Technical Topics Scrapbook
1985–89

Radio Society of Great Britain

Published by the Radio Society of Great Britain, Cranborne Road, Potters Bar, Herts EN6 3JE.

First published in book form 1993

ISBN 1 872309 20 8

Cover design: Geoff Korten Design.
Production: Ray Eckersley, Seven Stars Publishing.

Printed in Great Britain by Bell & Bain Ltd, Glasgow.

Contents

087793463

Preface

When in 1958 a new column entitled 'Technical Topics' began to appear in the *RSGB Bulletin* (which in January 1968 was renamed *Radio Communication*), it soon became apparent that the bringing together of a varied collection of new and established circuit ideas, HF/VHF antennas, and general hints on running an amateur radio station on a modest budget – having in common only that they were practical and relevant to day-to-day amateur operation – fulfilled a real and widespread need.

At that time, technical information tended to be presented, even in the amateur journals and handbooks, in a formal (and to non-professionals an often rather forbidding) manner, with a heavy lacing of mathematics. From the outset, 'Technical Topics', on the other hand, concentrated on providing simply a large number of hints and tips, circuit diagrams of transmitter and receiver stages, illustrations of antennas and details of simple test instruments that could be built literally on the kitchen table with a minimum of special tools. It is perhaps a mark of the success of this policy that a number of overseas amateur radio journals have since introduced roughly similar columns.

Although simplicity and KISS ('keep it simple, stupid') technology has been a prime aim, every effort has been made to introduce amateurs to advances in the basic technology of receivers, transmitters and simple antennas – although not by poaching on other regular *Radio Communication* columns covering the more-specialised technologies of data transmission and space communications.

As I wrote in the first 'TT': "To keep abreast of current technical progress and practice in Amateur Radio fields has never been an easy task. New ideas, circuits and components are constantly being introduced and old ones revived. Some have a short life, others are absorbed into the mainstream of amateur practice. Yet often, unless one has read the original article . . . it may be many months before one meets someone able to pass along sufficient details . . . to make it possible to try a new antenna or circuit device which may be just what the station needs.

"We cannot promise that this new feature will solve all these difficulties. All we can hope to do is to survey a few ideas from the technical press; a few hints and tips that have come to our notice, with perhaps an occasional comment thrown in for good measure."

That policy has been adhered to for over 35 years despite the changes that have occurred in the pursuit of a hobby that remains interesting, exciting and unique – and capable of being pursued within restricted budgets.

It has always been assumed that most readers already have and use the more-formal handbooks and no effort has been made, in general, to cover basic theory but rather to concentrate on new or little-understood concepts and techniques of proven or potential practical value – and to show ways in which good results can be achieved at low costs. 'Technical Topics' remains dedicated to amateur radio experimentation.

Within a few years, the first collected edition – *Technical Topics for the Radio Amateur* (1965) – appeared as a slim 100-page book, followed between 1968 and 1980 by progressively enlarged editions under the title *Amateur Radio Techniques*. The seventh edition, covering selected items from 'TT' between 1958 and 1980, runs to 368 pages and over 800 diagrams, and remains in demand, having been last reprinted in 1991.

This has meant that over 1000 pages of 'TT' published since 1980 have remained available only to those with a library of back copies of *Radio Communication*, and even these lack a consolidated index to enable items relating to particular topics to be accessed quickly. To further update *Amateur Radio Techniques* to encompass this mass of material has become impracticable. Instead, the decision has been made to reprint five years of 'TT' articles as published in *Radio Communication*. This volume thus includes all 339 pages of 'TT' from January 1985 to December 1989, together with a comprehensive index of all topics covered which, it is hoped, will enable the reader to locate rapidly all items relevant to a particular subject.

Grateful acknowledgement is made to all the many amateurs and engineers worldwide and to the amateur radio and professional engineering publications from which the material was originally drawn. It is my policy always to acknowledge fully the source of all abstracts and designs. Acknowledgement is also made to A W Hutchinson, who was Editor of *Radio Communication* from 1972 to 1988, Trevor Preece, G3TRP (Editor 1988–89), Dave Bobbett, G4IRQ (Editor 1989) and Mike Dennison, G3XDV, who is the current Editor and who has encouraged the Society to publish this collected edition of 'Technical Topics'; and finally to Derek Cole, the Society's Technical Illustrator, who drew all the several hundred diagrams in these pages.

Pat Hawker, G3VA
London, October 1993

Technical Topics
by Pat Hawker, G3VA

SAFETY is always an emotive subject which needs to be approached with a balanced and open mind. As a hobby, amateur radio has an extremely good safety record; but any activity that involves antennas, ladders and high places, connections to the 240V supply mains, high-voltage or high-current power supplies, high rf voltages, toxic chemicals etc, is bound to put an incautious operator at some risk, while even a normally prudent person can fall victim to a single rash act. Usually it is a matter of pain or injury or damage rather than a fatality. Constant vigilance and a healthy respect for electricity is the ideal; it can be argued that a little knowledge is a dangerous thing, since it can produce complacency and risk-taking. In electrical matters, there are few better pieces of advice than always to keep one hand in your pocket when fault-finding on a "live" piece of equipment, and so avoid the risk of a dangerous hand-to-hand shock with current passing near the heart.

So it is with some humility and with the help of some very experienced "professionals" that we open this month with a number of topics concerned with electric shock.

Safety and the ac mains supply

Recent items in *Members Mailbag* and *TT* on personal safety have sparked off a considerable flow of correspondence and comment on such questions as the value or otherwise of an rccb (residual current circuit breaker) and the safe limits and effect of current passing through the human body. In compiling the following notes I am drawing on information and comments from R. C. Taylor, GW2HCJ; Wing-Commander I. E. Hill, G6HL; J. Rickwood, G3JJR; Dr E. Leask, GM6UNQ, of the Scottish Health service; as well as material relating to the MK "Sentry" range and an article by Michael Neidle "Clean supply, new supply—and new rules" in *Electrical and Radio Trading*, (1 November, 1984).

It may also be worth emphasizing that the rccb has already been discussed a number of times in *TT*, most recently in May and August 1981, although the term rccb had not then come into general use. It was the 15th edition

of the *IEE Regulations for electrical installations* published in 1981 that renamed what had usually been known as a "current-operated earth-leakage circuit breaker (elcb)". This edition also made the fitting of such devices mandatory for new installations when mains-supplies are used outside of what is termed the "equipotential zone", for example for an electric lawn mower, and presumably including a garden-hut shack when this has not been permanently wired for electricity.

The result of the 15th edition has been to encourage manufacturers to produce a range of rccb-type devices, including sockets with a built-in rccb having a 30mA earth leakage tripping current. As GW2HCJ points out, an rccb depends for its action on a transformer with two heavy-current windings which are equal within close limits and a third winding which usually has many turns of thin wire. The thin winding is connected to a solenoid which operates an isolating switch through a trigger mechanism, usually mechanical: Fig 1.

In normal operation the current flowing in the live ("phase") conductor is nearly equal to that in the neutral conductor. The magnetic fluxes produced in the transformer core nearly cancel. The device, however, will detect any resistive leakage to earth that unbalances the two currents, and will automatically switch off the supply when this exceeds the rated current (which may, for example, be 30mA, 100mA or 300mA etc). If the leakage is from live (phase) to earth, current flows through one "heavy" winding only, inducing a voltage in the third "thin" winding. Some recent devices, GW2HCJ points out, intended to protect a single portable device, are also actuated should the mains-supply fail. The majority of rccbs, however, are *not* affected by a temporary mains failure and do *not* act as "no-volt" relays in the manner suggested in *Members Mailbag*.

In *TT* May 1981, G3KWJ noted that some devices rated at 30mA could be wired to provide 15mA tripping, and 10mA rccbs are available. However, the problem is then likely to arise of false or "nuisance" trips: it is most inconvenient to have your equipment tripped off in the middle of a contact only to find it all a false alarm. On the other hand the tripping of a 30mA rccb usually indicates a fault-condition that needs rectifying, and gives good protection as noted below. GW2HCJ is firmly of the opinion that *all* domestic power points (but not lighting points) should be protected by 30mA trips; he believes a 30mA rccb to be a worthwhile safety precaution, prefereably with power circuits separate from the lighting installation.

Should this appear to suggest that an rccb is the ideal answer to safety problems, it should be emphasized, as Llyr D. Gruffyd, GW4CFC, did in *TT* August 1981, that such devices may prove counter-productive in giving a radio operator a false sense of security since it provides *no* protection against electric shock from the *secondary-side* of any double-wound mains transformer. This includes the ht supplies to high-power valve amplifiers which can often be 1, 2 or even 3kV. GW4CFC contended from experience in laboratories that introducing rccb protection where ht and eht supplies exist "can lead to a false feeling of immunity to shock, and is thus psychologically bad when most severe shocks experienced by amateurs originate from the secondary side of transformers". However, there are many all-solid-state rigs in which dc potentials (but not rf voltages) may be limited to 12–24V, and the main danger from a low-current heavy-duty psu comes from a short-circuit by, say, personal jewellery such as a ring. For such stations an rccb *would* reduce the risks of "live" metalwork etc

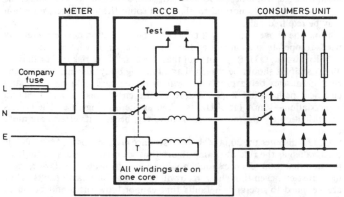

Fig 1. Showing an rccb installed to detect excessive earth leakage currents throughout a domestic installation. Such units may have a trip sensitivity of 100mA or more. Higher sensitivity 30mA units protect the output from a single power socket. Even higher sensitivity units (to about 10mA) are available but may prove susceptible to false tripping.

resulting from the primary of a mains transformer short-circuiting to a poorly earthed shield or a secondary winding etc (a by-no-means uncommon hazard).

It should be appreciated that the rccb is not only intended to provide protection against electric shock but also against fires caused by faulty wiring or appliances, and that even a 300mA rccb installed at the incoming supply offers significantly more protection than conventional fuses or miniature contact breakers (mcb).

My personal belief is that an amateur station should always have *one* heavy-duty double-pole switch (15A rating or better) that turns off *all* equipment rather than relying on the on-off switches in the individual units. As noted in *TT* several years ago, by no means all imported equipments are fitted with reliable double-pole on-off switches.

Impedance of the human body

Dr E. Leask, GM6UNQ, writes with the professional experience of representing the Scottish Health service on many BSI committees dealing with safety standards, as well as representing the UK on several IEC and ISO committees. He feels that the comments by G4CCM in the November *Members Mailbag* need to be corrected, particularly those concerning the measurement of hand-to-hand body impedance with a megger. GM6UNQ points out that these figures are wildly out, certainly for 240V 50Hz supplies. A megger turned at the correct speed produces 200Hz, but it is most unlikely that anybody would willingly stand the full output in order to make such a measurement. He writes:

"A megger is inappropriate for this purpose. To put the record straight, the following are quantitative figures for human body impedance, based upon official International Electrotechnical Commission (IEC) papers and experiments (including some on the writer) carried out in the course of drafting a new International Electrical Safety Standard which will be applicable to all measuring, test, process control, scientific laboratory, medical laboratory and educational equipment.

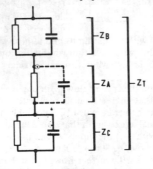

Fig 2. Body impedance can be thought of as the total of three impedances in series with the skin entry and exit points having a capacitive element that makes the total impedance depend to some degree upon the supply frequency. But note that there are very many variables. In practice, a rule-of-thumb approximation puts the total impedance between 1,000 and 2,000Ω.

"The impedance of the human body can be regarded as three impedances in series: Fig 2. ZT, the total body impedance, is made up of ZA the internal body impedance, which has a very small capacitive element, and ZB and ZC, the impedances of the skin entry and exit points. While ZA is largely resistive, the skin (acting as a semiconductor with conductive holes—the pores) has a large capacitive impedance up to skin breakdown.

"There are many variables in any situation: the contact area (the smaller the contact area the higher the apparent impedance); whether the contact areas are wet or dry; the type of current (ac, dc or pulse); the frequency; the touch voltage; the pressure of contact; and the ambient temperature.

"Up to about 50V the value of impedance varies widely with contact area, temperature and respiration; even for a single individual. I would postulate that G4CCM derived his figure with an idling megger and perhaps small electrodes.

"For large contact areas—50/100cm² at 50Hz, and for touch voltages from 50 to 1000V, 95 per cent of the population lie somewhere between 1,500 and 4,300Ω. Safety standards in the past have assumed a theoretical body impedance of either 1,000 or 2,000Ω. The new standard assumes 2,000Ω up to 100Hz, and a more complex impedance—including capacitive elements—from 100Hz to 1MHz, which approximates to 1,750Ω.

"The question of electric shock and its effects, with the many permutations of conditions, involves the duration of the applied current and the phase of the cardiac cycle when the shock is experienced. On the question of rccbs, the trip time is obviously the most important parameter."

I seem to recall an old saying: "Its volts that jolts, but mils (mA) that kills." Perhaps in the light of GM6UNQ's comments one should now add: "Pray the relay don't delay."

Effects of electric shock

There is still some controversy over safe limits and the effects of electric shock on the human body. Much depends, of course, on whether the current passes through the region of the heart. The IEC document 479 includes a diagram (Fig 3) reproduced here from an MK "Sentry" catalogue. This attempts to relate duration of shock to current and indicates four of the five "zones" of effect.

Zone 1 (not shown) relates to currents less than 0·5mA deemed to have no effect.

Zone 2 is regarded as usually presenting no damage to health.

Zone 3 indicates "usually no fibrillation, possible non-permanent effect". This could mean muscular contraction and loss of breathing, but capable of being corrected by artificial respiration if the shock current is removed in time.

Zone 4 "probability of fibrillation less than 50 per cent".

Zone 5 "probability of fibrillation more than 50 per cent".

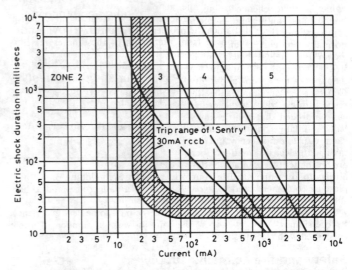

Fig 3. Showing how an MK "Sentry" 30mA rccb provides protection within the less dangerous Zone 2, as well as the much more dangerous Zones 3, 4 and 5. Zone 1 (not shown) involves currents of less than 0·5mA and usually has no effect. Zone 2 usually represents no damage to health. Zone 3 usually results in no fibrillation of the heart but possible non-permanent effects. Zone 4 represents a 50 per cent probability of fibrillation. Zone 5 more than 50 per cent probability of fibrillation. The zones are those defined in IEC document 479 and the diagram is as shown in MK information on their Sentry range. Trip range of other makes of rccb are therefore not necessarily the same.

Fibrillation is the highly dangerous condition where the current passing through the heart causes this to malfunction, reducing or stopping the circulation of the blood. Such a condition very quickly causes permanent brain damage, if not death. Removal of such a current does not cause the heart to return to its normal rhythm, and sophisticated medical attention may be required quickly.

From the above notes it will be seen that a protection device preferably needs to operate at a current and within a time period within Zone 2.

J. Rickwood, G3JJR, points out that, because of the risk of fibrillation, 30mA at 50Hz should be regarded as a limiting body current, but that the risk of muscles being paralysed—which in the case of a hand-to-hand electrical path would imply seizure of the chest muscles and eventual asphyxiation—10mA (at 50Hz) is taken as the limiting case. The effects of fibrillation are the more serious, however, because its effects are more rapid.

G3JJR disputes the 20,000Ω body resistance given by G4CCM; 1,000Ω is often taken as the rule of thumb figure (but see earlier). He is strongly of the view that total reliance should not be put on any protective device, rccb, mcb, fuse etc, even though an rccb will protect against earth faults. They are designed to operate on faults that cannot blow fuses and be quick enough to reduce the risk of human fatality if correctly chosen and installed.

The IEE Regulations emphasize the necessity that an rccb should be regularly tested, *not simply by pressing the trip button*. There are purpose-made instruments for use in making this test.

Earth-Neutral leakage

GW2HCJ emphasizes that an rccb protects against earth/neutral faults which often pass undetected and are a fire hazard. He writes: "As the current flowing in such a fault depends on the E-N voltage, which in turn depends on the supply cabling and the load being taken by other consumers, the trip in house A (which has an E-N fault) may operate only when the cooker in house B is turned on! This leads to confusion, and such faults may mistakenly be "cured" by removing the trip rather than the E-N fault. E-N faults tend to be caused by floor nails or missing sleeving on earth wires in fittings."

G6HL in the course of his service career encountered very varied standards of electrical installation. It should be noted that the British three-wire system is not used in most countries. In his present QTH an untidy fused distribution box was preceded by an old-style *voltage-operated* elcb ("Chilton") which proved erratic. Local electricity-supply staff pointed out that the voltage-operated devices are no longer fitted and advised a change to a current-operated device ("Wylex").

This resulted in a problem that he traced to his mains rf filter comprising two large single-layer rf chokes with $0\cdot1\mu$F feedthrough capacitors to earth from each end of the chokes. As has been pointed out on several occasions in *TT*, $0\cdot005\mu$F capacitance can represent the maximum safe leakage in this type of application, so that the action of several $0\cdot1\mu$F capacitors effectively in parallel caused the device to trip. When the $0\cdot1\mu$F capacitors were changed to $0\cdot01\mu$F mica the problem disappeared.

It should not be supposed from the length of these notes that large numbers of radio amateurs are being knocked out from shock or their homes burnt up. Nevertheless there can be few of us who over the years have not got ourselves across the mains or ht. I recall a 700V-plus "packet" that left me shaky and with extreme dislike of touching anything electrical for several hours! One should, of course, also watch out for charged high-voltage psu filter capacitors as a result of a "bleeder" resistor open-circuit. Protection that fails is a much greater hazard than no protection other than constant vigilance!

Lack a centre-tapped heater transformer?

Just as a problem exists these days in locating components suitable for high-voltage rf applications, so one finds increasing difficulty—or out-of-this-world costs, in providing the power for the valves still needed in linear amplifiers.

The 50W (10V at 5A) directly-heated filaments of the rugged and still-popular 813 tetrode have always been something of a problem, with their requirement for a hefty centre-tapped heater transformer, especially where several of these valves are used. W. M. Frost, G3OHE, has found a simple but effective solution to this problem that he has never seen suggested in print. His idea is shown in Fig 4. He writes: "D1 and D2 are 1A silicon power diodes, piv rating unimportant. In regard to anode current, the 813 filament(s) act as a centre-tapped resistor to equalise diode currents. Should a small amount of standing bias be required for the 813 over and above the $0\cdot7$V that always exists with this arrangement, several diodes can be used in series in each filament/earth connection, providing $0\cdot7$V times the number of diodes in each leg (which should of course be equal in number). Whether or not the mode of operation is precisely as outlined above may be open to question, but certainly the arrangement works well in practice."

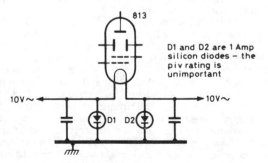

Fig 4. How a pair of 1A diodes can substitute for a centre-tapped transformer for the directly-heated 813 etc

Audio agc/processor

A high-performance agc system capable of converting an af signal with 50dB dynamic range input to near constant output, originally developed for broadcast applications, is described by Lee Barrett, K7NM, in *Ham Radio* September 1984, pp24-5: Fig 5. Heart of the device is a Motorola MC3340P ic which can provide 13dB gain or nearly 80dB attenuation, depending on the value of the resistance between pin 2 and earth. In practice a jfet

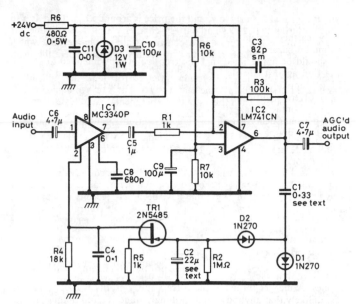

Fig 5. K7NM's audio automatic gain control circuit capable of converting 50dB input dynamic range to near constant output

(2N5485 n-channel fet) is used as a voltage-controlled resistor to control the ic.

Dynamic range is adjustable by selecting the value of R3 with the 100K shown resulting in a near—50dB range. To reduce the range (high for most amateur radio applications) increase C3, at the same time decreasing the value of C3 to maintain the time-constant represented by R3 × C3. R3 plus C3 form a low-pass filter to minimise the problem of overshoot (poppiness) caused by a very abrupt change from soft to loud input signal.

The attack time is governed by C1, with $0\cdot33\mu$F resulting in the fastest possible time; this value should not be exceeded or low-frequency oscillation may result. C2 controls the main recovery time, with 22μF recommended by K7NM for speech. A level control potentiometer may be added across the output.

One possible application for such a high-performance agc system mentioned by K7NM would be to provide constant modulation level in an fm repeater virtually regardless of the deviation of the incoming signal.

Alternative power sources

The operation of communications and electronic equipment completely independent of ac supply mains—even for battery recharging—continues to be a topic of more than passing interest not only to radio amateurs but also to sailing enthusiasts. Jack Tootill, G4IFF, who keeps an eye on the shipping and yachting periodicals, has sent along a wad of clippings that show the increasing number of small generating systems now being marketed for a variety of marine applications, although do-it-yourself electricity still does not come cheaply.

Two developing systems are evident: wind generators suitable for keeping batteries charged during periods when no engine is running; and the increasing use of solar cells to replace entirely mechanical generators.

Unfortunately for those with inland sites both wind and solar generators depend to a major degree on the weather, although it should be remembered that solar cells do deliver power during an overcast day. The contrasting weather dependence of wind and sun has encouraged broadcasters to experiment with a combination of both these forms of generation on the assumption that in coastal areas it is reasonably likely to be either sunny or windy, and without long periods of still fog. A note on and illustration of the IBA's wind and sun four-channel televison relay station at Bossiney, on the north Cornish coast appeared in *TT* January 1983, pp43-4.

It would seem that typical wind generators on the marine market include the Aerogen and Ampair ranges for 12V batteries, capable of delivering from about 25 to 75W at wind speeds of around 20 knots at prices that can go from roughly £140 as special offers up to about £200 for the 25W units. Typically they will begin to charge a battery at about $0\cdot5$A at wind speeds of around 10 knots. A voltage regulator is always necessary with a wind generator.

The UK is not the best region in the world for solar generators based on silicon photovoltaic cells, and although one often reads of how prices will soon come tumbling down this has not happened yet! Solarvent, who specialise in sun-powered ventilators, offer an M82 photovoltaic $20\cdot6$V module intended to charge 12V batteries, though the charging rate in typical daylight is probably fairly low, and the price is around £125. There is also a Lucas Marine MB1206 solar battery charger claimed as suitable for keeping unattended batteries in a constant state of charge, and which appears to be intended as a topping-up facility in cases where the main charging is from a generator driven by the ship's engine.

Many of the solar heating systems intended for domestic applications work on a different principle, the heating by the sun's rays of liquid in roof-mounted thin pipes. Then there are the experimental large scale electricity generators using large numbers of parabolic reflectors computer-controlled to track the sun. A very large array of this type is located in the south of France and is expected to be made available to French amateurs for moonbounce experiments using the reflectors as antennas rather than heat concentrators.

For those interested in other novel forms of energy conservation, G4IFF has provided some details of the growing number of sail-assisted ships of up to 30,000 tonnes deadweight that have been built recently in Japan. The largest of these, the *Aqua City,* with two computer-controlled sails each 16m high and 11m across, achieved a $20,000 saving in fuel during a single voyage from Japan to Vancouver.

The ageless W3EDP antenna
In a recent "first steps in radio" article on "Radio antennas and how they operate" (*QST* September 1984, pp30–4), Doug DeMaw, W1FB, comments: "I've known a number of new hams (*sic*) who thought they could get on the air with a random length of wire at whatever height they could manage. Grave disappointment often follows . . . the amateurs received no responses to the CQs because they had ineffective antennas, and thereby were transmitting weak signals."

This discouraging and only partly valid observation can be justified only because W1FB makes it clear later in his useful article that the newcomers' problems were primarily because, in the absence of effective matching of the transmitter into a reactive impedance, very little power was being radiated. In other words, it was the *antenna system* and not necessarily the use of a random length of wire at uncertain height that made the antennas ineffective. In practice, as many amateurs have discovered, a random length of wire even a few feet off the ground *can* bring plenty of contacts, even though nobody should expect it to outperform a TH7DXX at 60ft.

The secret, if there is one, is simply to ensure that the whole antenna system is brought into a conjugate match with the aid of a very good earth, radials or, usually better still, a counterpoise insulated from ground, using an effective transmitter-antenna matching arrangement, and avoiding very heavy circulating currents.

About the mid-'thirties there appeared on the scene an antenna system designed by W3EDP that exploited this very effectively, though the length of the antenna wire (84ft) was not entirely random but chosen so that a simple parallel-tuned circuit inductively coupled to the transmitter tank coil, plus a short counterpoise of length suitable for the band in use, was all that was needed to bring the antenna system into resonance. Basically it is a simple "Marconi" antenna, and any other reasonable length of wire can be substituted for the 84ft length but may require a somewhat more flexible transmatch and different lengths of counterpoise. I recall using a W3EDP in 1939 for my 10W on 7 and 14MHz, and being reasonably happy with the results, which were roughly the same as with a 66ft end-fed wire that I also favoured.

Les Parnell, G8PP, still uses a W3EDP antenna on all pre-WARC bands from 3·5 to 28MHz, and reports receiving on ssb such comments as "this is a new one on me. If it is a new type of Yagi let me know how long the elements are, as my yard is very small and any rotatable thing with less than

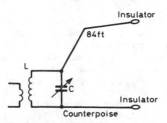

Fig 6. The traditional W3EDP 84ft end-fed antenna. L was often inductively coupled directly to the pa tank coil, but modern practice would be to use a low-impedance link winding on L. C is 250pF. L wound on 2in diameter former would be as follows:

3.5MHz	21 turns, 16swg spaced one diameter. 17ft counterpoise
7 MHz	7 turns, 16swg spaced one diameter. 17ft counterpoise
14MHz	5 turns 16swg spaced one diameter. 6·5ft counterpoise
28MHz	3 turns, 16swg 0·5in diameter. No counterpoise

Other bands will require some experimentation. G8PP uses a 3ft 4in counterpoise on 21MHz

12ft span would be more than welcome," and, again, "Is it omni-directional? You're coming in here 5 and 9 so I take it you've a reflector of some sort. If this is so, how do you radiate the other way? I'm using a three-element beam some 60ft high, and your W3EDP, as you call it, might have potential as you say it is only 21ft above ground."

G8PP comments: "These two quotes are not unusual responses to my saying that I'm using a W3EDP. So I explain that it is simply an end-fed wire some 84ft long with a short counterpoise that varies in length with the band in use: Fig 6. I first used this system in 1938–9, before we had access to 21MHz. I have since found that a counterpoise about 3ft 4in long gives the best results on that band."

It would be interesting to discover how well the basic W3EDP arrangement loads on 10, 18 and 24MHz (but remember, UK amateurs are not yet permitted to radiate a vertical component on 18 and 24MHz) and the optimum counterpoise lengths for these bands. It could prove necessary to use series tuning on one or more of the non-harmonically related bands.

Although it is unusual these days to hear anyone claiming to be using a W3EDP, the basic design remains in the hf antennas chapter of the *Radio Communication Handbook.* It is described in the current edition as "an excellent solution for 'awkward locations' where an antenna of orthodox type cannot be made to fit in". Although most diagrams still show the W3EDP coil as inductively coupled to the pa tank coil, in 'thirties style, the current edition of the handbook makes it clear that there is no basic reason why it should not be link-coupled to the transmitter, directly or via a lowpass filter, swr meter etc. It is also pointed out that "there is scope for much experimental work with alternative lengths of antenna and counterpoise". It also stresses that, in general, it is much easier to achieve efficient radiation with systems of this type (ie not grounded, but with a counterpoise) than those relying on earth connections (ie Marconi-type end-fed antennas).

The flexible centre-fed dipole
In his "First steps in radio" article, Doug DeMaw, W1FB, pays tribute not only to the basic single-band half-wave resonant dipole with coaxial feeder, but also to the much more flexible centre-fed multiband dipole or doublet with open-wire or 300Ω resonant feeders.

Surprisingly, however, he does not mention one of the most important advantages of the multiband version: the top span does *not* necessarily have to be, as W1FB suggests, 468/f(MHz)ft, ie an electrical half-wave, "at the lowest operating frequency" with all the real-estate problems this involves for 1·8MHz (250ft), 3·5MHz (132ft) and even 7MHz (66ft) operation. Provided the whole system, top/feeders/atu can be brought into resonance, a "top" span of only about half this figure (λ/4), or even less at the lowest band, will radiate quite effectively. Remember that any antenna system radiates all the power that is fed into it, less that dissipated in losses. Although losses tend to rise with a short top span, even a 66ft span can prove quite effective on 3·5 and 1·8MHz.

Our shrinking lifestyle
Les Mitchell, G3BHK, raises the problem presented to both hf and vhf operators by the gradual shrinking of our *lebensraum:* "Modern housing decrees short gardens. Buildings are becoming ever closer together. Not only does the amateur have difficulty in finding space for an effective and aesthetically acceptable antenna, but even the number of potential rfi hazards is increased by proximity.

"Just consider", he continues, "the items which absorb rf such as metal and trees on an average-type housing estate, and you begin to realize the extent of the problem (but see my remarks below—*G3VA*). The average house has electrical wiring which passes up the wall but branches out at the 8 and 16ft levels (approx). The water pipes extend upwards to around 20ft with horizontal extensions under the floor at the same levels as the wiring. The tv and vhf/fm broadcast antennas are around the 32–3ft level. To this mass of rf screening one must add street lamp standards (even if made of concrete they still house electrical wiring), trees and overhead cables.

"As the majority of amateur antennas appear to be about 25 to 30ft high, one wonders how they radiate at all! If you then go on to consider this screening material as vertical antennas, many will tend to resonate on amateur bands and add to our rfi problems. For instance, I cause my very near neighbour very little interference on his fm radio, except when I operate on 7MHz running just a few watts to a vertical erected at ground level. Reference to Fig 7 suggests that his fm antenna array resonates as a half-wave on 7MHz, giving him full benefit of the available rf.

"One wonders what effect rows of High Street lights and those along motorways etc have; some must resonate and their spacing cause peculiar radiation patterns.

"The different combinations of screening and resonance in different locations may explain why two amateurs living in the same locality and

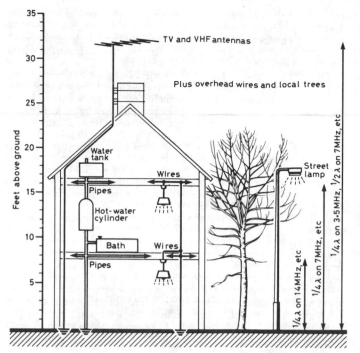

Fig 7. The possibility of unwanted resonances of metal conduits, pipes etc in a typical residential environment as suggested by G3BHK. The houses themselves can also have broadband resonances as noted in the text stemming from work by Canadian engineers

using exactly similar antennas often achieve very different results. Trees at least change resonant frequency with the passing years."

G3BHK's comments are generally valid but need some slight qualification. Objects surrounding antennas certainly affect their radiation pattern, but do not necessarily "absorb" as much transmitter power as G3BHK suggests. Many objects, particularly metal structures, do not absorb much rf but re-radiate most of it. This can, and often does, change the radiation pattern, tending to fill in nulls and to reduce the f:b ratio of directive arrays, introducing mixed polarization etc. In other words, they tend to act like poor mirrors rather than sponges. Quite distant electricity pylons have been shown to have significant effect on directional mf arrays.

A detailed paper by S. J. Kavanagh and K. G. Balmain of Toronto University (*IEEE Trans on Broadcasting*, Vol BC-30, No 1, March 1984) goes even further in showing how high-rise buildings re-radiate mf signals and can also cause detuning of nearby mf transmitting antennas. They have found that buildings can act like a thick, somewhat lossy monopole antenna, exhibiting a broad, quarter-wave resonance when a building having horizontal dimensions of about half its height has an overall height of about $0 \cdot 18\lambda$. Re-radiation from a building near resonance can be strong enough to distort significantly the pattern from an omnidirectional vertical antenna at distances of up to two or three wavelengths (ie up to about 1km at 1MHz). Moreover, for multi-element directional mf antennas, as widely used for radio broadcasting in North America and occasionally in the UK, serious null-filling can occur even when a "resonant" building is several kilometres away from the antenna site.

The paper describes successful "detuning" of a 12-storey building by the fitting of stubs, although the reduction of scattering (about 2dB with rooftop stubs, and $4 \cdot 4$ to $6 \cdot 6$dB for umbrella stubs) was not as large as could be obtained using simple models. The paper also observes that the predominant building construction material in which rf *losses* occur is concrete; the electrical properties of concrete are strongly dependent on its moisture content, which varies with age and environmental factors.

Building resonances resulting in re-radiation and rf losses can occur at hf without requiring the presence of high-rise buildings in the neighbourhood, though I am not sure how you could persuade your neighbour to let you fit an umbrella detuning stub on his house!

Fitting PL259 and bnc plugs

Brian Walters, GW3XHD, has sent along some useful notes on the fitting of PL259 and bnc plugs to coaxial cable based on his years of servicing mobile radiotelephones. He refers to his suggestions as "tips for newcomers", but I suspect that it is not only G0 and G1 amateurs who sometimes find it difficult to fit these plugs.

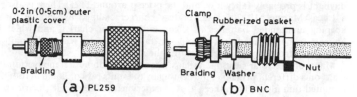

Fig 8. GW3XHD's recommended method of fitting PL259 and bnc coaxial cable plugs

GW3XHD believes that with the PL259 plug the problem when fitting is that afterwards it is found that a short-circuit exists across the insulation to the centre pin inside the plug. He avoids this problem, as shown in Fig 8(a), by placing a small piece of the outer covering of the cable to form an additional insulating washer as shown. When the reducer is screwed into the body of the plug, this washer is squeezed, insulating the centre of the plug and ensuring a snug fit of the cable to the plug.

With a bnc-type plug a similar problem can arise due to short-circuiting by stray strands of the braiding, and often the cable can later be all-too-easily pulled away from the plug. Fig 8(b) shows how both these problems can be overcome. The braiding is made long enough to go back over the clamp and then under the rubberized gasket, which can be eased over the cable. Then, when fitting to the body of the plug, the assembly will need to be eased in with the aid of a small screwdriver. Once a plug has been fitted in this manner, the cable is most unlikely ever to be accidentally pulled out; in practice, GW3XHD has found, the cable is more likely to snap before this happens.

Waterproofing and antenna accessories

P. G. Rollin, G4AFU (telephone (0768) 66131), draws attention to the uses to which a "Rubberlite" type 108 junction box can be put when erecting wire antennas; for example, when joining open-wire feeders to coaxial cable for a G5RV dipole or to provide a centrepiece for a dipole. The box is basically an eight-way connector block enclosed in a high-grade, watertight rubber enclosure with a removable transparent cover, and normally used for some vehicle electrics. There are two versions, one using synthetic rubber to provide greater resistance to oil. They are available from motor accessory dealers at under £5, although G4AFU offers to help out in case of difficulty. He has used one for a G5RV for several months with no trace of moisture ingress. He writes:

"After making the connections the window snaps back into place, providing a completely watertight enclosure. There are two blank inlet and outlet ports. These are opened by either cutting off sufficient of the rubber to make a suitable interference fit for coaxial cable, or by poking a small hole through for the open-wire feeder. A spot of silicone sealant at the point where the open-wire feeder enters the port then finishes the job. Coaxial cable does not need any other sealing provided the rubber has been cut for a push or interference fit."

It should be stressed that while it is possible to implement antenna systems without the use of watertight junction boxes, it is *essential* to ensure that the ends of coaxial cable are effectively sealed against moisture ingress. G3MCK (*TT* November 1981, pp1034–5) described a low-cost technique using a toothpaste-cap filled with Bostik or Evostick sealant.

For wrapping around other junction connectors etc, diy enthusiasts will probably be aware of the thick heavily-greased "Sylglas" tape intended for such purposes as temporary repairs to leaking water-pipes etc, though I would question the electrical characteristics of this very messy material. Mike Shepherd, G8YZW, draws attention to a "revolutionary" new waterproofing tape that would seem to be ideal for a number of outdoor and antenna applications. This is "Rubbaweld self-amalgamating marine tape" (C C Marine services Ltd, Eagle Road, Guildford, Surrey GU1 4HZ, telephone (0483) 35358).

It is a thin adhesive tape which, when bound around the dry surface of a pipe, cable, insulator etc, welds itself into a solid waterproof skin within about 1h, and is claimed to provide "complete protection against corrosion by seawater to electrical connections" and "high voltage insulation for rt connections". Two layers of overlapping tape are claimed to repair a leaking water hose.

G8YZW reports that a small roll of Rubbaweld marine tape (3m long, 25mm wide) costs about £1.30. He adds: "For outside joint sealing it is the best stuff I have come across next to well-applied Evostik, of which I make great use. It is not cheap but neither is the replacement of a length of watersoaked coaxial cable!"

For those who may believe that wire antennas have been displaced by "whips" for professional military and civil hf communications, attention is drawn to the fact that the British firm C & S Antennas Ltd has recently

Multi-purpose hf antenna kit with portable carrying case introduced by C & S Antennas Ltd for military and professional civil application

introduced a multi-purpose antenna kit for tactical communications or for civil exploration and survey applications. The kit enables any one of nine different hf antennas to be erected, including a base-fed "V" for short range use up to 8MHz, a sloping "V" for directional long-range skywave working, an inverted-L, various dipole delta and non-resonant "V" configurations, supported from trees, buildings or masts. The kit including wire, earth rods and accessories fits into a small canvas carrying bag.

For radio amateurs such a kit would be most useful, though experience suggests that products intended primarily for military purposes are seldom priced within amateur budgets, at least until they become available as "surplus".

In this connection, D. J. Harvey (ex-G8SSB) draws attention to a report last July in *The Daily Telegraph* headed "Equipment hoarded by MoD" and referring to a report of the Public Accounts Committee criticising MoD for its excessive level of stocks including: "obsolescent items, others which were almost out of date, and stocks awaiting potential overseas buyers." This explains why only a trickle of radio equipment has recently been released as "surplus". Those equipments that do reach the market still provide a happy hunting ground for home-constructors seeking the increasingly rare high-grade transmitting capacitors and coils etc, though the construction of military equipment has made it increasingly difficult to recover, for alternative use, the components.

ARQ rtty via satellite

Colin Richards, 9M2CR, in "Amtor spins a time-wrap around Oscar 10" (*Rad Com* July 1984, pp582-3, 589) described the problems that arise with ARQ (automatic repetition of errors) systems of rtty, such as Amtor, when the propagation delay increases. Admittedly, he showed that in certain circumstances it is possible to copy Amtor traffic through Oscar 10 provided that the error-rate is very low and there is no objection to losing the valuable advantages of error-correction offered by Amtor over all but the very longest terrestrial paths.

Belgian engineers have recently proposed a modified way of transmitting data blocks suitable for an ARQ system used on satellite circuits with their long propagation delay even under high error rate conditions (*Electronics Letters* 8 November 1984, pp986-7). If I understand their proposals

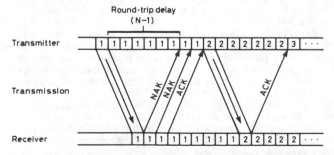

Fig 9. The proposed rtty ARQ system suitable for use over satellite circuits having long propagation delay. The minimum number of repetitions of each data block depends on the round-trip delay relative to block length. In practice, for Amtor, fewer repetitions would be required

correctly, the transmitter simply repeats the same data block until an acknowledgement is received. If this is the affirmative "ack", it immediately passes on to the next data block. If an error is signalled, "nak" or negative acknowledgement, the first data block continues to be transmitted until an "ack" is received: see Fig 9.

The Belgian authors present mathematical and graphical analyses that indicate a significant improvement in overall efficiency under poor conditions when compared to two alternative systems proposed for satellite ARQ operation: "go-back-N" or the system proposed by A. R. K. Sastry in 1975 ("Improving automatic repeat-request (ARQ) performance on satellite channels under high error rate conditions" *IEEE Trans* 1975 COM-23, pp436-9). The new proposal would seem to be confined to the data block transmission protocol, and at first sight it would seem feasible to develop an Amtor terminal switchable between the conventional transmission mode and the Belgian scheme, though I leave it to rtty enthusiasts to show exactly how this could be done, and whether it would be permissible within the current UK licence.

Unlike the go-back-N schemes, which have the disadvantage of changing the order of the data blocks, the new proposals by M. Moeneclaey and H. Bruneel, provide a continuous ARQ protocol while preserving the order of the data blocks. At low error rates, go-back-N, Sastry and the Belgian proposals provide virtually the same throughput efficiency, which is defined as the number of bits delivered to the total number of bits transmitted, but as the probability of a transmission error increases the new scheme shows a dramatic improvement. It provides the normal degree of error protection though clearly reduces the wpm rate, compared to conventional ARQ over shorter paths, by an amount that is governed by the propagation delay.

Nicad charger

Brian Walters, GW3YSP, recommends the use of a 7805 three-terminal ic

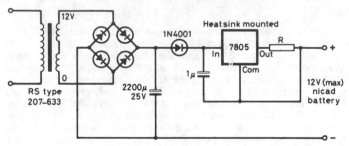

Fig 10. Constant current nicad charger using three-terminal ic regulator chip

regulator chip as a constant current source for charging nicad batteries. For the past five years he has been using this technique, which he took from RS data sheet No R/2854 issued August 1978, for batteries up to 5Ah capacity with a 12V maximum voltage.

The action of the 7805 results in the voltage-drop across R (Fig 10) remaining constant at 5V. Hence the voltage across the output and "common" terminals of the regulator chip is 5V, the regulated output voltage of a 7805. Table 1 lists the value of R for charging various cells, which may be single cells of 1·25V up to 10 cells in series providing approximately 12V. For other charging rates and cells, R is given by 5/(charge rate), remembering that the normal charge rate for long life of a nicad cell should be around 0·1C of its capacity, ie a 5Ah battery would charge at 500mA for 14h. Some nicad cells are suitable for fast-charge but with a simple charger without a timer or voltage sensing it is far safer to stick to the 0·1C rule.

Table 1

Nicad cell type	Charge current	Value of R Ohms	Watts
AA	66mA	75	0·5
C	250mA	22	2·5
D	500mA	10	2·5
PP3	9mA	560	0·5

GW3YSP suggests it may be possible to use the higher voltage 7812 (12V output) and a higher voltage mains transformer to charge 24V stacks using the same principle, although he has not tried this. He adds a timely reminder that nicad cells should generally be discharged to the 1V/cell level prior to recharging. Two or three complete charge/discharge cycles can often restore a battery which has developed a so-called "memory" to full normal working order. When discharging batteries the 0·1C rate is advised. ☐

Technical Topics
by Pat Hawker, G3VA

THERE IS a widespread but often fallacious belief that "you only get what you pay for". The implication is that if you buy cheap equipment it is most unlikely to prove as satisfactory or as reliable or as easy to operate as a "top of the range" model. Retailers in the consumer industries sometimes take advantage of this belief, particularly the food industry, by offering a choice of virtually the same goods but under different brand names, confident that the vast majority of the customers will instinctively choose either the middle or highest priced article, while still not losing the custom of those unable or unprepared to pay the higher prices.

The cost of amateur radio
In amateur radio, it is often the higher-priced models that sell best, and at times I have the impression that all the diy hints and tips in *TT* and elsewhere, most of which are intended to show how costs can be reduced, are little more than a hangover from the thirties when the "real cost" of both components and assembled equipment was far higher than it is today.

It is sometimes suggested that modern hf transceivers are simply not available within schoolboy or student budgets. Yet within the UK there are already several million home computers, many with a full range of peripheral units, many of them used predominantly for "games" even when bought by parents on the basis of being educational tools. It is a much older age group, the pensioners, who have been hurt most by inflation.

If, at times, the cost of equipment seems high to those who recall the days of stable money, it is vastly cheaper than what taxpayers in all countries pay for "mil-spec" radio communication equipment. A two-way satellite terminal for Oscar may cost several hundreds of pounds to assemble; one for a merchant ship, such as the Marconi "Oceanray" about £20,000, but this is still vastly cheaper than the naval SCOT satellite terminals that run to almost £2-million per frigate.

The demanding (over-demanding?) specifications for Defence equipment have been highlighted by reports of the American services paying $110 for electric plugs available in hardware stores for about 5c; $7622 rather than less than $100 for a 10-cup coffee maker fitted in large cargo aircraft; $170 rather than under $25 for battery-operated torches . . . . . There is little evidence that the costly coffee makers provide better tasting coffee than the standard machines. Mil-spec transistors etc are required to operate down to much lower temperatures than you expect to meet in your shack (even though much will end up permanently installed in well-heated base stations).

I have always taken the view that if an amateur is willing to spend thousands of pounds on complex equipment that is entirely his or her own affair; but at the same time it is important that newcomers should be made aware of the fact that with a bit of make-do-and-mend, and a willingness to devote time rather than money to the hobby, it is still possible to get on the air with equipment that does not occupy excessive spectrum space or cause unnecessary rfi, for a modest outlay.

It was Neville Shute, engineer turned novelist, who insisted that a good engineer can do for ten-bob (50p) what any damn fool can do for £5; and E. F. Schumacher who wrote: "Any third-rate engineer can make a complicated apparatus more complicated, but it takes a touch of genius to find one's way back to basic principles".

Low-cost budgeting in amateur radio may involve the modification of cast-off professional or military equipment, the use of diy materials never intended for such purposes, the use of buildings and trees as antenna supports, and the savings that come from not having to count the time-cost

---

THIS MONTH

The cost of amateur radio
How sporadic is sporadic-E?
Industrial eht generators
Using 300Ω balanced cable
Simple keyer
Circular polarization and crossed-Yagi antennas
Coaxial phasing lines
Simplified tuned circuit and inductance formula
FM, nbfm and the spectrum
GaAs and computer-aided design
Over-voltage sensing ic devices
Getting it taped
70MHz on the cheap

---

of the labour involved in design, production and testing, willingly contributed as part of the enjoyment of the hobby.

How sporadic is sporadic-E?
For many years, Ron Ham has provided an annual report in *Rad Com* on his monitoring of sporadic-E vhf signals, from which it has become clear that there is no surefire way of predicting, except in general terms, just when this rather mysterious form of propagation will suddenly bring in strong signals from all over Europe on frequencies that may extend over all or part of the range 20 to 150MHz or thereabouts.

Results of a consolidated nine-year study of this subject by a team at the University College of Wales have been published in a paper "Sporadic-E propagation at frequencies around 70MHz" by K. J. Edwards, L. Kersley and L. F. Shrubsole in *The Radio & Electronic Engineer* May 1984, pp231–37. This is based on studies of skywave propagation between 59·25 and 77·25MHz by means of sporadic-E during 1972–81. It concludes that such propagation occurs mainly from May to August, with June and July being the months of both maximum number and maximum duration of these events. A small winter peak occurs (around December, early January) with February to April being the period of fewest events. The summer months show a double-peaked diurnal variation with a small pre-noon maximum and dominant evening peak at the lower frequencies in this range. At 77·25MHz, the double-peak disappears and is replaced by a steady rise to a single evening maximum. No regular trends associated with the solar cycle were detected, a conclusion found also in many of Ron Ham's reports.

In *Wireless World* April 1978, Dr E. B. Dorling, of the Mullard Space Science Laboratory of London University, described how knowledge of this curious phenomenon has been much increased from a combination of ground-based and rocket observations. He wrote:

"Sporadic-E was first seen to occur in the way it does, that is as very thin intense layers of ionization, by a British Skylark rocket flown from Woomera in 1958. By 1966 an association between these layers and sharp reversals in wind direction at high altitude had become recognized. Wind measurements in the very rarified atmosphere up to 150km or so revealed that a surprising pattern of wind reversals with height can occur; what is more, the measurements showed that the pattern often descends slowly over a period of hours, with, for example, a sharp wind shear first appearing above 150km height, then moving downwards to below 100km before fading. The cause of this rather unexpected wind structure appears to be the propagation of atmospheric waves horizontally over great distances.

"The sharp wind shears are at the root of the Sporadic-E layers, though in a rather complicated way. The winds, tenuous though they are at such heights, act to move the ions and electrons in the ionosphere across the earth's magnetic field, but interactions then occur in such a way as to displace the plasma vertically. Where strong wind shears of the appropriate sense exist, the plasma is squeezed into a thin concentrated layer, being moved downwards from above, upwards from below. As the wind pattern descends the layer descends too into an ever denser atmosphere, until finally at a height of about 100km it is brought to a halt . . . . .

"Sporadic-E then owes its transient character to interactions between atmospheric waves, the ionospheric E layer, and magnetic and electric fields. All but the magnetic field are constantly changing, so that the right conditions for layer formation occur—well, sporadically. If the question is asked why the explanation has been so long in coming—I should explain that physicists the world over have contributed to the solution—

the answer is that the region concerned, roughly 100–200km above the earth's surface, is inaccessible to satellites and therefore to regular on-the-spot measurements.

"One final point. Were the sporadic-E layers to be composed simply of ionized atmospheric gases, they wouldn't persist. They are, in fact, composed of ionized metallic atoms, mainly magnesium, silicon and iron, probably the remains of burned-up meteorites. The descending wind shears sweep up the metallic ions and bring them down as sporadic-E layers out of the thermosphere into the lower regions where atmospheric turbulence then churns them away into oblivion. Sporadic-E layers seem to be the product of Nature's vacuum cleaning!"

Thus I suppose that one could refer to sporadic-E contacts not as "meteor scatter" but as by "scattered meteors". And it is a relief to find that Nature's cleaning up is as sporadic and unpredictable as my own!

Industrial eht generators

Dr Dorling's letter on sporadic-E was prompted by some notes I had written on what at first promised to be an equally-mysterious phenomenon—the 27MHz "sweepers"—that were later proved to stem not from Nature but from long-distance propagation of unstable signals from industrial rf heating equipments, and since shown to be prominent also around 13–14MHz from glue-drying and similar industrial equipment.

In *TT* May 1984, p405, G3TDZ noted how these very-high-power self-excited oscillators, providing up to 25kW output, drift hundreds of kilohertz each time they are fired up. More recently, Ray Nicholson, G4SQG, who is professionally connected with the electric lamp industry, has sent along some details of lower-power rf eht generators. These use an oscillator and step-up transformer to provide a source of up to about 55kV, much as did some of the 25kV eht generators in early projection-tv models. G4SQG points out that they deliver quite a lot of rf, enough to light-up electric lamps of from about 10 to 40W rating.

He recalls the first unit of this type that came his way about 1950, comprising a power oscillator tuned to 200kHz. This completely blacked-out the BBC Droitwich sound radio programmes in the locality until the manufacturers supplied a large screened cage . . . . by the time he left that firm in 1969 there were 18 rf eht generators in virtually continuous operation during factory hours, used for checking the vacuum systems.

G4SQG enclosed some manufacturers' catalogue material and a circuit diagram of a typical eht generator from which it is clear that these generators are also used in connection with rubber and plastic coatings etc. Two of the three models are still listed as using 0·2MHz which, if accurately tuned, should hardly please local listeners to Radio 4. The third, however, is listed as 3·8MHz so that one must hope that it tends to drift higher rather than lower in frequency. All these units are in plastic enclosures with output leads to assist radiation!

His circuit diagram of a larger unit shows a single-valve seo working directly from unrectified 1·2kV ac; this one apparently is in a steel box but the rf output is fed to about 2m of wire. While the interference potential of these eht generators must be substantially less than the kilowatt rf heaters on (or near) the ism bands, it cannot be altogether negligible in view of the large number in almost continuous daytime use.

One wonders also what is the present dx record for 2·4GHz microwave ovens. These have grown rapidly in popularity, each containing a microwave transmitter of typically 1·5kW output or so, fed from rac. Admittedly attempts have been made by the manufacturers to reduce leakage of uhf power by improving the sealing of the doors (commercially necessary in order to reduce fears of safety hazards from excessive microwave radiation) but I recall commenting in 1980 on complaints by the Jodrell Bank radio-astronomers that they were receiving strong signals from microwave ovens on the sidelobes of their big dish at distances up to 20km or more. Later, Japanese broadcast engineers reported that harmonics from microwave ovens had proved a significant source of interference to the reception of 12GHz television signals from their experimental dbs trial using the BSE satellite.

Using 300Ω balanced cable

For many years I made good use of 300Ω ribbon cable for the element and feeder of single-band folded-dipole antennas. Ribbon cable was very economical, retailing then at around 6d (2·5p) per yard. In conjunction with a simple balanced form of pi-network atu (Fig 1) such an antenna provided a sure-fire, almost foolproof, system with a broad resonance that was not unduly affected by near-by objects, etc. I recall an indoor (roof-space) antenna of this type bringing me an RST589 report on 21MHz from BV1USB on Taiwan. Unfortunately, I never found any easy way of achieving good results on both 14 and 21MHz from a single folded-dipole antenna.

A practical snag was that the ribbon tended to deteriorate fairly quickly.

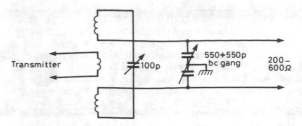

Fig 1. Simple form of pi-network atu suitable for feeding 300–600Ω balanced line, including folded dipoles fashioned from 300Ω ribbon feeder

Wind and ultraviolet radiation from the sun can cause such cable to split, although both black ribbon and the tubular form of 300Ω cable last longer. Soldered connections between ribbon feeder and ribbon element also tend to break due to the wind, unless care is taken to provide some form of protective clamping etc.

Brian Weller, ZS2AB, in *Radio-ZS* (April 1984) sets out some "tips for using ribbon cable" from which the following has been extracted:

"The cable has a very tough but relatively thin outer insulation, and the wire size is not very large. This combination tends to produce broken strands when the wire is stripped unless one is very careful. I have found a way to overcome this.

"When you are preparing to strip the cable for soldering, draw a line with a pen across the cable at whatever distance back from the end that you wish to strip it: lay a ruler or other straight-edge across the cable, and with a very sharp, fairly rigid blade, make a cut across the insulation. Do this gently, so as not to nick the strands inside. Turn the cable over and do the same on the other side. You will find that only a gentle pull with your sidecutters will cleanly remove the insulation from the wires. When making this cut, use a blade with a fairly rigid body. The so-called "carpet knife" blades are ideal. A razor blade is a bit thin, and not always easy to control.

"When soldering such a cable to a plug, slip a small piece of systoflex over each core and push this down over the completed connection after soldering. This supports the joint very well and will overcome the problem of broken wires after a bit of movement of the cable."

Simple keyer

Over the years, electronic keyers have become more and more complex, and it is rare to find an article describing a novel form of compact keyer intended primarily for use with a QRP transceiver that consumes less than 4mA, even on "key down" when fed from a stable 12V supply and with circuitry that fits on to 1·5in² of board space.

Jack Najork, W5FG, has come up with the circuit shown in Fig 2 *(Ham Radio* October 1984, p82) which uses a unijunction transistor (2N6027) as the basic timing device. It provides self-completing dits and dashes but without all the digital refinements and memories of so many modern designs. The unijunction transistor is a well-established and useful semiconductor device, though rarely used. It has a stable triggering voltage, very low value of "firing" current, good pulse current capability and low cost.

An exponential voltage is built up across C1 at a rate governed by RV2 until the unijunction transistor fires. Self-completion of dits and dahs follows, since the action of the ujt depends on the time constant. A "weight" control, RV3, in the emitter of TR2 controls the switching threshold (the on-off periods) of TR2 and TR3. TR3 is the keying

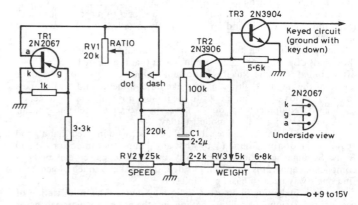

Fig 2. W5FG's simple electronic keyer for QRP. TR1 is a unijunction transistor, TR2 is pnp type 2N3906 or similar high-beta device. TR3 is npn 2N3904 or similar

(switching) transistor, and in the form shown is intended for keying the driver emitter, about 20mA, of a QRP transmitter. However, it is possible to use a keying relay (preferably reed type) in the collector circuit of TR3.

W5FG cheerfully admits the limitations of simple keyers and the precautions that need to be taken to achieve satisfactory performance. Of prime importance is that the dc supply (about 12V) *must* be stable, since poor regulation will result in erratic characters. Similarly this voltage once chosen, needs to remain the same unless all controls are readjusted. C1 should be $2 \cdot 2\mu F$, and TR2 should have a high beta, at least 60–70. If a keying relay is used, its characteristics are important and it should be capable of responding to a triangular waveform; there can also be problems of reed contact welding if one attempts to key an inductive load.

Circular polarization and crossed-Yagi antennas

The notes in *TT*, September and November 1984, on circular polarization continue to attract comment. Not surprisingly, Bill Sykes, G2HCG, does not accept the views of Dr Neill Taylor, G4HLX, as altogether valid, at least from a practical point of view. Although this is a debate unlikely to be readily settled one way or the other, it is only fair to provide space for G2HCG's reply:

"The radio amateur is noted for considering the practicalities of a situation, but G4HLX asks us to accept that the losses inherent in any method of phasing two feeders are unacceptable . . . Altering the phase of two feeders requires that their difference in electrical length be changed by a maximum of $\lambda/2$ to achieve 360° phase change. Surely the addition (or even subtraction) of this length to the total feeder length is hardly a measurable quantity and would not affect the noise factor of the system.

"On mast effect, G4HLX states that the reduction of vertical radiation from a + mounted crossed-Yagi is the result of currents induced in the conductive mast. True, but one should consider other factors that are involved. An important effect, especially on phased systems, is the mismatch caused by the presence of the mast in the plane of the elements. Unbalance in the matching of two antennas fed in quadrature to produce circular polarization means that in addition to correct phasing of the feeds, the power levels in each antenna must also be controlled, a much more difficult proposition. Mounting the antennas in the 45° × configuration, instead of +, ensures that the effect of the mast on matching is equal, this virtually ensuring equal power distribution to each antenna.

"The question of which mast effect is the most important, especially as currents induced in the mast would be dependent on the length and type of material used, can be answered only by practical tests. Signal strength measurements over a short path with × mounted Yagis show no measurable difference between vertical and horizontal components, indicating that the theoretical mast currents in this configuration have little or no measurable effect.

"A daily 'sked' over a 130-mile path between the south coast and Northampton has been carried out for more than 30 years with 100 per cent contact on fm with only occasional necessity to use ssb. Noise figures are obviously of first importance, but complete control of polarization has proved particularly interesting. On this long path horizontal polarization is, as theory predicts, better than vertical. There is, however, a quite consistent polarization shift of some 45° with a total loss of polarization in the troughs of fades. Circular polarization has always been the optimum on this path, and the recent discovery of the 45° shift explains why, since the use of circular polarization means that signals remain unaffected by the shift.

"Reception of Oscar 10 on 144MHz is also interesting. Those familiar with the reception of this satellite will be aware of the regular fading caused by its rotation. Turning the knob of the "Polarphaser" (as I now call the device outlined in the September *TT*) alters the signal strength and the apparent speed of rotation, sometimes virtually eliminating the QSB, as the varying polarization lobes of the satellite antenna are explored."

Coaxial phasing lines

Bob Roberts, G2RQ, is concerned with the problem of setting up a crossed-Yagi to obtain circular polarization on 144MHz or 435MHz which requires that the pieces of coaxial cable feeding the two parts of the antenna should differ in electrical length by exactly a quarter-wave. He writes: "The dimensional accuracy desirable at these frequencies is high, being measured in parts of an inch, yet it is difficult to determine this parameter with any satisfactory precision using conventional techniques.

"One possibility is to calculate the physical length from the velocity factor quoted for the cable. But that factor may not be known or may only be known uncertainly; and, in any case, not every batch of cable will show coincidence with a quoted average figure.

"Another possibility is to determine by cut-and-try the resonant frequency of an approximate length shorted at one end, that end being then coupled to a dip meter. But stable dip meters are not commonplace at 144MHz, and rare, indeed, at 435MHz. And when that determination has been made, it is still necessary to compensate by arbitrary judgement for the effect of the shorted coupling end and for the effect of subsequently adding connectors. (*Note*: I recall an idea for coaxial tuning stubs is to use a pin to short-circuit temporarily inner and outer, to adjust stub resonance without actually cutting the cable—*G3VA*).

"I would like to call attention to a straightforward method of determining the correct length absolutely, by electrical measurement. It requires only patience, an swr meter and a willingness to sacrifice a foot or two of cable. The swr meter can be of ordinary, inexact, quality: only comparative readings are needed.

"The procedure begins by the attachment of any arbitrary length of cable, through the swr meter, to a transmitter set at low power (1 to 2W will be enough). The cable, which can be the whole length provided by the supplier, is left open-circuited and the swr is measured and recorded. The cable is then progressively shortened in equal snips: a 1in snip is convenient for 144MHz and 0.5in for 435MHz. It is then practicable, and desirable as a cross-check, to record the remaining length each time a measured snip is cut off. Each swr reading should be taken with care, with the meter reset as necessary each time. The method will average the errors, but it is still desirable to make each measurement as accurately as possible. One *can* plot the resulting sequence of figures, but experience shows that not to be necessary. The turning points of the curve can be determined quite precisely because the rate of change slows down at the peak and at the trough. Any supplementary calibration happening to be present on the meter face can be used to assist this operation: it need not be linear. Note that most simple swr meters give their most reliable performance at the lowest power which will adequately operate them.

"The two pieces of cable required for the two parts of the antenna to be phased can then be cut to any length convenient for the phasing harness so long as they differ by exactly the length determined in this operation. If identical end connectors are then fitted, in an identical manner, one may have confidence that the correct phasing requirement has been exactly and securely obtained. The method can also be used in other applications where phasing by feeder length is necessary."

Simplified tuned circuit and inductance formulas

Walter Borland, G3NXM, feels that readers may be interested in simplified forms of two of the basic formulas used in calculating resonance and inductance, as follows:

(1) The basic formula for a tuned circuit is $f = 1/(2\pi\sqrt{LC})$ but f, L and C are in the basic units of: hertz, henrys and farads. It can be changed to the more useful form of: $f^2 = 25,330/(LC)$ where f is in megahertz, L in microhenries and C in picofarads.

(2) Another formula inconvenient in its basic form is that for winding a multi-layer coil: $N = \sqrt{[3d \times 9l \times 10t \times L/(0 \cdot 2d^2)]}$ where N is number of turns, d is diameter of the coil former, l is the winding length, t the thickness of the winding, and L the inductance. This involves several variables, so a lot of trial and error may be required. However, the formula can be simplified to: $N = 1350L/(dn^2)$ where n is turns per inch of the wire. Decide on the length l, multiply by n (tpi), divide it into N, and the result will be the number of layers. The result may include part of a layer but, as G3NXM points out, that does not matter.

FM, nbfm and the spectrum

Steve Whitt, G8KDL, has rightly noted a misleading over-simplification in my comments (*TT* November 1984, p964) on the possibility of radiating higher-quality speech when using the vhf fm channels for local contacts. I inadvertently gave the impression that restricting the af range on fm had no effect on spectrum occupancy. I should have made it clearer that what I had in mind was that with carefully limited deviation it is possible for local contacts to transmit audio up to at least 5,000Hz within a 25kHz channel.

Theoretically, the sidebands of an fm transmission extend to infinity, although in practice the energy in the outer sidebands falls off very rapidly. A working expression used to determine the minimum i.f. bandwidth of an fm receiver is $2\Delta f + 2B$ where Δf is the peak frequency deviation and B is the highest baseband frequency (this assumes a stable local oscillator). Thus, in a stereo broadcast signal where the maximum deviation is ±75kHz, the af maximum around 15kHz, but with stereo and (in the USA) up to two "subsidiary communications" (sca) subcarriers, B may be 50 to 75kHz or more, so that the spectrum required could be as much as 300kHz. An amateur *nbfm* transmission with ±5kHz deviation and af restricted to 3kHz occupies at least $10 + 6 = 16$kHz. With a 5kHz af range this increases to $10 + 10$ or 20kHz. This still fits quite well into a 25kHz channel. Figs 3 and 4 show the basic spectrum distribution of fm signals at various frequencies and modulation indices.

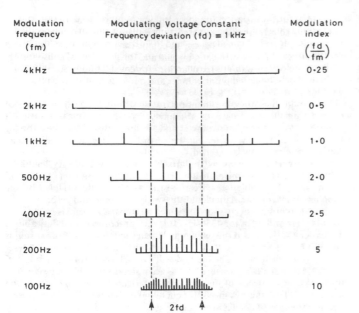

Fig 3. Sideband components of an fm signal with constant modulating voltage and ± 1kHz deviation at different audio frequencies

Modulation frequency (fm)	Modulating Voltage Constant Frequency deviation (fd) = 1kHz	Modulation index $\left(\frac{fd}{fm}\right)$
4kHz		0·25
2kHz		0·5
1kHz		1·0
500Hz		2·0
400Hz		2·5
200Hz		5
100Hz		10

2fd

Modulation frequency (fm) = 200Hz	Modulating Voltage	Frequency deviation (fd)	Modulation index $\left(\frac{fd}{fm}\right)$
	1	50Hz	0·25
	2	100Hz	0·5
	4	200Hz	1·0
	8	400Hz	2·0
	10	500Hz	2·9
	20	1kHz	5
	40	2kHz	10

Fig 4. Sideband components of an fm signal modulated with 200Hz tone at various modulating voltages

Thus on fm, as G8KDL noted, one *does* conserve spectrum by limiting af bandwidth, even if this is only one of the factors determining the transmission bandwidth, but the practical channelling protocol means that what is saved has little practical significance.

With the disappearance of most conventional amplitude-modulation with carrier, the old debate about the relative communications efficiency of different modes has largely vanished, but it may be worth pointing out that to arrive at a valid conclusion one *must* take into account the form of detection used in the receiver.

Communication theory tells us that we can exchange bandwidth for snr and hence transmitter power, which is why, for direct broadcasting from satellites, the video signal will be transmitted as wide-deviation fm, and the channels at 12GHz will be 27MHz wide (with some power radiated in the adjacent channels). This means that a geostationary fm transmitter of 100–200W peak output can do the work of an a.m. transmitter of about 10kW or so. But remember that part of the power advantage is lost if the detector has a high minimum "threshold". This is why there has been so much interest in recent years in "threshold extension" detectors, such as those based on phase-locked loops (pll). And, of course, you achieve virtually none of the power advantage of fm with an nbfm deviation of around ±5kHz.

A paper "Receiver techniques for reception of C-MAC dbs signals" by D. K. W. Hopkins and B. Beech of the IBA (*IEE Conference Publication*

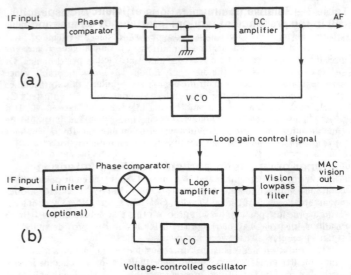

Fig 5. (a) Basic phase-locked-loop fm demodulator. (b) Threshold extension vision fm demodulator proposed for C-MAC/packet dbs. Second-order loop, natural frequency 18MHz nominal. Damping factor 3 (zero in loop 500kHz)

No. 240 "Tenth International Broadcasting Convention") discusses some of the ways in which 12GHz dbs receivers can be improved, including the use of low-cost pll threshold extension demodulators (Fig 5) for the vision signal, with separate discriminator detection for the psk digital sound/data signals.

Many years ago I reprinted in *TT* a table stemming from R P Haviland of General Electric (US) that showed the relative communication efficiency for speech (in decibels) in the presence of random interference from a signal using the same mode (Table 1). This showed how widely efficiency varies depending on the form of demodulation. The six demodulation systems examined were: envelope detection; slope detection (this is a normal fm discriminator and not the "slope" demodulation of fm with an envelope detector); product (synchronous) detector; select product (product detector with sideband selection); lock-loop (synchronous (product) demodulation using a phase-lock loop): and bi-aural demodulation (a specialized form of lock-loop); and bi-aural demodulation (a specialized form of lock-loop synchronous demodulator with independent presentation and selection of usb, lsb and permitting bi-aural presentation of double-sideband signals): Fig 6.

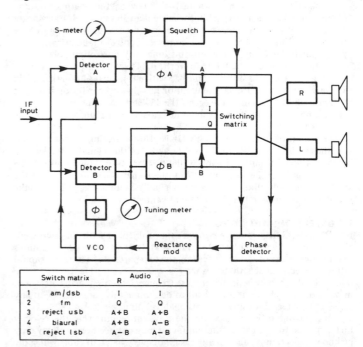

Switch matrix		Audio	
		R	L
1	am/dsb	I	I
2	fm	Q	Q
3	reject usb	A+B	A+B
4	biaural	A+B	A−B
5	reject lsb	A−B	A−B

Fig 6. Block outline of a flexible detector system developed by R P Haviland to investigate communications efficiency of a.m./fm/ssb/dsbsc modes, including bi-aural synchronous exalted-carrier detector (*Wireless World* November 1972 pp525-8)

Table 1—Relative communications efficiency for speech (dB) in the presence of random interference (same mode).

Mode	Envelope	Slope	Product	Select Product	Lock-Loop	Bi-aural
AM (dsb with carrier)	−3·2	—	−6·2	−3·2	−3·2	+2·8
NBFM	−20·4	−7·4	−10·4	−7·4	−7·4	−1·4
SSB	—	—	+10	+10	+7	+10
DSB (suppressed carrier)	—	—	+7	+10	+10	+16

It will be noted that nbfm emerges rather poorly from this comparison (about 4dB down on a.m. and 17dB down on ssb) and that the efficiency of all modes depends on the form of demodulation. The real attraction of nbfm to amateurs is that it causes less rfi and is more suited to the limitations of solidstate power amplifiers. It is also apparent from Table 1 that the *most* effective form of transmission is not, as commonly assumed, ssb, but dsb with suppressed carrier when this is received with a bi-aural demodulator.

It seems worth repeating this comparison in view of some recent articles in various journals that have been singing the praises of fm without distinguishing carefully between narrow and wide deviation. There is the problem, of course, that many fm rigs are set up with a deviation of ±7/10kHz rather than ±5kHz or so—but that is another story.

GaAs and computer-aided design

In the late 'sixties I recall going on a press jaunt to Racal at Tewkesbury on the occasion of the opening of what I believe was the first centre in the UK dedicated to computer-aided design (cad) of electronic circuits. Although crude by modern standards of sophistication, it was demonstrated that one could feed in the required response characteristics and specification of an amplifier and out would pop the optimum component values for the circuit.

I was much impressed, at least until one of my colleagues was told by the computer to fit a capacitor of an impossibly high value, of the order of farads if I recall correctly. No doubt he had specified some impossibly low frequency response, but the incident stuck in my memory as underlining the fact that if you ask a computer a stupid question the beasts are quite prepared to give you a stupid answer, unless the software tells it not to.

Yet one notices of late that the amateur radio journals are increasingly providing circuit and antenna information based on computer analyses, not always supported by practical experiments or measurements. Seldom is the warning given that the results and conclusions may be right or wrong, depending upon the correctness or otherwise of the information fed into the machine, the quality of the software programming and the validity of the basic mathematics.

An otherwise well-informed article "Quiet! preamp at work" by Paul Shuck, N6TX (*Ham Radio* November 1984, pp14–16, 19–20) on the problems of intermodulation distortion and other effects on vhf receiver performance of adding a low-noise, high-gain preamplifier, is marred by the author presenting some sweeping conclusions purely on the basis of computer imd analyses.

N6TX claims that while there is little difference in optimum performance at 144MHz with either good bipolar or mosfet devices in vhf/uhf preamplifiers, "an undisputed winner in all areas of vhf and uhf performance" is the gallium arsenide field effect transistor. This type of device, he claims, offers exceptionally high gain, low noise and wide dynamic range performance. Yet I cannot help feeling that his computer tells him this is so simply because he has fed into it device characteristics that may or may not represent what can be achieved in practice.

In *TT* (April 1984, p315) on the basis of practical experience, Chris Bartram, G4GDU, of Mostek argued that it is far from certain that GaAs devices, available at acceptable cost, are capable of doing all that is popularly claimed for them on 144MHz, even though such devices undoubtedly provide superior noise and gain performance on the microwave bands: Fig 7. For example, he had found the third-order intercept point is unlikely to exceed 6dBm and more likely to be about 0dBm. Yet N6TX uses the figure 11dBm, so it is not surprising that he is

able to claim for GaAs devices (no specified type numbers given) a spurious-free dynamic range of 84dB compared with 78dB for similarly unspecified bipolar and mosfet silicon devices, and 107dB for a high-level doubly-balanced mixer. This inevitably leads him to conclude that the optimum choice for any vhf/uhf receiver front-end is a GaAs fet amplifier followed by a high-level doubly-balanced mixer.

He may or may not be right. In his notes, G4GDU questioned where "the myth of exceptionally good dynamic performance with GaAs devices came from", although he showed how, unless interpreted very carefully, some manufacturers' literature can suggest a third-order intercept point above 10dBm.

N6TX, however, is on less contentious ground in drawing attention to the problem of biasing semiconductor devices to achieve a valid compromise between low-noise and wide dynamic range.

It may also be recalled that G4GDU drew attention to the extremely good strong-signal performance that can be achieved in vhf receivers by the use of complex non-dissipative negative feedback, though this technique is generally confined to specialist high-cost professional equipment. Although, rightly, there is much interest in the use of GaAs devices on shf and above, in view of the extremely attractive low-noise/high-gain characteristics of these and other "3–5" semiconductor materials, it has to be recognized that there remain considerable difficulties in these materials, both in the laboratory and in the bulk manufacturing process, limiting availability and increasing the cost. It is unlikely that they will ever be as cheap as good silicon devices.

Over-voltage sensing ic devices

The three-terminal ic voltage regulators have established a firm and popular place in the homemade psu firmament. Originally for 1A maximum current rating, but later for 5A and, most recently, I gather, available for up to 10A, they are gradually replacing the discrete series-pass regulators except for the really heavy-current units.

A further step towards simple but safe power units is the introduction by Motorola of three-terminal and pin-programmable over-voltage sensing circuits in integrated form. Two devices, MC34061 and MC34061A, combine with two external programming resistors and a thyristor to provide quick-acting crowbar protection for a psu. The MC34061, a three-terminal ic, has a ±2 per cent tolerance on trip voltage; the similar looking MC34061A ±1 per cent. For power supplies above 11V, a resistor in series with the thyristor gate is recommended to limit the power dissipated by the protection circuit to approximately 2W. Adding an external capacitor across this resistor provides a time-constant "delay" to give noise immunity and thus avoid the trip functioning on extremely short transients.

Also being introduced is an eight-pin dip device (MC34062) which provides a pin-programmable crowbar circuit in conjunction with an external thyristor (scr). The on-chip tapped resistor allows the circuit to be programmed for trip voltages from 3·5 to 40V with each of the five programming pins set to the standard trip point for a psu output of 5, 12, 15, 24 or 28V. Both devices sell in the USA, in 100-up quantities, for less than a dollar.

Getting it taped

Stan Kaplan, WB9RQR, in the Ozaukee Radio Club Newsletter and Hints and Kinks (*QST* October 1984) has drawn attention to the usefulness of adhesive copper tape. Such tape, as has previously been reported in *TT*, is made specifically for use in the electronics industry for such purposes as rf screening. However, the material that WB9RQR discovered is sold in the USA (and possibly the UK?) for use by hobbyists making stained-glass windows, so enabling the pieces of stained glass to be soldered together. It is made in widths from $\frac{1}{32}$in upwards, and the adhesive on the tape withstands the heat of soldering.

WB9RQR considers that, for amateur radio, "the possibilities for such tape seem endless". Among those that he has found useful are: making circuit traces on plain board for simple pcb projects, if necessary cutting the tape into narrow strips with scissors or razor blade; winding coils on

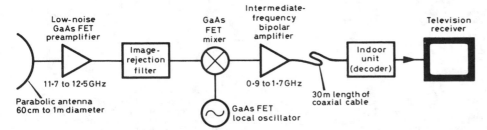

Low-noise GaAs FET preamplifier

11·7 to 12·5GHz

Parabolic antenna 60cm to 1m diameter

Image-rejection filter

GaAs FET mixer

GaAs FET local oscillator

Intermediate-frequency bipolar amplifier

0·9 to 1·7GHz

30m length of coaxial cable

Indoor unit (decoder)

Television receiver

Fig 7. Block outline of experimental 12GHz receiver for dbs television reception showing the important role of GaAs devices. It also underlines the potential tvi problem from 1·3GHz amateur transmissions breaking into the 0·9 to 1·7GHz i.f. cable

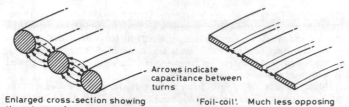

Enlarged cross-section showing three turns of a conventional coil

'Foil-coil'. Much less opposing area means much less capacitance

Arrows indicate capacitance between turns

Fig 8. Cross-sectional areas showing how the distributed capacitance of a coil is reduced by using copper-foil tape

cylindrical formers, adding "Such coils are ideal for a transmatch atu because they exhibit low distributed capacitance" (Fig 8); and for the conversion of a standard reel relay insert into a switchable coaxial connector (an idea he based on an article in *Design News* 28 March, 1983 "Foil tape converts reed switch to switchable coaxial conductor"): see Fig 9. The copper on the hobby tape is 0·0015in thick, so that the current rating for a given thickness of strip may need to be considered. The adhesive provides insulation of an uncertain quality, but this matters little if the base material is suitable for the particular application.

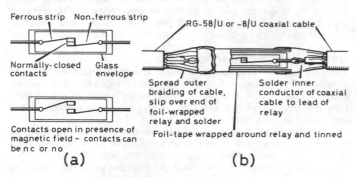

Ferrous strip   Non-ferrous strip

Normally-closed contacts   Glass envelope

Contacts open in presence of magnetic field – contacts can be n c or no

(a)

RG-58/U or –8/U coaxial cable

Spread outer braiding of cable, slip over end of foil-wrapped relay and solder

Solder inner conductor of coaxial cable to lead of relay

Foil-tape wrapped around relay and tinned

(b)

Fig 9. (a) The anatomy of a reed switch; (b) how a coaxial reed relay can be made with the aid of copper-foil tape

70MHz on the cheap

Even if high-quality MoD surplus is in short supply, there are other useful pickings. R. A. Sansoni, G4MWR, points out that many of the "illegal" cordless telephones are now becoming available at give-away prices. Approved frequencies for cordless telephones are now 1·642 to 1·782MHz (base transmit) and 47·456 to 47·543MHz (remote transmit), but there are still in use or in the shops a large number of units with base transmit frequencies about 49MHz and remote transmit 70 to 72MHz. BT have the power to confiscate any unauthorized equipment found connected to their network, and users and dealers are faced with equipment for which there is now virtually no market.

G4MWR finds that the 70MHz base receiver and 70MHz remote transmitter can form the basis of a 70MHz band transceiver of useful performance. He writes: "The sets are crystal-controlled (receiver 59MHz, transmitter 14MHz) with fm deviation of 5 to 7kHz. I have found some models with a receiver sensitivity as good as 0·175μV. Transmitter power can vary from 0·5W to 1·5W on the remote units (authorized models are limited to 0·1W). And there is another bonus; the versions using the 70–72MHz portion for both transmit and receive correspond in channels to the 25kHz spacing and location. The only modification required is to choose the crystals, replace them and disable the logic coding in the receiver or take the af out from the discriminator to a small af amplifier."

Tips and topics

G6ZCY draws attention to a possible source of conductive paint "Chipshield" as demonstrated on "Tomorrow's World" for BBC1, for reducing rf radiation from home computers but which could be applied to any plastics enclosure etc to reduce rfi by providing screening: Bee Chemical Co (UK) Ltd, Kangley Bridge Road, Lower Sydenham, London SE26 5BA. However, at the time of writing he had no details of prices, quantities etc.

G3KXF approves of the publicity given to the recent power-line tragedies, but was surprised to see than nobody referred to the problem of power-line noise radiation which should deter operators from siting antennas anywhere near dangerous power lines. With his motto of "put amateur back into amateur radio" G3KXF fears that "off the shelf" equipment operators may learn little about the does and don'ts of antenna siting and so run into danger. He recalls that one of the first lessons he learned was to avoid "power line QRN".

Dr A.F. Gerrard, G4TFU, was recently caught out by assuming (on the basis of the rather misleading Ambit catalogue details) that the SBL1 double-balanced mixer has the same pin connections as the now less readily available MD108. I recall this point has been made previously in *TT*, but it is worth repeating. You cannot simply substitute an SBL1 for an MD108 without changing the pin connections.

Feedback on the "underground hazards" item in the November *TT*. G3ZPF notes that the mention of manholes should read: "Manholes are usually about 1m deep. Bases should be at least 900mm (*not* 200mm) deep in order to be immune from seasonal movements in the ground." The point he was trying to make was that on large, flat housing developments manholes could be much deeper. Normally the bottom of the base should be about the same depth. □

Technical Topics
by Pat Hawker, G3VA

AS SOMEONE who increasingly finds it difficult to wax very enthusiastically about "new technology", I find it necessary from time to time to remind myself that Rab Butler, sometimes described as "the best prime minister Britain never had", warned us that "all too often those who do not seek to change with the times find that the times leave them changed for the worse." The battered British consumer-electronics industry has been known to dismiss the highly-successful Japanese technologists as being mainly derivative rather than creative, yet, as *Nature* has put it: "From ships to video recorders, Japanese technologists have been able to design and manufacture high-quality products more cheaply than others, and at the same time make sure they function reliably. If this ingenuity is not creative, many of us should be wondering what is meant by creativity".

It may have been true in the 'sixties, when Japanese amateur-radio products began to appear on the world market, that those first designs used strikingly familiar ideas, but there was a new emphasis on cost-effective production engineering that brought them within the reach of far more amateurs. It has long been apparent that reliability of modern equipment is related more to mechanical engineering, metallurgy and chemical engineering than to innovative electronic circuitry.

Hybrid microelectronics—the coming thing?
As we indicate below, current developments all over the world in how equipment is assembled will bring about changes that many of us will much regret, since inevitably they make further inroads into some of the traditional do-it-yourself and learning-by-doing aspects of the hobby. But one must hope that there will prove to be at least some compensating advantages for those who are prepared "to change with the times" and turn more to those areas of radio communication where there are still opportunities for genuine experimental work.

THIS MONTH
Hybrid microelectronics—the coming thing
Stuck with what you buy
Whither experimentation?
A poor man's log-periodic
Comparision with log-periodic arrays
Wires in parallel
Safety standards
Mercury is dangerous
144MHz, 134MHz and dbs tvi
Ripple on dc supplies
Testing a high-current psu
Flash-over protection for high-power linear amplifiers
Self-amalgamating tape—a cautionary tale

In *TT* December 1981 (pp1127–8) and more recently in *TT* January 1984, I drew attention to new forms of "hybrid microelectronics", "surface-mounted multi-layer assembly" and other closely-related methods of assembling equipment using tiny chip-type components, with the ic devices and semiconductors automatically located and then glued into place on compact printed circuit boards before being wave or dip soldered. It was pointed out that because of the very small size of chip-components and chip-carrier-type semi-conductor devices, complex circuits could be assembled economically at high rates on much smaller boards than with the established forms of pcb technology. I expressed the opinion that the economics of these forms of assembly would ensure that they would find their way into the factory construction of amateur radio equipment, at least in those areas which justify the setting up of high-volume production lines.

To quote what I wrote in January 1984: "While there are obvious advantages to the manufacturers, the users benefit from the improved reliability and consistency of performance that is possible (but) at the same time it does represent a further step along the path towards 'throw-away' electronics; that is, the disposal of the complete circuit board (or even the complete equipment) should a fault occur. Tracing and replacing individual faulty components in such assemblies is virtually impossible. The chip components of millimetric dimensions are often far too small to carry identification marks or values, while the high packing density renders traditional forms of fault-tracing extremely difficult . . . it is not technology for experimental bread-board units."

Some of these new constructional techniques are already being used in recent Japanese models, and fully bear out the points made above, although the user advantages in terms of better value-for-money, due to reduced manufacturing costs, are being rendered invisible in the UK by the dramatic decline in the pound-sterling/yen exchange rate.

But there is one important consequence of the new technology that was missed in my earlier notes: the virtual impossibility of making *any*

Photo 1. Comparing the size of two boards that fulfil identical functions. In general, boards using surface-mounted devices, chip components etc require only a third of the board area of conventional pcb assemblies. *(Mullard Ltd)*

Photo 2. Examples from the Mullard range of components used in surface mounted assemblies. Included are chip resistors, wet aluminium electrolytic capacitors, blue chip capacitors, ceramic multilayer capacitors, SOT packaged transistors and diodes, and SO packaged integrated circuits. All are of miniature dimensions, and few carry any identification or values. Similarly packaged components are increasingly being used in many countries in conjunction with automatic assembly

Photo 3. A far cry from the kitchen table! A modern, multi-head automatic placement machine. Typically with eight placement heads, each mounting 25 components, some 200,000 components are put on to 1,000 boards in an hour. Despite the need for specialized servicing and virtual impossibility of d-i-y modifications, this—for better or worse—is the way the electronics industry is going. *(Mullard Ltd)*

modifications to equipment made using the new production techniques, either to improve performance or to modify for UK use models intended for operation elsewhere.

Stuck with what you buy

Kjell Stroem, SM6CPI, who is currently the European representative of Yaesu Musen based in Italy, admits that in the past, he—like many other European amateurs—has occasionally by-passed the "authorized dealers" and brought in Japanese transceivers as personal imports, then changed a few components to make them work to European standards, frequency bands, channelling etc; tackling the odd bit of troubleshooting and repair during the initial phase of the bath-tub reliability curve that is normally taken care of by the guarantee. This practice meant that equipment could be acquired at prices below those set by authorized dealers to cover the cost of guaranteed after-sales service, the stocking of spares etc. (See *TT* January 1984, p 45).

SM6CPI now writes: "From correspondence arriving at the headquarters of Yaesu Musen, I understand there is now a further complication that can lead to disappointment and embarrassment to those attempting personal importing.

"With the advent of melf-type chip components there is no longer any easy way of modifying equipment from one version into another. It is also extremely difficult to troubleshoot and repair them without access to the specialized techniques that are now required. Some of the complications include:

(a) There is no identification on components; only on the parts magazine that is used for automatic assembly.

(b) The part is secured not only as the result of dip soldering but also because it is glued on to the pcb with epoxy glue (in order to stay put during the soldering); this is then oven hardened and further hardened by the heat during the soldering process.

(c) There is always the risk that if you attack the epoxy bond with, say, a chisel, you will also remove a number of the under-lying fine-line foil conductors.

"One result, is that it is no longer practicable to add repeater shift and change from 20kHz to 12·5/25kHz channel spacing on a Japanese home-model of a 144MHz transceiver by just moving a couple of diodes (as often possible in the past). In many cases not even the factory can carry out such modifications once the soldering process has been carried out.

"This may be seen as an undesirable loss of flexibility, but there are several good reasons why these forms of assembly have come to stay. A highly automated production system makes it possible to offer better value for money. Production costs have been rising rapidly in Japan, and new production techniques are being constantly introduced to counter this trend. It has already been shown (for example with the Walkman type of portable cassette players which have been based on the new techniques for several years) that equipments manufactured in this way prove more reliable and require less servicing.

"The problem of rising costs is one reason why so many new models are being introduced; few people like to pay substantially more this year than they would have paid a few years ago for the same model. Gone are the days when the FT101 or FRG-7 could stay on the production lines until their metal stamping tools were completely worn down."

SM6CPI notes also the problems that come from the high rate of inflation and the decline in exchange rates which tend to distort the pricing of both new and secondhand equipment in the UK, and which conceal the fact that there has been almost continuous improvement in real value-for-money terms. He wonders why, in the UK, unusually high prices are asked for the second hand equipment that he sees advertised in "Members Ads" etc. "In most countries the value of electronic equipment drops some 30 per cent just after you have opened the box and plugged the lead into the wall socket, yet it seems to take some five years of use before the same price drop is reached in the UK."

He also believes, with some justification, that there is little demand for simple, low-budget equipment. Attempts to introduce "economy" designs have not met with the sort of response that would be needed to encourage the Japanese firms to make further efforts in that direction. "Is it a question of a status symbol, the strange practice whereby amateurs announce to the world what brand and model of radio they are using, that is to blame for this?" SM6CPI wonders. He also raises some other matters on which *TT* has commented, including the standard of the equipment reviews that appear in many magazines. He shares some of my own views on this subject, including the fact that there will always be a spread in the measurements made on different models, and the evidence that by no means all of the readers, or apparently even some of the writers, are really sure of the practical significance (or otherwise) of some of the measurements—although he specifically excludes *Rad Com* reviewer Peter Hart, G3SJX, from this criticism.

SM6CPI thus echoes the theme of my 1981 paper "Effect of receiver specifications on practical performance" in which I suggested that it is increasingly difficult to interpret makers' and retailers' promotional material in terms that relate meaningfully to operational performance, and noted that "the assistance that can be provided by 'reviews' in the technical journals is often limited by the circumstances under which these normally have to be prepared (generally based on a single receiver selected and loaned for the purpose by the manufacturer or importer)". I also added that "many of the features now found on receivers intended for the amateur market add only marginally to the on-air performance in the amateur service; complexity is a disease".

Whither experimentation?

The new factory production techniques are here to stay, even though they remove some opportunities for amateur radio operators to engage in experimentation and development in the course of improving or "personalizing" their black boxes. These changes, however, need not be accepted as implying that the traditional role of the experimentally-minded amateur, or those seeking to "learn by doing", has now vanished and the soldering iron and multimeter finally discarded. But they may well mean that for the majority of us, emphasis and technical interest must swing increasingly away from basic electronic circuitry for transmitters and receivers into those other areas where opportunities still abound for d-i-y innovation: "kiss" and QRP rigs; linears; power supply units; microwave technology etc.

One major such area still offering tremendous opportunities for innovation is that of hf antennas. A few years ago for the IERE Radio Receivers and Associated Systems Conference at Leeds, I wrote: "Long- and medium-distance amateur two-way communication is often conducted under marginal conditions; increasingly the relative performance of different (and often 'competing') stations tends to be determined primarily by the strength of the signal received by the distant station; in turn this will be set by propagation conditions; power-gain, directivity, height and siting of the transmitting antennas. Amateur radio, in the professional jargon, has increasingly become a competitive, interference-limited service, rather than signal-strength-limited as in earlier days".

The performance of the transmitting antenna represents the single most important factor affecting station results—and the most promising area for further development. The old adage "if you can't hear them, you can't work them", putting emphasis on the receiving side, has almost lost its point. Most hf receivers, even with a moderate antenna, will bring in all the dx that we have any hope of working. The *useful* sensitivity of hf receivers tends to be limited far more by local levels of electrical and signal interference than by their design. Of course, the classic criteria of good sensitivity, selectivity filters of good shape factor and providing minimum noise bandwidth, reasonable stability and freedom from spurious responses —and in some circumstances a wide dynamic range—continue to be important. But both for transmission and reception it is the efficiency and particularly the directivity of the antenna, and the skilful exploitation of site factors and hf propagation that contribute to consistent dx performance. There is nothing more frustrating than to have an extremely sensitive receiver but an inefficient transmitting antenna!

Fortunately for the future of amateur radio, the development of practical antenna systems for the wide variety of situations and locations in which we may wish to establish a station continues to provide the chance to engage in genuinely useful development work, ranging from those who seek only to find a new low-cost flexible solution for undemanding bands and undemanding contacts, to the most professional and painstaking investigations of fundamentally new principles. Which brings us, naturally, to the latest instalment of Les Moxon's painstaking work on hf antennas.

A poor man's log-periodic?

TT (April 1984, pp316–7) under the heading "Antennas that slow the wave" provided detailed information on a novel form of loaded folded dipole element developed by G6XN. Though, as he pointed out, the design lacked "sales appeal" it had the remarkable property that, despite its small size and multiband properties, it could be fed with any length of open-wire feeder without degrading its 14MHz bandwidth. This, G6XN reported, was in marked contrast to his experience with other multiband systems based on the use of open-wire lines which tend to involve fairly critical adjustment of the atu. G6XN admitted that this characteristic had been completely unexpected and was, in effect, yet another case of the serendipity that from time to time comes to the rescue—the obverse of Murphy's Law.

Fortunately, G6XN is of a disposition that does not just accept an apparent anomaly but seeks to find out just why it occurs and then to investigate whether it might provide a clue to further useful developments. In this instance, he confesses that it took him quite a long time to arrive at the explanation and to appreciate fully its practical significance. He writes:

"What has now emerged is, I believe, an entirely new and (potentially) very important family of multiband beam antennas. These can include many different forms of construction and a wide range of options. The earlier "loaded folded dipole" owes its membership of this family to the fact that, at the lowest frequency of operation, although physically reduced in size, it is electrically a full wavelength loop *with the two half-wavelengths having different values of Z_0 so that they act as quarter-wave transformers providing an impedance step-up equal to the square of the Z_0 ratio.* The current is stepped *down* by the Z_0 ratio, so that in the case of, say, a quad or delta loop having low Z_0 at the top, *most of the radiation comes from the top of the loop, thus increasing the effective height.* This effect tends to be greatly augmented in practical designs which in most cases lead to relatively short lengths and less uniform current distributions for the high-Z_0 portions of the loops.

"Fig 1 best illustrates the principle; Fig 2 shows the first version of the new beam to be tried in practice. The helix loading of Fig 1 has been

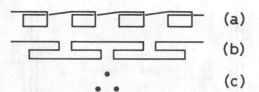

Fig 3. (a) VK5HA-type planar loading is preferable to helix loading and is a near optimum solution. (b) Meander-line loading is another alternative. (c) Triangular configuration for three parallel wires

replaced by 'planar loading', an idea for which I am indebted to VK5HA. This involves a string of one-turn loops as in Fig 3 (a). For these I have used three cords arranged as in Fig 3 (c), with appropriate spacers, instead of a solid former. With three loops each side of centre, I was able to fold a half-wave dipole element into about one-third of its normal length, at the cost of an increase of only some 15–20 per cent in total wire length. This is a big improvement over a helix or another alternative such as a form of 'the 'meader' system shown recently in *TT* (November 1984 Fig 6 (b)) as a means of reducing the overall span of a dipole element and which can be implemented as in Fig 3 (b).

"A Mark 2 version, dubbed by others 'The Claw', shown in Fig 4, has

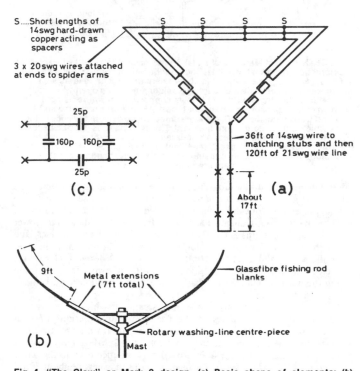

Fig 4. "The Claw" or Mark 2 design. (a) Basic shape of elements; (b) construction of supporting arms; and (c) matching/coupling network for 10MHz switched in by relays at point X in the feeders

been my main antenna for several months, but has not been without problems due to a number of mechanical design errors. Planar loading, unfortunately, is ideally suitable for getting caught up in bushes etc, and the antenna sustained considerable damage en route from the lawn to the mast. Flimsy construction, relying partly on nylon fishing line ties, plus bending the top section down along thin glass-fibre arms, meant that the whole thing is top heavy and (the nylon line being elastic) wobbles like a jelly! Almost unbelievably, it survived the severe gales of December 1984.

"Worse problems have arisen from the resulting asymmetry (one arm broke in transit) in conjunction with a resonant mast which, on 10MHz, caused the current in the reflector to be either normal or zero depending on whether I was holding on to the wooden or metal part of the mast! Confusion abounded. Erratic results on 21 and 28MHz can be attributed partly to this and partly to other factors which came to light during development of the Mark 3 array, shown in Fig 5.

"This has now been completed and is being evaluated at relatively low height pending the advent of better weather (G6XN's letter was written in January). This is a relatively neat and clean arrangement and so far appears to have no vices. Inductive loading has been avoided by going to a larger loop size, and it has been found just possible to achieve this without pattern break-up at 28MHz, where the current zeros occur in the exact centre of the

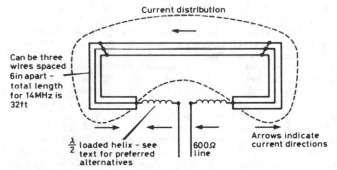

Fig 1. Basic concept of the reduced-size multiband folded-dipole element. The 600Ω feeder can be any length but, if long or thin, matching stubs switched in at ground level are an improvement and may be essential at the highest frequencies

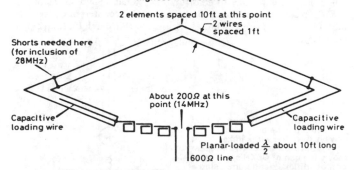

Fig 2. Practical implementation of arrays using multiband folded-dipole elements. This is G6XN's Mark 1 design. With 6ft spacing at the bottom, and 2ft at the ends between the two sections, there was severe overcoupling on 14MHz, cured by neutralization. Total span about 20ft

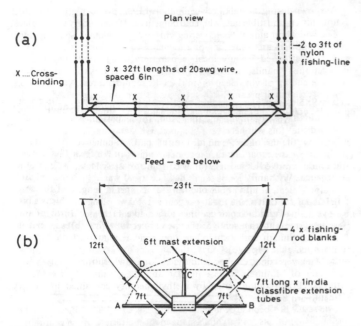

(a)

Plan view

X ....Cross-binding

3 x 32ft lengths of 20swg wire, spaced 6in

2 to 3ft of nylon fishing-line

X   X   X   X   X

Feed — see below

(b)

23ft

12ft   6ft mast extension   12ft

4 x fishing-rod blanks

D   E
C
7ft   7ft
A   B

7ft long x 1in dia Glassfibre extension tubes

Fig 5. G6XN's latest Mark 3 design. (a) Shows basic shape, but when erected the elements are almost invisible. The arrangement is similar to the VK2ABQ flat array, and only one element is shown here in full. The feeders are single 20swg wires dropped down through the spider arms, then open-wire resonant lines (40ft) to the transmitter. (b) Shows supporting structure using fishing-rod blanks and glass-fibre extension tubes. AB is a 6ft dural tube and there is a short transverse tube at C, the arms being guyed back to the ends of these tubes which are insulated from the mast. The spacing rods (6ft of tube, 0·5in od, with insulated end pieces) are located at the glass-fibre rod junctions. Horizontal metal rods, if used, must not exceed about 8–10ft. The metal extensions almost certainly causing problems even though the elements in Fig 4 are are held clear of them

sides, which should therefore not radiate. This should maximize the effective height, but there is a bandwidth penalty unless one is prepared to retune; this can be done in the shack provided the feeders are not too long.

"The larger loops mean increased effective height at the lower frequencies, though this is largely offset by radiation from the sides, and the main incentive for the larger loops has been an improvement in gain, as predicted, of about 2dB at 10MHz. The Mark 2 design (Fig 4) has a predicted gain of only 2 to 3dB at 10MHz, after allowing for losses (and curing the mast resonance), but has given a pretty good account of itself over the long path to Australia.

"So far I have used only two elements, and this inevitably involves compromises at the extremes of the frequency range because of non-optimum spacings. With three elements a spacing of 8ft would be consistent with optimum performance all the way from 14 to 28MHz. The use of the outer two elements would give improved performance (due to the wider spacing) on 10MHz. However, for feeder lengths in excess of about 30ft it is essential to use some form of switched matching at 10MHz; this also provides independent control of coupling between the elements, as shown in Fig 4.

"This introduces yet another valuable feature of the new system: the ability to control coupling by the connection of small capacitors between the feedlines in a readily accessible position. The array of Fig 2 was so badly overcoupled that at 14MHz there was no f:b ratio at all, but neutralization produced (at the first attempt) 38dB of rejection! The array of Fig 4 was badly *undercoupled*, giving at first only 10dB f:b ratio, but with the in-phase connection of a pair of 5pF capacitors about 8ft from a current maximum I am getting 20–30dB of rejection. The null can be set for any frequency or back direction with a single knob at the operating position, controlling the resonant frequency of the reflector.

"The design of Fig 5 resembles very closely the well-known VK2ABQ design. Drawing on past experience (as reflected in *TT* items and in *HF antennas for all locations*), the coupling has turned out to be very nearly optimum on all three bands (14/21/28MHz) without further adjustment."

Comparison with log periodic arrays

It will be appreciated that the object of this new family of designs is to provide a rotatable, directional antenna that can be used on 10MHz and on any frequency between 14 and 28MHz without the radiation pattern breaking up, characteristics normally associated with large and heavy log-periodic arrays whose use is virtually confined to professional communica-

tions and hf broadcasting. G6XN continues his explanatory notes as follows:

"With three elements one can expect a gain of 6dBd from 14 to 28MHz, plus 4dB at a spot frequency of 10·1MHz. This is directly comparable to what can be achieved with the size of log periodic arrays practicable for amateur radio. The log periodics have the advantage that there is no tuning operation needed and no theoretical limit to the frequency range. Nevertheless with the new array the tuning could be preset. Similarly, extending the coverage of a log-periodic to cover 7MHz would require an extremely large structure unlikely to be within the means of many amateurs. The new family of beams, on the other hand, offers the possibility of achieving the ultimate in lightness, low cost, low windage and miniaturization. They could be designed to 'look good', although it must be admitted that supplies of glass-fibre rods are difficult to find and it may be necessary to settle for compromises that would make it look less aesthetically attractive.

"The arrays have the big advantage that they can be made instantly reversible from the shack so that sufficient rotation can be achieved using two cords from a single position, so eliminating the need for a beam rotator. No adjustment is needed before erection, and dimensions become critical only when the operating range is being pushed to its limit. The need for symmetry, noted earlier, applies to *all* horizontal beams (lack of it may well account for the disappointing results of, for example, the TET antenna based on the principles formulated by VK2AOU). Mast resonances are probably the cause of much confusion. In this respect, serious problems arose on 21 and 28MHz due to resonances of metal struts used to reinforce the Fig 5 design at its centre, leading to considerable mechanical redesign. A slight tendency to overcoupling (rather than the anticipated undercoupling) at 21MHz is believed to be due to two short spacing rods, the ends of which are insulated but come close to points of high voltage."

Wires in parallel

The use of parallel wires rather than tubular elements in the new arrays has brought to light an important finding that would seem to apply to virtually any use of this technique for multiband systems. This is the need to make *several* cross connections between the wires. G6XN identifies a link between this and his experiences with groundplane antennas (*TT* March 1981). It may be recalled that G6XN then noted that the *one* length of radial which should be avoided is the *usual* quarter-wave. This is because the impedance of a quarter-wave radial changes very rapidly near resonance; phase reversals could thus occur were it not for losses which have never been specified or investigated! Unfortunately this message, expressed both in *TT* and in G6XN's book, has failed to get through with the use of λ/4 radials still apparently universal.

This rapid change of impedance near resonance turns up in other guises. G6XN himself was caught out twice in quick succession. In one case he had a vertical monopole with three thin wires joined in parallel at the base, but operation was haywire until the wires were joined also at a point some 2 to 3ft up from the base: Fig 6. With the beam of Fig 2, care was taken to put the short-circuit at a voltage point (14MHz). Nevertheless a big difference in wire currents resulted at 28MHz because the points of maximum voltage on 14MHz were current points on 28MHz.

G6XN therefore postulates, *as an axiom*, that wires in parallel must *never* be connected *only* at points of current maximum. This axiom clearly condemns virtually all conventional groundplane antennas (I shudder to think of the irate letters this statement may attract!). G6XN points out that the cure is trivial; it remains the fact that there is no *need* for long radials, and only a single radial is needed provided that it is short enough not to upset the radiation pattern. Planar loading in the VK5HA style (Fig 3 (b)) should prove a good way to construct such radials. Fig 6 shows one of G6XN's recommended forms of helix-loaded "counterpoise" type of radial for a groundplane antenna as discussed in *TT* (March 1981, pp 235–6) and *HFAfal*.

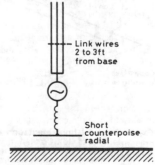

Fig 6. Multi-wire vertical groundplane antennas should always have the wires linked 2–3ft above the base. The diagram shows the use of G6XN's preferred form of artificial earthplane using a single-loaded counterpoise "radial"

Link wires 2 to 3ft from base

Short counterpoise radial

Fig 7. Current distribution of loaded elements: (a) distributed loading results in sinusoidal current distribution; (b) centre loading gives triangular current distribution

The basic principle of the short multiband folded dipole element, such as those shown in Figs 4 and 5, can provide other options. For example, single-elements or arrays could be suspended between two masts or trees, using spreaders for the arrays. Similar principles can be applied to any shape or size of loop provided that it is small enough not to result in pattern break-up at the highest frequency. As a challenge, G6XN has considered trying to build an antenna with flat folded-dipole elements and a 12ft diameter turning circle, yet providing a gain approaching that of full-size performance. This would require either helical or, probably better, multi-turn planar loading.

Finally, G6XN adds a note on the impedance of multi-wire elements: "Three thin wires spaced 6in provide a Z_0 of about 600Ω compared with 1,100Ω for a single wire. The latter figure can be expected to be increased by inductive loading, and one can use either distributed loading *or* centre loading (see Fig 7). The latter may be preferable, a reversal of the usual situation arising from the fact that we are not in this case trying to *increase* radiation but rather to *stop* the wrong part of the loop from radiating. The top portion of the loop can be *capacitively* loaded (stretched) as is done to a small extent in the arrangement shown in Fig 2."

For this type of array he considers three wires in parallel are about optimum. Beyond three, one is in the region of diminishing returns, but with only two the impedance ratio is reduced significantly.

Safety standards

As discussed in *TT* on various occasions, consumer electronic products are expected to conform to the safety standard BS415:1979, including the fitting of double-pole on-off mains switches, non-accessibility of high voltages, the use of isolation components on antenna sockets in the absence of double-wound mains transformers, etc. Television set makers and others go to considerable lengths to ensure their products meet BS415, and issue warnings when things are found to have gone wrong. For example a large firm recently told dealers that: "It has become known that a component used in the manufacture of Brand X tv sets during 1977–80 is susceptible to an ageing defect which can give rise to the risk of fire". Local authorized dealers were requested to carry out a modification to such sets for which they would be reimbursed by the manufacturer. One hopes that the warning was followed up and the sets duly modified.

There would appear, however, to be no obligation for distributors or retailers to ensure that imported amateur radio equipment complies fully with BS415, and it would take a sharper legal brain than mine to unravel the extent to which the Consumer Safety Act, 1978 covers such equipment; noting that, if it does, then it would apply also to buying or selling second-hand equipment.

In *Electrical and Radio Trading* (22 November 1984, p22) Sant Kharbanda, G2PU, chairman of Labgear Cablevision Ltd, notes that the many smaller manufacturers of tv accessories, such as mains-powered antenna masthead and set-top preamplifiers, do not necessarily carry out the detailed attention at the design, development and production stages required by BS415. This should involve the correct choice of raw materials and components; the manufacturing processes; and testing and quality control. He quotes tests on a competitor's masthead preamp power supply which showed:

(a) mains transformer windings substantially exceeded the maximum permitted temperature rise after 17min;

(b) the transformer core similarly after 55min; and

(c) the housing similarly after 32min.

There was also non-compliance with BS405 in the mains cable being directly soldered to the conductors of a printed circuit board; with the result that, in the absence of a thermal cut-out etc, under fault conditions this might result, in extreme cases, in fire, release of noxious fumes or a shock hazard.

G2PU drew attention to the importance of adequate creepage and clearance distances between "live" and accessible points even under extreme humid conditions.

Elsewhere it has been pointed out that the Home Office advice on removing the mains plug of a tv set from the mains socket overnight is being modified. It is recognized that fires can arise through "spontaneous combustion" of tv sets even when these are turned off and disconnected; presumably this is due to overheating during operation, with later combustion.

As shown during the Falklands campaign of 1982, pvc-insulation on cables is not only combustible but, when burning, gives off extremely toxic fumes.

The wideband amplifiers (covering vhf *and* uhf channels) used in some tv preamplifiers are something of a menace to amateurs, as they may be greatly overloaded by any local transmitters using bands intermediate between the tv bands, such as 70, 144 and 430MHz. It is to be hoped that with the ending of vhf television in the UK, manufacturers will take steps to ensure that their preamplifiers are less sensitive to signals below 470MHz and above 860MHz. However, since virtually all other countries are continuing to use both vhf and uhf bands for television, it should not be assumed that this will necessarily happen. UK amateurs benefit in several ways from the use of uhf-only tv, but this hardly applies to either British tv viewers or the broadcasters. As somebody not entirely disinterested in tv transmission, I would still argue that Band 3(175–216MHz) is the optimum tv broadcasting band!

Mercury is dangerous

As a very small child I reputedly once bit a medical thermometer and must have swallowed at least some of the mercury. I seem to have survived the incident, although some unkind readers may suggest that it obviously resulted in brain damage. Today, the dangers of mercuric poisoning are more widely recognized, particularly in Japan where there were major outbreaks of Minimata disease in 1956 and 1964, caused by the victims eating shellfish contaminated by methyl mercury contained in factory effluent.

One result has been growing alarm in that country over the disposal of the many millions of alkaline-manganese batteries which contain a significant amount of mercury and which are regularly used in the popular walk-about audio recorders etc. Japan now manufactures some 3,000-million dry batteries a year, the majority finishing up on municipal rubbish dumps and later used as landfill. There is also, of course, mercury in the small mercury button cells and some in discarded fluorescent lighting tubes etc. Some part of all this mercury becomes converted into organic mercury by the action of bacteria and leached away. Such sites, it has been calculated, have an average battery-derived mercury content of about three parts per million, or roughly a thousand times more than the permissible level of mercury in water supplies.

There have been public demonstrations in Japan over the risk from batteries. As a result Japanese battery manufacturers are reportedly seeking ways of making high-energy batteries free of mercury, and seeking to encourage more use of incineration in the disposal of alkaline-manganese batteries.

But this provides an interesting example of how hazards can arise initially unnoticed when a change in technology, such as the introduction of walk-about audio, alters the pattern of consumption and so changes what was virtually a negligible risk into one requiring positive action.

Fortunately, for most amateur radio applications, the traditional carbon-zinc battery or, more especially, the rechargeable nicad, is considerably more cost-effective.

144MHz, 134MHz and dbs tvi

In the February *TT* (Fig 7, p116), I included a block diagram showing a typical arrangement for future 12GHz dbs television receivers, *inter alia* noting the vulnerability to breakthrough of 1·3GHz amateur transmissions with the broadband first i.f. of 0·9 to 1·7GHz. In practice, however, there is hope that the receivers will avoid tuning through 1·3GHz by shifting the lower edge up to about 1·4GHz.

But there is another, potentially far more serious problem facing the many thousands of amateurs who use 144MHz. This is the question of breakthrough into the second (fixed) i.f. amplifier stages, which need to have a bandwidth of around 30MHz in order to cope with the wide-deviation fm vision signals. G8AAE notes that Philips, for example, are currently offering surface acoustic wave (saw) i.f. filters for satellite receivers having a nominal centre frequency of 134MHz, with pass bandwidths of either 28 or 30MHz; in other words, passing signals between about 120 to 148MHz.

It is certainly the case that 134MHz is already being considered as a "standard" i.f. by a number of committees, and is being supported by the results of investigations into potential problems of emc. But there is no doubt whatsoever that receivers using this i.f., to be clear of tvi from local 144MHz signals, will need to be built to standards higher than those usually found in mass-produced consumer-type receivers.

I recall the days shortly after the second world war when a number of British tv receivers, before the adoption of the standard tv i.f. between 34 and 40MHz, had i.fs that impinged on several of our hf bands, including 14, 21 and 28MHz. Curing tvi on such sets was extremely difficult and at times virtually impossible.

The DTI(RRD), BREMA and broadcast engineers (with RSGB representation) have certainly been at pains to check that 134·2MHz can be used without tvi being inevitable. They have recognized the problem of 144MHz pick-up on the coaxial cable linking indoor and outdoor units, or from direct breakthrough into the indoor unit. Their conclusion, which personally I suspect is rather over-optimistic, is that 134MHz is suitable provided that manufacturers observe a series of recommendations.

Using an experimental receiver, they have shown that it is *possible* to build-in sufficient isolation in respect of cable pick-up and direct breakthrough provided that, for example, the indoor unit is in a complete metal enclosure, the linking cable has excellent braid coverage and is used with high-quality connectors, and the 144MHz signals are attenuated by entering the building etc. In other words, *if* all dbs receivers are mass-produced to the proposed very high standards, a local 144MHz transmitter should not cause tvi—though the margins âre narrow.

Even if all the recommendations are accepted by British and European industry, this is no guarantee that they will be followed elsewhere, particularly as there is much pressure for the costs of dbs receivers to be reduced to a minimum. And initial isolation of a tv receiver can soon degrade, or be reduced by inexpert servicing. Even if the RIS teams are prepared to tell affected viewers that their tvi is due to the receiver and not the amateur transmitter, we have learned how unsatisfactory this can be, with irate viewers then using every possible means of harassing the amateur.

Clearly it is very difficult to find a suitable i.f, but a choice that includes the most heavily populated amateur band is storing up trouble for years to come. The West Germans have proposed 471MHz, which would certainly be far more acceptable to amateurs, but shifts the problem to broadcasters using Channels 21, 22 or 23 at up to 1,000kW erp!

Ripple on dc supplies

The technique of float-charging heavy-duty lead-acid batteries to form a relatively low-cost and almost ideal form of self-regulating power supply capable of supplying the high peak currents required for ssb transceivers etc, has been discussed several times in *TT*. It is normal practice to use low-cost garage chargers for this purpose, relying on the battery to smooth out the heavy ripple on such units.

However, it needs to be recognised that even a small residual ripple can sometimes degrade the performance of equipment powered in this way. This has been pointed out by Jerry Connolly, an engineer with the UN field operations in conjunction with Middle East peace-keeping activities and based in Cyprus. He writes:

"Unfortunately the ripple level on many battery chargers can prove a serious nuisance on the various transmission modes, including cw, ssb, fm, rtty etc. I encountered some serious problems last year in cases where our people used some fairly cheap (and some not so cheap) battery chargers without first checking, with the aid of an oscilloscope, the ripple content riding on the battery 'bus'. This ripple level increases as the output current drawn from the charger increases, with particularly deleterious effects on the filtering of multiplexed channels.

"I found that if the ripple on the bus is between about 2 and 20mV all is well; otherwise queer things can happen. Many (professional) transceivers today use complex logic and expensive chip-type regulators complete with over-voltage protection, reverse polarity protection, current fold-back, soft-starting, switching-mode systems, and often appear to have a distinct dislike for 'fuzzy-dc' supplies."

While nobody has reported to me similar problems arising from the use of float-charged batteries with amateur radio equipment, it may well be a point worth investigating should incoming reports suggest that all is not well—or equally if all other transmissions seem to have problems.

Testing a high-current psu

Testing and setting-up a high-current psu is clearly not something to be carried out using expensive equipment as a test load. One needs a substitute load that is capable of taking the full output of the psu, and a common practice is to use vehicle headlight lamps in parallel. However, these can easily be fused by excess voltage, and have a number of other disadvantages. They are fairly delicate physically, and also exhibit a very low switch-on resistance that can present problems when used with a fast-trip current-sensing circuit.

B. Bracewell, G3GED, suggests an alternative solution which he has

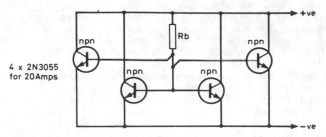

Fig 8. G3GED's use of power transistor to provide test load for heavy-current power supply units. Rb should be a 5–15Ω wire-wound resistor

found more satisfactory than lamps. This is to use a number of inexpensive power transistors, such as the 2N3055. Even devices rejected because of high leakage should prove satisfactory for this application. He writes: "Two, three or four transistors may be grouped around a single brass nut and bolt, to secure and provide a terminal tag point for the collectors: Fig 8. Coat the unit in silicone grease and immerse in a pot of cold water".

Flash-over protection for high-power linear amplifiers

From Stuart Jones, GW3XYW, comes the circuit diagram (Fig 9) for a flash-over protection unit suitable for the 430MHz K2RIW high-power linear amplifier. This was originally published in K2VYH's *Lunar News Letter* and has proved very useful over the past three years. He writes:

"If standard 1A glass cartridge (1·25in) fuses are used for ht flashover protection, the filament sometimes evaporates and recondenses on the inside of the glass fuse enclosure; where it again forms a current-path, with dramatic results. I have had a fuseholder actually disintegrate. Since fitting the protection circuit, a flash-over is hardly noticed; the unit is just reset, and if it happens too often the 4CX250B valves are changed. It is quite fast in operation, thus limiting electrical and physical damage.

"While I use the K2RIW amplifier on eme and may be pushing it a bit, there must be quite a few similar amplifiers in general use for tropospheric propagation etc with similar problems."

GW3XYW also mentions that a colleague recently tested a BICC type C2218 20μF (BB-7-70) capacitor packaged in an oval aluminium case, and confirmed that it contained a considerable amount of dangerous polychlorinated biphenyls (pcb) (see *TT* October 1984, p861).

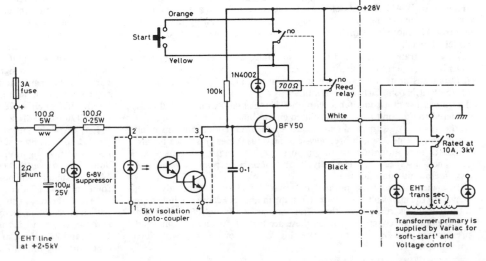

Fig 9. EHT current trip at about 2A to provide protection for flash-over in high-power linear amplifiers, and avoid unnecessary blowing of fuses. D is an RS high-speed pn silicon transient voltage suppressor (6·8V), stock No 283-225 *or* 5-7V 10W zener diode. The opto-coupler is an RS high voltage opto-isolator, stock No 302-148

Self-amalgamating tape—a cautionary tale

TT (January) carried an enthusiastic report from G8YZW on his discovery of "Rubbaweld self-amalgamating marine tape" and his use of this thin adhesive tape as a means of waterproofing outside joints in feeders and antennas. Nev Kirk, G3JDK, has no knowledge of this particular brand of tape but two years ago he bought some self-amalgamating tape from RS Components and used it to seal the various bits of a new trap vertical antenna. When completed, this looked as though it should last for many years. Unfortunately, in practice, one good summer reduced the sealing to a tattered pinholed mess.

He contacted the suppliers and they advised that self-amalgamating tape is intended for *indoor use only* as it is rapidly destroyed as a sealer by the action of the ultraviolet component of the sun's rays. G3JDK has no information on whether CC Marine Services Ltd who sell the tape for marine applications have overcome the uv problem, but will be interested to learn whether, by the end of the year, G8YZW still believes that "for outside joint sealing it is the best stuff I have come across next to well-applied Evostik." Evostik, at least, has a proven record for waterproofing cable joints.

Tips and topics

Numbers of readers have commented on, or provided additional information on, topics discussed recently in *TT*, including the adjustment of semi-automatic keys, antenna tuning units, safety and the ac mains, rccbs, Goyder-lock oscillators etc. I hope to return to these subjects in turn, but with space limitations it is necessary to strike a balance between introducing new ideas and continuing with previously discussed topics. But writers can rest assured that none of their letters has gone into the wpb.

Mullard have recently introduced plastic TO-220 versions of the popular 2N2955 and 2N3055 power transistors, respectively the MJE2995T and MJE3055T. Mullard have also introduced a number of uhf power transistors intended primarily for 900 or 470MHz mobile radio equipment, but some of which are suitable for use on the 1·3GHz amateur band. For example, the BLU99 can provide 4W output power at 900MHz with a typical gain of 7dB from a 12·5V supply in an SOT-122 package.

Dave Sugden, G4CQS, adds his vote in favour of the use of a float-charged car battery rather than a heavy-current mains psu. His elderly car battery with a 4A Halfords charger is well able to provide 30A or more peak for 100W ssb operation, and has proved the ultimate in "kiss" technique. □

Technical Topics
by Pat Hawker, G3VA

ONE OF THE PROBLEMS facing any columnist writing over a period of years is trying to keep abreast of the changing interests of his readers. When *TT* began 27 years ago in April 1958, ssb was still a minority mode with amplitude-modulation far in the lead; fm operation was confined to a tiny minority; 144MHz and above almost exclusively bands for home-construction; the Japanese had not yet set up amateur radio production lines; rtty, mobile operation, sstv, atv and the whole gamut of solidstate were in their infancy; home-computers, integrated circuits and surface-mounted assemblies not even on the distant horizon.

This is not to say that the bc (before computer) years of amateur radio were any less interesting, less fun or less rewarding. Indeed some old-timers would echo the remark of the cross-channel passenger when asked if he had eaten on the voyage: *"au contraire"*.

Be that as it may, a general column must recognize the changing pattern of interests and be steered gently towards majority present-day practices (or hopefully sometimes lead the way in introducing them) while leaving the more exotic developments mainly to the specialist columns.

It is not easy to discover the current interests of those many, many thousands who now hold UK amateur radio licences. Have we become, as sometimes alleged, "an international conversational club", a crowd of QSL-card collectors and "square'" workers, contest or computer buffs? Is manual cw going the way of a.m.? Are current licensees interested in the technical side of radio communication only to the extent of scraping through the RAE and the "need to know" of how to connect up a transceiver? Or regard cw as an obsolete mode forced down their throats by an absurd international regulation—rather than a highly effective and enjoyable craft skill based on a digital non-return-to-zero code?

The latest issue of the *IARU Region 1 News* reports an illuminating survey carried out by the Austrian national society, ÖVSV, based on a questionnaire sent to 300–400 hf band users and resulting in 152 completed forms (a very high proportion for this form of market research). The survey, unfortunately, was confined to hf bands only, and operating rather than technical usage, but some of the results seem pertinent.

Preferred mode: 53 per cent cw; 36 per cent ssb; 10 per cent rtty; 1 per cent sstv or fax; 69 per cent do not or only seldom take part in contests; 79 per cent are not yet using computers for communication purposes, but 34 per cent are thinking of doing so in the future.

Hans Berg, DK6TJ, chairman of the Region 1 HF Working Group, points out that there can be very wide variations in band usage between different parts of the world and even between different countries in the same continent. He suggests that African countries now show nearly 100 per cent usage of ssb, while amateurs in his part of West Germany split roughly 30 per cent cw, 60 per cent ssb and 10 per cent rtty. On the other hand one suspects that in Eastern Europe the percentage using mainly cw would be even higher than in Austria. Such wide variations do indeed make life difficult for columnists and editors alike!

The 200Ω vertical

Traditionally, radio amateurs have tended to think of hf antennas in terms of resonant half-wave dipoles or quarter-wave monopoles, and then either accepting these as single-band systems or alternatively taking advantage of the harmonic relationship of the pre-WARC bands. Admittedly, on 144MHz the $5\lambda/8$ element has achieved some popularity as a mobile whip despite the tendency for the longer elements to flex during motion.

Yet, for military and professional communication, a single hf vertical whip antenna is normally used over a wide range of frequencies, emphasising once again that there is nothing magical about element resonance other than that it tends to make it easier to feed in rf energy without having to worry about a reactive feed impedance.

Over 20 years ago in *TT* I included some items based on the experiences of George Barratt (ex-G8IP, 5B4IP and ZD7IP) and later F. Regier (ex-OD5CG, who made the news media last year when he was kidnapped and held hostage for several weeks in Beirut). These reports showed how a 22ft vertical element (about 113° physical, 110° electrical on 14MHz) could be used effectively with horizontal radials or an earth mat, with the aid of quite simple matching networks, indeed on 14MHz all that is necessary is to insert a series capacitor between the element and the inner conductor of a 75Ω coaxial feeder. OD5CG provided information on a matching network for 14, 21 and 28MHz. ZD7IP quoted the classic antenna textbook by Laporte to show that at electrical lengths of 110° and 220° the resistive component of the feed impedance passes through 75Ω, with 110° having a series inductive reactance and 220° a series capacitive reactance.

John Share, GW3OKA, revives interest in this work in writing: "Last summer I was messing around with my antenna and came to the conclusion that the mast might prove more effective than some of the wires it was supporting. The mast is 25ft high and made from 1·5in aluminium tubing —my immediate impression was that this would not prove of much use for 14 or 21MHz, though I decided to work out the feed impedances. Here comes the surprise! On both 14 and 21MHz it proves to be about 200Ω (see Table 1 and Fig 1).

"These feedpoint impedances are of course reactive, but I remembered the comments on the 5B4IP vertical and also the 4:1 ferrite transformer and it proved all too easy. Connect the transformer to the 50Ω feeder and *voila* 50Ω becomes 200Ω! Series connect a capacitor to the antenna and tune for minimum swr. For the other band replace capacitor with an old roller-coaster and again adjust for minimum swr. Band change? A lead and a crocodile clip.

"When fed against an earth mat comprising lots of odd-length radials the system performed very well, working as a $3\lambda/8$ vertical on 14MHz and $5\lambda/8$

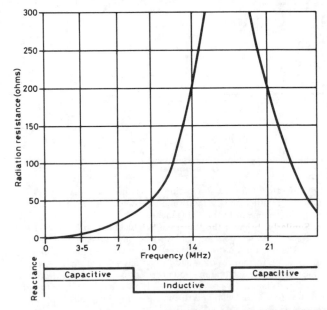

Fig 1. Feedpoint values for a 25·5ft vertical as plotted by GW3OKA

Table 1—Feedpoint values of 25·5ft vertical

MHz	a(°)	b(Ω)	c(X) (pF)	Feed	SWR
3·5	34·37	4		4:1 down	High
3·7	37·31	5			
7·0	68·74	18	120	4:1 down	1·5:1
10·0	98·20	46		1:1	2:1
10·2	100·16	50	75	1:1	1:1
14·0	137·48	200	300	1:4 up	1:1
14·3	140·00	208			
21·0	206·22	198		1:4 up	1:1
21·5	211·13	190		1:4 up	—
28·0	274·90	Much too long		Not suitable	—

SWR readings may vary from those indicated according to individual circumstances

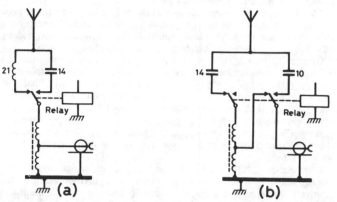

Fig 2. Dual-band operation of a 25·5ft vertical using a remotely-controlled relay rather than crocodile clips

(well almost) on 21MHz, on both bands giving good low angle radiation and all round coverage: Fig 2. The arrival of winter stopped me 'messing around' further with the design for other bands: Fig 3. Later, the arrival of planning permission and a new tower to support an hf beam stopped work on this promising 200Ω vertical altogether. By the way, my definition of 'messing around' is what I do for free: 'research' is much the same, but done for payment!"

How high the antenna?

When it comes to horizontally-polarized antenna systems there is an old adage that says "if it stays up it's too low"—at least for the dyed-in-the-

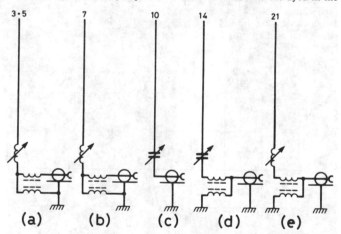

Fig 3. Suggested matching for five-band operation. Use on 28MHz not recommended

wool dx operator. On several occasions it has been pointed out in *TT* that it may be preferable to use a lightweight two-element hf Yagi rather than a heavier three-element beam if this means that the bigger array has to be lower. Similarly, because the "average height above ground level" of a quad is lower than its top wire, this form of antenna is at a *disadvantage* to a Yagi. Believe it or not, there is no real basis for the long-standing myth of superior performance of quad antennas at low heights. It has, conversely, been stressed that in good propagation conditions, chordal-hop and grey-line dx is entirely possible on simple antennas only a few feet above ground. It is for *consistent* dx performance that height really comes into its own.

Yet it has to be recognized that the provision of really high masts or towers is usually expensive and can involve difficult neighbour/local-authority problems. It is for these reasons that the question of "how high is high enough?" arises, even for those whose bank manager does not blanche at the idea of 60ft-plus tiltover towers etc.

First one must stress the general truth of "the higher the better" and attempt to kill the myth that certain critical heights (multiples of λ/2) significantly improve matters by reducing the vertical radiation angle.

It is, unfortunately, extremely difficult to measure "height gain" on hf, though rather more straightforward on vhf/uhf, since so much depends on site factors, ground conductivity etc. There is also the problem, when making measurements or contacts, of the constantly-changing band conditions and the tendency of all hf signals to fade quite rapidly.

An attempt to obtain meaningful results based on the reception of 14, 21 and 28MHz signals over paths exceeding 5,000km, and 145 and 435MHz signals over a path of about 20km, was made several years ago by a German antenna manufacturer, H. A. Rohrbacher, DJ2NN, from a reasonably good and uncluttered site. His results were published initially in *QRV* and then in English (translation by H. M. Lillienthal, F6DYG/DL7AH) in *Short Wave Magazine* (December 1981) and more recently in *Break-in* (June 1984). His measurement techniques and instrumentation are set out fully in his article and show that he went to considerable trouble to eliminate most of the usual problems, though it could be argued that any receiver measurements assume the "reciprocity theory" that equates the receiving and transmitting characteristics of a given antenna. This is by no means always true where radiation resistance is involved. Compare, for example, the performance of a small frame or ferrite-rod antenna on 1·8MHz for reception to that achievable when it is used for transmitting. Nevertheless this would not have been a problem in DJ2NN's project. He indicates once again, how misleading can be any attempt to access hf antenna performance on the basis of near-field signal-strength measurements.

DJ2NN measured incoming dx signals on an hf array which could be rapidly raised from about 2·5 to some 20m above ground, recognizing the problems of element detuning at very low heights.

His measurements (Fig 4) show that received signal strength increases continuously with height; but the increase is, as might be expected, greater at the lower levels above ground. On 14MHz, lowering the height of an array from, say, 25 to 12·5m reduces incoming signals by only one genuine S-point (6dB), Yet curiously, there is much less flattening of the height gain as the frequency increases.

DL2NN concludes on the basis of cost-effectiveness that an overall height for an hf array of about 17m (56ft) is about optimum, any additional height

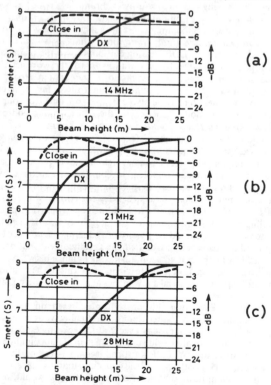

Fig 4. DJ2NN's antenna height-gain measurements. (a) 14MHz; (b) 21MHz; and (c) 28MHz. Note that increasing the height above about 15m shows relatively little improvement on 14 and 21MHz

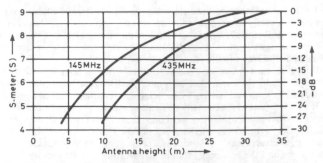

Fig 5. Antenna height-gain measurements on 145 and 435MHz

adding much more to cost than to performance. For many of us, 17m is an impossible dream, and perhaps the more important finding is that between 2·5 and 10m an almost logarithmic increase of signal voltage occurs. An array height of less than 10m above ground, even on a clear site, is definitely disadvantageous. At 10m an array should be capable of putting up a good performance on 14, 21 and 28MHz, at least when the site is reasonably uncluttered, though the presence of trees usually has relatively little effect on a horizontally-polarized array.

On vhf/uhf, useful height-gain continues to be obtained even above 25m, and DJ2NN recommends that on a shared tower the vhf/uhf antennas should always be mounted *above* the hf array: Fig 5. He admits that his investigation left open some questions, including vertical radiation patterns (which really require an aircraft as a measuring tool). Nevertheless his results do appear to provide some useful practical guidance, including the unanticipated conclusion that extreme height is less valuable on 14MHz than on higher-frequency bands.

More on the W3EDP antenna

The January *TT* (p35) item on "the ageless W3EDP antenna" brought comments from readers with long memories. Brian Bower, G3COJ, recalls, while operating the BBC club station G3AYC in 1975, having a contact with W4AG in Florida who mentioned that it was he who had been W3EDP and had devised this simple multiband antenna. As W4AG is not listed in the 1985 Callbook, and as Florida is the retirement centre of the USA, it may well be that he is now operating only from that great shack in the sky. G3COJ also mentions that another antenna man from the 'fifties— "Dickie" Bird, G4ZU, of Mini-Beam fame—now hides under the callsign F6IDC, having retired to southwest France where he has been busy working on a new form of miniature beam.

Charles Bryant, G3SB, comments on the suggestion in *TT*, quoting the current *Radio Communication Handbook*, that it is unnecessary to inductively couple the W3EDP loading coil directly to the pa tank coil, as it can be link coupled—directly or via a lowpass filter, swr meter etc—to the normal low-impedance output socket of a transmitter. He recalls that early descriptions of the W3EDP suggested that direct inductive coupling was necessary in order to provide also a degree of capacitive coupling.

G3SB's memory is good. A check with the first (pre-war) edition of the RSGB's *The Amateur Radio Handbook* shows the counterpoise end of the coupling coil coupled to the "hot" (anode) end of the tank coil with the following text note: "The counterpoise, which is 17ft or 6·5ft long according to frequency, is taken away at right angles to the aerial, and may also be bent to fit the space available. The counterpoise is connected to the end of the coupling coil nearest the pa coil, because a certain amount of capacitance coupling to this part is necessary for correct working. For the same reason it is necessary to have the coupling coil proportioned correctly. The coupling coils should be made of the plug-in type, arranged to swing against the pa tank. It should be possible to tune up the coupler and then swing up until the pa is fully loaded. If the aerial current falls off, before what is considered correct load is obtained, the balance between capacitive and inductive coupling is not quite right, and this is best adjusted by trimming the length of the aerial a few inches at a time, up to a possible total of 2ft."

I cannot help feeling that this procedure is based on what W3EDP actually did in the 'thirties, rather than theoretical considerations. Such a procedure would be ruled out today except at the very lowest powers, since it would appear to be an almost ideal way of ensuring maximum harmonic radiation. I suspect that W3EDP's procedure was based on the problem that (except on 7MHz) both ends of the coupling/loading coil are "hot" to rf, and this can complicate the use of a link winding. It would, of course, be possible to incorporate an additional "tank" circuit, link coupling this to the transmitter, but I would expect the reassuring comment in the current edition of *RCH* to be valid.

A problem with any form of coupling to this antenna, as with most long-wire antennas operated in an upstairs shack with a long earth-lead, is the tendency for the transmitter chassis to become "hot" to rf. G3SB experiences a form of this problem when using 66 or 132ft antennas with a pi-coupler on mains-operated transmitters, finding that rf is injected into the mains earth-lead, causing various difficulties. In my experience an almost sure-fire cure for a "hot" chassis is to attach to it a quarter-wave wire (or several for different bands), and there would seem to be no reason why this should not be done when using a W3EDP provided that no direct connection is made to the short counterpoise.

ATU round-up

Several comments have been received in connection with items on antenna tuning units in the December 1984 *TT*.

Alan Royle, G3FQE, reminds us that the original notes on the Z-match unit modified by the Australians appeared in the *RSGB Bulletin* December 1956, stemming from Vic Scott, GD3UB, and influenced by a design including an swr meter in *QST* May 1955 by Allen W King, W1CJL.

George Clarkson, G3RHM, is a firm believer in the Z-match atu but believes that when 50Ω cable is used the link windings should be reduced by two or three turns. He praises the Z-match for effective harmonic suppression, superior to that usually achieved with the conventional lowpass filter that does not take into account the multiband, multi-reactance, multi-impedance requirements of amateur hf operation (absorption type lpf designs tackle this problem—*G3VA*). He also notes that the Z-match atu is entirely suitable for use with balanced feeders without a balun.

Brian Sandall, G3LGK, reflects on the great difficulty these days of finding suitable high-quality components for a high-power atu. It is relatively simple, he points out, to punch out capacitor plates in aluminium sheet and assemble them with lengths of studding and spacing rings, washers (or even drilled-out nuts). Yet he finds very few amateurs who are prepared to tackle such an approach. A high-voltage capacitor of even relatively modest maximum capacitance can set one back £50 or more if bought new, and if a source can be located. He greatly welcomes the efforts of G4OGP of Tau in introducing a range of well-made British components and complete units (mentioned in the December *TT*). While they may appear "pricey" to those with memories of the components of the 'fifties, they appear to be excellently designed and made, including the roller-coasters. He enclosed a couple of the photographs he took at the Leicester exhibition as an enthusiastic but disinterested observer.

G4OCP holding one of the new Tau atus on the company's stand at the Leicester exhibition. *(Photo: G3LGK)*

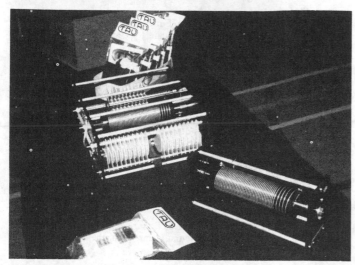

Some of the British-built components being designed and marketed by Tau to overcome the growing gap in the supply of components suitable for rf applications at high power. *(Photo: G3LGK)*

AGC on a BC348 hybrid receiver

I.M. Waters, G8ADE, still uses a ruggedly-built American wartime BC348 receiver, bought for £8 in 1954, as his main station receiver, though this has been subject to some drastic modifications over the years. It is used for hf, vhf and uhf bands, the latter with the aid of converters. Currently, the hf "front-end" retains the use of valves, but all subsequent stages are solidstate. The receiver caters for the original a.m. mode (10kHz bandwidth) but incorporates a 2·4kHz ssb filter and product detector as well as a quadrature fm detector with squelch—it is wonderful what you can do with sets built before new technology came on the scene!

One problem proved to be to devise a flexible agc system controlling valves and solidstate i.f. amplifier. Fig 6 shows the arrangement adopted, which G8ADE feels may be of general interest to those who still like to keep the old warhorses in harness rather than confining them to collectors' corner.

Audio derived ssb agc at 0 to +4Vdc from the SL1621 agc generator

controls the ssb i.f. amplifier (SL1612) directly. This is also fed to a 741 op-amp functioning as a "valve agc inverter" to give 0 to −6Vdc to feed forward to the valve stages. SWA1 selects the agc feed to the valve stages depending on the mode in use. On ssb an S-meter is driven from the SL1621 directly via a set-fsd potentiometer. To allow the S-meter to work on a.m. and fm, the original agc is also inverted by a second 741 op-amp shown as the "S-meter inverter". This has adjustments for setting the fsd and for setting zero. S16 selects the S-meter feed.

Radio equipment in cars

In "Mobile operating—safe not sorry" (*TT* July 1984, p579) I referred briefly to a RoSPA article that had drawn attention to EEC regulations in respect of radio equipment fitted in cars. I wrote then: "(These are) intended to ensure that a driver will not be cut by any part of a radio, will not get his hands stuck nor receive any electric shocks. Equipment must be reasonably easy to operate and with rounded, recessed controls—though I am uncertain to what extent these EEC regulations apply to amateur radio equipment or to the extent to which they are enforced in the UK."

Dr Bryan Roe, G4LVR, who is in the automotive industry, has recently explained the situation. He reports that every significantly different model of any vehicle intended for retail in the UK and Europe must have type approval. The approval regulations include a number relating to "interior projections" and "external protrusions" which refer respectively to anything which sticks out inside and outside the vehicle. He continues:

"The test for the interior projection part of the regulations is carried out by placing a hemisphere of a specific dimension—this represents a small child's head—anywhere around the interior and exterior of the vehicle. Any surface contactible by this hemisphere must have a certain minimum radius. Such surfaces are not confined to radio equipment, they can be anything, ie heater controls, steering wheel, sunvisor, door handles, headrests/restraints etc. The test is basically to ensure there are no sharp objects around which in normal use or in an accident could cause injury or death.

"Manufacturers normally carry out these checks before submitting a vehicle to the Department of Transport. Where items represent a risk to obtaining the type approval, they are normally redesigned or often, in the case of equipment such as radios, recessed into their mounting positions, such that sharp areas like the edges of switches, knobs etc are not contactible by the test hemisphere.

"Now for the 'crunch'. While these regulations apply to the original vehicle manufacturer, they do not apply to the purchaser or user. So once you have bought your vehicle, you could install any amount of equipment

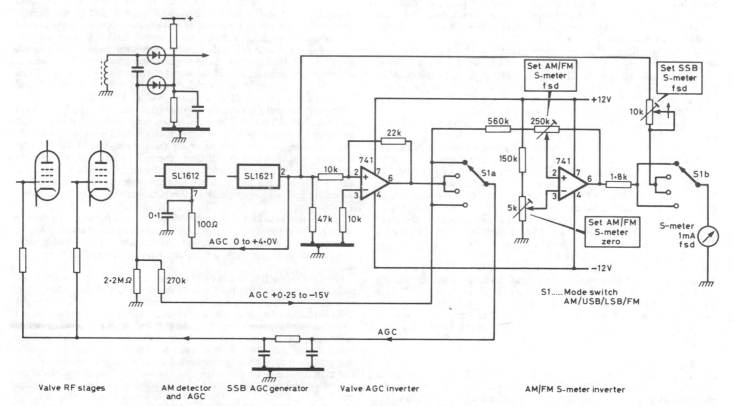

Fig 6. G8ADE's essentials of the agc/S-meter arrangements used with a hybrid valve/solidstate receiver

with sharp edges. All the manufacturer is required to do is to ensure that the vehicle is safe to sell. How you kill yourself or your pasengers is your problem!''

For those who have no wish to add to the slaughter on the roads, it would clearly be wise voluntarily to take heed of these recommendations and at least reduce to a minimum the addition of sharp edges in interior projections or external protrusions in the form of radio equipment that transgresses the spirit of the EEC recommendations.

Electric shock

The January *TT* described the dangers of electric shock in some detail, but there was one omission that needs to be put on record: the extra risk when the power supply is ac rather than dc. According to the informative if terrifying paper "Death by lightning" by Dr R H Golde and Professor W R Lee (*Proc IEE*, Vol 123, No 1OR, October 1976, *IEE Reviews*): "The effects of electric shock from direct current are less severe than from power-frequency current of the same rms magnitude. Direct currents and alternating currents producing similar effects (including fibrillation) are generally in the ratio 5:1." By this token, 240V ac mains should be considered as potentially dangerous as about 1,000V dc. Lightning is of course ac at a high (rf) frequency.

Harry Ashcroft, G4CCM, also makes this point in his reply to criticisms of his body resistance tests. It was his letter in "Members Mailbag" that sparked off this debate. He notes the "animated response" to his megger measurements, but remains unrepentant, and comments: "The megger reading was based on memory from 60 years ago when I was an apprentice and tester, but I assure you that I knew how to use a megger. Before writing the letter I took a rough check with a 3V multimeter and have since taken further tests with the multimeter and with a Mullard CR bridge energized at 6V 50MHz. Electrodes were similar to those of early 'shocking coils': 0·6in (16mm) diameter by 3in (76mm) long of polished copper, gripped as firmly as possible:

Condition	Multimeter	Bridge
Dry	45kΩ	22kΩ
Wet (tap water)	6kΩ	6kΩ
Wet (salt water)	3·5kΩ	2kΩ

"Using the same electrodes, the hand-to-hand current on 12V 50Hz was 1mA dry and 3·5mA with tap water. Gripping the electrodes hard at 3·5mA is beginning to feel unpleasant, and at my age I am not prepared to go further. I agree that people are non-linear resistors and that the resistance will fall with increasing voltage. The IEC body resistance is taken out of context. If it were specified for the assessment of safety transformers for portable equipment it should be set near the bottom range. A 'standard' body resistance of assessing shock protecting equipment should be set near the top of the range. Very few shocks occur with such perfect contact conditions as in my test.

"All the contributors to the debate exept G3JJR ignored the most important feature—the let-go current, which he quotes as 10mA. Between 10 and 30mA on the IEC curve is a zone where people could be killed if there is nobody to pull them off or break the circuit. The rccb is an excellent device for earth-leakage protection but it gives only partial protection against shock in a range that could be fatal.

"The advantage of dc over ac is that muscular contraction usually breaks the circuit."

The Golde & Lee paper includes some fascinating descriptions of the early attempts, over 200 years ago, to investigate the effects of electricity on the human body. Benjamin Franklin, after taking a discharge from two "six-gallon" Leyden jars wrote: "It seem'd an univeral Blow from head to foot through the Body, and followed by a violent quick Trembling in the Trunk . . . It was some Minutes before I could recollect my Thoughts . . . . I afterwards found it had rais'd a Swelling there (back of the hand) of the Bigness of half a Swan Shot or Pistol Bullet. My Arms and the Back of my Neck felt somewhat numb the remainder of the Evening, and my Brest Bone was sore, for a Week after."

At the French Court of Louis XV, spectacles of 180 soldiers of the guard and subsequently 800 monks, leaping simultaneously in the air with "a precision out-rivalling the timing of the most perfect corps de ballet" were staged by Abbé Nollet (the official court electrician). Highly diverting it must have been—and at least less horrifying than some of the ways in which the use of electric shock is put by torturers in this more enlightened (?) age!

Tips and topics

Gerald Stancey, G3MCK, noted the hints on simplifying tuned circuit formulas from G3NXM (*TT*, February 1985) and recalled another useful approximation that came to him from a Belgian old-timer: "Take the wavelengths in metres at which you require resonance. divide it by two and

this gives the inductance in microhenries and the capacitance in picofarads. Then scale to get the correct LC ratio. For example: 10MHz = 30m. Then L(μH) = 30/2 = 15. C(pF) = 30/2 = 15. Scale by, say, three to give more practical values: L = 5μH, C = 45pF".

Although RSGB publications changed from "aerial" to "antenna" almost a decade ago, the British public and even some electronics publications have yet to follow suit. David Pratt, G3KEP, notes that the IEE's *Electronic Group News* has attacked the present confused situation in which British antenna engineers are "antenna engineers" at work but "aerial designers" at home, adding: "Both antenna and aerial are technical terms whose original meaning was quite different. Antenna is a noun and comes from 'biological sensor'. Aerial is strictly an adjective and means 'in or belonging to the air' . . . . Both appear to have been conceived at about the same time. Marconi, in the IEE journal in 1899, wrote: 'a vertical conductor wire which I shall call the aerial conductor' . . . . J. A. Fleming in 1902 wrote: 'the great improvement introduced by Marconi was the employment of this vertical air-wire, aerial, antenna or elevated conductor'."

But at least the IEE confirms that dictionaries are largely agreed that while the plural of a biological antenna is *antennae*, the correct plural of radio antenna is *antennas*.

Dank u weel en tot horrens!

The ceremonies last summer commemorating the 40th anniversary of the Normandy D-Day landings were unfortunately something of a political jamboree and tended to give the impression that the second world war in Europe was as good as over once the assault forces were ashore and the beach-head established. This was far from the case: the Normandy campaign lasted three bloody months; then the euphoric liberation of France and Belgium, halted by the "bridge too far" disaster at Arnhem; followed by that long, bitterly cold winter of 1944-5—and for the Dutch in the northern, still occupied half of their unhappy land, near famine hunger. Also throughout the period: the heavy losses of the tactical and strategic air forces; the assaults across the Rhine; and, what should never be forgotten, the all-important Eastern Front moving ever closer to Berlin. Tragic days that should be recalled in humility, not military jingoism.

Among my personal recollections of that winter, there stands out the work of the various Dutch "underground" organizations, and in particular the internal clandestine radio networks set up by the RVV and OD resistance groups. Whereas most western Europe secret radio links were largely run by, supplied by, and with training facilities in, the UK, the internal Dutch radio service was set up, run and equipped by the Dutch themselves, using radio operators drawn from pre-war PA0 radio amateurs, KLM and merchant navy radio officers, and former Service telegraphists. By chance I was one of two English operators loaned to the Netherlands Intelligence Bureau from 1 January 1945 until the end of the war in Europe to help out at the Eindhoven control stations, and I recall, all too vividly, the experience of having one after another of the stations in the north go permanently off the air as the result of enemy raids. The frequencies used for these short-distance links were between 2·7 and 2·9MHz and 3·0 to 3·3MHz particularly vulnerable to df.

The two networks sprang into action after the "Mad Tuesday" of 5 September 1944, but the heaviest losses were suffered in the weeks following Christmas 1944. In the network with which I was concerned, only one clandestine station survived on-air right through until VE Day—at Alkmaar, just north of Amsterdam, manned by two highly-proficient operators who sent literally hundreds of cipher messages to Eindhoven (and also, I believe, ran a link with my former colleagues in the UK control station for Special Communications); perfect cw at more than 25 groups per minute.

In 1983, thanks to Dick Rollema, PA0SE, I finally discovered the identity of the surviving member of that successful team: Jan Zandbergen, PA0ZY, an aeronautical Civil Service ground operator, and still an active radio amateur; his colleague Jack, a merchant navy operator, died some years ago.

Since the recent BBC series on SOE, which featured the disastrous and shame-making (but from the German viewpoint very skilful) North Pole operation, British viewers may have been left with the feeling that secret radio in Holland was an unmitigated disaster. The full story of the Internal Radio Service has never been told in the UK; with all of its hazards, not just to the operators but also the young cipher clerks, couriers etc, many of them young Dutch girls. May I be excused for taking this 40th anniversary opportunity of paying a long overdue tribute to one of the most remarkable and most prolific Underground intelligence and sabotage operations of the second world war; to the skill of those who survived, and in memory of the many who lost their lives. An operation in which Dutch radio amateurs played a significant role. □

Technical Topics
by Pat Hawker, G3VA

Some years ago, when the promise of reliable, 24h, high-capacity microwave links via satellite began to be achieved with the launching of Early Bird in April 1965, it was widely, if rashly, assumed that the use of hf, with all its many propagation variables and its limited (often non-coherent) bandwidths would soon be relegated almost entirely to hf broadcasting and amateur radio. Some believed that even these two services would finally become primarily *via satellite* services.

Satellites, hf and the Services

While this was never my belief, I recall a press trip in 1965 to Hughes Aircraft at Culver City, Los Angeles, a few weeks before the launching of Early Bird (later renamed Intelsat 1), the very first geostationary communications satellite to go into commercial service in July 1965. The complex, clean-air assembly and stringent environmental testing of satellites, together with laser research at the firm's Malibu Beach laboratories, tend to merge in my memory with the opportunity it gave to visit the original Disneyland at Anaheim and to see the west coast premiere of the film *Sound of Music* (how that dates the period!).

Hughes Aircraft had found it necessary to bend the ears of that party of visiting European journalists because of the great reluctance of European PTT authorities to recognize the advantages of the synchronous orbit, with, for example, the UK still pushing for a lower orbit with station-keeping satellites involving tracking and hand-over with multiple earth terminals. The great protagonist of the 22,300-mile geostationary orbit was Dr Harold Rosen, who had earlier expounded his ideas to me on a visit to London in 1964. He led the team that developed the techniques for putting satellites into geostationary orbit, and was convinced that the British Post Office's doubts on excessive time-delay with the high orbit could be largely overcome by the use of better echo-suppressors—as indeed proved the case.

The developed countries have transferred their long-distance telephone circuits from hf to satellite, and are still in the process of developing higher-capacity ocean cables based on fibre optics. But the developing countries still need cost-effective, thin-line, medium-distance communications for which hf and vhf meteor scatter continue to offer many attractions. But hf is also being increasingly reclaimed by the Services, both for communications and for radar, due to the growing doubts about the vulnerability of satellite communications to jamming and anti-satellite weaponry. Currently, the US Navy, for example, is committed to a massive investment in new hf systems that will use frequency-hopping techniques and digital encryption for voice and data. This will make hf communications extremely difficult to intercept, to disrupt by jamming, or to locate by other than the most sophisticated df systems. Digital encryption of vocoded speech can provide completely "secure" links with a data rate of 2·4kb/s.

The present sunspot minimum, with the use of frequencies above about 7MHz restricted largely to mutual daylight paths, has resulted in the lower half of the hf spectrum becoming more crowded than ever. For amateurs, new threats are arising. With what are called "adaptive" systems and embedded real-time channel evaluation techniques, both commercial and Service transmissions are seeking and using any relatively clear channels they can find, often regardless of whether or not they have registered these with the International Frequency Registration Board. Frequency hopping at rates of tens or hundreds or even thousands of times per second, as now being planned, may superficially appear to present other users of the spectrum with few problems since, for most of the time, any particular frequency is not in use. A transmission of a few milliseconds duration will not seriously disrupt other transmissions unless the transmitter is very local. Unfortunately this situation rapidly degrades when there are a

considerable number of frequency-hopping transmissions. The effect then is similar to a rise in the continuous background noise, reducing the opportunities for weak-signal dx operation. Let us hope that the Services of all nations restrict their frequency-hopping and frequency-agile transmissions to outside the "exclusive" amateur allocations, though this may be asking too much. Spread-spectrum and adaptive systems may turn out to be dirty words to the civilian users of the spectrum!

Another unfortunate consequence of the renewed interest of the Services in hf and vhf is that they seem obsessed with achieving ever higher volumes of "instant" traffic—gone are the days when the Royal Navy aimed at maintaining "wireless silence" during operations unless within sight of the enemy (a change brought about by remote-sensing of ships by satellite radar, etc). This is tending to result in many more broad transmissions using various forms of phase-shift-keying of digital data streams that can blot out 3, 6, or even more than 10kHz of precious spectrum.

Nor are the Services keen to maintain the spectrum efficiency of hand morse, with the result that they are endeavouring to substitute keyboard systems that are highly resistant to interference. In this way they hope to avoid the cost of training morse operators despite the many advantages of retaining "kiss" systems. One technique currently being field tested by the Admiralty Research Laboratory (formerly ASWE) requires a full 3kHz ssb bandwidth to transmit messages at about 12wpm (10bits/s), repeating each "bit" five times on different audio frequencies by occupying, in effect, 10 100-baud channels. The tests they have conducted appear to have been heavily weighted in favour of the complex keyboard system—and against cw—and one hopes that the Navy will think again before abandoning morse as its fall-back system!

Many of the new techniques were discussed at a recent international "HF communications systems and techniques" conference held in London. A number of well-known amateurs—mostly wearing their professional hats—were present. Papers were presented by Dr Ulrich Rohde, DJ2LR/W2, on current work by RCA, with special emphasis on digital and frequency-hopping techniques; Professor Mike Underhill, G3LHZ, on "silent tuning" of transmitter antenna tuning units; Pat Gowen, G3IOR, on the fascinating hf ducting uncovered by amateur satellites; Maurice Hately, GM3HAT, on his "dipole of delight", etc. It was also a personal pleasure to meet Rich Rosen, K2RR, editor of *Ham Radio*, who came over to London especially to attend this conference. An article based on DJ2LR's paper is due to be published shortly in that magazine.

Trigonal reflectors

For most vhf arrays, operators accept the backward-looking lobes of Yagi antennas as an inevitable fact of life. In *TT*, November 1982, pp959–60, G8SEQ proposed the use of a second resistive-loaded reflector as a means of improving the back-to-front ratio of a 144MHz Yagi array, though subsequently theoretical considerations showed that even with an accurately-matched load in the centre of the second reflector half the energy in this element would inevitably be re-radiated, thus somewhat limiting the effectiveness of this approach.

It is perhaps surprising that more attention has not been paid to the use of trigonal reflectors—a technique first described (for a 120MHz array) by A Wheeler Nagy in 1936 and analysed by Dr George Brown in his definitive study of directional antennas (*Proc IRE*, Vol 28, No 1, January 1937, pp120–2).

In the UK the value of trigonal reflectors has perhaps been underestimated due to what appears to have been a long-standing error in several

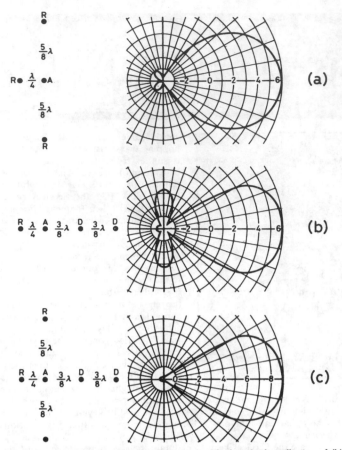

Fig 1. Use of trigonal reflectors compared with the single reflector of (b) shows the improved side and back lobe performance. But note that these diagrams originally used in *Radio Handbook* of 1938 are drawn to a linear rather than a logarithmic scale as would be done today. A logarithmic scale would make the side lobes more prominent on all diagrams. Note also the element spacings are those that were commonly used in the 'thirties, with the reflector a full quarter-wave behind the driven element

editions of the RSGB's handbook where what purports to be a "Yagi array with trigonal reflectors" (Fig 13.19 in *Radio Communication Handbook*, 5th edn) shows the three reflectors mounted in a flat plane.

In *Break-in* (September 1984, pp10–11), Rex Cassey, ZL2IQ, reproduces some diagrams from the *Jones Radio Handbook* of 1938 which show (Fig 2) that the three reflectors should be located on a parabolic curve which has the feedpoint of the driven element as it focus.

He provides the following up-dated design criteria:

(a) the added reflectors should all be the same length as the normal reflectors;

(b) the three reflectors should lie on a parabolic curve, $y^2 = 4ax$ (Fig 2) but note that in modern practice a is usually much less than the $\lambda/4$ of the pre-George Brown era or Yagi antennas;

(c) if the added elements are directly above and below F, their distance away will be $2a$. However, they can be placed anywhere on the parabola. For example, if $x = a/2$, then y will be $\sqrt{2}a$.

It seems worth adding that there is no reason why more than three reflectors should not be used provided that they all lie on the parabola and are symmetrical (ie 3, 5, 7 reflectors).

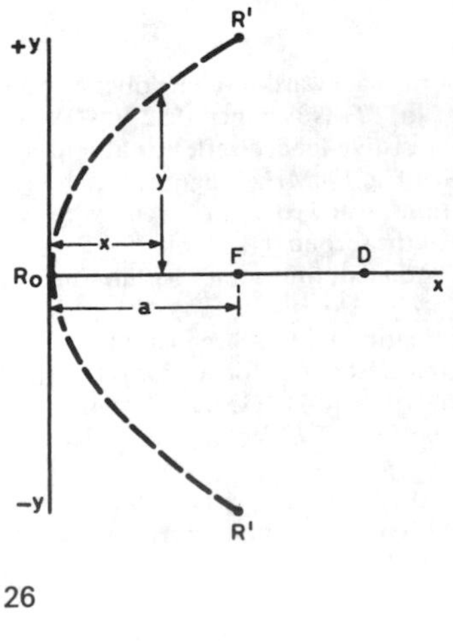

Fig 2. Trigonal reflectors should be located on the parabola having its focal point at F where the driven element is located

More on the rccb

L J Carpenter, G4CNH, is a little concerned that Fig 1 of the January *TT* showed an rccb connected directly between the supply meter and the customer's consumer unit, even though the prime purpose of the diagram was to show the principle of an rccb rather than provide a practical wiring diagram. G4CNH admits the diagram may appear correct but warns that, as shown, the rccb has no input protection itself apart from the company fuse. A fault in the rccb or even accidental contact of its terminals would not only be very dangerous, but also blow a fuse rated at about 60A! He believes that an rccb is best positioned *after* the consumer unit, and this arrangement lends itself very easily to having an rccb-protected outlet socket, as available from a number of sources, introduced into the normal ring main circuitry. In this case the 30A fuse fitted inside the consumer unit also protects the rccb. He adds:

"Houses with a modern electrical installation should have separate ring main circuits for upstairs and downstairs. The downstairs ring main is the circuit normally used to supply such appliances as washing machines, spin driers, electric kettles, garden tools and shacks. It therefore makes sense to fit an rccb to this ring main, at the very least.

"You are right to encourage the fitting of an isolator (eg heavy-duty double-pole switch) in the shack. I personally use a four-pole 240V ac contactor with one pole providing a latching supply. A shrouded push-button activates the contactor which can then be de-activated simply by interrupting the latching supply. To achieve this I have two switches wired in series, one switch at the operating position and the other switch by the door. This arrangement allows anyone to remove power safely from the equipment, *or you*, in the event of an accident. The use of a contactor or heavy duty relay is a must, the strong return spring fitted to such devices will easily part any contact(s) attempting to 'stick together'.

"And finally, the outside shack *must* have a separate earth. If for some reason the mains earth became detached at the supply, then the metalwork of some equipment could acquire a very unpleasant potential indeed. This is where the fitting of an rccb may possibly help."

John Nelson, G4FRX, has spotted an error in the reference (*TT* January) to the rccb as a "no-volt" detector. He writes: "The point about the no-volt relay is *not* that it falls out and stays out in the event of a temporary mains failure; it does no such thing. The facility is used in industry, and especially in traction applications, to isolate a piece of equipment if *a phase or neutral* voltage disappears. In the case of, for example, the B&R socket-outlet 13A rccb (which can readily be added to an existing socket not protected by an rccb) this does occur as an added bonus to normal rccb operation. A number of other rccbs, although definitely not all, act in this fashion.

"I believe that several bodies choose rccb devices based on their ability to act as this form of 'no-volt' relays, presumably with a view to the hazards which could conceivably arise if the neutral wire went open-circuit not far upstream of the socket."

G4FRX also stresses the point made by GW4CFC in the January *TT* that an rccb can in no way protect the user against faults arising downstream of an isolating (double-wound) transformer of any type. "Those of us who still enjoy high-power operation should not be deluded into thinking that rccb will in some magical way protect us against getting across the high-voltage anode supply required for a 4CX250B or 813 or what have you. But in these cases the rccb might still prove useful in the not unknown event of the primary developing an intermittent short-circuit to the core—something that unfortunately still happens with almost irreplaceable transformers. But they can do little more and should not be allowed to become counter-productive in giving a false sense of security."

Des Shepherd, G3LCS, and Paul Mullineaux, G3XEN, both draw attention to the RS "Powerbreaker" 13A rccb, stock No 334–094, but in a rather different way. G3LCS feels the £18.25 is well worth the investment for a bottom-of-the-garden shack run off a 13A plug for over 25 years. On the other hand, G3XEN has been concerned with five of these particular devices in the engineering department of Lancaster University. He provides a word of caution: "Five of these are in use on extension distribution board leads, but when we decided to test the trips they all worked fairly well for small leakage currents, though the trip time proved variable. But when we applied a short-circuit to earth to the miniature trips, they did not trip at all—instead two 13A hrc mains fuses blew, one in the trip and one in the 13A plug which was supplying it. So much for 30mA, 30ms!"

EMC and cable tv

The problem of signal leakage into and out of multichannel tv cable networks has become a matter of considerable concern to American vhf amateurs since there is now widespread distribution of programme channels on carriers within amateur radio bands; for example, US Channel E has its video carrier on 145·25MHz. Phil Karn, KA9Q ("Hints & Kinks" *QST*

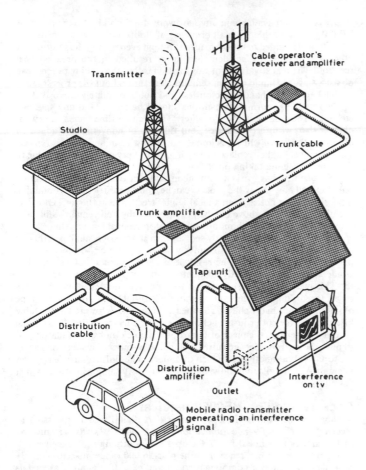

Fig 3. A typical tree-and-branch cable-television network showing the main component parts. The link between studio and the cable operator's master receiver often takes the form of a geostationary satellite distribution link

November 1984, p55) describes a novel, but apparently effective way of tracking down leaky cable "taps". This is to tune a mobile ssb transceiver to obtain a low audio beat of the carrier and then listen for the Doppler frequency shift that occurs as you drive past the signal source. At 40mph (64km/h) the shift on 144MHz while passing a source is twice the 9Hz Doppler shift (ie 18Hz), which he finds readily detectable on the receiver.

He reports that driving past a leaky tap thus results in both S-meter peaking and a sudden change in beat note. If the vehicle passes close to the leak—for example, from a cable pole close to the roadway—the shift is more sudden and the signal will peak higher than when the leak is at a greater distance; eg from a subscriber's installation in a house. A number of leaks tend to produce a confusing interference pattern. Once a serious leak or leaks is located it is then up to the cable company to deal with it.

Although it is now clear that, in the UK, multichannel cable is not going to spread as rapidly as was widely believed in 1982–3, the problem of cable tv in-band emc has already been encountered in some locations, eg Milton Keynes. The Electrical Research Association (ERA) has recently completed a major study which confirms the view that more stringent technical standards need to be established before wideband cable tv systems are generally introduced into the UK (ERA Report No 84–0059, price £135 to non-members, the availability of which has been brought to my notice by John Wilson, G8KIS).

ERA points out that the leakage of rf energy through imperfect connectors, cables and other components can cause interference to radio and tv reception and that the cable tv system may itself suffer interference due to the fields produced by transmissions from "broadcasting authorities, police, gas boards and even cb users".

ERA has investigated both a conventional "tree and branch" cable system (Fig 3) and a more advanced "switched star" system. Components and elements such as cables, taps and isolators were individually assessed. Radiated emissions from trunk and distribution cables were found to be negligible, but the emissions increased significantly as more components were added to build up the systems. Two components stood out as having significantly more effect on system emc behaviour than others, namely the tap-off units and safety isolators; clearly, ERA suggests, much depends on the quality of their design and construction.

ERA's conclusion is that while radiated emissions from the systems examined might not cause unacceptable interference, the immunity to external fields required substantial improvement to avoid interference—particularly from amateur and mobile radio transmitters. It may well be that the levels of radiated energy with which ERA were concerned were high enough to have interfered with weak-signal amateur radio reception, even if "acceptable" for other services, though I have not yet had an opportunity of studying the complete ERA report.

Testing high-current power units—another look

In the March *TT*, p193, G3GED noted the advantages of using a number of parallel-connected power transistors rather than lamps in order to provide an electronic test load for heavy-current power supply units. John Brown, G3EUR, is concerned that G3GED's arrangement (March Fig 8) does not include any low-value emitter resistors to ensure correct load-sharing between the four 2N3055 transistors. In practice some degree of load sharing can result from the finite resistance of the emitter connecting leads but, as in series regulators, it is unwise to rely on this. G3EUR writes:

"I use the same idea of a 2N3055 'electronic load' but with load-sharing and a small potentiometer to vary the current. The gain of different 2N3055 devices can vary a lot, and the arrangement shown would not be a very stable or safe load. In my version (Fig 4 (a)) the use, when required, of a separate 12V 1A psu for a driver stage provides a near-constant current load and opens the way to turning the electronic load into a useful tester.

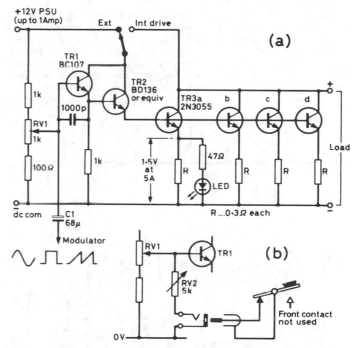

Fig 4. (a) G3EUR's electronic test load for high-current power supply units incorporating load-sharing 0·3Ω resistors and facilities for dynamic testing. (b) Use of the back contact of a morse key for dynamic testing in the absence of a function generator, etc. See text regarding the adjustment of RV1 and RV2

"Switching the dc at the base of TR1 (or just twiddling RV1) 'perturbs' the load so that the response of the psu can be seen on an oscilloscope connected across the load. The load current can be conveniently monitored by the voltage developed across one of the 0·3Ω resistors. Note that the driver will need about 1A to provide the base current for the 2N3055 devices at full current. An l.e.d. connected as shown in Fig 4 (a) across one of the 0·3Ω resistors can form a simple, cheap maximum-current indicator."

Incorporation of a driver arrangement enables the psu to be tested under various conditions. A function generator, 600Ω source or af generator, can be used to check the output under sine-wave, square-wave, triangular-wave conditions. A morse key connected as shown in Fig 4 (b) provides a useful way of checking output under varying current conditions, the maximum current being set by RV1 with "key down", and minimum current conditions set by RV2 with "key up". All this can be done without having to connect an untried psu to vulnerable solidstate equipment.

A similar technique could also be used with float-charged battery supplies to check ripple, etc, which (as mentioned in a separate item in the March *TT*) can sometimes affect the performance of communications equipment supplied in this way.

Digital signal processing

In *TT* (October 1984, p859) I referred briefly to the new Rockwell-Collins communications receiver model HF2050 as the first production model (currently being delivered to the Canadian Department of National Defence) to incorporate digital signal processing in all stages beyond the analogue double-conversion front-end. It includes the use of digital filtering under software control to provide the main selectivity in lieu of the traditional crystal or mechanical filters. As noted later, further information on this new receiver was given at the *HF communications systems* conference.

Another presentation which discussed alternative approaches to this form of receiver came from V Considine of Birmingham University. This paper ("Digital processing architectures for hf radio receivers" *IEE Conference Publication No 245,* pp86–8) underlined the basic problem of achieving a spurious-free dynamic range of 90dB required to achieve a dynamic range comparable with modern analogue receivers.

If one accepts the 90dB figure, then an adjacent channel (3kHz) suppression of 30dB is a normally acceptable minimum for high-grade professional receivers. However, since signal levels in adjacent channels may differ by the 90dB figure based on a statistical study of signal levels in the hf band, this suggests that a final requirement for dynamic range is of the order of 90 + 30dB, and that a dynamic range of 120dB is desirable for all early wideband stages of a receiver (this may be *desirable* but there can be few front-ends that reach this figure without taking into account the use of attenuators/agc, etc—*G3VA*).

The two basic design approaches for hybrid analogue/digital receivers (a/d) are shown in Fig 5. Fig 5 (a) outlines an upconversion approach using a conventional roofing filter. Fig 5 (b) adopts a 0kHz i.f. (that is, a direct-conversion or homodyne technique) in which quadrature (I, Q) channels are used to overcome the ambiguity as to whether the required signal is above or below the original local oscillator frequency, and thus dispenses with the requirement for an analogue filter. These two arrangements differ in that in (a) a bandpass signal is digitally processed in a single channel, whereas

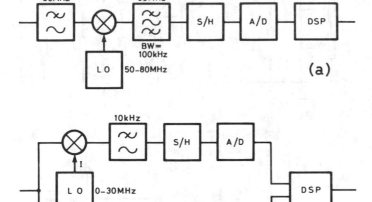

Fig 5. Basic arrangements for hybrid analogue/digital receivers incorporating digital signal processing. (a) Single-channel, single-conversion superhet (in practice a double-conversion analogue front-end is more likely to be employed to bring the i.f. signal down to 1·6 or 3MHz). (b) Dual-channel homodyne approach: s/h, sample and hold; a/d, analogue/digital converter; dsp, digital signal processing

in (b) two lowpass signals are produced in a homodyne arrangement.

The Birmingham paper notes that a 120dB signal range requires analogue/digital conversion with a 20-bit precision and that this is at present still beyond the capability of available devices. For an experimental receiver, Bagwell and Considine adopted the single-channel approach. On the other hand the Collins HF2050 uses the dual-channel zero i.f. or homodyne configuration.

Etching and drilling pcbs

R P Bown, G3PCN, describes a method of etching printed circuit boards which he has used for many years and which does not involve the use of any form of ferric chloride that can so easily result in yellow fingers and holes in the carpet. He writes:

"The liquid I use is a 1:1 solution of hydrochloric acid (spirits of salts,

30 per cent w/w) available in any hardware store, and hydrogen peroxide BP (20 vols) available from all branches of Boots and other chemists.

"The acid is added *to* the peroxide, although even mixing the solution the other way around by accident has never resulted in the dreaded heat reaction! The real advantage of this method is that the etching process can be seen, since the liquid etchant remains clear throughout the process; also, any etchant on the hands is colourless and not immediately corrosive!

"Nevertheless, normal precautions should be taken, and any splashed etchant washed down with cold water. The etchant time seems somewhat quicker than with ferric chloride, but this can be conveniently judged by observing the board while it is immersed. About 10 min at 65°C is typical. The etchant should be replaced when it appears very green in colour due to the copper reaction taking place.

"Anyone who has worked with the usual ferric chloride etchants knows only too well how messy the process can be, plus the difficulty of obtaining a supply at short notice from a local High Street shop at the weekend. The chemicals suggested above can be procured locally and remain stable and safe for long periods without any special storage problems arising."

Alf Hussey, G4KUN, recently sent along a sample of a small pcb that he had produced in a matter of minutes without the use of any chemicals or photographic techniques. The result looks a little crude but nevertheless would appear to be perfectly adequate for many purposes. He writes:

"This method may be of interest to other radio enthusiasts who have access to a drilling machine. By mounting a ⅛th-inch slot drill (this is a type of milling cutter) in the chuck, and then with the chuck lowered or the table lifted so that the cutter just touches the copper surface. After drawing the required pattern on the piece of board, it is a quick and simple matter just to push the board under the cutter, using it as a router. This just cuts away the top few thousandths of an inch of copper. The finished article requires a few strokes of a file to remove the slight burr. My sample board took just 6min to produce."

Rockwell-Collins HF2050 receiver

A paper on the Collins HF2050 receiver ("A digital signal processing hf receiver", *IEE Conference Publication No 245* pp89–93) was presented by D T Anderson. As noted in *TT* October 1984, although this receiver is a high-grade professional receiver in the plus-$6,000 range, it seems entirely possible that the lower component count and ease of assembly, as well as the good characteristics of digital filtering, will prove attractive for the designers of equipment for the amateur service when the necessary large-scale integrated circuits (lsi) become more readily available.

Fig 6 shows the overall arrangement of the HF2050, with its first i.f. at 99MHz then converted down to 3MHz under the control of a low-noise synthesizer providing signal frequency coverage that includes vlf/lf/mf/hf. The digital signal processing is shown in Fig 7, with quadrature processing on the digital bit stream derived from sampling the 3MHz i.f. signal using a 12MHz clock. The processing is described as follows:

"The 3MHz i.f. signal is buffered and then digitized by an a/d converter. The output filter of the rf translator acts as an anti-aliasing filter for the a/d input signal. The a/d is a flash-type and is operated without a sample-and-hold. The a/d output is a digital 3MHz i.f. sampled at 12 megasamples/s (msps).

"The a/d output samples are inputted to the i.f. translator. The translator mixes, filters and reduces the sample rate (decimation) of the signal. It outputs a baseband (0Hz i.f.) signal consisting of an in-phase (I) and a quadrature (Q) component. Each component is in 2's complement form and is sampled at 48 kilosamples/s (ksps). The finite-impulse-response type (fir) which produces no phase distortion. A patent application describing the i.f. translator was filed by Rockwell.

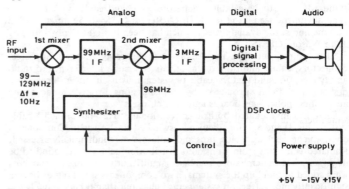

Fig 6. Block diagram of the Collins HF2050 receiver, the first production model of a general-purpose communications receiver incorporating digital signal processing and filtering

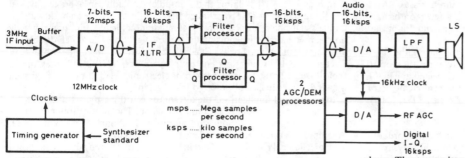

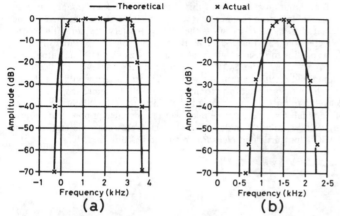

Fig 7. Block diagram of the digital signal processor incorporated in the Collins HF2050

Fig 8. (*a*) Amplitude response of the ssb digital filter in the HF2050. (*b*) 300Hz cw filter response. Differential delay responses of such digital filters is very much better than with mechanical or crystal filters, a factor of importance for rtty and digital data operation

"Next, filtering is done on the I-Q components separately using filter processors. This filtering provides the final selectivity of the receiver, and is equivalent in function to the mechanical and crystal filters found in all analogue receivers (but note that in effect the filtering is carried out on the 0kHz i.f. signal and is thus the equivalent of af filtering in a superhet or direct-conversion receiver—*G3VA*). The excellent filter responses are shown in Fig 8. The filter processors are vlsi digital signal processors containing a filtering program. Receiver bandwidth, ripple and selectivity are determined by programmed data within the processors. In the first production deliveries of the receiver, six different filtering operations (two cw, two a.m., ssb and isb) are implemented within the two I and Q filter processors . . . . the filter processors decimate the sample rate to 16ksps for each of the I and Q components.

"The agc/demodulator processors are the same type vlsi processor as used for filtering except that they contain agc and demodulating programs. Each agc/demod processor (one for cw, ssb and a.m., and one for isb) inputs the I-Q signal from the filter processors . . . ."

Those of us who are more used to analogue than digital technology may find the above description a little obscure, although the overall arrangement is reasonably clear.

Choosing the right material
John R Hey, G3TDZ, is concerned about the use of unsuitable materials noted in some constructional articles etc, particularly the use of "lossy" plastics at rf. He writes:

"It has been known for many years that certain plastics are very poor at rf, especially at vhf. Perspex, nylon, and colour-filled plastics such as pvc, are very lossy indeed and dissipate significant amounts of rf energy. A friend wound a 'rubber duck' antenna on to a nylon tube; it collapsed in a heap after only 15s of rf being applied! Every old-time tv service engineer remembers the fate of line transformers built from perspex. They went yellow, then turned brown, then black, and finally burst into flames.

"Polythene, polystyrene, polyester, polycarbonate and polypropylene are all fine, as are glass, ptfe, ceramics, and those old paper-based materials Paxolin and Tufnel.

"For many years I have used successfully a J-stick 144MHz antenna which is mounted inside a polypropylene tube. The popular grey pvc drainpipe, often used for this purpose, is much too lossy and sends the swr meter soaring. The white polypropylene tubes made by Marley and sold at

d-i-y shops are quite good.

"Some years ago, after the publication of one of my constructional articles in *Rad Com*, a constructor sent me his transmitter which he said could not be tuned up. Each stage appeared to tune in itself, but there was a net loss at each stage so that there was hardly a sniff of rf at the antenna socket. All components were correct and his soldering was impeccable. It was not until I inadvertently put a finger on one of the coils that the truth emerged—preceded by some bad language. The coil was almost red hot!

"I replaced each tuning slug with Aladdin slugs. The transmitter came to life and worked perfectly. If readers are reminded of the losses in materials periodically, constructors may have fewer disappointments."

It is indeed worth noting that there are still unknown factors in the use of materials in different environmental conditions and demanding applications. It was not until after the early Comet aircraft disasters of the 'fifties that much attention was paid to metal fatigue. Even today every very cold spell seems to be accompanied by a quota of gas explosions caused by leaks in the pipes.

Alun Williams, G3KSU, recently drew my attention to the sudden collapse on a calm but very cold morning of a 298m-high, 15-year-old cylindrical steel television transmitting mast near Detmond, West Germany, following a week in which the temperature had never risen above −15°C. Did the sustained cold cause one of the enormously strong guy cables to snap? Was there a sudden ground subsidence? Are tall cylindrical steel masts inherently less reliable than the traditional triangular steel lattice masts? Even the most experienced constructional engineers appear to be baffled by some of the questions that have arisen from this and other tv mast failures.

Plumbers' ptfe tape
Ken Lanyon, GM4GSJ, draws attention to the ptfe tape used in the plumbing trade for sealing water joints in mechanical couplings. He writes:

"This useful tape is quite cheap, and, although fiddly to handle owing to the static engendered as it is unwound, is not messy, as are most pvc adhesive tapes. When it is used for 'making-off' cable joints and terminations, it moulds itself neatly around soldered joints and does not show any tendency to peel off or unwind, even though it has not specific adhesive coating. I believe that if carefully applied it should prove waterproof.

"A further merit is that it will withstand soldering-iron temperatures, and this led me to use it, instead of pvc tape, while making one of the baluns described in *HF Antennas for All Locations*. After 'stretch-straightening' the 18swg wire and spiral wrapping it with ptfe tape for sufficient length (about 10in) the windings lay close and smooth on the ferrite rod: not too difficult to achieve with bifilar winding but much more problematic with trifilar construction.

"When wrapping three wires they naturally fall into a triangular configuration, and as winding proceeds they tend to twist, suggesting that achieving neat and close coupling of the conductors may be difficult when applied to the ferrite rod. But I found that in practice this procedure flattened the triangular format and, at the same time, tightened the wrapping, thus ensuring close and even coupling.

"In addition, the electrical properties of ptfe must be reflected in this type of tape and so far I have never heard of any disadvantages in using it for amateur radio applications."

G E Birkhead, EI9DZ (G4KOQ), recently constructed an atu which required the use of a balun (*Radio Communication Handbook*, 1974 ed, p585). This suggested the ferrite core should be covered with two layers of "3M No 27 glass-cloth insulating tape" which is not readily available on this side of the Atlantic. He purchased instead a roll of pure ptfe tape from the plumbing department of the local hardware store and wound approximately three layers around the ferrite core. This makes a neat job with the insulating properties of ptfe.

Adhesive copper tape
A Rawlings, G1CIJ, has found adhesive-backed copper tape (*TT* February) very useful for constructing the directors and driven element of a roof-space 144MHz ZL-Special antenna. He writes:

"I used 1 by 1in timber as the frame, and ran the tape around the timber element in a double row. The driven elements were built similarly and cross-joined to give the correct phasing. A small variable capacitor was added to adjust the swr down to about 1·3:1. This type of tape is available in 33m lengths in four sizes (4mm, 4·75mm 6mm and 8mm wide) from:

Copperfoil Enterprises, 141 Lyndhurst Drive, Hornchurch, Essex RM11 1JP. For the 4mm size I paid about £2.95 plus 50 p&p a few months ago. Soldered connections can be made satisfactorily, and I have no doubt that such tape could find many other applications.''

I suppose it could be argued that using the copper tape on a timber base limits the rf insulation, though this would not apply to tape stuck on to window glass, for example. A number of references have been made in *TT* to the use of very-low cost aluminium kitchen foil to form elements of indoor wideband hf and loop-type vhf antennas (see *TT* July 1983, p609).

Alternative energy—pedal power

The use of a static bicycle or hand generator to charge batteries in order to keep radio equipment working in remote locations has a long history. It has been shown that an energetic "cyclist" can generate over 100W of electrical power; though it can be exhausting to keep up this output over extended periods unless the overall efficiency of the system is high.

A recent article by Penn Clower, W1BG (*Ham Radio* December 1984) on ''The bicycle-powered station'' adopts the unusual approach of using a vehicle alternator to provide a regulated 110V ac output. This he uses directly to power a 100W ssb transceiver with no attempt to provide any form of energy storage other than adding some 2kg ''flywheel'' weight to the rim of the bicycle wheel which drives the alternator. This technique makes it essential to achieve high-efficiency if only to eliminate excessive huffing and puffing on the part of the energetic operator/rider. An effective and relatively sophisticated voltage-regulator is also necessary because of the large swings in the load presented by an ssb transceiver, and the significant variation in the power delivered by the rider during each pedal revolution.

In practice, W1BG claims that a middle-aged adult in average physical condition should be able to produce 50W continuously for an hour without undue strain; he reports that a 30–40min contact leaves him damp but by no means exhausted when using his static 10-gear bicycle which doubles as an exercise machine. For receive-only he loads his machine with a 40W electric light bulb. For less energetic operators, W1BG indicates that a typical Delco-Remy car alternator plus electronic regulator could be driven by wind, water or petrol-powered installations.

In its original application, the alternator is a three-phase machine with a y-wound stator driven by a rotating field coil. The three output phases are full-wave rectified to produce dc output with about 14 per cent ripple. Windings are arranged so that seven electrical output cycles occur during each mechanical rotation of the shaft, accounting for the advantage shown by an alternator at low rotational speeds compared with the more common two-pole dc vehicle generator. For a given field current, W1BG notes, the unregulated output of either type of machine is directly proportional to the shaft rate, but an alternator of this type, with its 7:1 advantage, can reach a reasonable output at a much lower speed. In a vehicle a relatively crude regulator is satisfactory since the storage battery regulates the output delivered to the various loads. W1BG connects a step-up transformer into the ac portion of the low-voltage alternator to provide 110V ac output. This could, of course, be 240V for European rigs, though the use of an unmodified rectified alternator with a 12V car battery would avoid many of the voltage-regulation problems. With either approach, the supply delivered to the equipment must be regulated to within about five per cent of nominal. Care needs to be taken with solidstate equipment to suppress any voltage spikes. For details of the elaborate electronic regulator etc, W1BG's long article in *Ham Radio* should be consulted. □

Technical Topics
by Pat Hawker, G3VA

THOSE OF US who do our best to provide technical information for the columns of journals and magazines seldom retain our youthful illusion that people read and remember everything they can lay their hands on, even about subjects of interest to them. Technical papers and articles on radical and innovatory topics seldom attract wide-spread attention—at least not immediately. It is left to the historians to pin-point (or argue about) just when a new idea was first published—and by whom.

The experimental tradition

Today, some members are much concerned at the apparent lack of curiosity into technical matters. How different it was, they say, in the old days of home-brew —or was it? Idly thumbing through some old copies of the *RSGB Bulletin* my eyes fell on an editorial I wrote for the June 1949 issue: *The experimental tradition*. To quote briefly from that 36-year-old piece:

"There can be few members who have not been assailed at times by the doubt that as Amateur Radio becomes technically more and more complicated, so the old experimental zest will recede further and further into the background.

"What was important, in the early days, was an alert, observant mind, backed by some mechanical skill and unlimited patience. Possessed of such assets, an amateur could, in a matter of months, assimilate current ideas and practices and pass rapidly to the stage where he was able to contribute usefully to work of a genuine experimental nature. Much good work was accomplished by amateurs while in their teens and even—as in the case of one of our notable pioneers, Cecil Goyder (2SZ Mill Hill School)— while still at school.

"What is the position nowadays? During and since the war, millions of pounds have been poured into radio research establishments. Techniques have advanced so far that the experts themselves can hope only to specialise in some relatively small section of the field of electronics.

"Does this mean that the experimental work of the amateur has become valueless? Or are there still opportunities for the average amateur who makes no claim to more than a moderate technical knowledge coupled with unbounded enthusiasm?

"We believe, most emphatically, that the amateur can and will continue to play an important role in experimental research and development . . . The history of science provides many examples to prove that it is a new approach towards, or a fresh outlook upon, a subject rather than profound learning that leads to far-reaching discoveries. There are many unexplained gaps in the science of radio . . .

"The amateur, today, should be ready to search amongst the accumulated mass of scientific data for ideas which are capable of application to our problems. By refusing to be overawed by the complexity of modern radio, by turning a receptive ear towards new ideas and by encouraging those who—whether they are new or old hands at the game —have something fresh to say, so shall we all ensure that the experimental tradition of Amateur Radio is fully maintained."

With the advantage of hindsight, it is possible to see that indeed the radio amateurs of 1949 to 1985, both young and old, have successfully maintained the experimental tradition; have still, despite the far greater complexity made possible by integrated circuits, contributed to the development and practical application of novel techniques. Perhaps one reason for this is that so much of the progress in radio communication is still based on the implementation (with modern components) of ideas first propounded many years ago.

Joshua Sieger, a noted innovator, puts it thus: "In my many years associated with television in the pre-war days, with radar during the war, and my gas detection company post-war, I have always found that looking backwards at the inventive genius of people in the latter part of the last century and the early part of this century exercises the mind to invent again with all the devices which have become available . . ."

Safety, mains equipment and high-energy batteries

The March *TT* included some items dealing with safety regulations, BS415, and also raised the question of mercury in high-energy batteries. This prompted Peter Poole, G3ENV, who is Electrical Adviser in the DTI's consumer safety unit, to send along some further useful comments. On mains equipment he wrote:

"Mains-powered equipment is subject to the Electrical Equipment (Safety) Regulations, 1975 as amended in 1976. These regulations apply at the point of sale irrespective of the source. If you find an item of electronic equipment which appears not to comply with BS415 it is highly likely that it will contravene the safety regulations and I would advise anyone to bring the matter to the attention of their local trading standards department. The regulations also apply to the sale of second-hand goods, although there are certain exemptions which relate to the supply of maintenance spares which might have been acceptable at the time of the original equipment sale."

This sounds a formidable barrier to the sale of a lot of imported equipment, but regulations are only effective in so far as they are fully enforceable and I suspect that a lot of equipment changes hands that would not meet all of the stringent provisions of BS415 as mentioned in the March *TT*.

On the question of mercury in alkaline-manganese batteries, G3ENV takes issue with my use of the phrase "significant amount". He recognizes that the Japanese public has become extremely sensitive to the issue of mercuric poisoning (my notes were based on a report in the scientific journal *Nature* from their Tokyo correspondent) but considers that the amount of mercury contained in alkaline batteries is so small as to be insignificant. He writes:

"What there is being in the form of amalgam on an electrode. They do, however, contain potassium hydroxide and have a much higher output power capability in that they can produce 15A on short-circuit and achieve surface temperatures of up to 120°C in the process—lithium and nickel cadmium cells even more so.

"Button-type mercury cells do, of course, contain a significant amount of mercury, and it is for this reason that the Japanese normally specify the much more expensive silver cells. Although mercury cells probably do not present a large hazard to public health, we are concerned at the number which are swallowed by young children. Although this only rarely leads to death it often does involve hospitalization and great distress to parents, and unnecessary expense to the Health Service. May I therefore ask for the hospitality of your column to ask people not to leave button cells lying about in places where they might be picked up and swallowed by infants.

"Modern high-performance batteries need to be treated with great respect, since they are a very potent source of energy and contain toxic materials. However, you may be pleased to know that the use of mercury in cells is likely to fall with the development of new technologies."

Chris Cheney, G3RSE, also takes up the question of the many toxic materials in common use in our shacks. He writes:

"In the 'Mercury is dangerous' item you seem to imply in the final paragraph that nicad batteries are comparatively safe. However, as you have pointed out in past *TT* items, cadmium salts are toxic. I cannot comment on the relative safety of different types of battery but I am certain that we all assume that many common items are safe, when in fact they are not.

"I have been concerned for some time about the lead in solder—especially the fine powder which results from the use of a 'solder-sucker'. Yet I have not seen anything in any technical literature about the hazard of lead in solder."

In this connection it may be worth reminding readers of an item in *TT* some years ago about the danger of using cored solder over long periods without good extraction of the flux fumes which can lead to asthma-type coughs and wheezing.

Crystal filters and the stenode receiver

If I had to pick one single event in the development of communication receivers as of the greatest importance, without question I would opt for the *QST* articles in which James Lamb of ARRL staff advocated the use of a crystal-gate i.f. filter, so opening the way for high-performance superhet receivers. But Lamb, as he frankly admitted at the time, was not responsible for the initial development of the crystal filter. The credit for this belongs to the UK work of Dr J Robinson and Ernest Gardiner, G6GR, in connection with their development of the "stenode radiostat" principle. Yet I suspect that only a minority of readers will ever have heard of stenode reception, even though some elements of their work is found not only in communication receivers but in virtually all medium-wave broadcast receivers.

A stenode radiostat receiver was intended to have sufficiently high selectivity to permit the frequency separation between broadcast transmitters to be reduced to perhaps 5kHz without impairing the quality of reception; this was achieved by providing a high degree of compensation in the af section of the receiver. As noted in *TT, ART,* etc many years ago, a receiver fitted with the original form of sharply-peaked filter based on a single crystal can be used very successfully for ssb reception simply by incorporating a suitable form of high-rise coupling network within the af chain: Fig 1(c). This will turn muffled, boomy and virtually unintelligible speech into reasonable quality speech. The principle depends on the shape factor of a single-crystal filter not being as steep as we nowadays expect from a multi-pole bandpass crystal filter. The peaked filter passes the higher audio components of the sideband, although these are greatly reduced compared with the low audio frequencies.

In broadcasting, signal-processing with pre-emphasis of high audio frequencies is increasingly being used for medium-wave a.m. broadcasting to overcome the narrow bandwidth (2 to 3kHz at 6dB down) of most broadcast receivers. In fact, although the term stenode radiostat has passed into history, the principle is still very much alive, although broadcast transmitters still need to be spaced 9 or 10kHz apart.

I was reminded of the stenode principle by finding a detailed article "The stenode radiostat system of wireless reception and its application to television", by E L Gardiner, G6GR, in the June 1931 issue of the *Journal of the Television Society*. To be brutally frank, I do not think the stenode system ever did prove to have any direct application to television, but G6GR's article provides a survey of highly-selective receivers based either on the use of a crystal filter or alternatively on the use of an i.f. of the order of 20 to 50kHz (a technique which became popular in amateur radio in the 'fifties in the form of the old Q-5er/BC453 adapter). The 1931 article includes a diagram (Fig 1(b)) of the balanced-bridge crystal filter that was

subsequently adopted by Lamb. Dr Robinson, accompanied by Ernest Gardiner, made a lecture-demonstration tour of the USA in 1930, and the idea was taken up by the Crosley Radio Corporation. It also came to the notice of James Lamb.

Some years later, G6GR wrote several excellent series of articles on crystal filters, including two-crystal bandpass units, for the *T & R Bulletin,* later incorporated into the war-time edition of the RSGB's *Amateur Radio Handbook*. G6GR is still active in retirement in the Torbay area. With Robinson and Lamb he was one of the founding fathers of the modern crystal filter.

Fishing rod antenna supports

Robin Greenwood, G3LBA/PA3ACQ, noted the use of glass-fibre fishing rod blanks by Les Moxen, G6XN, for his "poor man's log periodic" antenna arrays (*TT* March) and his comment that these are difficult to find. Writing from Holland, G3LBA reports that very long glass-fibre rods are available there at modest cost (hfl 100) and that he has found them superb for antenna use and apparently indestructable even in the high winds that sweep across Holland. He reports:

"I have a vertical antenna mounted on the end of the house. This is made of a combination of a faulty wind-surf mast (wind surfers are extremely fussy about any blemishes) and a 6·5m fishing rod. The overall length of the unguyed vertical is 9·5m, and it is crowned by a 1m-diameter capacitance hat made of stainless-steel welding rod. The antenna is used on 1·8 to 10·1MHz in conjunction with loaded counterpoises.

"During an equinox, winds here regularly peak up to 160km/h and yet these rods survive, presumably because they bend dramatically. After such a blow, I look and find the antenna is still there and absolutely vertical. Such rods would lend themselves well to the type of construction suggested by G6XN, particularly for those of us who operate on the lower portion of the hf spectrum.

"These very long fishing rods are available in the UK, but as usual the price is higher than over here: for the wealthy they are available also in carbon fibre. They are delivered in concentric form, each section plugging into the next. I bind each joint with self-amalgamating tape, and the joints do not work loose. The wire up the centre needs a light foam silencer to stop it from rattling, and for this I use central-heating pipe insulation which I cut for thin sections. The tubes must not be clamped but be a tight fit at the points of contact with the support, which should overlap about 1m."

RFI and home computers

Sources of rfi, or the many domestic electronic systems that are vulnerable to rfi, range from smoke detectors to burglar alarms to almost anything fitted with a cmos microprocessor. Similarly, weak-signal reception can be affected by almost any digital system that uses "clock" oscillators and has high-frequency pulses rushing around in unshielded, unbypassed circuits. This can include electronic telephones which often have pulse diallers with crystal-controlled "clocks". High-speed pulses can be quite a potent source of rfi (particularly on lf and mf) but fortunately the power involved in many devices, such as digital watches, is very low indeed. Home computers are a different kettle of fish, with many of the models on sale in the UK unlikely to pass the strict limits now laid down in the USA for maximum radiation levels.

Despite the tighter control exercised by the FCC in the USA, interference arising from electronic consumer equipment and from home computers is still recognized as a difficult problem. In *Ham Radio* September 1984, Dale Williams, K3PUR, discusses the whole question of "electromagnetic interference and the digital era", showing the importance of component selection, earthing and shielding in attempting to reduce interference. He notes that "digital electronics has overwhelmed the rf environment with binary clocks that produce harmonics into the gigahertz range, plastic equipment enclosures, wall-plug power supplies and unshielded ribbon cable that acts as an antenna". The shielding characteristics of coaxial cable, he points out, not only depends on the braid coverage, but also on the quality of the connectors used at both ends of the cable; it is pointless to use the best-quality double-shielded cable with connectors that are incapable of providing more than 60db attenuation to leaking signals. The bolting together of a shielding enclosure can reduce isolation by some 25dB when the hole spacing is increased from 1 to 5in. He suggests, as a general rule of thumb, that where rf gaskets are not used, or the enclosure contains discontinuities such as corner bend strain relief openings, multiple bolt-together sections, openings for switches, fuses, etc, maximum attenuation is likely to be limited to about 30dB. In most cases, fortunately, the provision of decoupling capacitors and some ferrite beads will at least minimize the problem.

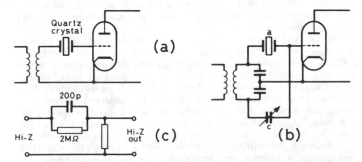

Fig 1. (*a*) Simple crystal filter, and (*b*) the well-known balanced crystal-gate filter with balancing (phasing) control as used in hf receivers over many years prior to the general adoption of multi-crystal bandpass filters. Both diagrams are from G6GR's 1931 paper on the stenode radiostat receiver principles devised by Dr J Robinson in 1929. (c) Simple tone correction network which enables ssb to be received through a crystal filter of the type shown in (b). Values are suitable for high-impedance (old-style phone output sockets) and require modification for low-impedance af circuits

Variable bandwidth ladder filter

The low-cost variable-bandwidth crystal filter based on a handful of 4·43MHz PAL colour-tv crystals, a few capacitors and a multipole switch remains a useful and effective economy for anyone building or improving an ssb/cw transceiver. Although a number of designs have already appeared in *TT* and elsewhere, it was interesting to note a full constructional article, including pcb layout in a compartmentalized screening box appearing in the East German publication *Funkamateur* Nr 1/85 by H R Langer, Y27YO.

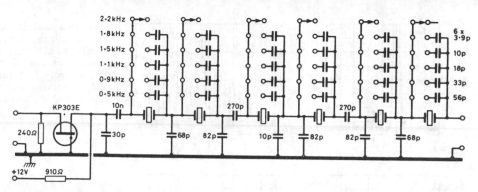

Fig 2. Y27YO's low-cost variable-bandwidth ladder crystal filter using PAL-tv 4·43MHz crystals. Careful layout and shielded construction are needed to achieve optimum results

While it has been made clear in earlier articles that there is more than one style of PAL crystal, requiring slightly different capacitances to achieve a stated bandwidth at a given impedance, the values suggested by Y27YO should prove a useful starting point: Fig 2.

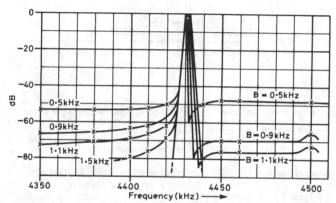

Fig 3. Response curves of the Y27YO filter. The reduced ultimate rejection of the narrower responses reflects the higher value of capacitors connected across the crystals

The slope of the filter on the high-frequency side will tend to be steeper than on the low-frequency side, and account should be taken of this when the filter is used in ssb receivers or exciters. The ultimate rejection of the filter decreases at narrow bandwidths but should always exceed about 50dB and may be considerably greater than this for ssb: Fig 3. The use of shielding plates and careful layout play an important part in any filter, but construction need not be unduly difficult.

Quartz crystals, holders and oscillator stability

Some basic notes on quartz crystals—emphasizing that these are one of the most vital, yet perhaps least understood, components used in amateur radio equipment—were given in *TT* (January 1984, and see also April 1984, p317). Useful additional information can be found in "Choosing quartz crystals" by Gordon Huyler of Cathodeon Crystals in *Electronics & Wireless World,* April 1985, pp51-3, 55). This shows that modern crystal holders are of four basic types: solder-seal holders, the least expensive but subject to significant long-term "ageing" drift; resistance-weld holders, currently the most popular type and suitable for the vast majority of applications; cold-weld holders that give a further improvement in long-term ageing but cost more; and glass holders for the most rigorous applications such as frequency standards.

Table 1 shows typical tolerances, ageing characteristics etc for these four types of holder.

Table 1. "Accuracy" of crystals in different holders

	Solder-seal	Resistance weld	Cold weld	Glass
Adjustment tolerance, ppm	± 15	± 10	± 7·5	± 5
Frequency/temperature tolerance	± 15	± 10	± 10	± 10
ppm at −10°C to +60°C				
ppm at −40°C to +90°C	± 40	± 30	± 30	± 30
Ageing at 85°C ppm/annum	± 10-15	± 3·5	± 2	± 1·2

(*Note:* These values are dependent also on other factors, particularly frequency).

Gordon Huyler similarly divides crystal oscillators into a series of increasingly accurate categories: simple "clock" oscillators; simple "packaged" oscillators (spxo) with frequency-trimming capability to permit use in voltage-controlled oscillators (vcxo); temperature-compensated oscillators (tcxo) having a temperature-dependent reactance in the frequency control loop (expensive although home-built versions have been described in the past in *TT*); and oven-compensated oscillators (ocxo) which can achieve stabilities of one part in 10^{10} per day when using a built-in double oven and vacuum flask in conjunction with careful circuit design and used in "secondary standards". A single-oven design can give stabilities of about one part in 10^7 in respect of temperature variations. These characteristics are summarized in Table 2.

Table 2. Stability of four main types of crystal oscillator

	Accuracy in ppm	Remarks
(1) Clock oscillators	50 to 2000	Low cost; logic compatible
(2) Simple package	5 to 100	Standard crystal oscillator Tuneable to frequency
(3) Temperature compensated	0·2 to 5	Low power consumption; instant warm up; modest cost
(4) Oven controlled	0·001 to 1	High precision; long warm-up; high power consumption; cost rises rapidly with stability

(*Notes:* The clock oscillator is the basic crystal oscillator. The distinction drawn between simple-package and clock oscillators is that clock oscillators often do not incorporate any means of frequency adjustment). Tables 1 and 2 from *Electronics & Wireless World* April 1985.

Linear transmitters with cartesian feedback

If you consider that the ssb sections of most amateur bands always seem crowded and noisy, it is interesting to speculate to what degree this situation is due to spurious emissions from transmitters of uncertain linearity. Unwanted intermodulation products cause transmitters to spread out over many kilohertz, and this may be inherent in their design or due to gradual deterioration as valves age and cause flat-topping or the circuits drift out of alignment.

The intermodulation characteristics regarded as acceptable for amateur radio transmitters are considerably more relaxed and less rigorous than those specified for military or professional equipment. The near-in noise output during a two-tone test may be only around 25–30dB down on the peak tones, compared with 40–50dB for high-grade professional communications.

It would significantly help to clean up our bands if spurious noise and unwanted sideband suppression could be reduced to around −60dB, though this would not really be possible without adopting new techniques —and only the public-spirited would rush to buy a new, sanitized rig!

For the past five years or so, V Petrovic and others at Bath University have been developing a special form of negative feedback (polar-loop or cartesian feedback) that offers not only extremely good linearity but also has other advantages, including high efficiency power amplification. These techniques have been discussed before in *TT* and have been implemented by the Bath team to provide hf and vhf transmitters at powers up to about 1kW.

At the recent hf communications conference, a paper by V Petrovic and A H Brown ("Application of cartesian feedback to hf ssb transmitters" *IEE Conference Publication No 245*, pp81-5) describes a 1·6 to 30MHz 100W p.e.p. transmitter in which feedback reduces the third-order products by a massive 37dB, with the products on a two-tone test a remarkable 67dB below the tones. Image sidebands are suppressed 68dB: see Fig 4.

The use of cartesian feedback not only improves the spectral purity but also results in: (*1*) lower output noise, achieved by reducing the overall gain of the transmitter; (*2*) improved efficiency, obtained by operating the pa

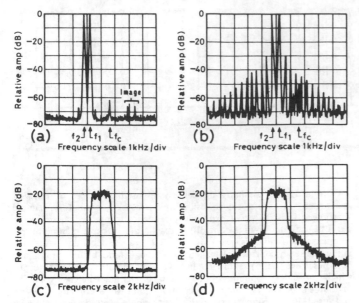

Fig 4. Output spectrum of the 100W p.e.p. hf transmitter developed at Bath University with and without the use of cartesian feedback loops: (a) and (b) are for two-tone input, (c) and (d) are with white noise input; (a) and (c) with feedback, (b) and (d) without feedback

with reduced bias and using an unregulated power supply; and (3) simplified design of the power amplifier, since neither its linearity nor frequency response need to be exceptionally good.

Basically, this cartesian loop transmitter employs phasing-type ssb generation (Weaver third-method) to which the *modulation information* obtained by synchronous demodulation of a sample of the output signal is fed back in quadrature form. In other words, audio signals at 90° to each other are recovered and used as negative feedback. Since the bandwidth of the af signals is much narrower than with rf negative feedback, as used on some ssb transmitters, much larger amounts of feedback can be applied.

The problem of obtaining af signals over the range 300 to 3,000Hz in accurate quadrature by means of phase-shift networks is well known and has been the reason why relatively few phasing-type ssb transmitters are used, particularly where they need to operate over a wide temperature range. The vast majority of amateurs continue to use filter-type ssb generation despite the attractions of third-method and polyphase networks.

The novel feature of this latest transmitter is to use a combination of third-method ssb generation with *filter-type* demodulation to supply the quadrature feedback, using 10·7MHz ssb crystal filters.

Delightful dipoles?

One of several papers presented by well-known radio amateurs (though usually in the professional *alter ego* guise) at the hf conference was one by Maurice Hately, GM3HAT, on the multiband dipole which he is currently marketing as a "dipole of delight". This antenna is based on a UK patent application made in September 1981 on his behalf by the National Research Development Corporation (UK Patent Application GB 2112579, published 20 July 1983).

In effect, GM3HAT claims that by inserting suitable-value capacitors at the feedpoint of a dipole element fed from coaxial cable, he achieves an efficient form of matching/balun that significantly reduces the effect of pick-up on the outer braid of the coaxial cable and thus provides not only an efficient radiator but also a receiving antenna that is much less susceptible to local rfi from tv sets, home computers, electrical appliances and the like. The insertion of capacitors involves a phase-shift that "stretches" the element so that its half-wave electrical resonance approximately equals a physical half-wave; in other words the usual five per cent end-correction does not apply.

The insertion of two capacitors in the element creates an electrical centre-point to which the braid of the coaxial feeder is connected, with also a low-impedance feedpoint (whose impedance can be made to match the cable) on the outer side of either of the two capacitors, and it is to one of these two points that the inner conductor of the cable is connected. It appears to me that this arrangement provides a form of gamma match that minimizes the age-old problem of joining an unbalanced feeder to a balanced element. In practice, GM3HAT then forms a multiband antenna by a series of resonant parallel wires in the accepted manner: Fig 5.

Provided that the capacitors are of the correct value for the frequency involved, the GM3HAT principle would seem to offer useful advantages in achieving a good match on each band over a reasonable bandwidth, and also minimizing pick-up of stray electrical interference on the feeder. Whether all of the advantages claimed by GM3HAT can be fully justified on theoretical grounds is a little more difficult to assess. As I mentioned at the conference, his paper seems to assume that the outer braid of a coaxial cable feeder, regardless of its length, represents an "electrical earth" point. To my mind, it doesn't.

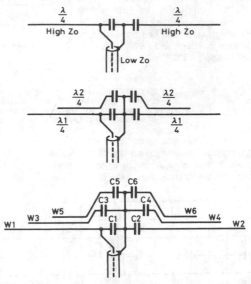

Fig 5. GM3HAT's patented "dipoles of delight" which use capacitors to improve the match between unbalanced coaxial feeders and the balanced elements. The capacitances should have a reactance at the frequency concerned equal to the impedance of the feeder. The incorporation of the capacitors "stretches" the element and at resonance the electrical length is roughly the same as the physical length

But perhaps more important than theory is practice. GM3HAT is enthusiastically convinced that his dipoles are a delight to use and that in time all dipoles will come to have phase-shifting capacitors at their feed points. Only time will tell, but at least full credit to GM3HAT for what is clearly a novel idea that has already won support from a number of those now using this antenna.

Constant-k crystal filters

In *TT* (November 1980, p1157) I drew attention to the symmetrical variable-selectivity crystal filters used by the Germans in a number of their high-grade military communications receivers during the second world war. This form of constant-k filter, the basis of the modern ladder filter, unlike the more usual half-lattice configuration, provided a substantially symmetrical passband which could be narrowed while retaining a reasonably good shape factor from about 10kHz to 200Hz, and could be further improved by using more than one such filter in separate mf i.f. stages.

The arrangement shown in Fig 6, as given in the 1980 *TT*, was taken from one of the articles by Dick Rollema, PA0SE, on German wartime receivers.

A more detailed description of this type of filter has appeared recently in *cq-DL* (March 1985, pp138–40) by Ulrich Fleischmann, DL9LX, together with a bibliography (mostly German text) of sources dating back to 1937, from which it is fairly clear that this type of mf filter was

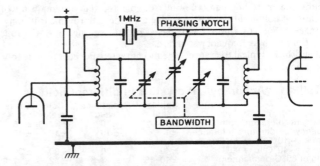

Fig 6. The constant-k 1MHz crystal filter as used in a number of German wartime communication receivers providing a variable-bandwidth symmetrical response plus a phasing notch control

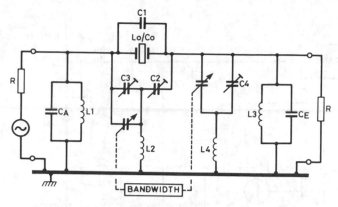

Fig 7. Filter circuit from DL9LX's article

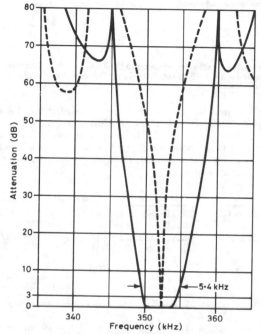

Fig 8. Response curve of a 352kHz filter in a medium-wave receiver possibly with similar filters in two i.f. stages

developed by Telefunken engineers. DL9LX provides information on the design, adjustment and performance of this type of filter. I have not tackled the German text, but Figs 7 and 8, taken from the article, show that for an intermediate frequency filter at mf (352kHz) this filter has much to offer.

Reducing ultra-violet radiation damage

Recent items in *TT* on 300Ω ribbon feeder and self-amalgamating rubber tape have noted the damage that can be caused to materials used outdoors in strong sunlight due to u-v radiation, as well as the better-known degradations brought about by wind, rain, humidity, moisture ingress, etc. Several informative comments have been received from readers.

Dr Constantino Feruglio, IV3VS writes:

"In order to avoid the deterioration of 300Ω ribbon feeders, I put my ribbon inside a length of plastic hosepipe. Since I leave the ends of the pipe open, no problem of condensation arises inside the pipe. I do, however, carefully bend the pipe over at the top to prevent the entry of rain. The weight of the ribbon and plastic pipe is no greater than many coaxial cables (eg RG8U), and rf losses appear to be insignificant. After *four years* in operation my ribbon is still practically 'new'!".

IV3VS does not mention any problems of u-v affecting the plastic hosepipe.

Mike Shepherd, G8YZW, who originally raised the subject of self-amalgamating tape (*TT* January, with comments about u-v from G3JDK in the March issue) comments further as follows:

"Deterioration caused by u-v has always to be taken into account with materials used in full sunlight, as shown by the deterioration of the outer

covering of coaxial cables. Similarly, plastic rope often used for mast stays becomes hardened and brittle after exposure to sun and rain.

"In reply to G3JDK I cannot say how 'my' tape will perform, especially as, following my usual procedure, I gave the wrapped areas a good coat of outdoor-quality paint for added protection. Incidentally, I use marine varnish, 'u-v resistant' for all *metal* items, including antenna elements. But as a result of G3JDK's experience of his tape performing badly, I am making up a small test rig with short lengths of tube, coaxial cable and stranded wire all having *tape-only* wrapped joints, and will mount this out-of-doors to find out how it performs when unprotected by paint."

John Tye, G4BYV, also comments on RS self-amalgamating rubber tape as follows:

"I have used this for several years on the coaxial cables on my tower and for my mobile antenna loading coils without experiencing any water or u-v radiation problems. But I do spray it with Holt's damp-start ignition sealer."

Cliff Ranft, BRS1418 (ex-G5RF, VK3NR and VK7FG), notes that while working as a senior radio technical officer with the Australian Department of Civil Aviation in the 'fifties and 'sixties, he used what was called "Bi-seal tape" which he believes stemmed from the USA. This tape was also used by their lines section for outdoor use, including repeater stations located on mountains up to 4,600ft high in bright Australian sunshine. He does not remember any problem being experienced from u-v radiation. He recalls that the mechanism of applying the tape was to do so under a lot of "stretch", as this was said to change the molecular structure and the separate layers then merged to form a homogeneous solid. He writes:

"The problem of u-v is often called 'photo-degradation', and we had problems when using coaxial cables with a black or brown outer cover. We overcame these temporarily until the introduction of white-covered coaxial cable by covering significant lengths of cable with ordinary 'household' white adhesive tape. Until this was done the brown cable particularly used to come up in rough 'bubbles' and even sometimes crack. The white wrapping shaded the cable from direct sunlight and, more importantly, *reflected* it. The white adhesive tape, of course, contributed nothing to the actual waterproofing.

"White adhesive tape might well overcome any u-v problems with self-amalgamating rubber tape. I am not sure if 'Bi-seal' tape is available in the UK. Personally, I use a good dollop of 'not-properly-stirred' gloss paint for sealing purposes. This is very effective for foam-type coaxial cables, but goodness knows what its electrical properties are!".

Finally on this topic, a note from T. A. Sear, G4MGD, a planning engineer with British Telecom, who has been professionally involved with life-expectancy tests on various sealing and weatherproofing techniques, including self-amalgamating tape. He writes:

"A self-amalgamating tape seal is expected to last several years even in exposed locations. However, it is important that the seal is performed correctly, as follows:

(1) As with any seal, the sheath must be clean, dry and grease-free.

(2) Do not use old self-amalgamating tape. One-year-old should be the maximum.

(3) Warm the tape by keeping it in an inside pocket prior to use.

(4) Stretch tape until it is about 75 per cent of its original width.

(5) Apply tape under tension and with 50 per cent overlap, ruck-free.

(6) Cover entire seal with pvc tape at 50 per cent overlap, and extend pvc tape, ruck free, overlapping ends of seal by approximately 2in."

Getting on air with homebrew QRP

It is always an unexpected pleasure to be the very first station contacted on-air by a newly-licensed amateur. Recently, I had this experience when working Peter Hall, G4ZPT, on 3·5MHz while he was using a home-built QRP transmitter.

In a subsequent letter G4ZPT wrote: "Surely you could impress upon your readers the extraordinary pleasure awaiting anyone who can establish radio contact for the first time on home-built equipment. It is so easy to take the whole of radio communication for granted. Yet if one only stops to think about it, with just a handful of components, a morse key, and a wire antenna strung up into a tree, it is possible for anyone to radiate tiny oscillating signals and converse with fellow human beings miles away. This is, by any reckoning, an extraordinary and wonderful thing—too often forgotten by the many who buy all their 'gear', plug it in, switch on and talk. The remarkable combination of natural phenomena and electronics makes possible what must be the most exciting and interesting part of amateur radio; there, waiting to be grappled with, experimented and understood.

"I realize my station is primitive and largely devoid of new features, but I defy anyone, with any equipment, to derive more enjoyment from the

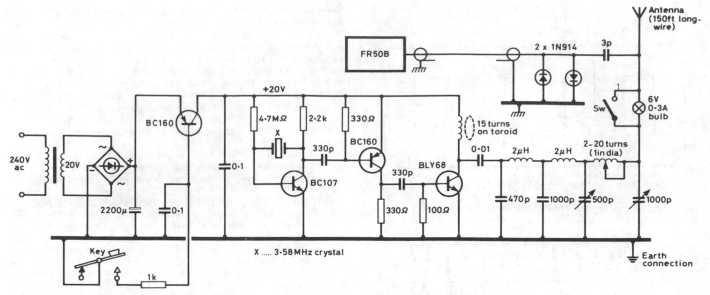

Fig 9. The "first contact" QRP home-brew transmitter of G4ZPT that emphasizes the miracle of radio communication with a handful of components. No transmitter/receiver switching necessary in view of the protective diodes across the input to the FR50B receiver. Tune the pi-network output circuit for maximum brilliance and then close switch

miraculous short waves. PS: I am not an old fuddy duddy, but a 23-year-old medical student."

Without wishing to trespass on G3RJV's domain, I cannot refrain from providing details of G4ZPT's simple rig: Fig 9, in the hope that it may encourage others to experience the pleasure of home-brew gear. Even though I still feel that most newcomers to cw operating would be happier with an input power of, say, 10 to 15W, although 5W can bring good contacts on 3·5 and 7MHz even with indifferent antennas.

Monopoles, vertical dipoles and the five-eighths vertical

A three-part article "The feed impedance of an elevated vertical antenna" by Guy Fletcher, VK2BBF, in *Amateur Radio* (VK) of August, September and October 1984, explores in some depth the facts and fallacies surrounding the effect on vertical antennas of its elevation above ground and its effect on antenna gain. While there are several nuggets of useful information (eg Fig 10) in all three parts, there is space here only to quote some of the points made in the final part:

"It should be clearly understood that the ground-level monopole, an elevated monopole and an elevated half-wave vertical dipole should all have approximately the same gain over an *unobstructed, good ground*. The magic 3dB gain sometimes claimed for a λ/4 monopole over a dipole never existed. The argument for it is based, I think, on the fact that the same power is radiated into only half of all space (above ground level) so the signal should be doubled. This is not a fair comparison, since a vertical dipole over a ground has exactly the same advantage, and in free space (interplanetary) neither antenna has this advantage.

"Finally the 5λ/8 monopole. It can be shown that over a perfect ground and for the same total radiated power, the field strength due to an antenna of height 0·64λ (which is close enough to 5λ/8) exceeds that due to a λ/4 monopole by a factor 1·43 due to the sharpening of the radiation pattern; 0·64λ is the optimum length, and the field falls quickly for longer monopoles. This corresponds to a power gain of $1·43^2 = 2·03$ or 3dB.

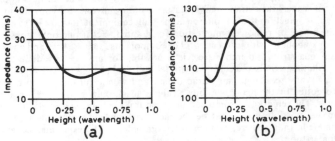

Fig 10. Base feed impedance of (a) λ/4 vertical monopole antenna; (b) base feed impedance (reactive) of 5λ/8 vertical monopole. Both as functions of height above ground

"Thus a vertical 5λ/8 antenna, whether elevated or not, has a built-in advantage for low-angle radiation of 3·07dB over a vertical λ/4 antenna, and presumably 3·07 − 0·26 = 2·81dB over a vertical half-wave dipole. If this advantage is not observed in practice, it is almost certainly due to incorrect matching of the antennas, and to different power levels delivered to each by the transmitter."

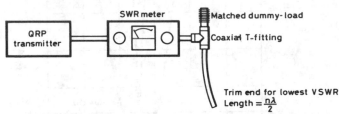

Fig 11. G3SEK's method of trimming coaxial cable to length

For hf operators who cannot reach 5λ/8 (225°) it is worth mentioning that the 110° vertical mentioned in the April *TT* (200Ω vertical) does show a useful sharpening of the vertical radiation pattern, though less than the optimum 5λ/8.

Adjusting vhf phasing lines

Several comments have been received in connection with G2RO's notes on "coaxial phasing lines" (*TT* February 1985, p114). Ian White, G3SEK, writes:

"G2RQ's method of cutting coaxial cable to equal lengths is very interesting. I am sure it works, but I am uneasy about *how* it works. Any short length of unterminated low-loss cable should theoretically give an "infinity" (forward = reflected) indication on an swr meter, so G2RO is relying on his swr meter doing what it shouldn't! (A *lossy* cable, particularly a long one, does *not* result in an infinite swr reading, and this can mislead the operator who believes his antenna is far better matched to its feeder than is the case in practice—*G3VA*).

"If you use a T-adapter to connect a matched dummy load to the swr meter, as well as the length of coaxial cable (see Fig 11), this allows the swr meter to work properly. It will indicate a perfect match whenever the length of the coaxial cable is a whole number of half-wavelengths, if the trimmed end is left open-circuit. With a good swr meter the null in reflected power is very sharp and deep. This idea came from K1WHS, and I have used it to cut eight equal long lengths of coaxial cable for 432MHz within an accuracy of a few millimetres."

Noiseless negative-feedback on 144MHz

Apropos my notes in the February *TT* on "GaAs and computer-aided design", I must first apologise to Chris Bartram, G4GDU, of muTek, for mixing up both his call-letters and the name of his firm. He writes:

"It may be of interest to readers that we do now manufacture a GaAs preamplifier for 144MHz (GFBA144e) using non-dissipative "noiseless" feedback circuitry. We are, to the best of my knowledge, the only company in the world to offer this level of performance to amateur vhf enthusiasts. As an amateur, it is possible to buy a standard of performance better than many professional users would believe possible . . . However, I fully endorse your comments regarding the misuse of computer modelling by amateurs. The computer is no substitute for a full understanding of the problem.

"The figures for spurious free dynamic range quoted by N6TX seem rather short of the state of the art. Using a silicon mosfet (BF981) with a standard level mixer we are achieving 90dB-plus sfdr (in ssb bandwidths) quite routinely in our production front-end boards. We are currently producing a transverter for 60MHz (also using BF981s) which has, typically, an input third-order intercept point of + 4dBm with an associated noise figure of 2·2dB. This represents around 97dB sfdr in ssb bandwidths. It is possible to exceed this by some decibels, but at a cost unlikely to appeal to radio amateurs.

"I agree that our North American friends seem rather overwhelmed by the GaAsfet, and it seems that trendiness is sometimes replacing engineering. These devices have their uses, but good receiver design is not just a matter of choosing devices and throwing them together in a 'traditional' circuit . . . The environment that the receiver is to be used in is as important a parameter as the noise performance of the first stage— as being emphasized by Ian White, G3SEK . . . Once a suitable noise floor has been decided upon, the rest of the front-end can be optimized for dynamic range. Computers *are* useful here: by juggling with gain distribution within a suitable analysis program, it is possible to optimize dynamic performance within the constraints of the system components (amplifiers, mixer etc).

"It is very easy to waste money on system components, such as high-level mixers. With standard-level mixers such as the SBL-1 it is possible to obtain input third-order intercept points for a complete front-end of around + 6dBm with an associated noise figure of 2dB. The limitation usually lies in the choice of the rf amplifier device. With a correctly-terminated mixer, modern mosfets, bipolar transistors or GaAsfets are all capable of a genuine noise figure of around 1dB but with input third-order intercept points of around 0dBm at best, even with the gain distribution properly optimized. Significantly better performance can *only* be achieved at the expense of more complex amplifier circuitry."

In the GFBA144e, a "noiseless" negative-feedback circuit is used around a MGF1202 GaAsfet. This can result in a low noise figure combined with excellent dynamic performance, so achieving an input third-order intercept of 10dBm and output intercept of 23dBm, still with a noise figure of under 1dB. The feedback adds only about 0·15dB to the noise figure but almost 10dB to the intercept point.

Hard-to-come-by components

The difficulty these days of obtaining small quantities of out-of-the-ordinary components is too well-known to need emphasizing. Distributors often are "trade-only" or have swingeing "minimum-order" charges. Firms catering for the home-constructor have, in the main, long gone over almost exclusively to low-voltage semiconductor-type components that are unsuitable for any valve-type equipment.

It is not usually the policy of *TT* to devote a whole section to promoting the services of a particular firm, but I feel that the following note from Nick Valentine, G3KWJ, in Avon, could prove the answer to many prayers. He writes:

"The G2DAF Mark 2 receiver which I am building has reached the stage of wiring. Despite our very good local electronic surplus stores, I had been unable to locate some 240pF 250V (or higher) close-tolerance capacitors. I remembered reading in *TT* that STC (formerly ITT) Components Ltd deal with the public, though having experience of working for a manufacturer I hesitated to get in touch with them, thinking of the usual £20-minimum invoice charges together with quantities I felt sure would apply.

"However, finally I phoned their Bristol number. A charming girl answered the phone and I gave her the Suflex part number from my 1980 catalogue. She said they had discontinued the range but her computer brought forth the equivalent Mullard one per cent tolerance components and the information that these were in stock. No question of a minimum invoice charge and (for capacitors) no minimum quantity, although some components such as resistors are supplied only in lots of 20. I simply gave her my credit card number. Three days later the capacitors arrived. The cost? £1.89 post free. I did not believe that such service still existed in this day and age.

"Each branch of STC Components has a copy of the STC Electronics catalogue. My 1980 catalogue runs to over 1,000 pages.

"I once built a digital clock from individual ics because I could not locate

the National Semiconductor clock chip with bcd output. It is listed by STC and would have saved me weeks of work. I cannot recommend their services too highly."

Tips and topics

George May, G4RZF, draws attention to a useful and readable book *Noise in Receiving Systems* by Raoul Pettai of Raytheon (published by John Wiley & Sons, 1984) which he was recently able to borrow from the British Library at Boston Spa (and may also be found in some of the better technical libraries). He feels this book would be of interest to amateurs trying to get the most out of uhf and microwave equipment, even though some of the same topics are being covered in the current article by Ian White, G3SEK. There are 12 sections, three appendices and a useful general bibliography listing some 59 references, all in about 270 pages. It is perhaps not a book for the beginner, but enthusiastic uhf and microwave enthusiasts will find a lot of the information clear and useful and "bringing the entire subject of thermal noise, as encountered in engineering applications, under one roof". The sections are: introduction; overview of common noise sources; thermal noise; random variables and processes; single-port networks; two-port networks; distribution of gain; noise temperature; noise factor and noise figure; multi-response transducers; measurement of noise parameters; and signal and noise in crystal detectors.

Further to my notes on the trend towards surface-mounted miniature components (*TT* March), *Electronics Week* (8 April 1985)—in a detailed survey of this new technology—reports that currently 47 per cent of all electronic components in Japan are for surface mounting, compared with 5–6 per cent in the USA. It forecasts that by about 1990, the USA figure may grow to 70 per cent. Many new types of components are becoming available for surface mounting, including connectors, crystals, switches and relays. A variety of different "packages" and connecting leads are being used, with considerable need for rationalization. Some packages include: three small-outline transistor packages (SOT-23, SOT-89, SOT-143); plastic leaded chip carrier; plastic quad flat pack; metal-electrode face bonding (melf) as used by Yaesu; mini-melf small cylindrical leadless packages; small-outline integrated circuits (soic) including a miniaturized dual-in-line package); leadless chip resistors etc. There are also chip inductors and toroidal transformers for surface mounting.

Norman Burton, RS11494, writing from New South Wales, recalls with affection the high-impedance earphones of yesteryear. He owns a pair of Ericcsons from 1923, a pair of Gecophones from the same era, a pair of Brown Type A, and a year ago he bought very cheaply a pair of the once-famous Brown Type F that still works "damn well". He does all his serious listening on the Brown phones, mostly the Type A model. Although initially Brown "cans" seem uncomfortable, he believes that one's ears soon become bent to accommodate them and then they become extremely comfortable to wear. He recalls the sorbo sponge rubber ear caps that one could buy in the 'twenties—and an old *WW* tip of glueing a sponge rubber washer on to the ebonite of the caps. I must confess that after a decade of using fairly modern AKG lightweight phones, I have recently brought out of retirement a pair of Telefunken adjustable-diaphragm (4,000Ω) phones, and after an initial period of noticing the hardness of the ebonite caps, now find them comfortable to wear and sensitive to use. Maybe they bend my ears better than the heavier Brown Type A ever did when I had to wear them for eight hours at a stretch in the second world war!

It is often difficult to keep track of the many publications now aimed at the amateur radio market. Myron "Bud" Weisberg, K2YOF, recently sent along a detailed resumé of the long yet traceable path between the first publication of *Pacific Radio News* in January 1917 and the present day *CQ*. Mergers, changes in name, and the sale of titles from one firm to another are a common feature of publications on both sides of the Atlantic! *Pacific Radio News* became *Radio* in 1921. *Radio* merged with *R/9* in 1936 but continued as *Radio*, but with the entry of America into the second world war its direction changed away from amateur radio. However, "Sandy" Cowan, business manager of Radio Magazines, assumed control and in January 1945 launched *CQ—The Radio Amateurs' Journal*, roping in a number of the old *Radio* contributors. *CQ* has weathered several difficult periods and was taken over by its present management in 1979. *Radio* also spawned *Jones Radio Handbook* in the 'thirties, Jones being Frank Jones, W6AJF. This soon became the *Radio Handbook* and is up to its 21st edition, although *Editors and Engineers* is now an imprint of Howard W Sams, which is (or possibly was until recently) part of ITT, with Bill Orr, W6SAI, as editor.

STOP PRESS

There is a potential hazard in using the pcb etchant described in the May TT. Details next month.

□

Technical Topics
by Pat Hawker, G3VA

WHAT DO YOU LOOK FOR when buying a major new factory-built item for the shack? The highest possible technical specification? The lowest possible price? Reasonable performance at reasonable cost? Flexibility and versatility? Convenience of operation? Something you can use mobile or portable when the need arises? The latest and most innovatory technology? Reliability based on the maker's reputation?

Some or all of these features may turn you on. But it seems likely that you would also like to have some assurance—yet have to take on trust—that the manufacturing company will still be in business, and in the amateur radio market, when the time comes for the product to need servicing or spare parts.

The electronics industry

It is a feature of most technologically-based industries, in times of boom-and-bust economies, that companies come and go within relatively short periods. Firms, even if they survive and prosper, tend to merge and coalesce into a small number of international suppliers. Think of all those 35 to 45 separate firms making British television sets in the early 'fifties, admittedly many of them fitting a Plessey chassis. Booms in consumer electronics build up rapidly but subside almost as quickly. In the UK in 1982 and 1983 some 2·2-million video cassette recorders were delivered to the trade each year; by 1984 this figure had dropped to 1·4-million. Personal computer sales last Christmas were about the same as Christmas 1983, but the manufacturers had banked on a further large rise.

There used to be 600 car manufacturers in the USA; today there are four. How many of the personal computer manufacturers (200 in the USA alone) will be around to celebrate the diamond jubilee of Alan Turing's classic proof in 1935-6 that while there was no possibility of a "miraculous machine" that could solve *all* mathematical problems, the feasibility existed of a universal machine that could take over the work of *any* machine by performing the equivalent of human mental activity and computation, albeit for many years in only a crude manner compared with the human brain: the "universal" machine with artificial intelligence, the computer.

Much of the present attraction of solidstate is not so much a question of performance as the fear that thermionic devices, high-voltage components etc will either not be around when they are needed or virtually priced out of the market. As several articles in *Radio Communication* have shown, we are being forced back into a new era of making your own specialized components!

It is a sobering thought that few of the firms whose products are currently

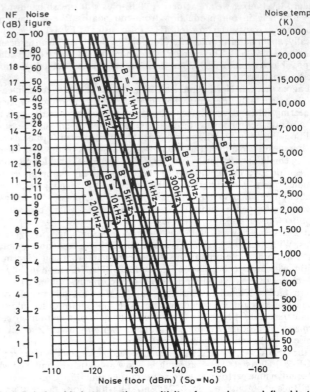

Fig 2. Relationship between the sensitivity of a receiver as defined in terms of noise factor (dB), noise figure or noise temperature and the noise floor (noise = signal) in dBm for various receiver bandwidths. Note how the minimum detectable signal reduces with narrower bandwidths for the same noise factor. From the article by ON4VN

advertised in *Radio Communication* were around 20 years ago—and that even fewer of those that were then well-known are still active in this field. Perhaps as we move relentlessly towards an era of "throw-away electronics" with no attempt to repair modules or even whole equipments, nobody will be worrying about the state of the industry ten, or even five, years ahead!

Weak signal reception

In the 'thirties the sensitivity of a communication receiver was normally defined as the weakest input signal that could be received, in terms of microvolts at the antenna input socket, for a given signal:signal + noise ratio in a *stated bandwidth*. It was to remove the requirement to specify the different bandwidths that the concept of a noise figure or noise factor was introduced in the 'forties. This rapidly became established for vhf receivers, and to a lesser extent on hf where today it competes with such concepts as the "minimum detectable signal" and "noise floor".

But it sometimes seems that we are in danger of forgetting that on any receiver the ability to receive very weak signals with a reasonable snr is governed not only by the internal and external noise but also by the *noise bandwidth*. Look at a smaller portion of the rf spectrum and the less will be the noise with which the signal has to compete: Fig 2.

Clearly there are limits. One needs to look at enough of the spectrum to gather in all the significant information contained in the transmission. In other words, we need ideally to match the received bandwidth with the transmitted intelligence-carrying signal. For double-sideband a.m. we need a minimum of rather more than 6kHz (unless we receive this as ssb, in which case you can reduce the noise bandwidth but throw away half of the information-carrying sidebands). For ssb the bandwidth needs to be about 3kHz or possibly a little less; for nbfm with, say, ±5kHz deviation and maximum af of 3kHz you need a minimum bandwidth of 16kHz; for cw at

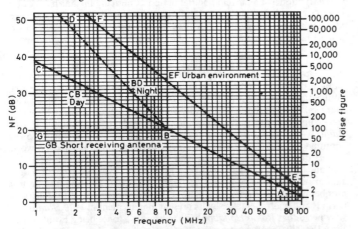

Fig 1. Relationship between maximum usable sensitivity, minimum acceptable sensitivity and frequency from an article by ON4VN/ON4EG in CQ-QSO. Note that on hf it is seldom necessary to have receivers with a noise factor much below about 15-20dB, below about 21MHz, unless a very short and inefficient antenna is being used. The line BC and BD represent reception on half-wave dipoles about a half-wave above ground. Minimum acceptable sensitivity is represented by the line EF reflecting a noisy urban environment. An hf receiver with a noise factor of about 10dB can usually be designed to have better strong-signal performance than the typical figure of 6dB of many modern receivers

less than about 25wpm theoretically you need only about 25Hz, though this would assume a very high standard of frequency stability in both the transmitter and receiver. A cw or fsk signal, incidentally, also has the advantage of containing a very much higher average power content than the peaky waveforms of speech, even processed speech.

Slowly-sent morse or data can be contained in less than 10Hz of spectrum, though a receiver matching this can be difficult to tune and to keep on tune. Nevertheless it is worth remembering that an experimental 100mW hf pocket transmitter developed by RCA in the 'sixties and intended as an emergency system for search and rescue (*RCA Review* March 1966, reported briefly in *TT* September 1966) had a filter only 0·75Hz wide in the base receiver and provided reliable daytime communication on 13 to 16MHz over distances of up to about 2,000 miles. The signalling rate was limited to only three bits/*min*! Similar data rates are also used in the extremely low frequency systems being developed for communication with submarines on *radio* frequencies below 100Hz where transmission bandwidth is extremely limited.

For QRP enthusiasts working at around 100mW it may be noted that the RCA report commented on various portable antenna systems for use with the pocket transmitter, and considered that "the most successful, yet most simple, was a quarter-wave vertical with a driven quarter-wave element laid in the direction of the desired transmission" using thin wire elements. In other words, a half-wave dipole bent to form a vertical radiator with a single quarter-wave radial pointed towards the target area, using for example a branch of a tree less than 20ft high. An alternative system would be an inverted-V dipole, again using a branch to provide the skyhook.

For this emergency system, special receiver techniques were developed to sweep over about 20Hz in order to cope with the problem of achieving a high degree of frequency stability with a portable battery-operated miniature transmitter. To provide a high degree of frequency stability, a zero-temperature-coefficient crystal was cut for a turn-over temperature of 99°F (body heat) and mounted in a small arm-pit enclosure to form a "natural-energy" crystal oven.

The secret of this system was, of course, that *noise power* is proportional to receiver bandwidth, and *noise voltage* to the square root of bandwidth. Yet, there must be a considerable number of amateurs happily using a 2·7kHz ssb filter (with no af filter) for cw reception!

It needs to be recognized, however, that there can be a practical snag with many very sharp narrowband filters: their tendency to "ring". A crystal filter that has a slight ring can actually enhance a wanted (stable) signal, but ringing has an altogether less desirable effect on incoming noise pulses. They cause the filter to ring, prolonging and emphasizing the interference to the wanted signal.

There are many reasons why most modern receivers are less than ideal for the reception of narrowband cw/rtty signals. For example the increasing use of a fairly broad "roofing filter" with the narrowband selectivity achieved late in the receiver may severely limit close-in dynamic range; similarly, frequency-synthesizer phase noise may result in excessive reciprocal mixing. Again, an early narrowband filter followed by the bulk of amplification coming from wideband amplifiers may severely restrict the final signal-to-noise ratio. But perhaps the most obvious drawback when using many modern receivers in the cw/rtty modes is the use of "hang agc" with the control signals derived from a wider bandwidth so that the wanted signal will be reduced in the presence of strong unwanted signals up to about 2kHz or more off-tune; then again the finite attack time of an agc system can reduce the instantaneous dynamic range of the receiver. My personal preference has always been not to use any agc for cw reception but to protect my ears by using a back-to-back (anti-parallel) diode audio-limiter located at a point of reasonably high impedance (for example, directly in the leads to high-impedance headphones).

In any discussion of weak-signal reception one must emphasize the role of the antenna which can amplify wanted signals without introducing additional noise, and can also reduce man-made noise and interference by the use of directional characteristics, electronic null-steering etc. The receiver also benefits from good front-end selectivity in order to reduce the many millions of intermodulation products that can result from the reception of the considerable number of extremely-strong broadcast signals that may be reaching the mixer.

Narrowband receivers

The communication receiver is essentially a general-purpose instrument designed to work reasonably well on a variety of transmission modes: ssb, cw, rtty and, possibly, a.m. and nbfm. This means that the basic i.f. amplifier has to be designed to cope with bandwidths that may even exceed 12 or 15kHz, yet expected to perform well on signals a few tens of hertz wide, inevitably resulting in compromises. It is worth remembering that for many years high-performance receivers used for point-to-point hf

communication were produced specifically as radiotelegraph or radio-telephone designs. Ideally a cw/rtty receiver should have distributed selectivity over the entire receiver chain.

The desire to reduce costs by eliminating multiple-ganged signal-frequency front-end tuning and replace this with wide-band or sub-octave front-ends has contributed to the problem of avoiding the generation of intermodulation products due to non-linearity. With a wideband front-end, only a receiver designed to have exceptionally-wide dynamic range can be expected to cope with the extremely-strong signals from broadcast transmitters, or local amateur stations.

In *TT* (October 1982) I drew attention to a paper by R A Barrs of Rediffusion Radio Systems ("A reappraisal of hf receiver selectivity" *The Radio and Electronic Engineer*, Vol 52, No 7, pp315–20, July 1982). This provided a detailed assessment of the limitations still found in professional hf receivers, and suggested that many of these could be minimized by improving front-end signal-frequency selectivity. He pointed out that during daytime there are about 28 transmissions between 2 and 30MHz delivering signals of about 100mV emf at the input of the receiver. For an imd characteristic of $90dB\mu V$, these are liable to produce:

14,644 imps up to third-order at $+30dB\mu V$ emf;
175,000,000 imps up to seventh-order at $+10dB\mu V$ emf; and
84×10^{12} imps up to 15th order at $-10dB\mu V$ emf.

This enormous number of spurious imd products will have the effect of increasing the noise floor of a receiver to about $+15dB\mu V$ and, possibly, noticeable interference on wanted input signals of up to about $+30dB\mu V$ emf. The noise floor resulting from a mass of imd products will not normally show up in laboratory measurements of receivers.

To minimize this problem R A Barrs advocated a front-end selectivity on the signals applied to the mixer of the order of $-37·5dB$ at five per cent off-tune, and $-20dB$ at $2·5$ per cent. He noted that this can be achieved and bettered with four rf ganged-tuned circuits each with a working Q of 30 to 40. Such an arrangement, requiring a matching accuracy of the tuned circuits of about one per cent over the tuning range is difficult, and very expensive, to achieve. This is one reason why so much effort has been put into improving the performance of packaged doubly-balanced mixers to better than a respectable $90dB\mu V$.

The use of an input rf attenuator can help to overcome the problem of strong signal imd when used expertly and with understanding, although clearly introducing limitations on very weak signal reception.

Signal-frequency crystal filters

Is there any other way, apart from rf attenuators, of improving front-end selectivity at moderate cost? One technique which has been described previously in *TT* is the use of passive or low-gain preselectors external to the receiver proper. Without ganging, a number of tuned circuits can certainly improve matters in those circumstances where the very strong signals are not in, or immediately adjacent to, the amateur bands. Incidentally it is worth stressing once again that the use of variable-capacitance tuning diodes in lieu of variable capacitors is not recommended for really high-performance receivers or preselectors.

A potentially very effective system for those who are prepared to accept the limitation of restricted channels is the use of a front-end crystal filter. This technique was advocated 20 years ago by Stuart Meyer, W2GHK, in an article "Front-end crystal filters for amateur radio use" (*Interadio, 4U1ITU Calling*, 1965). He drew attention to the use at 4U1ITU of a series of filters supplied by Hammarlund to facilitate the simultaneous use of several transmitters. Typically a 14MHz bandpass filter permitted reception over about a 30kHz ($\pm$15kHz) segment of the band while providing over 80dB attenuation at more than about 30kHz off-tune. W2GHK noted that the practical nose bandwidth of this range of filters was around 30kHz at 14MHz, 15kHz at 7MHz and 7·5kHz at 3·5MHz, while filters for 21 and 28MHz presented considerable technical problems due to spurious responses etc.

I suspect that the concept of using signal-frequency crystal filters was developed for professional and Defence communications, aimed primarily at overcoming the severe problems experienced on modern naval vessels where a number of transmitters are located in close proximity. I do not think the idea ever caught on widely, at least for amateur applications. In practice, to obtain maximum benefit from a filter used in this way it is necessary to reduce the amount of rf leaking into the receiver, either directly or around the filter. This is not so easy as might be imagined.

It was therefore interesting to learn from P W Haylett, G3IPV, of his efforts over a number of years to develop effective signal-frequency crystal filtering to provide a high degree of rf selectivity without the complexity of multiple LC circuits. He writes:

"I have been experimenting with front-end crystal filters in external preselectors for many years and have at last, after pursuing a number of false trails, more or less got it all together. One of the main problems has been to produce an amplifier with extremely low levels of internal (positive) feedback when high-Q crystals are placed in its input and output circuits.

"The other problem of leakage of signals around the crystals and via the crystal-holder capacitances can be largely overcome by ensuring that all circuitry is at low impedance.

"I still have one final problem, which consists of a peak of noise which occurs at the centre of the crystal filter passband and which can override weak signals. This peak appears to be associated with the crystals rather than the amplifiers, and can be overcome by keeping down the drive level to the crystal filters."

Presumably the noise and intermodulation signals associated with this peak of noise are not just part of the external noise in the passband of the filter, and may be a manifestation of the non-linearity and non-reciprocity that has been previously noted in *TT* in connection with i.f. crystal filters.

G3IPV continues: "The number of crystals required varies with the band in use and propagation conditions. On 3·5MHz during daytime it is often only necessary to use one crystal, whereas on 14MHz I often use 10 or more crystals.

"In spite of the various development problems which I experienced, but which I have now largely overcome, I am getting some very good results. Often on 3·5MHz around lunchtime at weekends I hear YU, SM and HA stations that nobody else in the UK seems to be receiving. I feel the day is coming when amateurs will no longer tune bands but operate more on fixed hf channels in order to avoid front-end overload and intermodulation problems, especially in densely-populated areas." His arrangements are shown in Figs 3, 4 and 5.

While personally I would not go all the way with G3IPV's views on fixed-channel operation, and would not expect a front-end crystal filter, as such, to improve weak signal reception in the absence of strong signals on nearby frequencies, at least when used with a receiver having a good dynamic range, there is no doubt in my mind that there are already circumstances in which an effective front-end crystal filter could prove valuable. For example, for amateurs using specific "net" frequencies or, again, to protect a QRP calling frequency etc. The prime value would still seem to be for the 4U1ITU-type of situation where a number of transmitters are being operated in close proximity. Nevertheless, for weak-signal reception it would be a more attractive technique than throwing away both wanted and unwanted signals in an rf attenuator pad.

To reduce rf leakage and circulating earth currents, G3IPV appears to have concentrated on developing what he calls "earth-isolated rf technology", with no direct rf connections to chassis. He has also developed a broadband amplifier module having a wide dynamic range to provide sufficient gain to compensate for the attenuation of cascaded filter modules.

Broadband vhf/uhf antennas at ICAP85

The series of IEE/URSI international conferences on antennas and propagation tend to produce some pretty esoteric, highly-mathematical papers, many of them concerned with millimetric and satellite studies,

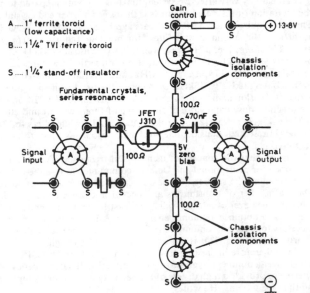

Fig 3. Basic signal-frequency crystal filter module using earth-isolated construction as developed by G3IPV

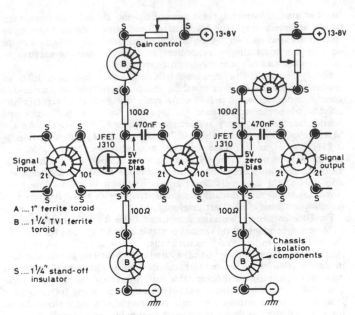

Fig 4. G3IPV's broadband amplifier module using J310 jfets

complex electronically-steered adaptive arrays, massive df systems and the like. The fourth of these, ICAP85, was apparently no exception. The 120 or so papers in *IEE Conference Publication No 248*, 584 large double-column pages, are not exactly light reading in either a physical or metaphorical sense. But here and there one finds papers that give practical guidance applicable to amateur radio.

For example, a BBC paper on "Aerial (*sic*) developments for television outside broadcast links" summarizes a considerable number of broadband uhf designs that have been developed and are now in use. These are for either the 580 to 854MHz band or the 2·5GHz band, and include a number of circularly-polarized arrays used to relay pictures from helicopters or roving vehicle-mounted cameras at race meetings etc. The following is a very brief summary of some of the types of array involved that seem to have possible applications on our bands:

UHF 5-element log-periodic array. This is a fairly conventional log-periodic dipole (lpd) array with a back radiation of −20dB and fairly modest forward gain for use over the range 580 to 800MHz.

1·2m dish with log-periodic feed. Suitable for use 580 to 950MHz. Gain about 14–15dBd. Vertex plate to improve impedance match.

Conical logarithmic-spiral antenna. Circularly-polarized "rove" antenna based on a balanced conical spiral array. This again is for 580 to 950MHz and is constructed from a pvc cone (surely not the most suitable material, see May *TT*) with the two-arm spiral painted on its surface in silver conductive paint, and with feeder and matching networks concentric with the spiral arms. About 6·4dBd gain, front-to-back ratio between 21dB (600MHz) and 29dB (860MHz).

1·2m dish with crossed log-periodic feed. This is a circularly-polarized version of the dish array mentioned above, with a quadrature drive to the two crossed elements provided by a 0dB output ratio wire-line coupler. Vertex plate matching not required. Gain about 14·6 to 16·5dBd, axial ratio 0·8 to 1·8dB.

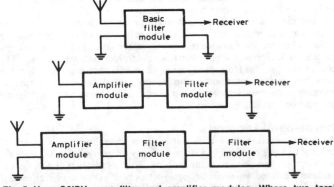

Fig 5. How G3IPV uses filter and amplifier modules. Where two toroid transformers come together in the interstage coupling, one is removed. The ferrite transformers have low capacitance from input to output to simulate transformers using Faraday screens (an alternative technique)

UHF manpack antennas. (1) A vertically-polarized sleeve dipole using a choke and ferrite bead to reduce outer-braid current. **(2)** A horizontally-polarized antenna based on orthogonally mounted end-fed unipole elements in the form of a quadrant antenna. To provide near omni-directional radiation pattern. Both these antennas are in two versions: *(a)* 580 to 780MHz; *(b)* 720 to 860MHz.

2·5GHz helicopter-link antennas. To replace a linearly-polarized Franklin antenna, circularly-polarized arrays have been developed. **(1)** With crossed, bent elements mounted in front of two reflector discs. Omnidirectional horizontal radiation pattern with about 1·8dBd gain. **(2)** A 2·4 to 2·7GHz disc Yagi receiving array for use on the ground to receive circularly-polarized signals from helicopters. Driven elements are crossed folded dipoles whereas the large reflector plate and some 16 parasitic directors are discs, all mounted on a common metallic boom. Gain about 13·5dBd, fbr about 25dB. Can also form the basic of higher-gain arrays using two or four of these structures. This type of disc/rod array has become increasingly popular for tv applications in many countries, and a commercially-manufactured version is the "Golden Rod" antenna. For microwave bands it would appear to be a relatively simple form of construction.

Another ICAP85 paper "The analysis of the directivity properties of the lpp antenna" by R J Katulski of Gdansk University, Poland, includes a formidable mathematical analysis of the "log piramidal periodic" (lpp) antenna described by G J Monser (1964, *Electronics*, 4, pp91–4). But don't be put off by the unfamiliar name. It is simply two log-periodic dipole structures in two planes that come together at the shortest element ends: Fig 6. The Polish work is aimed at providing a practical wideband antenna of good directivity gain for vhf/uhf television reception throughout the range 150 to 900MHz, though I seem to recall having seen this form of structure being used for military surveillance systems etc. The ICAP paper confirms the influence of the separation angle on the directivity gain, and concludes: "an lpp array has the best properties when the value of the separation angle is about 40°. The results of numerical modelling and experiments confirm the usefulness of this antenna for tv broadcasting systems".

Remember that inherently a broadband antenna should prove less critical to build and adjust than a narrowband array, so that in practice the gain can approach or even exceed that of a less-than-optimum narrowband array of the same number of elements. Log-periodic structures which, at least in theory, can be extended to cover any required frequency range are renowned for good sidelobe/fbr characteristics and so help reduce multipath problems.

Adjustable l.e.d. level meter

The use of solidstate devices to replace mechanical meters is becoming common practice and, indeed, echoes the traditional usage of torch bulbs as rf indicators. Light-emitting diodes are well suited to bar displays for such applications as modulation meters and audio level meters. With the aid of a single driver/decoder integrated circuit they can be used to form a column of light to replace a VU meter or peak-reading modulation meter etc.

Fig 7 shows the basic circuit diagram of a 12-l.e.d. level meter described, as a constructional project, by David Edwards in *Electronics Australia* January 1985, intended for connection directly to the speaker leads of a stereo audio amplifier. However, he also provides a diagram (Fig 8) of a small auxiliary amplifier to increase input sensitivity when used at lower af levels in lieu of a VU-meter in a tape recorder and suitable also for amateur radio applications.

Heart of the unit is an 18-pin dil Siemens UAA180 decoder ic (stocked by Electrovalue Ltd, 28 St Jude's Road, Englefield Green, Egham, Surrey TW20 0HB, tel Egham (0784 outside London) 33603, price £1.59). With this device a dc voltage applied to pin 17 is decoded to drive a column of 12 l.e.d. devices with the length of light directly proportional to the input voltage. The upper and lower points of the light bar are set by the voltages applied to pins 3 and 16 respectively. When the voltage on pin 17 exceeds that on pin 3, all 12 devices light, and in this application pin 16 is at zero potential. An increase in input level of 0·5V gives a gradual transition; a difference of over 4V an abrupt transition.

Control of l.e.d. intensity is obtained by varying the potential applied to pin 2, preferably using evenly matched l.e.d. devices. With the values shown, the light intensity is about maximum but can be reduced by

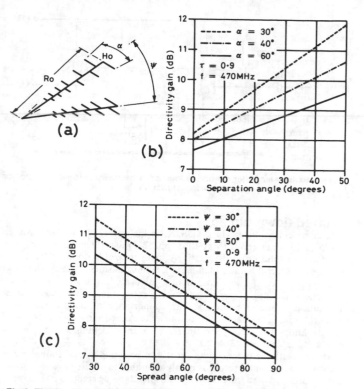

Fig 6. The log piramidal periodic (lpp) antenna comprises two log periodic structures arranged in two planes diagonally. *(a)* Basic arrangement of lpp. *(b)* Showing how directivity gain increases with the separation angle. *(c)* Showing how it decreases with the spread angle. 40° is about optimum

decreasing the value of 100kΩ leg of the potential divider supplying pin 2. Reference voltage for pin 3 is governed by the 4·7V, 400mW zener diode.

The input arrangement shown has two input connections for stereo applications—only one will normally be needed for amateur radio applications.

The input has a voltage doubler arrangement; the attack time is governed by the 1kΩ, 1μF time constant; decay time by the 100kΩ, 1μF tantalum capacitor. Note that the input 1μF capacitor should be a 50V wkg *bipolar* electrolytic. A 100kΩ trimpot adjusts the input level to the ic via a 100kΩ isolating resistor. The unit is designed to work from either ac or dc supplies.

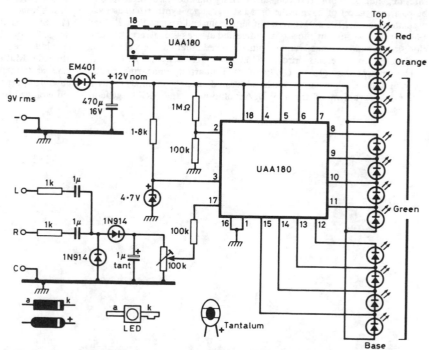

Fig 7. Circuit diagram of the audio level indicator described in *Electronics Australia*

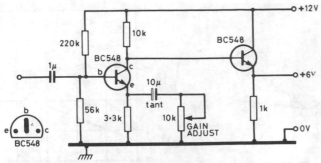

Fig 8. Auxiliary amplifier needed to increase sensitivity of the level indicator at lower signal levels

Slowed-down tuning

The comment by Peter Hart, G3SJX, in his review of the Yaesu Musen FT757GX hf transceiver (May 1985, pp352–6) that "The slow tuning rate of 10kHz/revolution of the relatively small control knob made frequency changes of several hundred kilohertz a tedious business" set me thinking. For many years I have consistently advocated, primarily for hf cw operation, the use of very slow tuning rates, preferably under 5kHz/revolution, while stressing the vital importance of having a "velvet-smooth" tuning mechanism, free from all backlash, and a reasonably-sized tuning knob that suits your fingers at a convenient height above the operating table (about 3–4in).

In fact, with the older equipment still to be found in operational use at G3VA I have usually found it highly desirable to fit an *extra* out-board slow-motion drive to the electrical bandspread tuning spindles of receivers, and to the vfo of an old LG300 transmitter. In fact, a main grumble at the slightly more modern hf ssb/cw transceiver that I sometimes use is the poor tuning mechanism made worse by a knot in the difficult-to-get-at drive cord and the fast tuning rate.

With a tuning rate of 3 to 5kHz/revolution one can really "explore" the response curve of a peaked cw filter response, even with evidently clumsy rather than "safecracker's" fingers. The idea of a plus-100kHz/revolution tuning knob (even on vintage receivers such as the AR88) has always seemed too high a price to pay for the ease of sweeping in a matter of milliseconds from one end of a band to the other, particularly if one only seldom wishes to check the ssb segment. At one time I fixed a small handle to my tuning knob to cater for such eventualities. I recall descriptions in the 'thirties of amateurs fitting small motors to cope with 400:1 reduction mechanisms fitted to general-coverage receivers not having electrical bandspread. Some modern receivers with microprocessor control provide fast and slow tuning rates depending on how fast you start turning the knob, but these tend to be part and parcel of having the dreaded frequency synthesizers as local oscillator (see G3SEK's "Modern vhf/uhf front-end design, Part 2" May 1985 for the reasons why those of us interested in weak-signal reception and close-in dynamic range remain unconvinced that a typical digital synthesizer vfo represents "progress" in transceiver design).

The enterprising *QUA—G4IRC* (1/85) quarterly magazine of the Ipswich Radio Club in its "Workshop 'ints and tipses" column by G4TVT, tackles the problem of the 175kHz/revolution of the SRX30 general-coverage receiver by explaining just how to fit an ex-R1155 16-1 reduction gearbox to the tuning spindle, though this involves a good deal of machining and the addition of two miniature ballraces; clearly not a process that could be tackled by everyone, even if they can locate a spare R1155 drive.

It is, however, usually quite a simple process to add an extra "integral reduction drive" plus a piece of fixing metal (even an old Mecanno strip bent to shape can be used). Similarly some of the very old slow-motion drives can be used provided that they are of the continuously rotatable (360°) type rather than the more common 180°-only type which cannot be used as a second step-down gear for obvious reasons.

QUA also includes some notes on the series of Hammarlund Super Pro receivers (first version 1935; SP10-series 1937; SP110 and 200 (BC779) 1939; SP210 (BC1004) 1942; SP400 1946; SP600 1950) a high-grade built-like-a-battleship receiver that tends to get forgotten in the "vintage" HRO/AR88 debate. The Super Pro also inspired the lower-cost pre-war HQ-120 and the immediate post-war HQ129x models that can still give a reasonable account of themselves (if you can tolerate a large warm-up frequency drift) or can provide the basis for a modernized receiver. A feature of the Hammarlund models was a six-position selectivity switch based on a single-crystal filter.

PCB etchant and chlorine gas

In the May *TT* (p359) R P Bown, G3PCN, suggested that a mixture of hydrochloric acid and hydrogen peroxide provides a pcb etchant with several plus features compared with ferric chloride. Apparently, however, as a "stop press" note inserted at the end of the June *TT* warned, it has also some major disadvantages. Before attempting to use this etchant readers should be aware of a possible hazard both to health and equipment. Dr Tony Webb, G4LYF, writes:

"Attention should be urgently drawn to the dangers associated with this etch mixture. A mixture of hydrochloric acid and hydrogen peroxide will slowly evolve chlorine gas, which is extremely poisonous and which will also, if left near electrical equipment, bring about spectacular corrosion! If the mixture is used at all, it should be out of doors, and should be rinsed away with plenty of water after use. If it is bottled after mixing, the gas evolved will pressurize the container and may eventually burst it."

G4LYF does not indicate the amount of chlorine gas likely to be produced in a given period, but it would seem wise to pay heed to this warning. He adds, on a lighter note, "I was alarmed at W1BG's suggestion that a reasonably-fit middle-aged man should be able to generate 50W continuously for 30–40min from a 'bicycle' generator. Is amateur radio about to join jogging and squash as a pastime causing the premature demise of the middle-aged?" I must admit to being grateful for the availability of the electric supply mains when using my rig!

Tips and topics

Frank Rogers, G3BFR, reports finding another use for plumbers' ptfe tape (*TT* May, p360). It is excellent for tightening "slack" ferrite/iron-powder slugs. If wound so as to tighten when the slug is first screwed in, it does not unwind when the core is unscrewed, and seems almost to become part of the slug. Multiple layers can be put on successfully, for it is difficult to unwrap the tape once it is well bedded into the thread. This is akin to the intended purpose of using such tape on screw threads. G3BFR also uses it on wrapped (non-soldered) joints in wire antennas.

Technical Topics
by Pat Hawker, G3VA

THERE IS a widespread, though in my opinion a mistaken, belief that the rate of innovation in radio and electronics is growing faster and faster, resulting from the often-quoted fact that there are currently said to be more professional research scientists and engineers than the aggregated total of past history. In such circumstances, it might be thought, the role of amateur radio in generating practical innovation and implementation and as a training ground for both the amateur hobbyist and for young "professionals" must be coming to an end.

Amateurs and the experimental tradition

There are several different approaches to bringing new ideas into radio: the purely theoretical and mathematical, as exemplified by Clerk-Maxwell who predicted the existence of radio waves well over 100 years ago; investigation motivated by purely scientific curiosity, as exemplified by the work of Heinrich Hertz, the centenary of whose pioneering work in demonstrating the existence of radio waves is fast approaching; practical commercial development by those who perceive a need or first recognize the potential value of new discoveries, as exemplified by Marconi and his team of engineers, who may not have "invented" radio communication but who successfully pioneered it.

History shows us that no matter how brilliant the concept, no matter how painstaking the mathematical analysis, in the end what counts is the ability to take some pieces of wire and make things work. The illustrious first President of the Wireless Society of London (now RSGB), A A Campbell-Swinton, FRS, 2HK, was the very first man to conceive and describe, in the early years of this century, a fully-electronic system of television, the basis of all present-day tv. Unfortunately, materials research was still at an elementary stage and he was never able to make his system actually produce pictures, no matter how crude. The result is that his historic contribution to television is recognized by relatively few people, and many believe that either Baird or Jenkins "invented" television in 1923-5.

Campbell-Swinton was only one of many notable pioneers who have combined "professional" engineering with an interest in experimental amateur radio. The great Howard Armstrong, responsible for the regenerative detector, the practical superhet receiver, super-regeneration and wide-deviation frequency modulation, retained a close connection with the hobby throughout his life; he was deeply involved with the successful transatlantic tests of 1921, while the very first transmissions of his fm system were made on 112MHz (the old 2·5m band) by his friend Randy Runyon, W2AG, of Yonkers, New York. For several months W2AG put out the *only* frequency-modulated transmissions anywhere in the world!

Happily still with us is Dr John Kraus, W8JK, recently awarded the prestigious Edison Medal of the IEEE. In 1937, W8JK, drawing on the newly-published work of Dr George Brown of RCA, designed, put-up, tested and then described the first *close-spaced* bi-directional "flat-top" rotary 14MHz antenna array, and so created the whole new family of driven-element "8JK" antennas, shortly in advance of the first close-spaced unidirectional (Yagi) array built by Walter Van Roberts, W2CWO, of RCA. Less well known among amateurs is that W8JK was later responsible for the introduction of folded and multiwire dipoles; for the corner reflector; for the helical antenna (inspired by the helix of a travelling-wave tube); and for the massive radiotelescopes of Ohio State University, including the famous "Big Ear" array. In the UK, the late Sir Martin Ryle, G3CY, innovated the use of aperture synthesis for radiotelescopes and made many other notable contributions to radioastronomy.

The coming of radar

Recently I had the pleasure of attending several of the sessions of a three-day IEE seminar to mark the 50th anniversary of the development in the UK of radar (formerly "RDF" and "radiolocation") by the team led by (Sir) Robert Watson-Watt. This seminar, attended by many of the surviving pre-1945 pioneers, brought home two important features of this work.

First, the remarkable way in which engineers in many different countries independently and secretly developed basically similar forms of radar during the 'thirties. It is clear that the German radar "hardware" in 1939 was at a more advanced stage than the British, but we had the advantage that more effective operational procedures had been worked out by better co-operation between the scientists and the RAF. Firm evidence was also presented showing similar "invention" and rapid development of radar in the USA, France, Holland, Japan, Italy and the USSR. The French actually fitted and publicly described a crude collision radar on the passenger-liner *Normandie* in the mid 'thirties.

The most striking feature of all this work, certainly the work in the UK, is the sheer speed at which it was carried out when compared to major R&D projects today. Watson-Watt with A Wilkins, for example, carried out the first feasibility experiment within a matter of days of his first putting forward the possibility of using reflections from aircraft. They simply used the 6MHz transmissions from BBC Daventry; this was February 1935. Again, within a matter of days, he had submitted his report and been authorized to go ahead. He had an experimental installation at Orfordness working by *July* of that year. Originally it was all hf radar, 6MHz being considered the optimum frequency had it been free of interference; then the idea was to use 12MHz, but finally the original Chain Home (CH) worked on 24MHz, and many of the ideas soon also influenced hf communications.

The single most important UK contribution to radar was the cavity magnetron. This opened the way to 10cm radar. It was developed in a matter of weeks by Randall and Boot at Birmingham University, and first powered up in February 1940. It is often forgotten that this was only a crude laboratory model working directly on a vacuum pump. The important work of getting such a device into production, and in doing so incorporating valuable contributions of his own, and also those of his French friend Dr Henri Gutton, fell to Eric Megaw, G6MU, of the GEC Research Laboratories, Wembley. G6MU had been actively interested in vhf, uhf and microwaves throughout the 'thirties, both as an amateur and as a professional. His "Some experiments on 30,000kHz and above" appeared in the *T&R Bulletin* as early as April 1929. G6MU ranks as one of the major contributors to microwave vhf scatter technology.

I was also interested to learn that it was at Orfordness that it was noted that the "transposition blocks", so commonly used in those days for open-wire feeders (suitable blocks were marketed by Eddystone Radio and others), added nothing to the actual performance of open-wire transmission lines!

Our hobby can be extremely proud of its long "experimental tradition" and the training it provides in "making something actually work before somebody else beats you to it".

Remember that every idea, every circuit, every antenna, every component in modern radio technology had to be conceived and tested by somebody. Many who founded the science of radio communication were closely associated with the early days of experimental amateur radio.

Longer life for nicads

A topic that has turned up many times over the past decade or so is the question of premature failure of sealed nickel cadmium cells and batteries, and a number of experimental cures have already been suggested in *TT*. It is commonly claimed by the battery manufacturers that nicad units will withstand some 1,000 charge/discharge cycles, but many users experience problems long before that number of cycles have been completed. Yet basically the nicad cell, treated properly, is a very reliable and cost-effective device.

Premature failure can often be prevented, or at least significantly delayed, if care is taken during charging and use; the experience of readers has also shown that it is sometimes possible to rejuvenate apparently "dead" cells—a worthwhile process, since nicad batteries are fairly expensive items.

A very detailed two-part article by Rod Cooper ("Avoiding failure of sealed nickel-cadmium cells", *Electronics & Wireless World* May 1985, pp61-3, and June 1985, pp60-3) describes a number of the most common failure modes, suggests ways in which these can be avoided or minimized, and provides hints on experimental cures.

He stresses that water (H_2O) is an essential part of the chemical process and that loss of even small amounts from the electrolyte will result in a large reduction in the capacity of a cell. Loss of water can occur due to "reverse charging" of one or more cells in a battery, or from overcharging.

Loss of water due to reverse charging is a common failure mode. The

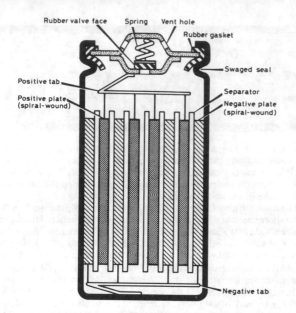

Fig 1. Construction of a typical sealed nicad cell (*E&WW* June 1985)

reasons why reverse charging occurs in deeply-discharged batteries has been previously described in *TT*. Basically it is because no battery consists of cells of exactly equal capacity, so that some cells are exhausted before the others —which promptly begin to reverse charge the exhausted cell(s), Fig 2(a), progressively bringing about further inequalities in capacity. Some users attempt to avoid this by using low-voltage sensors, cutting out the battery when the total voltage drops to around an average of 1V/cell. Rod Cooper suggests that this precaution is useful but of only limited value, since such sensors, applied across a battery, cannot distinguish between, say, six healthy cells at 1·25V, plus one cell being reverse charged at −0·4V, and alternatively seven cells at 1V. He considers, however, that the problem can be reduced by connecting a reverse-biased diode (preferably a Schottky diode) across each cell (where this is physically possible): Fig 2 (b). This precaution is more effective for larger cells that are charged at around 0·5A.

A better solution, he suggests, is to avoid using nicad *batteries* but instead to use a single (higher capacity) cell in conjunction with a small dc–dc converter such as the one using the Texas Instruments TL496 switching regulator ic shown in Fig 2(c). This will step up the 1·25V to about 7V at 40mA. It would, unfortunately, be rather difficult to use such a small dc/dc converter with the average handheld transceiver in view of the considerably greater load drawn during "transmit", but nevertheless the idea seems worth considering for many applications.

Loss of water due to incorrect charging, including lengthy overcharging even at the standard C/10 rate, occurs quite frequently due to the build-up of oxygen pressure and its escape via the safety vent. Rapid charging, at rates above C/10, is not advisable except with nicad cells specifically designed for such treatment. Rod Cooper describes a successful technique for introducing small quantities of distilled water, using a syringe, during several successive charging cycles afterwards resealing the small hole drilled to take the syringe: I recall a similar technique being described by David Foster, G3KQR, in *TT* (June/July 1980, p636), for cells showing a loss of weight.

A different failure mode can be induced by low charging rates extending over long periods: the so-called "crystal deformation" of the narrowly-spaced plates resulting in internal short-circuiting of the cell. Although not mentioned by Rod Cooper, a similar effect can arise from small "whiskers", and in this case the short-circuit can sometimes be removed by discharging a large-value capacitor through the affected cell. Rejuvenation of a cell in which the plates have actually buckled seems more problematic; the best way of avoiding this condition is to charge at C/10 using a sensor to detect and curtail overcharging. I must admit that it is still common practice to leave cells charging at C/10 for hours without worrying whether or not they are fully charged.

Electrolytic creepage through the seals, giving rise to a furry white deposit that is highly corrosive, is another problem and may account for the so-called "black death" syndrome. The deposit is highly corrosive and can cause havoc if it spreads to nearby circuit boards etc. No effective way of combatting this problem seems to exist, although Rod Cooper observes that some makes of cell appear to be more prone than others: he has found that nylon-topped cells made by Saft appear to be free of this trouble, but believes that it is better to throw away a cell suffering from electrolytic creepage rather than to risk corrosion damage to surrounding equipment.

Corrosion problems can also affect the outer steel case whether or not assisted by electrolyte creepage particularly in damp atmospheres; he suggests it is sometimes better to remove the outer plastics coating which traps moisture, if necessary using adhesive tape to provide electrical insulation. It is also advisable to keep dissimilar metals, such as copper and zinc, away from the steel casing. Zinc, for instance, can rapidly cause pin holes if left in contact with the steel casing.

The diagnosis of failure modes can be complicated by the fact that more than one of the above modes may be involved. Rod Cooper provides a short but useful list of "do's and don'ts":

Recharging. Don't recharge cells connected in batteries if at all possible, preferably recharge cells separately. Avoid temperatures above 50°C and below 5°C. Don't persistently overcharge cells. Recharge standard cells at C/10.

Discharging. Preferably, don't use cells connected in batteries. Where batteries are essential, use protection diodes or low-voltage cut-out.

General. Avoid encapsulated batteries such as substitutes for PP9 batteries. Don't replace dead cells in a battery with brand new ones; do not add partly-used cells to a new battery.

One should emphasise that, with care and a good-quality charger, nicad cells *can* provide excellent, cost-effective, trouble-free service and last for from 500 to 2,000 charging cycles.

Another look at fishing rods

Recent items on the use of long glass-fibre fishing rod blanks as antenna supports (*TT* March and June) have brought in several informative comments. For example, Pat Painting, G3OUC—an advocate of homebrew station equipment—writes:

"I have used a 22ft hollow glass-fibre roach pole for 15 years, loaded inductively for either 3·5 or 1·8MHz, and mounted without guy lines in the top of a birch tree in my garden to a height of 60ft: Fig 3.

"With a loading coil of 208 turns of 14/36 plastic (pvc) covered wire on the handle end of the rod, the antenna is resonant on about 1,930kHz, and by using an atu the whole of the UK 1·8MHz band can be covered. In particular, the winter season 1984–5 gave many excellent contacts with stations all over Europe and the USSR using 25W p.e.p. ssb.

"Roach poles come in various lengths, the most popular being about 22ft long, the collapsible, hollow, glass-fibre rods weighing a total of about 2lb. These rods are extremely strong, telescopic in form, and have no fishing line 'runners', the line being simply tied to the end of the rod.

"Currently, the cost of a roach pole is about £15–£20. One maker is the Shakespeare company, but any fishing tackle stockist should be able to help, provided that you make it clear that it is a roach pole that you require.

"G3LBA is correct in his assessment of the great strength of these rods; mine has suffered no damage during many gales despite its exposed

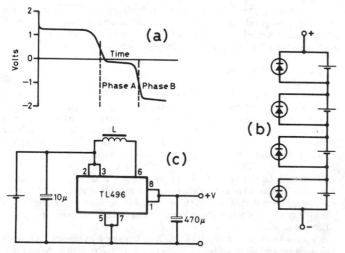

Fig 2. (a) Discharge curve of a nicad cell of reduced capacity when connected in a battery of cells and thus extending into the reverse-charging mode. Electrolyte decomposition occurs during both Phase A and Phase B periods, leading to further permanent reduction of the capacity of the cell. (b) Reverse-charging damage can be reduced to some degree when Schottky diodes are connected across individual cells. (c) A better solution is to use a single cell with a dc–dc converter. This arrangement can step up 1·25V to about 7V at 40mA. L should have a value of about 40–50 μH and very low dc resistance of less than 0·15Ω (wind on RM5 or RM6 core) for operation at about 10kHz (*E&WW* May 1985)

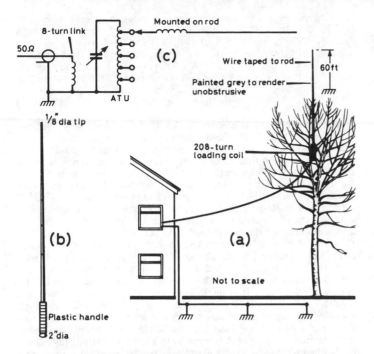

Fig 3. Use of collapsible hollow glass-fibre roach pole as support for 1·8/3·5MHz antenna. The 22ft rod breaks down to about 4ft with self-locking (interference-fit) sections of total weight about 2lb. Roach poles are not fitted with runners or reel fixtures and cost about £20. One firm making them is the Shakespeare Fishing Tackle Company. (c) Matching system used by G3OUC

position; it is advisable, however, not to make the structure 'top heavy' by attempting too much top capacitance loading. The performance of my antenna has attracted many enquiries and resulted in much letter writing!''

Dave Burley, G4WIZ, however, is less confident at the suggestion that even stronger (but much more expensive) support could be provided by using carbon-fibre fishing rods, with a wire running up the centre. It needs to be taken into account, he suggests, that carbon is a conductive material (though not a very good one) so that one might end up with a screened antenna or an unterminated length of lossy "coaxial cable"!

By coincidence, G4WIZ had written an article on "carbon antennas" for the May 1985 issue of the Basingstoke ARC newsletter in which he had warned against using carbon materials as antenna elements in view of the appreciably higher ohmic losses involved. While this would be less apparent when a wire is run up outside a carbon-fibre element, this could still prove a "lossy" form of support. Such considerations would probably not impair the performance when a carbon-fibre rod is used as a support for a G6XN-type of array (*TT* March) though his array used glass-fibre supports. But, as G4WIZ points out, the electrical characteristics need to be taken into account before spending a lot of money to obtain the advantage of extra mechanical strength. The less-costly glass-fibre rods, such as G3OUC's collapsible roach poles, should suffice for most applications, even when modest top capacitance loading is used, as in G3LBA/PA3ACQ's installation.

Opto-isolator current limiter

Lionel Sear, G3PPT, in the "Circuit Ideas" column of *Electronics & Wireless World* July 1984, p51, showed how an opto-isolator device can be used in conjunction with a 317-based variable voltage power supply to provide current limiting for such applications as the protection of rf power transistors during the development of solidstate power amplifiers etc.

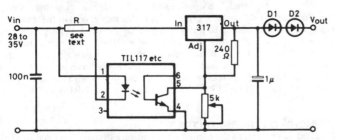

Fig 4. G3PPT's opto-isolator current limiting system on a 317 ic regulator variable voltage psu (*E&WW* July 1984)

Fig 4 shows his arrangement. When the voltage across R exceeds about 1V, the isolator photodiode begins to light, thus turning on the isolator phototransistor and so reducing the control voltage applied to the ic regulator, normally governed by the 5kΩ potentiometer. Two silicon diodes, D1, D2, rated to carry more than the maximum output current, keep the regulator output voltage 1·5V above the control voltage in order to limit maximum output current and so protect the psu should the load become short-circuited. The value and rating of R are chosen to suit the required current limit by developing the 1V potential at the limiting current value.

Active add-on cw filter

While personally I must admit to a bias towards passive rather than active af filters for cw reception, and an ingrained belief that narrowband filters are better placed before rather than after the signal demodulator, there is no doubt that a simple filter based on a couple of low-cost op-amps can be very useful for those attempting to receive cw through an ssb, fm or even a 600Hz cw filter. Tom Hall, GM3HBT writes:

"I think it is a pity that the major manufacturers of amateur transceivers often do not incorporate what to me is an indispensable aid to comfortable reception of cw—a simple audio filter. The effect on the overall price would be negligible, but the improvement even with such good rigs (in my experience) as the TS520S, TS530S, FT77 and my present delight, the Corsair, is quite remarkable.

"Over the years to each of these rigs (and also receivers R1000 and FRG7700) I have added a little two-stage op-amp (741) active filter, always at the same point in the circuit. This is at the 'top' or input of the audio gain control. I have never failed to find an unused front panel switch or button to switch the filter off and on (eg an unused CAL button).

"CW reception using the filter—audio bandwidth around 150Hz—in conjunction with the usual narrow i.f. filter (500–600Hz) improves the subjective clarity of cw signals by a useful factor; if the components in each stage of the filter are closely matched it even provides a slight gain at the centre frequency. (Often a useful feature, since overall gain of many hf transceivers is insufficient to allow one to take full advantage of the lower noise floor resulting from the narrow noise bandwidth—G3VA.)

"The use of the filter on receivers lacking a narrow i.f. filter also gives excellent results, the only limitation being the reduction of the wanted signal caused by other strong signals in the wide i.f. passband, which although unheard by the listener through the filter, may cause the agc to depress the wanted signal. (One reason why some of us regret the loss of the former ability to switch off the agc when receiving cw on older-style receivers—G3VA.)

"No claim is made for originality in the standard op-amp filter circuit design (Fig 5) but the following notes should prove useful to anyone

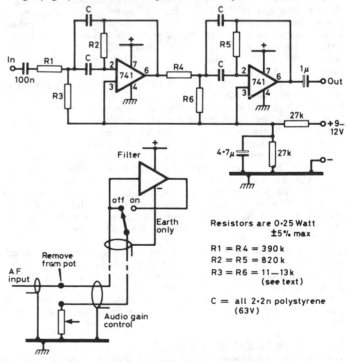

Resistors are 0·25 Watt ±5% max

R1 = R4 = 390k
R2 = R5 = 820k
R3 = R6 = 11–13k (see text)

C = all 2·2n polystyrene (63V)

Fig 5. Active op-amp cw, filter recommended by GM3HBT as an add-on unit suitable for many hf transceivers etc

building this useful and simple unit. I attempt to match the values in each stage as closely as possible, normally around one per cent, although even unselected five per cent tolerance components give good results. The centre frequency can be calculated from:

$$fo = \frac{1}{2\pi} \sqrt{\frac{R1 + R3}{R1 \times R2 \times R3}}$$

"I juggle with the value of R3/R6 to make the centre frequency coincide with the specific sidetone frequency of the rig involved. The circuit Q is low enough (around 4) not to cause any sign of ringing.

"The whole unit can be built on a 'postage stamp' of Veroboard, even smaller with a 747 op-amp, and is 'stuck' anywhere handy inside the rig (except near a mains transformer) using the ubiquitous 'Sticky Fixers' adhesive, and connected with miniature screened audio cable. I use this adhesive for all small modules as it provides the obvious advantage that should the unit ever be removed for resale of the rig etc, this can be done without leaving any trace, and the original connections made to the audio gain-control.

"To prevent hum loops, I always use the earth point of the gain control, via the cable screen, as the only earthing point for the filter.

"CW acquaintances are always most impressed by the performance of this compact filter, and I have fitted quite a few to other peoples' rigs— well worth about £1.50 for components and a couple of hours of enjoyable work!"

The Powerbreaker rccb and those fuses

The May *TT* notes on the pros and cons of rccb safety-protection devices included a critical comment from G3XEN reporting that when attempting to test a 30mA Powerbreaker rccb, as marketed by RS Components Ltd, by applying a short-circuit to earth, he was surprised that the device did not trip but instead the 13A mains fuses blew.

John Power, G8LXG, applications engineer with RS Components, was dismayed to read G3XEN's comments as he feels that they show a common misconception of the true role of rccb/elcb devices. G8LXG emphasizes that an rccb is *not* an overload-protection device and should never be thought of as a substitute for conventional fuses or miniature contact breakers. A mains short-circuit should blow a heavy current fuse in much less time than the 15 to 30ms trip-time of an rccb. In fact the situation reported by G3XEN would apply generally and is not peculiar to the Powerbreaker. G8LXG writes:

"A fuse blows accordingly to a heating effect which is characterized by $I^2t =$ a constant. At, say, 100A a healthy mains fuse will therefore blow in a considerably shorter time than the 15–30ms needed to trip an rccb. It is therefore not surprising that G3XEN's fuses blew before the breaker tripper. We would be seriously concerned if they had not!

"We have received many enquiries about this effect, and we have had to remind users than an elcb/rccb can never, under any circumstances, be considered to provide overload protection but is to protect individuals against dangerous electric shocks. A phase (live) to earth short-circuit, although representing a large overload which will blow a fuse, does not simulate the conditions under which the rccb is intended to operate, and may even weld the contacts together.

"As pointed out in *TT*, the average human body would represent an impedance of around 8kΩ from phase to earth, and an rccb should always be tested with a resistor of around this value. As noted in January, all rccbs have a test facility which simulates this order of leakage and provides a simple and valid test. If a user is not satisfied by this built-in test, a number of suppliers, including ourselves, stock purpose-made test instruments which check that installations conform with the requirements of the IEE's 15th edition *Wiring Regulations* in respect of tripping times and current.

"In short, elcb/rccb devices are there to protect the user, and fuses/overload circuit breakers there to protect the supply wiring. Where there is a risk of accidental contact with the mains wiring, both should be installed (my shack is so protected) and I would certainly never recommend that anybody deliberately applies a metallic link from a live conductor to earth."

Personally I suspect that some confusion exists between a relay-type rccb and a miniature relay-type contact breaker. An mcb is a substitute for a fuse and has the advantage of being resettable. I recall finding 2A and 6A mcb devices installed in homes in Germany in 1945, and was sufficiently impressed to acquire one for use on a home-built transmitter. Very much more convenient than the old-fashioned fuses still in use at my QTH in 1985!

Microwave radiation hazards

The long and often heatedly-debated question of possible hazardous effects of non-ionized microwave radiation other than the known hazards arising from thermal effects on sensitive organs such as the eyes, continues to rumble on. In 1982 the National Radiological Protection Board recommended that the official safety limits should be lowered at vhf/uhf, and suggested also a base standard for microwave exposure to be reduced from 1W/kg of body weight to 0·4W/kg. However, it would appear that none of the 1982 recommendations has been acted on officially to-date. The British authorities are currently opposing some draft EEC proposals that would reduce safe exposure limits well below even the 1982 NRPB recommendations.

According to reports in *Electronics Times* (11 April and 2 May, 1985) the situation has been further confused by a Polish report that military personnel who have been exposed to microwave radiation are statistically more likely to suffer from some forms of cancer than those who have not been so exposed. Polish scientists believe this ranges from a factor of three for stomach and skin cancers, about four for thyroid cancers to almost seven for cancers of the lymphatic system and blood forming organs.

Clearly, a single statistical study, no matter how well conducted, is unlikely to be widely accepted without a great deal of further investigation and assessments of the actual levels and periods of exposure involved. However, if it could be shown convincingly that low-level microwave radiation does in fact pose health hazards other than those arising directly from thermal effects, it would be bound to re-open the whole issue regarding radiation from radar and communications transmitters, microwave ovens etc. It is increasingly accepted that ionized radiation (nuclear radiation etc) has no absolutely safe threshold, although statistically it can be shown that at very low levels the effects merge into those resulting from natural radiation levels. The moral for radio amateurs, in the interim period, would seem to be to keep out of strong microwave fields wherever possible, particularly over regular extended periods, and make sure any microwave oven doors fit tightly—just in case.

Radiation and leukaemia risks

Further studies relating to the hypothesis that electromagnetic fields may be carcinogenic have been reported in letters published in the highly-respected medical journal *The Lancet* (April 6, 1985 pp811–2) and brought to my notice by Ned Row, G8GZZ.

The first relates to the apparent increased risk of leukaemia among electrical workers. A study in New Zealand of 546 male leukaemia patients aged over 20 years registered during 1979–83, and contrasted with 2,184 matched controls, divides "electrical workers" into eight categories. As a result, the study highlights an apparently significantly increased risk to only two of the eight categories: "electronic equipment assemblers" and "radio and television repairmen"; whereas the other six categories of electrical/electronic engineers, electrical/electronic technicians, electrical fitters, telephone installers, linesmen and power-station operators, show only a small, if any, statistical difference from the controls. This study, by members of the New Zealand Department of Community Health thus suggests that the apparent additional risk to assemblers and repairmen is more likely to be due to exposure to metal fumes and substances such as polychlorinated biphenyls (pcbs) than to exposure to non-ionizing radiation from electromagnetic fields from transformers, power generators and the like.

On the other hand, a letter "Silent keys: leukaemia mortality in amateur radio operators" by Samuel Milham of the Department of Social and Health Services, Washington (state), carried in the same issue of *The Lancet* does provide some further evidence in support of the electromagnetic radiation hypothesis. Milham, who presumably is an amateur operator himself, collected "cause of death" information on 1,691 amateurs formerly resident in California and Washington relating to those listed between 1971 and 1983 in the "Silent keys" column of *QST*. Of the 1,691 deaths, 24 were ascribed to leukaemia as compared with an expected 12·6 from statistical averages. The excess was confined almost entirely to myeloid leukaemia (16 compared with an expected 5·7). Milham also notes that the statistical excess among radio amateurs does not appear to relate to their professional occupations ("occupational exposure alone, therefore, probably does not explain the leukaemia excess in these men"). However, before rushing to pull the big switch before it is pulled on you, it is perhaps worth noting that in this study the excess seems to have amounted to just 11·4 out of almost 1,700 deaths. There is also the fact that modern amateur stations usually involve much lower levels of non-ionizing radiation than in the shacks of the mainly old-timers who became "silent keys" between 1971 and 1983. (See also statement by NRPB in "Amateur Radio News"—*Ed.*)

Bilateral harmonic mixer

Bilateral mixers are, as the name implies, mixers that are intended to work equally well in converting a higher frequency signal down to a lower

LA8AK's bilateral mixer with dummy load when used with 145MHz transceiver

frequency, or without changing the configuration, converting the lower frequency to the higher frequency. Such mixers are finding increasing application for a variety of purposes in transceivers, transverters and test instruments. Packaged doubly-balanced diode mixers (eg SBL1, MD108) can readily be used as bilateral mixers, but tend to be rather costly components for some applications.

In *Sprat* (No 42, Spring 1985) Mike Roblic, GW4GIU, describes a home-built bi-directional mixer he uses in a low-power transverter to provide 7MHz output from a 144MHz IC202, and similarly to provide a 144MHz receive output from incoming 7MHz signals, using a 137MHz crystal oscillator chain (45·7MHz crystal). This has a balanced mixer with two jfet J310 devices, and 6dB of attenuation is applied to the 144MHz output from the 3W IC202 (later type with sideband selection).

Jan-Martin Noeding, LA8AK, has built a 14/145MHz bi-directional mixer using two anti-parallel diodes in the harmonic mixer configuration

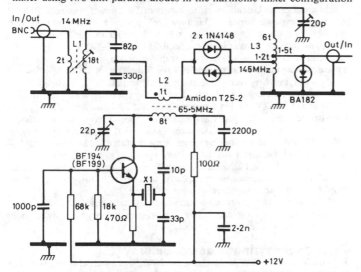

Fig 6. LA8AK's 14/145MHz bilateral mixer using anti-parallel diodes (eg 1N4148). L1: 5mm dia with core, 18 + 2 turns closewound, 0·3mm enam copper wire. L2, Amidon T25-2 core, 8 + 1 turns, 0·3mm enam copper wire. L3: 6 turns, 6mm id, 2cm long, 18swg tinned copper wire tapped at 1·2 and 1·5 turns. Conversion loss approximately 7dB

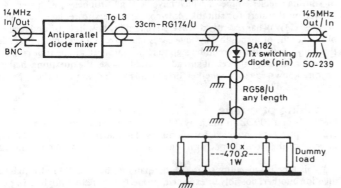

Fig 7. How the bilateral mixer is connected to a 145MHz transceiver. A dummy load is used to protect the mixer in case the "transmit" button is accidentally pushed

popularized by RA3AAE for hf direct-conversion receivers (described a number of times in *TT*). With his mixer, (Fig 6) LA8AK uses this device primarily to align "14MHz i.f." equipment from a 145MHz fm transceiver, but many other applications seem possible since it converts a 145MHz signal to 14MHz, or vice versa, with a conversion loss of only about 7dB. For example, it could be used to provide calibrated levels of test signal in the 144MHz band using a 14MHz rf signal generator etc.

When used with a typical fm transceiver it is advisable to incorporate a dummy load (shown in the illustration) as protection against inadvertently pressing the transmit button: see Fig 7. This is in addition to the protection provided by the BA182 or similar pin-switch on the 145MHz side of the circuit.

Adhesive aluminium tape

The May *TT* (pp360–1) included some suggestions for using adhesive copper tape or kitchen aluminium foil for indoor antennas. This has prompted Ernie Sumption, G3DQL, to comment that the 9mm adhesive *aluminium* tape used in burglar alarm systems could be used in place of copper tape.

He writes: "These adhesive aluminium tapes are far cheaper and have the advantage that suitable connectors are available. The connectors are made of acrylic plastics but could be mounted on glass-fibre or other more suitable materials for good rf insulation. One source for these items is Maplins."

While aluminium is not quite such a good conductor as copper, the lower cost of this material has encouraged increasing use of aluminium wire for professional applications, including antennas, earth mats and radials; 9mm or wider tape should prove entirely suitable for hf or vhf antennas.

ICs that simplify receiver construction

From time to time attention has been drawn to the availability of low-cost consumer-type integrated circuit devices that can form much of the "heart" of home-brew hf or vhf communications receivers or can provide "tunable i.f." systems for use with pre-converter front-ends from hf to microwaves. The use of one or more such device can greatly simplify construction of receivers suitable for many applications.

Mats Espling, SM6EAN, in *QTC*, Nr 3, 1985, presents a tabulated compilation of 21 devices of this general type, listing the main capabilities of each device, maker, operating voltage etc. Unfortunately this takes up three large pages with Swedish-language text, but the following very brief summary may at least draw attention to the wide range of devices now available.

Philips TDA1072. Intended for a.m. receivers to 30MHz (agc amplifier intended for 455kHz i.f.) and tuning indicator facility. 12V. Recommended by SM6EAN.

Philips TEA5560. Much as TDA1072 but without tuning indicator facility. 12V.

Philips TEA5570. Intended for a.m./fm clock radios, includes fm detector with internal oscillator for use below 30MHz. Tuning indicator for a.m. 6V.

Philips TDA7000. Intended for miniature fm-only receivers. 110MHz capability with pulse-counter type fm discriminator for 70kHz i.f. 4·5V.

Motorola MC3356. Device suitable for nbfm/fsk reception to 100MHz, including digital fsk. Recommended by SM6EAN for fsk applications. 5V.

Motorola MC3357. Similar to MC3356 but with frequency limitations, but suitable for use in nbfm receivers at 10·7MHz. Recommended by SM6EAN. 6V.

Motorola MC3359. Roughly similar to MC3357 but with afc facility. Recommended by SM6EAN in preference to MC3357. 6V.

Toko KB4420B. Similar to RCA CA3089E. 12V.

Toko KB4454. Intended for a.m./fm broadcast radio or clock radio with 10·7MHz fm i.f. 3V.

Siemens TBA120S. Intended for television sound providing i.f. strip to 12MHz. 12V.

Siemens TCA440. Intended for a.m. receivers to 30MHz but suitable for ssb with an external product detector. Recommended by SM6EAN. Note that the use by ZL1NB of this device to form the basis of a simple 3·5MHz df receiver was described in *TT*, December 1983, while in *TT*, March 1984, DJ1ZB outlined how two TCA440 devices could provide the major part of a high-performance hf receiver, including ssb demodulator, for use with modular front-ends.

RCA CA3089E. Intended for fm broadcast receivers with separate front-end. Recommended by SM6EAN for nbfm 10·7MHz i.f./detector etc. 12V.

RCA CA3189E. Much as CA3089E but with additional facilities. Recommended by SM6EAN in preference to the CA3089E ("on channel" indicator etc). 12V.

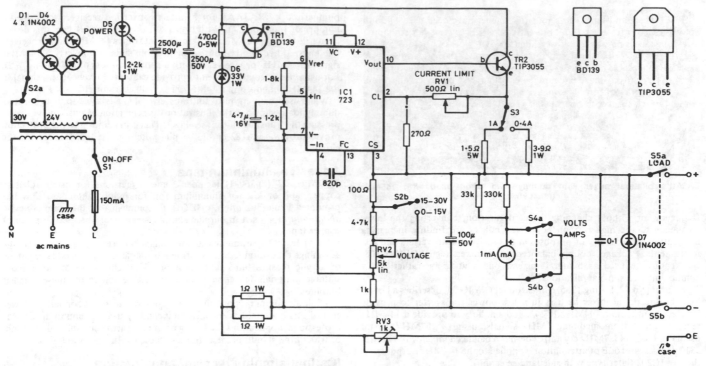

Fig 8. Circuit diagram of the versatile 30V, 1A power supply described in *Electronics Australia*

Plessey SL6601C. Specifically intended for use with nbfm (10·7MHz) with pll demodulator. 7V.

Toko TK10420. Similar to Motorola MC3357. 6V.

Plessey SL6700C. Can form a 10·7 or 21·4MHz i.f. system for a.m., or for ssb with external demodulator. Incorporates noise blanker. Recommended by SM6EAN. 4·5V.

Plessey SL6691C. 455kHz i.f. section for mobile fm receivers etc. 2·5V.

SGS TDA1220L. Intended for a.m./fm clock radios etc. Devices to 30MHz and 10·7MHz fm i.f./455kHz a.m. i.f. 5V.

Siemens TCA1046. Intended for a.m. receiver to 30MHz and suitable for ssb with external detector. Recommended by SM6EAN in preference to TCA440. 10V.

Siemens TCA1047. Intended for fm receivers (10·7MHz i.f.) 12V.

Siemens S469. Intended for fm receivers (i.f. to 30MHz). Recommended by SM6EAN for nbfm.

Note that Philips devices are marketed in the UK by Mullard with the same type numbers.

Experimenters' power supply

Most of the power supply ideas that have been featured in *TT* in recent years have been heavy-current units for the operation of 12V solidstate transceivers from ac mains. But there is often a need for a flexible bench unit providing a regulated output of up to about 1A at an adjustable output voltage up to about 30V. Preferably such a psu should incorporate overload protection and metering and be capable of providing a full 1A output over most of the voltage range and generally be suitable for testing equipment based on 5, 9, 12 and 24V devices.

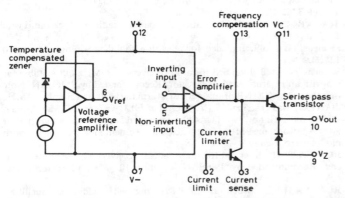

Fig 9. The 723 ic regulator contains a series-pass transistor (150mA), an error amplifier and a voltage reference source

A design (Fig 8) fulfilling such a specification has been described by Greg Swain and Franco Ubaudi, staff members of *Electronics Australia* ("30V/1A benchtop power supply", January 1985, pp60–5). This is built around the 723 ic regulator and a transformer with switchable secondary (24V, 30V), and provides two voltage ranges 0–15V and 15–30V (1A up to 27V). In the absence of a suitably-tapped transformer, a single range could be provided. The tap is needed to permit the full rating of 1A to be provided at *low* voltages where heat dissipation problems tend to be most severe. In the Australian arrangement the bridge rectifiers provide a no-load voltage of either 37V or 47V. TR1 is a preregulator and TR2 an external series-pass transistor driven by the internal (maximum 150mA) series-pass transistor. TR1 and TR2 are mounted on a common heatsink (high efficiency fan type, 105 by 58mm). Current limiting ranges are adjustable 0·15 to 0·4A and 0·4 to 1A. A 1mA fsd meter is used to show voltage/current output.

The useful 723 ic regulators, available from a number of semiconductor manufacturers, incorporate a 150mA series-pass transistor, an error amplifier and a voltage reference source: Fig 9.

The original article gives full constructional details based on components readily available in Australia, and this brief note is intended only to show some useful design features for this class of psu.

Disposable syringes as spreaders?

Richard Thurlow, G3WW, has long used 600Ω open-wire transmission line to feed a 7MHz Lazy-H antenna array. The spacers for most of the 128ft line are good-quality ex-WD ceramic spreaders, but the final 10ft use a motley assortment of ballpoint pen cases and old toothbrush handles, while the line between the higher and lower sections of the Lazy-H uses chunks of knitting needles, some of which have become "rubbery" with age.

Ever on the alert for suitable, low-cost spreaders to replace the ailing needles, G3WW has recently discovered that many hospitals use and throwout hundreds of disposable syringe cases made from a transparent plastic that looks as though it could be a good rf insulator. If so, the tubes would make convenient, lightweight spreaders. But he poses the question whether anyone knows for sure whether or not this is the case and the type of material used?

Creeping ptfe tape

GM4GSJ and EI9DZ in the May *TT* drew attention to some uses for the type of ptfe tape intended for plumbers. Dr Martin Sweeting, G3YJO, director of the UoSAT spacecraft engineering research unit, comments as follows:

"This tape is indeed most useful to amateurs, but I should also like to mention another, possibly unexpected, property of ptfe that might give rise to later difficulties: that of 'cold flow'. PTFE under mechanical stress exhibits the tendency to 'creep' or flow away from that stress. This can result in failure of electrical insulation if not used with care.

"PTFE sheet and tapes of various thicknesses have been used on both UoSAT spacecraft successfully, but early experiences were not so happy. Several instances of 'cold flow' were identified on UoSAT1 before launch, necessitating rework and relief of the relating stress. In one case, the ptfe insulation on a cable had 'crept' away, leaving an exposed conductor! This can happen with no more encouragement than just tight bending radii. Different varieties of ptfe/Teflon are more or less prone to creep, but the 'white' tape or sheet seems particularly fluid. The creep may take months to occur but, fortunately, we identified this problem early on and were able to take appropriate action. If undetected it could, however, have proved disastrous."

Star Wars and the ionosphere

Several years ago there was a certain amount of concern, particularly in the USA, that the increasing use of aerosols would release more freon gas into the upper atmosphere and that this would gradually destroy the ozone which not only plays an important part in the formation of the ionospheric layers but also protects us all from the bulk of the sun's ultra-violet radiation. Whether this was, or perhaps still is, a real danger to our environment I do not know, though I have seen few references to the problem in recent years.

Now, however, G4JBR has drawn attention to an article "Star Wars" by John Draycott in *Resurgence* No 110, May/June 1983, which appears to be a journal committed to the peace and environmental movements. This article claims that the launch by NASA on 14 May 1973 of Skylab on a Saturn 5 rocket knocked a temporary "hole" some 800 miles wide in the F layer of the ionosphere, due to the ton or so of water vapour from the five J-2 liquid oxygen hydrogen engines. The extra oxygen, it is suggested, combines with the ozone to form molecular oxygen and thus reduces the amount of ozone, permitting more ultra-violet radiation to reach the earth's surface.

The point made by John Draycott is that the "strategic defence system", sdi or more popularly known as "star wars", would require the frequent launching of rockets very much larger than even Saturn 5. He claims that "the mere deployment of sdi could have a major effect upon all life on earth. It would alter the whole structure of the upper atmosphere, with resulting effects upon radio transmission, weather and on the level of surface ultra-violet light".

I have no idea how realistic is this warning; it may well be that concern with hf dx could be the least of our worries!

Switched capacitor bandpass filters

The use of switched-capacitor bandpass filters to provide receiver selectivity is already being exploited in the Collins HF2050 receiver (*TT* May, p359) and a switched-capacitor tunable notch filter was described in *Electronics* (24 February 1983). In practice, device limitations have so far meant that most of this form of filter have been confined to relatively low digital rates representing audio rather than radio frequency filters.

A team of engineers at STL and Imperial College (including I A W Vance, G3WMS) has recently reported (*Electronics Letters*, Vol 21, No 11, 23 May 1985) the implementation of second-order switched capacitor bandpass filters at carrier frequencies up to 4MHz (switching clock frequencies up to 100MHz) using integrated-circuit devices made from gallium-arsenide semiconductor material. They forecast that it will prove possible to extend clock frequencies up to 250MHz, which would presumably permit centre frequencies of the order of 10MHz. The published response curve of a two-pole filter having a 1·6MHz centre-frequency, as might be expected, does not approach in shape factor or ultimate rejection the characteristics of a modern multi-pole crystal filter, but presumably in practice a number of such filters could be cascaded. GaAs ic devices still tend to be laboratory devices, and it may be some years yet before this type of filter at typical intermediate frequencies will come into widespread use. But it could happen eventually.

Tips and topics

David Seddon, G4VCO, adds to the saga of rf interference to "Statesman" telephones. A unit (type GNA 83/1) installed in his office experienced much interference whenever an hf TIG welding machine was in use. A local telephone engineer claimed nothing could be done. Later, however, G4VCO—with the advice of G3YXZ—was able to induce another engineer from BT's rfi department to pay a visit. He quickly solved the problem with just four 1nF capacitors, connected as follows: the first capacitor was soldered across R4; the second across the zener diode D6; and the other two on the ic amplifier (TMC 1302), from pin 11 to pin 10 and from pin 7 to pin 10. G4CVO is not sure whether this cure would prove equally effective for vhf rfi but it might be worth trying in the absence of a knowledgeable BT engineer.

Technical Topics
by Pat Hawker, G3VA

LAST MONTH'S NEWS that the DTI has accepted the recommendation of the interim report of the Merriman independent advisory panel and is to allocate the band 50 to 50·5MHz to British radio amateurs should indeed be music to the ears of all experimentally-minded amateurs. For it is not just a question of a little more vhf spectrum to relieve the often overcrowded 144MHz band. It needs to be stressed that 50MHz is uniquely suitable for all those interested in the exploitation of an unparalleled number of different propagation modes. For 50MHz, rather than 30MHz, stands at the critical junction between hf and vhf and is a frequency more responsive to the ionosphere than the lower troposphere that dominates propagation on 70 and 144MHz and higher frequency bands. We will be acquiring a band that combines many of the features of hf and vhf. The external noise levels are significantly below those found on 28MHz, the antenna arrays more compact, yet suitable for equipment that is less critical and less demanding than for the vhf and uhf bands.

50MHz—a valuable acquisition

Perhaps only those radio amateurs who have also some professional involvement in the use of the limited radio spectrum will fully appreciate the significance of the award of this 500kHz to British radio amateurs. For they will be more aware of the ever-increasing pressure on the hf/vhf/uhf radio spectrum, much of which is already bursting at the seams, particularly in the European Region 1 area. At the recent IEE conference on hf systems, it was indicated how difficult it is during the present sunspot minimum and at some times of the day and night to locate *any* usable "gaps" of more than a couple of hundred hertz during sunspot minimum periods.

Similarly, the intense pressure from mobile users and industry for more radiotelephony and data channels in the vhf spectrum is still acute despite the banishing of all UK television broadcasting from Bands 1 (41–68MHz) and 3 (174–216MHz). Broadcasters have even had to fight hard to obtain a limited number of vhf allocations for their many "ancillary services" that range from radio microphones to outside-broadcast programme and communications links.

The success of the RSGB in convincing the 1982 "Independent review of the radio spectrum (30 to 960MHz)" that there was a real need for a UK amateur band at 50MHz is comparable only to the success achieved by the RSGB representatives (Stan Lewer, G6LJ, and John Clarricoats, G6CL) at the 1947 Atlantic City conference in saving for UK amateurs access to the 1·8MHz band.

There is, unfortunately, the disadvantage that the prospects of transmission (at least during television hours) on 50MHz by the many thousands of experimentally-minded amateurs in Continental Europe must be regarded as dim. For most countries (Norway is an exception) 50MHz is, and likely to remain, firmly in the heartland of television broadcasting, swallowed up in Channels E-2, E-2A and the East European R-1. There will thus be a dearth of medium-distance stations at work, and the international obligation for British amateurs to avoid causing interference to television reception in any of those countries. Nevertheless the shape of our islands does provide paths stretching from the Channel Islands to the Shetlands —and there is plenty of 50MHz activity across the Atlantic, in Australia, Japan etc.

In the UK it will also be necessary to ensure that 50MHz transmitters have low harmonic output. The second harmonic between 100 and 101MHz is a part of the spectrum due to be used for one of the two new national vhf/fm sound radio networks planned for when the broadcasting Band 2 is extended up to 108MHz during the next few years, and still used in many parts of the country for the emergency mobile radio service (police, ambulance and fire services).

But just consider the possibilities offered by the following basic propagation modes:

(1) Worldwide F2 ionospheric propagation in daylight at periods of very high sunspot activity, with occasional, though possibly rare, openings towards the south in most phases of the cycle.

(2) Transequatorial and field-aligned F2 propagation (te) in the evenings, even though the UK is often considered too far north for this to be at all common.

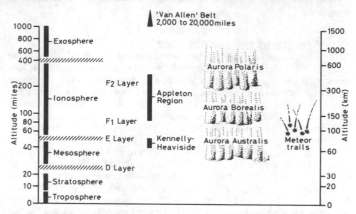

Fig 1. The atmospheric and ionized layers that play a vital role in the propagation of all radio waves. At night the F1 and F2 layers combine, resulting in dawn and dusk "tilts" that give rise to chordal hop rather than multi-hop propagation of long-distance signals. Meteor-trail reflections, auroral reflections and sporadic-E reflections all occur about 85 to 115km above the earth so that the maximum range of all these forms of hf/vhf propagation is roughly the same, about 2,000km

(3) Ionospheric scatter modes (with very high power) can provide reliable 24h communication over distances of from 500 to 2,000km.

(4) Almost the optimum frequency for sporadic-E and meteor-burst communications.

(5) Reasonable for auroral propagation.

(6) Some degree of tropospheric bending, ducting and tropospheric scatter modes, though less pronounced than at 144MHz and above.

(7) Significantly better propagation over hills and down into valleys than at 144MHz.

HF operators can expect to be reliably warned of sporadic-E and/or high muf on 50MHz by the presence of "short skip" signals on 14, 21 and 28MHz.

Antennas and 50MHz

The dipole element length for 50·25MHz is about 9ft 3·5in (282·2cm). While this may seem massive to 144MHz operators, it will seem welcomingly small to hf operators, making two, three and four-element Yagis, two and three-element Quads, delta loops etc practical for most locations. But it should also be recognised that 50MHz also lends itself to high-gain, fixed beams such as rhombics and V-beams. It is a matter of history that the first experimental radio relay system for television distribution links from London to South Wales was around 50MHz and used rhombic antennas.

There are also the benefits that accrue from the larger elements, compared to 144MHz and even 70MHz, as well as the lower losses in coaxial cable feeders.

The signal voltage delivered by a receiving antenna depends on: (a) the *frequency* of the signal; (b) the gain of the array; (c) the loss in the feeder cable, which in turn depends on the cable characteristics, the frequency and the length of the cable; (d) the field strength of the signal; and (e) the height of the antenna. Similar considerations apply to the use of an array for transmission.

It is sometimes forgotten by newcomers that the voltage developed by a dipole element decreases inversely with frequency. For a given field strength a 50MHz dipole will provide about three times as much signal as a 144MHz dipole. The hf operator will also appreciate the fact that a 50MHz array just about 18ft high will nevertheless be a full-wavelength above ground and should be capable of providing excellent low-angle radiation to exploit the ionospheric propagation modes.

While there is no call on 50MHz for the degree of receiver sensitivity that we associate with 144MHz and above, we can still significantly improve on 28MHz where it is seldom possible to obtain any advantage from a noise factor of less than about 7–8dB. For 50MHz we can usefully aim at around 4–5dB well within the capabilities of low-cost devices.

Thus, in general, the techniques suitable for 50MHz can have as much or more affiliation with those used at hf than at 144MHz. It is also more logical to concentrate on the narrower-band modes such as cw, rtty and ssb than channelized nbfm(though nbfm may prove a useful cure for rfi). It will be a pity if the band is viewed primarily as an "overflow" band for 144MHz, although with a 500kHz allocation and a little goodwill by users, there should be space for both weak-signal and local operation. But there is surely some obligation to take every opportunity to exploit to the full the many possible modes of propagation and to uphold our claim, as experimental amateurs, to this valuable stake in the spectrum.

Scatter modes of propagation

The scatter modes of vhf propagation have been used for some 25 years to provide reliable 24h communication for commercial and defence systems. Many of these have been tropospheric scatter systems between about 400MHz and 5GHz, with hops of about 100 to 700 miles. A typical example of the use of tropo scatter is to provide communication with many of the North Sea oil rigs.

But there have also been a number of very high power ionospheric scatter systems operating between about 35 and 50MHz, and used to provide continuous 24h multi-channel rtty communication over single-hop distances of up to about 1,200 miles. For example, ionospheric scatter was adopted to provide the links between the American "dew" (distance early warning) radars within the Arctic Circle and continental USA. Such installations often have enormous "billboard" antennas (about 20dB gain) and around 50kW transmitter power. This does not mean however that ionospheric scatter or tropo scatter is not possible for amateur operation, at least for intermittent, narrowband operation at favourable times.

It is interesting to recall that the early pioneers of vhf scatter propagation included Dr Eric Megaw, G6MU, of GEC Research Laboratories, "Scattering of electromagnetic-waves by atmospheric turbulence", *Nature* 166, 1100 (1950), and the English-American team of H G Booker and W E Gordon, "A theory of radio scattering in the troposphere" *Proc IRE,* Vol 38, 401 (1950).

The first recorded observations of tropospheric scattering are usually ascribed to Katzin in 1945, who noted that even when ducts were not present the signals did not disappear altogether or fall to diffraction levels. New vistas of extended range, over-the-horizon working on vhf opened up in the late 'forties and early 'fifties when radio scattering theories were combined with the idea of irregular and patchy structures in the troposphere, stratosphere and ionosphere.

Megaw established a link from Wembley to Cornwall. In the USA a number of prominent physicists, including Booker and Gordon, and with the co-operation of a number of radio amateurs recruited by the ARRL, established an experimental ionospheric scatter link between Cedar Rapids, Iowa and Sterling, Virginia, a distance of some 1,250km, roughly half the span of the USA, on a frequency just below the 50MHz band.

From this work, several interesting and important findings emerged. For instance, the signal strengths of 50MHz scatter signals tend to decrease at lower sunspot levels (but never entirely vanish), apparently as a result of a decrease in the ionization of the D region. However, the *opposite* effect is observed during the sudden ionospheric disturbances (sids) which result from solar flares and which can black out communication at hf as a result of the increased absorption in the D region. But at these times 50MHz ionospheric scatter signals peak up: Fig 2 is taken from "Radiowave propagation and the ionosphere" by Ya L Al'pert, first published in Moscow in 1960.

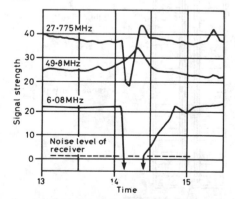

Fig 2. Variation in signal strength at 6·08, 27·775 and 49·8MHz over a 1,243km path during a sudden ionospheric disturbance. Whereas the low hf signal blacks out completely, and the 22MHz signal shows a marked reduction, the 49·8MHz scatter signals rise appreciably (After Al'pert)

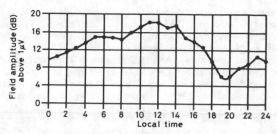

Fig 3. Diurnal variation in the strength of 49·8MHz ionospheric scatter signals over a 1,243km path as recorded in April 1951 (After Al'pert)

Al'pert points out that propagation due to scattering by ionospheric irregularities needs to be distinguished from two other propagation modes which play just as important a role at around 50MHz and permit reception at about the same distances. These are reflections from ionized meteor trails and ionized auroral formations where the propagation path passes through the polar region.

Ionospheric scattering can be distinguished from meteor-trail reflections by the less pronounced and smoother amplitude variations. Then again, the optimum time for ionospheric scatter is around local noon (Fig 3) when the lower regions of the ionosphere tend to be more ionized. On the other hand, the optimum period for bursts from meteor trails is during the morning when meteor activity is at a maximum.

It should thus be possible on 50MHz to communicate over distances of the order of 1,000 miles by noting various optimum periods spread conveniently through the day: meteor burst in the mornings; ionospheric reflections in periods of high sunspot activity or ionospheric scattering around noon; transequatorial effects possibly in the evenings, auroral effects in the evenings and night; and of course *frequent* sporadic-E openings during the summer months and with a less pronounced mid-winter season at the end of December and early January. Remember that meteoric activity tends to be a minimum around twilight.

Al'pert was perhaps treading on thinner ice when he stated: "Good correspondence was also observed between the intensity of reflections from auroras, the frequency of occurence of the sporadic-E layer, and the ionospheric propagation of (50MHz) vhf". Subsequent work has tended to discount the idea of any clear correlation between sporadic-E and the sunspot cycle.

Meteor bursts on 50MHz

Much of the early work (in the mid-'fifties) by the Canadian Defence Research Board ("Project Janet") on meteor-burst communication systems was carried out at approximately 50MHz, and the 30 to 50MHz range is still regarded as the optimum band for operational Defence or commercial meteor-burst systems designed to exploit even the very short (typically 0·2s) bursts that result from the billions of small meteorites that enter the upper atmosphere every day. This differs from normal amateur practice where, at least up to now, most effort has been concentrated on the much longer-lasting highly-ionized trails that tend to be associated with the regular "shower" periods, on the less favourable frequency of 144MHz.

Project Janet showed that with a 100W transmitter and five-element Yagi antenna arrays it is possible to communicate over distances of about 600 miles, in bursts of 600wpm transmission, at an average rate of 60wpm. More recent systems tend to use computer-controlled systems with burst rates of around 4,800 or 9,600 bits/s over distances of up to 2,000km and usually experience maximum periods between bursts of just a few minutes. Transmitter powers are of the order of 1kW with about five-element Yagi antennas. *Reliable* meteor-burst communications are thus possible with installations relatively modest when compared with the enormous Defence ionospheric scatter systems. There is clearly great scope for amateur work at 50MHz, particularly in the development of systems capable of exploiting the far more numerous short bursts, rather than relying on the occasional long bursts of the major shower periods. Remember that 50MHz is the *ideal* band for this mode of propagation.

Experimental results on 50MHz

The availabiltiy of 50MHz (outside of tv hours and with limited power) to a relatively small number of British amateurs since February 1983 has amply confirmed the interesting propagation modes to be found in this unique part of the spectrum. An illuminating summary, compiled by Ray Cracknell, G2AHU (and former ZE2JV of te-propagation fame) on behalf of the RSGB Propagation Studies Committee, has recently been published in the journal of the IARU Region 1 Division. Without wishing to trespass on G8VR's 4-2-70 preserves, the technical aspects of this report should encourage widespread use of 50MHz once it becomes available to us all.

For example, transatlantic contacts have been made on 50MHz in June 1983, June 1984 (and June 1985) by what is often believed to be multi-hop sporadic-E. However, such openings seem to be limited to a very few days each year, at this phase of the sunspot cycle.

In general, reliable ranges of about 200 miles (320km) seem possible on most days, with up to about 1,000 miles (1,600km) in favourable tropo conditions. 50MHz has been shown to be "pre-eminently" suitable for sporadic-E propagation, "frequently disappointing" for auroral propagation, "excellent" (better than 70MHz and much better than 144MHz) for meteor-burst communication. Some F-layer ionospheric openings have been observed despite the unfavourable sunspot conditions. Field-aligned/te-modes hae not yet been positively identified.

The report makes no mention of ionospheric or tropospheric scatter modes, but it is of course difficult for amateur observers to identify with any degree of certainty the various propagation modes, particularly since there can be mixed-mode signals. The power limits of 16dBW (22dBW p.e.p.) also mitigate against scatter modes. These limits have always applied to the British 70MHz band (which, like 50MHz in Region 1, is a national rather than international assignment) and it remains to be seen whether the DTI will give us the 4dB power gain that would bring 50MHz into line with most hf/vhf bands, and be extremely useful for scatter modes.

7MHz sloping delta loop antenna

The full-wave 7MHz loop antenna has been shown by G3UML and others to be an effective dx antenna but tends to require a fairly high support in the form of a tree, pole or building. From Kjell Norlich, SM6CTQ, in his Swedish dx column in *QTC* (Nr 3, 1985, p112) comes the sloping form of delta loop shown in Fig 4 that he reports to be a useful dx performer and with a more modest height requirement. The impedance match is improved by the quarter-wave transformer (though this will tend to make such an antenna a one-band antenna). The formulas used were: loop $(1,005 \times 0\cdot305)/f$ where the length is in metres and f in megahertz, and for the transformer $(246 \times 0\cdot305)/f$ multiplied by the velocity factor of the cable $(0\cdot66$ for RG59/U). Omission of the $0\cdot305$ factor gives the result in feet.

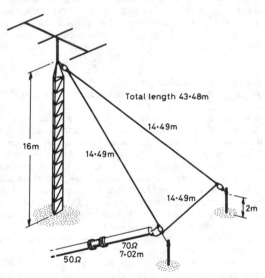

Fig 4. 7MHz sloping delta-loop antenna

Radiation wrongly blamed?

In a follow-up to the correspondence in *The Lancet* (6 April, 1985) reported in the August *TT* (p628) on the statistical studies that apparently link electronic equipment assembly, radio and tv servicing and amateur radio with some leukaemia and cancers, a letter from J Seager of Arrowe Park Hospital, Upton (*The Lancet* 11 May, 1985, pp1095–6) stresses that the possible environmental hazard found in these studies is most unlikely to have anything to do with the presence of electromagnetic fields.

He writes: "As pointed out by Bonnell (the New Zealand study of electrical workers), there are many possible hazards such as fluxes and the tin/lead alloy used in soldering to which the amateur radio enthusiast (and the other two categories—*G3VA*) is exposed. Electrical components and synthetic materials used for tagboards and insulators may all overheat and emit fumes when soldering is being done. The radio amateur has traditionally not only operated but also built much of his equipment. This tends to be done in far from ideal workshop conditions, though allergy to

resin flux may limit exposure to solder fumes in some . . . . A more precise analysis of the risk factors is needed, but in the meantime it might be advisable for readers of *QST* and other electronics periodicals to do their soldering in short sessions in a well-ventilated room or out of doors."

This letter thus echoes the suggestion made in *TT* several years ago (based on advice in the *British Medical Journal*) that extraction fans or other good ventilation are advisable during soldering sessions—although this was in connection with a clear tendency for electronic assemblers using cored solders to develop asthma-type coughs and wheezes.

In general there does appear to be a tendency today for "radiation" (ionized or non-ionized) to be labelled as the likely cause whenever there is any statistical evidence of an apparent health hazard that cannot be clearly identified. A notable example is the long-standing controversy over the alleged effects of using visual display units over long periods. Many investigations have shown that the radiation from vdus, monitors and tv sets of modern design is miniscule.

In my purely layman's opinion, a far more likely cause of headaches, nervous strain etc often reported as symptoms by vdu operators is the degree of 25Hz inter-line flicker on the closely-observed screens. Undoubtedly a small proportion of the population is sensitive to various optical effects such as flicker, and this has been found to act as a trigger for those who suffer from epilepsy, and there is some evidence that flicker can also trigger migraine headaches.

Water-loaded antennas

Alan Williams, G3KSU, draws attention to an intriguing UK patent application (GB 2, 001, 804A) filed by Plessey (inventor J G Brett) in 1978 for "improvements in or relating to aerial systems."

It has often been pointed out in amateur journals that if we could submerge antenna elements in water, the resonant length would be greatly decreased. In effect, the idea proposed in this patent is a variation of this principle of dielectric loading which can also be implemented by cladding the element with ferrite material.

The application points out that "it has been proposed to submerge an antenna consisting, for example, of a metallic rod in water, but this has been found to suffer from the practical disadvantage that through contamination and absorption of CO_2 into the water, degradation results and the antenna efficiency rapidly deteriorates."

It is therefore proposed to use an antenna structure surrounded by water or similar acceptable liquid by including a sealed container shaped so that the element is completely surrounded by the liquid. This can take form of a sealed glass or plastics container filled with water (some anti-freeze can be added for low temperature conditions): Fig 5. The process of filling and sealing the container is preferably carried out under chemically-clean conditions.

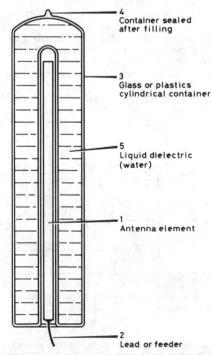

Fig 5. Short "water-jacketed" dielectric-loaded antenna as disclosed in UK Patent Application GB 2,001 804 by the Plessey Company

It is claimed that, for example, an antenna rod length of 15cm used at a frequency of 100MHz gave an increase in signal strength of over 200 per cent compared with a rod of the same length in free air. Where the sealed container is not completely filled, any remaining air space should be substantially evacuated.

While one needs to view patent claims with some reservation, there is little doubt that dielectric loading has been shown to be an effective method of achieving reasonably-efficient antennas with miniature resonant elements. The construction of a sealed water container might present problems, but perhaps there is someone able to overcome the problems and give the idea a trial on the amateur bands.

The idea of surrounding an element with water reminds me of a problem known to exist with some wideband television receiving arrays: a significant fall-off in performance on the higher-frequency channels when it rains and water collects on the elements. Clearly what is happening is that the resonant frequency of the array is being lowered by the rain—further proof of the effects of dielectric loading.

The idea of a 1·5m rod antenna at 10MHz is sufficiently attractive to encourage practical experimentation. Remember that it is entirely permissible for an amateur to use the ideas of any patent provided that no attempt is made to market the resulting product.

But one foresees an unhappy operator reporting: "Sorry, om, signals are fading, my antenna has sprung a leak." Shades of Tony Hancock!

Solidstate polarity protection

To protect solidstate equipment from being accidentally connected to a battery with the polarity of the leads reversed, it has long been common practice to connect one or more diodes in series with the load: Fig 6. This, however, results in voltage drops of about 0·3V (germanium diode) or 0·7V (silicon diode) or twice these figures where the current passes through two diodes as in Fig 6 (c).

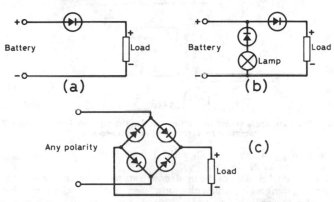

Fig 6. Polarity protection using diodes in power supply line. In (b) the lamp lights if the battery is wrongly connected. In all arrangements there will be a fixed voltage drop due to the diodes

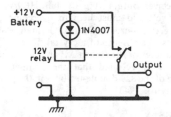

Fig 7. Polarity protection combining a relay with a diode in such a way that there is no voltage drop to the load

In some applications even these modest voltage drops may be unacceptable. Fig 7 shows a variation of diode protection reported by Winfried Mederer, DL4RW (cq-DL, Nr 6/85, p315) that provides protection without incurring any significant voltage drop. In this case the diode ensures that a suitable relay closes only when the battery is correctly connected.

Spark hazards from transmitters

Several references have been made in *TT* to the work of Dr Peter Excell and others at the University of Bradford on the controversial subject of the risk of spark ignition of flammable substances by very strong local radio transmissions (eg *TT*, September 1984, p774). Some of his papers drew particular attention to the fact that some amateurs, particularly those working hf mobile, use transmitter powers considerably in excess of those normally associated with commercial vhf/uhf radiotelephones etc.

It is therefore interesting to learn that, together with Dr Alfred Keller, he has been awarded a £33,572 SERC grant to carry out further studies, with emphasis on taking into account "probabilistic factors" when determining realistic safety margins, on the grounds that some current BSI standards relating to "hazard zones" have proved "unrealistically onerous", being based on the assumption that a number of unlikely events will occur simultaneously. It is now claimed that: "By themselves, each of these events may be seen to be 'just possible', ie at the limit of reasonable probability. In fact, for a sequence of such events to occur simultaneously the probability would be so low as to be negligible compared with numerous other generally-accepted risks: the costs involved in elimination of the radio-frequency hazard on oil rigs and large chemical plants etc might be better spent on more urgent safety matters, such as improved scaffolding, or road safety."

Refraining from the comment that Dr Excell appears to be attempting to disprove Murphy's Law, the announcement of this work does offer some other useful background information:

"Radio waves from high-powered transmitters can sometimes cause sparks to form on metal structures (unintended receiving antennas) located in a zone around the transmitter. Potentially hazardous conditions exist, for example, around oil and gas plants should these be co-incidentally located within the predicted 'hazard zone' of a transmitter. The purpose of the work is to determine viable safety margins within which transmitters can be built and operated. This will be done by assessing the 'probabilistic factors'—in other words, the likelihood of an explosion occurring, since a number of conditions must simultaneously exist, such as appropriate orientation, a spark-gap of the correct size, and flammable mixture at the optimum concentration around the spark-gap at the time of the spark."

Fleeting history

Although, basically, *Technical Topics* is dedicated to the advancement of new technology, it has always been my firm contention that the future cannot be disassociated from the past. Even though amateur radio is now well into its third era of solidstate, the influence and value of the ideas that abounded and were pioneered in the earlier eras of valve and spark are still important—right back to such classic patents as the Marconi Company's "7777" that introduced the concept of tuning and so opened the way to there being more than one usable transmission at a time!

There is, I find, a growing appreciation that the history of technology is important, and that more care needs to be taken to collect, preserve and display not only the fascinating hardware of yesteryear but also archival material in the form of documents, publications and the like. British amateurs should be grateful for the efforts of the Science Museum (not forgetting the associated new Film and Television Museum at Bradford); the various Service displays at Blandford, Hendon etc; Douglas Byrne, G3KPO, and his National Wireless Museum on the Isle of Wight; Ron Ham; George Jessop, G6JP; and a growing number of other private museums and collections. There is, for instance, an extensive private collection of early radio and television sets and memorabilia in West Dulwich, south London, and similar collections are being built up elsewhere. Unfortunately various attempts to set up a broadcasting museum at Alexandra Palace or in BBC buildings still seem to be stymied by lack of funds; the IBA has long had a "broadcasting gallery" at 70 Brompton Road (prior appointment required) though this is mainly concerned with the establishment and organization of Independent Broadcasting. However, there is a small but interesting historical section. In 1982, I was fortunate enough to have a chance to look round a broadcasting museum in Dallas, Texas, that included a significant number of amateur radio exhibits, not behind glass but open virtually to "hands on" examination.

The recent diamond jubilee issue of *Radio Communication* prompted Arthur Milne, G2MI, to make a renewed plea that the RSGB, itself, should do more to establish its own museum or collection, and to appoint an official archivist. G2MI, like others, is concerned that various gifts and bequests of historic radio material that have been made over the years to the Society, are nowhere on display. I recall the unique collection of early equipment donated by Mr Maurice Childs of the London Telegraph College and an early vice-president of the Society. G2MI mentions a model made by Professor G G Blake (one of the first historians of radio) showing the principles of the valve, a Marconi magnetic detector in working order, a working syphon recorder, various Post Office telegraph keys, a coherer, his own 3·5MHz transmitter used for GB2RS, and many other artefacts.

Unfortunately, museums and archivists (unless volunteers) cost money and space, and the same can be said of library collections, and tend to be given low priority. But let us hope that the Council will not overlook the

Gerry Marcuse, 2NM, the founding father of the *T&R Bulletin* in his elaborate early station. This shows his equipment about 1922 and is probably a "440m" set-up in the days before he became one of the most successful of the pioneers of the "short waves". (Photographed from a radio display at the IBA Broadcasting Gallery by Adrian Good)

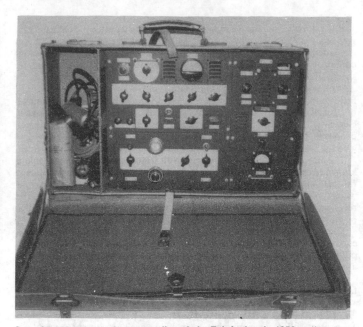

One of a 100 or so "suitcase sets" made by Telefunken in 1952 as "amateur radio apparatus" but most likely meant for "unofficial" diplomatic communications. This equipment is now in the possession of HB9AQS of Gstaad, Switzerland and still performs well on the amateur bands

need to do something positive before the bits and pieces are scattered and lost—and I feel certain that, if displayed, they would soon encourage others to find a permanent place for fast-vanishing equipment and components of historical significance. Perhaps the RSGB could co-operate with one of the smaller London museums to arrange a special exhibition —I was much impressed last December to see a display of Alfred Midgeley's pioneer work in radio, electronic music, car electrics etc organized at the Watford museum, not all that far from Potters Bar!

G W Thomas, G5YK, has written to say that the "unidentified" member of the early editorial committee in one of the illustrations in "Sixty Glorious Years" was Archie Alliston, G5LA, and that he and the others were a great help in putting together the *Bulletin*.

It had also been my intention to provide an illustration of the unforgettable Gerry Marcuse, G2NM, who initiated Empire Broadcasting, was an outstanding dx operator, an RSS Group Leader etc, all in addition to his being "the father of the *Bulletin*"', but the print arrived too late. It shows Gerry's impressive station about 1922–3 at a time when he was still interested in "440m" as well as the opening of the short waves.

The suitcase-set mystery

For those who share my enjoyment of the John Le Carré (David Cornwell) novels of post-war intelligence intrigue, Hans Zimmermann, HB9AQS (ex G5EIH, DJ0RW etc) sets a poser worthy of the Master. He has a hefty "suitcase set" that was clearly strongly influenced by SOE's wartime B–2 as designed by John Brown, G3EUR, including a two-stage co-pa (6AG7–6L6G), a four-stage, three-waveband superhet receiver (two ECH42, two EAF42) covering 3 to 16MHz and similarly built in three sections, though with rather more controls and with a suprising lack of miniaturization that would have been technically possible at the time it was built.

It would appear that a batch of at least 100 of these equipments was built by Telefunken at Hannover in 1952 and were intended for, and used by, diplomatic radio networks for a number of years. So far so good, but why, asks HB9AQS, were the Telefunken drawing office circuit diagrams clearly marked "Amateurgerät Empfänger" and "Amateurgerät Sender" when it seems certain that they were not designed or ever intended for the amateur radio market? HB9AQS has found that, like the B–2, they can still form an effective cw rig.

My own guess is that these sets were never "clandestine" equipments for agents or paramilitary purposes, but for diplomatic networks in the days before the Vienna Convention finally made such communications entirely legal once the consent of the host country is obtained. For many years before that, Foreign Offices, including our own, set up extensive hf radio networks on an "unofficial" basis and under the control of Intelligence Services rather than the pukka Foreign Offices.

Thus the "amateur" designation on the Telefunken diagrams may have been to keep the true purpose of the sets from Telefunken employees, or possibly from any over-inquisitive British officials of the Civilian Control

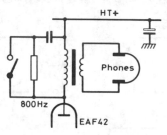

Fig 8. The switchable 800Hz audio filter used in the mystery Telefunken 1952 "amateur receiver" for the suitcase set

Commission that still, in 1952, wielded some power over the emerging Federal Republic of Germany.

But one final element of the mystery defeats me. Why, if they were for German government communications, were the instruction manuals printed in French?

Technically, the Telefunken sets have at least two features not found in the B2. A voltage-regulator tube in the screen-grid supply to the 6AG7 apparently to improve keying characteristics, and a simple switched 800Hz af filter in the receiver output (Fig 8) that HB9AQS reports finding "suprisingly effective" and must help to overcome one of the major problems with the receivers used in British, German, Polish and American wartime suitcase sets: the absence of a crystal filter.

As a long-time admirer of the Polish AP and BP clandestine sets, it was only recently that I appreciated that the compact, high-power BP3 equipment used one of the 829 double-tetrodes in the power amplifier, very advanced technology for 1943!

Tips and topics

Hector Cole, G3OHK, queries whether there is any simple but effective way of paralleling several low-cost, medium-current power supply units so as to provide a high-current, voltage-regulated and protected output with the aid of a single "magic" mixer-regulator.

John Wilson, ex-G8KIS, notes a comment from British Telecom Research at Martlesham (*Electronic Letters* 20 June, 1985, page 553) which indicates that the flash from a strong photographic flash-gun or a laser used close to some forms of cmos memory devices can result in a destructive latch up, and less serious latch-up problems at lower light levels.

George Cripps, G3DWW, commenting on the principle of using narrow bandwidths and good rf selectivity as an aid to weak-signal reception (*TT* July) writes: "If we accept the desirability of introducing a narrow bandwidth as early as possible in the receiver chain, then the use of a signal-frequency Q-multiplier was used to good effect by W1DX in his "Miser's Dream" receiver (*QST* May 1965 and *Amateur Radio Techniques*, 7th edition, p78). He very neatly utilized the normal antenna coupling and first tuned circuit coils. It seems to me that this technique could now be exploited using a low-noise fet device.'' The 1965 receiver was a valve model with a 6C4 Q-multiplier directly before a 7360 beam deflection mixer capable of a very wide dynamic range.

In connection with the signal-frequency crystal filters developed by G3IPV (*TT* July), he has further refined his units based on shunt rather than series crystals, and it is hoped to return to this subject later.

Dr Constantino Feruglio, IV3VS, adds to his comment on using plastic hosepipe to protect 300Ω twin-feeder by pointing out that his hosepipe is dark-yellow and probably acts as an effective filter against u-v radiation. The hosepipe itself, as well as the ribbon feeder, remains in excellent condition even after four years in the strong Italian sunlight.

A A Butcher, G4SIB, who owns a Trio 930S transceiver, suggests that owners of this or similar equipment may be interested to learn that memories can be stored without using batteries to form a non-volatile memory since the large, low-leakage capacitor alongside the battery can retain a charge for 24h or more. He writes: ''I went on a week's holiday and the frequencies remained stored. The rig has been used for 18 months and this arrangement has the advantage that the owner does not have to worry about battery leakage.'' It should perhaps be stressed that it would be unwise to rely on charged capacitors for those rigs where the memory is essential for the functioning of the equipment, and not just for storing frequencies.

I ''priced'' the Rockwell-Collins HF2050 receiver (*TT* May) in the plus-$6,000 price range on the basis of the first $6-million Canadian order for almost 1,000 receivers. An unsigned note from an ''swl'' complains that he received a quote for a single receiver which puts it in the £16,000-plus-options category. It only goes to show that things come cheaper when you buy in large quantities. In practice many current high-performance *professional-grade* communication receivers tend to be priced in the £10,000 to £20,000 range depending on the options etc. Thus, basically, it would seem that digital signal processing is already roughly cost-competitive with analogue designs, and offers considerable scope for becoming more so. That is not to deny that there is still a lot to be said for sets based on analogue crystal filters etc.

John Stocking, G4INI, ran into interference on all hf bands (KW2000 at about 90W p.e.p.) on all tv signals passing through his Panasonic NV333 video cassette recorder. He traced the problem to the wideband rf amplifier in the vcr, and fitted a Labgear CM9700 cb-type highpass filter in the tv antenna coaxial cable feeder lead as close as possible to the vcr antenna socket. He reports ''This effected an immediate and complete cure to the problem, proving cheap and easy to install''.

The Spalding & DARS has now published an enlarged second edition of its useful ''Digest of horizontal wire aerials'' compiled by Dennis Hoult, G4OO, and containing some 91 different designs of simple wire antennas and 14 antenna tuning units, including an appreciable number that have appeared over the years in *TT*. A handy 46 pages, it can be obtained, £3 post free, from D Hoult, Chespool House, Gosberton Risegate, Spalding, Lincs PE11 4EU.

Technical Topics *by Pat Hawker, G3VA*

RECENTLY, in reviewing the circumstances behind the almost universal worry about the apparent diminishing ability of amateur radio to attract and/or retain the interest of youngsters in these days of personal computers and worldwide subscriber-dialling telephones, I wrote in *Electronics & Wireless World*: "While some believe that in order to appeal to younger newcomers it is necessary to stress new technology in the form of packet data, spread spectrum, Oscar satellites and microwaves, others believe that the fundamental attraction lies in the use of relatively simple equipment for speech and manual morse communication."

I quoted 23-year-old Peter Hall, G4ZPT (*TT* June 1985, pp454–5): "With just a handful of components, a morse key, and a wire antenna strung up into a tree, it is possible to converse with fellow human beings miles away. This is, by any reckoning, an extraordinary and wonderful thing—too often forgotten by the many who buy all their gear, plug it in, switch on and talk."

First rigs and the young newcomers

It was therefore interesting to find basically similar views, though concerning teen and pre-teenagers, expressed strongly in the correspondence columns of *QST*, June 1985, p52, by B N Ensanian, KI3U. He wrote: "The average adolescent has grown up surrounded by advanced electronics from cb to computers, vtr machines to wristwatches that do everything but feed the cat. To them, hands-on contact with a very broad variety of electronics is routine.

"Yet many simple old pleasures, such as playing baseball with the gang, aren't declining so drastically in popularity. I think I understand. When I got licensed at the age of 12 in 1960 I was a kid with a strong sensitivity for 'I can do that', 'I can build a radio', 'I can do it all by myself'.

"Some friends of my parents demonstrated cb radio. It was interesting, but seeing them operate commercially-made gear just didn't capture my imagination. . . . What had hooked me on radio was a magazine picture of a young boy wearing a headset connected to a homemade crystal set. I knew I could wind a coil, mount it along with some other parts on a piece of wood, string up a wire to a tree, and then claim 'I did it all myself'.

"When I started as a Novice, there was an unwritten rule that no matter how easily you could afford commercially-made gear, you built your first transmitter and, perhaps, even a simple receiver. Only after having made contacts with your own homemade rig were you considered to be truly initiated into the fraternity as a 'real' radioman.

"I don't advocate reversing the progress in commercially-made rigs. I've operated my share of appliances and will continue to . . . but as for selling the appeal that making contacts with such rigs is somehow irresistibly challenging and exciting to today's teenage computer veterans, I doubt it.

"We need to reintroduce the ethic of building your first rig—of rising to the challenge of creating your first signal by your own hands. We need to revive the beauty and wonder of radios constructed from a few simple old parts and much ingenuity. And we need to let the youngsters know we are proud of them for having done it all on their own."

It was an unfortunate, entirely unforeseen and unintended effect of the UK Class B licence that it has meant that so many amateurs here *start* on 144MHz where it is so much more difficult to build the type of first rig that KI3U has in mind. It is on the 1·8, 3·5 and 7MHz bands that a simple, crystal-controlled, one or two-stage, 5–20W cw transmitter with a tree or chimney-stack-supported wire antenna can still keep alive a practical and enjoyable do-it-yourself concept, aided perhaps by the rest of us taking more trouble to search ±5 or 10kHz after making a CQ call rather than assuming that answering stations can always net exactly on frequency. The proposed "intermediate licence" may help, but is surely not a complete answer since it still implies that the first steps, after taking the RAE and getting a Class B licence, will be to acquire a factory-built vhf rig.

KI3U is surely right in believing that a strong element of "I can do it myself" is an essential prerequisite to attracting and retaining the long-term interest of youngsters.

Frank Hughes, VE3DQB, recently drew my attention to a letter in *The Canadian Amateur* from Harry Gloster, VE3IT, who had just finished building and erecting a new quad antenna, and who has never purchased a commercial antenna. Not bad going for someone who has been an amateur for *77 years* and built his first transmitter and receiver from an article published in 1907 in the *Boys Own Paper* when he was 10 years old. Clearly that spark rig hooked him for life!

While it may be argued that commercially-made and ex-Service equipment was widely used in the UK for "first rigs" throughout much of the past 35 years, this still involved (until recently) a good deal of auxiliary equipment and the ability to assemble the various separate items into a working radio station. The modern transceiver is a very different kettle of fish: plug it into the mains and the cable from a factory-built antenna into it—and, hey presto, that's often all there is to it, except talking and listening; or at least that's how it must appear to many youngsters! As surface-mounted components become the norm, even home modification or home maintenance will become impracticable.

Yet without a significant element of do-it-yourself, we are all in danger of becoming merely the ageing caretakers of a once great and unique hobby. I wish it were possible to be more optimistic!

Curing rfi without the RIS

The decision of the DTI to switch the diminished resources of the Radio Investigation Service towards "enforcement" while carrying out a "phased withdrawal from the time-consuming effort put into dealing with domestic tv and radio reception problems" is understandable, but will be regretted by many amateurs who have been able to rely not only on the specialized technical skills of the RIS teams but also the diplomatic way they handle the vexed social problems.

Indeed over the years RIS built up what must be unique expertise in identifying, tracing and suggesting cures for tvi and bci. It is unlikely that this can be readily replaced, even where viewers and listeners are prepared to pay the trade to carry out such work. The promise that manufacturers will be legally obliged to build sets with better immunity to strong local signals, at least to the standards suggested in BS905 Part 2, is indeed welcome news. But even here a word of warning is in order. A check with BS905 shows that this specifies immunity measurements only between 26 and 30MHz and is clearly directed primarily at achieving immunity to legal, low-power cb 27MHz fm signals. While immunity to such signals should help in cases where transmissions are on amateur hf bands, it will not cover such problems as the wideband vhf/uhf amplifiers, widely used in pre-amplifiers, vcr machines etc, that can so easily be overloaded by 144 or 430MHz signals. Nor should we expect BS905 to provide the degree of immunity required to cope always with a legal-limit amateur radio transmitter next door.

Having had an opportunity to read in draft the text of the new DTI booklet *How to improve television and radio reception* (which should be

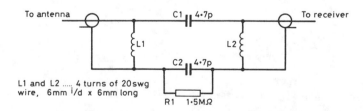

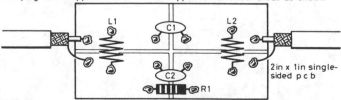

Fig 1. Combined braid-breaker and high-pass filter as included in the DTI booklet *How to improve television and radio reception*. This is intended to prevent hf signals from flowing down either the inner or outer of a coaxial cable feeder. R1 provides a static discharge path. This filter uses single-sided printed circuit board

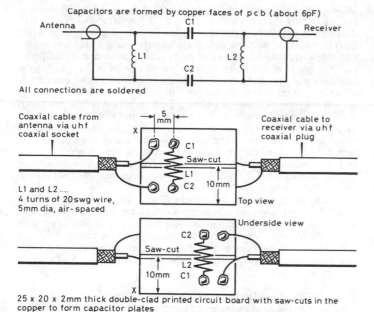

Capacitors are formed by copper faces of p c b (about 6pF)

Antenna — C1 — Receiver

L1   L2

C2

All connections are soldered

Coaxial cable from antenna via uhf coaxial socket

5 mm

X

C1
Saw-cut
L1
C2

10mm

Coaxial cable to receiver via uhf coaxial plug

Top view

L1 and L2 ....
4 turns of 20 swg wire, 5mm dia, air-spaced

Underside view

C2
Saw-cut
L2
C1

10mm

X

25 x 20 x 2mm thick double-clad printed circuit board with saw-cuts in the copper to form capacitor plates

Fig 2. An alternative design by G8YOM as published some years ago in *TT*. This uses double-sided copper pcb with the capacitors formed by the copper faces (about 6pF). Note that it would be advisable to add a static discharge resistor as in the DTI design

available free-of-charge from main Post Offices by about October/ November) I would strongly urge all British amateurs to obtain a copy. The DTI admits that this useful booklet has been modelled on a similar FCC booklet first published in 1977 at the height of the American cb boom. The DTI points out that American viewers have never had a free interference investigation service on which to draw. The booklet is divided into two parts. Part 1 is intended for householders and very firmly emphasizes that the vast majority of reception problems are due to the receiving installation; it also provides check lists, illustrations of some common tv reception problems, including weak signal reception, "ghosting" (multipath), reception of distant co-channel signals at times of tropo propagation, as well as various forms of electrical interference such as vacuum cleaners and thermostats. This section includes notes on possible simple remedies and on "how to fit a filter". On audio equipment, which these days is often more of a problem to radio amateurs than uhf television, it says simply: "Audio equipment which does *not* incorporate a radio tuner is designed to reproduce music and not to receive radio signals and is therefore outside the scope of this booklet. If you are suffering interference a modification to the equipment will be necessary. Please consult your dealer."

Part 2, "For the tv and radio dealer", provides an excellent, though necessarily summarized, guide to interference mechanisms, with check charts outlining procedures to follow in determining interference mechanisms for pick-up on the receiving antenna and feeders, as well as

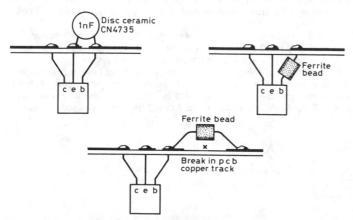

1nF
Disc ceramic
CN4735

c e b

Ferrite bead

c e b

Ferrite bead

x

c e b

Break in pcb copper track

Fig 3. Another illustration from the DTI booklet to show how to fit ferrite beads and rf bypass capacitors. The capacitors should be disc ceramic and fitted with the shortest possible leads. Ferrite beads should preferably be fitted directly on the base lead of the transistor, but where this is not possible it should be fitted across a broken lead on the board as shown

direct pick-up in the receiver. There are also 10 appendices, including information on toroidal choke filters, braid-breaker and high-pass filters (Fig 1), the fitting of ferrite beads and rf bypass capacitors (Fig 3), as well as listing a selection of available commercially-manufactured filters, manufacturers' addresses, regulations affecting reception problems and relevant British Standards. There is also a form for viewers to seek RIS help for those prepared to send £21 in advance.

Most amateurs will note with relief that nowhere in the sections on "radio transmitter interference" is there any suggestion that interference is the fault of the transmitter—indeed neither the householder nor the dealer is given much guidance, apart from a mere mention or two, of the possibility of harmonics other than a note to Appendix 1 which lists amateur radio frequency allocations and states: "It should be noted that most of the frequencies used by amateur radio operators are often obtained by using oscillators at other frequencies and the final frequency then obtained by a mixing process; hence there can be low-level radiation of the fundamental oscillators or any of their harmonics or mixing products."

The DTI is thus shifting responsibility for dealing with rfi problems pretty firmly on to viewers, retailers and manufacturers, though if it steps up "enforcement" it would clearly be inadvisable for amateurs to shrug off or show an unhelpful attitude towards complaints of rfi, but rather to do whatever possible to help overcome the problem and keep the neighbours happy. Few viewers willingly blame their own equipment for rfi problems, and unfortunately many do whatever possible to put the amateur/cb operator off the air by putting pressure on local authorities etc. Many of the restrictive planning ordinances in the USA have resulted not from environmental considerations but more from tvi and bci problems.

In other words, British amateurs are going to have to learn to live without the active assistance of the RIS, and the first step, I suggest, will be to obtain and study the new booklet. It's worth queueing for at your nearest main Post Office!

Window-pane 144MHz antenna

Many broadcast engineers responsible for advising viewers on the reception of uhf television seem to be besotted with the idea that outdoor antennas are *always* essential in order to obtain good quality pictures. While I recognize that for very many viewers this is indeed the case, on occasions I find myself in disagreement with my colleagues since I remain convinced that, in some circumstances, perfectly good pictures, free of multipath "ghosting" and the effects of local movement *can* be achieved with window-pane loop antennas—provided of course that the window is looking roughly in the right direction and the local signal is reasonably strong and clean of multipath.

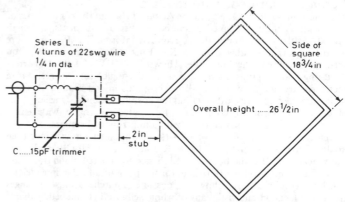

Series L ....
4 turns of 22 swg wire
1/4 in dia

Side of square 18 3/4 in

Overall height .... 26 1/2 in

2 in stub

C ....15pF trimmer

Fig 4. The aluminium-tape 144MHz "window pane" antenna used by G4WEA/ A. This can be fed either side of the loop, as convenient, providing vertical polarization. For horizontal polarization feed at bottom corner. Mark the window with a felt-tip pen and then stick down the tape. The spacing of the stub was governed by the "burglar alarm" connectors which came as a pair, about an inch apart between centres

I was reminded of this ongoing debate by a note from John Wells, G4WEA, who has for several years used very successfully a 144MHz "quad loop" antenna formed from self-adhesive aluminium foil tape (see G3DQL's notes in the August *TT*) while operating /A with about 1·5W from an IC2E at the Medical Physics and Clinical Engineering laboratories of Barnsley District General Hospital. His antenna (Fig 4) uses burglar-alarm tape (readily obtainable from RS Components, Farnell etc) stuck on to the metal-framed laboratory window. A 2in (5cm) stub at one corner is fed with 50Ω coaxial cable via a simple matching network mounted on plain Veroboard, which is fastened to the tape's connectors with 4BA solder tags.

G4WEA acknowledges that the idea came from G6IDL, and reports that performance has been excellent—including even a contact with Holland under "lift" conditions. He points out that an added advantage is that, even at work, it does not have to be put away after every session, as it takes up virtually no room space!

Adjusting hf stubs and antennas

Bill McLeod, VK3MI, was interested in the report by G3SEK (*TT* June, p455) of the technique used for the accurate adjustment of vhf phasing lines using an swr meter as the device to indicate resonance, since he has been using a basically similar arrangement at hf for several years not only to facilitate accurate cutting of coaxial line sections but also to adjust the two halves of dipole antennas. VK3MI writes: "For full versatility and protection the arrangement (Fig 5) needs a 6dB pad between the QRP transmitter or exciter and the swr meter in order to protect against short- and open-circuit mishaps and to allow the reflected wave to indicate the low-Z dip from half-wave lines in parallel on a T-connector with the load.

"The system works with single wires and also the outer shield of quarter-wave coaxial cables used as radiating elements! For convenience, these antenna sections are fixed about 8ft above ground on a temporary wooden support (eg a reach off a packing case) then stretched to the test bench at 3ft for a thin wire to subtend, say, 600Ω and a coaxial outer 50 to 75Ω for 3·5MHz. The elements should initially be cut about one per cent longer than required to allow for the change in earth capacitance when the element is raised to operating height.

"Then, start about 10 per cent too long, find the 'dip' frequency and calculate the percentage error. Snip off 66 per cent only of this error length and at the third try the accuracy should be close to one per cent without any change of overshoot. When required a further stage can be used with an accurate frequency read-out from the rf generator.

"The swr meter needs to be a sensitive, toroid-transformer type, capable of full-scale deflection on about 0·75W, suitable for use with 3–12W of rf power, but the scarcity of power film resistors for the 6dB pad can be a difficulty. Mine are elderly 6W tin-oxide resistors but the 2·5W type PR52 resistors in parallel are satisfactory, as shown in Fig 5.

"This arrangement can safely dissipate 9W and pass 3W to the load. Such a pad is very useful for low-power antenna tests as well as forming a resistive load for transmitter adjustments when terminated with the 50Ω load. The transmitter sees only a change from 30 to 80Ω when the antenna side of the pad varies from short- to open-circuit conditions all too familiar during text work. Even in normal transmission, the 6dB pad can be pressed into service as a 'lie detector' if the distant station claims that your 5 and 9 signal disappears into noise when the pad is inserted!''

Spreaders for open-wire feeders

The question posed by G3WW in the August *TT* about the rf properties of disposable syringes prompted a number of useful comments, although nobody actually came up with the required information. Perhaps more important was a warning given by Ken Ruiz, G4SGF (ex-ZB2MD), on syringes used for medical purposes. He writes: "G3WW is indeed correct in stating that hospitals use many disposable (single-use) syringes, but in fact these are not thrown out. All the hospitals in and around Sheffield incinerate their syringes, often within the hospital grounds. Once used for blood sampling or injection they are coated internally with either potentially infectious material or with dangerous substances, and are therefore disposed of in this way."—(**Note:** this warning has since been made even more strongly by Dr K R Johnston, GW4BCB, and Dave Lankshear, G3TJP, who both stressed that contaminated blood traces can prove fatal, and **never** worth risking for the price of a feeder spreader.)

G4SGF continues: "It is, however, possible to purchase unused syringes from your local pharmacist, many of whom sell insulin to diabetic patients (prescription only) and the syringes can be purchased 'over the counter'. Pharmacists may, for fairly obvious reasons, be reluctant to sell large numbers to strangers unless convinced that they are to be used as spreaders, or you have your GP on your side."

G4SGF sent along syringes of various sizes: 0·5, 2, 5, 10 and 20ml. There is also a 1ml size about twice the length of the 0·5ml size and of similar small diameter. It was, in fact, the small 0·5ml size (about 8cm in length) that G3WW had in mind, and the bigger-diameter sizes would prove very unwieldy as spreaders as they would tend to catch the wind. As G4SGF puts it: "The barrel of the larger syringes would present a fairly high wind resistance when you have, say, 128ft of feeder with a spreader every 2ft or so, unless you use the readily-available 1ml size. If the cylinder is used, to prevent the entry of water or whistling in the wind the hole at both ends should be sealed, the small needle end perhaps by just glueing and the larger by glueing the rubber 'piston head' into it. The head can be very easily prized off the 'cam rod'. The rod itself might prove more useful as a spreader, lighter than the cylinder in most cases and, apart from the 0·5 and 1ml sizes, perhaps easier to secure to the feeder wire. It might also be possible to obtain just the rods from hospitals since these have not been in contact with the contents.

"All my syringes were manufactured by Becton Dickinson in Ireland, but no information is given as to the material and it is anybody's guess how they would stand up to the elements and rf. As I am thinking of making up some feeders in this way I would appreciate any further information."

My present feeling is that buying syringes for this purpose is hardly likely to prove economical, particularly in view of suggestions that have come in from other readers.

Spreaders, plastics and the environment

Arising out of the notes on suitable materials for the spreaders of open-wire feeders by G3WW (*TT* August) and G3TDZ (*TT* May), John Stebbings, G4BTV comments as follows:

"My own 6mm diameter polystyrene rod spreaders became corroded and brittle after only five years and began to drop off. The brittleness is presumably due to ultra-violet light.

"Unable to find more polystyrene, I obtained some polythene strips 50 by 3 by 340mm. These were easily cut into spreaders 50 by 10 by 3mm and, by the use of a steel jig, notched and drilled as described in the various amateur radio handbooks. The total cost was under £3, and I still have enough material left to provide another complete replacement.

"The source of the material was K R Whiston, New Mills, Stockport, Cheshire SK12 4YA. For those who are interested in electrical, mechanical and other surplus 'goodies' a large stamped-addressed envelope will bring his catalogue."

A S Hussey, G4KUN, of Viola Plastics, 36 Croft Rd, Hastings, points out that G3WW or others need look no longer for cheap spreaders. His company manufacture neat-looking spreaders at 18p each, about 75mm spacing. He adds that as a broad guide to choosing plastics for outdoor use it is advisable to pick a dark colour, black or grey for example.

Norman Sedgwick, G8WV, with many years of experience of using open-wire feeders for professional hf communications, mentions that he has become cynical about the quality of spreaders, for all of them soon become sooty and are often soaking wet! It is better, he believes, to have long spans kept taut by tension, without spreaders. He adds that personally he would not use open-wire line for the short distances involved with amateur radio antennas: "Coaxial cable or twin 75Ω cable matched to the load by a toroidal transformer is much easier to install and maintain. They can also be run in plastic pipes under the ground." (This is true of matched lines but a major attraction of open-wire line is the multiband facility given to dipole elements etc where the line forms part of the resonant system and may have a very high swr—*G3VA*).

But G8WV's main plea is to make the point that it is a simple matter for anyone worrying about losses on transmission lines to check using non-inductive resistive loads and an rf voltmeter. He writes:

"Unfortunately, the rf voltmeter seems to be out of fashion, although it is such a useful instrument for a large variety of test measurements that I would have expected it to be regarded as an essential instrument in every shack. Recently, when, in an article, I called for one to be used for testing

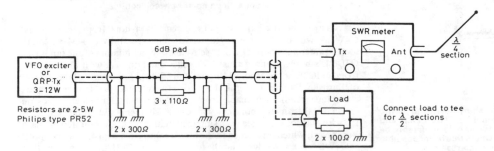

Fig 5. VK3MI's arrangement for testing and adjustment of quarter-wave and half-wave cable and element sections

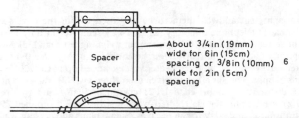

Spacer

Spacer

About 3/4 in (19mm) wide for 6in (15cm) spacing or 3/8 in (10mm) wide for 2 in (5cm) spacing

6

Fig 6. Simple and inexpensive method of constructing 600Ω open-wire transmission lines, as recommended by G6XN. Plastics piping of 2-3in (5-8cm) diameter is cut into short lengths and then sawn lengthwise into strips, a pair of small holes being drilled near each end of each strip. Spacing may be 2-6in (5-15cm) with spreaders at intervals of some 12-15 times the line spacing. With wide spacing, losses are reduced and construction is quicker but symmetry is more easily upset. Note that the spacers are slightly curved and this helps to prevent slippage (from *HF antennas for all locations*)

toroidal transformers, one of the 'reviewers' commented, 'We don't all own rf voltmeters!'.

"In general, one can find out what one needs to know using the transmitter power turned well down. Provided the measurement is made across a correctly loaded circuit of reasonably low impedance, the diode in a conventional rf probe should be safe enough. Voltage at 10W in a 600Ω line is only 77·5V, and across a loaded 50Ω line only 22·4V. These figures make it reasonable to use a point-contact diode probe having a piv of about 115V or so.

"If G3WW terminates his line with 600Ω non-inductive resistance and measures voltage at the input and output, he can soon see if he is losing power in the line, and by simple calculation determine roughly the actual power loss. The rf voltmeter does seem a necessity for an amateur wishing to check easily the matching, balance and loss in transmission lines."

Allan Taylor, G3JMO, was tempted to use flexible polythene tubing held tight by the 18-gauge feeder wires but this proved very inefficient. Over a few months the plastics attracted dirt on the outside which did not completely wash off in rain. But the major trouble was inside the hollow tube. He writes:

"The internal diameter is perhaps 0·125in or so, and here on the northeast coast we get misty, sometimes foggy, weather, often decidedly damp for a day or two. At these times the resistance across the feedline would fall to about 100kΩ, but as soon as the sun broke through it would return to infinity. The problem was condensation.

"It may well be that G3WW's ballpoint pen cases fare no better. Plastic hair curlers are usually recommended and would probably be satisfactory. They are usually perforated and of generous diameter. It seems to me that any tubing used for spreaders needs to be of adequate diameter to permit a breeze to blow through. The form of spreaders recommended by Les Moxon, G6XN, in his *HF antennas for all locations* avoid this difficulty although they might suffer from external condensation; however, this would disperse more quickly. My advice is to keep off small-gauge tubing of any sort for spreaders!"

G6XN's technique, referred to above, is shown in Fig 6 and consists of spacers made of sections cut from plastic piping (diameter 2 to 3in, 5 to 8cm). For those worrying unduly about relatively small losses arising from finite insulation, it is perhaps worth pointing out that G6XN stresses that, "very considerable liberties can be taken without adverse effect . . . the

usual labour-intensive instructions for the construction of a 600Ω line are best ignored, and for most purposes can be substituted by the rule that 'anything goes' . . . for long straight runs in an accessible position a spacing of 6in (15cm) is recommended with very few insulators . . . an average of about 8 to 10 spacers per 100ft (30m). A spacing of 2in (60cm) with spacers about every 2ft (60cm) is recommended where a feeder has to be run close to a mast, trees or other 'lossy' objects."

PSU with hexfet pass transistor

Robin Greenwood, G3LBA/PA3ACQ, noted with interest the use of a 723 regulator ic in the Australian "experimenters" power supply (*TT* August 1985 p630). He has a soft spot for this low-cost, docile and flexible ic regulator, using about half-a-dozen of them in various pieces of equipment in the shack. One such item is a 13·4V psu capable of providing a regulated output at up to 20A (continuous output about 9A) for use with an hf rig. He writes:

"This psu uses a 723 and a single IRF150 hexfet to provide a regulated 13·4V at 20A with only two active devices in the regulator circuit proper. Fig 7 shows just how simple such a psu can be, with just a single hexfet instead of the usual parallel power transistors and two-transistor driver stage. The high input impedance of the hexfet eliminates the need for any drivers, while a single IRF150 hexfet can pass 28A at its maximum current rating.

"The essential thing to note about the hexfet is that to drive it to 20A the gate voltage must be 6-8V above the source voltage. However, the drain voltage; can be as little as 2V above the required regulated output voltage; a considerable advantage when device dissipation (and hence heatsink requirements) and value of the storage capacitor are considered.

"In my unit the transformer is a 300VA toroid with a 15V secondary winding, and I have hand-wound a tertiary winding to provide the 9V for the regulator ic. (The number of turns per volt can be established with a test winding.) A 24V zener stabilized voltage is provided for the regulator; this enables it to drive the fet gate to a sufficiently high voltage to permit the device to pass 20A.

"The gate-to-source voltage limit of the hexfet is 20V, and another zener diode is used to protect the hexfet at switch-on when the source is at earth potential; this also serves to protect the device in the event of the output of the psu being short-circuited.

"The regulator and hexfet arrangement shown in Fig 7 can provide a continuous 9A with an 'adequate' heatsink, and will supply 20A with the duty cycle encountered with ssb with adequately low output variation (300mV, 0-18A). My version 'remotes' the voltage divider with two sense wires to bring the point of regulation to the connector at the rear of the rig. This is conventional and not shown in the circuit diagram, and is not really essential. The overvoltage protection senses the terminal voltage of the supply; if the output exceeds 14·8V the crowbar thyristor fires and blows the 20A fuse. The crowbar and fuse are placed before the pass transistor to ensure that the charge in the main storage capacitor is not absorbed by the hexfet during overvoltage firing or overcurrent conditions. The capacitor on the MC3423 device prevents spurious firing. This feature is essential and should never be omitted in any psu to which expensive equipment is connected! No rf decoupling is shown, but I recommend that the unit be totally screened and an IEC mains filter fitted. Each output lead is decoupled to case by a 0·1µF ceramic disc capacitor.

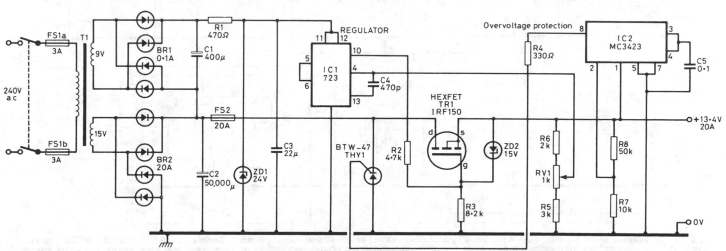

Fig 7. High-current psu providing 13·4V at up to 20A (peak) used by G3LBA/PA3 showing the simplicity made possible by the use of a hexfet (six power fets in a single package) pass device

"The IRF150 hexfet is an International Rectifier product (available through distributors) and is not cheap, but is well worth considering in view of the reduced metalworking required to reach a given current. Lower cost plastic versions are available rated at 15A, and two in parallel could be used; in this case source ballast resistors must be fitted and the gate-to-ground resistor duplicated and returned to each source."

The Danish "telephone-directory" clandestine radio

In the April *TT*, I paid a long-overdue tribute to the clandestine inland radio service run by a mixture of Dutch amateur and professional radio operators and engineers during the period from September 1944 to May 1945. I mentioned that I recalled only one station (that at Alkmaar with PA0ZY as one of the two operators) surviving throughout the period, although I did stress that my personal recollections covered only one of the two control stations located at Eindhoven.

As a result of that item I have been relieved to discover that at least one, and possibly two other stations in the inland network—plus also quite a few of the Anglo-Dutch clandestine links direct with the Special Communications control station near Stony Stratford—survived the many German raids. It is now clear that following the tragic loss of a number of transmitters in Amsterdam in December 1944, the copious traffic from there was handled by the inland stations at Alkmaar, Haarlem and Hilversum. Operators at Haarlem included Ko de Lee and Evert Kaleveld, PA0XE/DJ0XJ, both of whom survived. Following the raids and closures of January and February 1945 all three stations in this group were told to lay low for a period and the Amsterdam traffic was diverted to the UK links. Later they were reactivated, although I still believe most of my contacts from Eindhoven were with the Alkmaar operators. Both the Alkmaar and Haarlem operators had many narrow escapes in a highly dangerous situation.

The Dutch (and Poles) were not the only people in occupied countries to design and produce some of their own equipment. In the Danish journal *OZ* (May and June 1985), Erik Gørlyk, OZ1HJV, describes the remarkably successful work by Danish amateurs, led by L A Duus Hansen, OZ7DU, an engineer with Bang & Olufsen. In 1943 OZ7DU became dissatisfied with the suitcase-sets and hastily trained operators infiltrated into Denmark by SOE (who had assumed responsibility for much of the intelligence work as well as sabotage in that country). The group decided they could develop and operate sets more suitable for use in the less restrictive conditions that still existed (although soon to vanish) in Denmark. OZ7DU with the help of Svend Bagge, OZ7SB, and Steen Hasselbalch, OZ7T, designed and built some 60 "Telefonbogen" (telephone book) transmitter-receivers to a size

and weight that allowed them to be disguised within the covers of the Copenhagen telephone directory (21 by 14 by 7cm, weight only 1·5kg).

The secret to building a 10W transmitter weighing less than 1·5kg was the adoption of ac/dc "transformerless" techniques, using seven 0·1A series-heater valves whose combined heater voltage added up to the 220V Danish mains supply. The superhet receiver used three UCH21 valves. The two-stage transmitter comprised a UF21 crystal oscillator and two parallel UBL21 valves, plus the UY1N half-wave rectifier which supplied 250V to the transmitter and 200V to the receiver. Signal plans and crystals were sent out from the UK and the stations were operated by a number of Danish amateurs including, apparently, Bo Brøndum-Nielsen, OZ7BO, who became very well known to British amateurs after the war, not only for his superb operating but also for the design of an electronic keyer published in the *RSGB Bulletin*. The group also introduced the use of high-speed keying on clandestine circuits, using a GNT auto-sender, and had 300MHz vhf r/t links, operated among others by Edith Bonnesen, OZ7DU's secretary.

The Danish story has a happier ending than the Dutch. Very few, if any, of the Danish amateurs involved in this work appear to have lost their lives, although some saw the inside of Gestapo prisons.

Incidentally for those who feel that any mention of "valves" now belongs only to history, I wonder if they could produce today a *complete* mains-operated hf transmitter-receiver providing 10W output yet weighing only about 1·5kg? To have done so in 1943 using only standard consumer-type components in an occupied country surely deserves to be remembered!

Not that Danish clandestine operators always endeared themselves to the British control stations. I recall a message out of Copenhagen during 1943 that complained that afternoon calls often went unanswered and suggested that the British operators were taking time off for tea! Since the only tea-making facilities at that station comprised a temperamental primus stove and water from a village pump—later condemned as unfit for human consumption—and as the actual problem was the crude receiving antennas (later much improved) and the variable propagation conditions of the UK/Denmark path on about 7MHz during summer afternoons, this message did not go down too well!

An example of the Telefonbogen set was on display recently at the "Resistance in Europe" exhibition at the Imperial War Museum; also to be seen was an early, crude home-made transmitter used by the Belgian "Clarence" intelligence network organized by Walthère Dawé, Belgian director of posts and telegraphs (later killed while resisting arrest).

The Danish articles were kindly brought to my attention by Dick Rollema, PA0SE, and Colin Turner, G3VTT. Evert Kaleveld, PA0XE, has recently provided a detailed account of the Haarlem clandestine operation. □

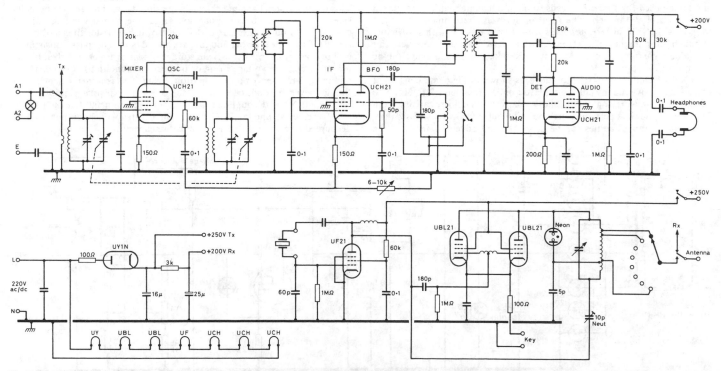

Fig 8. Circuit diagram of the Danish "Telephone Book" transmitter/receiver designed and manufactured in Denmark in 1943 by OZ7DU, OZ7SB and OZ7T. Note that "live chassis" transformerless construction is not recommended for amateur equipment for reasons of electrical safety, but in its intended application resulted in a total weight of only about 1·5kg. It is believed that about 60 such units were built. The antenna tuning lamp was switched out in operation to prevent chirp

Technical Topics
by Pat Hawker, G3VA

AT A RECENT "Home Entertainment Technology" symposium at the University of Sussex, Dr Alex Stark, of Mullard, forecast that: "By 1990, nearly half of all electronics components used in Europe will be surface-mounted devices (smd)." The elimination of many plated-through holes, the dramatic reduction in size of smd assemblies and the highly-automated processes (see *TT* March 1985) all ensure that surface-mounted technology will become dominant in many forms of electronic equipment.

Components for home-building?
As I attempted to make clear last March, smd and hybrid microelectronics technology is already fast creeping into the all-pervading Japanese amateur radio equipment. Undoubtedly it offers a number of significant advantages, but also—for experimentally-minded amateurs—significant disadvantages. Greater reliability, better value-for-money, consistent performance etc are among the "pros" for those content to buy and use ready-made equipment. But for the others the disadvantages include the virtual impossibility of carrying out any home servicing or any modification of the factory rigs. There is also the problem that as smd technology takes over, components suitable for home-construction and for high-voltage or high-current applications seem likely to become increasingly difficult to obtain, and then only at a cost rising far faster than the rate of inflation.

The vanishing of components suitable for home-construction by those of us who are not professionally involved with electronic design or assembly is nothing new. It merely continues a trend that stretches right back to the days when, in the late 'thirties, it became necessary for the first time to use a soldering iron to build a short-wave receiver! From about 1920 until the start of the second world war, it was possible to obtain virtually all components, valve holders etc, equipped with screw terminals and intended to be mounted on wooden boards with the aid of a screwdriver. Soldering, metal-working, chassis-bashing etc were all largely later developments!

The phasing-out of home-built broadcast receivers (remember the Scott-Taggart ST series?), the need to tame "hand-capacitance" effects on tuning hf receivers, screening to prevent high-gain i.f. amplifiers from bursting into oscillation, and harmonic suppression to overcome bci and tvi brought about the end of the screw-terminal era and the change from breadboard to metal chassis and the enclosed rack and panel.

Today there is a struggle to convince the newer generations of enthusiasts that perfectly good equipment can still be built by connecting components together with lengths of wire rather than via printed circuit boards. It is perhaps, unfortunate, that the term "ugly" has been appended to non-pcb construction.

It is difficult to foresee any great use of the really tiny smd-type discrete components for home-built equipment—at least by those of us who are already ham-fisted enough with existing small components.

Soldering to Litz wire
One result of the changes in technology has been the loss of some of the old "workshop skills". For example, G H Lucas, G3TWE, writes:

"The other day I came across a youngster attempting to clean Litz wire prior to soldering. He was using fine emery cloth and getting nowhere fast, and it occurs to me that some of the tips from old-time constructors may be becoming lost.

"The answer in this case is simple. Fill a small container with methylated spirits (a bottle-cap is ideal) and light it. Place the end one inch or so in the flame to burn off the insulation, remove it and blow the burning insulation out. Next replace the wire in the flame and heat until the wire is red hot, then quench the wire rapidly by immersing it in the unburnt spirits, and remove quickly. The result is clean multi-strands of wire that may be twisted together, tinned and soldered in the conventional manner.

"Finally, don't extinguish the burning methylated spirits by attempting to blow out the flame, or you may end up with burning spirit all over the workbench. Instead, always snuff it out by covering it completely with a lid or other convenient cover."

It occurs to me that there may indeed be many readers who have never even come across Litz wire, comprising multiple strands of very thin insulated wire at one time widely used for high-Q medium- and long-wave coils. The term "Litz" was derived from the German *Litzendraht* (*Litz*

strand, *draht* wire) and is correctly applied to conductors which are built up by successive stranding of wires or groups of wires in groups of three, each individual wire being insulated with enamel or silk, although often applied also to what are more-correctly termed "textile-covered bunched enamelled-copper wire conductors". Litz wires were developed for use in rf applications in which "skin effect" (the tendency of the current to flow along only the surface of a conductor) becomes significant. The result of skin effect is that the resistance of a conductor at high frequencies may be much greater than its dc resistance. Skin effect can be reduced by using a large number of small wires, each completely insulated from all the rest, twisted together in such a manner that, throughout its length, an individual wire occupies in turn all possible positions in the winding section.

Make your own pcb
For those projects for which "ugly" construction does not appeal, S Males, G8XEH, emphasizes that even for the uninitiated it is easy to make your own circuit boards, particularly where a full-size track layout diagram is available, as will often be the case with a published constructional project. His suggested procedure is as follows:

(1) Obtain a piece of good quality pcb (preferably glass fibre) roughly the required size.

(2) Obtain a copy of the pcb layout (copiers are generally available in public libraries, Post Offices etc). Cut out the layout and "Sellotape" it on to the copper side of the pcb. Then, using a small centre punch (or even a hardened nail) and hammer, centre pot as accurately as possible each hole marked on the track layout. Check that no holes are missed and then remove the paper layout. The board must then be thoroughly cleaned to ensure that the copper is shiny and free of grease.

(3) Now comes the "fun bit". Using a special etch-resist pen (available from component suppliers etc) join up the centre pot marks as in the track layout diagram. With care even ic pads can be marked on to the copper. Ensure that no copper shows through the resist. Allow your board to dry and then check very thoroughly for mistakes, omissions etc, if necessary tidying up and scraping away any track bridges, using a scalpel or modeller's knife.

(4) Obtain a supply of ferric chloride either as liquid or granules, water being added if the latter. This is used to etch the unwanted (uncovered) copper away by pouring some of the solution into a plastic tray, and immersing the board until all unwanted copper is etched away. Etching is speeded up if the tray is rocked occasionally. Rinse the board thoroughly under water and then dry. **Note:** ferric chloride is corrosive and must be kept clear of skin and eyes.

(5) With the aid of drills of sizes to suit the component leads (generally 0·8 to 1mm) drill out all centre-potted holes. Finally, clean off the etch-resist with solvent and your board should be ready to use.

Using the low-cost TBA120 ic device
The August *TT* included a summary of ic devices listed by SM6EAN as being of potential interest to amateur constructors. Since then the prolific Jan-Martin Noeding, LA8AK, has sent along information on two specific applications for the Siemens TBA120 device, originally intended as a consumer-device for an fm i.f. amplifier/discriminator. He also has some views on the appearance of good pcb artwork that avoids the "spider's web" appearance that often emerges from the "would-be professional" constructor.

Fig 1 shows what, in effect, is the Mk 3 version of LA8AK's well-known af up-converter for use when recording high-speed meteor scatter signals (see *TT* September 1982 for earlier version).

Fig 2 shows the latest "1497" pcb layout, prepared by LA8AK in conjunction with SM4LLP. This same pcb layout can also be used to build a balanced dsb modulator suitable for an ssb transmitter when used in conjunction with a suitable filter.

For the af up-converter, the limiter section of the TBA120/SN76660N is used with a 7kHz Wien-bridge af oscillator. The signal at pin 6 must be in-phase with pin 14. The balanced modulator section converts an incoming af signal to around 7kHz for tape recording, so that the recording can be played back at a slower tape speed and still provide a convenient audio tone.

Fig 1. Mark 3 version of LA8AK's audio-frequency up-converter for tape recording meteor-burst high-speed morse signals for playback at lower speed. Integrated circuit device TBA120/120A, but SO41P and TBA120S/120AS may also be used. Component values are not critical, with two tested values indicated on the diagram. Electrolytic capacitors are small bead tantalum types. LA8AK cannot supply pcbs for this version, but suitable pcb artwork is shown in Fig 2

Fig 2. LA8AK's pcb layout "1497" for use in either an af up-converter as in Fig 1 or a dsb modulator as shown in Fig 3

Fig 3. Modified circuit arrangement permitting the pcb of Fig 2 to be used as a crystal oscillator/balanced modulator for use in ssb or dsb transmitters. Carrier suppression about 40dB. TBA120/SN76660N or TBA120A, SO41P. For complete circuit information read in conjunction with Fig 1

In practice, LA8AK has found that there is no advantage in filtering out the "image" sideband, a simple af filter being used primarily to prevent harmonics affecting the bias oscillator in the tape recorder. This ic operates over a wide range of voltages, but for optimum performance is within 9–15V input. At 6V input the "gain" (about 0dB) is reduced.

Earlier versions of LA8AK's up-converter have been built by some 100 to 150 amateurs in about 15 European countries, if the number of pcbs supplied by LA8AK/SM5CHK is anything to go by.

With some changes in values and external circuit arrangements, the same pcb can be used to form a dsb modulator (crystal oscillator) for an ssb transmitter: Fig 3 shows the modified part of the circuit diagram.

LA8AK notes that since the Siemens TBA120 consumer ic is basically similar to the higher-cost "professional" Plessey SL624, the application notes for the SL624 can be used for this type of application. With the TBA120/SN76660N or TBA120 the current drain is about 15mA, but this can be reduced to 5 to 7mA if a Siemens SO41P device is used. Carrier suppression should be about 40dB.

LA8AK considers that the TBA120 should prove equally suitable for use as a very simple bfo/product detector. He has also seen published designs for this multipurpose ic including fm i.f./quadrature detector; a.m. synchronous detector; ssb product detector, vco and phase-detector etc.

Multiband doublets

The two most popular hf multiband antennas currently appear to be the W3DZZ/G8KW trapped dipole and the G5RV dipole, although one notes that delta and quad single-loop elements (full-wave) are rapidly increasing in popularity. The great attraction of the trapped dipole is that it can be used on many hf transceivers without any form of atu or astu. This is less true of the G5RV, which for greatest flexibility and optimum performance does require an astu on at least some bands. This remains true of the computer-aided modified-G5RV designs presented in *Rad Com* August 1985, pp614–17 and 624, by Brian Austin, ZS6BKW. But once we accept the need to have a flexible astu in the shack, surely we can free ourselves from the need for W3DZZ traps and the specific top dimensions of the G5RV!

Most people building a G5RV use sections of open-wire (or 300Ω) balanced line and then finish off with low-impedance feedline, either twin-wire balanced line or coaxial cable. This is often convenient but is not an inherent feature of the design.

For it is not always appreciated that the G5RV is simply a convenient variation of the earlier multiband, centre-fed dipole or doublet which used open-wire feeders not as a matched transmission line but as part of the resonant system (ie often tuned feeders, but essentially forming part of a resonant antenna system). Dipoles of this type, widely used in the 'thirties, did in fact often have resonant "tops" made possible by the harmonic relationship of the amateur bands of that period. But such antennas were also widely used in professional communications (frequently with twin-wire or multi-wire "cage" horizontal spans) with the same antenna used at virtually any frequency from about 2 to 20MHz. Provided that the whole system was brought into resonance by means of an astu (which often simply took the form of a resonant circuit parallel-tuned for a voltage feedpoint, series-tuned for a current feedpoint) then the antenna would radiate effectively. A resonant top simply meant that it presented a purely resistive feedpoint, but any resonant *system* will radiate all the power that is fed into it other than the usually very small losses arising from the rf resistance of the wire or poor insulation, provided that the atu really is putting power into the antenna and not just creating large circulating currents.

G H Lucas, G3TWE, in setting out to modify a "G5RV" antenna has, in some respects, re-invented the wheel in the form of a loaded centre-fed doublet. Nevertheless he makes a number of useful and valid comments in providing a design which fits into a 70ft span of garden yet performs satisfactorily on all bands from 1·8 to 30MHz. He writes as follows:

"The article by Brian Austin, ZS6BKW, on the "Computer-aided design of a multiband dipole" prompts me to write on modifications to the original G5RV design that I have been working on for several months, and has finally led me to an antenna that is proving to be very effective as a 1·8 and 3·5MHz radiator, loads on all bands up to 28MHz, and above all fits into my garden which is only 70ft long from the eaves of the house to a 10m-high pole at the far end.

"First, why all the effort to get the feed impedance to 50Ω or thereabouts? In his original articles, Louis Varney, G5RV, pointed out that the preferred method was to run the open-wire or 300Ω feeder section all the way into the shack and via a good atu rather than bringing it down to an odd length of 75Ω coaxial cable.

"Second, there is surely nothing to prove that any particular or critical length is better than another. Some lengths are easier to tune/load on some frequencies, and admittedly the radiation patterns become less predictable, but provided that the whole antenna system can be brought to resonance and finally presented to the transceiver as a 50Ω load it will assuredly work.

"Third, for those of us who are not blessed with sufficient real estate to erect a top-band dipole at a height of about a half-wave, the prime object of the whole exercise is to get the current carrying section of the antenna as high and in the clear as possible (true of horizontal spans not necessarily true of vertical sections—G3VA).

"My 'G5RV' (Fig 4) has a 65ft top plus two ends of 22ft each which drop vertically down, loaded with identical inductors in the vertical sections. The whole system is brought to resonance (with the aid of a dip meter) in the shack, by adding ferrite rods, salvaged from old transistor broadcast receivers, as cores to the inductors. The chosen resonant frequency was 1·93MHz. At this frequency the swr presented to the transmitter, without an atu, is less than 1·5:1 from 1·90MHz to 1·96MHz. There is nothing magical about the dimensions. I just happened to buy all the wire that remained on a drum, about 200ft, made 32ft of it into open-wire feeder to the top centre insulator, led it out to insulators 3ft from the supporting masts, and then down to end insulators on the garage and garden shed roof. What was left over was wound on to plastic formers of 1·25in diameter, coin tubes from an old fruit machine, 14ft from the ends of the antenna.

"Apart from cutting the original length into halves there are no joins in the feeder/antenna, and it has already survived one winter exposed to the east coast winds at Gorleston-on-Sea, Norfolk, without any breakages. Every effort has been made to preserve symmetry, lengths are identical, similar loading coils (69 turns) and identical amounts of similar ferrite

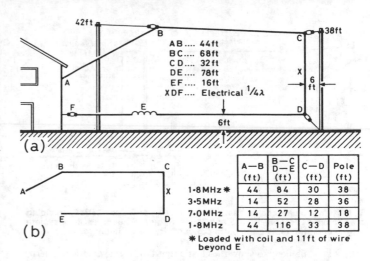

Fig 5. The "G8ON" multiband antenna as developed by the late Harold Chadwick in order to obtain a maximum vertically-polarized component radiated from the "X" section. Although the dimensions and shape are not unduly critical, the bends should come in approximately the places shown

	A—B (ft)	B—C D—E (ft)	C—D (ft)	Pole (ft)
1·8MHz *	44	84	30	38
3·5MHz	14	52	28	36
7·0MHz	14	27	12	18
1·8MHz	44	116	33	38

* Loaded with coil and 11ft of wire beyond E

AB.... 44ft
BC.... 68ft
CD.... 32ft
DE.... 78ft
EF.... 16ft
XDF.... Electrical ¼λ

material used in each coil. The system is fed via a home-built Z-match atu, again much modified, and a 1:1 balun, but any atu providing a balanced output would work. No atu is used when operating between 1·9 and 1·96MHz.

"Among trials carried out, I have increased the amount of ferrite material to provide resonance at 1·6MHz; thus the main current carrying section would be in the top horizontal span on 1·8MHz rather than folded down the feeders. This led to a superb receiving antenna on 1·9 to 10MHz, but signal reports were reduced by about two S-points when transmitting on 3·5 and 7MHz. Perhaps the extra ferrite material was too lossy.

"Another test was to remove all the ferrite material and bring the system to resonance on 1·93MHz by adding 22ft lengths of wire to each end and draping them along the garden fence. This works well but has led to an unacceptably high impedance on 14 and 18MHz, necessitating changing the balun in the atu to a 4:1 type, in order to tune the system, and then it would not load on 7MHz! Perhaps switchable baluns would be the answer. Incidentally the baluns I use are the type described in *HF Antennas for all locations* and in *TT* February 1984 with bifilar or trifiliar windings on more ferrite rods.

"It is clear that there is much scope for further development, and it will take another winter season to evaluate the system fully on the 1·9 and 3·5MHz bands; but I do not expect to provide one of the really hefty dx signals from a small garden in a residential area.

"Nevertheless the design appears to be very flexible and capable of working well provided the long-established rules are followed: viz
(1) Get the maximum current-carrying section of the system as high and in the clear as possible.
(2) Preserve symmetry.
(3) Use high-efficiency open-wire feeders all the way to the atu.
(4) Use a proven atu of high efficiency, with a balanced output."

I feel that for completeness some further points should be made: *(1)* If the series/parallel form of antenna loading/atu is used with no other form of balun, and if you have no objection to having voltage-fed (high impedance) feeders coming into the shack on some bands, even greater flexibility could be achieved. *(2)* It is arguable whether on 1·8/3·5/7MHz the advice to aim at maximum current in the horizontal span will result in optimum dx performance, since on these bands a vertically-polarized component is desirable (eg slopers, sloping inverted-Vs etc).

If an unbalanced end-fed "long wire" type of antenna is used, again implying a high-voltage, high-impedance feedpoint in the shack, there is much to be said for the "G8ON" type of arrangement (Fig 5) which aims at putting current in the vertical section, with the lower horizontal span, in effect, forming a counterpoise earth. John Heys, G3BDQ, has been heard recently on 1·8MHz extolling the virtues of an inverted-L "long wire" about 40ft high from which, at the far end, he has three identical wires dropping down to buried earth rods, thus putting maximum current in these three vertical wires. The multiple earthing points reduce the earth losses. A "half" trap dipole can also give this effect on 3·5 and 7MHz: Fig 6.

For medium-distance working on 1·8/3·5/7MHz, on the other hand, a low horizontally-polarized system will tend to provide the stronger signals and will usually prove to be virtually omni-directional. It is not always recognized that a dipole or half-wave antenna less than a half-wave above

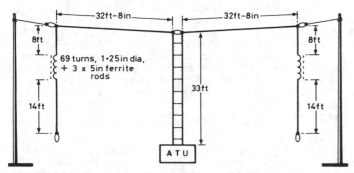

Fig 4. G3TWE's "modified-G5RV" multiband doublet with the open-wire feeder brought through to the atu. The ferrite rods in the loading coils are adjusted to bring resonant frequency to 1·93MHz, equivalent to an effective electrical length of about 242ft but with a top span of less than 66ft

32ft-8in   32ft-8in
8ft
69 turns, 1·25in dia, + 3 x 5in ferrite rods
33ft
14ft   14ft
ATU

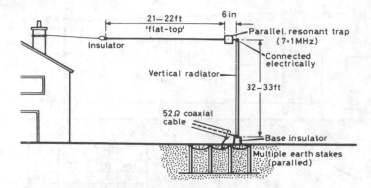

Fig 6. Half-trap antenna as described in _ART_ by M R Lee, G3VYF, providing an effective dx antenna on 3·5 and 7MHz. Requires a good earthing system and preferably good earth conductivity for optimum results

earth is most unlikely to show the classic figure-of-eight radiation pattern, but rather will be virtually omni-directional apart from any effects induced by nearby houses etc.

Corner reflector antennas

Antennas in amateur stations seem to follow cycles of fashion, often without any close correlation with their actual merits and demerits. For example, it is only seldom these days that one hears of people making use of the corner reflector first described by Dr John D Kraus, W8JK, in _Proc IRE_ November 1940, pp513–19. Yet, at least for vhf/uhf, this remains an antenna system which in a fairly compact structure offers relatively high gain, reasonably broad bandwidth, and is much easier and cheaper to construct than a parabolic reflector, either with a simple dipole feed or, for higher gain, using a line of dipoles. With a suitably large screen it is possible to achieve a very good front-to-back ratio, low sidelobes and good polarization discrimination.

The 5th edition of _Radio Communication Handbook_ is one of several handbooks that provide basic design and construction information; it is also described in _The Radio Handbook_ and the _ARRL Antenna Book_ although not in the RSGB's _VHF-UHF Manual. RCH_ is perhaps a little off-putting in stressing that as the corner angle is reduced to increase gain, the feed impedance of the dipole radiator falls to a very low value (under 20Ω for an angle of 45°) making matching rather difficult. One should, perhaps, therefore stress that the feed impedance is more manageable for angles of 60° or 90° and with such angles there should be no undue difficulty in achieving a gain of around 10–12dB with a single dipole feed. This is a reasonable figure for what is essentially a non-critical antenna system (far more so than a uhf Yagi array). The corner reflector itself can consist of metal sheets, perforated metal sheets, possibly even chicken wire, or the more usually closely-spaced reflector elements that offer less wind resistance than metal sheets.

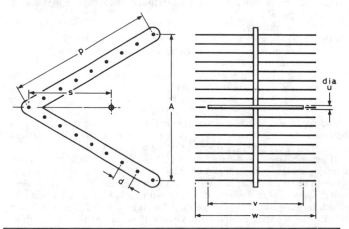

Band	Dimensions (inches)							
(MHz)	p	s	d	v	w	A	u	λ
144	100	40	6	38	50	100	0·375	168
432	35	13·25	1·5	12·5	20	35	0·25	27·25
1,296	12	4·5	0·5	4	8	12	0·125	9·125

Fig 7. Design for corner reflector (60° angle) for 144 or 432 or 1,296MHz bands as described in _Radio Communication Handbook_. Gain about 13dB. Feed impedance of dipole element about 75Ω

Fig 7 shows a typical arrangement as described in _RCH5_ p13.18, together with some suggested dimensions for 144MHz and for bands for which it seems more suitable, viz 430 and 1,215MHz.

Broadband corner reflector

Corner reflector antennas with a simple dipole feed, as described above, have adequate bandwidth to cover any single amateur band, but it is interesting to note that Jimmy Wong and Howard King, of the American Aerospace Corporation, have recently shown (_IEEE Trans on Antennas and Propagation_ Vol AP-33 No 8, August 1985) that the corner reflector technique can also be used to provide a very-wide-band antenna (bandwidth ratio of about 1:1·8) by using an "open-sleeve dipole" as the feed element. They present detailed measurements for two antennas covering 240 to 400MHz, a band used for military avionics. With a 90° corner reflector made from perforated aluminium sheets (48in wide by 41·13in long) the gain varied only from about 12·2dB to 10·5dB throughout the range 250 to 400MHz, with an swr that varied from about 2·2:1 to under 1·5:1.

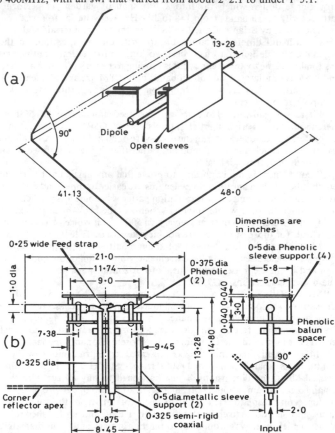

Fig 8. (a) Broadband corner reflector antenna covering 250 to 400MHz with a gain varying between about 10·5 and 12·25dB. Made with perforated aluminium sheeting and using the "open-sleeve dipole" system described by J Wong and H King. This technique could be used to broadband other types of antennas using dipole feed elements. (b) Details of feed arrangement

The novel feature, the open-sleeve dipole, comprised a conventional dipole element with two closely-spaced parasitic elements of flat sheets of metal closely spaced to the dipole element, as shown in Fig 8. The addition of these "sleeves" (which could consist of large-diameter cylindrical elements) extends the bandwidth of a conventional dipole from about 1·25:1 to 1·8:1, and the same technique could be applied to other antenna systems; it was originally described in _IEEE Trans Ant & Prop_ Vol AP-20, pp201–4, March 1972. Measured E- and H-plane patterns at 240, 290 and 400MHz exhibit good front-to-back characteristics, the worst case being about 23dB at the lower edge of the band, ie 240MHz. The on-axis crossed-polarization level was measured at 400MHz, and it was found to be about 35dB.

For amateur applications the main advantage of using an open-sleeve dipole would be to make the system more tolerant. One can imagine, however, that such a system would be particularly attractive for uhf television reception, since a frequency span of 1·8:1 would accommodate virtually the whole of Bands 4 to 5 (470 to 850MHz); many of the existing designs (groups A, B and C/D) show a decided fall-off in performance at one or the other ends of their respective bands.

Plug-in low-cost psu

Recently, while passing a local general-purpose disposals shop, I noticed a large box of small power units in brand-new condition. These were built directly on to a more or less standard (except for a dummy earth pin) 13A three-pin plug, and had apparently been intended for domestic television preamplifiers. The label gave a rating of 18V dc at 170mA, "for indoor use only" but "conforming to BS415". At 50p each it seemed worth investing in one if only to find out just what it consisted of. I had never previously come across this type of plug-in psu.

In fact it comprised a small double-wound mains transformer, mains fuse, two diode rectifiers, 220µF (25V) reservoir capacitor and the output lead and plug: Fig 9(a). I have to confess that after testing that it was working, it went into my junk box awaiting some suitable application. I might have forgotten it altogether had I not come across a *QST* (June 1985, pp36–8) article "Plug in wall transformers—a super bargain" by Doug DeMaw, W1FB. This describes a wide range of American 110V plug-in transformers and dc power units that appear to be stock items in the USA, including some that were basically similar to the British-made unit for 240V supplies that I had chanced upon.

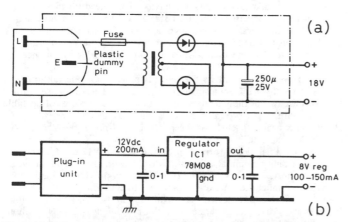

Fig 9. (a) Wall socket power supply unit found in a disposals store. The complete psu is built into an enlarged plug. (b) A method of adding voltage regulation to a dc wall socket power unit as described by W1FB. The two 0·1µF capacitors and three-terminal ic regulator are added externally

W1FB notes that such units tend to have too much ripple and insufficient voltage regulation for the more critical amateur radio applications (eg vfo unit) but with the simple addition of an external ic regulator and two 0·1µF capacitors one can provide a useful, low-cost psu for many applications: Fig 9(b). It must be remembered that several volts must be allowed for the operation of the regulator, so that, for example, to provide 9V regulated dc output, the unit should supply at least 12V. My 18V unit would be suitable for a regulated output of 13V or less with the regulator removing most of the ripple. There must be quite a few such units going for a song, to judge by the number in my local store a few months ago.

Forecasting hf propagation

For many years detailed predictions (such as those on page 875) have been published relating the likely "openings" along specific paths to local time and month. Most operators will have found that while such forecasts give a useful indication of what to expect when averaged over the coming month, unfortunately they cannot provide us with the likely propagation conditions or muf, for specific days or even weeks, or predict the onset of solar storms etc. But in addition, even when averaged over the whole month, like long-term weather forecasting, they are less reliable than one might have hoped after almost 50 years of regular forecasting.

This applies not only to amateurs seeking to take advantage of favourable conditions and working as close as possible to the muf, but also to the higher power commercial services who use the "optimum working frequency" (owf) roughly 15 per cent lower than the predicted muf.

Forecasts are normally based on the anticipated sunspot number index, using as a base the smoothed 12-month number. However, in the past few years, scientists at the Rutherford Appleton Laboratory, including J W King, P A Smith and R Y Liu, have shown fairly convincingly that, for prediction of hf radio propagation conditions six months or more ahead, significantly more accurate forecasts can be derived from figures based on past ionospheric measurements as made by the ionospheric observatories located in many parts of the world. They have estimated that their proposed system provides roughly 15 per cent more accurate f_oF2 predictions at any location, for any month and local time. Similarly, the muf can be predicted more accurately using the ionospheric records although, contrary to the situation when using sunspot numbers, the monthly ionospheric index has been found to provide better results than the 12-month smoothed version.

The RAL scientists have published tables (*Telecommunication Journal* Vol 50, No 8/1983) showing how the f_oF2 figures in various parts of the world differ (linear regression equations to obtain local effective sunspot number from measured median f_oF2 values) together with the statistics of what they define as the "global effective sunspot number" (gessn) over the period July 1943 to June 1981 (both monthly values and 12-month running mean values). It would presumably be possible for an experienced computer programmer to write the software for a prediction program which should prove more accurate than with conventional techniques.

Incidentally, taking the 12-month running mean values of the gessn, it can be seen clearly that new phases of the solar cycles begin around the middle of the year; past maxima include 1958, 1970 and 1980; past minima 1955, 1964 and 1976. Unfortunately, there still seems no reliable method of forecasting the shape or even the dates of maximum and minima of the next cycle. This could have begun in June this year, although there seems little indication that this has happened and it could be 1986 or even 1987. Once the new cycle begins we can hope for a fairly rapid rise in critical frequencies, unless of course the next maximum turns out to be a low one. Using the RAL technique it may prove possible to predict whether this is likely once we are a little way into the new cycle.

Norman Richardson, VK4BHJ, ex-G5HJ, draws attention to the exceptionally poor conditions this year, with the usually reliable 14MHz chordal-hop path to Europe failing except for extremely brief periods. He wonders just what has been happening to the ionosphere—though this may perhaps be just a sign that 1985 represents the end of solar cycle 21.

Using high-current batteries

Despite the popularity of high-current power supply units, the alternative approach of using float-charged vehicle batteries has many attractions when it comes to powering ssb and fm transceivers. However, despite the apparent fool-proof nature of such systems, problems can arise, including the possibility of the charger voltage being accidentally applied to the load equipment and the charger ripple affecting the operation of some equipments (*TT* March, p193) even though in theory such ripple should be much reduced by the battery.

Both of these problems have been raised in a helpful letter from Earl Hornbostel, DU1AE, of Republic Crystal Labs. He writes: "I heartily agree with the view expressed several times in *TT* that the best power supply for a standard 100W hf transceiver is a lead-acid storage battery . . . However, there is one vital condition that is essential when making such an installation. It must be foolproof with regard to the connections of the charger and the load equipment to avoid any possibility of the charger output being applied to the equipment without the voltage regulating effect of the battery. In other words it needs to be impossible, or virtually so, for the charger to become the source of power for the equipment by itself. Otherwise serious and expensive-to-rectify damage is almost bound to occur.

"There are two ways of preventing this from happening. The first is to use a charger having the voltage limited to approximately 14·2V, with the voltage regulation of the charger arranged to be reliably fail-safe.

"The second method, which I much prefer, is not only simple to implement but also eliminates the need for a special charger. It comprises a method of attaching the battery charger to the battery terminal posts in such a way that the transceiver can *never* receive power directly from the charger.

"The way I do this is to drill a small hole downwards from the top of each terminal post and insert a self-tapping screw. The screws should be solder-coated or terne-plated to minimize contact problems or subsequent corrosion. Then the lead from the transceiver should be taken to the screw, wrapped around it, preferably soldered, and then each screw driven in. This will make tapping-in difficult, unless the battery cable is unplugged or disconnected from the transceiver. The use of a terminal lug should be discouraged and the insulation of the battery cable should extend as close as possible to the soldered point; this is in order to remove the temptation to clip the battery charger on to the transceiver cable lead.

"Instead, the charger leads should be clipped directly on to the battery posts. This arrangement accomplishes two things. It eliminates the possibility of the battery not forming part of the circuit and also greatly reduces the common impedance which gives rise to unwanted ripple being passed to the equipment. With such an arrangement it should be almost impossible to measure any ripple on the leads to the equipment. Common impedance problems can arise in other forms of power supply where it may sometimes be found extremely difficult to achieve a sufficiently low ripple where earth returns of the various main components have not been made correctly. An altogether too common problem that deserves to be stressed every two or three years in *Radio Communication*, if only to prevent each new generation of constructors from making the same blunders as their predecessors. At the age of 70 years I have been involved in introducing several generations of young engineers to electronic design. I have repeatedly found this type of mistake to be a common one, seldom dealt with in the theoretical studies of university courses."

Fusing a fuse

Paul Essery, G3KFE, noted G8LXG's comments on the differences between fuses and rccbs in the August *TT* but clearly feels that this is a subject in which things are seldom as simple or as straightforward as one might imagine. He writes: "Many years ago, when I was with Belling-Lee, we did a long exercise on fuse-blowing in connection with obtaining standards approval for low-current fuses and meeting airborne requirements for the large 'Airfuse' range. Quite clearly, the conventional statement, I^2t = a constant, was shown *not* to be true in practice.

"The reasons for this seem to be: (1) the end-caps of a cartridge fuse and the fuse-holder clip form a heatsink; (2) when the temperature is reached at which the fuse begins to melt, further energy is required to turn the wire into molten metal (analogous to the boiling or freezing of water); and (3) Ohm's Law. The fuse wire is a resistor (and to some degree an inductor). A 1A fuse hit by a 'prospective current' of 1,000A will not in practice pass 1,000A even for a short time: its resistance would be too high. It is also worth noting that fuses have memories; if you apply the same test to a 'virgin' fuse and to one that has already been subjected to its rated current for, say, 5s, you will get different results. In our trials, over several months, we subjected 144 fuses to 5s of current at their rated value each day, photographing the meters and time clock to prove this had been done. Producing 144 whole-plate prints with 12 rolls of film every day put me off photography for years!

"In effect, when we put a very high current into a fuse we never saw it blow in much under, if my memory serves me right, about 10ms. This is why, as many have found out, a transistor is usually quicker than a fuse! The minimum blowing time of a fuse did not seem to vary greatly, whether a small domestic fuse or the large Airfuses.

"We also did some work on the behaviour of fuses at their rated currents and slightly above. In practice, at its rated current a fuse would last nicely; at twice this figure it would blow nicely; but at about 1·5 times rated current there existed a situation where one specimen would blow smartly but the next one would last for more than 2h (the limit of our test). However, when a fuse that had lasted for 2h was switched off, removing the fuse could be very difficult because the solder would have melted and soldered the fuse into its holder; for this reason we changed over to open-type holders.

"Back in the 'fifties test gear was cruder than today, but it is interesting to recall that we could obtain 7,000A-prospective out of our collection of car batteries and breakers in dc mode, or 200A at 500V dc, or 250A ac—though we always carried out the later test in the lunch break for fear of tripping off the main circuit-breakers and closing down the whole factory. Incidentally, a bit of multicore solder subjected to 7,000A-prospective can be quite spectacular!

"To revert to G8LXG's letter, we could assume that the fuse would have gone in about 10ms and the rccb in 15–30ms; but we should add the rider that a fuse is in essence a short-circuit protection. Were his assumptions correct, we would never be able to switch our rigs on as the initial surge would take the fuse straight out every time! The reason why a 1A or 5A fuse, rather than a standard 13A fuse, tends to be used in the power plugs of our equipment is, presumably, the hope that we can protect the equipment better. In practice, as noted above, even a low-rated fuse in the primary of a psu is likely to hold on long enough to do the circuit on the secondary of the transformer a severe mischief, as most old-timers will have found out from painful experience. For a small overload, modern electronic protection is both quicker and more reliable. There is little need to worry about whether to use a 1A or 2A fuse when you are legislating against a short-circuit on the mains-lead! It all amounts to the old story of engineers tending to forget the basic laws of physics and Nature, I fear."

More on nicad dc–dc converters

In the August *TT* I drew attention to the informative series of articles by Rod Cooper in *Electronics & Wireless World* on improving the reliability of nicad cells and batteries. My notes were based on only the first two articles, "Avoiding failure of sealed nickel-cadmium cells" in the May and June issues. Since then two further articles by the same author have appeared: July pp32–6 "Recharging system for NiCd cells" and September p73 "NiCd cells—part 4". These have described in detail the design and construction of a practical charger designed to avoid some of the pitfalls

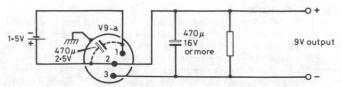

Fig 10. The Verkon V9—a high-efficiency dc–dc converter device allows a 9V battery to be replaced by a single alkaline or nicad cell

outlined in the first two articles and so help to obtain reliable performance from nicad cells. This is quite a complex unit incorporating timer, low-temperature cut-out, automatic turn-on and turn-off etc, having as a prime objective the avoidance of premature failure of cells due to dendrites forming between the plates, as described in the August *TT* notes.

I have also received a letter from Rod Cooper saying how glad he was to see the *TT* comments on the advisability of using (and subsequently recharging) *single* cells rather than cells connected in series to form batteries. He clearly feels strongly that this is a message that needs to get through to more nicad users.

However, he takes me to task for having reproduced his diagram of a simple ic dc–dc converter using the Texas TL496 to raise the voltage of a single cell to the necessary working voltage (my Fig 2(c)) without pointing out that in his text he had stressed his preference for the Verkon range of dc–dc converter devices which can provide "far superior" performance. He writes:

"The TL496 is really at its best with two cells, not one, although as indicated it will work from a single cell with reduced performance figures. Indeed, I use two of these devices myself in a couple of pieces of portable test gear, with single Type D nicad cells, but the converters are then only about 50 per cent efficient. For sheer efficiency, I prefer the Verkon V9a and single nicad cell."

He enclosed detailed information on the Verkon V12 dc–dc converter device providing a nominal 12V output (or 9V with an ic regulator) at up to about 50mA, and also the V9-a (Fig 10) which provides a nominal 9V over the recommended operating range of 1 to 80mA.

Both these Verkon devices are available in the UK from J Biles Engineering, 120 Castle Lane, Solihull, West Midlands B92 8RN, at about £5.25 each. Verkon have a useful introductory leaflet *A cost-saving alternative to batteries* which shows that their original application was to allow small batteries such as the alkaline PP3 to be replaced by a single (larger) alkaline "D" cell (eg Duracell MN1300) which provides about three times the electrical energy at half the cost, so soon saves the cost of the dc-dc converter. Rod Cooper's suggestion of using one of these devices powered by a rechargeable nicad would prove even more economical to anyone making regular and frequent use of battery-powered equipment although, as mentioned in the August *TT*, the devices would not be really suitable for providing the "transmit" currents for the majority of handheld transceivers, except the lowest power units.

RF and medical electronics

In the September *TT* ("Radiation wrongly blamed?", p708) I noted the letter from J Seager (*The Lancet* 11 May 1985) which suggested that the statistical environmental hazard seemingly affecting radio amateurs, electronic assemblers and radio and tv servicing technicians (but not other occupations in electronics) was most unlikely to have anything to do with electromagnetic fields, and that a more likely cause was to be found in the fluxes and tin/lead alloys used in soldering, the fumes from synthetic materials when overheated (or the very toxic pcb compounds found in large transformers, high-voltage capacitors and dummy antenna loads manufactured until the danger was recognized in the late 'seventies).

Ned Rew, G8GZZ, has brought to my attention further letters in *The Lancet* (29 June and 13 July) on this topic. The one on 29 June was from the members of the ARRL Electromagnetic Compatibility (emc) Committee attacking certain aspects of the statistical study carried out by Dr Milham on amateur mortality in California and Washington. This provoked a strongly critical comment from Michael Coleman, of the ICRF Cancer Epidemiology and Clinical Trials Unit at Radcliffe Infirmary, Oxford, who, in turn, found fault with the ARRL's comments on the use of "proportional mortality ratios", and suggested it was most unlikely that the study by Dr Milham was far wrong in this respect, although of course this does not mean that electromagnetic radiation is accepted as necessarily the culprit.

In view of the almost never-ending controversy surrounding the possible health hazards of ionized and non-ionized electromagnetic radiation, it was refreshing to read a detailed paper by R E Sharpe and N B Hornback, of the Indiana University School of Medicine ("The friendly fields of rf" *IEEE Spectrum* June 1985, pp64–9) showing how valuable use is now being made, particularly in the USA, of electromagnetic fields for fusing fractured bones that have otherwise proved extremely difficult to heal (this application uses pulsed low-frequency, low-power waveforms), and also their use for healing wounds and for inducing local or whole-body heating (hyperthermia) to disperse malignant tumours, a subject that surfaced in *TT* in 1977 when Reg Patrick, G2BBX, reported on a 14MHz cure effected on his pet goose! Robert Colson, G4GYN, brought the value of low-frequency, low-level electromagnetic radiation to my attention in 1981. Some 60,000 difficult fractures are reported to have been healed in this way in the USA.

This does not mean that we should regard non-ionized electromagnetic radiation as necessarily benign, but at least it is good to be reminded that very many thousands of people already have reason to be grateful for its "friendly" nature when correctly administered. It is perhaps a great pity that in the UK there are relatively few medical specialists (other than those who are also radio amateurs) who are equally at home with medicine and rf generators.

Mobile radio and the frequency spectrum

The rapid growth over the years of emergency service and private mobile radio (pmr), and more recently 900MHz computerized cellular radio systems, has gobbled up large sections of the vhf/uhf spectrum—to the extent where, in the UK, broadcasting has been ousted (except for some ancillary services) from Band 1 (41–68MHz) and Band 3 (172–216MHz). This once again raises the spectre of the UK being out of step with the rest of the world, with all the problems that that involves. Yes, I know that, as amateurs, we will benefit greatly by gaining access to 50·0 to 50·5MHz, but I still think it would be a far happier situation if we could harmonize frequency allocations throughout Europe.

The problem that unilateral declarations of independence in frequency matters can give rise to has been underlined throughout the many years in which UK emergency services have squatted in a large part of the Band 2 broadcasting band, with the result that not only has vhf fm broadcasting been unduly restricted but, perhaps more importantly, the criminal fraternity has been furnished with low-cost "look-out" receivers to ensure that they are alerted to any "suspects on premises" messages!

Then again, to complicate the mobile scene, the pmr services in different countries have traditionally adopted different allocations and different channelling: 30, 25, 15 and 12·5kHz, just to list a few! In the UK 25kHz channelling for ±5kHz deviation fm has become the accepted standard for amateur mobile/repeater operation, in general providing only four channels per 100kHz, though with some use of split channels representing 12·5kHz channels.

Over the past 10 years there have been many efforts to develop a commercial ssb system for pmr that would be as easy to use and with equally good speech quality as fm, yet would require only 5kHz channelling. A number of firms, including Pye, developed prototypes for the Wolfson Project centred initially on Swansea university. However, by about 1980 it became clear that the effects of fading were making it very difficult to develop ssb equipment that could seriously compete with fm in overall performance and cost.

On the other hand, it was shown that the basic problem of frequency stability, including that posed by doppler shift on mobile signals, can be overcome by using a "pilot carrier" (ie not suppressing the carrier to the 40dB or so normally found in amateur ssb, but only by about 6 to 12dB) to facilitate the use of a phase-lock-loop demodulator that can cope with frequency changes of about ±150Hz without significant change in speech quality.

Fading and mobiles

William C Y Lee's paper "Estimate of local average power of a mobile radio signal" (*IEEE Trans on Vehicular Technology* Vol VT-34, No 1, February 1985) provides a useful introduction to the basic problem of the severe fading invariably occurring during mobile vhf/uhf operation. He writes:

"A mobile radio signal envelope is composed of a fast-fading signal superimposed on a slow-fading signal. . . . Severe fading always occurs when the mobile unit is in motion. The cause of this severe fading is due to two factors: *(1)* The multipath phenomenon—in the mobile radio environment, the unique situation is such that the mobile antennas are always lower than the surrounding structures such as houses, buildings etc. Thus the signal transmitted from the base station is usually blocked by the surrounding structures, and many reflected waves are generated, as shown in Fig 11. Summing all the multipath waves at the mobile unit results in a fast variation in the received signal, called short-term fading. *(2)* The path-loss fluctuation (local mean), that is the variation of the average signal power as the vehicle travels, is called the path-loss fluctuation of the signal;

this is due to the different terrain configurations affecting direct-line propagation between the base station and a moving mobile unit. This is long-term fading, since the location of the vehicle, and hence the path loss, varies relatively slowly: Fig 11 (b)."

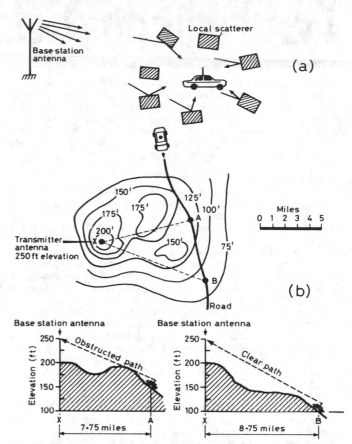

Fig 11. *(a)* Fast fading in mobile vhf/uhf operation results from the constantly changing summation of many signals reflected from buildings etc. *(b)* The changing path loss due to hills and other major obstructions result in pronounced but slower, long-term fading. The receiver needs to be able to cope effectively with the superimposition of fast fading on a slower fading signal

This combination of fast and slow fading is thus inherent in mobile operation on vhf or uhf, and the only practical way of combating the serious effects that it has on ssb reception lies in the development of improved agc systems. A good deal of work has been done on this problem both in Europe and the USA, with some very promising results achieved in the UK at the University of Bath by a team under Dr Joseph McGeehan (now University of Bristol) using a technique called "feed-forward signal regeneration" (ffsr). A paper discussing the application of ffsr and a new optimized form of ssb called "phase-locked transparent tone-in-band" (ttib) has been published recently ("Speech and data communications over 942MHz TAB and TTIB single-sideband mobile radio systems incorporating feed-forward signal regeneration", *IEEE Trans on Vehicular Technology* Vol VT-34, No 1, February 1985).

The paper presents preliminary results for both speech and data communication at 992MHz, and shows that the quality of the speech, compared to 25kHz fm, and the low error rates for data, "clearly demonstrate that pilot tone companded ssb should be considered as a suitable modulation form for mobile radio over all operational frequency bands up to 1GHz. The improvement in speech quality over 25kHz fm may amount to as much as one point on the (five-point) CCIR scale for all signal strengths". The preliminary trials also encompassed 12·5kHz channelling fm, but this was so markedly inferior to the 5kHz channelling ssb system that further trials were confined to comparisons with 25kHz fm.

It will be noted by amateurs that the thrust of this work is to obtain as good or better performance in 5kHz channels (right up to 1GHz) as can be obtained with 25kHz channelling: it is not primarily to extend range. However, the basic feed-forward signal regeneration technique with companded pilot-tone ssb may well prove to have applications other than for mobile operation. It would seem to be a technique that, as amateurs, we should keep an eye on. ☐

Technical Topics *by Pat Hawker, G3VA*

IS "HAM INGENUITY"—the junk-box syndrome—a dying art? In the pioneering days experimental amateurs were forced to improvise since component parts suitable for operation above about 1MHz were often not available to buy. Then came several decades in which schoolboy and other budget-limited enthusiasts found it possible to put together effective amateur stations by salvaging parts, valves, power transformers etc from discarded broadcast radio and television sets.

The art of improvisation

The rise and rise of the industrial muscle of the Rising Sun has ushered in an era where, for the past decade, only a small minority of newcomers even contemplate building their own equipment. Old-timers, other than a few QRP enthusiasts, tend to claim (to quote Doug DeMaw, W1FB's introduction to "The fine art of improvisation" *QST* July 1985, pp22–4): "I gave up building ham gear because parts are hard to find and they cost too much"—perhaps simply a more acceptable excuse than to admit that most of us (and I certainly include myself) are simply not capable of designing or constructing modern solidstate transceivers of the complexity and packing density of many current off-the-shelf equipments.

Those who cannot find the wherewithal to buy brand-new equipment now tend to acquire 'seventies secondhand transceivers rather than seek out the cheaper, bulkier "separates" or the once popular kit-built a.m. rigs that can make effective cw rigs and are amenable to home modification. I find, when admitting that I still often use an old Labgear LG300 transmitter, that other amateurs frequently express regret that they ever got rid of this once-popular and extremely rugged rig with its trusty 813 power amplifier, "built like a battleship".

W1FB wrote: "It is conceivable that we might have to spend $15 for a tuning capacitor and a vernier drive, when the circuit with which it will be used contains only $3 worth of small parts. Prices of items such as tuning capacitors, drive mechanisms, cabinets, slug-tuned coils and new meters can discourage even those builders who have a large amateur radio budget . . . What alternatives do we have? The ingenuity of a true experimenter must be summoned from within if speedy solutions to these common problems are to be found. In decades past it was a regularly practiced art among hams to solve design and procurement problems by using materials on hand. Most hams were inveterate experimenters, and it was considered a challenge to come up with new electrical and mechanical ideas—it was a stimulating learning experience to get on the air and talk about circuits and projects. Each of us has the potential to build radio equipment, to find shortcuts to design objectives, and to enjoy using something we built ourselves."

W1FB thus puts into print what has become all too apparent: decline of the art of junk-box ingenuity, the recycling of surplus and salvaged components and the use of low-cost materials for purposes far removed from those for which they were originally intended. The term "you get what you pay for" seems to be steadily replacing the old idea that with lots of ingenuity and a dash of technical know-how, an amateur experimenter could build for a song what would cost him an arm and a leg to buy new. It was an approach that bred some very resourceful people.

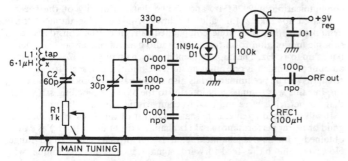

Fig 1. W1FB's "reactance tuning" technique applied to a vfo that uses a 2N4416 or MPF102 fet. C2 sets the frequency spread provided by R1 and eliminates the need for a high-quality tuning capacitor and slow-motion drive. Maximum tuning range is also governed by the position of the tap on L1

Low cost-tuning mechanisms

W1FB in his *QST* article shows a simple method of tuning a vfo that he has devised to eliminate the need for an expensive variable capacitor and tuning drive. Fig 1 shows an example of his "reactance tuning" which has fine control of the frequency using a high-quality potentiometer. He writes:

"I had some reservations about how it might work, but after breadboarding a test circuit I was pleasantly surprised with the results. R1, a high-quality Allen Bradley potentiometer, is located close to C2 and L1 in order to keep the leads from R1 as short and direct as possible.

"Why does this system work? Well, as R1 is adjusted, the presence of the trimmer C2 becomes more prominent. The series combination of C2 and R1 form a capacitive reactance and resistance that cause a frequency shift as R1 is adjusted. The smaller the value of R1, the lower the operating frequency.

"What are the bad features? The tuning is nonlinear in the sense that the frequency is more spread out at the maximum-resistance end of the R1 range (how about using an anti-log law potentiometer?—*G3VA*). Also if a poor quality control is used you might hear a slight scratching noise as the control is adjusted if the vfo is used for a receiver."

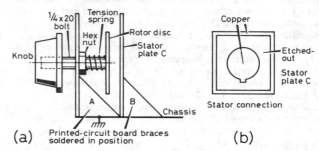

Fig 2. Homemade disc drive described by W1FB. A tension spring ensures good stability of the rotor portion. Side brackets help to keep the unit mechanically rigid. (b) Shows how the stator disc is etched on pcb material

For those who require a multi-turn variable capacitor, W1FB also comes up with a straightforward design for a simple disc tuning capacitor, very reminiscent of the old Eddystone neutralizing capacitors of the 'thirties: Fig 2. He also describes a cylindrical tuning capacitor (Fig 3) that I suspect could also be adapted to provide the mechanism for a permeability-tuned oscillator.

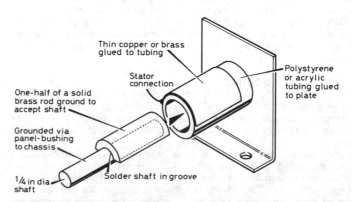

Fig 3. Alternative cylindrical format for a tuning capacitor. The rotor unit is semicircular brass or copper to which a 0·25in diameter tuning rod has been soldered. The station section is plastic tubing to which thin copper or brass sheeting has been glued

Bob Lombardi, WB4EHS, in *Ham Radio* August 1984, pp32–4, discussed how to buy, use and recycle surplus electronic parts, including the surplus pcb boards that tend to be disposed of these days in large quantities. He concluded, perhaps a trifle over-enthusiastically: "It seems strange to me that homebrewing should be on the decline today. This should be a 'Golden Age' of homebrewing if there ever was one! Just look at what's available! Integrated circuits that perform all manner of digital and analog functions are at our disposal, and most are quite cheap. Using reasonable parts counts, we can build circuits capable of performance that was no more than the stuff of dreams in the 'fifties and 'sixties; in the 'fifties, who would have dreamed of a three-terminal voltage regulator? (How about the once-popular gas-filled voltage-regulator tube?—*G3VA*). We can build things more cheaply today than we could when taking inflation into account.''

Incidentally, if you fear homebrewed equipment may have that "old-fashioned" look, take comfort from the fact that a British radio manufacturer (Ross Electronics) is attempting to get the UK back into the portable radio set market by introducing a model designed to have a 'fifties look. Fashions, like sunspots, come and go in cycles!·

Ceramic resonator oscillators

The search for variable-frequency oscillators of high stability and low phase noise ("jitter") stretches back over many years. For some 60 years the dominant control element has been the quartz crystal; more recently a number of other control elements have emerged, including cavities, ceramic dielectric resonators, yttrium indium garnet (yig), surface acoustic wave (saw) devices, steel and glass delay lines (eg PAL television delay-line components) etc. The problem comes when one wishes to vary the frequency over an appreciable range.

The variable crystal oscillator (vxo) in which the crystal frequency is "pulled" by external LC components is an excellent system where the change of frequency can be limited to about 0·1 per cent of the crystal frequency (ie about 7kHz at 7MHz, 150kHz at 144MHz etc) but is less satisfactory for applications requiring a tuning range covering an entire amateur band.

The digital pll frequency synthesizer has tended to be hailed as the ultimate answer but, in practice, unless extreme precautions are taken its phase noise remains a significant problem that can limit the performance of a receiver or transmitter. Mixer-type synthesizers can give much-lower phase noise but tend to be much more complex and costly.

In a long article in *Ham Radio* (June 1985, pp18–26), Albert D Helfrick, K2LBA, shows how ceramic filter resonators, combined with mechanical or diode variable capacitors, can form very useful vxo/vco (voltage controlled oscillator) systems. In conjunction with a low-cost 10·7MHz ceramic i.f. filter resonator, as used in many consumer-type vhf/fm broadcast receivers, he reports that a stable tuning range of almost 200kHz is achievable, although compared with an AT-cut crystal vxo the temperature-induced frequency drift tends to be rather high. This represents about two per cent tuning range compared with 0·1 per cent of a quartz crystal.

For a fixed frequency oscillator using a ceramic oscillator the temperature drift could be minimized by using special −4400ppm/°C ceramic capacitors as the feedback elements.

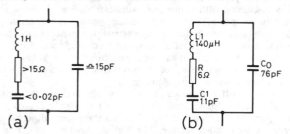

Fig 4. Equivalent circuit of (a) quartz resonator and (b) 4MHz ceramic resonator as described by K2BLA

More generally, a ceramic-resonator vxo/vco can be considered as providing a useful compromise, offering much of the low-phase noise and short-term stability of a crystal oscillator and the wide tuning range of an LC oscillator. The Q of a crystal can be as high as 500,000; for a ceramic resonator, although the series resistance is *lower*, the equivalent inductance is much lower and the Q is typically about 600: Fig 4. While this is much lower than for a quartz crystal it is significantly higher than can be achieved with an hf LC circuit which typically is under 60. The ceramic resonator is also much less microphonic than an LC tuned circuit.

Another significant advantage of the ceramic resonator is the ability to pull its frequency, without losing stability, by as much as seven per cent. In practice, with a limited capacitance-diode variation of, say, 200pF, a typical tuning range with a 4MHz resonator would be about three per cent.

K2BLA provides circuit diagrams (Figs 5, 6) of both capacitor- and varactor-tuned ceramic resonator oscillators using a 10MHz resonator

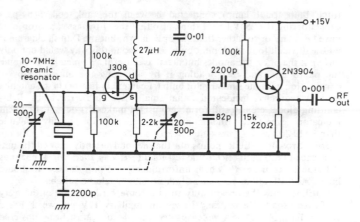

Fig 5. Mechanically-tuned ceramic resonator oscillator

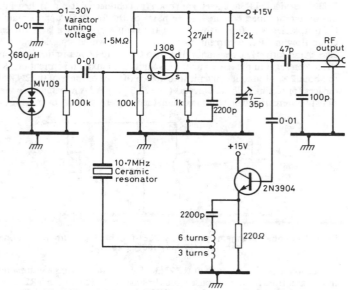

Fig 6. Varactor-tuned 10MHz ceramic resonator oscillator

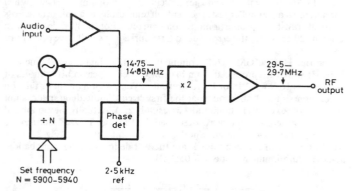

Fig 7. Outline of a 28MHz fm transmitter using a 14MHz ceramic resonator oscillator

capable of covering the entire 10·1 to 10·15MHz band; admittedly this has a temperature variation of approximately 230Hz/°C and is not readily amenable to simple temperature compensation: nevertheless it could provide a very useful performance if kept away from heat sources. He outlines arrangements for a synthesizer for 50MHz based on a phase-locked ceramic resonator vco, and also a simple 28MHz fm transmitter with a phase-locked 14·75 to 14·85MHz vco (Fig 7).

Setting the record straight

No matter how hard one tries, errors *do* creep into print unnoticed! I introduced a stupid error into the circuit diagram of the wartime Danish "telephone directory" transmitter-receiver (*TT* October, Fig 8, p786). As shown, there is no ht applied to the pa anodes, but a "neon" bulb is connected across the tank coil. In reality, there was no "neon" but a small torch bulb (pilot lamp) connected between the tank coil/rf by-pass capacitor and the 250V line. I think also that the rf bypass capacitor must have been 5nF or so rather than the 5pF shown, but the Danish diagram is a little difficult to read. A pilot bulb connected in this way would not only have put the ht on the anodes but acted as a useful "dc meter" for tuning the pa to dip, and then loading it by adjusting the antenna taps in conjunction with the similar pilot bulb (rf current indicator) in the antenna lead. A reminder, incidentally, that small pilot bulbs, car bulbs, light-emitting diodes etc can still form very useful makeshift dc and rf current indicators, even today when miniature meters are more readily available than in 1943!

John Brown, G3EUR, points out that he inadvertently showed the npn transistor (TR2) in his electronic test load (*TT* May 1985, Fig 4, p358) as "BD136 or equivalent" which unfortunately are pnp devices. It should have read "BD139 or equivalent". A 2N6099 would be suitable.

G3EUR takes the opportunity to add some further notes on his very useful test load. He writes: "I used an auxiliary 12V psu which has a current-limit set at 1·5A which protects the load against being powered when it is not connected to a psu under test. When the collectors of the 2N3055 devices (TR3a, b, c etc) are open (not connected to a psu) then TR2 has an emitter load comprising the bases of the 2N3055s, approximately 0·1Ω in series with 0·7V (the Vbe of the transistors) and a large current could flow in TR2. A current-limited 12V supply would shut down in this case. Alternatively, a resistance of 4·7 to 6·8Ω can be put in the line from "Ext" on Fig 4 to the + 12V line. This limits the maximum current in TR2 to about 2A. I found it convenient to switch off one or more of the 2N3055 devices for testing at lower currents (one 2N3055 per 5A maximum) so that only two were used when the maximum load current was 10A or less (Fig 8).

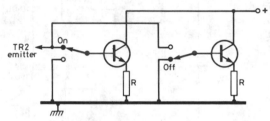

Fig 8. Switching arrangement used by G3EUR in his high-current electronic test load (*TT* May 1985). See text

"To avoid problems, each of the 2N3055 b, c, d devices has a spdt switch in its base, transferring the base from the base of TR3a/emitter TR2 to the negative line, so that there is no current in the collector. Even so, I found the odd 2N3055 with a leakage current of a milliamp or two. When connected to a psu under test, the load current results in a volt-drop across the 0·3Ω resistors, proportional to load current. For 2N3055 devices with gains of 20 or more, the error due to base current is small, five per cent or less."

Maurice Hately, GM3HAT, commented on the diagram (*TT* June, Fig 5, p453) which I reproduced from his conference paper on his "dipoles of delight" as follows: "In order to prevent anyone wasting a lot of time on experiments, may I point out that the first circuit in the diagram does not actually work very well (minimum swr usually 2:1). Actually the monoband capacitor antennas that were described in the paper *(IEE Conference Publication No 245)* contain another component shown in Fig 2 of the paper. Only with this component are the full delights of the monobander achieved (minimum swr about 1·05:1)."

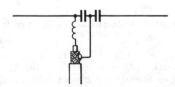

Fig 9. GM3HAT's monoband "dipole of delight" showing improved form with an inductor. Both capacitors and inductor have reactances numerically equal to the cable impedance at the frequency of operation

His Fig 2 is here reproduced as Fig 9, about which he explained: "The tuning problem can be alternatively cured if a series inductor is connected between the coaxial feeder and the capacitive balun. While a half-wave dipole constructed in this way is only a singly resonant device, it is nevertheless attractive in view of the accurately resistive input impedance over a wide bandwidth (some six per cent before the swr exceeds 1·5:1), minimal received interference and preclusion of overtone radiation."

Brian Bower, G3COJ, noted the 7MHz sloping delta loop antenna of SM6CTQ (*TT* September, Fig 4, p708) which adopts the ideas of W1FB and W1SE in their *QST* article of October 1984: "The full-wave delta loop at low height". However, he feels that the dimensions given by SM6CTQ are unduly pessimistic in suggesting that the support mast or tower needs to be 16m high. If the centre of the base of the antenna is spaced out at, say, 5m from the base of the tower, and the wire 2m above the ground, the apex would not reach the top of a 16m mast but would be some 13·5m above ground. However, this is only about 1m less than with the loop in the vertical plane. On the other hand, G3COJ suggests, if the plane of the loop slopes at 45°, then its apex would be at 10·88m, representing a worthwhile saving in mast height. Alternatively, for a given apex height, moving the loop out from the mast and raising it more than 2m above ground would raise the average height of the antenna. "It would be interesting to know whether this height improvement would be cancelled by the loop becoming less vertical", G3COJ writes.

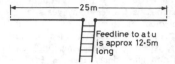

Fig 10. All-band centre-fed doublet antenna as recommended by VK5RG, for use on all hf bands from 1·8 to 28MHz

As *TT* has frequently noted the attractions of a centre-fed doublet antenna using open-wire feeder, it may be appropriate to reproduce from Rob Gurr, VK5RG's "Wire antennas" (*Amateur Radio (VK)* September 1984) an antenna he recommends as a flexible all-band system: Fig 10. He writes:

"This multiband general purpose system has the following radiation properties:

1·8MHz (with feeders tied together and tuned against earth) omnidirectional;

3·5MHz as a shortened dipole, excellent general coverage;

7MHz as an extended dipole, some bidirectional gain at right angles to the wire;

10MHz as shortened two halfwaves in phase, some bidirectional gain (1·8dBd);

14MHz as two extended halfwaves in phase, 3dBd gain;

18, 21 and 28MHz as a general-purpose centre-fed "long wire" with multiple lobes, some providing useful gain (eg 2·5-waves long on 28MHz for gain of 2dBd in each of four lobes at 30° with respect to the wire).

For this type of system one does need a flexible astu with balanced output that can be varied from high to low impedance.

Flash-over and transient suppression

Although the problem of short, sharp voltage spikes ("transients") is usually associated with vulnerable, solidstate devices, it can also affect thermionic equipment. For example, in high-power valve linear amplifiers, transient voltages can develop on any electrode that is not at earth potential. This can include the grid of a cathode-driven triode amplifier, or more commonly the screen grid of a tetrode amplifier, such as those based on the 4CX series. Unless suitable protection is provided, transients arising from flash-over can result in costly damage.

Protection is often provided in the form of a surge arrestor, taking the form of a simple "spark gap" or its rather more sophisticated gas-filled counterpart that ionizes and "fires" when the potential across the gap exceeds the breakdown voltage. The high-power KW-1 amplifier with a 8875 power triode described in *Radio Handbook* (22nd edition) incorporates in its grid circuit a surge arrestor of this type made, for example, by Siemens, Signalite, Reliable Electric etc.

However, John Nelson, G4FRX, of RSGB headquarters, is not convinced that a spark-gap arrangement can be relied upon always to provide adequate protection. He writes:

"There currently seems to be a school of thought among constructors and users of tetrode amplifiers (especially those using the 4CX250B) that advocates the use of spark gaps to provide a measure of protection to the screen grid in the event of flash-over. Having carried out a good deal of work in this area in connection with a forthcoming RSGB publication, I would like to point out some relevant facts and to suggest a much better alternative.

"It is true that flash-over in 4CX-series tetrodes can damage the screen grid, typically resulting in internal short-circuits. However, the real component at risk is the valve base or, more correctly, the built-in screen decoupling capacitor in the SK600 and SK620 series of bases. These are rated at 1kV working and, in my experience, this rating is *not* conservative.

Flash-over is very likely to cause this component to go short-circuit, especially in the case of the SK620 series which are (or should be) generally used at uhf. Given the current cost of these components, one consequence of a flash-over is likely to be deep QSB in the wallet.

"Small spark gaps can indeed be placed between the screen voltage pin (pin 1) and earth, and may give some measure of protection. However, the spark gap has several disadvantages in this application. The inevitable manufacturing tolerances mean that the striking voltage can in some cases be ± 75 per cent of nominal, and this voltage also has a marked temperature coefficient. Because the manner in which the spark gap works is statistical in nature, there is a random variation in striking voltage for successive operations; there is also usually some difference between the striking and the sustaining voltage. A discussion of this subject can be found in *Transient Voltage Suppressor Manual* published by General Electric (USA) and available from Jermyn Distribution.

"A much better way to protect the valve and its base is to use a voltage dependent resistor (vdr). For this application, the best form of vdr would seem to be the zinc oxide devices "GE-MOV II", manufactured by General Electric (USA): the current ratings and response times of these components are excellent and they are also not expensive. For a typical 4CX250B amplifier with 350V on its screen grid in Class AB1, the V275LA40B offers excellent protection, with a Vmin of 389V and a Vnom at 1mA of 430V. With this component the maximum voltage appearing at the valve in the event of a flash-over is unlikely to exceed about 650V even under the most severe flash-over conditions, and both valve and base are fully protected.

"These devices will handle enormous current for the relatively short duration of the event. They are about the size of a 1nF 3kV ceramic capacitor and can be connected directly between the screen pin on the valve base and earth, with lead lengths suitably short. I have recently, in the cause of science, deliberately induced a series of flash-overs in a 144MHz amplifier using a pair of 4CX250R valves and am satisfied that the vdr devices function excellently. Even with the aid of a very fast oscilloscope, no excessive voltages can be detected at the screen grid: emphatically not the case when the devices are removed!

"Incidentally, I believe that the vast majority of amplifier designs using this series of valves, which feature a low-value series resistor in the screen-grid feed, are positively inviting disasters in the event of flash-over, but that is another story."

I feel that it is worth adding that these metal oxide varistor transient suppressors, to which attention was drawn in *TT* as long ago as December 1972/February 1973, have many other applications, such as the elimination of mains surges, switch-on transients etc. They were originally developed in Japan by Mashushita who called them zinc oxide non-linear resistors (znr). They act as very high resistors when normal low voltages are applied across them, but once the voltage exceeds a critical value they become virtually conductors, behaving as back-to-back zener diodes and sometimes capable of passing currents of hundreds of amperes for brief periods. Devices are manufactured suitable for direct connection across 110V or 240V ac mains; among many possible applications in power supply units

they can simply be connected across the secondary of a power transformer or used to protect the pass-transistor of a series regulator: Fig 11. Another use is to protect transistor output stages in audio output stages.

Metal oxide varistors should not be confused with another form of protective device, the ptc thermistor which has a very pronounced positive temperature coefficient and can be used to provide current overload protection in applications where very quick action is not required (*TT* March 1981, p236) such as current protection of relays, loudspeakers, meters etc, or in ptc devices with very low initial resistance directly in power supply units intended to deliver up to about 1·9A. A range of ptc thermistors is made by Siemens. They can also be used for temperature stabilization of crystal oscillators.

The frequency-modulation paradox

In the February *TT* (pp114–5), under the heading "FM, nbfm and the spectrum", I wrote: "Communication theory tells us that we can exchange bandwidth for snr and hence transmitter power, which is why, for direct broadcasting from satellite, the video signal will be transmitted as wide-deviation fm in 27MHz channels with 100 to 200W peak output doing the work of an a.m. transmitter of about 10kW or so."

Yet, as readers have pointed out, in the July *TT* I stressed that, in amateur practice, weak signal reception is more effective, and a better snr achieved, by narrowing the bandwidth of the receiver. That is to say, snr of most amateur signals is inversely proportional to noise bandwidth. So why widen the tv signals from 8MHz channels and vestigial sideband transmission to 27MHz fm?

This apparent contradiction has puzzled some readers. Surely, they suggest, it is well-established that ssb and even a.m. packs a greater punch than fm. This curious paradox stems from the fact that, as amateurs, we are more accustomed to *narrow-band fm* than to broadcast-type wide-deviation fm which has a maximum deviation of ± 75kHz for an audio baseband (monophonic) of about 15kHz and occupies roughly 2(75 + 15) which is 180kHz with 200kHz or more channelling.

For an fm signal the *modulation index* represents maximum frequency deviation divided by the baseband. Amateur nbfm has a modulation index of around unity (eg ± 5kHz deviation, 3kHz baseband) whereas broadcast fm usually has a modulation index of about five.

It is with wide-deviation fm that one can achieve what is usually called "the fm improvement" which, on reasonably strong signals, provides a post-discriminator snr equivalent to that provided by about a 23dB increase of the carrier power of a double-sideband a.m. broadcast signal occupying, say, 30kHz of spectrum. For speech communications (3kHz baseband) a modulation index of five represents a maximum carrier deviation of ± 15kHz and a spectrum bandwidth of (for significant sidebands) of 2(3 + 15), ie 36kHz. Taking into account frequency drift of receivers, this implies 50kHz channelling (100kHz in some of the older systems). With a very stable receiver we could reduce i.f. bandwidth to, say, 40kHz, but such transmissions would not be popular on, say, 144MHz! Furthermore, range would not be improved to anything like the extent you might expect from the large "fm improvement". This is because the type of fm detection we use in our receivers falls to pieces on weak signals due to the high "threshold", often anywhere below a carrier-to-noise ratio of around 12–15dB.

Thus the question of overall communications efficiency of different modes of transmission is quite a complex matter, and one must take into account the way the receiver responds to "noise" which, in the main, is random amplitude-modulated transients. The fm improvement stems partly from the fact that the modulation content is conveyed as a frequency

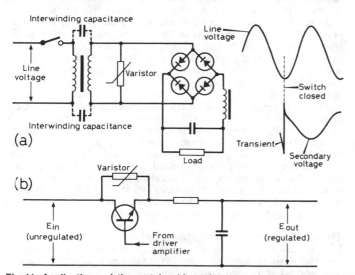

(a)

(b)

Fig 11. Applications of the metal oxide varistor transient suppressor. (a) Elimination of switching transients on power step-down transformer by connecting varistor directly across secondary winding. (b) Varistor protecting a pass-transistor in a psu from switch-on transients. Varistors can also be used to protect audio output stages etc as well as for G4FRX's application to flash-over protection

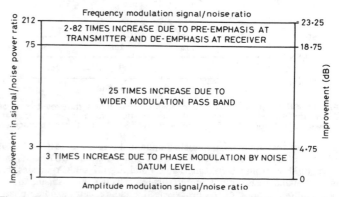

Fig 12. The signal-to-noise ratio improvement of wide-deviation (modulation index 5) over a.m. broadcast signals

deviation, so that a modulation index above unity is akin to distortionless over-modulation of an a.m.-type signal with the sideband power much greater than carrier power.

In the second place, a large reduction in noise output from the receiver on a strong fm signal stems from the fact that most "noise" is an amplitude change and can quite easily be separated from the frequency-modulated carrier by the amplitude limiters that are inherent in an fm receiver. Acting on a broadband signal in which the pulses have not been heightened by the action of a narrow i.f. passband, they can be very much more effective than the type of noise limiters found in communications receivers. As long as the peak carrier of an fm signal exceeds the peak noise, fm reception produces about 4·75dB less aural noise output than a.m.

Fig 12 shows the "fm improvement" in terms of how the snr of an fm receiver output compares with a double-sideband a.m. broadcast system. But it is important to remember that this type of power gain is not obtained with nbfm, although it is feasible on the microwave bands provided that this is not ruled out by licence conditions.

When considering communications applications it is necessary to take into account such matters as spectral efficiency, whether the system is expected to be noise-limited or interference-limited, the form of receiver *demodulation* as well as the transmitted modulation.

Table 1—Comparison of amateur nbfm and ssb parameters

	SSB	NBFM
Bandwidth	3kHz	16kHz
Transceiver complexity	More complex	Less complex
Weak-signal performance	Good	Poor
Threshold effect	No	Yes
Capture effect	No	Yes
Audio quality	Fair	Good

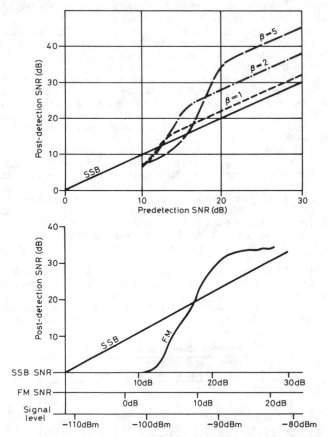

Fig 13. SNR curves for fm with several modulation indexes based on theoretical analysis. The linear ssb curve is shown for comparison. (b) Data measured by KB0CY for 28MHz nbfm on the TS43OS multimode transceiver

Some of these matters are touched upon in a recent article by Robert A Witte, KB0CY, "A close look at frequency modulation" *QST* September 1985, pp31–6, from which come Table 1 and Fig 13. KB0CY stresses that in weak signal areas nbfm is appreciably less effective than ssb, and that hf propagation, because of frequency-selective fading, can introduce phase-related distortion on the broader fm signals.

Communications theory

For those who would wish to delve deeper into the complex question of the effectiveness of different modulation/demodulation systems in different conditions, it is worth pointing out that digitally-coded speech or data transmissions can take even more advantage of extra bandwidth than wide-deviation fm. Coded transmissions (remember that the morse code is basically a non-return-to-zero binary digital system) offer the opportunity to overcome a number of the impairments that affect analogue transmission, and also make it possible to have error detection and correction as very powerful weapons against fading and interference. It is interesting to note that consideration is being given to using a 32kb/s digital system (100kHz channels) for such purposes as cordless telephones using what is termed "continuously variable slope delta modulation" (cvsdm) transmitted using a modulation method such as tamed frequency modulation (tfm) or filtered fsk. Amateurs do not seem yet to have seriously tackled digital speech/data systems, though it seems increasingly likely that such techniques will be widely used by professionals on uhf and microwaves. Some interesting ideas and many useful references can be found in a recent special issue of *IEE Proceedings F* devoted to "Land Mobile Radio" (Vol 132, Part F, No 5, August 1985). Digital bit rates of 16kb/s are already being widely used for military "secure" speech/data systems.

All such systems have been developed as a result of the growing awareness of basic communication theory. The elements of this theory stretch back to 1924 when Nyquist first showed that the number of discrete pulses (for example, morse dits) that can be sent over a channel of finite bandwidth is directly proportional to its bandwidth in Hertz and cannot exceed twice this figure. Later R V Hartley (of Hartley oscillator fame) developed this finding to include the effect of the restricted ability of a receiver to estimate the amplitude of transmitted pulses; in an amplitude-limited channel this puts a limitation on the amount of data per second that can be accurately communicated. In 1948 Shannon, of Bell Telephone Laboratories, concluded that in a noisy channel of restricted bandwidth and limited signal amplitude, it is always theoretically possible to communicate information with arbitrarily high accuracy by using signals of sufficiently long duration—a fact that should be known by experience to every cw operator: *slow down* when the going gets tough!

Shannon's work, however, did far more than just confirm what we have, or should have, found out for ourselves. For the first time it became possible to achieve a deeper insight into all possible modes aimed at permitting the transfer of information and to determine the extent to which practical modulation/demodulation systems fall short of the theoretical ideal. Shannon, in other words, was the Einstein of communications! In effect, Shannon showed for the first time that increased bandwidth could, *for a given rate of information exchange*, provide an improved signal-to-noise ratio.

By applying Shannon's theory it can be shown that systems in which the information is "coded" (such as pulse-code-modulation, delta modulation etc, or even morse coded) require more bandwidth but less transmission power than would be required to achieve a similar accuracy for non-coded systems (such as analogue speech) at the same rate of information exchange. That is to say, bandwidth can be exchanged for transmitter power. Thus systems that spread the information over more of the spectrum, such as wide-deviation fm or pcm, can use less power than where the spectrum bandwidth is less than, or equal to, double the baseband as with a.m./dsbsc/ssb. By similar reasoning it can be shown that with suitable forms of demodulation dsbsc would be *more* efficient than ssb—but that is another story.

All communication systems, in accordance with Shannon's theory, can reduce the minimum usable snr either by reducing the information rate or by increasing the bandwidth actually used at a given information rate. This is why, for example, multi-tone teleprinter systems, such as Piccolo, which involves integrating the signalling tones over a period, can provide "clean" copy without Amtor-type error correction even on very weak signals. Conversely, by reducing the overall signalling rate in an extremely narrow bandwidth, cw can be reliably transmitted over the very long eme paths. On shorter paths, very slow cw can be reliably transmitted in the absence of interference, with miniscule power of a few milliwatts.

Those disposable syringes again

In the October *TT* it was emphasized that disposable medical syringes of the type widely used by doctors and dentists can present serious health hazards once they have been used, and that there are more economical means of making open wire spreaders than attempting to buy new syringes.

However, Dick Pascoe, G0BPS, The Anchorage, 3 Limes Road, Folkestone, Kent CT19 4AU, writes to point out that he could supply (to *bona fide* radio amateurs only) "out-of-date" stock that has not been used.

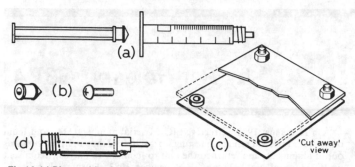

Fig 14. (a) Disposable plastic syringe. (b) Neoprene insert from the end of the plunger and how a No 6 machine screw can be used to make rubber equipment feet. These inserts can also be used to mount a circuit board, transformer etc to chassis as shown in (c). The syringe barrel makes a good coil former. (d) How W5MY fashioned a plug-in coil for a gdo using a piece of the tubing and a phono plug

He believes that it would be possible for him to obtain and supply large quantities of these from about £5 per 100. If you are interested drop him a line, though we still have no information on the rf properties of the plastics or how they stand up to uv radiation etc.

However, by coincidence, I recently came across some suggestions for other uses of these disposable syringes (*QST* January 1985, p40). George B Bean, W5MY, provided an illustration showing details of disposable plastic syringes and wrote: "The neoprene inserts on the end of the plunger can be used as grommets to protect wires going through a hole in a metal chassis if you cut a hole in the tip. They also make excellent rubber feet for equipment or shock mounts for circuit boards, transformers, relays, blowers or other sources of hum and vibration.

"Fig 14 (b) shows one of these inserts. The head of a No 6 screw is just the right size for a snug fit into the insert. These can be fastened to the bottom of a project case to serve as feet. Secure the screw with a lock washer and nut. To use the insert as an insulated shock mount, drill a 0·25in hole in the chassis, then insert the grommet into that hole, add a No 6 machine screw and attach the circuit board or other device. Fig 14 (c) illustrates this technique. You may want to use a nut and lock washer above and below the board for extra security.

"I have also found that the barrel of the syringe makes a nice coil form. If you use a sharp knife to cut off a section of the tube, it will fit nicely over the outside of a phone plug. I have made plug-in coils for my gdo using this method. Fig 14 (d) shows an example of how that is done."

Dr Maurice Sasson, W2JAJ, came up with another use: "Cooling fans can be oiled very easily without removing them from the chassis, or even removing the covers, if they are in an accessible position. I use a 3ml (3cc) syringe and a long metal needle.

"Needles that fit on the hub of a syringe are available in many bore sizes and in lengths from 1 to 6in in increments of 0·5 or 0·75in. The necessary size depends on the physical structure of the equipment. Measure from the area of the motor to a convenient height that allows freedom of operation. These needles are flexible enough to bend slightly for various working angles.

"Filled with a few millilitres of very light machine oil, the needle can be placed right on the motor shaft, keeping the bevel towards the motor and applying gentle pressure on the plunger until an adequate amount of oil has been 'injected'."

I recall that, several years ago, *TT* included a number of items showing how useful hypodermic needles can be as a soldering aid etc. At the time, several readers warned against attempting to acquire needles *after* they have been used. I can only repeat the warning.

Tips and topics

Peter Delaney, G8KZG, commenting on the August *TT* item on the difference between an rccb (residual current circuit breaker) and an mcb (miniature contact breaker) notes that RS Components do in fact market combined rccb/mcb devices, apparently made by GEC, that protect against earth-leakage (trip at 30mA in 30ms) and also provides short-circuit protection (mcb rated at 6, 10, 16, 25 or 32A). But he warns that these are not particularly cheap and are also not intended for fitting into plug tops.

John Haydon, G3BLP, raises the question of whether the action of an rccb when tripping can itself create a transient voltage spike capable of damaging, for example, the psu of an hf transceiver. In his case it appears that the rccb was tripped as the result of a nearby lightning strike, but that damage to his Icom psu resulted not from the lightning emp but from the tripping of the rccb, if I have understood his letter correctly. Certainly the problem of destructive mains transients on a wide range of solidstate equipment (including domestic tv sets) can be a difficult one. Varistor-type transient protectors are claimed to prevent this type of damage, but it is seldom that one comes across consumer-type equipment fitted with such a device.

Technical Topics

by Pat Hawker, G3VA

RECENT COMMENTS in *TT* that the hobby of amateur radio needs to include at least some element of diy and homebuilt equipment, if it is to survive and flourish and continue to provide genuine self-training, have brought in several letters. Most writers agree that ideally it would be fine if newcomers could be persuaded to start off by building their own simple hf transmitter or at least "assemble" a radio station from a number of separate units, put up a simple wire antenna and cut their teeth operating cw on the 1·8, 3·5 and 7MHz bands—rather than starting off with a 144MHz factory-built fm transceiver. Then, later, graduating to even more complex equipment, possibly hf ssb with rotary beam antenna, automatic tuning units etc—equipment of a complexity far beyond anything required to pass the RAE. Domestic appliance users seldom understand (or need) to the equipment they use, whether this be a colour tv set, a vcr machine or a microwave oven. You do not learn to understand radio equipment purely from books and operating via the local vhf repeater!

This is not, in any way, to decry modern factory-built equipment or to suggest that many of us could build equivalent equipment. It is not a question of expecting newcomers to stick to homebuilt equipment, but simply to imply that to understand how a transmitter works in practice needs more than using an on-off switch. However, John Tuke, GM3BST, highlights a real problem when it comes to the homebrewing of complex equipment. He writes: "I think one of the main disadvantages of homebrew equipment is the very low (if any) secondhand value. If one were to construct a transceiver with all the operating conveniences, compact size and facilities to be found on modern Japanese black boxes, the cost would not be all that different from the purchase price of the factory item. But its resale value would be very, very different. If one *did* make such a rig it would mean in most cases being stuck with it for life, as few of us could afford to build another every few years. Commercial gear, on the other hand, does have a secondhand value, and can be traded in like a car.

"I think the 'homebrew' ability today is more sensibly directed to auxiliary equipment, much of which is either highly priced commercially or almost impossible to obtain. For example, I have homebuilt facsimile receiving and transmitting equipment, homebuilt rtty modems together with character recognition circuitry, auto-start, auto-stop etc. It is all home designed and practical to build—but there is no way I could build an FT757 transceiver!

"Just for fun about a year ago I built a 'short-wave receiver' using component parts from the 'thirties; baseboard and panel construction, 1-v-1 (ie rf amplifier, regenerative detector and audio output using three 2V battery valves). It covered 6 to 15MHz and I found that weak signals which were not adjacent to strong ones had a signal-to-noise ratio marginally better than my FT757! Of course it would be foolish to pretend it could cope with today's 14MHz band, but it was fun to play about with 'reaction' once again."

Reliability

As factory equipment becomes more and more complex, there is little chance of home servicing except by those in the profession. There is also an increasing tendency for users to label as "hardware faults" what are in reality operator errors or failures to integrate different pieces of equipment correctly. There is also the problem that few of us have the test equipment necessary to check whether a new rig is really up to spec.

I remain amazed at the degree of reliability that *is* achieved in complex transceivers, but there are still cold solder (dry) joints, mechanical problems with switches, sockets, potentiometers, and inevitably some missing or wrong components, incorrectly positioned components etc, as a result of human or software errors.

An example of the problems that can arise, even with well-designed and carefully-produced equipment from a reputable manufacturer, turned up in a *QST* (January 1985) review of the Icom IC751 hf transceiver claimed, in 1983, as "the most advanced, highest performing hf transceiver for the amateur world today."

Reviewer Paul Pagel, N1FB, reported: "Although the review transceiver worked flawlessly during the review period, obtaining a working IC751 proved to be a real task. The following is a log of the problems we encountered:

"On 11 August 1983 we received IC751 serial number 1114 from Icom on loan for review. During lab testing we discovered that an i.f. section was out of alignment, and returned the unit to Icom on 16 August. Icom sent us IC751 serial No 1227 on 21 November 1983. During lab tests we discovered that this unit suffered from reduced power output as frequency increased. Power dropped from full output on 1·8MHz to zero output on 28MHz after the rig was on for a few minutes. We returned the unit to Icom for repair on 23 November. The problem turned out to be defective final power amplifier transistors. After this repair, the unit operated normally.

"Meanwhile we purchased an IC751 from an authorized Icom dealer on 27 December 1983. During lab testing we discovered that this unit (serial No 1982) would not go into transmit. We returned the rig to the dealer who found a burnt-up resistor. Serial No 1982 was returned to us 24 January 1984. Again, lab testing revealed a problem. This time the IC751 would not transmit fm properly—the output power dropped rapidly in transmit. We again returned the rig to the dealer, who found a defective 8V regulator. On 5 March 1984 we were able to perform the necessary lab testing and begin the review."

WARC-bands trapped dipole

Although not everyone favours the use of traps, the trapped dipole does have the useful feature that it is possible to achieve a sufficiently low swr on each band to make it unnecessary to use an atu with most transmitters, unless any solidstate protective circuits have a low threshold. But few designs of trapped dipoles cover 3·5, 7, 10, 18 and 24MHz using eight traps constructed from coaxial cable. Such an antenna has been described by Brian J Warman, VK5B1, in *Electronics Australia* June 1985, pp100–1. He has not attempted to cover 14, 21 or 28MHz for which bands he uses a triband beam array. The total span of the dipole is about 25m and could thus fit many gardens, yet providing a resonant antenna for 3·5MHz: Fig 1(a).

The traps comprise RG-58U cable wound on formers cut from a 1m length of 32mm polypipe; VK5B1 suggests checking its rf properties by putting a bit in a microwave oven for 1min: there should be no reaction. Ten metres of RG-58U are used (Fig 1(b)) to the following dimensions:

7MHz trap	1,800mm of cable	110mm of pipe
10MHz trap	1,330mm of cable	90mm of pipe
18MHz trap	830mm of cable	70mm of pipe
24MHz trap	710mm of cable	70mm of pipe

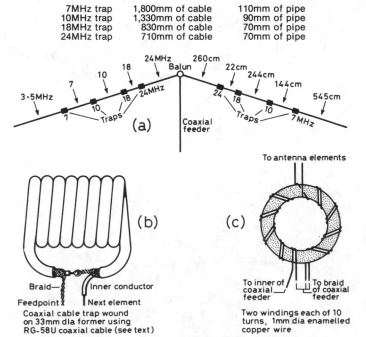

Fig 1. "WARC-bands" trapped dipole by VK5B1 covers 3·5, 7, 10, 18 and 24MHz. Element lengths shown on the right, while the corresponding bands are shown on the left. (b) Details of coaxial cable traps. (c) Winding details for optional balun

TECHNICAL TOPICS   January 1986

The pipe is first drilled with three holes: one 5mm hole, 25mm from one end to secure the beginning of the coil; two 2mm holes 10mm from each end to attach the antenna wire. He proceeds as follows:

"Strip 75mm of jacket off each end of the length of coaxial cable followed by 50mm off the centre conductor. I have found the neatest way of finishing off the braid is to part the strands near the jacket and then fish the centre conductor out through this hole. In this way the weaving remains intact and makes for a very neat finish. Push one end of the cable through the 5mm hole at the end of the former until 5mm of the jacket is inside. Wind the cable to form a coil on the former, then mark a hole at the finish to allow 5mm of jacket to be pushed inside to finish the coil. Pull the remaining cable through this hole. You will now have approximately 70mm of cable inside the former at each end.

"Solder the centre conductor from one end of the coil to the braid at the other end. Fig 1(b) shows the general idea, but note that the connection will be inside the former, not on the outside as shown. (The figure has been drawn this way for clarity.) The remaining braid connects to the element coming from the feedpoint (centre) of the antenna, while the remaining inner conductor goes to the next element."

VK5B1 used a ferrite-ring balun (Fig 1(c)) between the feeder and the element, primarily to reduce current flowing on the outer conductor of the cable to minimize tvi on vhf tv channels. It would probably have little effect in the UK, but be sure to seal the end of the cable to prevent moisture ingress.

The antenna sections comprise:

24MHz	2 × 260cm	
18MHz	2 × 22cm	
10MHz	2 × 244cm	
7MHz	2 × 144cm	
3·5MHz	2 × 545cm	

plus in each case wire allowance for terminating the wire to the trap (about 30mm extra).

VK5B1 stresses that trap dimensions are correct only for RG-58U cable, although even in this case it would be advisable to check resonance with a gdo, before drilling the second 5mm hole in the former, by temporarily connecting the inner conductor at one end to the braid at the other end. Resonance points to aim at are: 7·1, 10·1, 18·1 and 24·9MHz. Similarly, it is advisable to gdo-check element lengths as they are assembled progressively from 24MHz.

Loops and dipoles

Few authors ever seem to agree on the theoretical gain, radiation resistance etc of full-wave loop, quad and delta antenna elements. Since, for real antennas, the characteristics will be affected by such questions as height above ground etc, it could be argued that the published variations are of limited practical significance. However, James L Dietrich, WA0RDX, with the support of Walter Maxwell, W2DU, has tackled this problem once more, and has come up with a useful tabulation of four basic loops as a basis for the determination by trial and error of characteristics in a real situation.

Table 1—Summary of loop and dipole characteristics

		Gain over isotropic (dB)	Gain over dipole (dB)	Radiation resistance (Ω)	Rel level at vertical (dB)
λ/2	Dipole	2·15	0	73	0
1λ	Square loop	3·14	0·99	117	−3·01
1λ	Circular loop	3·49	1·34	133	−3·74
1λ	Diamond loop	3·14	0·99	117	−2·70
1λ	Delta loop	2·82	0·67	106	−2·09

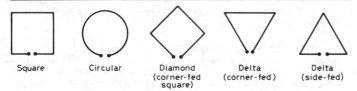

Fig 2. Five full-wave loop shapes. The delta loop is an equilateral triangle, each side one-third of a wavelength (from QST)

In general, it will be noted from Table 1 and Fig 2 that the greater the area enclosed by the loop, the greater the gain. Unfortunately, at least for hf, the large circular loop is the most difficult form to construct. Loops with a perimeter greater than 1λ will show more gain, just as a 3λ/2 dipole has gain over the conventional λ/2 dipole: Fig 3.

It is worth stressing that the "gain" of an antenna derives from its directivity in the horizontal and vertical planes. An isotropic antenna is an imaginary antenna that radiates equal power in all directions. In practice

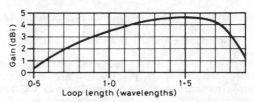

Fig 3. Computer gain versus length of a circular loop in the direction broadside to the loop. In practice, loops less than a full wave in circumference will have increased losses due to low radiation resistance

radiation patterns and "gain", as well as radiation resistance etc, are affected by height and ground conductivity, and also by nearby buildings, structures, trees etc.

The original zepp

An interesting sidelight on the once-popular (and still occasionally used) zepp antenna is shed by a letter from Alois Krischke, DT0TR/OE8AK, in *Ham Radio* November 1985, p8. He points out that the zepp antenna, so-called on account of its use on the German Zeppelin airships, is now more than 75 years old, having been patented by Dr Hans Beggerow in Germany as early as 1908. Its classical form is a full-wave, current-fed antenna with a λ/4 section folded back on itself to form a λ/2 radiator with a quarter-wave matching transformer.

The usual form in the 'thirties was to have the λ/2 radiator as a horizontal element (Fig 4(b)), but it is interesting to note that in the original patent it was shown as a vertical radiator suspended from a balloon, just like an inverted J-pole or Slim-Jim antenna: Fig 4(a). DJ8TR suggests that the design had a particular value for use in balloons and airships: the current-fed matching section was a big improvement over the dangerous practice of using a high-voltage feed in close proximity to the oxyhydrogen gas with which balloons were often filled. The zepp radiator was essentially fed from one end of the radiating section and poses the problem of a "balanced" transformer feeding an unbalanced radiator, though it has to be admitted that the system usually works quite well.

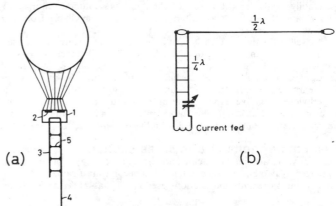

Fig 4. (a) The original zepp antenna as patented in 1909 by Dr Hans Beggerow for suspension from a balloon or airship. (b) Commonly used form of zepp in the 'thirties

Antennas where open-wire tuned feeders are connected to the centre of a dipole antenna were in the past often (and sometimes still are) incorrectly referred to as "centre-fed zepps". They constitute dipole or multi-band doublet antennas and are, as noted frequently in *TT*, highly reliable antennas. In this connection John Tuke, GM3BST writes: "I don't have room for a centre-fed doublet where I live now (I use an HF5 vertical), but in the past I have used large centre-feds, and they all seem to work well. I think dimensions are really quite unimportant unless you are stringing them between 100ft-high masts where one can get true radiation patterns because the antenna is well in the clear. But for the average location, directivity means little because of the low elevation and interference from surrounding objects. If I had room, I would be back with a centre-fed antenna with open-wire feeders—you can't beat them!"

Self-amalgamating and adhesive tapes

Philip Hutchinson, sales specialist (cable & electrical products) of Rotunda Ltd of Holland Street, Denton, Manchester M34 3GH, has shed further light on questions raised in *TT* during 1985 concerning the use of self-amalgamating and adhesive tapes. He writes: "Rotunda Ltd is the only UK manufacturer of self-amalgamating tapes, and the largest UK producer of pvc adhesive tapes.

"I have been reading, with interest, the articles published in *TT* January, March, May and June 1985, in particular applications and problems associated with sealing tape and self-amalgamating products. I would like to answer some of the queries posed.

"The first point is that two of the three self-amalgamating tapes mentioned (CC Marine and RS Components) are one and the same: polyisobutylene (pib) self-amalgamating tape (Rotunda Ref 2501) initially designed for use as a sealing tape in the telecommunications industry. The major user in the UK for this type of application is British Telecom, who have approved it for water and corrosion sealing on moulded plastic sleeves jointing to their Specification No BTRB 071309. In this application the seal is further strengthened by overwrapping the pvc adhesive tape (Rotunda Ref 2702). PIB is also used as an insulation tape and has a voltage breakdown of 40kV/mm.

"As a waterproofing and sealing tape, pib has proved itself in a wide range of environments from the North Sea (tested to 6,000 psi in a saline water tank for water ingress) to the harsh arctic conditions of Canada: Bell-Canada/Ontario Hydro being among the major users.

"In all outdoor sealing applications u-v performance (ie resistance to ultra-violet radiation) is the critical characteristic which governs efficiency. Rotunda 2501 pib is u-v resistant and is expected to perform outside for a very long span of time as a waterproof/corrosion proof seal. For extreme and high voltage applications above 1kV, a layer of outdoor pvc tape (Rotunda Ref 2705) is advised, mainly as an abrasion protection. As far as application of pib is concerned, I completely agree with T A Sear, G4MGD, who outlined the basic requirements for a good seal (*TT* June 1985, p464). The pvc tape again being an added precaution against abrasion.

"In the May 1985 *TT*, Ken Lanyon, GM4GSJ, outlined the use of ptfe tape for sealing joints and terminations. I believe that a pib self-amalgamating tape would give a better seal due to its self-amalgamation which eliminates layers. In a recent study on water 'treeing' in power joints (where water ingress prevention is one of the most important factors) self-amalgamating tape was found to be the best type of tape used because once applied it forms a solid rubber seal without layers. In the same issue, G E Birkhead, E19DZ (G4KOQ), referred to a 3M 27 glass cloth tape, which is not readily available on this side of the Atlantic. Rotunda Ltd makes a similar tape (Ref 3107 glass cloth tape) which is available from our stockists.

"As well as the two previously mentioned companies, Rotunda products are available from our regional stockists. These include: Nu-Pax of Wythenshawe; Intech Tapes of Burgess Hill; Pebody & Muston of Leicester; Graham Tennant of Darlington; and Tayforth Storage Systems of Glenrothes. Apart from self-amalgamating tapes, Rotunda make polyethylene adhesive tapes, waterproof cloth adhesive tapes, cloth adhesive tapes, electrical jointing tapes, pvc electrical insulating tapes, pvc industrial adhesive tapes, double-sided adhesive tapes etc.''

Elements of non-uniform cross-section

Some 50 years ago mf broadcast antennas moved away from T designs supported by two high masts and tended to become mast-radiator designs. Some of the more ambitious stations used masts that tended to start thin,

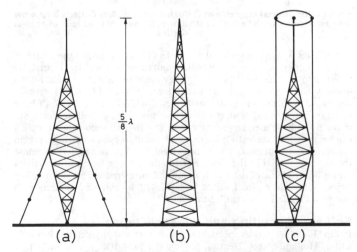

Fig 5. (a) Form of broadcast antenna tower promoted by Blaw Knox in the early 'thirties and used in a number of American stations until the problems were realized. (b) Another form of tower with non-uniform cross-section occasionally used in early 'thirties. (c) How wires were suspended at WCAU to restore proper current distribution

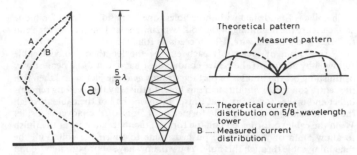

Fig 6. (a) Showing the non-sinusoidal current distribution that was found to occur with towers of non-uniform cross-section. (b) Field strength measurements made on WABC from aircraft that showed how vertical radiation pattern differed from theory

become wider at the centre and then taper off in the top section: rather like a squeezed diamond, though usually termed a "vertical guyed-cantilever antenna": Fig 5 (a). Alternatively tapered self-supporting towers were used.

It was left to the redoubtable Dr George Brown and Herman Gihring of RCA to show that the vertical radiation pattern of a typical $5\lambda/8$ antenna of this type, a 500ft high installation at WCAU in Philadelphia, differed significantly from that of a $5\lambda/8$ mast-radiator of uniform cross-section, with the result that its coverage area was well below expectations. In the course of this work the RCA engineers built an hf model antenna 7ft 10in high (1:64 scale) as a result of which the WCAU antenna was successfully modified (Fig 5 (c)). Since the results of the investigation were published in April 1935, mf tower antennas have been either structural steel towers of uniform cross-section or guyed flagpoles. The story is told in George Brown's very entertaining and outspoken autobiography *and part of which I was—recollections of a research engineer*.

I was reminded of this work by finding a detailed reference to it in the monthly "Techniques" column by Bill Orr, W6SAI, *Ham Radio* November 1985. He points out that the RCA work proved that the current distribution along a non-uniform cross-section element is non-sinusoidal, and that the theory governing the design of elements of constant cross-section does not apply. (W6SAI notes that the unexpected characteristics of a tapered element, although discovered from an hf model, escaped the notice of radio amateurs for many years.) This does not imply that an hf or vhf horizontal antenna element should never be tapered, but it does mean that you cannot use the conventional formulas for physical length etc, or assume that the vertical radiation pattern of a monopole will be exactly the same as for a uniform thin mast radiator.

W6SAI states that, for resonance, a tapered element, surprisingly, tends to be *longer* than for uniform cross-section. It was left to the late Jim Lawson, W2PV, to come up with computer programs that can be used to calculate the resonant lengths of tapered elements, but this can be done by trial-and-error provided that you recognize beforehand that its trimmed length may be longer than that given by the usual formulas.

In his refreshingly blunt manner, George Brown has written of this incident: "The vertical guyed-cantilever antenna promoted by Blaw-Knox was no doubt a mechanical marvel, but it was an outstanding example of the arrogance of ignorance. Apparently no consideration was given to the electrical performance of the structure before inflicting it upon a number of broadcasting stations who accepted the design in good faith . . . we all expended thousands of hours of engineering time to achieve a result which now comes routinely by using towers of uniform cross-section."

On the other hand, it provided an outstanding example of the value of using small model antennas at a correspondingly higher frequency, a technique that had been suggested by Professor Tykociner of the University of Illinois in 1925.

Antennas for long, long waves

Around the turn of the century, when radio communication was in its infancy, Marconi and his associates moved away from the ultra short wavelengths used for the earliest experiments by Heinrich Hertz, Lodge, Marconi and Chandra Bose to the lf and vlf spectrum with wavelengths of several thousand metres. Soon the "short waves" of 200m and down were declared useless and, in the USA, given to the newly-licensed "amateurs" in 1912.

To radiate signals on vlf/lf it was soon found that the more wire you could put up in the air the more power you could radiate. Antennas similar to those in Figs 7 and 8 were used. Even so the antennas were short in terms of wavelength. In the late 'twenties the most powerful transmitter in the world was Rugby Radio, GBR, on 16kHz (wavelength 18,750m) which could be relied upon to reach all parts of the globe due to the propagation of the signals via the earth–ionosphere waveguide. Such signals even

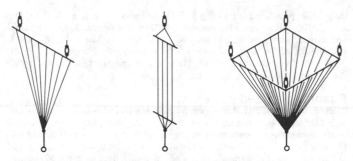

Fig 7. Fan, grid and square cone antennas popular at the turn of the century for long-wave transmissions

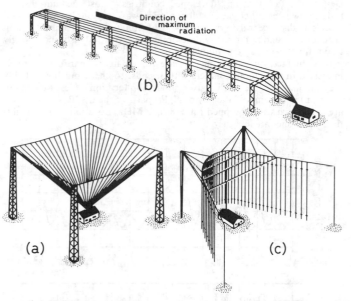

Fig 8. (a) The Poldhu antenna of 1901. (b) Inverted-L antenna of 1905. (c) Early hf directional antenna with parabolic reflector at Poldhu, 1923

penetrated some distance below the surface of the sea, permitting vlf to be used to broadcast messages to submarines.

However, vlf signals have a limited penetration in salt water, and for the past 20 years or so there has been work going on to exploit the elf spectrum below 3,000 hertz, including, for example, Project Sanguine (*TT* July, 1974) using frequencies as low as 45Hz. To radiate electromagnetic waves at such frequencies you need to send enormous power along many miles of wire—and then you are lucky to radiate, say, 1W! But the attenuation is so low (down to about 1·5dB per 1000km) that such signals can be picked up (even well below the sea's surface) on quite compact loop antennas. The snag is that you can send data only at about 1bit/s or less.

Ivan James, G5IJ, recently drew my attention to some fascinating work in northern Norway to use the hf "ionospheric heating" transmitter at Ramfjord to "modulate" the enormous natural currents in the polar electrojet. This then forms an extremely long antenna radiating up to about 1W in the frequency range 1 to 1·5kHz for hf effective radiated powers of

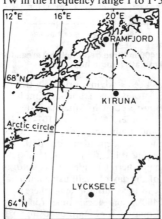

Fig 9. Map of Northern Scandinavia showing the location of the hf ionospheric heating transmitter at Ramfjord and the elf receiving sites at Kiruna and Lycksele

270MW (*Nature* 12 September 1985, p114 and pp155–6). This may not seem a highly efficient system but it avoids the problems of having to erect antennas up to a hundred miles or so long! The prime purpose of hf ionospheric heaters is to produce field-aligned scatter of vhf signals based on the non-linearity of the ionosphere producing cross-modulation (first observed in the 'thirties as the "Luxembourg effect"). Ionospheric heaters provide a practical way of extending the range of vhf transmissions. During the tests the hf transmitter was modulated at 1 and 1·5kHz and the ionospheric "mixing" resulted in elf signals being received at Kiruna and Lycksele: Fig 9.

Those PoW receivers

For sheer grit and "ham-ingenuity" it would be difficult to equal the efforts of those who built and operated their own equipment under the dangerous conditions of enemy occupation; in several countries all radio receivers were supposed to be handed in, and it was a serious offence to be found in possession of a broadcast receiver let alone communications equipment. But perhaps an even more difficult problem arose for those pre-war amateurs who became prisoners-of-war and found themselves involved in secret efforts to listen to the BBC news bulletins in huts that were regularly subjected to meticulous searches and sometimes having to "acquire" components by bribery, blackmail or theft where they could not be built from junk.

Amateurs who successfully built camp receivers include Herb Dixon, ZL2BO, in Hong Kong, Tom Douglas G3BA, in South-east Asia and, in Germany, "Shack" (Ernest Shackleton, G6SN) who in the 'thirties had been a regular contributor of "workshop notes" to the RSGB's *T&R Bulletin*, and had similarly contributed the workshop chapter for the RSGB's *Amateur Radio Handbook*.

Tom Douglas, talked about his experiences in Burma in the 1979 "Open Door" television programme and, since then, to a number of local societies.

Herb Dixon was a lieutenant in the RNZNVR who was taken prisoner in Hong Kong at the end of 1941. He played a leading role in the construction and operation of no less than three hf receivers that picked up bulletins from the UK for many months until September 1943. In one camp a derelict Austin 7 provided wire, nuts and bolts, and the rim of the horn formed part of a vernier tuning dial; headphones were constructed; flux obtained from pine-gum; solder scrounged from tag boards of defunct power equipment; fellow prisoners contributed more than 300 precious torch batteries. Valves were located in and smuggled out of a prison operating theatre when an unwitting PoW complained of a pain, lost a perfectly sound appendix but brought out three valves in his bandages. In one camp the receiver was hidden in a watertight container in a lavatory cistern; at the North Point camp a hole was dug under a hut under cover provided by the Canadian Brass Band. But on 21 September 1943, after a four-hour search, a receiver was discovered. Herb Dixon was one of nine officers interrogated and sentenced to long terms of imprisonment under extremely harsh conditions; he served two years before the war ended.

Captain Ernest Shackleton, was, in peacetime, a professional radio engineer with GEC. He was taken prisoner early in the war while serving with the Royal Signals; this was at St Valery-in-Caux in 1940. He then spent three months in hospital at Rouen recovering from wounds before ending up at Rotenburg-am-Fulda (Oflag 9A/Z). His story, published in the *Ilkley Gazette* in 1945, provides a vivid glimpse of what "ham ingenuity", when combined with professional skills, can do.

At a camp at Warburg the Germans permitted the prisoners to buy a "talkie" film projector, but insisted on having a sentry present with the equipment. This projector was later taken to Oflag 9 and impounded for several months. Then a film arrived, but the exciter lamp for the sound track was found to be broken and the Germans (fortunately) lost interest in the projector.

"We were able to remove a valve and a few capacitors etc. Variable capacitors were made from scrap; the spindles from clinical thermometer cases, the plates from Rowntree's cocoa tins rolled out flat on a table with a beer bottle. Two toothbrush handles provided insulation. Valve holders were made from a Bakelite ash tray laboriously cut and drilled with a penknife, with the contacts made from more cocoa tins, which were just the right size. Coil formers were toilet roll tubes impregnated with candle wax. Plug-in coils covered the broadcast bands needed to cover the varying seasonal propagation conditions.

"At first the set was fitted under floorboards and operated by two knitting needles that engaged with the capacitor extensions. Mains lead, telephone leads, antenna wires went via cracks between boards. The set could be closed down immediately and everything quickly made to look entirely innocent should any of the guards approach the hut.

"A warning system was devised by having a small group of prisoners apparently engaged in conversation some way from the hut. If a guard was spotted, one of the group simply sauntered away. This was observed by a look-out stationed just outside the room with the radio. He then opened the door and walked inside. Opening the door was the signal to close down the radio immediately.

"Following intensive searches, the set was moved to the canteen, where a similar system of 'stooging' was operated. Here the set was built into the wall behind a false side of a cupboard, but in an extended search about half the set was lost, only to be replaced in about 10 days, and the nightly 'secret listening service' resumed."

This set remained in operation until the final liberation of the camp in late March 1945. It was eventually recovered and later presented to the Imperial War Museum, though it is now some years since it was on display there.

There have been suggestions that one or more secret transmitters were built and operated in the PoW camps, but I have never seen any evidence of this and certainly do not recall any w/t links (a secret "letter code" *was* used). In 1945 "Shack" gave the following account of *preparations* to have a transmitter ready for use, and it is just possible that he was then reluctant to admit that one had actually been built. Those who knew him believe this may have been the case, but his 1945 story was as follows:

"In the summer of 1944 it was realized that there were possibilities of the camp being over-run in the near future, and some means of communication with the advancing Allied forces seemed desirable. The remaining cinema talkie gear was carefully examined and parts ear-marked for a future transmitter should such be found necessary. However, as the German guard and camp officers lived in the same building, and it was not known whether or not a short-wave receiver existed there, it was decided that any transmission by the prisoners would be highly dangerous. Plans were ready for the construction of a transmitter and this could have been built and working within 48 hours of orders from the British camp authorities. Unfortunately the Arnhem landings were not so successful as had been hoped, and before the Allied forces neared the camp the British officers had been marched some 150 miles east. Consequently no transmitter was ever built or existed in that camp."

Acknowledgements to Neil Glover, G3AAV, one-time Royal Signals and SAS, for reminding me of the radio equipment improvised by G6SN, and also to Diana Condell of the Imperial War Museum for providing extracts from the *Ilkley Gazette* of October 1945 and for pointing out that while "escape" activities by PoWs were legitimate under the Geneva Convention, prisoners caught in direct communication with the "enemy" would have been liable to be shot as "spies". She shares my doubts that any w/t links were established from the camps.

Many miniature receivers were made in the occupied countries. I recall being shown a very compact mains-operated hf receiver with an "acorn" type valve, built into a small tobacco tin and capable of good reception of 6 and 7MHz broadcast transmissions. Built by a member of the Dutch underground, it survived a careful search of passengers on a train, during which the resourceful Dutchman took the tin out of his pocket and pretended to be refilling his pipe.

Monolithic vhf crystal filters

Many years ago in *TT* and *Amateur Radio Techniques* I drew attention to the development of miniature hf and vhf bandpass monolithic crystal filters by American firms such as Collins, Bell Telephone Laboratories, Piezo Technology etc. Such filters have tended to be used primarily as "roofing filters" in commercial mobile-radio receivers etc.

An article in the Japanese industrial journal *JEE* (October 1985) by Yoshiaki Ogawa and Toshiki Suganuma of Nihon Dempa Kogyo, "MCFs move toward low price, miniaturization, and indispensable for hf communication" translated into rather quaint English text, claims that the mcf (Fig 10) has now been found to be suitable for mass production, and discusses in some detail i.f. filters centred on 58·1125MHz (a recently-adopted standard i.f. for Japanese mobile communications equipment) and also 45MHz, with characteristics that would appear to make them suitable for roofing filters in both hf and vhf communication receivers.

The 58MHz filter is an overtone filter with an ultimate rejection of more

than 80dB, pass bandwidth of ±8·5kHz or less at −3dB, ±25kHz or less at −25dB, 4dB or less insertion loss, 2dB or less ripple, 3,000Ω terminal impedance, and mounted in an HC−45/U holder. The 45MHz filter is suitable for nbfm receivers with a −3dB passband of more than ±3dB passband of more than ±16kHz. These monolithic filters are thus roughly the size of a modern single crystal.

Spanning a fixed path

There is a major difference between operating hf radio as an amateur and as a professional. Most amateurs, most of the time, tend to seek casual contacts either over convenient strong-signal paths or as weak-signal long-distance paths. Professionals, on the other hand, are often more concerned at being able to communicate over a specific path over as much of the time as possible, and consequently to be able to predict accurately the optimum frequency to use at any given time to pass traffic to specific destinations. Despite the fact that in "developed countries" most medium-distance traffic now goes either via broadband microwave radio-relay systems and most long-distance traffic via satellite, "hf circuits" are still important (on grounds of economy) in many developing countries and also, increasingly again, for "Defence" communications.

It is, in fact, an interesting exercise for amateurs, particularly those interested in scheduling contacts with friends, to check out how reliably they can make contact with a given single-hop location (ie less than about 4,000km) at any time of the day or night: parts of the USSR, Germany etc are easy for anyone equipped for 1·8 to 21MHz. Locations within night-time skip zones are less easy.

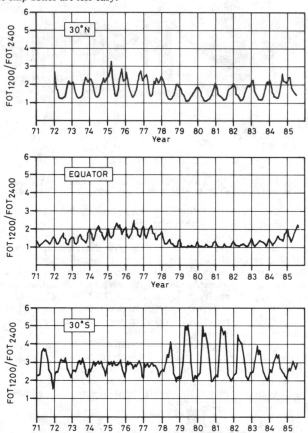

Fig 11. Variations of the FOT at 1200 and 2400 in three geographical areas for propagation over a 1,200km path (single hop)

I note that B A Austin, ZS6BKW, has been studying, primarily from a professional viewpoint, this problem: "Ionospheric and geographical effects on the choice of tactical and point-to-point hf antenna systems" (*Electronics Letters*, 7 November 1985, Vol 21, No 23, pp1107–8). He shows that the span between maximum and minimum frequencies needed to work over given single-hop distances is dependent on both the ionospheric conditions and on the geographical location of the terminals. In effect he notes that pairs of stations in northern latitudes and equatorial zones can maintain contact at any time of the day or night using antennas having less system bandwidth than those in the southern hemisphere.

He has analysed the FO1200/FO2400 hours local time for three geographical areas: 30°N, 30°S and the Equator, for longitudes 0° to 50°E

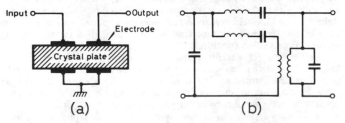

Fig 10. Monolithic crystal filter: (a) structure, and (b) equivalent circuit

and for a 14-year period from 1971 to July 1985 covering more than a sunspot cycle, including the December 1979 maximum and June 1976 minimum, based on predicted SSN numbers of the South African National Institute for Telecommunications. Fig 11 shows the variations of FO1200/2400 in three geographical areas for a 1,200km (745 miles) path. Whereas for equatorial 1,200km circuits an antenna system with a 2:1 frequency range would suffice, post-1979 operation at around 30°S necessitates in winter a near 5:1 span of frequencies. The 30°N variation does not exceed about 3:1. Unfortunately he does not appear to have analysed the situation at, say, 55°N where I suspect the span would need to be significantly more than 3:1. Again, his analysis is based on predictions rather than actual measurements. It would still seem to be open to others to investigate this problem in the light of actual experience—although it is easier to cover 24h continuously on a computer simulation than actually on-air!

Dump the decibel?

It always seemed to me a curious decision by the UK licensing authorities to change from "watts" to "dBW" in the amateur licence at a time when there was no mention of decibels in the RAE syllabus! In my opinion, plain, old-fashioned "dc input" or, as a second choice, "rf output" in *watts* was perfectly satisfactory. I suppose, like the camel, it was a decision made by a committee!

C W McCutchen, writing in the "Technically speaking" column of the *IEEE Spectrum* (September 1985, p17) seems to feel far more strongly than I do about the decibel, and not only in this specific connection. He writes:

"The decibel is an obsolete nuisance. When the only non-integral powers of numbers easily available were those of e or 10, the decibel was useful for working out the attenuation of cables. It was then convenient to describe the amplifier gain in decibels, NdB gain in the amplifier compensating for NdB loss in the cable. But there were costs that we are still paying. The decibel is not the physical quantity that does things. What the designer and the wise user most need to know is potential.

"The only remaining accomplishment of the decibel is mystification. In acoustics this is a resounding success. Layman talk about decibels and are misled. How many know that a 130dB sound has 100 times the pressures and 10,000 times the energy of a 90dB sound? And how many engineers truly understand these magnitudes?

"Let us forswear the mumbo jumbo. Let us say what we mean, be it volts, watts, dynes/cm², or watts/cm²."

I can think of few better ways of confusing newcomers to amateur radio than to regulate power in terms of dBW actually reaching the antenna

elements, but perhaps that was the intention. I can think of no other valid reason!

Admittedly, the logarithmic base of the decibel makes it convenient and meaningful for antenna gain (though it is easy to confuse dBd with dBi) but one could still use a log scale of ×1, ×10, ×100, ×1000 etc without bringing in the decibel. Personally I would not wish to see the decibel vanish, except in the regulation of amateur transmitter powers!

Low-cost "mechanical" audio filter

An ingenious low-cost form of audio filter to improve cw reception published in the Australian *Radio Experimenter* has been brought to my attention by Dave Bevan, G4DMR, on his return from a trip down-under.

In effect, in place of the usual metal diaphragm of an old-style headphone, new diaphragms are fashioned, with tin snips, from a piece of (non-ferrous) aluminium (say 1/32in thick) in which a small rectangular slot is then cut in the centre. A metal (ferrous) reed of the type used in musical instruments is then riveted (or fastened with a very small nut and bolt) at one end of the slot in such a way that it extends into the central opening for the same vibrating distance that it would in a musical instrument.

A headphone modified in this way will respond to signals at the resonant frequency of the reed (eg 440Hz (A) or what you consider a suitable beat note). Note that modern stereo-type and low-impedance headphones are not suitable. Headphones modified in this way will be highly insensitive to frequencies other than the resonant frequency of the reed; the writer puts it that the silence is uncanny.

I must admit that while I can see that this idea might work very well on low-speed morse, I cannot help wondering whether the decay time of a vibrating reed would not cause unacceptable "lag" at higher morse speeds. This point is not covered in the *Radio Experimenter* article, and it would be interesting to have some feedback from anyone tempted to give the idea a whirl. Since, if it does not work satisfactorily, the original diaphragms can be replaced no damage would be done. A friendly music shop might even be prepared to supply a spare reed at virtually no cost.

Tips and topics

Francis Rose, G2DRT, found it difficult to find a source for a Varian/Eimac SK1920 thermal heat link from the 8873 valve in his Heathkit SB230 linear to chassis until he located a UK manufacturer of beryllium oxide ceramics: Consolidated Beryllium Ltd, PO Box 5, Marble Hill Road, Milford Haven, Dyfed SA73 2PP; (tel (06462) 7681).

Technical Topics
by Pat Hawker, G3VA

AMATEUR RADIO means different things to different people and I would not wish to give the impression that only the do-it-yourself, home-constructor is the true inheritor of the legacy of the experimental era. Indeed I would readily admit that it is the enjoyment of manual cw operating that primarily has maintained my own interest in the technical aspects of radio communication over the years.

Morse and the deaf

Then again there is the special bonus that the hobby can give to handicapped persons, including the house-bound, the blind and the deaf and hard-of-hearing. In each case, two-way radio provides the means of communicating virtually on an equal basis with the rest of the world.

In the December "Mailbag", Professor Alex Comfort stressed the potential value of the morse code in the field of medical robotics for the severely handicapped. Morse, he stressed "has a far greater potential as a language interface for the disabled than most of the experimental systems seem to realize." If you missed his letter "Radio and medicine" turn to the December issue, p922.

By coincidence, a few weeks before it appeared I received a very long letter from Nigel Neame, ex-G2AUB, who urged me, on the basis of his experience over many years of increasing deafness, to stress the international importance of cw communication for the deaf. For many of the hard-of-hearing, morse is the only aural means of communication. Even for the profoundly deaf it is possible to receive morse by means of a vibrating sensor etc. Nigel Neame would like to see morse taught in schools, at the very least in all schools for the deaf. Because of their handicap many of the profoundly deaf cannot afford all-singing, all-dancing transceivers, but could manage a simple cw-only hf rig of the classic "beginners style" that I have often suggested in *TT*, which can still bring plenty of interesting cw contacts on the lower hf bands.

He writes: "CW enables a licensed deaf amateur to communicate *on equal terms* with any other person virtually throughout the world. The words 'on equal terms' are most significant, since there is no other means of direct *human* to *human* communication available between the deaf and non-deaf apart from 'signing' and lip-reading—and how many non-deaf people learn those skills?"

He would like to see frequencies reserved for deaf operators, though this would, I suspect, not be necessary except perhaps on 14MHz.

It is extremely good news for all handicapped persons that the RSGB intends establishing some 70 local centres where it will be possible to take the morse examination. Ex-G2AUB feels that more information should be published on simple, "kiss" receivers, transmitters and transceivers that could be built within the limited budgets of many handicapped people.

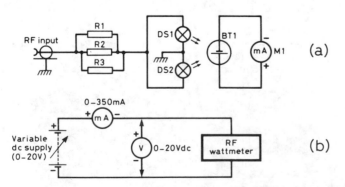

Fig 1. The simple rf wattmeter described in *QST* (November 1979) by James Kennedy, W7MID (see *TT* February 1980). Suitable as shown for use up to about 30MHz at powers up to 5W. Two small pilot bulbs (6 to 9V, 0·15A) form part of a 50Ω dummy load and are mounted in a lightproof enclosure about 3in from the face of a solar cell. M1 is 1mA fsd meter. R1, 2 and 3 are 100Ω 2W carbon resistors. Calibrated against dc as shown in (b). The scale is likely to be compressed towards fsd and maximum sensitivity at fairly low output above a minimum threshold

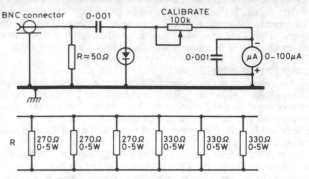

Fig 2. W9QB's 5W rf wattmeter suitable, with careful construction, for use to 144MHz and above

Dummy load/power meters

While all must admire the sheer ingenuity of the design by Ian Braithwaite, G4COL, of his "Accurate rf power meter for the hf bands" (*Rad Com* December 1985, pp924–930), I could not help feeling that it offended against the "kiss" concept (keep it simple, stupid). With a component list filling half-a-page, digital read-out *et al* it seemed to require a lot of effort to achieve the claimed accuracy of ± 10 per cent for a range of 40 to 400mW.

How much simpler, yet providing reasonable accuracy, is the technique of measuring the voltage across a matched dummy load—provided the analogue meter scale is calibrated correctly. Alternatively, if you want to use optical methods, there is either the traditional "grease-spot photometer" or simply the use of a solar cell calibrated against dc: Fig 1.

A number of dummy load/power meters have been described in *TT* and *ART,* and a recent design by Harry Neben, W9QB, specifically intended for 144MHz handhelds, appeared in *QST* March 1985: Fig 2. With care, W9QB reports that even with paralleled 0·5W carbon-composition or film resistors it is possible to obtain low swr (indicating minimal inductance in the load) throughout the vhf range. At hf, construction would be even less critical. Many years ago Dick Halls, G3EIW, provided very useful notes on this type of combined power-meter/dummy-load, that can indicate power output to within about 10 per cent of true value and is capable of being used from 50Hz to about 144MHz: Fig 3.

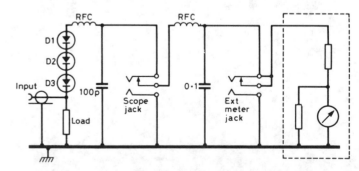

Fig 3. G3EIW's general-purpose power meter/dummy load. A single diode of suitable piv could be substituted for D1, D2 and D3. The scope jack will be found useful for ssb applications

He simply measured the peak voltage developed across a non-inductive matched dummy load. In order to convert the voltage into watts, a high-resistance voltmeter can be built into the unit and calibrated in watts. Alternatively, it is quite practical to use an external test meter with a conversion table as shown in Table 1.

It was pointed out at the time that the only constructional precautions are to make the load "look" like lossy co-axial cable to the transmitter; to screen the detector from the load resistor to avoid direct pick-up; and to provide effective decoupling to prevent pick-up on the meter wires.

Table 1
WR = V²

W	R	V²	V	V peak
1	70	70	8.32	11.6
5	70	350	18.7	26.2
10	70	700	26.2	36.8
20	70	1400	37.4	51
30	70	2100	45.8	63.5
40	70	2800	52.9	72.5
50	70	3500	59.2	83
60	70	4200	64.8	91
70	70	4900	70.0	98
80	70	5600	74.8	104
90	70	6300	79.3	111
100	70	7000	83.6	116
120	70	8400	91.6	127
150	70	10,500	102.5	143
200	70	14,000	118.3	165
0·75	70	52	7·2	10·05
0·5	70	35	5·8	8·05
0·25	70	17·5	4·05	5·65

From the basic power relationship, $W = I^2R$ and $W = I \times V$ it follows that $W \times R = V^2$. A typical table of values is constructed as in Table 1, extending over the power range to be measured, the final value being the peak V to be used as an indication of power. If a built-in meter is to be used this should have an fsd current not greater than 200μA, and a suitable series resistance can be calculated from volt range required/fsd current in amperes. For small increments of meter deflection and to take any inaccuracy in the series resistor, the damping resistor across the meter coil could be varied by up to 10 per cent of its nominal value.

A new scale can be constructed once the fsd is known in terms of volts and will be linear.

In his original unit Dick Halls used a 67·7Ω Morganite non-inductive high-wattage resistor. However, it is quite possible to make a 100W load using six 1W resistors in an oil-filled jam-jar, as described by F Lees, G3PD, (*TT* May 1984, p404). For low-power, as in the W9QB unit, the resistors can be air-mounted.

A note about this general type of unit has come recently from Chris Trayner, G4OKW. He writes:

"One often uses a dummy load with an attenuator attached and a diode rectifier and capacitor following that. This allows one to 'take a snifter' and measure the power dissipated. With a built in meter the scale can be calibrated to provide a reading in watts. But, commonly, use is made of a general-purpose multimeter and then it is necessary to perform a calculation to deduce the power.

"My suggestion is simply that a suitable choice of the attenuation ratio simplifies the arithmetic, by making the power in watts numerically equal to the attenuated voltage (in volts) squared. For a 50Ω load, for example, the ratio should be 7·07:1, for a 75Ω load 8·65:1. In practice these ratios can be approximated.

"The maths can readily be verified; in general the ratio should be the square root of the impedance in ohms. Fig 4 shows the use of 5·6kΩ and 3kΩ resistors with a 50Ω load."

Fuses and safety

At one time it was common practice with mains-operated equipment to use twin mains-lead, no earth-wire, and a fuse in each lead to cope with the reversible mains plugs. Mains practice on the Continent differs in several respects from UK practice, and the use of two fuses continues to be a common, indeed sensible, precaution where plugs can sometimes be reversed.

In the October *TT* (Fig 7, p785) Robin Greenwood, G3LBA, who is licensed also as PA3ACQ and operates normally from Holland, incorporated two fuses in his high-current "hexfet" psu, one in the live ("phase") lead and one in the neutral lead.

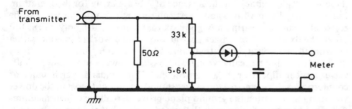

Fig 4. G4OKW suggests that a suitable ratio attenuator can simplify the arithmetic of a simple power meter

This has prompted Chris Trayner, G4OKW (64 Sydney Street, Brightlinsea, Essex CO7 0BE, telephone 0206 303931) to comment as follows:

"This practice may be sensible on the Continent where often plugs can be reversed, but could represent a safety problem in the UK: if the 'neutral' fuse blows first it could still leave mains voltage reaching the equipment, etc. But I have been unable to verify that this practice is 'dangerous' and possibly even illegal. Neither the IEE's Wiring Regulations nor BS415 appear to cover this point, and indeed there are still UK designers continuing the practice (possibly on the grounds that not all ac mains sockets are correctly wired —G3VA). Although most of my colleagues agree that there is a safety hazard, nobody can quote any specific regulations. Can anyone point to an official regulation covering this practice?"

Old technology that doesn't die

One of the difficulties that arise from all the new technology that has flooded into the amateur radio world in the past couple of decades is that it has not entirely replaced the old.

The thermionic valve power oscillator completely displaced, in a matter of a few years, the spark coil. But the valve is still very much with us, at least for high power, even though all-solidstate radio and television broadcast transmitters are now available up to about 50kW mf and 5–10kW and even 50kW vhf. However, the manufacturers, if pressed, will admit that many problems have marked the development of solidstate broadcast transmitters, not least the vulnerability to the effects of lightning discharges. There also remains an economic cross-over that still makes the valve approach less costly beyond a certain level—Marconi for instance in relation to vhf television put this at around 2·5kW. For amateur linear amplifiers it is probably a few hundred watts p.e.p.—and it is still possible to make a low-cost valve linear more linear than a low-cost solidstate linear!

One consequence of all this is that not only old-timers but also many newcomers, more especially those interested in hf, still need to know a good deal about valve principles and practice. And as valves, particularly high-power valves, steadily become more and more costly so it becomes more and more advisable to learn how to ensure that we get the maximum life from them. *TT* June 1982, p498 had something to say about "the use and abuse of valves" with emphasis on careful control of the voltage applied to thoriated tungsten filaments.

But it is perhaps appropriate to recall how excessive heat and electrode dissipation affects the life of valves and to note that the gradual and almost inevitable loss of cathode or filament emission is not the only problem.

"Soft" valves

Basically, as cathode emission falls, so does the gain (mutual conductance). In many applications this means that to restore the gain, the bias applied to the grid is lowered—automatically or manually—and current rises.

This not only increases the rate of cathode deterioration but the added heat will tend to liberate the traces of gas which inevitably remain "bound" to the metallic parts of the valve, producing positive ions which may poison the cathode or cause negative (reverse) grid current. In other words, the valve becomes increasingly "soft" with a tendency for the anode current to rise causing further overheating.

Early valves and cathode-ray tubes tended to be "soft" even when new. But quite early on techniques were introduced that made it possible for valves to be produced that had a "hard" vacuum and a "getter" to maintain this under normal conditions.

In order to provide as near a vacuum as possible, valves were heated by passing them through a heated chamber, and by the use of rf heating while the air was being withdrawn. Despite this, a small amount of gas usually remained occluded in the assembly, and later may be released when the valve becomes hot in operation. To remove virtually the last traces of free gas, some barium or magnesium called the "getter" was usually evaporated within the valve envelope just before sealing, fired by hf eddy currents. After evaporation this tended to condense on the envelope near the getter-holder (the small metal holder welded to the electrode assembly). In the 'forties and 'fifties the glass "foot" with connecting wires pinched in, gave-way to the pressed-glass base with stouter wires moulded into the glass base serving as lead-in wires and valve pins.

Even with correctly applied gettering a small amount of gas usually remains and can be released by overheating.

Normally the flow of grid current through the mandatory grid resistor produces a negative bias on the grid. But should a negative grid current flow, the grid resistor produces a positive bias (or reduces the negative bias) resulting in an increased space current and internal dissipation within the valve.

To quote from a long-out-of-print 1948 RSGB publication, *Valve*

Technique, reversed or negative grid current can arise from three causes: **(a)** Internal leakage paths within the valve or its base. **(b)** Positive ion current, due to faulty vacuum as traces of free gas are released from the metal structure (ie the valve becoming "soft"). **(c)** Electron emission from the grid (grid emission). All these factors tend to increase with an increase in the valve operating temperature. As increased temperatures result from increased dissipation, such defects, once developed, tend progressively to become increasingly serious.

The first signs tend to be excessive anode current (sometimes rising progressively after the valve has been switched on for a time) and/or heavy damping of the input circuit, so that there will appear to be lack of drive from the preceding stage. By the time the problem is spotted it will usually be irreversible and the valve has to be replaced. But it needs to be stressed that the problem is unlikely to arise if due attention has been given to the following points:

(a) Ensure the filament or heater voltage is within the specified tolerance. This is usually ± 5 per cent but it is better to keep to ± 3 per cent for thoriated tungsten filaments and longest life is achieved by careful regulation and management of this supply, at 95% of the nominal voltage. Such a procedure, while specifically aimed at delaying loss of emission, will also help prevent the valve becoming "soft".

(b) Do not permit excessive dissipation. Make sure you understand particularly in Class C stages the difference between power input and power output (power dissipated internally is the difference between the two). In other words check that the valve is operating within the correct characteristics for the application concerned.

(c) Limit the total dc resistance of the grid-cathode path to a safe value. This need may be less obvious.

Valve Technique suggested that where a safe value is not included in manufacturer's data, a rule-of-thumb guide is:

Fixed bias: total cathode current (mA) times grid resistance (in megohms) should be less than 15.

Automatic cathode bias: total cathode current (mA) times grid resistance (in megohms) should be less than 25.

Where several valves are connected in parallel or push-pull with a common grid resistor clearly the total cathode current of all must be considered.

With, for example, a set of three matched 6146 valves for an FT102 now costing around £40, it is prudent to pay attention to the type of good operating practice that prolongs active life. Valves, properly treated, can give good, rugged service over many years. I recall the old Dollis Hill Post Office Research Station developing valves for ocean cable repeaters having a guaranteed continuous life of 20 years. I suspect that many ordinary valves are still giving good service after 40 or 50 years use in receivers (certainly some are at G3VA!).

There is a growing interest in collecting and restoring early broadcast receivers. One of the best private collections is that of Gerald Wells (Vintage Wireless Museum, Rosendale Road, West Dulwich, south London). Recently, at an IEE lecture on "The history of sound broadcasting" given by Dr G.J. Phillips, Mr Wells announced that he hopes soon to have the necessary equipment for rebuilding old valves, including replacing burnt-out filaments and re-vacuuming. It created more interest than any new semiconductor device could hope to arouse!

"Project 6L6"

It is not only in the amateur radio field that the younger generation is showing a diminishing interest in "kitchen table" home-construction of equipment. It applies virtually to all electronic hobbies, particularly since the large-scale introduction of personal computers, and is reflected in falling circulations of many long-established magazines.

Conversely there is a growing nostalgia among old-timers for the days when a simple transmitter could be put together in an evening and an 0-v-1 or 1-v-1 receiver could cope with band conditions (as indeed direct-conversion can still do reasonably well on the lower frequency bands).

Dean Manley, KH6B, writing from Hawaii, draws attention to the fact that 1986 is the 50th anniversary of the introduction of the once highly popular 6L6 beam tetrode valve by RCA Radiotron. It rapidly became popular not only for its intended audio applications but also as a crystal-controlled power oscillator which when run at about 20 to 25W input could put out a very effective signal on 3·5, 7 and (in a tritet configuration) on 14MHz. *QST* May 1936, mentioned the 6L6 for the first time; the following month showed the use of a 6L6 as a crystal oscillator. As KH6B puts it: "The rest is history". The 6L6 soon led to the 807 beam tetrode intended for either af or rf applications and the host of later single and double beam-tetrodes.

KH6B is seeking to encourage a Project 6L6, not only to mark the golden jubilee but also to revive interest in simple ("kiss") rigs as club projects etc.

He writes: "It seems only natural for amateurs to build and experiment. A simple rig with a 6L6 would fill this bill. Building your own rig is half the fun. The other half is putting it on the air and convincing the disbelievers that you've really a metal 6L6 or glass 6L6G in the final, then taking the rig along to the local club and enticing others into the homebrew game."

Such rigs are not necessarily confined to cw. Amplitude (Heising) modulation of a crystal oscillator is not recommended practice, but many did it. A few brief contacts, just to prove it still works (and can be received as ssb), would hurt nobody. Indeed there is little reason why a.m. should not be reintroduced more widely on 1·9MHz or 29MHz. The 6V6co 6L6/807pa combination is better than a power oscillator.

One would like to see Project 6L6 extended to include, as a next step, "kiss" forms of solidstate. One has to accept, even if reluctantly, that the old order changeth. Even RCA, itself responsible for so many major contributions to radio engineering (not to mention the AR88D!), is being merged with General Electric (USA).

Axeman spare that tree!

Les Moxon, G6XN, has been busy developing a delta-loop beam intended for the long-path to Australia on 7MHz ssb, subject to constraints imposed by lack of space and the need to minimise visual impact. In this connection he writes:

"Compared with my previous QTH, results with vertical polarization have been poor. I estimated my signal to be at least one S-point worse, relative to horizontal polarization, and sometimes considerably more depending on the placement of the vertical element.

"The factors involved are trees and sandy soil. I feel there is an urgent need for more research into the effect of trees near a vertically-polarized antenna. I did a few crude experiments, scaled to 28MHz, and found marked 'shadows', often to one side of a tree rather than directly behind it, although proximity of pylons and power lines may have confused the issue.

"Even with an array of two vertical elements on 7MHz, I was not able (except for one or two dubious reports) to improve on the performance of a simple inverted-vee dipole with its apex at 37ft.

"This has led me to investigate the design of horizontal (fixed) beam arrays suitable for 'burying' in trees, and I have been surprised by the completeness with which the tree appears to have 'swallowed' the antenna without absorbing the power.

"In this antenna, which is along the lines of my earlier contributions to *TT*, 33ft horizontal tubing elements, 44ft above ground, are end-fed with 41ft of 18swg aluminium alloy wires dropped to a point 6ft above ground.

"With the current nulls coming in the centre of these wires all radiation should effectively come from the horizontal element 'top'. (See *TT* March 1985). "This involved a tricky bit of tree climbing but I was able to enlist the services of a tree-surgeon's apprentice who works on his own account at weekends; an idea that I recommend to others having 'unclimbable' (to them) trees in their gardens.

"To use such assistance to best advantage it is necessary to adopt an antenna array that is basically simple and does not require tuning before erection, hence my use of loops with open-wire stubs. By good planning in advance of the entire operation, the antenna cost me £25 (three hours work) a lot less than a conventional, commercial 'beam' antenna. And although my initial requirement was for 7MHz only, the loops are, in effect, 10MHz loops, so there is no problem on that band; on 14MHz performance (gain) equals that of my 'Claw' array (*TT* March 1985) at the same height. I hope shortly to phase the two arrays together and so get an extra 3dB gain".

It is hoped to discuss this "claw in a tree" antenna in more detail over the next few months. The point we are trying to make this month is the significant effect of trees on vertically polarized signals, yet they have very little effect (and can be very useful as supports) with horizontal polarization.

Vertical antennas and real earth

How many times have you read articles that start off by emphasizing that vertical antennas provide omni-directional low angle radiation and are therefore ideally suitable in the absence of a beam array for dx operation. Indeed if you listen with a good vertically-polarized antenna you can be reasonably sure of hearing any good dx that's going. It's only when, too often, the dx fails to come back to you and instead works someone with a horizontally-polarized dipole that doubts begin to creep in.

There's nothing basically wrong with a quarter-wave monopole, a half-wave vertical dipole or a $\frac{5}{8}\lambda$ vertical etc. With radials, earth mats or counterpoises there is no reason why it should not put out most of the power you feed into it. Often the ground plane proves a really excellent medium-distance antenna and gives you the added bonus that the reports you are given are often two or three S-points above those you hand out to the stations you contact.

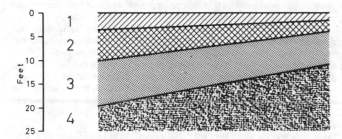

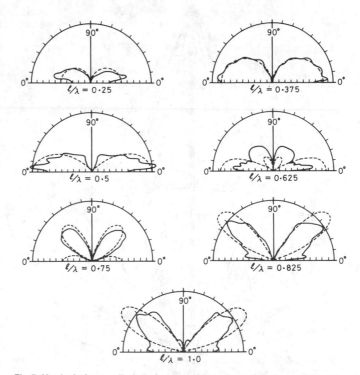

Fig 5. Typical section of earth's crust showing geological strata with several layers of different electrical conductivity. (1) Alluvial soil having relatively good conductivity (about 20 × 10⁻¹⁴ emu. (2) Sandy soil about 4 × 10⁻¹⁴ emu. (3) Chalk about 10 × 10⁻¹⁴ emu. (4) Young rock about 1 × 10⁻¹⁴. Sea water has conductivity about 4 × 10⁻¹¹, ie about 4,000 × 10⁻¹⁴. Effective conductivity depends upon depth of penetration of the earth currents and is thus a function of frequency: the higher the frequency the more the current will be concentrated in the uppermost levels. (From "The ground beneath us" G3HRH, 1966.)

If you operate maritime mobile you are likely to find that a 30-ft all-band vertical really does live up to the claims of excellent dx performance. By now the penny will have dropped. With a ground plane consisting of conductive salt water you can confidently expect to achieve excellent low-angle radiation. In country areas in those parts of the UK that have good earth conductivity, or for the chap who can establish an earth mat stretching out for several wavelengths towards a desired direction, the 14/21/28MHz vertical is an excellent dx performer. See Fig 5 and Fig 6.

It is for the many of us who live in urban areas, or areas of poorish earth conductivity that the low angles are not achievable on transmission, though remaining reasonably unaffected on reception—a notable exception to the theory of reciprocity of antennas that seldom gets mentioned.

It is difficult, of course, to find out (except by frustration) the vertical radiation pattern of an antenna above "real earth". The professionals who measure such patterns by flying aircraft around the area take care not to locate their vertical antennas for long-distance working in areas of poor conductivity or where the signals are likely to be affected by the many vertical structures that clutter our sites (trees, houses, electricity pylons etc).

On 14MHz and above, provided you can get a horizontal dipole 25ft or more above ground and in the clear, it will generally out-perform a vertical antenna unless you live in an area of extremely good earth conductivity or, conversely, in an area of extremely poor earth conductivity (where effectively the supergain "image" is not formed). This can apply also to antennas for 1·8 to 7MHz. Peter Chadwick, G3RZP has pointed out that

Fig 7. Vertical plane radiation characteristics of small-scale model antenna with effective groundplane

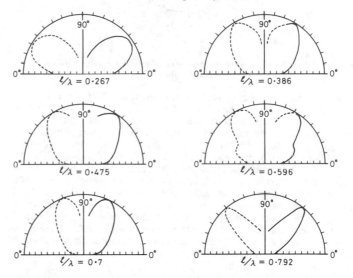

Fig 8. Vertical plane radiation characteristics of full-scale model of the biconical monopole antenna of Fig 10. Ground conductivity 8 × 10⁻² mho/m. Note the much higher angle of maximum radiation

his late father's "G8ON" antenna tends to perform better in areas of very poor conductivity, than in more conductive areas. The problem with verticals is mainly in areas of medium or poorish ground conductivity or where there are trees and other vertical structures.

Digging back in the literature to 1963, before the days of computer simulations, I found a set of diagrams relating to a broadband hf biconical monopole developed for the Royal Navy that does show very clearly that low-angle radiation is not an inherent feature of vertically polarized antennas: compare Figs 7 and 8.

This design, and the associated vertical radiation patterns, come from "Some factors influencing the design of broadband hf monopole aerials" presented by H P Mason at the 1963 IEE Convention on hf communication (IEE publication ED4, pp114–20). This antenna was designed to cover the range 10 to 26MHz with a support pole of the order of 25ft and 36 ground radials: Fig 9.

The conductors were 7/19swg cadmium copper wire to a total semi-perimeter length of 25ft 10in, including the terminating sections. The wires were spaced equidistant around a concentric steel supporting mast of 1in

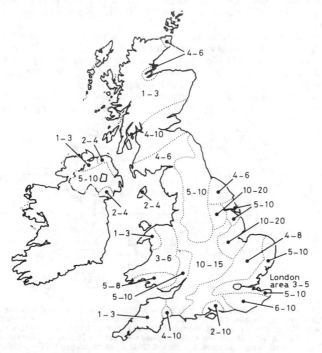

Fig 6. Rough ground conductivity map of the UK (figures quoted are for 1·5MHz). Conductivity is moderate to good in central and southeast England, poor in London, west and northwest. Urban areas tend to be of lower conductivity than farmland and rural areas

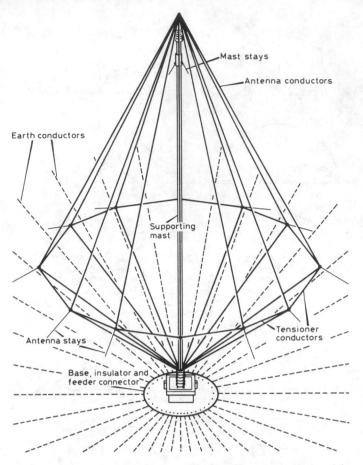

Fig 9. General arrangement of biconical monopole antenna designed for broadband operation

radius . . . for structural reasons it was found to be of advantage to make the height of the lower cone less than the upper, in this instance the slant height ratio of the upper to lower cones was 2·6:1. Added rigidity was given to the conductors by fitting horizontal wires at the point of maximum diameter and maintaining the correct section by the use of insulated radial stays. The whole structure was supported upon a special low-loss insulator and base-plate assembly, designed to produce minimum discontinuity to the terminal characteristic. Connection to the feeder was made by means of a conductor, mounted concentrically within the insulator. The associated ground conductor system consisted of 36 equally spaced radial wires of 7/19swg. It was claimed the system could be designed to match either 50Ω (lower cone half-angle 38·5°) or 75Ω (lower cone half-angle 23·2°) to cover bandwidths of the order of 2·6:1 without any matching or tuning units with swr not exceeding 2:1. Operational designs covering also 4 to 11MHz and 2 to 5MHz were developed.

Polarization and meteor scatter

The increasing use of meteor scatter burst systems by professionals as well as by amateurs is causing a number of research establishments to look more closely at the propagation characteristics. John Wilson (ex-G8KIS) draws attention to a recent report (*Electronics Letters*, Vol 21, No 24, 21 November 1985) from H Nes of the Shape Technical Centre at The Hague. Nes notes that several of the finer details of this type of forward scatter remain either unpredictable or unexplored. He writes:

"One such area of uncertainty relates to the polarization properties of the echoes. Classical theory predicts that the performance should be the same

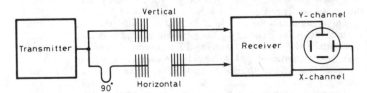

Fig 10. Measurement system used to check polarization of signals received via meteor trails. Arrangement shown for circular polarization

for horizontal and vertical polarization, but definitive experimental support for this has been lacking.

"A 40MHz carrier was transmitted from Tangen Fort, near Oslo and received in The Hague, a distance of 850km. The transmitting station comprised a 1kW transmitter, a power splitter and a crossed Yagi antenna on a glass-fibre mast on a 40m cliff overlooking the sea. One 5-el Yagi was mounted for horizontal polarization and one for vertical polarization, arranged for horizontal, vertical or circular (90° delay) polarization. An identical crossed Yagi on a 40m tower overlooking flat countryside, a two-channel receiver and an oscilloscope in the x-y mode (Fig 10) with the dynamic patterns video recorded and studied in detail.

"Measurements in June 1985 included about one hour of video recording for each of the three modes . . . For transmission with horizontal polarization the received echoes were typically also horizontally polarized with a deviation of about ±20°.

"Long-lasting echoes (as usually exploited by amateurs not using computer-controlled probing systems—*G3VA*) were characterized by the reception of random polarization, the randomness starting approximately one second after the creation of the echoes.

"With vertical polarization, vertical polarization was usually received for the first second, then random polarization. With circular polarization, ellipses predominated, the ratio between horizontal and vertical axes being approximately 1·5, corresponding to 20 log (1·5) = 3·5dB.

"Conclusions to be drawn are: (1) typically (on short echoes) the received echoes have the same polarization as the transmitted signal; (2) horizontal polarization performs 3–4dB better than vertical polarization."

Most amateur ms is already made with horizontal polarization, but these measurements confirm the advantage so gained, particularly on short echoes.

More signal-frequency crystal filters

Since the item on signal-frequency crystal filters (*TT* July 1985, pp541–2) Peter Haylett, G3IPV, has continued his work and, like a true experimenter, has introduced a number of variations and second thoughts. The most important of these has been directed towards making the front-end crystal filter tunable over a limited section of a band using the crystal "pulling" techniques associated with variable crystal oscillators (vxo). A steady stream of ideas have come from him to the extent where it becomes a little difficult to determine which ideas have been carried forward and which have been abandoned!

However it seems safest to start at the end, and report his latest technique for a 3·5MHz tunable filter that uses electric-field coupling between two toroids spaced about 2in apart. Fig 11 shows his basic arrangement, together with winding details etc, for tuning ranges of 25kHz and 50kHz. He believes this arrangement should prove to be the end of the road in basic design, though he intends to continue work on more complex multi-section filters.

It would be interesting to know the insertion loss of such a loosely coupled filter, although in view of the high external noise level on 3·5MHz, insertion loss is of only minor importance on that band when used with a low-noise receiver: it is signal-to-noise that matters on 3·5MHz and the insertion loss affects external noise and signals equally.

G3IPV has also been experimenting on the use of tunable signal-frequency filters for ssb operation, using stenode-type boosting of the

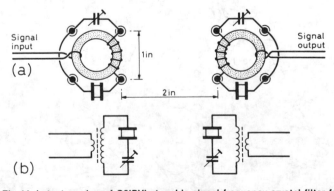

Fig 11. Latest version of G3IPV's tunable signal frequency crystal filter for 3·5MHz. Toroids Siemens KO618X001 from Electrovalue, Surrey. For a tuning range of 25kHz wind 5ft 24swg enam copper wire (about 50 turns). For a tuning range of 50kHz wind 7ft 24swg enam copper wire (about 70 turns). Trimmers 25pF airspaced vane. Crystals 3·5 to 3·810MHz (as required) HC6U holder McKnight, Southampton. Note that tuning range varies with different crystal manufacturers etc. Latest experiments show that highest voltage appears across the coil and not the crystal so that filters should be constructed as above rather than as shown in Photo 1 of an earlier version.

Photo 1. Example of a G3IPV basic crystal filter showing the use of earth-isolated rf technology. This is an earlier version of the filter shown in Fig 11 which has electric field coupling between the coils rather than the crystals. Greater attenuation can be obtained with more filter sections

higher audio frequencies. It would appear that the prime consideration in sf filters is to minimize rf leakage around the filter, requiring careful isolated-earth construction. In this case a minor problem had to be overcome due to leakage between the metal holders of the crystals (possibly forming a loop with stray capacitors and the metal box).

To achieve "stenode-mode" operation the af output from the receiver is modified by placing an 0·47μF capacitor in series with the low-impedance headphones (possibly 100pF in series with high-impedance headphones). G3IPV reports that it has proved possible to tune ssb filters over several kHz giving improved reception by attenuation of adjacent channel interference and (presumably) also helping to reduce intermodulation problems etc. For tunable cw filters a two-crystal filter does not provide particularly high off-resonance attenuation but it is possible to add extra crystals and achieve higher attenuation.

300W dc/ac inverter
The general use of 12V dc equipment has tended to reduce the requirement to generate 110, 220 or 240Vac in locations where there are no public supply mains. Where the need arises it tends to be met by the use of petrol-electric generators.

But it should not be forgotten that an alternative approach is possible unless extended periods of operation are required. In the old days there were the rotary converters which could achieve an efficiency of around 50 to 60 per cent with outputs of from about 50 to 350W ac from large capacity lead-acid vehicle batteries. The rotary converter has been long superseded by the higher-efficiency solidstate inverters using power transistors or silicon-controlled rectifiers (thyristors). Unfortunately simple switched-mode inverters tend to provide a square-wave rather than a sine-wave output, and this can cause problems with communications equipment. However, it is possible to obtain near sinusoidal waveforms by tuning the primary winding of the transformer or synthesized by switching on, in an ordered sequence, a series of silicon-controlled rectifiers. A compromise is a simple stepped-waveform such as that shown in Fig 12.

An interesting design for a compact 12/230V 300VA inverter, with full constructional details, appears in *Electronics Australia* (September 1985, pp40-44, 46-47, 50-52). The 50Hz frequency is derived from a 4MHz crystal with ic dividers and then buffered to drive four 2N3771 in a parallel push-pull switching arrangement with a voltage step-up transformer. This may seem simple but the complete unit features the use of a compact toroidal transformer, automatic starting, voltage regulation, current limiting and thermal overload protection with about 10 ic devices, a dozen transistors and assorted diodes, l.e.d indicators etc. It delivers a waveform of the type shown in Fig 12.

This is one of those units for which it would be virtually essential for a

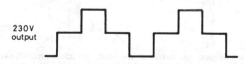

230V
output

Fig 12. Output wave form of the 300VA 12/240V inverter

constructor to consult the full text and diagrams of the original article by John Clark.

For a 40W load the input current from the battery is 4·6A, so that a 40Ah/20h battery could provide about 4h operation without recharging. For a 200W load the input current rises to 21·7A and battery-life reduces to 50min. At 300W it's down to 28min since the current drawn is a massive 30·3A. A kit from Altronics Pty Ltd is offered at $A199.

A lower-power, less complex inverter has been described in *Electronics Australia* (August 1985).

Stabilized 11GHz oscillator/mixer module
The growing use of low-power 11GHz distribution satellites for providing satellite programme feeds to cable networks has led to the development of television receive-only terminals (tvro) for use in leisure centres, hotels, and even homes with parabolic dish antennas of about 1·6 to 2·5 metres. It is now possible to obtain a licence for their use.

Stuart Jones, GW3XYW, has built an 11GHz tvro along the lines described by Hugh Cocks in *Television* (February 1985) and featuring the use of the Mitsubishi FO-UP-11K oscillator/mixer module developed initially for radar. This incorporates a dielectric resonator oscillator, as discussed on several occasions in *TT*. GW3XYW writes:

"I am not a 10GHz enthusiast, my interest being in 11GHz tvro, but it does cross my mind that this receiver unit might be useful for the amateur band. The oscillator can be tuned from about 10·4 to 11·4GHz, so that with a first i.f. of 432MHz the 10GHz band could be received. These units are relatively cheap for microwave devices: the FO-UP-11K is about £24.32, and the FO-UP-11KF (with flange) about £27.60. I must stress I have not tried this myself as my interest is with television reception. Charles Suckling, G3WDG, has borrowed my unit and is getting good pictures off Intelsat."

The local oscillator is a GaAsfet with dielectric resonator. A Schottky diode is used as the mixer. Noise figure is about 7·5 to 8dB and reasonable pictures can be received with this unit without a low-noise-amplifier on a 1·8m dish. Adding an lna/bandpass filter reduces the noise figure to 2·5-3·5dB in the 10·95-11·7GHz Ku-satellite band and can give excellent pictures with that size of dish. For anyone building such a unit, Hugh Cock's article is essential reading.

Computer propagation predictions
In my notes (*TT* November 1985, p864) on the work at the Rutherford Appleton Laboratory aimed at improving hf propagation predictions, I questioned whether it would be possible to write a program for use on a personal computer based on past ionospheric measurements rather than sunspot numbers.

Richard Limebear, G3RWL, writes to say that he has a "maximum useable frequency program" that he downloaded from an American amateur radio bulletin board. This program was originally developed by the US Navy to allow almost any mini or micro computer to be used to determine the muf between any two points. It was initially derived from a much larger program designed to run on very large computers, which has been extensively tested. The original sounder data base encompassed 196 path months (4,784 test points) of observed mufs measured over 23 different hf sounder paths.

The mini-muf program was found to have an rms of ±3·8MHz for muf predictions out to 6,000 miles but accuracy degrades for paths less than 250 miles. It is a single-layer F-region model. Because of lag in F-layer response to 10·7cm solar flux activity, it is best to use a 5-, 15- or 90-day running average of the 10·7cm flux. The flux value can be acquired from WWV at 18min after each hour. The conversion from 10·7cm flux to sunspot number has been accomplished by breaking the curve of the graph which accompanied the reference article into five sections, and deriving a formula for each section and then using that formula to convert from solar flux number to sunspot number. The original program is used from that point onward. Note that any intervention by E-region modes of propagation are not predictable by this program, but represent only a very small percentage of cases. The original author was Robert Rose, K6GKU (*QST* December 1982, p36), adapted to MBASIC by Jerry Hale, K0JH, and again by J W Barron, WA4LHT. Various modifications were introduced by G3RWL during 1984.

Richard Limebear (60 Willow Road, Enfield, EN1 3NQ) adds that the program is written in Microsoft Basic and is available for public use. It runs to about 400 lines (18 kilo-bytes). He would be willing to pass on copies via 8in disc, 300-baud modem, or even a printed listing. In effect, as his sample run shows, you can end up with a read out of the predicted muf based on current WWV data or, say, *Radio Communication* predictions for each hour of the day. In this case Falkland Islands to UK with a minimum muf at 0600gmt of 11MHz and maximum at 1500gmt of 29MHz.

Technical Topics
by Pat Hawker, G3VA

LETTERS CONTINUE TO ARRIVE expressing concern at the way home-construction and improvisation are becoming a declining art, though most stress that it is difficult to oppose market forces that persuade us to buy new facilities, such as a multiplicity of hf "memories", that add relatively little to on-air operation.

Phil Horwood, G3FRB, in reply to GM3BST's comment on the low resale price of home-built gear, points out that in earlier times "we didn't ever consider selling home-built gear, we just tore it down and built something else". But then it has to be admitted that modern constructional techniques, based on printed circuit boards, do not lend themselves to easy re-use of components.

Rules of the game?
John Gardner, GW4KUJ, one of the many amateurs who have taken up the hobby after retirement from another branch of engineering, stresses that factory-built rigs do provide an incentive "to assimilate microamperes, picofarads and rf impedances. After a lifetime of heavy current and ehv, this is not easy for those in their 60s". But it is clear from his letter that at least he has made a serious attempt to put up wire antennas etc. The problem is that some newcomers now show little or no interest in the technical aspects of radio communication.

As the Rev W J McKae, G4ILA, puts it: "The satisfaction of getting things to work is one thing, but just as important is the knowledge picked up on the way . . . The confidence and skills picked up while constructing equipment more than compensates any financial loss."

Jack Coomber, G4GYG, built up a company employing 500 people based on the following rules:

(1) Everything you want to know is in a book somewhere. The difficulty is finding the right b....., book.

(2) Whatever bits you want, however unusual, someone, somewhere, is making them in thousands and can't sell them.

(3) Drawings are practically useless, they include all your design mistakes plus the draughtsman's. (Hopefully not always true of Derek Cole's excellent *Rad Com* drawings!—*G3VA*).

(4) If you have found two design faults in an equipment, there is always one more you haven't found.

(5) The cheapest product is one designed as if you made it on the kitchen table—in early days we did just that.

And finally the key rule to improvisation:

(6) Almost anything designed specifically for one job, will do even better for another one.

Improvised rf components
Jack Coomber, G4GYG, is one of several amateurs who have submitted useful tips on improvising rf components now difficult to locate. Some ideas are being held over for the moment, but G4GYG writes as follows:

"Any re-use of disposable hypodermic syringes amazes and alarms me. It is all too easy to contract hepatitis etc.

"Almost every amateur has a source of polythene rod, ideal for antenna spreaders, in his junkbox in the form of the inner from old 0·5in coaxial cable. The trick is to remove the wire from the centre.

"Cut the cable into the required lengths, plus 0·5in, having first removed the outer sheath and braid. Carefully remove 0·5in of the polythene, leaving 0·5in of wire sticking out. Put all your cut lengths into a shallow baking tray, and, preferably, if appropriate with the permission of 'she who must be obeyed', put in the hot drawer or plate warmer of the cooker (*not* the oven). When good and warm, remove one by one and pull the wire out with pliers. A piece of metal with a slot or hole in it helps to pull the polythene (an eating fork would do if you can get away with it).

"It is at this stage that the pieces can be nicely straightened out before they harden again. A couple of self-tapping screws and some thin wire can be used to fasten the spreader to the feeder in the usual way.

"The same principle can be used very successfully to make stand-off insulators, choke and coil formers. For larger coil formers, the small tubes used by chemists for pills are very useful. My local chemist charges me only 1p each. They appear to be made of styrene which is an excellent rf insulator. The material dissolves in carbon tetrachloride or Thawpit, so it

is easy to secure the turns. Modelmakers' styrene cement is also useful and enables two pill-tubes to be stuck end-to-end if required. Since the tubes are rather brittle the safest method of drilling them is with a small drill in a pink-chuck held in the hand.

"For very large formers for antenna loading coils and the like, Paxolin tube used to be popular. Today it is expensive and difficult to obtain. I have seen plastic drain pipe used successfully, but take care; there is a type of pvc which does terrible things to the Q of coils.

"My answer is postal mailing tubes, which come in many sizes and are widely used for mailing large drawings, posters, certificates etc.

"Travel agents receive many and usually throw them away and may be persuaded to throw them your way. I keep a small stock in an airing cupboard (so they don't absorb excessive moisture). When needed, cut off the required length and put in a closed tin with 50 per cent yacht varnish and 50 per cent white spirit. Leave for several days with an occasional shake, then hang up to dry. When hard, finish off with a spell in the hot drawer (seize a suitable opportunity when nobody is around since the smell is terrible). After this treatment the tube looks like Paxolin and very nearly is Paxolin."

G4GYG sent along examples of rf components made from coaxial cable "inners" and pill-tubes, including an excellent-looking plug-in coil (four in-line pins, the former horizontally mounted).

Power transformers
One of the problems in keeping abreast of the changes that have flooded into radio technology in recent decades is that many standard handbooks tend to treat "fundamentals" primarily on the basis of long-established techniques. This can be justified on the grounds that fundamental "principles", by their very nature, do not change. But "practice" *does* change.

Then again some components are more interesting than others, more sexy, to use current parlance. Solid-looking lumps of ironwork such as high-wattage mains transformers or the audio transformers once commonly used in high-level amplitude-modulated transmitters tend to be taken for granted, despite such developments as grain-orientated "C" cores and the re-emergence of the now popular toroidal mains transformer.

In basic terms, the core of a low-frequency transformer is designed so that as much as possible of the magnetic flux developed by the primary winding encloses the secondary windings(s), using closed magnetic loops which concentrate the flux. Core design depends on the frequencies involved and whether the transformer is intended to operate at a specific frequency (eg 50 or 60Hz) or over a range of frequencies as for audio transformers. Conventional transformers designed for one specific frequency usually have an air gap in the core.

It is also usually highly desirable for the core to be arranged to minimize losses due to eddy currents induced within the core itself. For power and audio transformers those losses have been traditionally minimized by building up the core from a series of thin plates (laminations), stamped out in various standard shapes (Fig 1), and each insulated from its neighbours. The greater the cross-area of the core the greater the power handling capacity of the transformer without the core saturating. A core is said to be saturated when increased current in the primary ceases to produce any increase in magnetic flux so that, for example, a sine-wave input signal results in a distorted output waveform with flattened peaks.

The commonly-available plates of Fig 1 are formed from silicon steel having low hysteresis loss, or from nickel-iron alloys having very high permeabilities. About 30 years ago there emerged the C-core made from

Fig 1. Typical shapes of laminations from which conventional power transformer cores are usually built up, including a gap

silicon-iron sheets rolled so as to have greater permeability in one preferred direction. The practice is to cut this material into strips with the direction of major permeability along the major axis. Such cores are generally cut into two equal "U" shapes, with the windings inserted on the limbs, resulting in the so-called C-core. When required, a gap can be inserted between the two halves. Because of the greater permeability, a given core size is capable of handling more power than with non-grain-orientated cores, resulting in more compact and lighter transformers.

For power transformers involving the transfer of appreciable amounts of power between low-impedance circuits, core losses become the major consideration. This loss is expressed as watts per kilogram (or per pound) of core material as a function of maximum flux density with sine-wave excitation. If flux density is increased too much, rising core losses result in excessive core temperatures. The design of a power transformer is thus to some degree a matter of compromise. The alternative to high flux density is to use more turns per volt; for a given core size this results in the use of smaller diameter wire and hence greater resistive losses.

The toroidal power transformer

An alternative to the C-core transformer, while retaining the advantages of grain-orientated steel strip, is the use of toroids, and this can have very significant advantages in overall size, and in the reduction of external magnetic fields which can induce hum into low-level signals; the gapless toroid also has the advantage of generating much less acoustic hum, which in conventional transformers tends to come from vibration of the laminations.

The toroid is, in fact, the oldest form of transformer core, dating back to Michael Faraday! Nevertheless there remains, for most of us, an air of unfamiliarity and perhaps a danger of claiming too much for this approach. Its revival stems from the development of toroid winding processes and better wire technology and associated better insulation.

John Brown, G3EUR, formerly chief development engineer with Avel-Lindberg, is the author not only of that company's leaflet, *The ins and outs of toroidal transformers*, but also a useful guide to "Using toroidal transformers" in *Mercury*, The Royal Signals Amateur Radio Society Journal No 81, 7/85, and the following notes stem from these sources.

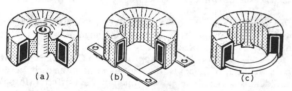

Fig 2. Mounting methods for toroidal transformers. The centre fixing of (a) is the most common arrangement

The toroid is exceptionally well-suited for use on printed circuit boards in view of the usual centre hole fixing (Fig 2), the low centre of gravity, and the pcb-compatible pins, which allow it to be mounted at the same time as other major components and then flow-soldered. G3EUR is careful to warn against the dangers of overkill by appearing to claim too much for the toroidal transformer. Nevertheless they are now being widely used in compact solidstate equipment, especially where the low external hum-field radiated from a toroid is of importance; for example in oscilloscopes and audio amplifiers.

Advantages of toroids

(1) In the general case, toroids, compared against traditional stacked laminated types, come out about 50 per cent lighter and 50 per cent lower volume—simply because they are more efficient.
(2) Because there is no air gap, there is far less reluctance (magnetic resistance) and consequently low magnetizing VA—important when used in "instant-on" circuitry. A toroid can give savings of 90 per cent open circuit power.
(3) A continuous strip (gapless) core can be wound at a controlled tension which gives a stacking factor of 95 per cent of its theoretical weight. All the molecules lie in the "preferred direction" along the strip, and this enables grain-orientated silicon steel to be used to give operation at a high flux density with very low iron losses, resulting in much higher efficiency.
(4) No air gap also means an 8:1 reduction in electrically-induced noise (hum) because most of the fringing flux which causes this trouble is concentrated at the air gap of stacked laminated types.
(5) With a toroidal core the windings completely envelop the core and thereby reduce audible noise caused by magneto-striction.
(6) The high efficiency which can be obtained with toroidal transformers enables them to be conservatively rated without incurring size penalties.

(7) Inherent in the toroidal type of construction is a low height profile which is compatible with components now being used in power supplies for contemporary "slimline" electronic equipment.

G3EUR writes: "The eight-to-one lower radiated field and the acoustic quietness are self-evident when the method of construction is investigated. A working flux density of 1·7 Tesla (17,000 Gauss) for the all-in-line grain-orientated toroid, as against 1·3 Tesla (13,000 Gauss) for a conventional transformer, is inherent in the design; as are iron losses of typically only 0·46W/lb (Fe) as against 1·25W/lb (Fe). The absence of the air gap means the toroid only requires a magnetizing current of one-tenth of that needed by a transformer with a gap. Centre-hole, single-point mounting, coupled with the ability to mount the toroid directly onto a pcb, make the production engineer's life easier. The typically 50 per cent lower weight and volume, with the lower height profile, must also contribute to easing the designer's ulcer when space is at a premium in high-component density equipment."

Using toroidal transformers

John Brown stresses that two points should always be observed when using toroidal transformers:
(1) Do *not* use toroids in half-wave rectifier circuits, since there would then

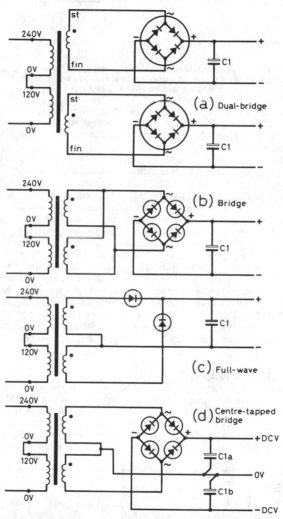

Fig 3. Four of the more common ways of using dual-winding toroidal transformers (other possible arrangements include dual and triple supplies, tripler, quadrupler etc). (a) Separate bridge rectifiers with minimum interaction. Either can have positive or negative earthed supply lines and can be used with a variety of ic or discrete voltage regulators. (b) Both windings in parallel to give single heavy current output. Note that the reservoir capacitor needs to be twice the value for (a) and a rule of thumb is 100μF/A at 12V dc, 2,000μF/A at 6V dc etc. Ripple-current rating may be taken to equal the direct current, and it is highly advisable to use computer-grade capacitors with stated ripple ratings of voltage rating preferably twice the rms voltage of the transformer secondary windings. (c) Alternative bi-phase arrangement using only two diodes. This is a better arrangement for low voltage psus (5 to 10V ac) where diode voltage-drop becomes more significant. A bridge has a 1·8V drop, two diodes about 0·7V but use bigger (higher current rated) diodes. (d) Centre-tapped bridge can give both positive and negative outputs, with different output currents. Treat each output as for (c)

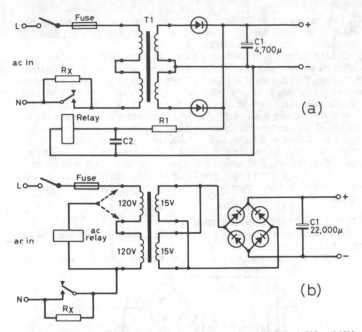

Fig 4. "Soft-start" systems based on dc and ac relays. In (b) a 110V or 240V relay can be used (240V across the whole primary, 110V across one half). The delay should be about 100ms

be an average (dc) current flowing in a winding. The gapless core of the toroid would become biased, resulting in saturation of the core and excessive heating. Even conventional laminated cores will not cope with much dc flowing in the windings.

(2) The very low impedance of a toroid transformer when used with silicon diodes and large capacitance filter capacitors results in high in-rush currents when the equipment is switched on. Unless some form of soft-start in-rush protection is used, fuses rated for normal load current will tend to blow. It is advisable to use "anti-surge" fuses of the correct rating, usually rated about 150 per cent of normal full load. In a large power supply unit, rated at, say, 100W or over, it is worth using a soft-start circuit or relay.

Many of the off-the-shelf toroidal mains transformers, suitable for home-construction, are wound with dual primaries (120V) which can be connected in series for 240V supplies or in parallel for 117V mains. The two secondaries can similarly be in series or parallel and used in "centre-tapped" full-wave configurations or in separate or joint bridge arrangements. This leads to great flexibility as indicated in Fig 3, derived from G3EUR's *Mercury* article, where he shows the large number of available options. Fig 4 indicates a relay approach to soft-starting, although, as indicated previously in *TT*, other techniques can be used.

Loop antenna amplifier

The directional characteristics of a tuned loop antenna make this an effective technique for sorting out weak dx signals on 1·8 and 3·5MHz. Eric Sandys, GI2FHN, provides information on a loop amplifier found to be the most effective of any that he has tried: Fig 5.

He writes: "It uses an MC1350 ic in the push-pull mode with output taken from pin 8. Additional amplification is provided by a hybrid cascade

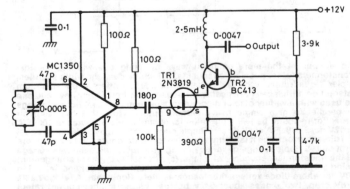

Fig 5. GI2FHN's receiving loop amplifier for medium waves, 1·8MHz and 3·5MHz

amplifier using a common-source jfet amplifier (TR1) driving a common-base amplifier (TR2). The loop itself is a conventional two-turn screened loop using coaxial cable on a frame made from 22mm polypropylene tubing, and covers both 1·8 and 3·5MHz when tuned with a 500pF capacitor. The loop is connected to a screen 'stereo plug' via a small diecast-aluminium box. A screened line socket mounted on the rear panel of the amplifier permits 360° rotation. As I am also interested in medium-wave dx, a separate loop is available for this band. The usual American and Canadian broadcast stations have been received at night, and during the day Radio Devon can be received here in Bangor as a signal of entertainment value. Some of the other loop amplifiers that have been published seem unnecessarily complex or require inconvenient power supplies."

The search for dynamic range

Even before the introduction of solidstate devices into communications receivers, it was being persuasively argued that the performance of high-grade valve receivers in the presence of very strong signals left a lot to be desired. The first bipolar transistor receivers in the 'sixties were a veritable disaster, putting back performance, at least in terms of dynamic range, by several decades. The reason was that the bipolar transistor is basically a steep slope device with no equivalent of the variable-mu pentode valve.

For some 10 years enormous efforts were put into bringing the dynamic range of solidstate receivers to the standard possible in thermionic designs, at least to those without such "special" valves as the 7360 beam-deflection valve. There was an added requirement resulting from the general adoption of broad-band input circuits and the growing use of a first "up-conversion" mixer (I have still to be convinced that this configuration is the optimum approach for receivers for the amateur bands).

But certainly, with care and the use of suitable devices, it is today possible to achieve good strong signal performance, with high-cost solidstate receivers. The use of 28V supplies rather than 12V for front-ends, combined with much better balanced or doubly-balanced active or passive mixers, has brought a great improvement. Limitations today tend to be oscillator jitter/noise and the use of broad "roofing filters" that result in the differential between the dynamic range when measured with closely spaced carriers and that when measured with signal generators off-tuned by 20, 50 or even 100kHz (see *TT*, August 1984).

But even today it is not easy to provide a mixer with a really high intercept point without driving this with a relatively high-power square-wave switching signal from the local oscillator. The drive required from some synthesized local oscillators is more appropriate to QRP transmitters! Ed Oxner, KB6QJ, of Siliconix, did a lot of work in the early 'seventies on balanced mixers based on power junction field effect (Mospower) transistors, and his pioneering work was frequently reported in *TT* and subsequently *ART*.

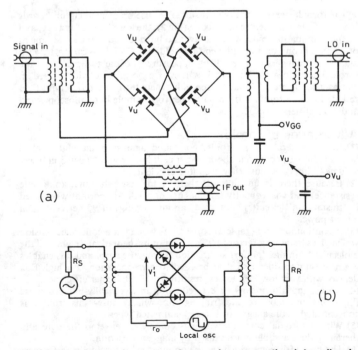

Fig 6. Typical high-performance mixers using conventional broadband transformers

Recently he kindly sent me details of new work on "A commutation (switching) double-balanced mosfet mixer of high dynamic range". His first paper on this subject is due to be presented at the 1986 RF Technology Expo, and will be published in the Conference Record.

To quote from the introduction to this still unpublished paper:

"Dynamic range remains the principal goal of hf mixer design. The intermodulation performance and overload characteristics of a mixer are fundamental qualities used in the evaluation of a good design.

"Heretofore, most mixers sporting a high dynamic range have been either the passive diode-ring variety (available from several sources) or the active fet mixer: Fig 6. The latter, not being commercially available, is often implemented from earlier published design notes (Ed Oxner, "Fets work well in active balanced mixers" *EDN*, Vol 18, No 1, 5 January 1973, pp66-72 and Ed Oxner, "Active double-balanced mixers made easy with junction fets" *EDN*, Vol 19, No 13, 5 July 1974, pp47-53).

"Common to both the diode and fet is their square-law characteristic so important in maintaining low distortion during mixing. However, equally important for high dynamic range is the ability to withstand overload that has been identified as a principal cause of distortion in mixing (H P Walker, "Sources of intermodulation in diode-ring mixers", *The Radio and Electronic Engineer* (UK), Vol 46, No 5, May 1967, pp247-255). Some passive diode-ring mixer designs have resorted to paralleling of diodes to effect greater current handling, yet the penalty for this apparent improvement is the need for a massive increase in local-oscillator power.

"This report examines a new fet mixer where commutation (switching) achieves high dynamic range without exacting the anticipated penalty of increased local-oscillator drive. Using the Siliconix Si8901 monolithic quad-ring small-signal double-diffused mosfet, third-order intercept points upward of +39dBm (input) have been achieved with only +17dBm of local oscillator power."

KB6QJ tells me that the figure of +39dBm, remarkable though it is, is proving conservative. One well-known communications firm claims that, under laboratory conditions, intercepts of +43dBm are being achieved. The Siliconix Si8901 is a commercially-available ic, suitable for use as a mixer at hf and the low-vhf region. A surface-mounted version may later extend performance to somewhat higher frequencies.

Si8901 as a commutation mixer

The design of this mixer is treated fully in KB6QJ's paper, which may appear later also as a Siliconix Application Note.

A few brief notes must suffice for the moment:

"To achieve a high intercept point the local oscillator drive must: (1) approach the ideal square wave; (2) ensure a 50 per cent duty cycle; and (3) offer sufficient amplitude to measure a full *on* and *off* switching condition, as well as to offer reduced r_{DS} when *on*.

"Furthermore, to maintain superior overall performance—both in terms of conversion loss, dynamic range (noise figure) and intercept point —some form of image frequency termination is highly desirable even though this restricts the bandwidth of the mixer.

"Consequently, the principal effort in the design of a high dynamic range commutation mixer is two-fold. First, and most crucial, is to achieve a gating or control voltage sufficient to ensure a positive and hard turn-*on*, as well as a complete turn-*off*, of the mosfet mixing elements. Second, and of lesser importance, is to terminate properly the parasitic and harmonic frequencies developed by the mixer.

"Local oscillator injection to the conventional diode ring, fet, or mosfet double-balanced mixer is by the use of a broadband, transmission-line transformer (C L Ruthroll "Some broad-band transformers", *Proc IRE*, August 1959, pp1,337-42), as shown in Fig 6.

"A major goal is the conservation of (oscillator) power. This goal cannot be achieved using the conventional design. Simply increasing the turns ratio of the coupling transformer is thwarted by the reactive load presented by the gates. The solution is to use a resonant gate drive. The voltage appearing across the resonant tank, and hence the gates, is $V = (P.Q.X)^{\frac{1}{2}}$ where P is

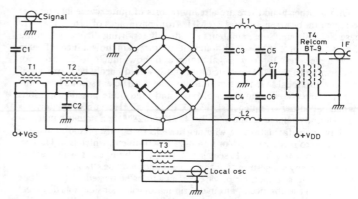

Fig 8. Ed Oxner's commutation double balanced mixer with resonate-drive transformer

the power delivered to the resonant tank circuit, Q is the *loaded Q* of the tank circuit; and X is the reactance of the gate capacitance.

"The gate capacitance of a mosfet is voltage dependent, so that the reactance of the gate becomes dependent upon the impressed excitation voltage. If this were permitted it would severely degrade the imd performance of the mixer; it can be minimized by using a combination of substrate and gate bias. A gate bias is, in any case, needed to ensure the required 50 per cent duty cycle.

"Implementing the resonant gate drive may take several forms. The resonant tank circuit may be merged with the oscillator, or it can be a varactor-tuned Class B stage, or, as in the present design, an independent resonant tank as shown in Figs 7 and 8.

"To ensure symmetrical gate voltage in 180° anti-phase, if the local oscillator drive is fed by unbalanced coaxial cable, an unbalanced-to-balanced must be used (see Fig 8), otherwise capacitive un-balance results with attendant loss in mixer performance."

Ed Oxner's paper goes into the theory, design and measurements made on this type of mixer in considerable detail at a technical level directed at professional designers, but it is felt that these notes will provide *TT* readers with at least an outline of this interesting design that could further improve the strong-signal performance of receivers. To quote his conclusions:

"Achieving a high gate voltage to effect high-level switching by means of a resonant tank is not a handicap. Although one might, at first, label the mixer as narrowband, in truth the mixer is wideband. For the majority of applications, the intermediate frequency is fixed, that is, narrowband. Consequently, to receive a wide range of frequencies the local oscillator is tuned across a similar band. In modern technology the tuning can be accomplished by numerous methods, not the least might be electronically using variactors. The resonant tank also may take several forms. It can be part of the oscillator or it can be a varactor-tuned driver electronically tracking the local oscillator.

"If the local-oscillator drive were processed to offer a more rectangular waveform, approaching the idealized square-wave, we might then anticipate even greater dynamic range."

EMC and the cordless telephone

Cordless telephones began to be used in the UK about five years ago, at first illegally. Subsequently an interim allocation of frequencies was made specifically for cordless telephones, and the use of units conforming to these frequencies and power limits became legal. In general, the base–handset links operate between 1·6 and 1·8MHz; between 49·8 and 49·9MHz is used for the return handset-to-base path. They are normally single-channel fm sets, the channel to be used being preselected at the factory from five or eight possibilities.

With only five or eight channels available and a nominal range of upwards of 100m, clearly severe problems of mutual interference will soon arise in urban areas. It has been estimated that by the year 2000 the number of cordless telephones in use may amount to some 10 per cent of conventional wired telephones. British Telecom are developing units operating at around 900MHz with digital modulation techniques, and foresee a need for some 6MHz of spectrum.

The use of cordless telephones seems likely to pose increasing problems of electromagnetic compatibility to radio amateurs, both in the form of rfi to the telephone units and, conversely, interference from the telephones to amateur reception. Clearly a 49·9MHz base receiver may prove vulnerable, for example, to local 50MHz transmissions, while the 1·7MHz receivers may be vulnerable to very strong local signals on virtually any band, though no cases have yet come to my attention.

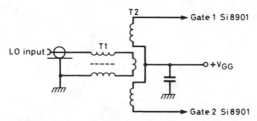

Fig 7. Resonant-gate drive transformer (T2) which resonates with C_{GG} of the Si8901 mixer ic and permits the use of significantly less oscillator drive

On the other hand there are already reports of quite severe interference to reception between 3·5 and 3·6MHz from harmonics of 1·6 to 1·8MHz base transmitters. Some amateurs are already reporting difficulty in using the cw end of 3·5MHz, although it is uncertain how much of such interference results from legal units and how much to models not conforming to the DTI specification. But it would hardly be surprising if any low-cost local 1·7MHz transmitter radiates sufficient second harmonic to cause interference on the 3·5MHz band, and quite possibly spurious signals at other frequencies: 1·750 to 1·800MHz, unfortunately, is harmonically related to the 3·5, 7, 14, 21 and 28MHz amateur bands!

I have no information on whether the RIS or BT are preparing to take any action to recognize and/or minimize this problem, which is still largely confined to a few areas. It seems odd that telephone users who react so strongly to any suggestion that their telephones may be "tapped" seem to be quite willing to let their private conversations be picked up (with slope detection in the absence of an fm discriminator) at a considerable distance! Perhaps they have no idea how far their words are winging! Even a few milliwatts do not stay within a user's own estate! Perhaps if they were made more aware of the facts of radio there would be far less than the millions of users anticipated by the year 2000, at least on the 1·7/49MHz bands.

Multiway 6A adapters

While some of us still live in houses having the old round three-pin 15A, 5A, 2A mains wall sockets, the majority must by now be using the standard flat-pin 13A socket. This often implies the use in the shack of a quite large four- or six-way junction box, or at least the rather cumbersome three-way 13A adapter.

Photo 1. (Top) Conventional six-way junction box adapter with 13A sockets. (Below) The Conblock six-way adapter

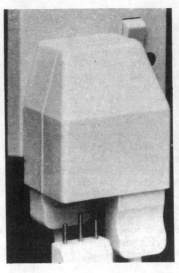

Photo 2. The new Conblock plug-adapter providing four outlets with 6A sockets

A recent press release, issued on behalf of Conblock Electrical Ltd (0686–27100) of Newtown, Powys, sings the praises of two new adapters, sold complete with plugs. They provide compact three-pin 6A sockets, so making for much smaller and lighter units for the many applications where the individual loads do not really require the use of 13A plugs/sockets (ie loads of less than about 1kW), and particularly where there are several separate units.

Conblock claim the new adapters are available at most electrical high street outlets and confirm fully with BS5733 and the latest electrical equipment safety regulations.

An in-line adapter for use with 13A sockets provides six in-line 6A shuttered sockets. They are also making a wallplug adapter that plugs into a 13A socket and provides four of the 6A sockets.

That earphone filter!

The January *TT* included an item on putting a resonant reed as the effective part of the diaphragms of a high-impedance as described in the Australian *Radio Experimenter,* of unknown date. I expressed reservations about this idea, particularly the "lag". It all seemed a little too good to be true. What I did not realize, until reminded by Eric Sandys, GI2FHN, was that exactly the same idea had been previously published in *QST*, but with a few significant differences! It was in the *April* (1976) issue and was ascribed to "Tin Ehres, WH0OP". Quite clearly it was one of the traditional semi-believable *QST* April Fool jokes!

My apologies to readers for including this idea in a January rather than an April issue—and thanks to GI2FHN.

There is, of course, no fundamental reason why the output transducer or impedance matching transformer should not constitute an effective filter. Douglas Byrne, G3KPO, writes:

"A horn loudspeaker from the 'twenties makes an excellent af filter for cw. Its 800Hz peak can be much improved by bunging a large wad of cotton-wool right down the aperture! Most of these early loudspeakers had high-impedance windings (about 2,000Ω) but can be fed from low-Z sockets via almost any small output transformer wired backwards (ie with the low-Z winding connected to the receiver)."

The German "diplomatic" suitcase set (*TT* September 1985) used the technique of resonating the output transformer, and in a pre-war *T & R Bulletin* an article showed how by cutting a gap in the core, the *Q* could be improved and the output peaked at the required frequency.

Technical Topics

by Pat Hawker, G3VA

THIS MONTH we range back and forth across the years of experimental amateur radio. From spark to smd, via valves. For it all began, at least in the UK, with the passing of the original Wireless Telegraphy Act, 1904. How easy it was at first: "It was only necessary to advise the Postmaster General of the intention to erect a wireless station (transmitting or receiving) and to fill in a form giving particulars of such installation, when an inspector would be sent to visit the station and a permit for its use would be handed to the owner. Later, one guinea began to be charged".

No RAE, no morse test, no being tied down to specific frequency bands. Little more than a morse key, earphones, a hefty spark, a crystal detector and lots of wire! But no wonder that the Wireless Society of London (forerunner of the RSGB) was soon alarmed at the number of complaints of interference with commercial and Government stations due to the use of "excessive powers and untuned aerials, by irresponsible experimenters". Regulations and morse tests came in the early 'twenties, RAE in the late 'forties. It seems we could not do without them.

First this month, an apology. Reading the page proofs of the March *TT* I panicked and decided I had inadvertently switched round two diagrams. The editor promptly made the correction and passed the issue for press. A day later I realised that the diagrams had been correct in the first place—so you got them with the wrong captions. What was shown in Fig 6(a) as a conventional active doubly-balanced fet mixer was in fact Ed Oxner's new mixer configuration. Fig 8 showed the conventional circuit. My apologies! Who would be a columnist!

Costs of reliability

There is little doubt that many UK amateurs resent the fact that the prices charged for imported Japanese equipment by "authorized dealers" tend to be significantly higher than those charged for identical models in some other countries and by non-authorized dealers who import indirectly. In *TT* January 1984, p45, Kjell Ström, SM6CPI, the Yaesu Musen representative for Europe, explained that Japanese firms "encourage their agents to carry the necessary spare parts and to take care of customers long after the final cheque has been cashed". He felt that the emphasis on quality assurance and initial "burn-in" procedures at the factories meant the probability of failure of each individual component to be microscopic . . . "Because it would not make economic sense for manufacturers to seek out the few remaining potential failures, they expect these to be taken care of in the after-sales service, performed and paid for by the authorized agents . . . Buying from an authorized agent is a form of insurance".

Cynics could interpret this as meaning that while manufacturers do their reasonable best to make their rigs reliable they accept that inevitably a small number of less-than-perfect rigs will leave the factories and end up in our shacks, with the retail price geared to covering the cost of putting these right.

This is a commercially understandable policy, by no means unique to amateur radio equipment. But for customers it can give rise to some justifiable misgivings. For example, equipment that has to be sent back to the dealer once, or even twice, needs to be dealt with promptly and effectively or the unlucky purchaser is bound to feel aggrieved. There is the even more insidious problem that few of us have the full range of laboratory test equipment to determine whether or not equipments meet their design specification.

The *QST* account of the reviewer's difficulties and delays in obtaining a fully effective Icom 751 (*TT* January 1986, p34) highlighted this problem and has encouraged some *TT* readers to unfold their own horror stories. Meanwhile *Members Mailbag* continues to keep the Trio/Kenwood pot boiling.

Owen Kemp, G4TLK, for example, lists some of his experiences with well-respected Yaesu equipment:

FRG7700: display driver ic failed after two months' use.

FT77: intermittent operation over the first three months caused by a dry solder joint.

FT757: various faults in both transmit and receive modes over a period of 18 months, cured only by replacement of the rf board.

G4TLK is a professional electronics technician and recognizes how perverse equipment can be. But he feels that faults could be eliminated in production by more rigid use of quality assurance procedures and less dependence on "after sales service" by authorized agents.

His place of employment has an effective three-day "burn-in" procedure which accelerates the ageing of components by operating them at an elevated temperature. This removes "infant mortality" and spotlights unduly temperature-sensitive components. Following this burn-in, each instrument is checked twice, once by a technician manually and then by an automated test system that avoids human error. Further checks are carried out independently by the quality assurance department, then finally by a standards inspector. This is very different, he suggests, from the simple batch testing usually considered sufficient for price-sensitive consumer electronics.

My own feeling is that we cannot have it both ways. Although the prices asked these days for amateur black boxes appear to be very high by historic standards, they are in fact very reasonable, indeed low, in comparison with the cost of British, European and American professional communications equipment. The Japanese cram a lot of facilities into their transceivers, largely because a few years ago they discovered a lack of demand for simpler "economy" models. Complexity implies less reliability without rigid quality assurance. But rigid quality assurance inevitably costs the customer a great deal of money. Few amateurs would be able to afford to buy equipment made to "mil-spec" and BS9000 standards, unless satisfied with extremely "simple" equipments. As long as amateurs go on demanding "all-singing, all-dancing" models they must necessarily accept that a proportion of equipments will require after-sales service and need careful "in-shack" checking out to the best of one's ability.

What the amateur has the right to demand is that if he pays the "insurance premium" of buying from an authorized dealer, he should receive courteous, prompt and effective after-sales service and, if necessary, prompt replacement of "rogue" models that never seem to be quite right. On the other hand, dealers are fully entitled to charge an "economic" fee for servicing equipments bought elsewhere—labour costs can be very high—though they may not do their reputation any good by simply refusing altogether to service models bought overseas.

The greatest difficulty that arises from complex equipment made to retail at budget cost is how the purchaser can ensure that his model is really up to spec. For example, the initial problem uncovered by N1FB in the ARRL laboratory on IC751, serial number 1114, was that an i.f. section was out of alignment. In some circumstances, in the absence of test equipment, slight misalignment of one or two stages could pass unnoticed for a considerable period of time.

SMD and homebrew

On several occasions attention has been drawn in *TT* to the increasing use of tiny surface-mounted devices and related forms of hybrid microelectronics in virtually all branches of electronics, including amateur radio equipment. SMDs have made very rapid progress in Japan; rather slower progress in the USA and Europe, where equipment manufacturers point to the problems of reflow soldering tiny leaded and leadless surface-mounted boards with components on both sides, techniques on which most manufacturers of mass-produced equipment are only just beginning to get a grip. Then there is the cost of installing new highly-automated production equipment in an era when so much of the consumer market has been captured by Japanese industry. A single smd assembly line consisting of machines for surface-mount placement, soldering, testing and repair can cost around a quarter of a million pounds. On the other hand, the technology offers both manufacturers and customers significant advan-

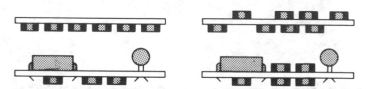

Fig 1. Surface-mounted components can be mounted on or below the printed circuit boards

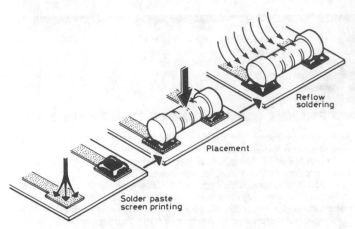

Fig 2. A standard procedure for fixing surface-mounted components on the upper side of printed circuit boards, using solder paste screen printing

tages: increased interconnection density, smaller pcb area, better and more consistent performance, and reduced manufacturing costs once the necessary production equipment has been installed (see "What's holding back surface mounting" *Electronics* 10 February 1986, pp25–29).

One result, both in the USA and Europe, has been the growth of specialized sub-contracting firms that undertake the design, production and testing of smd boards for the main manufacturers.

Recently I received a letter from Rex Waygood, technical director of Surface Electronics, a UK firm in Poole, Dorset, that specializes in miniaturization and surface mount production technology, thick-film hybrid circuits and the like.

He takes me to task for having suggested on various occasions that smd could represent a further blow to home-servicing and home-construction. Rather, he suggests, it offers amateurs a new set of challenges. He writes:

"Surface mount components are now available to the home-constructor, although I admit not as readily available as conventional components.

"To remove failed components, greater use has to be made of such devices as desoldering braid; solder suckers, other than expensive motorized versions, are of little use. (The outer braid from discarded coaxial cable can form an effective desoldering braid—*G3VA*.)

"For assembly, tweezers, a pot of RMA flux, a small soldering iron and a bench magnifier are really all that are necessary.

"In order to make the joints look more professional, a grill pan and a hot air paint stripper can be used to reflow the solder!

"The major difficulty with surface-mount assemblies is to design the pads and solder mask to produce a high first-time yield and a highly reliable joint for mass production. This is not a problem for the radio amateur, as his requirement is normally for a one-off board, therefore rework time is not significant.

"The major challenge to the home-constructor using sma comes in the manufacture of the board. The smaller pad sizes, pitches of 50-thou, 0·8mm and even 25-thou, and inevitably smaller tracks, 10-thou to 8-thou, will be a challenge. However, pcb manufacturers are using 0·5oz copper laminate to improve their own yields at these finer track widths. This will filter down to the amateurs. Also it will be found that, for several reasons, the board design will be double-sided.

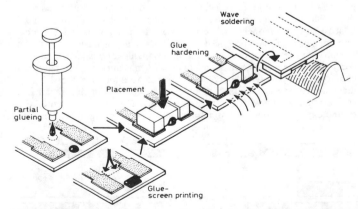

Fig 3. An alternative mounting procedure whereby glue is used to hold the component to the board during flow soldering, making subsequent removal of components rather tricky as it is easy to damage the board

"I accept the fact that it will be a brave amateur who applies a paint stripper to his newly-purchased surface-mount cmos micro, but no braver than the amateur with his first valve, first transistor, first fet, first gasfet or first micro!

"I am convinced that amateurs can and will rise to the challenges offered by sma and will come to exploit the size, cost and performance benefits offered."

A long and detailed article, "Surface mounted components—the quiet revolution" (*Electronics Australia*, July 1985) ended by discussing briefly their use by hobbyists:

"All the foregoing seems to indicate that electronics is progressing to the point where hobbyists will no longer be able to be involved because the components are just too small to handle. This is not necessarily the case. While chip capacitors and resistors are exceedingly small and difficult to handle, the larger packages are quite practical for use by hobbyists. Indeed, *Electronics Australia* has presently under development a circuit design using a surface mounting microprocessor."

One of the practical snags, it seems to me, will be identifying component values etc should they ever get mixed together. The situation for the ic packages, however, seems a little more hopeful, though I guess it will need those "hands-free" binocular magnifiers described in *TT* February 1983, p134 and May 1983, p428. It's a challenge we shall need to accept, though personally I still like components that are big and identifiable and carry their value with them, and can withstand lots of volts and/or milliamps. But who am I to stand in the way of "progress"?

Don't fuse the neutral

In the February *TT*, Chris Trayner, G4OKW, commented on the safety hazard represented by the practice of connecting fuses in both the phase ("live" or "line") and neutral leads of mains equipment connected to three-pin mains sockets. Twin mains fuses were once common practice and can still be found occasionally, particularly in equipment for use on mainland Europe etc.

However, he was puzzled at not being able to trace a definitive reference to double fusing in the IEE Wiring Regulations or BS415. A number of readers have pointed out that in fact the IEE Wiring Regulations do cover this practice in relation to advice never to fuse earthed neutral conductors.

Brian Castle, G4DYF, refers to Paragraph 13.12 of the current IEE Wiring Regulations (15th edition with May 1984 amendments):

"No fuse, or circuit breaker other than a limited circuit breaker, shall be inserted in an earthed neutral conductor, and any limited circuit breaker in an earthed neutral conductor shall be arranged to break also all the related phase conductors."

David Rolle, GM3GRG, writes: 1 think Appendix 5 of the IEE regulations may cover this point:

"If the circuit has one pole earthed, the socket outlet is of the type that will accept only two-pole-and-earth contact plugs with single-pole fusing on the live pole. . . ." and

"If the circuit has neither pole earthed (eg a circuit supplied from a double-wound transformer having the mid-point of its secondary winding earthed) the socket outlet is of the type that will accept only two-pole-and-earth contacts plugs with double-pole fusing. . . ."

I can see that there could be a degree of confusion in the use of the term "earthed neutral conductor" in referring to the mains supply "neutral" since, as previously mentioned in *TT*, this lead must never be "earthed" by users, as a potential often exists between "neutral" and "earth". Nevertheless it should be appreciated that the neutral *is* earthed at an earlier point in the system, so that a supply taken from either a two-pole "lighting" bayonet socket or from a three-pin socket has, in effect, "an earthed neutral conductor". As pointed out above, the output from a double-wound transformer will not inherently be earthed and can require double-pole fusing.

GM3GRG also pointed out that it is worth considering the comments in the 1986 edition of the ARRL *Radio Amateurs Handbook*, Chapter 37 "Assembling a station". Although the American public supply sustem is not the same as ours, the comments underline the care necessary in diy electrical work. In the USA, apart from safety aspects such work can give rise to insurance problems. The ARRL notes:

"In some areas this work must be performed by a licensed electrician. You may need a special building permit for the work, and even if you are allowed to do the work yourself, you might have to get a licensed electrician to inspect the work."

Presumably this applies to the installation of permanent wiring, rather than to the connection of equipment fed from an already installed domestic socket; but, as has been stressed many times in *TT*, anything connected to 240V ac mains needs to be treated with caution and a recognition of the safety and fire hazards that can arise.

GM3GRG concludes with a couple of extracts from the old, 14th edition of the IEE Wiring Regulations: F8 "Every plug containing a fuse shall be non-reversible and so designed and arranged that no fuse can be connected in an earthed conductor." F5: "In circuits in which one pole is earthed at the source of supply, every socket outlet and plug shall be of the non-reversible type, with provision for earthing. This requirement does not apply to extra low voltage circuits or to the special low-voltage circuits referred to in Regulation F7." (Since writing these notes, further letters putting a rather different view have been received. More next month.)

Valves—not just nostalgia!
The suggestion by KH6B of "Project 6L6" (*TT* February, p107), to mark the 50th anniversary of this once extremely popular valve and to encourage a degree of home-construction, has brought forth some nostalgic memories.

But is it just a nostalgic fad? Or are there still valid grounds for suggesting that those old valves can still play a valuable role in providing the means whereby simple, low-cost but effective cw-only transmitters can be built on the kitchen table? Unlike smd technology, there was little fear that an untimely sneeze would blow the equipment off the bench and leave you with the problem of trying to work out which component is which!

John Roscoe, G4QK, recalls the 6AG7, so useful as a doubler or driver, the pre-war RK39, the powerful wartime PT15 (used in the T1154). He strongly recommends the glass version of the 6L6; the metal version, apart from its inferior rf performance, tended to give off a nasty smell when it got really hot. He points out that an EF80 can furnish all the drive needed for a 6L6G.

Richard Q Marris, G2BZQ, makes no bones about still preferring valves to solidstate: "I use valves, as much as possible, for the simple reason that I *like* them—not that I have anything against transistors or those who use them. Similarly I use cw because I *like* t—I have a perfectly good 100W ssb transceiver but I seldom use it because it bores me. I have several of the old Codar AT5 transmitters and use these on 3·5MHz cw, deliberately under-running them at 10W input to preserve them. With a box of 7MHz crystals, a load of valves and a 'junk box' I am planning a low-power transmitter with a single 6V6 (the useful little brother of the 6L6). The old handbooks give plenty of advice and dodges on how to eliminate chirp from single-valve crystal-controlled transmitters. I enjoyed using valves in the old days. I enjoy using them now."

Coping with the 4CX-series
In retrospect, the rf power valves available to amateurs from 1936–9 onwards, including the 807 and 813 beam tetrodes, 808, T20, T55, 35T power triodes were ideally suited to home-construction, being both rugged —in that they would withstand considerable abuse—and reasonably docile once the art of parasitic-oscillation suppression and/or neutralization had been assimilated.

Post-war valves were designed to provide greater gain and efficiency at higher frequencies, and improved cathodes were of high perveance (in other words, permitted much larger transient peaks of emission). The introduction of ceramic instead of glass for valve envelopes increased mechanical strength, allowed smaller physical size for a given power dissipation, and enabled valves to operate at higher ambient temperature; more effective de-gassing during manufacture permitted greater emission for pulse operation. Nevertheless it must be admitted that high-perveance, high-gain valves require more care be taken in ensuring correct operating conditions if self-destruction is to be avoided. There is still much to be said for using the older style glass 813 for hf operation. And why leave those 807s in the junk box?

For high power at vhf/uhf, the 4CX-series has established a virtually unrivalled position. But it is important to realize that these valves, although rugged and capable of extremely good linearity, are "like no other" and require careful study of the data sheets, particularly in respect of close control of the screen volts if they are to approach the linearity of which they are capable. In *TT* December 1985, John Nelson, G4FRX, with long experience of these powerful beasts, drew attention to the value of metal oxide varistors to prevent damage, particularly to the built-in screen bypass capacitors in the costly SK620 bases, from the flashovers that are all too common with these radial-beam high-gain tetrodes.

Several letters have been received on the use of 4CX-series valves, including comments from John Fournier, DC0HW, ex-G8LRH, and G D Eddowes, G3NOH, together with further comments from G4FRX. While these correspondents do not agree in some respects on why and how problems such as flashover arise so often with these valves, I have endeavoured to sort through three long letters to find common ground on some of the operating precautions that should be taken to achieve good performance over a long lifetime, without the non-linear splatter that too often occurs.

G4FRX emphasizes that the inter-electrode spacing is extremely small in order to achieve good performance up to 500MHz, but that this is not the primary reason for flashovers, which he suggests can arise from at least four causes. Then again, in some respects, the 4CX-series resemble the older form of screen-grid tetrode: *all* radial-beam tetrodes display screen-grid secondary emission under some operating conditions of drive and anode and screen voltages. He writes: "All 4CX250Bs can be expected to source screen current under certain common conditions of drive and loading. For example, a correctly-loaded and driven 4CX250B with 2kV on its anode and 350V on its screen can be expected to source about 5mA of screen current when driven to 250mA anode current.

Varian-Eimac point out in their application notes that the single-tone screen current can be used to establish correct loading. Their data sheet shows that under several commonly-encountered operating conditions the screen current can be expected to be negative. This is due to a form of "secondary emission", though not quite in its classical form. Every 4CX250B pa, G4FRX stresses, should have a meter (preferably of off-zero type) in the screen circuit for tuning and loading purposes.

Light or no loading of a 4CX250B frequently leads to flashovers, as explained by G4FRX in *Short Wave Magazine* in considerable detail in a series of articles about five years ago.

There is no doubt that the screen-grid power supply for this series of valves needs careful design, preferably with shunt regulators and capable of sourcing and sinking at least 40mA for negligible change in the screen voltage. High-voltage transistors and improved regulators with higher loop gain are proving an important advance on the older valve regulators. DC0HW and G4FRX are in agreement about the vital importance of adequate cooling, with the blower "over" rather than "under" dimensioned.

G4FRX stresses that the correct heater supply is 6·0V ± 5 per cent, *not* 6·3V. He also mentions that loss of heater emission is uncommon and that these valves are more often pulled from professional sockets due to a degree of softness that increases secondary emission etc. Difficulties can thus be experienced with "ex-equipment" valves although, in view of the high initial cost, this is a common route for amateurs to take.

Control circuits for the 4CX250B
In a separate contribution, G D Eddowes, G3NOH (Flat 1, 47 The Avenue, Ealing, London W13 8JR) suggests some requirements in designing the control circuits for high-power 4CX250B amplifiers. He writes: "The 4CX250 type of valve can be expensive to buy new; the popular alternative is to obtain the 'used' version, and when a couple of gooduns are eventually found, the relieved owner obviously wants to take good care of them. Taking good care includes correct switch-on procedure and adequate cooling of the value. The circuits described achieve both of these requirements.

"The sequence of events I use when switching on is:
(*a*) Blower on.
(*b*) Heaters on, 10s later.
(*c*) Bias supplies on soon after or at the same time as the heaters.
(*d*) Anode volts on about 2min after the blower, and
(*e*) Screen volts on about 2min and 30s after the blower.

"Fig 4 shows a suitable delay to use for the switch-on sequence. Capacitor C1 is charged through R1 until the potential at pins 1 and 2 of the ic is high enough to produce a logic 0 at pins 3, 5 and 6. A logic 1 is then present at the base of the transistor, TR1, and the relay is made, thus making the particular circuit. Table 1 gives suitable values of C1 and R1 for the timings required.

"Another important contribution to the lifespan of the valve is to keep the blower running for at least 3min after switch-off, and this is achieved by the circuit of Fig 5. A separate 12V supply is needed, the mains supply of which is taken from the same mains supply that feeds the blower. On switch-off, C2 is charged and is supplying a logic 1 to pins 8 and 9 of the ic and, going through the logic a 1 is on the base of TR2 and the relay is

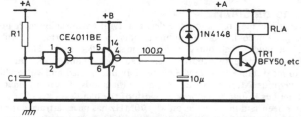

Fig 4. Delay logic for switch-on operations. Note that the supply for the ic is positive. For suggested component values for R and C, see Table 1

Table 1. Switch-on and switch-off delay

Delay	C1 and C2	R1 and R2
10s	4·7µF	2·2MΩ
2min	100µF	1·5MΩ
2min 30s	100µF	1·8MΩ
3min	100µF	2·2MΩ

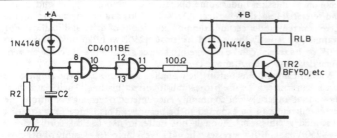

Fig 5. Delay logic for switching-off. Positive A supply is the general 12V line. Positive B supply must be maintained after switch-off and can be derived from the mains supply that feeds the fan. R2 and C2 component values are in Table 1

made. When the potential on pins 8 and 9 has dropped because of R1, the logic at the base of TR2 will be a 0 and the relay will break, thus disconnecting the blower.

"A snag I have come across is when the blower inductance is high and the relay contacts do not have much of a gap; the result is a chattering relay and burnt-out contacts! This is due to the spark inducing volts into the transformer that supplies the dc volts for the relay and charging up the smoothing capacitor. The answer is to keep the value of the smoothing to about 22µF, but this produces a side effect: not enough coulombs in the dc supply to keep C2 going. My 5min delay ended up with no R2 and a capacitor value of 220µF.

"As far as protection for the valve in the event of anode volts being lost, I have found that a 50mA quick-blow fuse in the screen supply is adequate. There are circuits around that detect the presence of anode volts, but I have never found one to be necessary. (G4FRX disagrees, he would not trust a 50mA fuse.)

"The mains supply switching is shown in Fig 6. The neutral is not switched, but if the live connector is fused and the polarity is correct it will be safe. If switching of the neutral is required there are four-pole mains switches available.

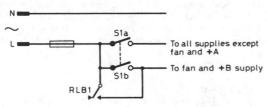

Fig 6. Arrangement of mains supplies

"The relays I use are 700Ω, and I have a limited number available but without bases."

G4FRX is a little uneasy about G3NOH's switch-on sequence. Eimac suggest that no other supplies should be applied until 1min after the heaters are turned on (although it seems unlikely that anything untoward could occur from earlier application of the bias supplies as in the G3NOH procedure). But the point he stresses is that the screen grid should always be tied to earth or to 300V and *never* allowed to float with anode volts applied, as this will almost certainly lead to flashovers etc. He adds that Eimac no longer recommend keeping the blower running 3min after switching off the heater.

Getting on 50MHz

Whatever one may feel about the desirability of encouraging more home-building or improvization of equipment, it is equally important that full use should be made of all our valuable frequency allocations. There is little doubt, for example, that, particularly in sunspot minimum years and after dark in maximum years, 28MHz is terribly under-used and vulnerable to take-over bids. More converted cb rigs, in the hands of licensed amateurs, could help us to retain the present width of the band!

It has been said that the reason why 70MHz has never attracted the level of activity justified by its useful propagation characteristics is because, being virtually a UK-only allocation, it has never been a target for Japanese

firms. This is not the situation on 50MHz. Not only are there plenty of transceivers available from the major manufacturers (including many at power levels that need to be fed to inefficient antennas through high-loss feeders if they are to meet the current power restrictions) but also 50MHz is within the frequency band used by military vehicles, including tank sets.

The commercial models include 10W and 85W transceivers, 2·5W handhelds etc, such as Icom 551 (10W), 551-D (85W), Trio TS-660 (10W), TS670 (10W), Yaesu FT680R (10W), FT726R (10W), FT690R (2·5W) etc. There are also transverters such as the Microwave Modules unit (144 to 50MHz) and Yaesu FTV700 (28 to 50MHz). Crystal-controlled receiver converters include the Microwave Modules MMC 50 to 28MHz for use with an hf communications receiver.

On the military side, the older Plessey units such as C42, B47 and PRC261 can get you on the band, though receiver sensitivity may need to be improved by a front-end or masthead preamplifier.

The vhf radio sets in operational use by Nato forces all cover 50MHz, though the tuning steps tend to be 50kHz or higher and bandwidth is a nominal 25kHz.

The following are some still operational models:

SEM-25	26·05	to 69·95MHz	in 50kHz steps
RT-68	38	to 54·8MHz	in 100kHz steps
VRC353	30	to 76MHz	in 25kHz steps
ANP524	30	to 75MHz	in 50kHz steps
RT3600	26	to 69·95MHz	in 50kHz steps
SEM-35	33	to 76MHz	in 50kHz steps
VRC-65	30	to 75·95MHz	in 50kHz steps
VRC-12	30	to 75·95MHz	in 50kHz steps

Some of the broadband masthead tv amplifiers, such as the Labgear CM8065 (42 to 800MHz), can be used to increase sensitivity, though it goes against the grain to draw attention to untuned vhf/uhf amplifiers which, in their customary application, make tv sets and vcr machines horribly susceptible to rfi due to overload from 70, 144, 430 or even 28MHz amateur transmitters.

The stringent erp restriction on UK operation suggests that for optimum performance it would be good strategy to use a non-gain omni-directional transmitting antenna (eg a "turnstile" arrangement of horizontally-polarized dipoles) *plus* a high-gain multi-element receiving antenna. Remember that even if separate antennas are used it will usually be necessary to protect the receiver or preamplifier front-end transistors.

Short backfire antennas

Many years ago in *TT* and *ART*, I drew attention to the backfire vhf/uhf antennas originally developed about 1960 by H W Ehrenspeck.

The basic principle was to mount a multi-element Yagi looking in the opposite direction to the target area, with the signal directed into a large plane reflector screen with a rim (rather like a large saucepan lid).

The theory was that the signals would be reflected back through the Yagi array so that the elements would, in effect, act twice. Attempts by amateurs to achieve similar results were not altogether successful.

However, one form of this antenna, known as a short backfire antenna (sba) dispensed with the line of Yagi director elements and comprised simply the large back "saucepan-lid" reflector plate (about 2λ diameter), the small front disc reflector (0·4λ diameter), plus the dipole. In this form, the backfire antenna has become well known among professional designers. The overall length of the structure was only about 0·5λ, and the structure

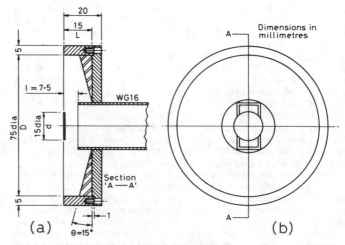

Fig 7. Mechanical details of the 10GHz rectangular waveguide (WG16)—excited short-back antenna with a conical rim

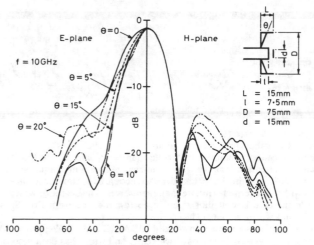

Fig 8. Measured E- and H-plane radiation patterns with conical main rim reflectors of slant angles (θ) of 0, 5, 10, 15 and 20°. 10 or 15° provides optimum pattern

was not unlike a Cassegrain parabolic-reflector antenna but without the production difficulties of the parabolic shape. It was claimed that an sba could give up to 15dBi gain, equivalent to a much longer Yagi of over 20 elements.

More recently various improvements to the basic sba have been reported both at vhf/uhf (L-band) and at 10GHz (X-band). It was found (*IEEE Trans AP-31*, pp644–6) that significantly improved bandwidth could be obtained by replacing the large plane reflector by a curved surface. Later it was reported by M S Leong and P S Kooi (National University of Singapore) in *Electronics Letters*, Vol 20, No 18, 30 August 1984, pp749–51, that a conical main reflector can lead to a compact antenna having a directive gain of 16·7 to 18·3dB, sidelobe level below 13·8dB, and input vswr better than 2·5 over a 20 per cent bandwidth. The experimental model (Figs 7, 8) was, in this case, a waveguide-excited sba covering 9 to 11GHz, and thus suitable for the amateur 10GHz band. At this frequency the beamwidth and sidelobe level of the antenna was optimum at 10GHz when the slant angle of the conical surface is around 10–15°. Construction is simplified by the fact that the main reflector is a separate unit as a plane surface, with the conical surface in the form of an attachment to this main reflector plate. The sub-reflector disc is positioned by means of a thin low-permittivity plastic support. At lower frequencies the same basic technique could presumably be used with a coaxial fed dipole element rather than wave guide excited.

Antenna basics

At virtually any frequency, hf to microwave, physical size is important, and it becomes difficult to use short elements, particularly in close-spaced arrays. As pointed out recently by Clifford H Freeman (Hazeltine Corporation) in "Wideband matching of a small disk-loaded monopole" (*IEEE Trans AP-33*, No 10, October 1985) electrically small antennas pose a major problem with respect to their electrical performance. He writes: "These types of antenna have radiation resistances which decrease rapidly with size. As a consequence, tuning and matching become very difficult to compute. With these concepts in mind, the antenna efficiency deteriorates and performance parameters, such as bandwidth, tend to decrease to unacceptable levels. Therefore, designing compact antennas which are efficient in spite of their electrical size is a very difficult task."

For microwave antennas, physical size is less a problem than the need for mechanical precision. For this reason alone, an antenna having a large effective bandwidth, relatively straightforward mechanics, and without the difficult doubly-curved parabolic shape, should prove attractive. The parabolic dish has many good points, including the potential of very high gain. The Yagi array gives excellent gain in relation to its size, but is frequency sensitive and by no means fool-proof in practice. With care, stacked Yagis can give even higher gain, though one should not expect that, for example, four stacked similar arrays will give more than some 5dB extra gain, and often less, rather than the theoretical 6dB.

There is, indeed, often so great a difference between free-space theory and practice when it comes to questions of antenna characteristics, that many amateurs have come to rely on commercial designs even though this is still no guarantee that their performance will meet fully the claims made for them. It is a pity that no matter how logical technically, the 50MHz power limits have been based on effective radiated power (erp), an entity that none of us can measure directly. I have for many years argued that even professional broadcasters are stretching credibility to the limit by listing transmitter powers in terms of kilowatts erp or emrp (effective monopole radiated power) to three places of decimals. The answer I am usually given is that this is the figure that comes out of the computer based on the requisite coverage area!

Loops and dipoles

A short note in January *TT* (p 35) commented on loop and dipole antennas from a *QST* article by J L Dietrich, WA0RDX. This has prompted Les Moxon, G6XN, to comment as follows, as he feels that readers could have been misled into attempting to put up some enormous loops as soon as the weather turned more spring-like.

"It is good to come across some recognition at last for the fact that 14MHz (1λ) quad loops work well on 21MHz. Unfortunately the claims made for larger loops generally based on computer studies appear to go well beyond the no-penalty multiband operation of loops featured hitherto.

"On theoretical grounds, as well as practical experience over many years covering this particular area, I find there is no substance in the suggestion that larger loops provide appreciably more gain or smaller loops less gain, nor is there any validity in the comparison, in this respect, with dipoles—though these do not show any significant gain variation with size either. The reference to a 3λ/2 dipole is presumably a misprint for 3λ/4, in which case the gain is 0·6dB over a λ/2 dipole, or 1dB over a very short dipole.

"What appears to have been overlooked is the strong vertically-polarized signal in the plane of the loop which results when the loop size is increased. For a 3λ/2 loop, ignoring ground effects, we have the following field strength ratios:

$$\frac{\text{vertical in plane of loop}}{\text{horizontal at right angles}} = \begin{array}{l} 0\cdot79 \text{ (square loop)} \\ 0\cdot61 \text{ (delta loop)} \end{array}$$

"This does not help with the QRM situation, but fortunately there is less energy wasted in the unwanted mode than these figures might suggest, since it is produced by an "8JK-pair" having a gain of 3 to 4dB. On this basis the losses due to the unwanted mode come to 1·17dB and 0·67dB respectively, and these must be deducted from the 'stacking gain' obtained by considering the loops as a pair of dipoles having the appropriate spacing. Another small correction arises because the length (or width) of the antenna affects the width of the forward lobe; this is the 'short dipole' effect mentioned above about which there is little published information. I have derived some very rough estimates by finding the centres of gravity of the current distribution of each half of the radiator and then treating it as a colinear pair having very close spacing. This can be done by using the mutual impedance data available in the handbooks. This gives a somewhat too low figure in the case of a λ/2 dipole (0·25 instead of 0·4dB) but this is to be expected in view of the unsymmetrical nature of a λ/4 current distribution, and the extra weight which should be given to contributions from near the ends. On this basis I feel that the method is basically sound and the other corrections unlikely to be in error by more than 0·1dB. This results in Table 2.

Table 2. Dipole and loop performance

Type of element	Stacking gain (dB)	Unwanted mode loss (dB)	"Length" correction (dB)	Gain (dB) dBd	Gain (dB) dBi
λ/2 dipole	—			0	2·15
λ/4 dipole, end-loaded*		Up to 0·2	−0·25	−0·45	1·7
1λ square loop	1·12	Very small	−0·32	0·8	2·95
3λ/2 square loop	2·5	1·17	−0·1	1·25	3·4
3λ delta loop	0·75	0·67	0	0·08	2·23
3λ/4 delta loop	0	0 (approx)	−0·25	−0·25	1·9

*eg, bent ends as in VK2ABQ antenna.
Note: Stacking gain for the 3λ/2 square loop assumes equal currents in the "dipoles". The actual ratio is 0·67 but it is very difficult to allow for this. The true gain figure could be as low as 3dBi.

"Note that the differences are in the main trivial, and single-element gain figures tend to disappear in the case of arrays, in line with normal stacking principles. In practice one is much better off with the *smaller* loops, since one can prevent sides or lower portions from radiating by arranging that current nodes occur in their centres. This increases the effective height, which may often be increased still further by taking advantage of smaller size and lower windage.

"Returning to the January *TT*, I am quite happy with Table 1, less so with Fig 3 in view of the misleading conclusions which appear to have been drawn from it. It may be no more than a coincidence that the gain for 3λ/2 *exactly* equals the stacking gain for dipoles spaced by the width of a 3λ/2 square loop, and it may be that the circular shape does provide extra gain equal to the 'mode loss'. Application of my square-counting methods to circular loops is extremely laborious and I have not attempted it."   □

Technical Topics
by Pat Hawker, G3VA

TT HAS ALWAYS DEPENDED on the efforts of others: the authors of the hundreds of articles published in overseas journals, both amateur and professional, plus the writers of the many letters that reach me, sometimes only a trickle, but sometimes in a flood. These include many useful ideas and comments, and no columnist in his right mind would wish to discourage such correspondence. But it can present the difficult problem of finding the space to do them justice; current economic restraints have meant that *Radio Communication* is often a little thinner than it was a few years ago. Inevitably the selection process results in the holding over of items that thoroughly deserve publication but cannot readily be condensed into the limited space available. I try to select a balance of items of interest to the majority of readers, though I realize not all readers share my particular prejudices and concerns.

My purpose in making this confession is primarily to apologize to those whose letters and drawings are still "on file" rather than in print. Quarts just do not go into pint bottles, even when spelt quartz.

But before getting down to business, I must pay a tribute, on behalf of us all, to Dick Thornley, G2DAF, who died in early March. It was Dick's designs of high-performance hf receivers and ssb/cw transmitters in the 'sixties that did so much to keep alive, at least for a time, the concept of home-construction as a means of achieving true "excellence". Even by today's standards, G2DAF designs are capable of a basic performance that is seldom equalled, let alone surpassed, by the black boxes. Dick was the "Collins" of the home workshop! It is sad that he has left us.

Morse, Shannon, eme and audio filtering

Recent items on the reduction of the noise bandwidth of a receiver to match the transmission bandwidth and the consequent theoretical advantage of reducing the bit-rate of morse or data transmissions "when the going gets tough" (see, for example, *TT* December 1985, p940) has brought in several pertinent comments.

Dr Ian White, G3SEK, seeks to destroy the myth that moonbounce (eme) communication takes place using extremely slow morse: "The plain fact is that moonbouncers use quite 'normal' speeds of 15 to 20wpm.

"The myth became established in the early days when just a few amateurs, using receiver, transmitter and antenna technology not available to the average experimenter, were involved. One of the blind alleys explored in that period was the detection of inaudibly weak signals buried in noise using integrators and pen recorders, for which extremely slow morse would have been appropriate. However, the technique never got anywhere, primarily because it did not provide the operator satisfaction of a normal, audible contact.

"With modern technology, moonbounce signals can be audible, though most are so weak that they are off the bottom of the normal RST scale! So why has the optimum speed been found to be 15 to 20wpm? With very slow morse a human operator loses the rhythm of the characters. Furthermore on eme the characters tend to get broken up by rapid fading. It needs concentration merely to copy the signals, without the extra effort of trying to copy signals that are either too slow or too fast. Fast morse has the advantage that individual characters are less likely to be chopped up by fading, and one technique is to send characters at the rate of 30wpm but spaced out to keep the average speed within the optimum 15 to 20wpm rate.

"The concession of Shannon's theory is that the basic message (callsigns, report, rogers, 73 etc) is repeated many times, so that in a sense moonbouncers do 'integrate' the signals over several fragmented repeats to extract the information."

This comment highlights the difficulty of interfacing the human operator into general theory—a problem that extends also to reception of morse in conditions other than eme. For example, the use of narrowband audio filters can sometimes prove disappointing simply because the human hearing process can provide a filter with an effective "noise" bandwidth of around 50 to 100Hz. However this characteristic cannot be relied upon to the same degree when it is a question of separating two or more audio tones with a spacing of less than about 15 to 20 per cent. This is one reason why many experienced operators prefer a beat note of, say, 400 to 500Hz rather than, say, 1,000Hz. You can separate a 500Hz note from either 300 or 700Hz far more readily than between 1,000Hz and 800 or 1,200Hz.

Wonders of morse

In the December "Members Mailbag", *TT* (February) and in my "Communications Commentary" column in *Electronics & Wireless World* (January), attention was drawn to the remarkable and unique value of morse code in enabling badly handicapped people to communicate *on equal terms* with those more fortunate than themselves. The degree to which this is truly the case is well illustrated in correspondence from Bob Smith, G6TQ, and B J Frost, G6UTN.

G6TQ describes a project in which he, RAIBC and the West Kent ARS have been involved over the past two years, and which has been described in a new book *Computer help for disabled people* by Lorna Ridgway and Stuart McKears (Human Horizons series, Souvenir Press, £5.99 paperback, £8.95 casebound).

This project has centred on a young man, Mark Brown, 22 years old, confined to a wheelchair, blind, profoundly deaf and, due to his deafness from birth, with a severe speech impairment. Yet he has achieved a "fantastic ability" to copy morse. G6TQ writes:

"We talk to him at 25 to 30wpm, but he can read at virtually any speed. He is unable to write and just reads it in his head like a book. This is achieved by a wheelchair-borne microcomputer which is programmed to translate plain language typed on the keyboard into fast morse. This he reads through earphones by bone conductivity, as he can sense the vibrations.

"With the help of WKARS, representing RAIBC, we have tutored Mark to the stage where last December he passed the RAE. Already, as a result of his new interests, he has put weight on his frail body, become more alert and lively. Via his keyboard he can talk with anybody. Feedback comes from him either in distorted speech or, for those who can read morse, he uses an auto-key (iambic type). He has mastered this keyer to perfection; an amazing performance, as he has such little use of his hands."

G6TQ adds that tuition was carried out with the equipment described, based on weekly visits together with morse instruction tapes. To me this seems a marvellous combination of the oldest and newest in communications—morse and computers yet with the emphasis on personally acquired skills.

The utterly-isolated world of those born both deaf and blind can be imagined. This condition is most often simply the unhappy result of the mother catching rubella (German measles) during pregnancy, and is all the more poignant in that the individuals concerned are often of high or at least average intelligence and are well capable, as the case of Mark Brown shows, of acquiring skills that can open the world to them.

B J Frost, G6UTN, similarly reports successful work for the deaf. He writes:

"A certain amount of successful work has recently been undertaken by the Great Yarmouth and Lowestoft branch of REMAP—a panel of engineers within a nationwide network who construct various kinds of mechanical and electronic aids for the disabled.

"This particular project commenced with my development of an aid for the family of a totally deaf girl to enable them to call her from within the confines of a house and garden. A very low-power receiver was developed (27MHz, 2V, 1mA) and used in conjunction with an indicating device mounted on the girl's spectacles. Her mother was then able to call her from a simple base transmitter using either simple pre-arranged codes or their pre-existing knowledge of morse.

"Due to the interest this caused, work has continued with a two-way aid intended either for a similar application or for use by two totally deaf persons. This consists of identical transceiver-type units in conjunction with a wristwatch-mounted indicator and push-button. When one person wishes to call the other, a single press of the button causes a motorized vibrating device to be actuated. Then two-way communication can continue using the indicators and buttons based on either pre-arranged or morse codes.

"A working prototype has been tested by the local social services and is attracting considerable interest. Unfortunately there are problems in licensing even these low-power units. 'Low-power non-speech devices' are only permitted to operate on specific frequencies and must obtain typed-approval from the DTI and require payment of an annual licence fee. This situation will ease later this year when such devices are due to become exempt from licence fees.

"At present the major difficulty is that the lowest available frequency for commercially-manufactured units is 173MHz, complicating the design of low-power circuitry. The DTI may allocate a new frequency at 49MHz, but up to late January it has still not issued technical characteristics for this band.

"While the DTI is gradually moving towards a more relaxed approach to such aids, the semiconductor manufacturers are also assisting in the greater integration of receiver circuitry. Plessey have helped with ics developed for their pocket radiopagers."

While clearly this type of equipment is aimed at short-range person-to-person communication of a fairly limited nature, it is easy to see that once the users have come to appreciate the value of morse it would be a very short step indeed to interest them in the wider horizons of amateur radio.

Optimizing coaxial traps

The use of coaxial to form resonate traps (eg VK5BI's WARC trapped dipole, *TT* January, pp34–5) has the unique advantage of providing an in-built high-voltage capacitor and offers other useful advantages. Geoff Roberts, G3ENY, points out, however, that they need to be carefully resonated and that cut-and-try methods can be tedious, time consuming and can result in an extravagant waste of expensive cable. He writes:

"It has been shown by Robert Sommer, N4UU (*QST* December 1984) that there is an optimum way to use this material to form an inductor, the whole acting as a parallel resonant circuit. The trick is to use the shortest length of cable (minimum capacitance) which can be closewound (maximum inductance) on a former of such a diameter to make a coil of correct inductance having a length to diameter ratio to give a good value of Q. Not so simple but very effective if it can be achieved. Final adjustment to resonance is done by stripping back the outer at the pig-tail (correcting the 'C') using a gdo and calibrated receiver.

"Eliminating the cut-and-try from construction requires the use of a computer to solve, by an iterative loop, the cubic equation which ties together the LC and diameter variables to obtain resonance. I have devised such a program in Sinclair Basic which gives results within a few per cent of design specification and has proved to be very useful. Coil diameters given in the VK5BI notes seem to be rather on the large side.

"As an example, the following are two designs of trap for 7,010kHz, one using standard coaxial cable and one miniature coaxial cable, which incidentally is quite satisfactory for most UK stations running legal power levels.

	RG-58/U	RG-174/U
Length of coaxial cable	61·6in	52·7in
Diameter of former	2·125in	1·6in
No of turns	7·8	9·6
Length of former	2·5in	2in
Coil inductance	3·35µH	3·78µH

"Knowing the coil inductance is useful in working out the length of wire in the next leg, another task for the microprocessor! As there is a limited range of pvc pipe sizes available from builders' merchants, the constructor would be well advised to choose a diameter which gives a length-to-diameter ratio of about 0·6, certainly less than one, or a square coil.

"The program listing is available, giving suggested pipe sizes for all amateur bands. It is quite long, but I would be glad to supply a listing or tape to interested enquirers; sae please. My address is 6 Highfield Road, Bridgnorth, Salop WV16 5AU."

The first transatlantic tv

This year sees the 50th anniversary of the formal opening of the Alexandra Palace television service (originally using alternatively 405- and 240-line systems) on 2 November 1936 as the world's first regular public high-definition tv service. There are many plans being made to mark this golden jubilee and to note also the earlier work on 30-line mechanical systems which, in the UK, stemmed from the work of the controversial John Logie Baird.

Baird in his early work had the lively assistance of a number of British radio amateurs, including Ben Clapp, now well into his 90s but then licensed as 2KZ. The pioneering work of Baird and his assistants deserves to be remembered. Unfortunately, many exaggerated claims on their behalf have been—and still are being—made, with the unhappy result that the real contribution they made in arousing interest and showing possibilities is in danger of being dismissed by the more serious students of the history of the technology.

Elsewhere I have been very critical of the claims made for a new book *The secret life of John Logie Baird* by Tom McArthur and Dr Peter Waddell (Hutchinsons, 1986, 274pp, £16.95). The publishers suggest that the book "radically rewrites the entire acknowledged histories of television, radar and secret signalling". Personally I find it impossible to accept most of the sweeping claims made in this book. A few years ago I spent several days

Simple, but unfortunately not very effective! A Baird 30-line disc receiver of the low-definition tv era

consulting the original files in the Post Office archives, and wrote the following notes on Baird's early attempts to put low-definition tv "on the air":

"Baird made many misleading claims about his early work, often giving the impression that his pictures were transmitted, if only between adjacent rooms, by radio. Yet all the evidence suggests that the very first time that the Baird signals were transmitted was about July 1927 when he persuaded H L Kirke of the BBC unofficially to let him put out signals on a BBC mf transmitter after the close of programmes. Three transmissions were made with no known record of successful reception, and then the Post Office realized what was going on and persuaded the BBC to stop the tests abruptly. It was not until September 1929, this time with the backing of the Post Office, that Baird gained "official" access to a BBC transmitter. Well before then Baird had obtained "experimental" licences 2TV and 2TW for use at Monograph House, near Leicester Square, and "Green Gables" at Harrow. There is, however, no reliable evidence that any transmissions actually took place from either of these locations, as the transmitters do not appear to have been completed.

"Baird, however, did transmit his signals by radio in February 1928 on about 7MHz from the home of Ben Clapp, one of his first assistants, who held the amateur experimental call 2KZ at Warwick Road, Coulsdon, Surrey. With this transmitter, modulated by tv signals sent over telephone lines from Monograph House, Baird staged his famous London/New York "demonstration" and subsequently a demonstration on the liner *Berengaria* during the return voyage. Fairly reliable records show that on the liner a few (barely) recognizable and fleeting pictures *were* achieved, even in the absence of any effective synchronization. In New York the "demonstrations" made front-page news, were extensively written up on the basis of what Baird told reporters, but there is little firm evidence about the quality or duration of the pictures actually achieved. The evidence of *successful* reception is far from convincing.

"The Post Office officials read with some alarm of the 2KZ transmissions and, on 26 April 1928 hastily and secretly arranged for a surprise inspection of the station. One suspects that they were not entirely pleased when their inspector duly reported that when he called at 7pm on 29 April 1928 he could find no evidence of any infringement of the terms of 2KZ's licence! For the period, 2KZ had a well-equipped hf station with two 60ft poles spaced 35ft apart and a five-wire cage counterpoise at a height of 12ft. The house was on the highest part of Coulsdon Down, with power taken from the public *dc* supply mains using an ht generator capable of providing 4,000V at 750mA (ie 3kW), although the two large Mullard valves in the power amplifier were run at about 1kW input, the licensed power of 2KZ. (The idea that all amateurs pre-war were restricted to 10W is one of those myths that have crept into the public domain.)

"Baird and 2KZ certainly made tv history in the first long-distance transmission by radio. Fair enough as long as we accept that the results were extremely crude and we discount the exaggerated claims made at the time by Baird.

"Later in the 'thirties, a well-known south London amateur, Don Price, G6HP, joined the Baird company's laboratories at Crystal Palace in charge of the experimental vhf transmitter. This had tragic consequences as he was electrocuted when he got across the eht."

Let's encourage beginner's rigs

The, to my mind, long overdue resurgence of interest in morse could hopefully lead to a renewed demand for simple hf transmitters having an rf power output of say 10 or 20W on 1·8, 3·5, 7 and 10·1MHz. Such rigs would, in effect, provide not only a valuable educational tool but they are still capable of providing effective contacts for those wishing to gain operational experience on cw without immediately plunging into highly-competitive "contest" or country/square-chasing working. A separate transmitter, possibly even crystal controlled, would suit those who have become interested in amateur radio by listening on a reasonably good receiver, and thus do not immediately require a high-performance transceiver.

John Roscoe, G4QK, puts it thus: "Obviously somebody will have to re-invent the B–2 transmitter! Actually that 1943 hf transmitter-receiver suitcase set had a lot going for it. The oscillator circuit would fire up just about anything, and the pa capacitors were fine compact devices. The chief snag for amateur operation was the inability to net. I built a small vfo with a stabilized psu. The other disadvantage was that the receiver was switched off completely on 'send' and did not always come back dead on tune. But at its post-war surplus price of £10!"

In practice, as I suspect John Brown, G3EUR, who designed that SOE equipment might agree, for its time the B–2 was relatively sophisticated and by no means a "simple" set, representing almost state-of-the-art miniaturization! The final version of that family of compact transmitter-receivers based on valves, but still very much in the B–2 tradition, was the Mark 123. I suspect that the unit manufacturing cost of that model, which was used well into the 'sixties or 'seventies, must have been higher than many "black boxes" when inflation is taken into account.

But certainly single- and two-valve transmitters had a lot going for them. One of the very first transmitters made expressly for clandestine operation in western Europe was designed for the German Abwehr (military intelligence) by the "Geheimer Funkmeldedienst" in 1936. It consisted simply of an adapter unit that plugged into the audio output socket of a domestic "all-wave" broadcast receiver (or preferably one of the low-cost communications receivers such as the "Sky Buddy" or "Sky Champion"). The original output valve was then plugged back into a socket at the top of the adapter where it functioned both as audio output and keyed crystal oscillator! No special psu, and all concealed in a standard receiver.

A much more potent German equipment was the SE90/40 used primarily on their military intelligence networks that were so assiduously listened to by the many British pre-war amateurs acting as "voluntary interceptors" for the Radio Security Service. Rudolf F Staritz, DL3CS, has recently published several detailed articles describing the German equipment which generally depended on "straight" 1–v–1 or 1–v–2 receivers, unless used with a commercial communications receiver. But even from the other side of the hill, he accepts that the B–2 design was technically in advance of what they were building even in 1944 or 1945. Though the models that I have seen were notably well constructed mechanically!

Based at Berlin-Stannsdorf, the Funkmeldedienst designed and built almost 100 different models of portable receivers and transmitters for use by the German Abwehr and RSHA police networks, ranging from battery-operated transmitters (sometimes used without a receiver) of up to 3W output, single-stage co transmitters using AL4, AL5, EL3, EL12, 6V6 and 6L6 valves for up to 14W output, and more powerful two- or three-stage compact transmitters of 10, 20, 30, 40, 80 and even 250W output, using simple variable oscillators (some a bit chirpy). Several models used the useful German RL12P50 valve, a bit larger than an 807, as shown in Fig 1 for model SE90/40. The most powerful transmitter, requiring two suitcases, had an RL12P50 driving an RS383 (Model SE93/250). DL3CS points out that they used the best existing degree of miniaturization and were invariably built for suitcase or canvas containers. Ruefully, he admits that many were carried in very elegant red-brown leather suitcases that could be recognized at a distance of 100m, and that this sealed the fate of many who were intended to use them until the wiser instructors and spy-masters changed them for cases that could be readily bought in the shops. The more powerful sets, that were in fact the main concern of the British VIs, were used primarily not as agent-sets but in the Abwehr offices in occupied countries (Asts) and in neutral countries (KOs). But certainly sets like the SE90/40 provided reasonable signals in the UK, but not being crystal-controlled they could come up several kilohertz away from their scheduled frequencies and required careful searching on the part of the interceptors!

DL3CS's articles appeared in *cq-DL* 6/83 and *Funk* 7/85 and 8/85. The *Funk* articles were kindly brought to my notice by Andy Emmerson, G8PTH/G9BUP.

The emptiness of "ten"

Ray Cracknell, G2AHU, is one of the increasing number of people deeply concerned at the lack of use being made of the 1·7MHz-wide 28MHz allocation during these sunspot-minimum years. He draws attention to an article by Z21GH in the *QUA Newsletter* of the Zimbabwe ARS which starts:

"I wonder how many stations have been listening on ten metres recently? With the sunspot cycle being what it is and at the very bottom of what is going to be a few years of minimal sunspot activity, I think that a lot of amateurs treat ten metres as a dead band.

"Far from it. With the return of our summer months (ie UK winter) there are, although infrequent, very good openings on ten metres on both the North–South and East–West paths. Good signals have been heard over the past two months from both Europe, mainly in the afternoons, and North and South America in the evenings up to as late as 1800gmt. The most disturbing aspect of the openings though is that the minority of signals heard are amateur.

"It looks as though the prediction made by some amateurs a few years back that ten metres was going to be inundated by non-amateur stations during the sunspot cycle lull has in fact happened. The band is full of pirate traffic, in all languages, right through from 28·0 to 29·7MHz. The most disturbing feature of all though is that amateurs themselves seem to be largely ignoring the band. Once amateurs "re-discover" ten metres, they may be sadly disappointed to find that they no longer have exclusive, or any, use of this very good dx band.

"It is a fact that in the recent past radio licensing authorities in a number of countries have been coerced into legalizing radio operation that was previously illegal due to the commercial and lobbying pressure of the illegal operators themselves. The precedent seems to have been set that if you have a problem with a large number of persons breaking the law, the easy way

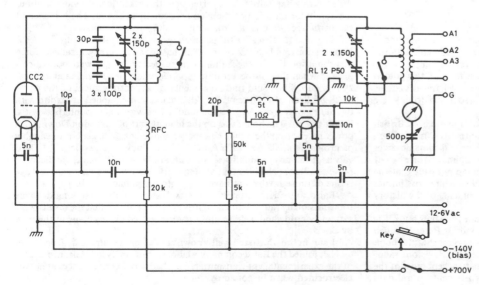

Fig 1. The wartime German suitcase transmitter type SE90/40, a simple 40W output hf transmitter used with a 1-v-1 receiver comprising three EF12 pentodes. The fixed capacitors in the oscillator tuned circuit provided temperature compensation

around it is not to prosecute the offenders but to legalize what was previously illegal. The problem then magically disappears.

"It is a consistent story you hear from amateurs in QSO on ten, they all bemoan the fact that most amateurs don't believe that ten metres is ever open, so very few are even taking the time to listen."

There are a number of ways of re-populating 28MHz for its assigned use. It is easy (some would say regrettably so) to convert low-cost cb rigs. It's a good band for mobile operation. But most of all it's open for long-distance F2 paths in a southerly direction (Africa, South America) far more often than seems to be generally believed. Like 50MHz, it is a band offering many odd modes, including meteor scatter, sporadic-E etc. With the legality of crossband operation now established in the UK, it could help reduce the pressure on 144MHz. One thing is certain, it is a part of the spectrum that other users would like. Use or lose!

Implementing "Project 6L6"

Several readers, including G2RX and G3KSU, have drawn attention to an article in *The Guardian* "Progress in a vacuum" that suggests that the US Naval Research Laboratory, Stanford Research Institute and possibly other establishments are currently hard at work developing new microminiature thermionic devices in order to provide greater protection of military equipment against nemp (nuclear electromagnetic pulses) though the sparse details given seem confused and, indeed, near unbelievable. But as has been noted before "if the valve had been invented *after* the transistor it would have been hailed as the answer to all our problems". For amateur radio it still has many attractions.

For those who wish to implement "Project 6L6" in the form of a duplication of the simple one-stage rigs of yesteryear, Roy Oliver has dug out an article by W8QBW from *QST* September 1939 (the design also appeared I recall in several editions of the *ARRL Radio Amateurs' Handbook*): Fig 2. This described a "Runt 60" 6L6G co transmitter claimed to provide 60W *output* (surely stretching the poor old valve rather too much!) on 3·5 or 7MHz and with a component cost (excluding valve, crystal and key) of only $3.86 which, in 1939, would have been well under £1!

Mike Shepherd, G8YZW, lists many publications that described simple valve transmitters, and provides the circuit diagram of a 6L6G rig with pi-network matching that appeared in *Practical Wireless* as late as June 1961 as "A 10-watt single-valve transmitter": Fig 3.

It should be noted that the American circuit includes a 60mA pilot bulb in series with the crystal to provide a warning against excessive crystal current when the tuned circuit is brought too near resonance. With power oscillators, even the physically large crystals of the 'thirties could be damaged in this way, especially when using the tritet harmonic oscillator. One would need to watch this carefully with small modern crystals.

Louis Varney, G5RV/CX5RV, whose amateur radio activities began as a schoolboy in the 'twenties, mentions that he still occasionally sets up and uses or demonstrates a Hartley self-oscillating transmitter he built in 1927

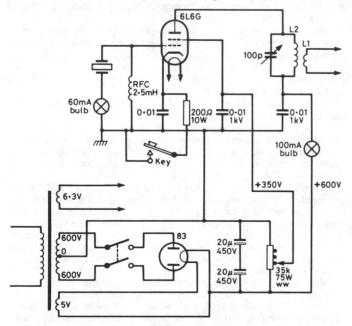

Fig 2. **Circuit diagram of the 1939 "Runt 60" 6L6G transmitter. But watch crystal currents at high power**

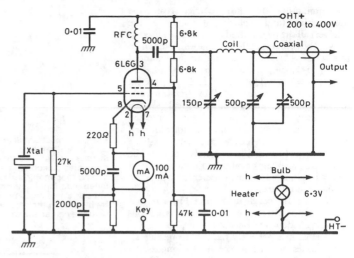

Fig 3. *Practical Wireless 6L6G transmitter (10W) of 1961*

that has its original DE4b dull-emitter af triode valve. This continues to oscillate on 3·5, 7 and 14MHz with a power input of about 3W that now comes from a 150V stabilized psu with 4V smoothed dc for the filament. Originally he used a 4V accumulator and 120V ht dry battery. When he could "touch" his father for the money for a second ht battery he could QRO to 6W.

Today, the note is a slightly chirpy T7 that provides a change from the ubiquitous depersonalized T9 of the black boxes. There is, however, no difficulty in copying it even on modern narrowband receivers. G5RV has demonstrated this "antique" transmitter in the course of many of the talks he gives to clubs when in the UK. He is currently building an exact replica of an O-v-1 Reinartz receiver with "original" components of the period for use with this transmitter. He may even, for complete authenticity, exchange his "G5RV" antenna for a Zepp!

Those steady carriers—the a.m. debate

The recent letters in *Members Mailbag* questioning how can it be (or confirming) that there is absolutely no information in the "carrier" of an amplitude modulated transmission underline a very real problem for newcomers, and for some who are not newcomers. For unless the concept of the steady carrier, contributing no information except that it is there, is firmly grasped, then it is virtually impossible to understand the principles not only of a.m. but also of ssb!

Much of the confusion arises, I suggest, from the many introductory books that still explain and illustrate "amplitude modulation" in terms of the "envelope" waveform. Such diagrams appear to show that the output of a fully-modulated a.m. transmitter is continuously varying between zeros and peaks. This makes it all the more difficult to appreciate that in reality the carrier of an a.m. signal remains at a constant amplitude in the presence or absence of modulation. It is essential to recognize this basic fact to grasp how ssb (which is in reality a form of a.m.) works.

It is all much easier once it is appreciated that the process of *amplitude modulation* is in reality the same process as *mixing*. An a.m. transmitter mixes the audio frequencies with a steady radio frequency in a non-linear stage. Mixing is the fundamental process of the superhet receiver, and newcomers are soon taught that mixing f1 with f2 results in outputs of f1, f2, f1 − f2 and f1 + f2. When af is "mixed" with (ie modulates) rf, the output contains f1 (rf) f2 (af) and f1 + f2 (upper sidebands) and f1 − f2 (lower sidebands). The f2 output, being af, is not developed in the tank circuit and vanishes, but we are left with the steady carrier, f1, and the upper and lower sidebands. Even if the audio frequency were only 1Hz, we would still have the pure f1 with the information carried in sidebands 1Hz away from the carrier.

Some years ago I explained this in *A Guide to Amateur Radio* as follows: In a.m. transmission the radiated power is contained in a steady carrier (representing the basic output of the power amplifier) plus, whenever there is speech, in two sets of sidebands, equally placed on either side of the carrier: see Fig 4 (c). All the power represented by the steady carrier is wasted, in the sense that it conveys none of the actual speech information. The sole use of the carrier is its value in making it easy for the receiver to recover the original speech information from the incoming signals (ie by providing a signal of the correct frequency and phase for demodulation, which again is essentially a *mixing* process). Yet during typical a.m. telephony, some 80 per cent or more of the power is in the carrier.

By eliminating the basic carrier from the transmission (and replacing it locally in the receiver) all the transmitted power can be used to convey the actual speech information. We can do this with a *balanced* modulator (ie balanced mixer). If the output signal from this is radiated, it is known as double-sideband suppressed-carrier transmission (dsbsc). However, correctly to demodulate such a signal, the local inserted carrier needs to be in phase with the suppressed carrier; by no means a simple operation although possible using phase-locked-loops etc. In ssb we go one stage further and eliminate not only the carrier but also one or other of the two identical sets of sidebands which emerge from the balanced modulator.

What should be gleaned from Fig 4 is that there is no difference in the information-providing sidebands between a.m., dsbsc and ssb. Hence it is perfectly feasible to receive all three modes on an ssb receiver so long as the characteristics of the selectivity filter provide the necessary filtering. It may also serve as a reminder of a technique that can be very effective on a.m.—known as exalted carrier detection—in which we enhance the incoming carrier, which will often be fading badly and hence be producing bad distortion since the fades may not coincide with those of the sidebands.

All this, of course, amounts to the A, B, C of a.m. and ssb, but it is clear that for historic reasons, and those envelope waveforms, misunderstandings still arise—particularly among those content to regard transmitters as black boxes to be plugged in and switched on rather than understood. In view of the complexity of current ssb transmitters it may be worth going back to basics with Fig 5.

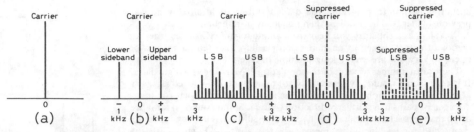

Fig 4. RF spectrum diagrams of various forms of transmission. (a) Basic unmodulated carrier, occupying only bandwidth of carrier. (b) Same carrier fully modulated with a 1kHz audio sine wave. Note that two exactly similar sideband signals are generated 1kHz away from carrier frequency. (c) A.M. speech transmissions contain many audio frequencies simultaneously, up to about 3kHz for communications, and corresponding sidebands appear on either side of the carrier frequency, each set of upper and lower sidebands forming a mirror image of the other. The total rf bandwidth is thus at least 6kHz. (d) DSB speech transmission is similar to a.m. except that the carrier is suppressed (unless received as "ssb" by filtering in the receiver, a synchronous demodulator must be used). (e) An ssb speech transmission with the carrier and the lower sideband suppressed. Note that the total bandwidth occupied is now less than half that for (c) or (d)

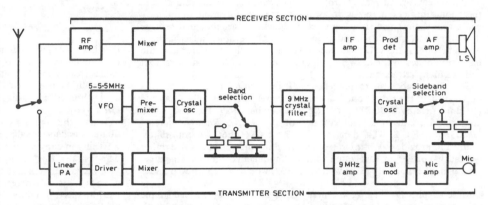

Fig 5. Block diagram of a basic ssb transceiver. Simplicity of this type can be found in early 1970 models, but modern black boxes are usually very much more complex. But once a newcomer can grasp Fig 4 and this block outline he or she can come much nearer to understanding how ssb is generated and works

Safety and the mains

Letters on safety and the fusing of ac mains supplies continued to arrive long after I had prepared the April *TT* item "Don't fuse the neutral" and the March item on "Multiway 6A adapters". These included items from Peter Poole, G3ENN, electrical advisor to the DTI's Consumer Safety Unit; D J Keston, G8FMC, of the BSI Testing Services; Dave Ackrill, G0DJA, who is concerned with safety of "grid" voltages up to 132kV; Harold Genton, G8GG; Bob Bastow, G3BAC; and Ivan James G5IJ. I have to admit to belonging to that generation of radio amateurs who, when we worry about safety in the shack, tend to think primarily in terms of the ht supplies rather than the frequently more dangerous 240V ac supplies. Some of us fell into bad habits!

G3ENN writes: "Apart from the very few countries in the world which use the BS1363 13A fused plug system, the vast majority, if not all, of the plug and socket systems for domestic use use unpolarized plugs. For this reason international standards work on the basis that the supply to appliances will not be polarized. Although BS415 is not yet a harmonized CENELEC document, the basis for the standard is IEC65, and the finalized CENELEC document is unlikely to differ greatly from the present standard.

"Equipment complying with the standard will be fitted with a supply cord of adequate dimensions to be protected by the BS1362 13A fuse or, as is likely to be the case elsewhere in the world, a 16A mcb (miniature contact breaker). Within the appliance, if the manufacturer is to satisfy the needs of the 'Low Voltage Directive' or, in Britain, the 'Electrical Equipment Safety Regulations', sufficient protection must be provided so that a short circuit occurring between any two points within the appliance, irrespective of the polarity of the supply, will not lead to a hazard. It is possible that one way in which this could be achieved would be by fusing both poles of the supply; however, there are many other ways of achieving this objective, and I am not aware of any cases in which this measure has been thought necessary.

"May I take this opportunity of making the following safety points:
● Always ensure that 13A plugs are properly wired and that the cord clamp is used, and remains effective.
● For Class 1 appliances never disconnect the protective earth connection; for radio amateurs, Class 2 appliances are to be preferred for a variety of safety and functional reasons.

● Never use tools and equipment in the garden without an rcd, and consider the use of a sufficiently sensitive rcd on all supplies.
● Never open up a piece of equipment without first disconnecting the supply main.
● When working on equipment, particularly live-chassis equipment, always use a safety isolating-transformer (double wound)."

G8FMC makes a number of the same points but adds:

"Double-pole mains fusing is certainly not illegal in the UK and is a requirement under some British standards, generally those harmonized with IEC standards.

"My own experience is with BS5724: part 1: 1979 *Safety of Medical Electrical Equipment* (IEC 601) and the requirements are briefly as follows:
(1) 'Fixed equipment', ie hard-wired from a fused spur outlet etc, shall have only one fuse and this must be in the line conductor.
(2) Portable Class 1 equipment (ie utilizing an earth) shall have a fuse in both line and neutral conductors.
(3) Portable Class 2 equipment (ie double insulated) shall have at least one fuse and this may be in either conductor. Mains switches where fitted must always be double pole and approved to BS or IEC Standards.

"Incidentally it is worth a mention that in this Standard, reversal of the mains 'line' and 'neutral' is considered a 'normal' rather than a 'fault' condition. (Presumably because it is so commonly found in practice— *G3VA*).

"The predecessor to BS5784 was a DHSS document called *HTM8*, and this required the 'line' only to be fused, and 'outlawed' double-pole fusing. Hence with medical Class 1 equipment we have had a complete 180° reversal of the requirements, the change having taken place in 1980.

"My personal opinion is that where one can be *certain* that your sockets have line (phase) and neutral the correct way round, then fusing line-only is possibly safer, but in any case one should always remove the plug before opening up any equipment.

"Many amateur radio equipments, particularly those imported a few years ago, have only single-pole on-off switches and a single fuse, sometimes in the neutral lead, both highly undesirable. Use of Class 1 equipment without an earth (or with an inadequate earth) is also a common but very dangerous practice.

"Finally it makes my blood run cold to encounter, primarily on the older valve or hybrid hf rigs, the main supply (switched and unswitched), ht (say 800V), low voltages and protective (!) earth all carried from one part of an equipment to another in a single multi-way connector. This can easily fall out, losing the earth connection: invariably it has totally inadequate separation between the pins to cope with the peak voltages encountered which are likely to be of the order of 1,150V."

G8GG points out that some modern equipment does not even switch the mains supply, merely switching the low voltage output. An example is the Trio R600 (and possibly associated models such as R1000 and R2000) where the *power* switch breaks the dc output from the rectifier system. While he admits that equipment should not be removed from its protective cover with the mains supply *on*, this may often be done when making adjustments, fault-finding etc.

G3BAC noted the March *TT* item on the problem of providing the large number of sockets needed in some shacks. He writes:

"I have just done a count and found 16 items plugged in and four adapters in use. We badly need something to replace the 13A plug, which is far too big for most purposes and yet inadequate for anything drawing large currents. These cause overheating of both fuse and socket, with the attendant risk of fire. Unless the socket blades are exactly parallel, poor contact results, as can be verified by taking a new plug and pushing it in and out of a socket a few times: the resultant score marks show the poor contact area.

"The old two and three-pin round plugs were much better in this respect. The original purpose of the three-pin 13A plug has been lost. People do not fuse according to the load, and earthing is becoming obsolete with many appliances that are plastic bodied. The only person I knew to be electrocuted was killed because of the provision of a large area of earthed metal.

"For a long time I used the old three-pin 2A plugs but, on moving QTH, changed to long strips of 'chocolate block connectors' tediously linked to provide LNE LNE etc, but these proved a chore when moving gear about.

"I like the American system of long parallel slots into which you can push large numbers of their small two-pin (albeit flat) plugs. I believe that a proposal for providing such slots around the skirting boards of new houses in the UK was rejected on grounds of high cost.

"Both the shack and the rest of the house need a new system . . . but what?"

G4COL's simplified rf power meter

In the February *TT* I was tempted to suggest that, while greatly admiring the ingenuity of G4COL's "Accurate rf power meter for the hf bands" (*Rad Com* December 1985) it was not exactly "kiss" equipment. As alternatives, I included several simple arrangements based on measuring the voltage across a matched dummy load and a unit based on measuring the electrical output from a solar cell.

Ian Braithwaite, G4COL, has taken my comments with refreshingly good spirit even though he feels that readers may have concluded from my notes that (1) his power meter was grossly over-complicated; and (2) an accuracy of ± 10 per cent can be obtained relatively easily using diodes to measure voltage across a load or by using the brightness of lamps. He writes: "The first point is, I feel, quite fair comment, and one which I take up later. In my defence, most of the circuit complexity arose because I was attempting to make an instrument which gives a direct reading of power, rather than requiring frequent calculation by the user. The signal change detector is optional and was included after I decided on a digital readout after finding out how linear the prototype was, and to improve its usefulness as a 'peaking indicator' when one wants to search quickly for peaks and dips.

"On (2) I believe one should not be too glib about accuracy. As pointed out in the December article, a signal source with a harmonic 20dB lower than the fundamental gives a reading that is uncertain by ± 10 per cent when measured with a peak rectifying meter based on diodes, as in the February *TT*. A transmitter output should be much better than this, but a driver stage may not be, since it would precede the lowpass filter. The major source of error in lamp systems, if the lamp brightness is allowed to vary, is likely to be the uncertainty of the match, since filament resistance varies greatly with temperature. This is the case with professional power meters which these days have very low internal or 'instrument' uncertainties indeed, and where great pains are taken to provide a very low input vswr. This (within the context of amateur use) is less likely to be a problem in the diode-based meters than in the lamp type since, in the former, the match can be made to be excellent.

"Ordinary lamp meters are subject to a variable input vswr as the filament brightness (and therefore its resistance) changes. Where a signal source with a 2:1 vswr is measured (surely by no means an extreme case for a transmitter) a power measuring device with a vswr of 1·35 would have a mismatch uncertainty of about ± 10 per cent. With a 1·1 vswr power meter, this would drop to around ± 3 per cent. With a perfect power meter (ie one

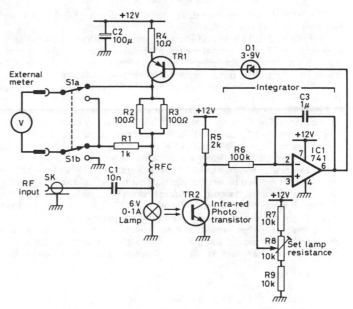

Fig 6. G4COL's simplified power meter capable of good accuracy

perfectly matched to the system impedance of, say, 50Ω) there would be no mismatch uncertainty, even though there may be mismatch loss if the source is not also perfectly matched to the system impedance.

"Running the lamp at constant brightness overcomes the variable mismatch problem of the simplest lamp method. It is also less sensitive to harmonics than a peak-rectifying diode since it responds to total power and not voltage. This is in essence a dc substitution approach widely used in instrumentation, and my aim was to show that relatively accurate measurements can be made with easily-obtainable lamp bulbs.

"However, on reading the comments in *TT*, the idea occurred to me that by dispensing with the facility for producing a direct reading of power, and instead asking the user to do a little calculation (much as for the diode meter), I could radically simplify the circuitry. I quickly set about building such a meter housed in a small diecast box. It proved a 'first time' success and now hardly offends against the 'kiss' principle!

"As shown in Fig 6 the optical feedback loop has been retained. The voltage across the lamp and the voltage dropped by the current source (TR1), monitoring resistors R2, R3 are both read on an external meter, preferably of reasonable accuracy. Because the current into the lamp flows through 50Ω, all that is necessary to achieve a good 50Ω match from the lamp is to adjust R8 until both readings are the same. As rf power is fed to the lamp, less dc power is required to keep it at its constant brightness, and the voltage readings drop. Since they are still equal (constant filament resistance) either can be used for calculating the power.

"If Vo is the reading with no rf input, and Vr the reading with rf applied, then rf power is given by $V_o^2/50 - V_r^2/50$ or $(V_o + V_r)(V_o - V_r)/50$. Since Vo will be constant (or very nearly so) for one sample of lamp, a look-up table, similar to that given in *TT* for the G3EIW diode meter, could easily be prepared.

"Two drawbacks still remain: the need for a power supply (12V at 100mA) and the fairly limited dynamic range. The latter can be overcome reasonably easily by adding attenuators (three 10dB attenuators would extend the range from less than 10mW to 400W).

Table 1. Measurements on simplified QRP power meter

RF power applied (dBm)	Voltmeter readings		Calculated rf (dBm)
	Vo	Vr	
10·2	4·42	4·36	10·2
13·3	4·42	4·29	13·55
16·5	4·42	4·15	16·7
19·9	4·41	3·81	19·9
23·0	4·41	3·11	22·9
25·5	4·42	0·73	25·6

Notes: Measurements were made by first measuring the source on a Marconi Instruments 6960 Power Meter (using a calibrated 10dB attenuator), then transferring the source to the QRP power meter under test. The dc meter used was a Beckman RMS 3030 digital multimeter set to the 20volt range.
Vo = Voltage reading with no applied rf power
Vr = Voltage reading with applied rf power
The term dBm refers to decibels relative to one milliwatt. For example, 1 watt = 30dBm, 0·5 watt = 27dBm and so on.
The instrument's maximum power reading is given by Vo²/50. In the case above, this would be 25·9dBm.

"Table 1 shows measurements made on the simplified meter and indicates reasonable accuracy.

"I would add that I have considerable sympathy with the 'back to basics' approach of *TT*, and regret the apparent passing of the 'surplus' or junk-box era when useful components could be obtained so very cheaply. One has to be careful these days when writing constructional articles to stick to fairly 'mainstream' components etc readily available to constructors, even if at some expense."

James Watt, G6ZC, draws attention to what must be an error in the circuit diagram of the long-established G3EIW dummy load/power meter (Fig 3, February *TT*, page 105), although curiously the identical diagram has appeared both in *TT* and *ART* over many years without adverse comment. But G6ZC is clearly correct when he writes:

"The circuit as shown would not work correctly on either hf or vhf. In theory we are entitled to assume that the first rfc has infinite impedance at all radio frequencies. It would therefore prevent the rf voltage at the hot end of the dummy load resistor from appearing *across* the diode(s). Accordingly, the diode(s) would produce no rectified output.

"In practice, what would happen would depend upon the precise characteristics of the rfc and upon whatever stray capacitance happens to exist between the junction of the diode(s) and the rfc and earth.

Performance would thus vary greatly over the frequency range, and on some bands is likely to be extremely inaccurate. It is for the same basic reason that in a psu a half-wave rectifier can never be followed by a choke-input smoothing filter.

"Can it be that, over the years, a by-pass capacitor of, say, 100pF connected between the output side of the diode(s) and earth has become lost?"

Checking back to the early diagrams it would appear that the necessary by-pass capacitor has been missing since the very beginning. If inserted the unit should work as intended.

Tips and topics

Dick Hawkins, G4XKO, adds to the saga of low-cost spreaders for open-wire or zepp feeders. He uses black plastic water main piping which is very slightly flexible and intended for use underground, under floors, in lofts etc. He writes: "It can be held in a vice and cut longitudinally with a Stanley knife, then cut to length with a "v" notch at each end corresponding to the required spacing. Holes are drilled near the notches so that a short tee can be made to hold the feeder wires in place. All spacers are mounted curved side up to shed rainwater etc. I feel confident such half-piping spreaders look and last a lot better than plastic pens or syringes." □

Technical Topics

by Pat Hawker, G3VA

KH6B's idea of celebrating this year's 50th anniversary of the introduction of the 6L6 beam tetrode family of valves by building a simple one- or two-stage cw or a.m. valve transmitter has tempted several more readers to delve into the depth of their junk boxes. Syd Fenwich, G3AIO, is putting together a 6V6–6L6 co-pa for 3·5, 7 and 10MHz. He even recalls a 3·5MHz contact with G3VA many years ago when he (G3AIO) was using a single KT66, the British near-equivalent of the 6L6G. J Bowling, G3FXP, agrees there is still a place for simple a.m. rigs on the underused 1·9 and 29MHz portions of the 1·8 and 28MHz bands. He mentions that there is a 1·9MHz a.m. net operating most afternoons in the Melton Mowbray area. He would like to see a spot frequency designated for a.m. about 29MHz, and suggests 29,160kHz as reasonably clear of other mode users. Though he notes a shortage of reasonably-priced receivers suitable for a.m. reception on the 28MHz band (best buys are probably the older communication receivers that still turn up in "Members Ads"). It is possible to get about 5W out of a single power fet and a 24V supply for those who regard valves as turning the clock back!

Screening cables to reduce rfi

The difficulty of screening equipment and interconnecting cables to minimize either or both incoming and outgoing rf signals is a reflection of the increasing use of digital techniques. With so many high-speed pulses being generated in computer-type equipment, the problems of radio-frequency and electromagnetic interference (rfi/emi) and electromagnetic compatibility (emc) are increasingly evident.

John Greenwell, G3AEZ, brings to attention an announcement by Holden Cords (Holden Cords Ltd, Bowater Road, London SE18 5TF, tel: 01-855 9821). This company has recently introduced a cable screening technique which they claim offers virtually "100 per cent screening against rfi/emi": Fig 1. This involves the use of two metalized foils, or one metalized foil and a braid. It is thus rather like some of the coaxial cables that have been introduced specifically for cable tv distribution. The method, it is stated, shows many benefits over the more traditional braided screening process only. The metalized tapes are constructed as a laminate of aluminum on a polyester base. The two tapes are then wrapped around the cable with the metalized surfaces in contact with each other and a drain wire sandwiched between. If a single foil and braid is used, the braid acts as the drain wire.

The screening of cables by laminated tapes provides 100 per cent coverage of the protected conductors, which cannot be provided by a braid alone.

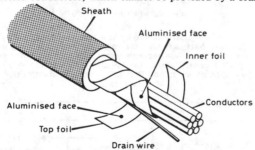

Fig 1. Use of twin foil screening to provide improved rfi/emi protection of multi-connector cables and cable harnesses (Holden)

Morse and the hard-of-hearing

Comments continue to arrive stressing the value of morse to amateurs facing the common problem of some progressive loss of hearing. Morse undoubtedly provides a bonus in the form of effective person-to-person communication for the many whose hearing loss ranges from slight to very severe.

Archie Couser, G3CZG, recalls the story of a former Merchant Navy radio officer who, while recovering from an operation for the removal of a brain tumour, was for some days quite unable to speak yet was able to communicate fluently, via another morse-wise patient, with the surgeon and medical staff. G3CZG also notes from personal experience that some loss of hearing has not impaired in any way his ability to copy even the weakest cw signals.

Syd Fenwich, G3AIO, experiences distortion of speech, particularly in one ear, that severely limits his use of ssb; yet, thanks to cw, he still communicates worldwide and chases the dx.

Roy Oliver mentions that WB4MBK is deaf but receives cw "on the tv set" presumably using automatic decoding. The value of the subtitling services on Ceefax and Oracle teletext services is well established, though I am not sure that I would regard microprocessor-decoded telegraphy and data as true person-to-person communication in the way that we have been discussing.

Nigel Neame, who launched us into this debate, mentions in a further letter that he hopes to remove that "ex" from his ex-G2AUB designation. He does, however, stress the need for the hard-of-hearing to take some care in the strength of signals when listening on headphones. He writes: "There are two main forms of deafness, 'nerve' and that caused by 'mechanical failure' (ie collapse or malfunctions of the tiny bones between the eardrum and the inner ear). Either can produce varying degrees of deafness, from slight to total. In each case, when headphones are employed, automatic limiting of peak audio output is *essential*, otherwise any hearing ability remaining could be further impaired, even destroyed."

Personally, I believe that all those who use headphones, no matter what the state of their hearing, should use peak audio limiting. My own choice for many years has been one or two pairs of back-to-back anti-parallel diodes across the leads of high-impedance phones (or alternatively, if low-impedance phones are used, at a suitably high impedance stage). Such a limiter protects the ears from loud crashes, particularly if the receiver is not fully muted during transmission. On the few occasions that my limiter has been disconnected I seem almost to blow my head off!

Those were the days

My recent confession that I still make good use of a 'fifties LG300 transmitter and a 'forties Hammarlund HQ129X receiver has found some echoes among those who fear that modern equipment has a greater degree of built-in obsolesence and may be destined for an appreciably shorter operational life.

Syd Fenwich, G3AIO, writes: "Like you, I run an LG300 transmitter for cw on the hf bands. It is about 25 years old. The 813 is still going strong after much use and abuse—and plenty of the latter. It runs 150W input quite effortlessly, the 813 merely ticking over at this power. The signals bring favourable comments from old hands. I wonder how many of the solidstate rigs will be performing as well after 25 years of knock-about use?

David Marsden, G4RMC, feels that the Japanese manufacturers may have misjudged the demand for simple, economy rigs. He is not convinced that amateurs do really want "all-singing, all-dancing" models as much as the marketing men would have us believe. He points to the continuing popularity of the FT101, TS520 in support of his view. He notes that Trio actually reintroduced the TS530 after discontinuing it for a time. He also mentions an incident concerning the problem of repairing equipment based on surface-mounted technology (smd). "Two or three days ago I happened to visit a radio repair shop as a radio pager unit was being repaired. I was shown one board, about 1·5 by 0·75in which was a masterpiece of miniaturization. No doubt it was very good in every respect, except that a film resistor is prone to frequent failure. When this happens the whole board is replaced at a cost of £47. I came away even more convinced of the continuing value of 'kiss' designs!"

Stable vfo with bipolar-assisted mosfet

It seems a long time since *TT* has featured a new design for a stable vfo, possible as a result of presenting in *TT, ART, Radio Communication Handbook* etc, what became virtually a standard vfo design by G3PDM using a 2N3819 fet as the basic Colpitts oscillator. With this design, it was emphasized strongly that good vfo performance depends as much or more on good construction as upon the circuitry. A total of some 15 constructional hints were listed, and these remain valid if minimum long-term and short-term frequency drift is to be achieved.

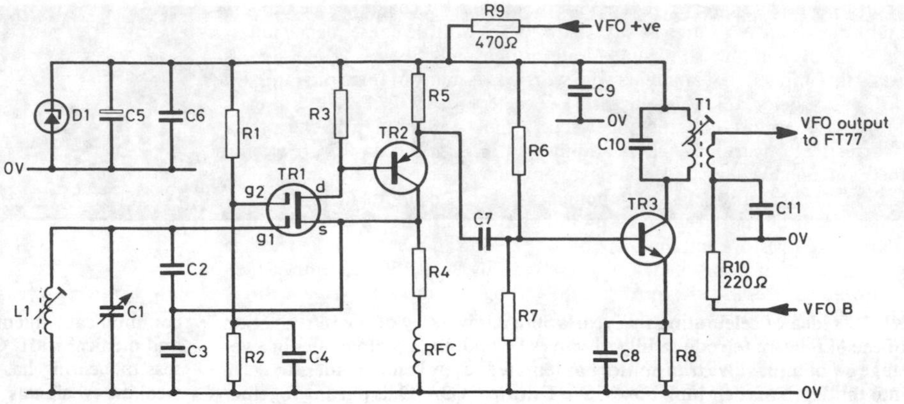

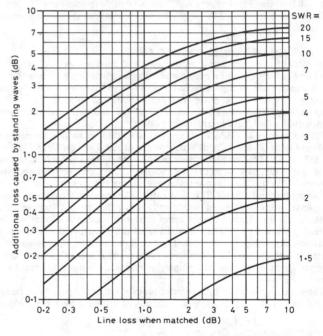

Fig 2. G4UAZ's 5 to 5·5MHz stable vfo. R1, 2—100kΩ; R3, 1kΩ; R4, 5–270kΩ; R6, 56kΩ; R7, 22kΩ; R8, 10—220Ω; R9, 470Ω; C1, double-bearing variable; C2, 3—2,200pF polystyrene; C4, 6, 7, 8, 9, 11—10nF ceramic disc; C5, 5·6μF; C10, 100pF silvered mica; TR1, 3N200 or 3N140 (but handle with care!); TR2, BFR99 or any high (1GHz) FT pnp; TR3, 2N2369 or 2N2222; D1 6·8V zener BZY88; L1, about 5t 18swg enamelled on 5mm former with "purple" core; T1, 30t primary, 15t secondary (same former as L1); rfc, 1mH choke

John Hawes, G4UAZ, however, believes with some justification that "the problem of building frequency-stable vfos has always been the bane of the home-constructor" often, unfortunately, ending in "a chase with a receiver to see where they have drifted to"—that is, the ones that can be persuaded actually to oscillate readily.

In the *CARA Newsletter* of August 1985 he expressed his delight in finally evolving a circuit for a vfo which seems to give good stability easily. This design evolved to meet a requirement for an 11MHz vfo for a 1·8MHz transceiver, but has been used also for the standard vfo range of 5 to 5·5MHz.

Earlier work had emphasized the difficulties that can be experienced in coaxing junction and dual-gate fets to oscillate in the Colpitts configuration. Bipolar transistors, on the other hand, oscillated readily but dragged down the Q of the tuned circuit and tended to result in drift. A high-Q is needed to give a sufficiently rapid change of phase at the frequency of operation.

The answer, G4UAZ found, was to use a compound circuit comprising both a dual-gate mosfet to provide very high input impedance and so maintain the Q of the tuned circuit *plus* a bipolar transistor to provide the gain necessary to ensure ready oscillation. Note that in Fig 2 TR2 is *not* a buffer stage but is essentially part of the oscillator stage.

The version shown in Fig 2 tunes from 5 to 5·5MHz for use as an external vfo, in G4UAZ's case, with an FT77. Component values are not unduly critical, the tuning capacitor being a junk box item in the form of a sturdy two-gang, dual-bearing type with each section having a maximum capacitance of about 100pF (only one section was used in practice). C2 and C3 are polystyrene film capacitors (the type in which the aluminium film can be seen being rolled up inside a transparent plastic casing). These capacitors are pretty stable, almost as good as silvered mica but with a negative temperature coefficient.

G4UAZ built his unit on Veroboard, and melted some candle wax over the coil, the tuned-circuit fixed capacitors and other nearby oscillator components in order to anchor the components and prevent short-term drift due to draughts around individual components. He strongly advises checking out the oscillator before applying the wax! Fig 3 shows his circuitry for interfacing the vfo with his FT77 via the external vfo socket. Despite his feeling that constant running of the vfo would result in optimum stability, he follows the FT77 practice in turning off the vfo when not in use.

The entire unit is housed in an ex-video-game sloping-front plastic box. Frequency drift is rarely sufficient to change the 100Hz digit of the FT77 frequency display in half an hour, easily adequate for any use. Switch-on drift is negligible, showing the degree to which oscillator frequency is independent of the sustaining amplifier.

G4AUZ claims it is the least critical vfo he has ever come across.

transmission line), is absorbed in the transmitter (possibly damaging the output stage) and is entirely lost. W2DU reminded us that, in practice: (1) any power returning down the feeder (and this really *does* happen), is not absorbed in the transmitter but is promptly reflected back up the transmission line and most of it radiated eventually; and (2) power losses due to a modest mismatch are usually so low as to be virtually negligible and related directly to the basic attenuation of the transmission line: Fig 4. It was shown that the power loss with open-wire transmission lines can remain very low indeed even when these are operated as a "resonate" line with an

Fig 4. A standard diagram showing by how much (or at hf usually how little), additional power is lost in a feeder having a moderate vswr compared with the same transmission line when accurately matched to the antenna element and thus having a 1:1 vswr. Remember that the transmission line vswr is *not* changed by means of an atu and that an atu may itself introduce significant power loss

Fooling the swr meter

A few years ago, following a lead by Walter Maxwell, W2DU, a serious attempt was made in *TT* to destroy the widely-held myth that power "reflected" from the antenna (due to a mismatch between the antenna element and the

Fig 3. Arrangement for connecting an external vfo, such as that of Fig 2, to a transceiver such as the FT77

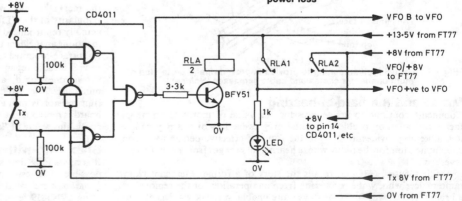

almost infinitely high swr. Even with more "lossy" coaxial cable the loss on hf due to an swr ratio of, say, 2:1 or 3:1 is of little consequence unless the transmission line is unusually long or unusually lossy.

All this implied that amateurs who worried, as many of them did (and still do), at not being able to make their swr meters read 1·0, 1·1, 1·5 or even 1·8 would almost certainly be wasting time and money if they took "corrective" measures such as adding *(for this reason)* an atu, trimming their antenna elements, discarding an antenna system as useless etc. There is even a range of expensive "antenna matchers" being made in the USA which are little more than a toroidal balun transformer shunted by high power load resistors and thus capable of offering an swr of only 1·4:1 even with no antenna connected! *QST* exposed this "con" in November 1984 and *Amateur Radio* (VK) in April 1985 (brought to my notice by J E Price, G4OIK). Offered as sealed units at prices up to $1,000 it took x-ray photographs to reveal that unwitting amateurs were buying dummy loads rather than antenna matching units!

But the attempts to wean amateurs away from the fetish of the swr meter and the pointless search for "perfect" (1:1 swr) impedance matching have been only partially successful. Just as the message was beginning to get through, massive "interference" in the form of solidstate protection circuitry began to blot out the weaker signals of technical commonsense! Because many solidstate amplifiers are vulnerable to the higher voltages that exist when feeding directly a transmission line having even quite a modest swr, it is an almost essential precaution for designers to incorporate circuitry that severely cuts back the power output of a transmitter when this is "looking into" an swr of more than about 2:1. In some cases the amplifiers begin to throttle-back when the swr rises to not much more than 1·5:1. This has meant that amateurs using such rigs do need to get the swr down to less than about 1·5:1 even though this usually has only a marginal effect on the efficiency of the antenna system.

As a result, the antenna matching or tuning unit has come back into favour, even though the use of an atu with a coaxial cable transmission line has *no effect on the cable itself* and, indeed, often introduces quite significant power losses since an atu can (and often does), dissipate a lot of power, at least on some bands. Admittedly, the atu may (or may not) have a useful function in reducing harmonic output, and is essential for feeding many types of antennas, but one must sympathise with the view of Norman Sedgwick, G8WV *(Rad Com* May 1986, p335 *et seq)*, when in this connection he regards "atus as rather sneaky devices which conceal the antenna's shortcomings from the operator but (also) conceal them from the transmitter, which is the important thing".

It is also paradoxical that many amateurs buy "broadband" transmitters that do not require retuning when changing frequency, but then find they need to use an atu which does! In turn this has brought about a demand for automatic tuning units that are by no means cheap. Remember that with a coaxial feeder the "sneaky" atu does absolutely nothing to increase the efficiency of the antenna system and may actually reduce the radiated power! It seems logical, wherever possible, to dispense with an atu for those antenna systems such as a dipole with coaxial cable feeder which do not inherently require a matching unit.

Increasing antenna bandwidth

As we have noted before, the wider 3·5MHz band (3,500 to 4,000kHz) available in some regions has encouraged the development of techniques that extend the bandwidth over which a dipole element and coaxial cable feeder results in an swr of less than, say, 2:1. A wire element will normally not do this over more than five per cent of its resonant frequency. Fatter elements, including the folded dipole element, have a lower Q and hence rather greater bandwidth. Bent and loaded elements tend to have higher Q and hence less bandwidth for a given swr ratio.

Bill McLeod, VK3MI, has tackled this problem in a novel way. In a recent article "Mis-matching for extended bandwidth", *Amateur Radio (VK)* April 1986, pp18-9, he shows how by the use of a quarter-wave impedance transformer and a compensating capacitance (which can be constructed from a length of feeder), an antenna element that is deliberately slightly mismatched at its resonate frequency can provide an extended bandwidth over which the swr remains below 2:1. Instead of about five per cent, which is, say, 180kHz at 3,600kHz with a conventional dipole, this technique can result in better than 10 per cent bandwidth for an swr of less than 2:1. This would enable a Region 1 operator to cover the entire 3·5MHz band with a wire dipole without an atu, yet without exceeding an swr of 2:1.

In practice, VK3MI has taken this technique to its extreme by using it in connection also with a "thick" dipole element made from a 15cm (6in)-wide ribbon of hot-dip galvanized wire mesh. This has a normal low-swr bandwidth of 300kHz, but his mis-matching technique extends this to 580kHz, thus covering the whole of the Region 2 and Region 3 band. To quote the introductory paragraphs to his article:

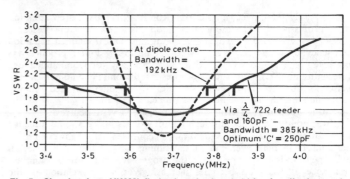

Fig 5. Showing how VK3MI finds that the bandwidth of a dipole can be increased by deliberately mis-matching a 50Ω dipole by feeding it with 72Ω cable and then providing capacitance compensation. In the example shown, the minimum vswr is about 1·5:1 but the bandwidth for which the vswr remains below 2:1 is increased from 192kHz to 385kHz

"The finicky transmitter that requires no greater than a 2:1 vswr from its nominal 50Ω implies that any load impedance from 25 to 100Ω would be satisfactory. There, matching it to a 50Ω load (in the conventional manner), that rises in a complex manner on either side of resonance, allows only half of the available range to be used.

"Why not match it to 25Ω at antenna resonance for a rising characteristic, or alternatively to 100Ω with an inverted impedance characteristic? Then, look at the hf coaxial feeder which is almost never a 'flat' 50Ω . . . The antenna, particularly for 3·5MHz, is usually a half-wave dipole of low height (10m or less), with a bandwidth around five per cent of resonant frequency (for 2:1 vswr), and a mid-band impedance about 55Ω. Only at the mid-band frequencies can a random length of 50Ω cable be successful.

"Now consider the quarter-wave transformer: *(a)* it transforms the load impedance across its Zo by the square of the ratio between the two; *(b)* it inverts the load impedance characteristic over the bandwidth from a u shape to an n shape; *(c)* it transposes inductive reactance to capacitive reactance and vice versa; and *(d)* only half of the total load/source vswr shows at each end (more accurately the root of the ratio).

"With an electrical quarter-wavelength of 72Ω coaxial cable (eg UR70) between the element and the transmitter, a 55Ω element impedance can be inverted and transformed for the transmitter to "see" 94Ω at mid-band, falling away each side down through the nominal transmitter output impedance of 50Ω for the bandwidth to increase by a useful factor of 1·5. This can be further increased to a factor of 2 by compensating the capacitance mis-match at the antenna junction: Fig 5.

"The compensation required for the quoted example of 55/72Ω is 300pF at 3·65MHz, consisting of the difference between the total capacitance of the quarter wavelength of cable actually used (920pF for UR70 at 69pF/m), and that for a similar notional cable matching the antenna (1,220pF for 55Ω). This value is not critical and can be varied by 30 per cent or more to adjust the lowest vswr point two or three per cent for convenient system corrections.

"The capacitor can consist of an open stub of the same cable, cut for the required capacitance (eg 4·5m of UR70 taped to the feeder, or a fixed mica capacitor of suitable voltage rating (250V or higher), depending on arrangements for waterproofing at the element feedpoint.

"For those with a transmitter sited more than 13m from the antenna feedpoint, there are two alternatives. One is to use a three-quarter wavelength of 72Ω cable, with any excess stored in the rafters or attic. The other is to extend the antenna centre using the first quarter-wave using a matching cable (eg UR43 52Ω cable), then transform with a further quarterwave of 37Ω cable."

Compact transmitting loop antennas

From time to time, ever since the publication in the mid-'sixties of the details of an octagonal loop antenna made up from six straight 5ft tubes and developed by the US Army Limited War Laboratory (see most editions of *ART*), references have been made in *TT* to electrically-small transmitting loops both for amateur and professional radio communications. The key features are that the loop *must* have extremely low ohmic rf impedance and that there must be no undue losses in the matching arrangements. These basic essentials point to the use of copper- or even silver-plated tubing of several inches diameter for the loop—although the outer braid of good quality 0·5in coaxial cable has been used with reasonable success—and the use of a capacitive matching network rather than having any coils in the matching unit. It must be appreciated that a small loop used on say, 3·5MHz is likely to have a radiation resistance of only a tiny fraction of 1Ω, and that in these circumstances ohmic losses assume great importance.

In *TT* July 1984, p580, a note from Ron Rew, G3HAZ, drew attention to a professional pedestal-mounted loop made by Antenna Research Associates. It was 5ft high and 7ft wide and had a claimed radiation efficiency of 98 per cent at 14MHz. A basically similar product was marketed several years before this by Technology for Communications International (TCI) for such purposes as diplomatic communications networks operated from embassies etc. These antennas used remote-controlled motorized vacuum-type capacitors to tune the loop to the operating frequency, offering a tuning range of several octaves.

It was pointed out that although manufacturers may claim a "directive gain" of around 5dBi, this should not be confused with "power gain"—particularly at the lower end of the tuning range where the radiation efficiency inevitably drops due to the progressive reduction of radiation resistance as the loop becomes increasingly small in relation to the wavelength.

The original claim for the US military loop was that it could perform almost as well as a dipole at a height of 40ft. It is a pity that some articles in amateur radio journals have made excessive claims based on the theoretical gain at low vertical radiation angles of short vertically-polarized antennas over perfect earth. Such claims lead only to disappointment and ultimate rejection of the whole concept. Nevertheless, a small transmitting loop, provided the losses can be kept low, does offer scope for use in some awkward locations. It is, for example, well suited for use in buildings having a small flat roof that would not permit the erection of a conventional dipole.

A contribution to this technique stems from J H Dunlavy, who obtained a US Patent 3,588,905 (28 June 1971), for a "wide range tunable transmitting antenna" based on a configuration that has become known as a "miniloop". In this antenna an electrically small, capacitively-tuned outer loop is excited by an even smaller inner loop that can be fed directly by the coaxial cable feeder. A technique that also forms the basis of A R Carr's US Patent 4,433,336 of 21 February, 1984 for a "three-element antenna".

Fig 6 shows the "miniloop" principle, together with equivalent circuits for both inductively-fed and directly-fed loops. In effect, inductive feeding of a high-Q resonant loop antenna is simply a version of the once popular "link coupling" between resonant circuits with the aid of a low-impedance line.

Operation and equivalent circuits are discussed in a paper by Donald E Barrick (Ocean Surface Research) in *IEEE Transactions on Antennas & Propagation*, Vol AP-34, No 1, January 1986, pp111–4. Although his paper points out that this technique is not suitable for hf radars designed to measure ocean currents and waves, since the Q is so high that it stretches and delays short pulses, he does point out its advantages over systems using the outer loop alone, fed directly, for communications applications. He writes:

"It's main features (and differences in operation from the outer loop fed along) are: (1) the input resistance to the inner loop can be large (eg 50Ω), although the input (radiation) resistance when the outer loop alone is fed is generally a fraction of an ohm (decreasing as f_o^{-4}; hence feeding is easier for the miniloop; and (2) a fairly good match to the line can be maintained over nearly a decade bandwidth as long as the outer loop is tuned to the desired operating frequency and is electrically small at the upper end of the band."

Inductive coupling to a resonant loop was also used in the professional Swedish design that was tested initially on the 3·5, 7 and 14MHz amateur bands and described at an IERE conference in 1981 (*TT* September 1981, p821). This comprised a three-turn silver-plated radiating square loop with 500mm sides and using a ferrite balun to match a 52Ω coaxial cable to a 200Ω feedpoint of the coupling loop.

There is no longer any doubt that compact hf transmitting loops can be made to work efficiently provided that great care is taken to minimize losses and to tune it accurately to the operating frequency.

HF active receiving loop antenna

While transmitting loops are still unfamiliar and rather strange beasts, simple loop receiving antennas date back to the earliest days. However, they are coming back into favour as the basic element of compact "active" antennas. John Hawes, G4UAZ, has drawn my attention to a design for a matching amplifier that he published in the *CARA Newsletter* (December 1984), of the Cheltenham Amateur Radio Association. He writes:

"Several active antennas have already been featured in *TT*, but I believe mine has the virtue of great simplicity yet seems to have good signal-handling capabilities, despite being essentially a broadband, untuned antenna."

The following notes are extracted from the original article:

"Small antennas (compared with the wavelength) are dogged with the problem of low radiation resistance. This means that an incoming signal must be transformed to the impedance of the receiver input with low loss. Conventionally this implies a narrow bandwidth, and matching difficulties. An answer is the so-called 'active' antenna with a small passive antenna element directly coupled to an impedance-transforming amplifier. Most commercial models use a small rod element and high input-impedance amplifier. Bipolar transistors do not lend themselves to this type of amplifier, and even fet devices have a large input capacitance.

"It seems more feasible to use a small loop antenna with a low input impedance. Such systems have been described before in *TT* but I wanted a simple amplifier that could be built in an evening or two: see Fig 7. I used BFW17A transistors, but any general-purpose rf type should work.

"The design uses a push-pull (long-tailed pair) configuration, presenting a balanced input to the loop. Shunt voltage-feedback is used to reduce the input impedance as well as to linearize the amplifier. Used with a square loop with 2m sides made from 16swg enamelled copper wire, it received

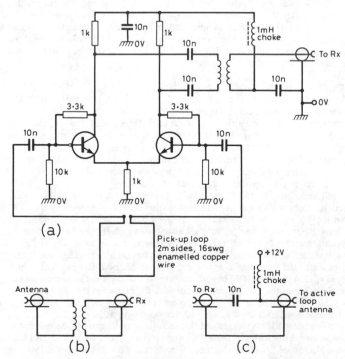

Fig 7. G4UAZ's active loop receiving antenna for use throughout the hf range. *(b)* Broadband toroidal coupling coil at receiver input. *(c)* Method of feeding active antenna over the coaxial cable transmission line

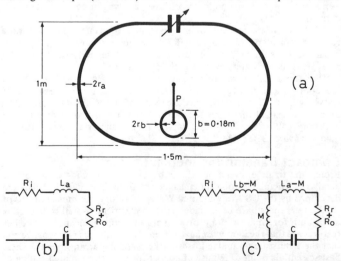

Fig 6. *(a)* Configuration of a typical miniloop structure designed as a transmitting loop from 3 to 24MHz. The outer loop is capacitively tuned to the frequency of operation. In this example the outer loop tubing has a radius of 0·04m and the coupling loop radius 0·006m, using copper tubing for both loops. *(b)* shows the equivalent circuit for an outer loop fed directly, while *(c)* represents the miniloop system with the inner loop fed and inductively coupled to the outer loop; in both cases, Ri represents the internal resistances of the source and transmission line

signals on 7MHz equivalent to my full-sized G5RV (with loop in vertical plane), and works over the full hf range. My amplifier was built on Veroboard with "ugly" wiring. The only difficult component is the 1:1 rf transformer for which I used a toroidal core from the junk box. Several turns of twisted bifilar wire were wound on the core, and checked as follows: First, one of the windings should be wired across the input of a receiver tuned to the lowest band of interest. The other winding must be open-circuit, and little reduction in signal should be noted provided the primary inductance is adequate. Then wire in receiver as in Fig 7(b). Before trying the amplifier, a dc check is worthwhile, about 10·5V on the collectors and about 3V on emitters should be found with a 12V supply. I power my amplifier through the coaxial feeder with the circuit of Fig 7(c), but if you do not wish to spend money on 1mH chokes, running a separate supply wire would be entirely satisfactory. It makes an interesting constructional project."

Top band antenna and atu

Dr Constantin Feruglio, IV3VS, uses a "double Zepp" (centre-fed dipole with balanced 300Ω ribbon feeder) plus atu. This works well on 3·5 to 28MHz, with the antenna having a horizontal span of 40m. However, he found that results were "only middling" on 1·8MHz, and has lengthened the top section by folding in extra wire as shown in Fig 8(b). While the folding results in a lower radiation resistance than had the "top" being in a straight line, the antenna works reasonably well on all bands from 1·8 to 30MHz and permits working "all over Europe" on 1·8MHz. Marconi "end-fed" antennas are ruled out on the grounds of tvi, IV3VS being a "third-floor" dweller.

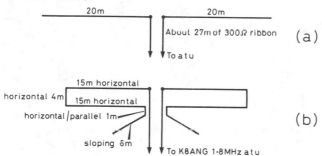

Fig 8. *(a)* Centre-fed dipole as used by IV3VS but providing only marginal results on 1·8MHz. *(b)* Additional wire loading to improve results on 1·8MHz.

As a flexible 1·8MHz atu he uses an arrangement described by John Skubick, K8ANG, in *73 Magazine* (date unknown): Fig 9(b). This is a variation of an atu that similarly delivers a balanced output based on pi-networks that have previously been described in *TT* and other RSGB publications (I used this arrangement for a number of years on 14 and 21MHz for feeding a folded dipole made from 300Ω line): Fig 9(a).

IV3VS constructed L1 and L2 using two perspex (lucite) pipes. L2 comprises 50 plus 50 turns on 56mm diameter pipe using 1mm diameter

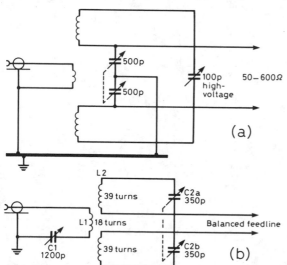

Fig 9. Antenna matching units that provide balanced output suitable for open-wire or 300Ω balanced feeders. *(a)* System used at G3VA for 14 and 21MHz for a number of years. *(b)* The K8ANG arrangement used by IV3VS and suitable for 1·8MHz

enamelled copper wire, winding length about 110 plus 110mm. L1 on 70mm diameter pipe comprises 20 turns of 1mm diameter enamelled copper wire, winding length 50mm and positioned over the centre of L2. C1 can be made from a three-section broadcast-type ganged capacitor. K8ANG advises not to earth any portion of L2 or C2 but leave them "floating" above earth on insulators.

Making a pcb—Mark 2

TT November 1985, page 860, included a note from G8XEH outlining a simple way of transferring pcb layouts from diagrams on to the boards using a scriber and centre punch. Jim Cookson, G4XWD (his callsign reflects his interest in restoring old ex-WD equipment!) suggests "an even easier way". He writes:

"Obtain a photocopy of the pcb layout drawing, Make the copy as dense as possible, then lay it toner side down on to the cleaned copper side of the laminate and, using an ordinary domestic electric iron just hot enough to scorch the paper lightly, firmly iron it down. (Note that the copy must be made with a modern electrostatic type of plain paper copier using toner powder). Leave it to cool, peel off the paper and it will be found that a good outline of the image will be seen on the copper board. This may need a little final touching up with a Dalo pen, but it is certainly a very quick and easy method of preparing boards. If a laterally-inverted image is required, a copy should be made on to a transparency and the other side copied. I work for Rank Xerox and have made quite a few pcbs in this way."

Restoring ex-WD equipment

In connection with his interest in restoring ex-WD equipment, G4XWD would like to see more sharing of information on circuit diagrams, ideas for making improvised component parts to replace those that are long out of production, etc. He points out, for instance, that it is often difficult to renovate the paintwork on ex-military sets but that many motor car accessory shops are selling off "old colours" in spray cans. In Birmingham it is often possible to buy about three cans for £1, and that frequently a good match can be obtained for an old set at minimum cost. Large old-style capacitors can be unsoldered and modern components fitted actually inside the cans which, when re-soldered and re-sprayed, retain the original appearance. He has just finished restoring an old Hallicrafters S27A receiver that had been reduced almost to scrap due to rust and the use on it of a "blowlamp" soldering technique. He removed most of the components from the chassis, emery-clothed the rust off and sprayed the chassis with silver paint, followed by a coat of clear cellulose. Although not original, the result is very attractive and the set now works well. G4XWD is anxious to obtain the manual for the ZC1 Mk2 transmitter-receiver (one time very popular in New Zealand and Australia as an amateur rig).

Tips and topics

Evert Kaleveld, PA0XE/DL0XJ, a wartime Dutch undergound operator, has raised a topic which is, perhaps, strictly operating practice rather than technical but nevertheless is one that surely needs airing. He notes that although the origins of such abbreviations as 73 and 88 stretch back into the 19th century American telegraph codes, the German-originated abbreviation 55 (often listed as *viele erflug* ie *much pleasure*) seems to be of quite recent origin, having been first listed in the German *QRV* journal of February/March 1947. Today it is very widely used in cw contacts, not only by German and Austrian amateurs.

But why 55? Could it be, PA0XE surmises, that in the immediate post-war years, when all operation by German nationals was covert, that some misguided humourist took a secret delight in simply modifying the "HH" (Heil Hitler) abbreviation that had been virtually obligatory for German amateurs from 1933 right up to May 1945 (Yes, some Germans were permitted to operate as amateurs throughout the war under the supervision of an SS general). He simply added an extra dit to the four dits of each H and so created 55.

HH was listed in the *Signal-buch fuer den Funkverkehr* published in Vienna in 1941. This also listed 73, 88 and even the little used 99, but had no trace of 55. Evert stresses that if, as he believes, 55 was a "black joke" it certainly does not mean that those German amateurs using 55 today have the slightest idea that unbeknowingly they may be perpetuating a Nazi salute. Personally, I suspect that HH may indeed be the origin of 55, and since the idea was first put to me I for one have stopped using it!

Chas Claydon, GM4GNB, following up the items on the April Fool resonate earphones, recalls the famous Brown Type A which were standard Naval issue for many years and suggests these used the principle of the "tuned reed" and had a natural resonance at 800Hz. As one who wore these phones for several years I agree in part, although they would certainly respond reasonably well to speech and music: the knurled knob on the side of each phone was, as GM4GNB says, to adjust the gap in order to obtain maximum sensitivity. The technique of adjustable diaphragms was used by Telefunken for lightweight phones widely used in the German forces, as Ken Mildren, G3FVD, reminds us, and as indeed I can confirm since I still often use a pair of these phones which have a captive diaphragm in the cover and a locking ring to adjust for sensitivity (but not for adjusting the resonance).

An unintended result of my notes (*TT* March) on cordless telephones is that it has apparently given some readers, who must remain nameless, a new interest in listening near top band. It contravenes the Wireless Telegraphy Acts, of course, but I am told it can be highly entertaining. It also confirms how far the fundamentals of these cordless phones can reach. My advice is watch what you say on them—better still, stick to the cord type!

Richard Barber, G4LXG, writes from Canada to suggest that it is possible to be misled by small-scale ground conductivity maps such as that given in Fig 6 of the February *TT*. He comments: "I fully appreciate that it is intended only as a rough guide, but from my own experience I know that proper testing of the site is the only satisfactory method of conductivity determination. My former QTH sat above rather more than 27ft of wet clay with only 9in of topsoil. Within a few hundred yards the clay gave way to a substantial seam of sandstone in which the local electricity board had difficulty establishing a good earth. Perhaps the recently updated map of soils of the UK may provide better local information. These maps are available from the Agricultural Development Advisory Service."

In the January *TT* (p37), it was noted that recent work at the high-power hf "ionospheric heating" transmitter at Ramfjord in northern Norway included the generation of frequencies in the range 1 to 1·5kHz by using the non-linear effects in order to modulate and radiate elf signals from the polar electrojet. This technique has now also been used in the USA. □

Technical Topics

by Pat Hawker, G3VA

TT HAS ALWAYS been dedicated to reporting "progress" in the technical development of radio communication, but increasingly it is becoming ever more difficult to define "progress". Aldous Huxley claimed "Technological progress has merely provided us with more efficient means for going backwards". Evelyn Waugh wrote "Never use the word 'progressive' to me . . . it makes me sick and agitated for hours . . . please, please never again." Havelock Ellis claimed that "What we call progress is the exchange of one nuisance for another nuisance." "Nothing" it has been said "dates faster than people's fantasies about the future."

Looking forward by looking back?

But such views are still anathema to many scientists and engineers. Recently, in the 1986 *National Electronics Review*, Dr William Gosling noted that "The whole pattern of Western technical and scientific thought is based on an assumption of ceaseless progress and development. It was Dr Ian Ross, president of Bell Laboratories, who said that technologies come in two kinds: those which are exponentially developing and those which are unimportant. We take it for granted that the science and technology of today will necessarily differ in essence from that of yesterday, and will be better . . . The assumption of progress is pervasive and irresistible . . . Technology either grows or dies . . ."

If one accepts this view of technology, then there would be clearly little place for continuing with conventional thermionics in amateur radio. But, on the other hand, history suggests that "progress" is cyclical rather than linear. Did not Poulsen develop magnetic recording at the turn of the century only to see it fade virtually out of existence until the revival of interest in the 'thirties? Did not the advocates of space communications a quarter-a-century ago suggest that hf and ocean cables would quickly fade away as communications media? Yet hf remains vitally important for Defence and low-cost "thin-line" communications. "Cable" in the form of fibre optics is re-emerging as the prime broadband carrier!

Should we not be cautious today, in accepting that electronic mail, packet networks and data transmission will replace paper? Professor Igor Aleksander, head of the Kobler Unit for the Management of Information Technology at Imperial College (*Business Computing & Communications* May 1986) writes of the "widely-voiced myth" of the "paperless office" adding: "Had computers been invented first and paper second, the latter would have been hailed as a remarkable achievement of high technology on which much information could be stored at a cost much lower than that of the magnetic medium."

There is surely no reason for amateurs to feel ashamed of sometimes advocating "old technology" although (unfortunately) changing fashions may result in old technologies fading away, not on grounds of inferior or unsatisfactory performance, but because falling demand may take them right out of the market place.

In *QST* March 1986, Greg Livingstone, WA2EHV, writes: "Are you looking for a new thrill in ham radio but can't afford packet or computer equipment? Does your super-duper all-mode transceiver do everything but fill out the QSL?. . . . Take a bold step backwards and build a transmitter. Not a solidstate QRP rig, but a 25W tube rig that you can use every day.

"After getting bored with guaranteed solid-copy QSOs on my HW101, I built a 6C5–6L6 rig on a breadboard. I run it at about 25W and have worked 24 states with my eight 7MHz crystals. I've never enjoyed ham radio so much. . . .

"If you're an old-timer, I'm sure you've built many such rigs, but there are a lot of hams out there who, like me, were licensed in the past 15 years and have grown up with the 'plug-in appliances'. If you're in that group, then dig out some old circuits, hit a few flea markets and be a 'born again ham'. My transmitter cost me $10, including the power supply."

So there is the quandary. Should one regard such activities as non-progressive, mere nostalgia or do they reflect something that is basic to amateur radio . . . the desire to get on the air with something that you have built yourself without first having to take a degree course in electronics?

Solidstate QRP

It is for QRP that cost considerations tend (for new components) to tip the balance in favour of solidstate. Again, for portable lightweight "week-end cottage" rigs working off batteries few would now advocate valves.

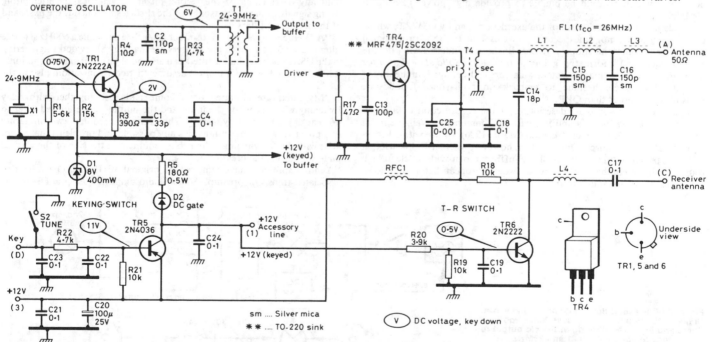

Fig 1. Overtone 24·9MHz crystal oscillator, keying switch, 4W power amplifier and transistor t–r switch as used in W1FB's low-power 24·9MHz cw transmitter with break-in facilities (*QST* February 1986). The buffer amplifier and driver stages are not shown. T1, 6t primary, 4t secondary No 28 enam on bobbin of Amidon L57–6 shielded transformer unit. T4 broadband transformer on stacked (two) FT50-43 ferrite toroid cores, 7t primary, 10t secondary, No 24 enam. Y1 overtone crystal, 30pF load capacitance, HC-6/U holder. Do not attempt to use 12·45MHz crystal. L1, L3 0·266μH, 8t, No 24 enam on Amidon T50-6 toroid core. L2 0·5μH, 13t No 24 enam on T50-6 core. L4 2·27μH 24t, No 26 on T50-6 core

In *QST* (Beginner's Bench, February 1986, pp23–6) Doug De Maw, W1FB, describes a 4W crystal-controlled transmitter for the 24·9MHz band with full break-in (QSK) facilities. It is intended to provide an opportunity to try the 24·9MHz band at minimum cost in conjunction with a companion 24·9MHz receiver converter (*QST* April 1985). This is a band on which, as the sunspots begin to return—hopefully we may see a start to Cycle 22 this autumn or next—worldwide cw communications should be possible with very low power at times when the muf along the desired paths is above 21MHz but still below 28MHz. It uses an overtone crystal rather than a fundamental 12·45MHz crystal (with doubling) since this would produce significant output at 12·45MHz. Transistor line-up is two 2N2222A (oscillator and buffer amplifier), 2N3866 (driver), MRF475 or 2SC092 (power amplifier), 2N4036 (keying switch) and 2N2222 (transit-receive switch). The circuit diagram of the overtone oscillator, keying switch and tr switch is given in Fig 1. This could be readily adapted for other bands etc.

Solidstate linear amplifiers

The article by John Matthews, G3WZT, on a single-stage linear for 50MHz with an rf output of 100W p.e.p rf output from 6–7W of drive (*Rad Com* June 1986, pages 402–7) showed vividly the problem facing amateurs who wish to retain a significant element of "home construction" in their stations yet would make no claim to being professional designers. For G3WZT, in his introductory notes, describes himself as a "self-confessed valve man where high-power linear amplifiers are concerned", more especially for the constructor "with a junk box brimming over with valves, bases and high-voltage transformers etc". But he notes that for the others, high-voltage valve equipment is fast becoming synonymous with high costs, unless constructors are prepared to salvage and re-cycle old equipment—and this can rule out the less-experienced constructors who would prefer to duplicate, or near-duplicate, a proven, published design.

For solidstate, G3WZT shows clearly the advantage, both in linearity and psu construction, of getting away from the 12V, 30A approach in favour of 24V or, better still, 48V (or even for some power mosfets 150V). But the article also reflects the fact that the design of a reliable medium-power solidstate amplifier still calls for significantly more basic engineering knowledge than a comparable valve amplifier, primarily in the need to cope with low and reactive input and output impedances, but also the added requirements for filtering and protection circuits—not to mention the stress that arises from the knowledge that rf power transistors are perhaps the fastest acting fuses yet invented!

It is perhaps worth remembering that not only the QQVO series of vhf double-tetrodes are capable of working satisfactorily at 50MHz. For example, even the 807 is usually listed for full ratings up to 60MHz. The same goes for the 6146B. There can be few of the television "sweep" (line-output) valves that would be unable to provide high power gain up to 50MHz.

This is in no way a criticism of the excellent design by G3WZT, whose potted biography, not unexpectedly, reveals him to be a professional development communications engineer. But it does indicate why, despite such excellent and informative guides as the ARRL *Solid state design for the radio amateur*, so many amateur-amateurs without much in the way of test instruments etc hesitate to embark on do-it-yourself solidstate transmitters at other than QRP.

A detailed, blow-by-blow description of the construction of a 100W solidstate 144MHz linear amplifier, with all components available in kit form, appears in *Electronics Australia* (March 1986) for use with a heavy-current 12V power source. One wonders, however, whether its linearity, at full rated power output, would really be sufficient to provide a "clean" ssb transmission acceptable in the more crowded European-band conditions. It is probably better suited to fm.

Close-in dynamic range of receivers

Modern high-performance solidstate hf receivers do not come cheaply, and are not necessarily an improvement, in terms of basic performance, on some of the better valve models that preceded them. This was well shown in a set of receiver measurements made by Sherwood Engineering Inc and drawn to the attention of *TT* readers by Peter Lonsdale, G3PVX (*TT* August and October 1984, pp677–8 and pp858–9). These detailed measurements underlined the way in which, in many receivers, the dynamic range deteriorates significantly when a very strong interfering signal is located only a few kilohertz away from the wanted signal (a not infrequent situation in amateur radio operations). This is due to the growing use of up-conversion to vhf implying a vhf first oscillator, the relatively poor noise (jitter) characteristics of most frequency synthesizers, the use of relatively broad "roofing filters" in the first fixed-i.f section and the lack of good pre-mixer selectivity. The Sherwood measurements showed that many highly-regarded receivers and transceivers have some 30–35dB less dynamic range when measurements are made with narrow spacing between the signals. It is gratifying to note that in his reviews, Peter Hart, G3SJX, is now including both conventional and narrow-spaced dynamic range measurements. There is also evidence that manufacturers are now paying more attention to this problem.

Ham Radio (December 1977) showed that after modifications (including the fitting of a narrowband cw filter to replace the roofing filter of the stock-models), the valved Drake R4C emerged at the top of the table of receivers in terms of narrowband dynamic range (85dB measured with 2kHz spacing).

Modifying an R4B receiver

It was therefore interesting to receive from Dave Johnstone, G4EVS (8 Newtondale, Cleveland Park, Guisborough, Cleveland TS14 8EY) a detailed account of his experiences in modifying an old Drake R4B receiver. Although the new filters that he has fitted do not come cheaply, the results appear to justify the cost and the effort.

"About four years ago I bought an old Drake R4B at a rally. Since that time I have spent many enjoyable and sometimes frustrating hours modifying and experimenting with this receiver to improve its performance. The changes I have made are in principle applicable to other valve equipment of a similar vintage, leading to signal performance levels comparable with many current hf black boxes. The modifications I have carried out are described below. (G4EVS's comments are set out at length as they provide a good insight into this whole area of receiver modification —*G3VA*.)

"**Filtering.** I have replaced the rather wide 5,645kHz filter in the first i.f with switchable crystal filters for the different modes of operation. These limit any overloading of the second mixer by significantly attenuating strong signals within the passband of the rf stages but outside the passband of the second i.f filters.

"A 5kHz eight-pole filter is used for lsb/usb/a.m, while a 600Hz six-pole filter is used for cw. Both these filters are made by Sherwood Engineering in the USA. I believe similar filters can also be obtained from International Radio Inc, the Kenwood/Icom/Yaesu newsletter organization, also in the USA.

"My filters are mounted on a home-made pcb together with relay switching which grounds the input and the output of the unused filter to prevent any unwanted bypassing. This technique requires two miniature two-pole two-way relays but avoids any possible imd problems that might arise with diode switching. The pcb is mounted on the side of the vertical plate supporting the preselector assembly.

"**Audio amplifier.** I have removed the original 6EH5 audio pa valve and associated transistor preamp. A new audio amplifier using a TBA810 ic

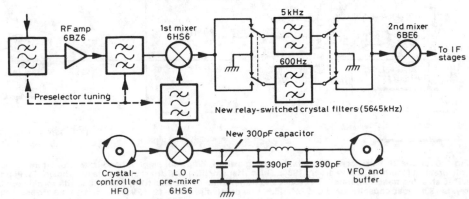

Fig 2. G4EVS's modified front-end for the valved Drake R4B receiver with switched "roofing" filters and improved filtering of the vfo output to reduce "birdies" on 21 and 28MHz

driven by a TL071 preamp has been fitted. This provides hum-free audio, as well as reducing the ht current demand by 30–40mA and the heater current demand by 1·2A. The mains transformer runs considerably cooler.

"**Power supply.** A small 15V 500mA transformer/rectifier/regulator (7812) assembly is mounted on a small pcb. This stands vertically in the space left by removing the 6EH5 tube.

The new 12V supply powers the new audio stages as well as all other existing solidstate stages in the rig, ie the vfo, hfo, bfo, a.m detector and calibrator. Previously all these stages were supplied by large (and hot!) dropping resistors from the 150V ht rail.

"**Product detector.** The original twin diode product detector does not give very good recovered audio, due both to an inadequate bfo injection level and a lack of balance providing poor isolation between the i.f, bfo and af ports. I have fitted a doubly-balanced product detector using an MC1496 active mixer. The SL640 chip also works well in this role. The imd performance of the MC1496 seems somewhat better than the SL640, but considerably more external components are needed.

"**Front-end modifications.** Assessing the effect of changes (Fig 2) to the receiver front-end can be done qualitatively. For instance, reducing the rf amplifier gain so that the preselector gives a less-pronounced peak on band noise is trading away sensitivity for hopefully improved overload performance. This kind of move is probably worthwhile for lower-frequency band operators with little interest in working 21/28MHz. To be more certain about these kind of trade-offs, I have found it necessary to build some simple test equipment as follows:

(a) A low-level (−89dBm) crystal oscillator on 14,030kHz for noise floor measurements.

(b) A pair of high-level (+4dBm) crystal oscillators on 14,040 and 14,060kHz respectively, together with a −6dB hybrid combiner for imd measurements.

(c) A 0–100dB attenuator (in 1dB steps) using nine slide switches and a compartmented box made from double-sided pcb.

(d) An audio voltmeter calibrated in decibels.

"This equipment, which is straightforward though time-consuming to construct, allows me to measure with reasonable accuracy receiver noise floor and dynamic range. The exact techniques for doing this are described in *Solid State Design for the Radio Amateur* published by ARRL (obtainable from RSGB Publications).

"Based on an information sheet from the USA, I changed the original arrangement of the first mixer (6HS6) so that the local oscillator was injected via a 10pF capacitor into the control grid with the signal instead of separately via a 0·005μF capacitor into the cathode. This change was claimed to reduce the loading on the tracking filter used on the lo pre-mixer output, as the mixer control grid has a much higher input impedance than its cathode. The reduction in loading improves the sharpness of the tracking filter response, eliminating a number of birdies which are particularly noticeable on 21 and 28MHz with the "stock" receiver. Tuning 21 and 28MHz after making this change certainly showed that the birdies had been significantly reduced. However, there was a marked reduction in overall gain with no significant preselector noise peak possible on the higher frequency bands.

"My R4B was in this modified condition at the time that the test equipment was ready for use. Initial measurements showed an mds (minimum discernible signal or noise floor) of −128dBm together with a dynamic range of 80dB with the ssb filters in use. This was disappointing, as published figures for the later Drake R4C, which has very similar front-end circuitry, showed an mds of about −139dBm together with an 85dB dynamic range.

"One of the requirements for high-level diode-ring mixers is adequate lo injection level. Increased noise figures and degraded strong-signal handling are characteristic of insufficient lo drive. I suspected there might be a similar problem with the R4B valve mixer. The lo signal on the mixer control grid on 3·5MHz showed 400mV p–p on a 20MHz bandwidth 'scope. This seemed rather low since a heterodyning ratio of some 10:1 for lo level:signal level is required for good performance. When calculating the expected signal levels at the mixer grid, remember that the preselector/rf amplifier combination will provide 20–30dB gain.

"I disconnected the lo signal from the mixer and measured its open-circuit value as 4V p–p. By using a selection of fixed resistors I established that a 50Ω load was needed before the lo voltage dropped to 2V p–p, suggesting that the output impedance of the lo tracking filter was about 50Ω. This was puzzling. How could the cathode input impedance of the R4B mixer (probably a few hundred ohms) cause any significant damping, as claimed in the information sheet, on a circuit with only 50Ω output impedance? The answer is that it does not! The information sheet is in error!

"Reconnecting the first mixer with lo drive to the cathode, the measured

lo level on the cathode was almost 4V p–p. However, not surprisingly, the 21/28MHz birdies had returned!

"I began to think more carefully about where the birdies were coming from. Harmonics of the crystal-controlled hfo seemed unlikely, the 4·9–5·5MHz vfo seemed a more likely candidate. I had noticed when tuning the R4B up and down the bands that the squelch on the 144MHz rig was sometimes opened by spurious signals! Examination of the vfo output circuit revealed a simple lowpass pi-filter made from a small series inductor and two 390pF shunt capacitors. A little experimentation showed that an extra 170pF capacitor across the output of this filter caused a marked reduction in the 21/28MHz birdies, while the resultant lo drive to the mixer dropped by only 0·2–0·3V—problem solved!

"The first mixer injection level after this change was about 3·5V p–p. However, the dc cathode bias is only about 2·1V. Therefore, during each cycle of the lo, the mixer was being driven almost into cut-off conditions. My understanding of this type of additive rather than switching mixer is that operation should be on a portion of the characteristic curve where there is a large amount of second-order curvature. It is the predominantly square law response of a fet which gives it good additive mixing characteristics.

"Accordingly, to avoid cut-off during the lo cycle, the lo drive level was reduced to 2V p–p. This meant that under no-signal conditions the mixer remained at least 1V above cut-off. A very strong mixer input signal (around 2V p–p) would be needed before the mixer would cut-off. The traditional wisdom used for setting up fet mixers is that the lo drive plus the maximum input signal should not cause the fet to pinch-off or (in the case of a depletion device) be driven into enhancement. Presumably similar arguments hold true for valve mixers?

"The lo level was reduced to 2V p–p by increasing the value of the extra capacitor fitted to the vfo output filter from 170pF to 300pF, which also further helps the 21/28MHz birdie situation.

"Measuring receiver performance now showed an mds of −136dBm and a dynamic range of 87dB—a worthwhile improvement relative to the lo injection into the control-grid case. These tests were made using a screen supply dropping resistor of 4·7kΩ (the original was 220kΩ) and a cathode resistor of 470Ω (the original was 2·2kΩ). Increasing the screen dropper to 220kΩ had no measurable effect on the mds but the dynamic range dropped by 4dB. This would lend weight to the principle that improved signal handling performance is obtained by having high standing currents on mixers and amplifiers.

"What more? How does one improve performance from here? The Drake R4C uses an EF184 mixer which has lower noise and higher mutual conductance than the 6HS6. Interestingly, in the R4C the lo is injected into the mixer grid with the signal! Using an EF184 in an R4B might allow the rf stage gain to be reduced while still maintaining an acceptable mds. There should be some consequent increase in dynamic range though the overall benefit is probably small.

"Some years ago in *TT* an article from the November 1968 *DL QTC* magazine was mentioned. This described how the first mixer of a Drake R4A was changed from a 6HS6 to a 7360 beam deflection tube, ie changing from additive to switching mixing. Can anyone let me have a copy/original of this? Even though the 7360 is now expensive and not too robust I suspect this change may prove most effective (Beam deflection valves can be susceptible to hum—*G3VA*.)

"High-level diode ring mixers are readily available today. Fitting one of these into an R4B/R4C would pose a number of problems:

(a) The lo signal (currently about 10dBm) would need boosting by about 10dB.

(b) A post-mixer amplifier (grounded gate fet or fet/bipolar with noiseless feedback) would need to be built.

(c) A satisfactory broadband input network to match the rf stage plate circuit to the 50Ω input of the diode ring would need to be constructed.

Problem (a) and (b) would be fairly easily achievable, though (c) may not be possible and a number of band-switched coils would have to be used.

"I would be interested to get in touch with anyone who has carried out investigations and modifications along similar lines to myself."

Modern filter technology

Eventually we may see the introduction of the all-digital receiver with high-grade digital filtering at i.f rather than the audio digital filtering used in the early professional hybrid analogue–digital communications receivers (eg Rockwell-Collins HF2050). But in the meantime the performance of receivers and ssb transmitters depends to a significant extent on the quality of their analogue fixed-frequency bandpass filters. Wire-wound lc filters, used for so many years in the form of i.f transformers, are still found, but the emphasis these days is on such devices as bandpass crystal filters, surface-wave (saw) filters, ceramic resonators and ceramic filters. There is

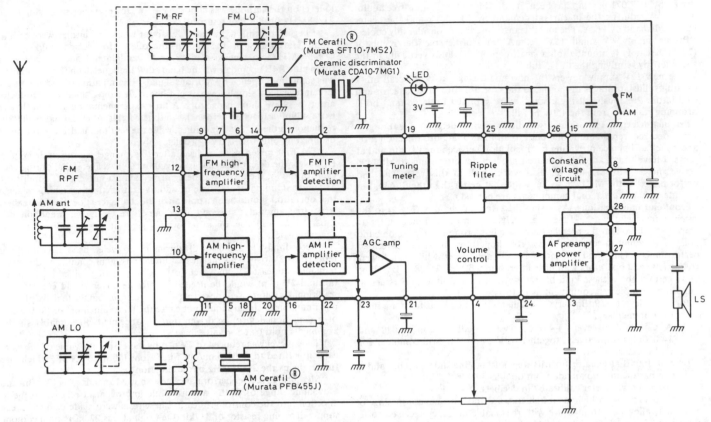

Fig 3. Japanese single-clip a.m/fm broadcast receiver showing use of ceramic resonators, filters etc

also still a role for mechanical filters, although these are limited to frequencies below about 500kHz.

An interesting series of articles covering all these forms of filters appears in the Japanese industry-orientated (English text) magazine *JEE* (April 1986, p58–74). These cover current filter units offered by Toyo, Nihon Dempa Kogyo (NDK), Murata and Goyo (the firm which took over production and marketing of mechanical filters from Kokusai). The range and forms of construction of filters are considerable, including mcf (monolithic crystal filters), dms (double-mode saw), ceramic filters mostly based on pzt (lead titanate zirconate), and including devices intended for use with surface-mount technology.

Ceramic resonators are finding increasing application in oscillators and filters (see *TT*, January 1984, p42) including clock oscillators for microcomputers. Fig 3 shows a single-chip a.m/fm broadcast receiver with a Murata CDA ceramic discriminator etc.

Fig 4 is a composite diagram showing the approximate frequency range to which each form of filter is applicable and the possible bandwidth. It will be noted that crystal filters up to well over 100MHz are now being manufactured in mcf form.

Goyo have an interesting range of 455kHz miniature mechanical filters that retain the good shape factor associated with this type of filter: Fig 5. Typically these are 28·5 by 16 by 10·5mm, although the MF-455-12GZ is 46 by 16 by 16mm.

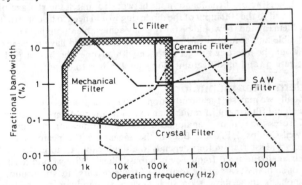

Fig 4. Typical frequency ranges for various filter techniques

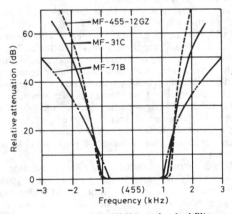

Fig 5. Characteristics of miniature 455kHz mechanical filters made by Goyo

Microphones in vehicles

In *TT* a number of references have been made, particularly in May and July 1984, to the safety aspects of the use of handheld microphones in moving vehicles, a subject that has come to the fore again partly as a result of the growing use of the mobile cellular networks, the use of cb and the general growth of two-way mobile radio. Attention was drawn to RSGB mobile safety recommendations, numbers six and seven, viz:

(6) The microphone should be attached to the vehicle so that it does not impair the vision or movement of the driver; and

(7) A driver/operator should not use a hand microphone or double headphone.

It was noted that these recommendations are disregarded by some amateur mobile operators and by many cb, pmr and cellular driver/operators; in fact, all of the early cellular microphone/earphones were in the form of quite bulky handsets. There exists the curious anomaly that a driver seen using an electric razor while driving is liable to prosecution, but the basically similar act of using a handheld microphone does not, in itself, constitute an offence. It was also noted that an attempt in 1966 by the then Ministry of Transport to introduce a draconian regulation that would have outlawed the use of *any* radio transmitter while driving was dropped as a result of the intervention of the mobile radio industry etc.

It does appear, however, that the Department of Transport (which now forms part of the large Department of the Environment) has taken up this question again, in the form of a draft revision to the *Highway Code*. While officially the department claims that this revision is not finalized, and has not been made available for publication, its press office confirms that the department is generally not in favour of the use of hand microphones while driving. Other sources are more positive that the revised code is likely to contain specific recommendations that handheld microphones should not be used while driving.

The *Highway Code*, issued under the Road Traffic Act, sets out rules for safety on the road. The Secretary of State is empowered to revise the code from time to time in such a manner as he thinks fit, subject to the approval of Parliament. Failure to observe a provision of the code does not, of itself, render a person liable to criminal proceedings but a failure to observe it may be used in either criminal or civil proceedings to establish liability.

T2FD antenna still has supporters

One of the very first unconventional and "experimental" antennas ever to be described in *TT* more than 25 years ago was the so-called "T2FD" derived from "terminated titled folded dipole", and the basic details have appeared in every edition of *ART*, although usually accompanied by a warning that its performance as an aperiodic multiband antenna may leave something to be desired, particularly on some bands where an appreciable proportion of the transmitter output power is wasted in the "terminating" resistor.

This antenna stemmed from a development by the US Navy as a technique for broadening the bandwidth of a folded dipole to a reasonable degree. However, it was, and still is, being publicized in the amateur radio journals as suitable for use on all bands from 3·5 to 28MHz.

Since the terminating resistor is usually specified as having a wattage for cw of about one-third or one-quarter of the input power of the transmitter, this suggests that, at least on some frequencies, a very large amount of power is being dissipated in the resistor. Unlike the terminating resistors used in rhombics, long-wire vee beams, etc. there is no compensating directivity gain. *Ipso facto*, there must be frequencies on which the aperiodic T2FD radiates a lot less power than a resonant dipole.

Having said that, one has to admit that the T2FD has always found supporters who consider that the advantages of omni-directional, multiband, mixed (slant) polarization etc compensates for the lower efficiency on some bands. John Heys, G3BDQ, resurrected the design in *Ham Radio Today* (June 1985). It has also won the support of several members of the West Kent Amateur Radio Society, as reported in their *Update* newsletter of 24 January, 1986 by Alex Korda, G4FDC: Fig 6.

The feedpoint impedance of a T2FD is considered as roughly 300Ω; and the antenna can simply be fed directly with any length of Ω balanced feeder or from 50Ω coaxial cable via a 6:1 balun or with a 4:1 balun plus transmission-line transformer, Fig 7. It is claimed that a low vswr can be achieved (with suitable atud), over at least a 4:1 frequency range. Undoubtedly, with a good site and with the element sloping at about 20° to 40° to the horizontal, then the 2 to 3dB of power that may be lost in the

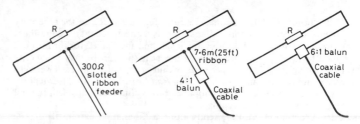

Fig 7. Some methods of feeding the T2FD antenna which has a feedpoint impedance of roughly 300Ω

non-inductive resistor (several resistors in parallel can give the necessary wattage) is not a serious drawback, though it always goes against the grain to develop expensive rf only to lose it all in a resistor, though there are other quite well-respected antennas where it is not unusual to have an efficiency of a similar order.

Tips and topics

Pat Painting, G3OUC, draws attention to the serious and growing interference to 1·8MHz operation resulting from illegal "cordless telephones" being used apparently as low-cost mobile units by garages and tv service technicians etc and operating around 1·95MHz. The fm signals spread over many kilohertz and some units appear to be considerably more powerful than the legal devices. To add insult to injury, it would seem that cordless telephones are covered by the "Interception of Communications Act 1985" that came into force in early April. Under this Act it is a criminal offence (liable to up to two years' imprisonment) intentionally to intercept "a communication in the course of its transmission by post or by means of a public telecommunication system". The Act makes it quite clear that this includes radio transmission where this is part of a public telecommunication system. It undoubtedly covers legal "cordless telephones" and possibly even when these are not of the approved type!

D J Bunyon, G4XHN, feels that it is time to remind readers of the effectiveness of the "single-turn transformer braid-breaker" as a means of reducing breakthrough of hf signals into vhf/fm stereo receivers which often use roof-top antennas to reduce stereo-hiss. This device (Fig 8) appeared very many years ago in *TT* and all editions of *ART* in connection with vhf/tv, but may be new to some as a means of combating interference to 88–108MHz stereo hi-fi systems.

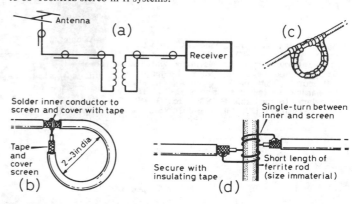

Fig 8 (a)–(c). Faraday double-loop "braid-breaker" filter using single-turn coaxial cable loops. (d) Alternative form of filter using short length of ferrite rod

The problems of electromagnetic compatibility (emc) now extend far beyond amateur radio, and increasingly the subject is being recognized as a vital aspect of electronic engineering.

Two universities in the UK now offer emc as a degree subject or as part of a postgraduate course. The IERE is organizing its fifth international conference on emc at York University from 30 September to 3 October, 1986. This will also cover the controversial subject of the potential hazards of non-ionizing radiation, including the accidental detonation of explosives etc.

Pat Painting, G3OUC, draws attention to the continuing problem of static discharges that can destroy solidstate devices, including ics, even when soldered into equipment. In his case, a 741 ic microphone amplifier in his homebuilt 28MHz ssb mobile transceiver went faulty following a period of cold dry weather in which high static voltages built up on the vehicle and sparks were generated between his hands and the car chassis when his feet touched the ground. One day he got out of the car while holding the microphone. . . .

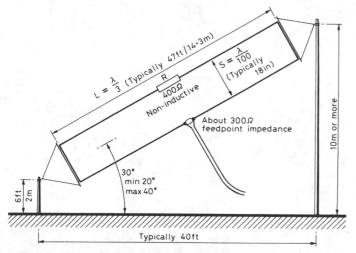

Fig 6. The controversial but often useful T2FD antenna. With a span of only about one-third of the wavelength of the lowest band of interest, it covers a frequency range of at least 4:1 and often more (3·5MHz design suitable for up to 14 or even 28Mhz)

C B Raithby, G8GI, welcomes recent references in *TT* to the reliability problems of complex transceivers. He is concerned that "equipment reviews" usually depend on equipment selected and loaned for the purpose by manufacturers or distributors who may be taking care to ensure that only fully-working models, 100 per cent within spec, reach the reviewers. In practice, not all equipments reviewed in *Rad Com* fall within this category, and some, I believe, arrive in unopened boxes. But it is a problem that all journals and reviewers recognize.

Cecil Broadhurst, G3PH, sends along a fascinating extract from *The Times* of 26 January 1922 reporting the findings of the Wireless Telegraphy Commission (the vice-chairman of the committee, incidentally, was Dr W H Eccles, an early President of the Wireless Society of London which became the RSGB). This committee was charged with deciding what type of transmission equipment should be used for the very-long-delayed Imperial wireless chain using extremely high-power on wavelengths of the order of 14,000m. The committee came out firmly in favour of thermionic valves, but recommended that initially all stations should be equipped also with arc transmitters, considered to need less skilled maintenance. In practice, following further delays, the vlf "chain" was abandoned in favour of beam transmission on "short wave" which by then had been pioneered by radio amateurs.

In the January *TT* (p37), it was noted that recent work at the high-power hf "ionospheric heating" transmitter at Ramfjord in northern Norway included the generation of frequencies in the range 1 to 1·5kHz by using the non-linear effects in order to modulate and radiate elf signals from the polar electrojet.

S. Ganguly (Rice University, Houston, Texas) reports on some basically similar experiments at the Arecibo Observatory, near Islote, Puerto Rico, where four 100kW hf transmitters can be fed to an array providing a massive 22 to 25dB gain. The transmitters consist of one pair on about 3,175kHz and one pair on about 5·1MHz. The transmitters were either pulsed at elf or alternatively operated with an elf difference in frequencies. Both these processes were shown to result in the generation and radiation of elf signals at 3, 5 and 6·25Hz and observed by three receivers including one sited on the island of Mona about 150km west of the transmitter site with a signal-to-noise ratio of up to 20dB.

The Japanese HRO

Few communication receivers have achieved such universal acclaim as the series of HRO models made by the National Company of Malden, Mass, USA, which spanned the years from 1934 to a final HRO-500 solidstate design with partial frequency-synthesis in the mid-sixties. The HRO-Senior (1936), HRO-M and HRO-5 (wartime models), HRO-7 (1947), HRO-50 (1950) and HRO-60 (1960) featured the famous HRO "PW" dial mechanism, and plug-in coil assemblies. The HRO was even paid the compliment of being closely copied as wartime receivers by both the Germans and Japanese.

An interesting collection of HRO receivers, including a Japanese copy, was assembled recently by members of the Welwyn-Hatfield ARC (see photo).

The rare Japanese model belongs to Norman Williams, G3BYG, who recovered it from an abandoned Japanese communications centre in Singapore in September 1945 and subsequently used it while he was VS1AC. It is still in regular use as a general-coverage receiver. It was one of nine in the Japanese centre, and uses the standard UX-based HRO valves such as the 6C6, 6D6 etc. Although not fitted with the classic "PW" dial, the gearbox and four-section tuning gang are similar and the circuit appears to duplicate the American design almost exactly, although the layout differs and the bfo and i.f transformers plug-in. The wooden cases that contain the plug-in coil assemblies fit like drawers into a compartmented wooden transit case. The receiver is built to an extremely high-standard, with superb workmanship and great attention to detail. It must have cost far more to manufacture than the original! Mechanically the Japanese version was of an altogether superior standard. ☐

Members of the Welwyn-Hatfield ARC with two "genuine" wartime HRO receivers (r) and the Japanese copy owned by Norman Williams, G3BYG, and modified psu (l). One of the genuine models comes from the Mosquito Aircraft Museum wartime wireless collection by G3LXP. The other belongs to Roy Cable, G4WSL. L to r: G3BYG (ex VS1AC), G1LQS, G3LXP and G4WSL.
Photo: G1HWH

Technical Topics

by Pat Hawker, G3VA

TRADITIONALLY, it has always been a feature of the UK amateur radio scene that much has been left to "self-regulation" brought about largely by the recommendations of the "national society" (ie RSGB) and a sense of responsibility on the part of licence holders. I recall, in the late 'forties, being one of those involved in drawing up the first RSGB "band plan" (hf only) designed to separate the a.m. sheep from the cw goats (or should it be vice versa?).

In those days the IARU (founded in 1925) was, to put it frankly, an almost moribund organization which, in the late 'twenties, had been rescued from complete oblivion by the ARRL and changed from being an "individual membership" society into a loose confederation of "national societies". It served mainly to give an international look to one or two pages each month in *QST* but did, at least, also publish a regular newsletter (IARU Calendar) that served to keep societies in touch with one another.

It was the setting up of the Region 1 Bureau in the early 'fifties that heralded a serious attempt to harmonize the "self-regulatory" activities of the fast-growing number of European amateurs. What had been the RSGB band plan became, with minor adjustments, the IARU band plan, later extended to cover vhf and uhf, including fm channelling, repeaters etc. IARU has also become involved in contests and the even more controversial "squares" debate.

This is fine in many ways, but it has left some Region 1 amateurs with the feeling that decisions that directly affect them are made by committees and delegates over which or whom they have little or no influence. In the jargon, there is little or no democratic "accountability" to individual members. There appears to be no way in which an individual can input and promote his or her views directly to the IARU unless these views have already been fully endorsed by the national society. Even in the well-known case of the separate or combined field days it has not proved possible for the RSGB to reverse completely an IARU recommendation that was endorsed primarily by delegates from countries that had never been closely involved with NFD.

What has this to do with technical topics you may be asking? The answer is that, for example, band planning can have very important technical consequences in encouraging or, alternatively, inhibiting technical developments. Take for example the IARU recommendation, in force now for several years, that no speech transmissions should be made in the 10·1MHz band.

Are we using 10·1MHz fairly?

As a 99 per cent cw-only operator I initially liked the idea that this narrow, 50kHz band should be reserved for telegraphy only, at least until the many point-to-point and other commercial stations move out in the fullness of time. But the lamentably low level of activity on what should be a most interesting and valuable allocation suggests that it is more than time that we pay attention to the seemingly-valid technical arguments in favour of ssb activity in part of the band. These have been repeatedly raised by Les Moxon, G6XN, and a few others over several years, but which somehow never seem to appear in print. Only recently, IARU headquarters declined to circulate to the member-societies G6XN's carefully considered views on the grounds that they can do this only when such views have already been fully endorsed by the national society. This is rather like saying that in an election only the governing body should be allowed to try and influence the voters!

I understand that RSGB committees are seriously considering G6XN's views, but it is surely important that these are understood by amateurs who still have the final say in whether they accept or reject those IARU recommendations that are not endorsed and made mandatory by their own licensing authorities. Decisions need to be made on the basis of a fully informed public opinion.

To summarize a few of G6XN's technical arguments:

Propagation: 10MHz is a part of the spectrum where long-path chordal-hop propagation is of particular interest and importance (see *TT* September 1979 and *Telecommunication Journal,* Vol 46, V1/1979, pp 320–7).

The *intelligent* use of ssb for *long-haul dx contacts* could do much to augment the contribution already made by amateurs to the initial recognition (by VK3AHH/DL3EC) of the extent of chordal-hop

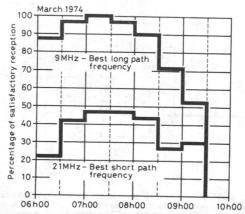

Fig 1. Percentage of satisfactory reception of German (Deutsche Welle) broadcast transmissions in Australia during March 1974 (sunspot-minimum period), showing the marked superiorty of the 9MHz long path over the 21MHz short-path route *(Telecommunication Journal)*

propagation at dawn and dusk periods. By force of the large number and variety of locations, amateurs are uniquely placed for contributing to the better understanding of this mode. At sunspot-minimum periods, 10MHz replaces the 14MHz band as the most consistent band for chordal-hop contacts to Australia and New Zealand with relatively modest antennas: Fig 1 relates to high-power broadcasting but underlines the value of 10MHz. A large number of amateurs well qualified to investigate long-distance propagation are undoubtedly discouraged from doing so on this band because of the no-telephony recommendations and consequent lack of activity. As a cw enthusiast, I recognize that not everybody shares this view.

Innovation: G6XN argues persuasively that the very narrowness of the 10·1MHz band constitutes a major challenge to developing new techniques that would reduce mutual interference between cw and ssb signals sharing the same channels; for example, using improved narrow-band audio filters for cw reception and improved, tunable and very deep notch filters for ssb reception. For many years it has been claimed by some amateurs that, with suitable filtering, cw signals, with their high average output power, can be copied effectively within the sideband region of even high-power broadcast transmissions. Mutual interference can also be further reduced by the use of directional antennas, by such techniques as radiated power control (rpc) etc. To the experienced cw operator, rtty is often a much more potent source of interference than ssb! For the commercial stations still legally entitled to use the band as primary users, the higher average power of a cw transmission can be more bothersome than ssb.

G6XN has obtained from Dr David Tong of Datong Electronics agreement that, with more suitable filtering, ssb and cw modes could co-exist reasonably happily, although this would place severe constraints on receiver linearity if the full benefits of af filtering are to be gained. Because the average power of a cw signal is higher than for nominally more powerful ssb transmission, the linearity requirements to avoid blocking etc by cw signals can be rigorous.

This is not to suggest that, generally speaking, separation of cw and ssb is not a good thing, but it seems tragic that because of the current IARU recommendations, 10MHz is so under-utilized that it is not even attractive to cw operators when, by making use of technological developments, some of the band could be shared, with the consequence that many more people would make the effort to come on the band. Equally important is that the IARU should be seen to be acting fairly towards *all* licensed amateurs so that its recommendations retain credibility.

The ills amplifiers are prone to

The essential ability of thermionic or semiconductor devices to amplify the voltage, current or power of an input signal has, unfortunately, to be qualified by the ever-present problem of potential instability. Basically, an amplifier is always liable to turn itself into an oscillator due to positive feedback from output to input in the presence of near-resonances in both circuits.

The classic "tuned plate tuned grid" (tptg) form of oscillator has been recognized since the earliest days of valve amplification at rf. Initially, with

triode-only devices available, it was countered by the process of neutralization; that is to say, by carefully arranging for an equivalent amount of negative feedback (ie 180° out of phase with the positive feedback), or by reducing inductive feedback by careful physical layout of the components and the use of shielding between input and output tuned circuits, and later by the introduction of tetrode (with effective screen by-passing to earth) and pentode valves to reduce the effect of the feedback-producing inter-electrode capacitances.

But tptg oscillation arises not only from the deliberate resonances of the tuned input and output circuits of an rf power amplifier. The problem also manifests itself in the form of "parasitic" oscillation, usually at vhf but also (particularly in the case of transistor power amplifiers) at very low frequencies, arising from the stray capacitances and inductances as in Fig 2(b).

Spurious tptg oscillation of this type can shorten the life of valves and occasionally destroy them; in the case of transistors an unwanted oscillation can be immediately destructive; it is particularly important in the case of a vmos power fet that the device should not go into strong self-oscillation, or instant destruction of an expensive device is likely to ensue. With valve amplifiers, parasitic oscillation may continue over a long period without necessarily being detected other than in the form of low efficiency, possible rfi problems, sparking over of high-voltage tank capacitors even when the amplifier is fully loaded, and burning up of the resistors, with a few turns of wire wound round them, used as parasitic suppressors.

More serious is that modern high-power (and high-cost) valves *can* be destroyed by parasitic oscillation along with a number of the associated components, in the form of inter-electrode short-circuits, flash-overs etc, together with bypass capacitors, zener bias diodes, tank-circuit switches, meter movements, filament transformers etc.

The unwanted (and often unsuspected) resonances in the input and output circuits are most likely to cause tptg oscillation when they are close to but not exactly on the same frequency. Even short lengths of straight wire leads have appreciable inductance at vhf/uhf and can result in parasitic oscillation. The purpose of parasitic suppressors is usually to provide additional, heavily damped, inductance. The smell of burning from a parasitic suppressor resistor is an infallible sign that despite its presence there is a vhf parasitic.

The following notes on the problems of valve amplifiers at hf and vhf are taken from P R Keller's long-out-of-print *VHF Radio Manual* (1957) but basically the same problems are found in solidstate amplifiers:

"As the operating frequency of an amplifier is raised the following effects become important:

(*a*) The input resistance of the valve falls, damping the grid circuit, and reducing the effective anode load of the preceding stage. Increased driving power is required.

(*b*) The small capacitances between valve electrodes can no longer be ignored, and give rise to undesirable effects, such as oscillation.

(*c*) The transit time for electrons to pass between the cathode and anode becomes an appreciable fraction of the time for a cycle and gives rise to increased losses.

(*d*) The inductance of internal connections, and external point-to-point wiring, has appreciable reactance.

(*e*) The self-inductance of capacitors used for tuning and decoupling must be considered when choosing components.

(*f*) The values of the inductors and capacitors in the tuned circuits become increasingly small and, at the higher frequencies, are difficult to achieve (in conventional *LC* form).

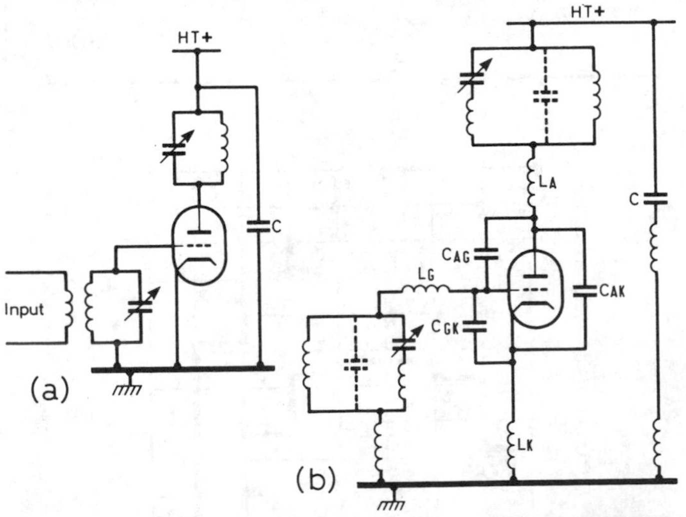

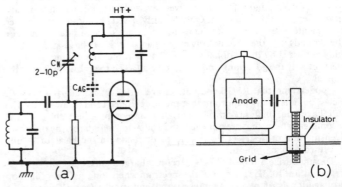

Fig 2. (a) The basic rf amplifier is also in effect a tuned-plate tuned-grid oscillator unless the two tuned circuits are not coupled either inductively or capacitatively with positive feedback. (b) The problem is made complex by the presence of stray capacitances and inductances that may also result in parasitic resonances at vhf. This is how the circuit of (a) appears at high or very high frequencies

Fig 3. (a) The basic form of neutralizing the anode-to-grid inter-electrode capacitance by providing a balancing out-of-phase feedback path. (b) With the low inter-electrode capacitance of valves intended for use at vhf, only a very small neutralizing capacitance is needed. This is one method of providing the high-voltage low-value capacitor

(g) At very high frequencies, the current in a conductor tends to flow only in the layers of the conductor close to the surface, a phenomenon known as skin effect. The effective resistance of conductors is thus increased so that circuit losses are higher. The depth of penetration of the current in a copper conductor at 100MHz is only a quarter of a thousandth of an inch, and most of the current flows in this shell so that circuit elements for vhf are often made of copper tube or strip and may be silver-plated and polished to give minimum losses.

"Triode valves in grounded-cathode circuits always require neutralising at radio frequencies: Fig 3(a). The grid-anode capacitance of a tetrode or pentode valve is lower, and these valves may often be used up to vhf without neutralising; the frequency limit, above which the valve must be neutralised, varies with individual valves and depends on the circuit application. . . . The anode-grid capacitance of a low-power tetrode valve is only a fraction of a picofarad . . . one method of obtaining the required capacitance is shown in Fig 3(b). Some twin-tetrode vhf valves include neutralising capacitances inside the valve envelope for push-pull configurations. Some types of twin-tetrode valve include the screen-decoupling capacitor inside the valve envelope. For optimum screen decoupling it is frequently better to use a small capacitor forming a low-impedance, series-resonant circuit with the screen-grid lead inductance, rather than to use a larger capacitor."

Parasitics and grounded-grid amplifiers

While grounded-cathode and common-emitter amplifiers have a 180° phase shift between input and output signals leading to positive feedback via the internal capacitances, the popular high-power zero-bias grounded-grid amplifier has zero phase shift and theoretically is an unconditionally stable amplifier not requiring neutralization. Unfortunately, this does not mean that in practice such amplifiers, even commercially available designs, are free from parasitic oscillation which can, if undetected, shorten the life of such high-cost valves as the 3–500Z, 8873, 8874, 8875 etc.

Richard Measures, AG6K, in "Grounded-grid amplifier parasitics—simple cure extends amplifier life" (*Ham Radio* April 1986, pp31–4) recounts some unfortunate experiences with his kit-built high-power hf linear using a pair of 3–500Z valves in grounded-grid configuration.

Over several years he noted a tendency for his tank capacitor to arc over occasionally and for the parasitic suppressor resistor to overheat. Then, shortly after fitting a new pair of valves, a grid-to-ground choke and a 200pF grid-to-ground capacitor exploded with the noise of a rifle shot. He learned that other users of grounded-grid amplifiers had suffered similar experiences, sometimes afterwards finding a valve ruined with a permanent grid-to-filament short-circuit.

He soon realized that the problem arises from vhf parasitic oscillation and that this stemmed from the combined effect of the grid structure inductance, inter-electrode capacitances, lead inductance etc. These created a resonant circuit connected, in effect, between grid and earth, even though the grid sockets appeared to be effectively bypassed to earth. Where a similar resonance occurs in the tank circuit there will be the 180° phase shift needed to form a tptg oscillator even though the main signal path shows no such phase shift. He suggests that in some conditions it is possible for the second resonance alternatively to be in the input circuit of the grounded-grid amplifier.

He believes that this problem is inherent in all grounded-grid amplifiers, and he discovered that Collins ran into the problem many years ago with their 30L-1 linear amplifier using the 811A valve. They solved the problem by adding a resistor shunted by a 200pF capacitor between grid and earth. The resistor lowered the Q of the unwanted resonance, and the series capacitor helped cancel some of the inductance of the grid structure, so *raising* the natural resonance of the grid. Since then other equipment manufacturers have picked up this technique but without realizing that the capacitor to earth was not functioning as a simple decoupling bypass

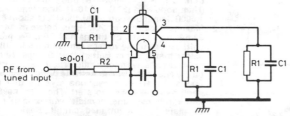

Fig 4. AG6K's grid and cathode modifications to reduce the tendency of hf grounded-grid amplifiers to parasitic oscillation at vhf. R1: 75 to 100Ω, 1 or 2W, non-inductive. R2: three 10Ω 2W non-inductive resistors in parallel; for two valves in parallel use three 10Ω resistors; for a single valve use three 20Ω, 1W resistors. C1: 47 to 75pF, 500V disc ceramic capacitors

arrangement. The result has been a tendency to increase the value of the capacitor in the belief that the bigger the better. For instance, in AG6K's amplifier instead of 200pF, as used by Collins, the total value of the capacitors from the three grid pins of the 3–500Z was 600pF from the three 200pF capacitors.

He recommends the arrangement shown in Fig 4 in which, as a further precaution found necessary primarily for the higher gain of valves when first purchased, he fits a non-inductive resistor in the cathode drive circuit to provide some degeneration even though this means that the amplifier must be driven slightly harder (no problem if the linear is being driven from a typical 100W transceiver).

The 3–500Z is a directly-heated valve, but the technique can also be applied to indirectly heated valves such as the 8877 with the degenerative resistor in the cathode lead. An rf negative-feedback cathode resistor is also useful in grid-driven linear amplifiers since it reduces intermodulation distortion (imd) products.

This is a short summary of a long article that goes into the question of parasitic problems in some detail.

Instability in solidstate power amplifiers

Despite steady improvements in bipolar and mosfet rf power devices, it remains easy to destroy devices during the building, adjustment and operation of amplifiers based on rf power transistors operating near their maximum ratings. This has led to development of various forms of protection circuits, but the basic problem arises to a considerable degree from the various forms of instability to which such amplifiers are prone. Parasitic oscillation can be defined as any undesired frequencies in the

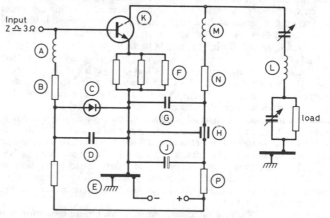

Fig 5. W4ATE's suggested safeguards for a typical medium-power bipolar transistor amplifier.
A. RFC must be low-Q (high Q causes i.f. oscillation).
B. Resistor lowers Q of rfc (typically 100Ω).
C. Bias stabilization diode.
D. Diode bypass (0·001μF).
E. Group all earth leads near emitter earth connection using short leads.
F. Low emitter resistor helps prevent secondary breakdown.
G. 0·001μF button vhf type.
H. 0·1μF feedthrough capacitor (hf bypass).
J. 10μF tantalum at by-pass capacitor.
K. High-level harmonics are generated due to non-linear characteristics of the transistor plus large dynamic voltage and current swings.
L. Network for load matching and reduction of harmonics.
M. RFC tunes out reactive component of admittance.
N. Low-value resistor lowers Q of the self-resonance of the rfc.
P. Decoupling resistor, typically 12Ω.
The heavy peak currents and low impedances should be reflected in the use of heavy gauge conductors and high-value capacitors with the tank coil carrying both rf and dc current.
"Mode jumping" in linear amplifiers is generally due to a tuned tank circuit having a different resonant frequency for a strong drive signal than for a weak one. This presents problems with the peaky nature of an ssb drive signal. Precautions include carefully choosing bias values, correct grounding, and using only transistors with low values of parasitic capacitance and inductance.
Make sure there is sufficient drive. Use triple bypassing for af, hf and vhf signal components; electrolytic capacitors for af bypassing should preferably be of the heavier tantalum type; i.f. bypass capacitors can be ceramic feedthrough or (second choice) disc ceramic types; vhf bypass capacitors should be silvered-mica button types with shortest possible leads.
The biasing circuit uses a stud-type silicon power diode bolted to the same heatsink as the rf power transistor (s) as near as possible to the transistor or between a pair of transistors. Any increased heat then lowers the diode resistance, thus helping to maintain a safe dissipation level in the transistor(s). A temperature-sensitive diode can be selected using an ohmmeter and soldering iron: measure the drop in diode forward resistance after touching the hot iron to the stud for a given number of seconds, selecting the diode with the fastest thermal response.

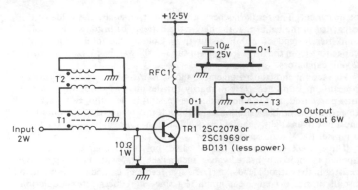

Fig 6. A useful arrangement for a single-ended wideband solidstate amplifier capable of providing about 4-6W output when driven from a 2W QRP rig. From *Solidstate Design for Radio Amateurs* (p61) with component suggestions from Stephen Ortmayer, G4RAW, who finds an amplifier with 10W dc input a great help to his home-built 3·5MHz d-c transceiver in poor conditions. RFC1 is a 25μH choke capable of passing 1A. T1, T2 and T3 have seven bifilar turns of two twisted pairs of No 26 enamel wire on Amidon FT37-61 toroid cores.

output not harmonically related to the input frequency. Unlike valve amplifiers this often includes sub-harmonics; transistor amplifier "parasitics" can thus range from a few hundred kilohertz to hundreds of megahertz, and may be short-lived or self-sustaining.

Parasitics seldom appear when an amplifier is precisely tuned, but rather when some change or adjustment is made. The degree of detuning can vary between wide limits. A particularly serious form of parasitic can occur when there is a variation of the load impedance which can result in virtually instant destruction of the device. It is also possible to destroy an unprotected transistor during the tuning up of an amplifier.

A Class C transistor stage, when dc current is flowing, becomes in effect a Class A amplifier superimposed on a Class C stage; it can then be prone to both the linear instabilities of a Class A amplifier and to various non-linear parametric instabilities in its Class C role. The major causes of Class A linear instabilities were identified many years ago as: (*a*) low-frequency oscillations produced by thermal feedback effects; (*b*) oscillations due to internal feedback in the device; (*c*) negative resistance and conductance instabilities due to transit-time effects, avalanche multiplication etc; and (*d*) oscillations due to external feedback, such as insufficient decoupling of the dc supply. Non-linear instabilities include parametric generation of harmonics and sub-harmonics. The tendency of transistor power amplifiers to burst into destructive self-oscillation at low frequencies has been called the "count-down" effect.

Fig 5 shows some useful safeguards applied to a typical medium-power transistor amplifier as suggested a decade ago by Gene Brizendine, W4ATE. He also listed a number of precautions to be taken during initial tune-up of such amplifiers:

(1) Always carry out initial checks with a low supply voltage and low drive, gradually increasing both together.

(2) It may be advisable to connect temporarily a relatively inexpensive transistor in order to gain the "feel" of tuning-up before risking the use of an expensive device.

(3) Degenerative (unbypassed) low-value emitter resistors offer useful protection during preliminary checks. Several 1W resistors in parallel present lower impedance than 0·5W types.

(4) Use generous heatsinking. During alignment it is worthwhile keeping a constant check on the temperature of the power transistor, using a finger, or a thermometer attached to the device with putty.

(5) Never operate a power transistor without a dummy load or matched antenna.

(6) Monitor collector current continuously; a climbing current is the earliest warning of junction heating. Remember that maximum rf current output does *not* occur exactly at the collector current dip.

A tunable rf indicator is useful since it is easy to tune an amplifier to an incorrect frequency and to check on spurious or harmonic output. Although harmonic output can be reduced by a high-C tank capacitor, nevertheless it must be recognized that the harmonic output of transistor amplifiers tends to be significantly higher than from valve amplifiers. A good lowpass filter is therefore usually built into the amplifier.

Fig 6 shows a typical low-power transistor amplifier from the invaluable *Solid State Design for Radio Amateurs* by W7ZOI and W1FB (ARRL).

Coaxial cable and contamination

In *Ham Radio* (October 1985) Joe Reisert, W1JR, wrote a detailed and useful article on coaxial cable, a subject well worth studying, particularly by vhf/uhf enthusiasts where a great deal of expensive rf can so easily be lost in relatively short lengths of cable—especially cheap cables or where some moisture has ingressed.

However, one piece of advice given by W1JR—that it is "penny-wise and pound-foolish" to opt for cables with "contaminating" jackets which use more plasticizer in the vinyl compound than non-contaminating cables —has been refuted by Ronald Steir, W9ICZ, a cable specialist (*HR* April 1986, p9). He suggests that insisting on non-contaminating cables, to avoid plasticizer migration, involves unnecessary expense. He does not believe that, in practice, plasticizer migration, either in exposed or buried environments, is ever likely to be the cause of increased attenuation. Invariably he finds the real cause is water or moisture getting into the cable, most commonly from inadequate sealing at the connector ends of the cable and/or cuts or pin holes caused by abrasion to the jacket.

Omni Tek universal crystal oscillator/tester

Robert Fransen, VE6RF (*Ham Radio* April 1986, pp 38–40) provides details of a useful device he has developed for checking virtually all types of crystals over the range 100kHz to 20MHz without adjustment, displaying crystal activity on a meter, providing an output for use with a digital frequency meter, or as a calibration "marker".

VE6RF claims that few if any previous circuits will readily oscillate over a 200:1 range, and suggests that the key component is the 10mH choke (scramble-wound miniature coil on a ferrite core). Fig 7 provides details of his arrangement using a fet oscillator, fet buffer and bipolar emitter follower with dual output, but versions have been built by VE6RF using the 6BH6 valve. An "activator button" is included to provide extra feedback for starting sluggish third-overtone or low-activity crystals, though it should not be needed often. When used as a spotter, additional harmonic output can be obtained by connecting back-to-back diodes across R2. The diode across the 200μA meter is to limit the voltage across the meter to

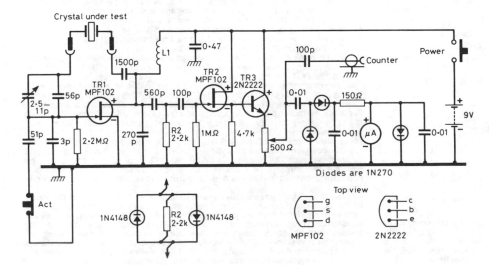

Fig 7. VE6RF's "universal" crystal oscillator (32pF load) used as a combined crystal checker/spotter etc. Diodes type IN270 or similar except IN 4148 diodes, across R2 for increased harmonic generation. L1 is scramble wound on ferrite rod (Hammond No 1530 C102) 10μH. Resistance about 1,000Ω. Minimum current at 100kHz is about 6mA. Maximum current at 20MHz is between 14 and 22mA, depending on the gain of TR1. Frequency shift over a supply voltage range from 5 to 10V dc is less than 0·5ppm. Battery is 9V dc type Number 1604. Some waveform distortion takes place below about 3MHz. The Activate button is used to test and start third overtone crystals that may need more feedback to start. The fifth, seventh and ninth overtone crystals will probably not oscillate in this untuned circuit. Basic circuit (with C1 and C4 left out) is for a 32pF load. Meter can be up to 200μA full scale, though 50 or 100μA is preferred. Minimum and maximum currents are for the whole circuit. R2 with 1N4148 diodes for increased harmonic generation

about 300mV because of the high output of some lower-frequency crystals.

VE6RF notes the problem of checking crystals which are soldered on to printed boards and which can easily be destroyed in attempting to remove them. He recommends cutting the traces to the crystal instead, putting two No 18 sewing-machine needles (with the mounting shaft ground off) in the oscillator socket holes and then pressing them against the traces to the crystal still on the board. C13 can be omitted if you intend only to use plug-in crystals. If this is done the crystal sockets provide a convenient test point for the battery voltage.

Crystal fundamentals up to vhf

Although monolithic bandpass crystal filters up to about 250MHz have been manufactured for several years, crystals based on mechanical lapping and polishing have been restricted to fundamental modes below about 25MHz (usually below about 15MHz) and overtone frequencies below about 150MHz.

Overtone oscillators should not be confused with harmonic oscillators: crystal in overtone mode produces no output whatsoever at its fundamental frequency. The overtone oscillator is a very useful device but is less easily "pulled" than fundamental oscillators; this means that they do not make a good vxo or vcxo, are less easily frequency modulated, and filters made from them are more restricted in bandwidth.

Recently STC Components Ltd of Harlow have announced the successful development by their affiliated research company STL of a new process for manufacturing crystals (Fig 8) which operate in fundamental mode up to 75MHz, or in third-overtone mode up to over 200MHz. A 75MHz fundamental implies a crystal thickness of only 22microns.

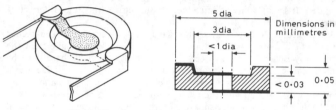

Fig 8. Structure of the new STC vhf crystals

STC believe that this represents an important breakthrough that opens the way to i.f. crystal filters up to 75MHz with low insertion losses, wider passbands and reduced spurious noise than previously possible. Used for oscillators, these crystals make possible temperature compensation at high frequencies, improved spectral purity, low esr (equivalent series resistance) and high pullability at high frequencies, while retaining an inherent temperature stability significantly greater than that of ceramic resonators etc.

During production up to 80μm of material is removed from mechanically prepared AT-cut quartz blanks. The process is based on the etching of quartz blanks in buffered hydrofluric acid; the crystals retain the required mechanical strength by the use of selective etching of high-purity, high-Q "zero tunnel" synthetic quartz. Using the new processes, 5mm AT-cut quartz elements up to 75MHz mounted in HC45 holders and TO5 packages are now being produced. Work is in progress to develop plasma etching techniques which should make possible fundamental-mode crystals up to 150MHz.

This new range of SQX-3000 (SQX-3001 fundamental, SQX-3003 third overtone) crystals is, at least initially, geared more to commercial and military budgets than amateur radio applications, ranging in cost from about £17 up to over £100 each. But it is clearly an interesting and potentially very useful development.

Polarization diversity at uhf

TT (November 1985, pp 866) noted how "multipath" propagation brought about by reflections leads to deep fades during mobile operation on vhf. This problem extends also to short-range communication using portable handheld equipment. Indeed, as noted in *Electronics Letters* 22 May 1986, pp609–10: "Radio transmission in the portable communications environment is plagued by deep rapid fading due to random handset orientation and multipath propagation". The problem can be particularly severe inside buildings, and for such applications as the use of radio microphones in lecture halls or television studios it has led to the common use of diversity reception.

In the USA, Bell Communications have been developing 816MHz portable/mobile systems that are required to be reliable and ubiquitous. Among the techniques that have been tried with considerable success is polarization diversity. In an *Electronics Letters* report, S A Bergmann

(State University of New Jersey) and H W Arnold (Bell Communications Research) note that: "Polarization diversity relies on the independence of signals received over two orthogonally-polarized antennas. Polarization diversity is both spectrally and spatially efficient. Frequency diversity requires the use of several frequencies, and space diversity antennas must be separated by at least one-quarter wavelength, while polarization diversity uses one frequency and the cross-polarized antennas can lie directly on top of one another."

Using a modified hand-held transceiver as a portable unit and a receiver with a dual-polarized microstrip patch antenna with approximately hemispherical coverage, the two outputs from the receiving antenna were fed to two spectrum analysers used as tunable receivers and the output sampled automatically every 2ms over a 20s period, with measurements made in both office and residential environments. The writers conclude that "Under non-line-of-sight conditions where deep fading occurs in portable communications environment, polarization diversity can be used to mitigate this signal impairment. In cases where there is a direct line-of-sight between transmitter and receiver, polarization diversity offers protection against random handset polarization." It is a further argument for the use of circular or mixed polarization on 144MHz and above.

American amateurs now have a frequency allocation at 902 to 928MHz, with an interim ARRL band plan providing segments for eme, digital communications, nbfm, fm repeaters, amateur television (a full 6MHz suitable for 525-line 60Hz transmissions to broadcast standards) and another 6MHz for wideband experimental systems including atv and spread spectrum. The band is shared with ism (industrial, scientific and medical) users, and there are restrictions in some states.

A move towards higher frequencies for mobile/portable operation may also come about as the result of the appearance on the market of models such as the Kenwood (Trio) TR-50 transceiver for the 1·3GHz band.

Digital signal processing

TT (May 1985, pp359–60) described the developing use of digital signal processing (dsp) in hf communication receivers, including the first production model (Collins HF2050) as described at an IEE *HF communications systems conference*. It was already clear that professional designers were becoming anxious to take advantage of the flexible high-grade channel filtering under software control made possible by the advent of mass-produced general-purpose signal processing ic devices. It was also noted that the limited speed of current lsi devices restricts such processing to af or low i.f. signals so that the existing approach is to use a conventional analogue-type front-end and have the digital filtering at af or a lowish i.f. Again, device speed still limits the instantaneous, spurious-free dynamic range of the digital filter, and particularly the A/D conversion.

Despite the present limitations, the advantages of flexible software control, the repeatability and reproducibility of digital performance, reduced component count and smaller size arising from the use of large-scale integrated devices, and reduced manufacturing costs with more automated production etc are all encouraging British and American firms to press ahead with experimental dsp receivers.

An article by A P Cheer of Plessey Electronic Systems Ltd in *PESL New Technology* No 2, Spring 1986 (brought to my attention by Alan Williams, G3KSU), describes the results obtained by modifying a high-grade Plessey PR2280 receiver to incorporate digital demodulation and digital filtering based on the Texas Instruments TMS32010 dsp ic. It also discusses the present options and architectures open to designers. The author leaves no doubt that he feels strongly that dsp will rapidly come into general use. He writes:

(1) DSP has arrived and can displace analogue circuit designs.
(2) DSP modules are smaller, cheaper and offer true modularity by software configuration.
(3) DSP circuits will shortly outperform analogue counterparts.
(4) Investment (by manufacturers) in dsp system elements is vital.
(5) To compete in future equipment markets we (PESL) must offer the attribute of configuration flexibility.

The demonstration model, based on the PR2280, incorporates the rf Option 2 and interface Option 1 (Fig 9). The analogue circuitry is retained up to the final 1·4MHz i.f., and the interface was a cmos eight-bit flash converter sampled at 5·6M samples/s. The data is split into I and Q versions of a square-wave local oscillator at 1·4MHz. The 12-bit digital-to-analogue converters provide a 72dB range. Data reduction is accomplished using a unity-weighted f.i.r (finite impulse response) filter and decimation process by accumulating groups of 128 samples to reduce the data rate to 40kw/s but with an increased word accuracy of approximately 12 bits. Channel filtering uses a lowpass, 60-stage, fir filter, implemented on a TMS32010 in each I and Q path. The demodulator uses a third TMS32010. The software for each lowpass filter requires a main programme of 150 words of

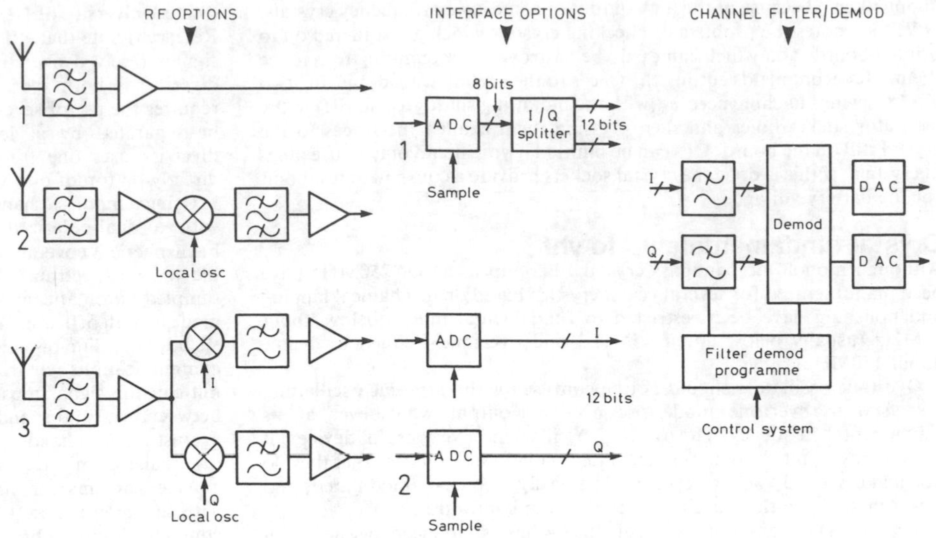

RF OPTIONS   INTERFACE OPTIONS   CHANNEL FILTER/DEMOD

Fig 9. The basic options for hybrid analogue/digital radio receivers. At the present state of the art only elf/vlf receivers would use rf Option 1 with conversion to digital form at signal frequency. The interface options depend on whether division into quadrature (1,Q) signals is before or after digitalization of the i.f. signal. (*Plessey New Technology*)

assembled code, plus 30 words for a set of filter coefficients. To add a new filter bandwidth requires only 30 words of extra storage. For demodulation of cw, a.m., usb, lsb, isb and fm, the software totals only 530 words.

The entire digital section is implemented on two double Euro cards reduced to fit into the receiver module box. It replaces two similar-sized analogue demodulator boards plus a further large board containing five crystal filters for the various mode bandwidths.

A P Cheer concludes: "It is essential that we rapidly exploit the now clearly established advantages of dsp in future communication systems . . . we are already in a position to develop a cost-effective standard i.f. transceiver module. . . . But the real competitive edge will be achieved in the future with the realization of a full custom chipset which would give an ultimately lower unit price and increase the performance to a level where the complete all-digital transceiver system would become a reality."

Since amateurs seldom require such a large choice of bandwidths as the professionals, the advantages of dsp for this application are rather less evident—and the disadvantages remain. However, I would guess that dsp will soon prove irresistible to the Japanese amateur radio firms, if only as a marketing ploy. So we need to understand what digital receivers are all about.

Tips and topics

The new high-dynamic range mixer with resonant-gate drive developed by Ed Oxner, KB6QJ (March *TT*, p187, with correction note in April *TT*) is fully described in a new 16-page publication by Siliconix *Designing a super-high dynamic range double-balanced mixer* including a data sheet for the Si8901 ring mixer ic and application note AN85-2 on the new mixer. This publication is now available from the Publicity Department, Siliconix Ltd, Morriston, Swansea SA6 6NE (tel (0792) 74681).

Dr Geoff Grayer, G3NAQ, noted the recent references in *TT* to the Conblock 6A three-pin mains plugs and sockets and adaptors, and admits that he uses this system for his hi-fi equipment. However, he is not in favour of introducing yet another "standard" plug because of the problems that arise when equipment is used away from the home location. The almost universal UK 13A plug has meant that we have at last almost got away from the old mixture of 2, 5 and 15A three round-pin connectors and all the various two-pin sockets found in a diminishing number of homes. The problem of multiple "standard" systems is well illustrated in the variety of coaxial sockets, audio and DIN sockets, standard and miniature mono and stereo jack plugs and sockets etc. With multiple mains standards a traveller needs to take along a formidable range of adapters, spare plugs etc. Writing from CERN, Geneva, G3NAQ adds: "The point I want to make is that the standard Swiss plug looks rather similar to the Conblock 6A system (*TT* March, p189) though slightly larger with 19mm rather than 16mm overall pin spacing, and has more substantial pins, being rated at 10A. By removal of the central earth pin (Heaven forbid that I should ever be guilty of doing such a thing!) it will fit the standard German and French two-pin sockets. Presumably because of its larger volume of production, it is substantially cheaper than the 'Con' 6A fittings. It would have been a simple matter to fabricate a lightweight compact distribution block based on the Swiss system, and this would have had a potential export market also. Perhaps an even more attractive alternative is the "Europlug", fast becoming a standard on electronic equipment. This is almost identical in size to my

'Con' plug and also possesses an extended earth pin. It is similarly rated at 6A though having flat pins. Although I have met it only as a male chassis socket and female plug, I see no reason why the opposite should not be fabricated for the kind of applications for which the 'Con' block is intended. It seems a pity to introduce a connector with yet another set of dimensions."

John Bird, G3GIH, adds to the saga of low-cost open-wire feeder spreaders cut from plastic containers. For his, he uses containers for the farm spray Betanal used on weeds in sugar beet, but feels there must be similar plastic containers for domestic and garden applications. He uses a triangular three-wire feeder (permitting choice of element legs) and has no problem with twisting into the plane of the feeders; when used with two-wire feeders it might be necessary to clip some small squares of the material next to each spreader for restraint. The spreaders survive wind and weather well, and can be slid up and down the wire for adjustment. The material is easily marked out and then cut out with a Stanley trimming knife. The original Betanal containers were white but they now come also in blue and green. G3GIH strongly recommends using green spreaders and putting a coat of green paint on any alloy elements etc. Green is much more environmentally acceptable and relatively inconspicuous against a background of sky and trees; he bemoans the fact that so many feeder cables, multiway rotator cables and some domestic coaxial cables are bright white.

For non-readers of "Members Mailbag" and *TT* (May) a 1min club quiz: "In what mode does the power of the constant-frequency carrier vary with the modulation index?" Anyone answering "amplitude modulation" should be given a three-months sentence of cw-only. Those giving the correct answer "frequency modulation" should be asked to try and convince the others—they are likely to find this as difficult as convincing those who continue to argue that an a.m. carrier is constantly varying in amplitude! It is permissible to quote P R Keller in support: "Frequency modulation differs from amplitude modulation, where the carrier remains

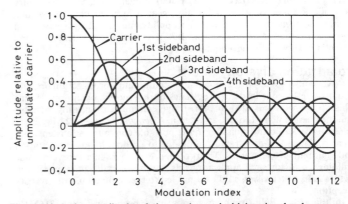

Fig 10. How the amplitude of the carrier and sidebands of a frequency-modulated wave varies with the modulation index (modulation index is the ratio of maximum frequency deviation divided by maximum audio frequency). Note that there will be some power in fifth, sixth, seventh etc sidebands not shown

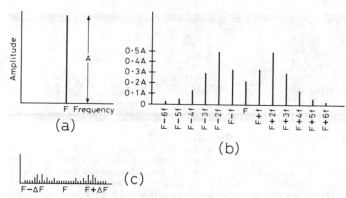

(a)

(b)

(c)

Fig 11. Frequency-modulation sideband spectrum. (a) Unmodulated carrier wave. (b) Carrier frequency modulated with a *single* audio tone (F carrier frequency, f audio frequency) with a modulation index of three. (c) Carrier frequency modulated with a *single* audio tone with a large modulation index

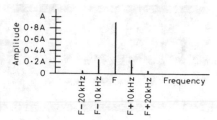

Fig 12. Narrowband frequency modulation using a modulation index of only 0·5 in order that the bandwidth is reduced to that required for a conventional a.m. signal. Diagram shows a carrier (F) modulated with a 10kHz af tone with 5kHz deviation

constant in amplitude and plays no part in transmitting intelligence, in that the amplitude of an fm carrier (and also that of its sidebands) varies with the modulation index. For certain values of modulation index the carrier disappears altogether. The values of modulation index for which the carrier is zero are approximately 2·40, 5·52, 8·65, 11·79 and thereafter at intervals of approximately 3·14 (π)." Just as amateurs tend to be misled by those a.m. "envelopes", so in elementary terms we are led to believe that the carrier of an fm transmission is constantly varying in frequency at a steady power. One seldom associates fm with sideband theory but they are really there, extending the transmission bandwidth theoretically to infinity though in practice the power in the higher-order sidebands drops off rapidly, and we usually assume a bandwidth of twice the frequency deviation plus twice the maximum audio based frequency. With a.m. the total (envelope) power output of carrier plus sidebands increases with modulation, though the carrier is of constant amplitude, whereas with frequency modulation the total power output (carrier plus sidebands) remains constant, as does the carrier frequency. Believe it or not! A reminder that some of the basics of fm, though not its spectrum analysis, were described in *TT* December 1985, pp939–40, under "The frequency-modulation paradox".

Technical Topics

by Pat Hawker, G3VA

AMATEUR RADIO in the UK is almost totally dependent upon the continued goodwill of the Radio Regulatory Division of the Department of Trade & Industry. In 1983, the RRD (previously called the Radio Regulatory Department) was transferred from the Home Office to the DTI after having moved in the late 'sixties from the Post Office to the short-lived Ministry of Posts & Telecommunications and thence to the Home Office.

It is often argued that the more things change the more they stay the same —but it could be dangerous to assume that this truism applies to RRD, since their attachment to DTI appears to have sparked off a series of far-reaching changes and investigations aimed at treating the radio spectrum less as a public service responsibility and much more as a marketable commodity. The idea of using "market forces" and "deregulation" as a means of producing more efficient exploitation of the spectrum could have very important repercussions on our activities.

Marketing the spectrum?

The extent to which such concepts will or could be applied to amateur radio regulation is by no means clear—though we are already seeing some quite daunting situations arising from the imposition last year of the £21 charge for the investigation by the RIS of viewers' and listeners' interference complaints—including the prospect of having "variations" imposed on our power limits, bands etc. Possibly even more fundamental to our activities is the determination of the DTI, spurred on by the present government, to "exploit" more fully the commercial possibilities of providing access to the radio spectrum.

At an IERE Conference on Land Mobile Radio last December, A J Nieduszynski, a senior official in the RRD, gave a keynote speech that included the following:

"Like coal, or gas, or oil, the radio spectrum is a limited resource. Unlike them, however, it cannot be used up or depleted in the same way because it can be re-used, day after day and year after year. Any moment that it stands unused because of regulatory constraints when somebody could be using it is an opportunity wasted—an opportunity *cost* or *loss* that makes the community that much poorer.

"Increasingly, therefore, we have come to appreciate that we regulators have a duty to ensure that that cost is minimized and that we put as few obstacles as we can in the way of the spectrum being used at any given moment to the fullest extent that can be justified economically . . . a piece of spectrum carries a potential price tag."

This is a crystal-clear expression of the British Government's wish to exploit more fully the radio spectrum by means of the market economy, using such techniques as "selling" or "renting" bits of the spectrum virtually to the highest bidder. Inevitably this is not an operation in which amateurs can afford to participate in competition with professional services. It means that the RRD is likely to become ever more anxious to seek out *under-used* frequencies and to transfer them to services willing to pay handsomely for using them. The RRD is already on record as suggesting that "The amateur radio licence fee is one of the least expensive, even within the category of licence taken out by hobbyist users of radio. In terms of the spectrum to which access is provided, the amateur fee is very good value for money." Could it be that they are already thinking in terms of a substantial rise in licence fees and/or reducing the amount of spectrum devoted to this non-profit-making activity? Remember that international regulations can be overruled nationally provided that this does not result in interference to authorized users in other countries.

This is yet another reason why it is surely essential to ensure that we make *full* and *responsible* use of *all* the frequencies to which we presently have access. It really is a case of *use or lose*—and using them for the internationally-defined purposes of "A radiocommunication service for the purpose of self-training, intercommunication and technical investigations". These are clearly "public service", "educational" and "scientific" rather than commercial arguments—but they remain the primary justification for our continued existence!

It is by no means reassuring—as happened to me recently—to be reminded by an American visitor (who had brought his handheld transceiver with him) of the continuing disgrace of the Crystal Palace 144MHz London repeater.

Valve and "kiss" aficionados

My mailbag continues to tell me that I am far from being the only operator still using thermionic devices and/or recalling the advantages of simplicity and easy repairability they bestow on home-built equipment. The other week my old HQ129X receiver produced thumps instead of cheeps; it took no diagnostic feat to decide immediately that the bfo was not oscillating, to guess that the emission of a near-40-year-old valve must at last have faded, to plug-in a replacement 6SJ7 and be back in business in a matter of minutes. I wish I could say the same for a non-functioning transistor broadcast radio that has been defeating my desultory attempts to trace and rectify the fault!

Alan Errock, G3HCO, built a 7MHz 6L6 crystal oscillator which gave 7W output, then a 6V6–6L6 crystal oscillator power amplifier that gave a more useful 20W output. But after studying some pre-war *QST*s he reverted to a single 6L6 as a cathode-coupled co that pushes out 15 to 20W and with which he has no difficulty working round Europe. His sense of achievement at getting 20W from a co was somewhat dimmed by finding in those old *QST*s an RCA advertisement that showed a circuit diagram for a single-valve oscillator providing no less than 150W output! The valve, needless to say, was not a 6L6 but an 813 with its 50W heater.

John Clarke, TK5FF/G8KA, living in Corsica, had some difficulty in locating a source of older-style crystals suitable for use in power oscillators, but draws attention to an advert that appears on the back pages of *QST* wherein CW Crystals, 570 No Buffalo St, Marshfield, MO 65706, USA, offers FT243 crystals ground to frequency of choice at what G8KA considers "a not unreasonable price". But to obtain further information it may be advisable to enclose $1 to ensure a reply.

For sheer nostalgia, however, the prize must go to Richard ("Badger") Farley, GW3SSJ, who has recreated early hf equipment in the form of an LS5A transmitter originally described by Frank Haynes, G2DY/G2DZ, in *Wireless World* in 1927, and has rebuilt, using components of the right period, a very decrepid *Wireless World* Empire Two (O-v-1) designed for "colonials" by H F Smith, including modifications suggested in 1928 for extending coverage from 80 to 190m.

GW3SSJ finds—as do several other readers—that regenerative 0-v-1 and 1-v-1 straight receivers can still be used to work consistently through the evening QRM on 3·5MHz, though such receivers tend to be difficult to "net" accurately. The modern form of the 0-v-1 is the direct-conversion receiver, but one misses the old sense of satisfaction you got from adjusting a really smooth "reaction" control for maximum sensitivity!

Richard Farley, GW3SSJ, with his re-constructed "1920s" equipment. The "Empire Two" receiver on the right uses 2V battery valves, lt, gb and ht batteries etc, with engine-tuned front metal panel. The single-valve transmitter was built about 25 years ago using an LS5A as specified in 1927 but now usually uses a 415PT valve dating from 1928 (4V directly-heated pentode) that runs at about 7W input. As a self-excited oscillator on 7MHz GW3SSJ got T7C reports but as a usable co gets good T9 reports from around Europe. The LS5A (but not the 415PT) gives enough light to operate by!

IERE "Radio Receiver" Conference

At the beginning of July, the IERE, in association with a number of professional institutions and the RSGB, held its fourth international conference on "Radio Receivers and Associated Systems" at the University College of North Wales at Bangor—a college that harbours and has bred many radio amateurs. Of the 130-plus delegates, an unusually large proportion were or had been licensed amateurs. Although most were wearing their "professional" hats, Ray Flavell, G3LTP ("Space and time continuity as an aid to North Sea transmission path studies") and L Sharrock, G3BNL ("Phase locking of Gunn diodes at 24GHz") presented papers solidly based on their amateur radio experiences, while my own paper "Dynamic range—fact or fiction?" brought together a number of topics aired in recent months in *TT*, coupled with the warning that current military radio systems, in attempting to design the human operator out of the system, faced the danger of introducing a software crisis into area networks and an ever-lengthening time between the formulation of an initial "requirement" and the production of operational systems. In other words stressing the need to retain a rapid "kiss" response to previously unforeseen requirements. I took, as an example, the way in which SCU, SOE and the Anglo-Polish teams were suddenly faced in 1940 with the need not only to distribute "Ultra" information to overseas commands on a secure (SLU) network but also to provide "suitcase" and pocket equipment for covert operations. Within a matter of months, a whole new concept of portable hf radio stations capable of providing, even with poor antennas, (reasonably) reliable communication over distances of hundreds of miles was developed, bringing "miniaturization" into radio systems, yet based on standard consumer and amateur-radio components and designs.

But what of current professional work on receivers, antennas etc? How much of what was disclosed in the 40 or so papers could have a direct bearing on amateur radio practice?

In an overcrowded spectrum there remains a keen interest in what can be done to minimize the effects of interference. A BBC paper described tests on a random sample of vhf fm broadcast receivers (often used with a uhf/shf converter for amateur portable operation). This underlined (as did some German tests a few years ago) that many receivers have adjacent channel selectivity well below the international planning requirements, particularly those for stereo-reproduction free of birdies and whistles. It is also clear that in this respect poor selectivity is found both in low-cost and high-cost models, with medium-price models tending often to be the best. Unfortunately the BBC tests did not extend to investigating why some receivers are so poor, though they do indicate that there can be a problem with dual 470kHz/10·7MHz i.f amplifiers, due to a peak in the response curve corresponding to the lower i.f. Since vhf/fm broadcast receivers are often used by radio amateurs as tunable i.f systems, this matter is of considerable interest.

Radio engineers have traditionally sought frequencies offering *good* propagation characteristics. However, for both military and civilian applications there is growing interest in the high-absorption gigahertz bands such as 60GHz. The military are interested because attenuation is so high that signals cannot (at least in normal conditions) be intercepted from any distance. Civilian applications such as short-range personal or mobile communiciations would allow very frequent re-use of the same frequencies.

Back-window vhf transmitting antennas

From an amateur radio viewpoint, one of the most practical papers was that by Dr J D Last, GW3MZY, and B Easter of UCNW and the associated "Industrial Development Bangor Ltd" on "Broadcast reception and mobile radio communication using vehicle rear-window heater aerials". Their system is currently being used by several vehicle manufacturers as broadcast (lf/mf/vhf) receiving antennas (see *Electronics & Wireless World* February 1985, pp64–67): Figs 1 and 2. Recent work has shown, however, that the technique can also be used for two-way vhf mobile radio, and it has been tested by the Essex Police. It has also been used successfully on 145MHz. Although window-heater antennas are not intended to outperform quarter-wave roof-mounted whips, they overcome the expense of fitting, the need for holes in the bodywork, the vulnerability to car-washes and vandals, aerodynamic drag etc. They can provide entirely satisfactory broadcast receiving antennas, provided they are not too close to the "rubber" (carbon-loaded plastic) flexible glass-retaining mouldings used on many vehicles.

It has been found that the characteristics of a typical window demister heater used as a transmitting antenna can be affected by the choice of the terminal configuration by which the heater supply and rf power are connected. Compared to broadcast reception, better impedance matching is needed at the operating frequency. It is also usually necessary to achieve nominally vertical polarization. For the police radio experiments (82 to 83MHz transmit, 97 to 100MHz receive) the natural choice is to connect the

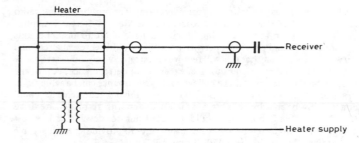

Fig 1. Basic back-window heater antenna isolated from the vehicle chassis by an isolating choke which is bifilar-wound to eliminate dc magnetization of the core. Problems arose on some vehicles due to the capacitance coupling to the "rubber" (often carbon-loaded plastic) flexible glass-retaining mouldings, but this is being overcome by increasing the physical separation

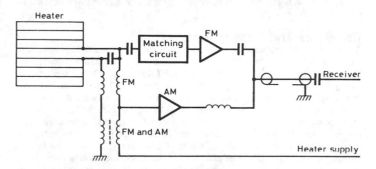

Fig 2. Arrangement for a combined lf/mf and vhf/fm antenna

two heater terminals in parallel (at rf) and to couple an unbalanced feed between this joint and the nearby metalwork. The structure is series resonant within the required frequency range, with a Q-factor of about 30. In this case, because of the separation between transmit and receive frequencies, a single matching network is not possible and relay switching of two matching networks was needed (this would not be the case for 145MHz). A vswr of better than 1·2:1 was achieved on transmission, but it was first necessary to remove the standard tailgate wiper arm which proved to have an unfortunate resonance, replacing a part of the arm assembly with a non-conductive component. The local field from an 18W transmitter at 83MHz did not present a safety hazard to passengers in the rear seat.

The authors conclude that the performance of a heater antenna, for pure vertical polarization, is (as might be expected) inferior to that of a centrally-mounted whip antenna. However, its superior performance for horizontal polarization strongly suggests that in many situations, especially where propagation is strongly perturbed and the polarization is altered, the overall performance will often be comparable, particularly in urban areas. Performance at 145MHz is substantially similar to that achieved on police frequencies.

Digital signal processing

Many of the papers were concerned with single-chip paging receivers and digital signal processing (dsp) both at i.f and with zero-i.f direct conversion.

As someone who helped to re-introduce the "homodyne" concept to UK amateurs in the 'sixties and 'seventies, I found it interesting to note the large number of presentations concerned with this alternative to the basic superhet. There are two main reasons for this: *(1)* the dc receiver facilitates and makes practicable the virtually complete integration of a "receiver on a chip" and is thus very attractive for radio-paging and cordless telephone applications; and *(2)* the dc approach brings signals down to baseband frequencies for subsequent digital signal processing within the present limitations of general purpose ic devices and analogue-to-digital converters. However, as a number of speakers emphasized, the Costas-loop direct-conversion receiver presents practical problems in achieving precise balance and 90° (quadrature) signals, and the future of dsp seems likely to depend on a/d converters that can cope with an i.f of, say, 1·6MHz and yet provide a resolution with sufficient dynamic range. It is also interesting to find that the snags as well as the advantages of direct-conversion are being re-discovered the hard way.

I was left with the impression that, as amateurs, we need to approach digital processing warily, particularly low-cost compromise designs. Of the professional designs now being developed, most seem to be aimed at a performance "as good as" the classical analogue designs based on crystal filters.

However, a paper "Design considerations for an hf digital radio receiver" by T H Pearce and S D Rogers of the Marconi Research Centre, outlined work on a receiver that should achieve a 120dB instantaneous dynamic range and provide a performance that would represent a real step forward. It was clear that this will require an extremely-low-noise frequency synthesizer and a front-end mixer of exceptional performance. Few of the professional designers seem to believe such performance can be achieved in practice with existing components. The mixer requirement could conceivably be met by Ed Oxner's Si8901 mixer with resonate-gate drive (*TT* March 1986) but you would be hard-put to develop a low-cost synthesizer with the required low noise and jitter to provide a practical drive for a mixer that could use a 120dB dynamic range.

A number of other developments of interest were also reported at Bangor but must await another month. A novelty was a receiver technique that is intended to recover a wanted signal from under a stronger interference signal by providing up to about 55dB of suppression on the unwanted signal. It sounds too good to be true but I'll include an outline of what is proposed next month.

Receivers and transceivers

A paper by D Holman, of Plessey Electronics Systems Research, on "Design techniques for low-cost transceivers" described some cost-cutting techniques used in the Plessey Model PTR5300, a 10/1W multimode battery-operated military "automatic hf transceiver" based on the premise that a soldier regards a manpack set as "a piece of unwanted junk that prevents me from doing my job (fighting) as well as I might" and that the true cost of equipment includes purchase, training, operation and maintenance. Personally I cannot help feeling that it might be better to spend a little more on training (or at least interesting) soldiers in the techniques of radio communication and a little less on making everything automatic and hence more complex. But it would, I suppose, be highly unfashionable not to incorporate microcomputer control!

However, there are some interesting concepts in the PTR5300, including the use of bilateral amplifiers, elimination of the usual output filter bank by re-configuring the atu into a variable lowpass filter when the 50Ω socket is in use (in the whip mode, the atu has sufficiently high Q to provide reasonable out-of-band rejection): Fig 4. An lcd alpha-numerical display tells the operator that he has set his unit to the correct channel/mode etc or reprimands him for his mistakes. Fig 5 shows the configuration of the bi-directional amplifiers used in this model, a control voltage switching from "forward" to "reverse" direction.

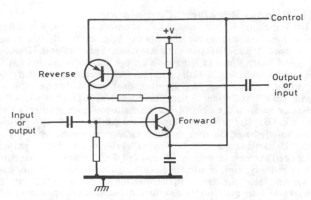

Fig 5. By applying a suitable switching "control" line, a bi-directional amplifier can provide gain in either the forward or reverse direction

The "msj" antenna

Most of the antenna technology used by radio amateurs is derived from professional research and development, some of it stretching back to the early days of hf radio. It is unusual to find a design presented as suitable for professional local broadcasting or communications that stems directly from a design originally developed for use on the amateur bands.

However, in *IEEE Transactions on Broadcasting* (Vol BC-32, No 1, March 1986) E Demacopoulos and P Zimourtopoulos, of the University of Thrace, and J N Sahalos, of the University of Thessaloniki, Greece, present a detailed description and analysis of a vertically-polarized "msj" antenna as developed for use at a local 101·8MHz experimental vhf/fm broadcast station. The "msj" turns out to stand for "modified slim jim" and the design is based with only minor modifications on the 144MHz "slim jim" (*j*-type *i*ntegrated *m*atching stub) antenna first described by F C Judd, G2BCX in *Practical Wireless* April 1978, pp899–901. It is pointed out that this antenna well meets the needs of broadcasters in offering omni-directional radiation concentrated in the horizontal plane, wide usable bandwidth and impedance stability.

The dimensions and geometry of the original Slim Jim (Fig 6) were first analysed theoretically using the so-called "method of moments". This showed that the antenna has an impedance of 50Ω at 155MHz and not in

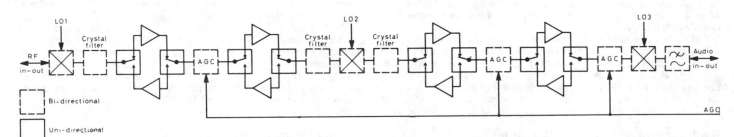

Fig 3. Block diagram of the Plessey PTR5300 10 or 1W hf manpack set using bi-directional techniques

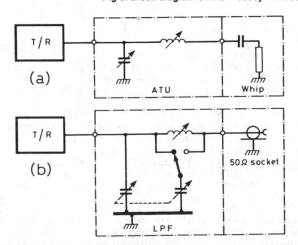

Fig 4. The use of an atu that can be re-configured to provide a tunable lowpass filter to eliminate the need for a bank of lowpass filters

the 144MHz band, but this is not considered a serious problem since it is possible to slightly redesign the antenna by scaling the dimensions. The main problem that emerged was that maximum radiation is at 22° above the horizontal, whereas it is usually desirable for a broadcast antenna to radiate most energy at 0° or even at a slight downward tilt. They retained the basic shape of the antenna but varied the place of the feedpoint, the leg distance and the place and the length of the gap.

The paper presents theoretical and experimental results of a number of variations of these dimensions, aiming at achieving maximum horizontal radiation while keeping the input impedance close to 50Ω.

Their final choice was based on that suitable for an antenna sited near a hill in the city. The actual dimensions for 101·8MHz are as follows: height 2·21m; leg distance 0·06m, height of gap (beginning) 1·10m; height of gap (ending) 1·25m; height of the feedpoints 0·37m; radius of wire 0·004m.

From an amateur viewpoint, the slight upward tilt would not be a disadvantage for some applications, but, for example, for a repeater station on a hill, the modified radiation pattern of the "msj" would be an advantage. The authors conclude: "We believe that with larger leg distance the radiation pattern will become directional in the horizontal plane." This will give some new ideas about the use of the msj as an element in directive arrays.

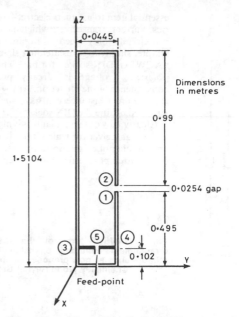

Fig 6. Dimensions of the original "Slim Jim" 145MHz antenna described by Fred Judd, G2BCX, in *Practical Wireless* in 1978 and now proposed in a slightly modified form as a Band 2 broadcast antenna

More on the T2FD

The Revd John Marshall, G3RKH, draws attention to an article "More on the T2FD" which appeared in *CQ* (February 1953) reprinted in *CQ Antenna Roundup 1963*. This included a 600Ω, open-wire version of the T2FD (*TT* July 1986) and some useful general design principles:

(1) Length of each leg should be $(50,000/f \times 3 \cdot 28)$ft where f is the lowest frequency of operation in kilohertz.

(2) Spacing is $(3000/f \times 3 \cdot 28)$ft.

(3) Angle of slope is about 30°.

(4) Terminating resistor should be non-inductive and rated at 35 per cent of dc input power (Note that this would have been for a.m operation, and a lower value would suffice for other modes—*G3VA*).

(5) The resistor value is quite critical: 390Ω for 300Ω feeder; 500Ω for 450Ω feeder; 650Ω for 600Ω feeder.

(6) If other than a non-inductive resistor is used, an atu will be necessary.

I must admit to a continued mistrust of an antenna system in which up to about 50 per cent of the rf power fed to it ends up (on some bands) in that non-inductive resistor. With open-wire feeder and a good atu, I strongly suspect that you could radiate equally effectively without there being any resistor in place, though this could result in what would amount to a voltage-fed arrangement on some bands. It must also be admitted that radiating half of your power effectively on a convenient multiband system that can be implemented at low cost is quite likely to result in a well-satisfied operator!

Roach pole plus sailboard mast vertical

A D Macfadyen, G3ZHZ, has been making good use of a multiband Windom (perhaps more correctly a variation of the VS1AA). This uses 300Ω ribbon feeder at roughly one-third the distance from one end (in practice a 140ft top, fed 44ft 5in from the end): Fig 7. This antenna, fed at the shack end through a 1:4 step-up balun, provides an swr of roughly 2:1 on most bands, with G3ZHZ using a transmatch to reduce the swr to near unity swr at the transmitter output. This works well on all pre-WARC bands from 1·8 to 28MHz.

Later, after reading the various notes in *TT* on the use of roach poles, he obtained one of these plus, from the local sailboard stockist, a *free* broken sailboard mast, 4·5m long. He found this could be easily repaired, at least for his purpose, with resin and glass-fibre tape. Among the masts from which he could choose were some made of carbon fibre. Again, recalling earlier *TT* notes, these were rejected. All the masts had carbon fibre

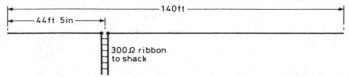

Fig 7. G3ZHZ's horizontal multi-band Windom with 300Ω transmission line

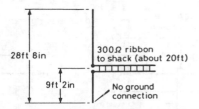

Fig 8. Vertical quarter-sized version of the 300Ω wire Windom used as a vertical dipole antenna by using a roach pole mounted atop of a repaired sailboard mast to provide an effective 33ft-high support. Resonate to 14·1MHz using gdo at shack end of feeder

reinforcement in the form of four thin strips running longitudinally along the mast. However, no problems have arisen in practice from these thin strips. The top of the sailboard mast fits neatly into the butt end of the roach pole, giving a strong self-supporting "whip" some 33ft long. G3ZHZ mounted this on tabernacles to facilitate easy raising and lowering.

After some experimentation he developed a quarter-sized version of his multiband Windom. Final dimensions, following work with a gdo and swr meter, were as shown in Fig 8. The antenna element comprises switchgear cable to BS6231, type BU, 1/1·78mm (2·5mm²). This is approximately 15swg copper wire pvc sheathed and is available from electrical wholesalers. Fed via the 4:1 balun, the swr is about 1·1:1 over most of 14MHz and about 2·5:1 on 28MHz.

G3ZHZ reports that this antenna works excellently on 14 and 28MHz. With careful adjustment of the atu, good results can be achieved on 7MHz. 21MHz is not currently in use at G3ZHZ, but there is no reason to believe that performance on that band would not be more than adequate. Unlike most verticals, no radials or elaborate ground connection are used even on 7MHz. During May/June 1986 a series of 14MHz cw skeds with ZF1JC (Cayman Islands) showed an advantage on receive of some 3 to 4 S-points over the horizontal windom. On 7MHz, once tuned up, signals are much the same on the vertical and horizontal antennas, suggesting that for those with tiny gardens or small flat roofs there is still hope of harvesting dx while growing vegetables rather than radials!

Electrets on the SACWRG connector

TT February 1984 included details of the DIN-connector arrangement proposed by Dr P J Best, G8CQH, and adopted as a "standard" by the Solihull & Chelmsley Wood Raynet Group (SACWRG). This comprised three elements: (*a*) a "rig adapter"; (*b*) a "line"; and (*c*) a selection of accessories or peripherals fitted with DIN connectors. The object of the exercise is to permit the use of microphones and speakers etc with different equipment and so help to overcome the operational and administrative problems that arise when groups of people depend on equipment owned by individual amateurs.

Dr Best now points out that to accommodate modern, miniature, lightweight accessories (eg headsets) which have electret microphones, whether of home construction or commercial manufacture, just two simple additions are needed. The first requires an alternative "rig-adaptor" to be constructed to add a voltage to the mic-high conductor via a 680Ω resistor which becomes the drain-load for the fet in the electret device. The second requires the electret accessory to be equipped with a DIN plug to replace the original connector if that caused the mic-lo and speaker-return conductors to be presented as a common connection. The required polarising voltage may be sourced at the transceiver's microphone socket from any pin which has between (about) +3V and +9V present. The voltage is not critical, and the current drawn is sufficiently small that pins allocated to scanning functions can be considered as suitable sources. If the source is above about 5V, further decoupled resistance should be considered, as shown (at about 2kΩ/excess volt). The added voltage must be blocked from the preamplifier stages (1µF or greater) to prevent conflict with the transceiver's internal arrangements for biasing and for superimposing tone-burst signals. This externally-added voltage has no effect upon passive microphone accessories when they are used instead, but gives the electret microphone a suitable impedance to match the specific transceiver; normally about 600Ω, due to the drain load which is shunted by the high-impedance fet amplifier in the electret device. The few extra components needed for this adapter may be housed in an in-line module (eg RS Components 456–201) with a seven-pin DIN socket set into one end-plate, and the body of the appropriate microphone plug soldered into the other. The finished item will have strong mechanical integrity and will protrude neatly from the transceiver like certain oscilloscope probe adapters. If preferred, an in-line version can be prepared.

Readers will deduce that this adapter is sufficiently general to surplant any specific adapters which manufacturers might otherwise claim to be an

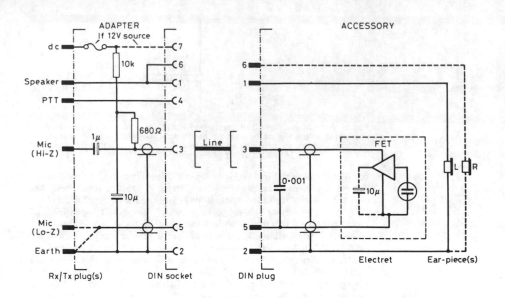

essential item to use their electret-based accessories. Further, transceivers which have series mic-ptt circuits only need a minimum form of adapter simply to translate their signals onto the SACWRG DIN-socket format. The necessary polarizing voltage is already present as a consequence of the ptt action. Any which require extra shunt resistance can have such a resistor strapped behind the DIN socket of their adapter.

Clearly, any of these adapters is highly specific to the transceiver for which it has been prepared and should not be swopped to other transceivers in any attempt to effect hurried repairs. ☐

Fig 9. Modified form of the DIN-connector arrangement including provision for electret microphones as now proposed by the Solihull & Chelmsley Wood Raynet Group

Technical Topics
by Pat Hawker, G3VA

AMATEUR RADIO now means very different things to different people. The strands that held the hobby together seem to be growing ever looser. At one time, it was fairly safe to assume that anyone who held an amateur licence had a basic knowledge of and technical interest in receivers, transmitters and the valves and components that went into them. This did not mean that everyone built their own equipment, at least not since the 'thirties, but it did mean that most of us could look inside a receiver or transmitter and relate what we saw to its circuit diagram, and had some idea of the identity and purpose of the various stages, components etc. Even if we did not all possess the skills to construct working equipment, most amateurs could keep them working and do their own repairs.

Of course, then, as now, some "newcomers" to amateur radio were at the same time also "professionals" and often already knew a lot about the theory of radio communication. But there were very few indeed, young or old, who did not rapidly acquire a nodding familiarity with radio components, circuit diagrams and the differences between good and bad equipment.

Today, this is no longer the case. Just as the modern car driver often has little idea of the role of the carburettor, distributor or even the spark plugs, so licensed amateurs can now become keen and proficient operators of what are virtually domestic appliances, with only the basic knowledge required to pass the RAE. This often bears little relationship to the complex "black boxes" that are used. You may, or may not, think this a good thing. Who expects every television viewer to know how a colour tv set works?

There would (at least in my opinion) be little point in raising the theoretical standard of the RAE higher. What is needed, at least for those who are not content to see the hobby become just one of operating an appliance, is something to bridge the gap between the basic elementary theory of the RAE and practical familiarity with the elements of modern communications equipment.

It is encouraging to note that a number of clubs, groups and educational centres are beginning to recognise this, and are introducing practical post-RAE courses. John Lawrence, GW3JGA, believes that home construction should remain an inherent part of the hobby. He writes:

"I taught the RAE at the local evening institute for two years, and after several dozen new amateur licences had been issued locally—mostly to ex-cb operators—I decided that I would try to correct the black box trend. For the following two years I ran, instead, a 'practical amateur radio class'.

"The students, all from previous RAE classes, had to choose from several constructional projects of varying complexity: morse oscillator, vhf reflectometer, hf directional power meter, 100W dummy load, fet-dip oscillator etc. Some projects I designed from scratch, others were based on existing designs, but in each case all the information, together with a built and working sample, was available on the first night, so that the level of constructional work and the performance could be seen at first hand.

"Each week I spent the first 20min covering some aspect of construction or setting up a station; for example, soldering, fitting coaxial plugs, simple metal work, antenna construction, tuning up a transmitter, tvi tests, safety etc. The rest of the evening I spent assisting with the constructional projects.

"At first there was a great lack of confidence. Some in the class had never used a soldering iron. Many had great difficulty in equating the circuit diagram with the physical components and the wiring. The physical wiring of switches appeared to be particularly difficult. The de-bugging of non-working projects needed to be covered in easy stages; visual examination, point-to-point checking, voltage measurements etc. This year I intend to cover simple fault-tracing early, so that checks can be made as the work proceeds.

"The results so far have been very gratifying. All of the class completed their projects successfully, and several of the group entered equipment in the constructional competition at the local radio club.

"Incidentally, the constructional notes for the fet-dip oscillator formed the core of my article published in *Practical Wireless* (October and December 1985). My 17-year-old son wanted some extra pocket money, so he advertised suitable sets of coil formers (cut and faced in a lathe). To-date he has sold 280 sets, which seems to prove that interest in home construction is still alive and kicking!"

What I find interesting about this commendable project is that it provided encouragement for those who had already passed their RAE but needed guidance on the practical aspects of building simple equipment. The Americans have an expression "Elmers"; the experienced enthusiasts who provide guidance for what they call "neophytes"—not exactly beginners but those without much practical experience. It is also important to note the concept of starting on simple projects before plunging in off the deep end and trying to emulate the black-box manufacturers.

Components are a problem. There are few local stockists, but some good mail order distributors. It is refreshing, for example, to learn that Radiospares (RS) are ceasing to be "trade only" and are now prepared to cater for the home-constructor.

Magnetic (small loop) antennas

The June *TT* item (pp418–9) on the use of large-diameter compact loops as transmitting antennas has resulted in a long and interesting letter from John Brown, G3EUR, who draws attention to articles in *cq-DL* (No 2/1983 and No 5/1984). The first of these, by Hans Wuertz, DL2FA, was Part 12 of a detailed series of articles on dx-antennas and their image. Part 12 dealt with loop and ferrite-loaded antennas in considerable detail, including the various ways in which they can be coupled to the 50Ω output socket of a transmitter.

I have also received from Ted Hart of W5QJR Antenna Products, PO Box 334, Melbourne, FL 32902, USA, a copy of his *Small High Efficiency Antennas—Alias The Loop* which runs to some 100pp (soft covers $11.95 plus $3.30 to cover overseas air mail). W5QJR also has an article on the loop antenna, which he insists is no "second-rate" antenna when it comes to dx operation, in *QST* June 1986.

While I have always stressed the need for extreme low-loss, low-ohmic construction, W5QJR is an unashamed enthusiast. His back cover proclaims: "At last a dream come true. The loop antenna provides high efficiency for transmitting and low noise for receiving. It provides an optimum radiation pattern for both local and dx communications. The pattern gain is second only to multi-element beam antennas. For the small city lot and for apartment dwellers, there is no other antenna that will provide equivalent performance in a small space—and it does all this when mounted at ground level."

While this is putting it a bit strong, the book does stress the practical problems that are involved with small loops of high-Q and hence narrow resonate bandwidth (although capable of being resonated over a wide frequency range). He provides an octagonal-loop design based on 0·75in copper pipe with motor driven remote tuning: Fig 1.

John Brown, G3EUR, has put together some useful notes on the fundamentals of small loops that will help put this approach in perspective. He writes: "Siemens and Telefunken have used loops and ferrite assemblies for many years, mainly for hf/df and selective reception in commercial stations where the ability to null out interfering signals arriving from a different direction to that of the wanted station is often more important than high efficiency in converting field strength into microvolts at the receiver terminals. The principles of frame and loop antennas go back many years, and were set out in the classic *Admiralty Handbook of Wireless Telegraphy* in 1927 alongside "jars" of capacitance.

A loop can be equated to a resonant tuned circuit: in the conventional full-wave "quad" the resonance results from the electrical length of the conductor; in the small single-turn loop the smaller inductance is tuned, with the aid of a capacitor, to the operating frequency. The Q can be very high, say 300 at 10MHz. Radiation into space (hence the radiation resistance) increases with loop diameter; this represents "work done" and results in a lowering of the working Q. By reducing losses in the inductor by using large-diameter copper tubing and low-loss insulation in the (high-voltage) tuning capacitor, the ratio of tuned circuit loss to radiated energy can be kept low and an efficient antenna for transmission and reception results. It should be noted that with a high-Q resonant circuit even a few watts of rf power results in high circulating currents in the loop and high voltage across the capacitor. Most loops of practical size are limited to transmitter powers of 100–300W, even when well protected from damp and stray power losses induced into nearby conductive material. The high-Q

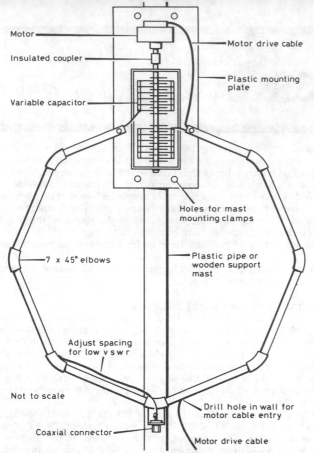

Fig 1. Suggested mechanical design of the magnetic (small loop) transmitting/receiving antenna as described by W5QJR in his book *Small High Efficiency Antennas—Alias the Loop*. The only changes are in the straight lengths of copper pipe that form the resonant octagon loop on different bands. Loops recommended by W5QJR include: (a) circumference of 8·5ft for use in 10/29MHz, approximate capacitance 125pF (10), 60 (14), 35 (18), 23 (21), 16 (24) and 9 (29); (b) circumference 20ft, capacitance 73pF (7), 29(10) and 6 (14)

results in a narrow bandwidth so that *accurate* retuning is necessary even for small changes of frequency. The radiation from a small loop is essentially via the magnetic field, hence the name "magnetic antenna".

Matching the loop into a receiver or transmitter can present problems. As a receiving antenna, the system is, in effect, a bandpass filter with some form of tap or link coupling between the element and the first stage (Fig 2). For a single-peak response the coupling (as in i.f transformers) must be critical; the first-stage tuned circuit needs to be high-Q so that its losses, coupled back to the antenna, do not reduce efficiency. By comparison, matching to a transmitter is easier since this can provide a low-impedance source from a broadband solidstate amplifier via lowpass filter and wideband transformer. Such an arrangement avoids the need to retune the transmitter tank circuit when changing frequency (but the high-Q loop itself *must* be retuned).

The loop radiation pattern is similar to that of a dipole, but efficiency will usually be lower. The advantages are primarily the smaller physical size, the ability to null unwanted signals during reception and the possibility of good performance close to ground.

Fig 3, derived from DL2FA's articles, shows options for matching a loop, including the use of capacitive networks and "miniloop" inductive coupling as discussed in the June *TT*. Fig 11 (e) is probably the optimum arrangement in practice. With optimum coupling between the primary and secondary loops, highest efficiency (maximum radiation resistance) occurs when the loop resonates with the tuning capacitance approaching 0pF. At frequencies above loop resonance, the system is no longer a true magnetic antenna, and electric fields develop in the neighbourhood of the antenna. This means that the loop circumference should not exceed about 0·4λ at the highest operating frequency.

Tuning with very small values of capacitance (about 5 to 10pF) is critical, and this usually requires a good remote tuning system. Small, geared "models" can be used, although tuning with them can prove rather slow. The power supply cable for the motor should be routed vertically from the zero point (mid-inductor).

DL2FA claims to have built and tested over 100 magnetic antennas, including ferrite types, with large area "air-cored" loops emerging as the most satisfactory. This checks with some wartime experiments made in 1943 by G3EUR with dust-core "loaded" wire antennas. Ferrite core losses tend to be significant for this application; the resulting smaller diameter loop for equivalent inductance reduces radiation (which is governed by the area enclosed within the loop). The reduced area offsets the concentration of flux via the core(s).

Among the advantages of the magnetic antenna, other than those already mentioned, is the fact that provided there are no masses of closed-loop or sheet conductors in the immediate vicinity, proximity to ground or to a typical building tends to result in lower losses than the electric field losses of a dipole or other conventional antennas. There is also, incidentally, less coupling to the human body.

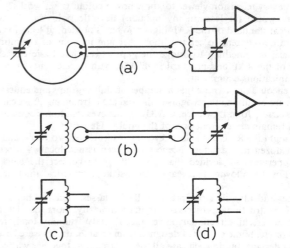

Fig 2. Coupling a resonant loop to a receiver. (a) Link coupling forming in effect a high-Q bandpass filter. (b) Electrical equivalent to (a). (c) Balanced and unbalanced tapped impedance coupling. Practical arrangements are shown in Fig 3

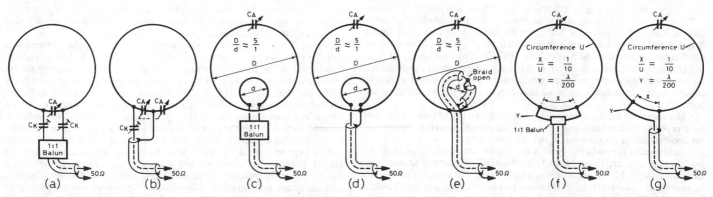

Fig 3. Matching a loop transmitting or receiving antenna to 50Ω cable as described in 1983 by DL2FA. The Faraday-loop coupling coil made from coaxial cable in (e) is considered optimum. (g) is the arrangement used by W5QJR

The magnetic field tends to result in less mutual interference (tvi and ivt) with television receivers. Small loop receiving antennas are less susceptible to all forms of local electrical interference. As df enthusiasts will appreciate, a loop antenna can be combined with a vertical element to achieve a cardioid radiation pattern (transmit as well as receive) but both antennas need to be resonated accurately (in amplitude and phase) to obtain useful gain in a desired direction.

A major disadvantage of the magnetic loop antenna is that using two or more closely-spaced loops to increase gain and directivity results in narrower bandwidths and individual tuning, so that a multiband antenna seems to be impractical (arrays of small broadband "active" loops have been used professionally as beam receiving arrays since the 'sixties). Some work has also been done commercially in the use of multiple loops for fixed frequency operation, using phasing networks in the feeder lines to reconcile the physical spacing of the loops.

Building your own stable vfo

John Hawes, G4UAZ, showed in "Stable vfo with bipolar-assisted mosfet" (*TT* June 1986, pp416–7) a novel idea of using a compound circuit in which the oscillator comprised both a dual-gate mosfet to provide high input impedance, thus maintaining the Q of the tuned circuit, and a bipolar transistor to provide the gain necessary to ensure ready oscillation.

Writing from British Columbia, Canada, Mike Koblic, G4GIU, congratulates G4UAZ on what he regards as one of the most brilliantly-simple technical ideas of the decade. He adds:

"I rushed to the work bench to try it out, and it certainly works! I built the vfo using the 'dry' method on a breadboard socket. Birkett's 'special' 40673-equivalent mosfet and a BC308 bipolar transistor were used, as I had nothing else suitable in my junk box. With the feedback capacitors of 3,000pF, a variable capacitor of 500pF, and a coil roughly similar to the original, the vfo tuned between 4·97MHz and 5·6MHz. The short-term stability at 7MHz (core removed from coil) was ±20Hz, remarkable considering the mechanical conditions. Blowing hot air onto the assembly from close-up hardly shifted the frequency by 100Hz (in conventional vfo units this test usually results in the frequency disappearing out of earshot!). With the feedback capacitors changed to 1200pF, the vfo tuned 9 to 13MHz with still pretty impressive stability.

"In agreement with theoretical calculations I found the tuning capacitance of 100pF maximum too small to tune the whole of the 5 to 5·5MHz range. I thought this might be improved if the tuning circuit were connected in series, thus changing the vfo into a Clapp configuration. It worked, but resulted in considerable degradation in stability.

"I feel G4AUZ may have provided us with an answer to every homebrew vfo-hacker's prayer."

Peter Hart, G3SJX, has also been busy putting together an external vfo unit for use with his Ten-Tec Corsair transceiver using a more conventional bipolar transistor oscillator. He writes:

"Earlier this year, after the frustrating experience of being unable to work two choice dxpedition stations through lack of a split-frequency capability, I decided to build an external vfo. The rf output of the internal 5 to 5·5MHz analogue vfo in the Corsair is routed via a jumper lead on the rear panel to the local oscillator mixer circuitry. A link on the accessory connector 'enables' the internal vfo. Adding an external vfo involves removing the jumper lead and applying suitable rf drive to the lo mixer input. Switching for internal/external/split operation may best be incorporated within the external vfo unit. The internal frequency display uses a frequency counter which will display correctly which vfo is selected, hence eliminating any requirement for calibration of the external unit. It is undesirable to have both vfo units running continuously in order to prevent spurious signal problems. For split-frequency operation it is necessary for the selected vfo to stabilize very rapidly, particularly for cw operation. This implies a clean keying characteristic. In my search for the ideal vfo to use, I

found that many of the 'classic' circuits have poor performance in this respect, taking several seconds to stabilize. The circuit finally adopted has an excellent keying characteristic and overall performance. It is derived from a source close to hand, being a slightly-modified version of the Corsair's internal vfo, but using variable-capacitor tuning rather than permeability tuning.

"Fig 4 shows the oscillator circuit, and Fig 5 the associated switching control circuitry for use with the Corsair—the basic vfo would be suitable for many equipments, but the control circuitry would depend on the equipment involved. The oscillator transistor is biased at all times, and uses feedback from collector to emitter. Only when the base is decoupled to ground is there sufficient gain to enable the stage to oscillate. A switching transistor in series with the decoupling capacitor effectively keys this stage. Note that there is no dc applied to the collector of the switching transistor.

"Oscillator construction should follow standard practice. Polystyrene film capacitors were used for C1 to C8, and a solidly-constructed 100pF small transmitting-type variable capacitor is used for tuning. This had ceramic end plates for supporting the rotor at both ends. The flywheel and reduction gear mechanism from an old Eddystone 898 drive gave a tuning rate and knob size similar to the internal vfo. L2 comprises 14 turns of 26swg enamelled copper wire on a 14mm diameter grooved ceramic former with no tuning slug (believed to have originated in an old Army No 19 set). C4 and the coil turns are adjusted to give the required tuning range. L2 comprises 35 turns of 35swg enamelled copper wire on a 5mm former with tuning slug. Transmit/receive switching makes use of the normally closed t/r relay contact (NC) available on the Corsair's accessory connected (short-circuit to ground on receive, open-circuit on transmit). The rest of the circuitry is fairly self-explanatory."

Bert Grayson, G3EVP, adds a further note arising out of the notes on the construction of the G4AUZ vfo, but which applies to any unit in which high-Q is desirable. G4UAZ built his unit on Veroboard and melted some candle wax over the coil, the tuned-circuit fixed capacitors and other nearby oscillator components in order to anchor the components and prevent short-term drift due to draughts around individual components. G3EVP, however, points out that many years ago he experimented with several materials for this purpose. With respect to achieving a high-Q coil, candle fat came down near the bottom of the list. If memory has served him correctly, a coil with a Q of around 140 with no impregnation came right

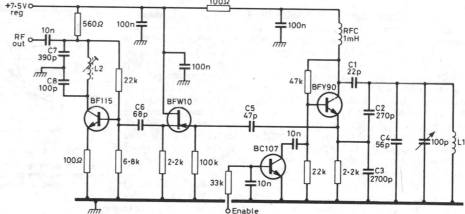

Fig 4. 5 to 5·5MHz external vfo built by G3SJX for use with a Corsair transceiver, but also suitable for use with many equipments having 5 to 5·5MHz analogue vfo systems

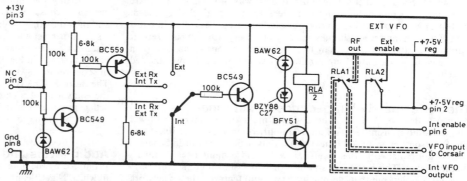

Fig 5. Internal/external vfo switching for the Ten Tec Corsair and the vfo shown in Fig 4

down to about 28 when impregnated with candle wax. He also tested sealing wax, shellac etc, as at the time he had access to a wave-winder and a high-quality Q-meter. He does not mention whether any of the alternatives proved significantly better. How about polystyrene dope?

G3EVP also notes that although extension spindle rods are now virtually unobtainable, a No 3 knitting needle can prove ideal for this purpose. It is slightly larger than a 0·25in spindle but can easily be rubbed down. A No 4 needle is just too small. Knitting needles are readily obtainable in alloy or plastic.

Clutter clunk? Synthetic voices?

At Bangor, a Dutch amateur, F Klinker, a QRP cw enthusiast, told me that in the last two or three years there has been a marked revival of interest in cw operation in the Netherlands. Similarly, in the London area one hears more new callsigns on groundwave on 7 and 14MHz cw than a few years ago. Could it be that the message is beginning to get through that manual cw and "plain ordinary speech" are the two fundamental modes most suited to amateur radio operation?—and tend to remain of lasting appeal to most operators. Keyboard and automatic data systems certainly offer interesting technical and software challenges, but once working satisfactorily can soon lose appeal to those who do not have large quantities of information to exchange but just wish to enjoy casual contacts or regular skeds. I hope that does not sound too much like the airing of personal prejudices. Rather it is a question of horses for courses—cw and 'phone may be slow nags but they do stay the course!

In a letter to *QST*, Charles P Krause, N7ESJ, puts it on a higher plane. He writes: "The centurions of ancient Rome, during the decline of their empire, sought to preserve Roman civilization and culture against the barbaric hordes.

"During the last quarter of the 20th century, a dwindling number of amateur and professional radiotelegraph operators seek to keep the Morse spirit alive during a time of encroachment by 'high tech', high-speed, fully-automated systems of communication.

"It is essential to preserve the cultured and civilized tones of the radiotelegraph signal as compared to the totally mechanical, barbaric, uncivilized and uncultured sounds of clutter-clunk, churgle, grunt, chirp-chirp, beep, oink, splutt, honk, hoot, howl, whine and buzz of high-tech communications . . . heralding the decline and fall of American civilization."

There is a similar threat facing phone operators. It was pointed out at Bangor that speech takes at least a 3kHz spectrum bandwidth (or more if you use what Professor Gosling calls "Armstrong's nightmare child", ie fm). On the other hand, control signals from a digital vocoder for reproduction from a voice synthesizer can use less bandwidth than a 100-baud teleprinter. As voice synthesis develops, "high-tech" and the pressure on the radio-spectrum will give us radiotelephone systems comprising automatic digitization and bit-reduction of speech, narrowband data link, with synthesized speech output that may (or may not) sound similar to the original speaker, though possibly adding a hint of a Japanese accent even to local contacts. However, even if synthesized speech can be improved to give us a recognizable rather than a purely synthesized "voice", we may have to learn not to talk in "connected" speech but as though giving dictation to a machine, ie in a "disconnected" manner.

Even Shakespeare's sonnets will sound pretty uncivilized: "Shall . . I . . com-pare . . . thee . . to . . a . . sum-mer's day . . . thou . . art . . more love-ly . . and . . more . . tem-per-ate . . . Rough . . winds . . do . . shake . . the . . dar-ling . . buds . . of . . May . . "

By comparison, even the Donald Duck noises of ssb may come to sound civilized. And what price amplitude modulation? Talking to machines and computers seems a rather sterile and antisocial way of passing one's spare time—though I notice that quite a few research groups (including a team at Hull University) are working towards digital speech that will fit into less than 100Hz channels, yet simple enough to be used with manpack sets. It would certainly allow more than 15 simultaneous phone contacts in each 3kHz channel—but only, I am afraid, with depersonalized, disconnected speech.

The series-parallel impedance transformer

Warren B Bruene, W5OLY (who designed many of the famous post-war Collins Radio transmitters and linear amplifiers, including the 30K-1 and 30S-1) introduces in *QST* (June 1986) an attractive form of impedance-transforming network that features wide and symmetrical bandpass characteristics. This is the series-parallel network shown in Fig 6(a).

W5OLY points out that, despite its very useful features, the s-p network is virtually unknown as a superior form of LC impedance transformation

circuit with potentially many applications in amateur radio. He writes: "It is hard to understand how this network has escaped wider recognition and usage for so long. It deserves a place beside the popular L, T and pi networks. I make no claim for originating the circuit, but perhaps some of the relationships have not been published previously. There are many ways to use this basic network, which simply behaves as two resonant circuits with a perfect transformer between them. Now that the s-p network has been introduced to you, perhaps you have a good application for putting it to work."

In his article he suggests that this impedance transformation circuit has been used in filter design, but it does not seem to be well known by transmitter, receiver and antenna-coupler designers. The s-p network uses four elements in contrast to the two of an L network and three in a T or pi network. It has the properties of a series-resonant circuit on the low resistance side, and a parallel-resonant circuit on the high resistance side.

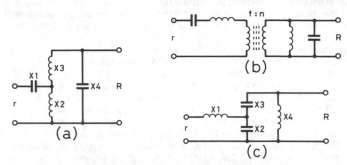

Fig 6. (a) Basic s-p (series-parallel) network configuration. (b) Equivalent circuit for the s-p network. (c) Reversing the sign of the reactances results in this alternative form of the s-p network

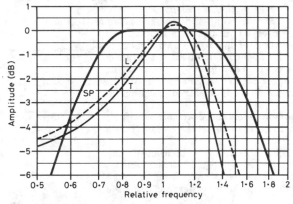

Fig 7. Relative responses for s-p, T and pi networks connected to a voltage source, showing the wide symmetrical bandpass characteristics of the s-p network. Actual s-p response is affected by the Q1/Q2 ratio

It provides a geometrically symmetrical bandpass response and zero phase delay at the centre frequency.

The designer may choose any desired impedance step-up (or step-down by reversing the input and output connections). The value of a single element is chosen with care (since this determines the frequency response) and then the other values are calculated as described in W5OLY's article. As for other networks, the signs of all reactances can be reversed, which means in practice that inductors can be replaced by capacitors, and vice versa, as shown in Fig 4(c). Component value relationships are: X2 and X3 in series resonate with X4, while X2 and X3 in parallel resonate with X2. The ratio -X4/X3 is equal to the voltage step-up ratio, n. The network is the equivalent of a classical form of two-pole bandpass filter. The *QST* article provides detailed information on the calculation of element values without resorting to complex mathematics.

Audio levels and "tinnitus"—a warning

Prompted by the notes in the June *TT* on morse and the hard-of-hearing, in which Nigel Neame, ex-G2AUB, warned those with partial hearing not to listen on headphones with excessive audio levels, I added that in my opinion anyone using headphones—no matter what the state of their hearing—should use some form of automatic peak audio limiting, such as that provided by a pair of back-to-back diodes. Reg Taylor, G3AVQ, draws attention to yet another reason why you should avoid overloud noises near your ears. He writes:

"May I suggest a further warning. Even if loud signals do not impair or destroy hearing they can cause 'tinnitus', otherwise known as 'ringing in the ears' or 'noises in the head'. Being a sufferer myself since May 1979, I did for a while act as a research patient for the Royal National Institute for the Deaf. I learned then that not only is excessive noise one cause of tinnitus but that it may not manifest itself until years after exposure to the noise (mine could have been caused by second world war gunfire and there is, I believe, an association of wartime air gunners who suffer from it). I have read that it affects as many as 17 per cent of the population, a figure that may well go up dramatically when the effects of the Walkman-type portable tape cassette machines begin to show! In my case, tinnitus takes the form of a constant, 24h/day, 7kHz purish tone at a level of S4 to S5 (on a 1 to 9 scale). For others the frequency may be in another part of the audio spectrum and may be intermittent rather than continuous. Whatever form it takes I can assure *TT* readers that it is something to be avoided if possible."

The 10·1MHz band

A considerable number of readers have commented, some constructively others abusively, on the suggestion (*TT* August) that it is time to consider whether a small segment of the narrow 10·1MHz band might logically be used for ssb, if only to encourage more amateurs to use this valuable band than do at present. I have to admit that virtually all those who took the trouble to write to me were highly critical of this proposal and of the technical justifications put forward by G6XN. While, personally, I have no wish to use ssb on this band, I make no apologies for providing a forum for G6XN's views, remembering that among many other feats, he was the first person in this country to draw attention to chordal hop.

Several correspondents have pointed out that such discussion is a little academic, since the main reason for the under-utilization of the band has always been the presence of so many high-power "primary users", ie the fixed (point-to-point) commercial service. The amateur allocation is strictly on a secondary, non-interference basis. It remains a paradox that for much of the time the spectrum just below 10·1MHz or just above 10·15MHz seems far less crowded with commercial signals than 10·1 to 10·15MHz! The 1986 edition of Joerg Klingenfuss's *Guide to Utility Stations* lists no less than 19 fixed-service stations between 10,100 and 10,150kHz. These include cw, rtty, fax and ssb stations, many of them concerned with the meteo (weather) service, and many putting strong signals into the UK for much of the time.

One of the problems is that commercial stations, in order to keep their channel open, often spend hours "idling". It has been shown by various professional investigations that in Europe after dark it is unusual, at least in sunspot minimum periods, to find, below the muf, *any* interference-free gaps exceeding about 200Hz.

David Sergeant, G3YMC, one of those firmly against any use of ssb on this band, points out that since it is a secondary allocation to amateurs there is little likelihood that the long-established high-power rtty, fax etc commercial stations will move out in the foreseeable future. This means that in reality only about half the band, or about 25kHz, is actually usable by amateurs. He feels that if ssb stations were encouraged to use the top end of the band, they would soon be forced to spread downwards until they occupied virtually the entire available spectrum. He accepts, nevertheless, that the band is seriously under-utilized at present. He believes that more cw activity would be generated by accepting 10·1MHz contacts for "award" purposes—though, like others, he feels strongly that the band should continue to be kept clear of "contest" operation.

Several readers doubt whether we are ever likely to see the use of notch and narrowband filters effective enough to permit spectrum sharing between cw and ssb. Some dismiss the very idea as nonsensical; my own opinion is that cw operators might come off better than ssb operators in such a situation!

Phil Stevens, G3SES, a regular user of 10·1MHz, notes that one reason for the lack of cw activity is the continued absence of Russian stations that provide so significant an element of the cw activity on 7, 14 and 21MHz. He also believes that the widespread use on other bands of trapped dipoles and trapped verticals not designed for 10·1MHz discourages use of the band. His more provocative suggestion (no letters to me about this *please*) is that the Class B licence should be scrapped and replaced with a cw-only 25W "novice" licence for 1·8, 10, 18, 24 and 28MHz. In his view this would ensure a better standard of cw operation and more use generally of hf. ☐

Technical Topics
by Pat Hawker, G3VA

Exactly 50 years ago, on 2 November, 1936, the world's first regular public service of high-definition (then 240 and 405 lines) television broadcasting began from Alexandra Palace, London. A few weeks before, as a schoolboy, I was one of the 100,000 visitors to the 1936 Radiolympia who had filed past an anonymous display of small tv screens that accorded a preview of the new novelty, infinitely superior to the earlier 30-line all-mechanical system.

TV was a slow starter with 10in and 12in sets costing almost as much as a small car. Only 2,000 sets were sold in the first 18 months of the service, later perking up to reach a bare 20,000 by 1 September, 1939 when the BBC service closed for the duration of the war.

Within a matter of weeks of the opening of Ally Pally, the late H A M Clark, G6OT, was writing in the *T&R Bulletin* (forerunner of *Radio Communication*) on cures for interference to television arising from the third harmonic of amateur 14MHz transmitters. Unfortunately, tvi is a problem that has never really gone away, although today in the UK the more serious emc problems are often concerned with other forms of consumer electronics and domestic appliances.

TV broadcasting created enormous demand for vhf, uhf and shf spectrum. Yet, despite the problems it brought to amateur radio, it has always for most of us been a love-hate relationship. For a considerable number of us it has even paid our salaries! Together with radar (rdf, radiolocation) it brought about the mass-production of components, valves, cathode-ray tubes and, later, solidstate devices suitable for use above 30MHz. So if sometimes we wish our neighbours were not so obsessed by the one-eyed monster, and that set makers would do more to give their products better immunity (see below), we can still wish tv a happy anniversary and admit that it was an invention that changed the world.

The old enemy—tvi

Interference to television receivers arising from radiated spurious signals on or near the frequency of the tv channels is far less common in the UK, with its uhf tv, than problems arising from breakthrough of strong local signals at frequencies far removed from those used by tv. The UK problem is essentially one of strong signals driving one or more of the tv receiver stages into non-linearity. UK amateurs, faced with a tvi or bci problem would be well advised to obtain a free copy of the DTI's useful 28-page booklet "How to improve television and radio reception" (which should be obtainable from main Post Offices).

In the USA, with both vhf and uhf tv channels, work is continuing on investigating emc problems that arise from signals on similar, or roughly similar frequencies, to the wanted tv channel. There is for example, a specific problem (for which amateurs are in no way responsible) that arises with vhf tv Channel 6 (vision carrier 83·25MHz, sound carrier 87·75MHz) and the educational vhf/fm radio stations which use 88 to 92MHz. Apparently, in many parts of the USA these two services have "been battling for years for supremacy on tv screens" according to a paper by L H Hoke of NAP (North American Philips) in *IEEE Trans on Consumer Electronics* (Vol CE-32, No 3, August 1986, pp290–294). In other words, the radio broadcasts cause patterning on tv screens on Channel 6. Of interest to UK amateurs is that this problem—plus the American decision to allow the land-mobile radio service to share parts of the uhf tv spectrum with tv, subject to various constraints—is leading to detailed investigation of the various interference mechanisms, the effect of the strength of the desired and undesired signals, the use of varactors in tv tuners, and the ways in which tv receivers might be made less vulnerable to unwanted rf signals.

The next paper in the same issue of the *IEEE Trans,* "Interference problems in proposed spectrum sharing between fm land mobile radio and uhf television" by Jouke Rypkema of Zenith Electric (pp 295–299), bears this out. Rypkema notes the large spread in performance measured on different tv receivers, and suggests that "many receivers could be improved if manufacturers fully understood the reasons for performance differences and were to invest the time and money to improve designs". He provides a detailed mathematical analysis of the effects of non-linearity, including intermodulation products and other spurious responses. His suggestions for reducing susceptibility to out-of-band signals include:

(a) Reduction in second harmonic content of the local oscillator to improve the rejection of signals at half-i.f.

(b) Balanced mixer design directed at reducing interference mechanisms.

(c) Development of higher-Q varactor diodes with adequate capacitance ratio and tight tracking tolerances to improve pre-mixer selectivity.

In connection with (c) many American uhf tuners still use variable-capacitance tuning and have no signal-frequency rf amplifier. This results in poor weak-signal performance (in the USA uhf tv is regarded as less important than vhf tv) but such tuners tend to have significantly better strong-signal performance in terms of dynamic range than varactor-type tuners.

Hoke puts emphasis on improvement of video detectors in which much of the Channel 6 / fm-radio interference is generated, noting that "the balanced multiplier circuit which makes up the synchronous or quasi-synchronous video detector in most currently available i.f. detector ic devices produces a much lower level of beat products than the older conventional diode detector. The internal balance of the multiplier is a critical parameter in lowering the cross-modulation product generated in this stage".

For the future, he notes that several devices and circuit concepts are being developed which may yield further improvement to a tv's ability to reject interference from fm signals. These include:

(1) Improved saw (surface-acoustic wave) i.f filters with lower out-of-band ripple. Some current saw filters have out-of-band lobes as high as −40dB from picture-carrier level while others have no lobes higher than −50dB.

(2) Adoption of double-balanced mixer techniques to improve dynamic range (although prototype designs by Texas Instruments were developed in the 'seventies using mesfets and double-balanced mixers, these ideas have never been put into production by the set-makers).

(3) Double rather than single conversion front-ends to improve selectivity, with ic devices providing this at low cost.

Suggestion (3) may seem surprising since for communications receivers designed for wide dynamic range and absence of spurious responses it is generally assumed the few conversions the better. In this case it seems to be a question of achieving better selectivity characteristics and so rejecting signals in adjacent or nearly adjacent channels.

Of course, there is not much that we as radio amateurs can do to lessen the susceptibility of neighbours' tv sets except by the addition of external filters. Nevertheless, it is worth keeping an eye on all such investigations. Who knows, we might persuade the DTI and BREMA that tv sets could be made much more immune to unwanted signals than the current models!

Military manpack with bilateral amplifiers

Fig 3 of the September *TT* showed a block diagram of the Plessey PTR5300 taken from the paper presented at the IERE receiver conference last July. However, as the author of the paper, D Holman, points out, the diagram was misleadingly captioned since this was the "before modification" version. The later substitution of the reversible amplifier described in *TT* eliminated eight relays and four amplifiers. He sends along the diagram (Fig 1) of the modified version (not in the original paper) and this gives a clear indication of the useful simplification made possible by adopting the

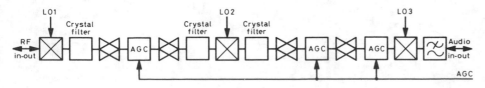

Fig 1. This is the block diagram of the modified Plessey PTR5300 military hf manpack transceiver fitted with the reversible amplifiers described in the Septembr *TT*. This diagram should be compared with the September Fig 3 which was the original version requiring eight relays and four more amplifier stages

bilateral amplifiers. This diagram should be compared with Fig 3 of the September issue.

He adds: "With regard to my 'manpack as unwanted junk' phrase, I admit to some hyperbole, but of course the intention was to draw the attention to us lovers of knob twiddling to the fact that not everyone shares our delights, especially when there is a rather more urgent task in hand (survival). I like to imagine the Consumers Association carrying out a test on hf transceivers as they might do for a dishwasher—after all, not many of us have a craving for washing dishes!"

Project 6L6 and the pi-tank

Impedance transforming networks such as the pi, L and T networks have long formed the basis of antenna tuning units and rf coupling circuits. The pi network with its three circuit elements was first introduced to radio amateurs in the form of the "Collins universal coupler" by Arthur Collins, W0CXX, founder of Collins Radio in the 'thirties, in both balanced and unbalanced versions. To the best of my knowledge the first person to conceive and put into practice the idea of using the pi-network as an unbalanced output circuit for the final stage of a transmitter was John Brown, G3EUR. This was for the 3 Mk1 (ie "B-1") SOE suitcase transmitter of 1941-2, which used a single 6L6G power crystal-oscillator and was the predecessor of the well-known two-stage (EL32co-6L6Gpa) 3 Mk2 (ie "B-2") suitcase transmitter of 1943-4 which similarly used the pi network.

G3EUR tells me that his 1941 "Project 6L6" drew upon the 1939 "Runt 60" QST design (see TT May 1986, Fig 2) but with the use of a pi-output matching arrangement to permit the transmitter to be used effectively with random-length (ie non-resonant) antennas.

He still believes that the B-1 arrangement (Fig 2) represents the most versatile one-valve transmitter, always provided that the crystals used are capable of handling up to about 50mA of current without cracking or mode-jumping. As an experiment he has run a B-1 from an 800V (key-up) power supply unit and obtained 50W cw output.

It should, however, not be forgotten that power oscillators generate considerable harmonic output. A pi-tank may help reduce this, but additional emc precautions are likely to be needed even if such a rig does not actually cause any interference to uhf television. You don't want replies on 14, 21 or 28MHz from your 7MHz "CQ" calls!

Universal interference suppressor?

How many times have you cursed when a loud interfering signal has suddenly appeared right on top of the station you are working or listening to? Most of us have learned to accept such situations as an inevitable part of amateur radio, but the professionals, particularly those concerned with military (C³I) communications, regard them as a technical challenge which needs to be overcome. In these days of "electronic warfare" they face the problem of intentional jamming in the form of electronic counter measures (ecm). Techniques for receiving a *weaker* wanted signal from under strong interference are becoming a recognized part of electronic-counter-counter-measures (eccm).

Certainly various approaches are possible, some already well known. A good directional receiving antenna can place a deep null in the direction of the unwanted signal provided always that this is not arriving along the same bearing as the wanted signal. The frame or ferrite-rod antennas despite (or perhaps because of) their simplicity, can be very effective—particularly at the lower mf/hf region of the spectrum—manually steering the nulls by rotating the antenna for maximum rejection of the unwanted signals. It is also perhaps worth remembering that frame antennas are less susceptible to local electrical interference than conventional antennas.

Slightly up the scale of complexity is the technique of phasing out an interfering signal by using two separate antennas with the aid of an electronic steering control box placed ahead of the receiver (see TT August 1982, pp684-5 or QST October 1982, pp28-32). A much more sophisticated form of electronic steering of rejection nulls is possible with computer-type adaptive arrays, though these are not exactly within amateur budgets! A lot of work is going on at the moment in devising systems that automatically identify wanted or unwanted signals by their modulation and other characteristics, and it would be feasible to hitch these up to either automatic d/f systems or automatic null-steering arrays.

But is there anything that could be done once the unwanted interference on the same frequency as the wanted signal has actually got into the signal path of the receiver? Apparently the answer, in some circumstances, could be yes. This would involve the use of notch-filter and signal-cancellation techniques, and would apply to signals on exactly the same frequency that no degree of receiver selectivity could separate and to signals arriving from precisely the same bearing, so defeating even the most sophisticated forms of electronic null steering.

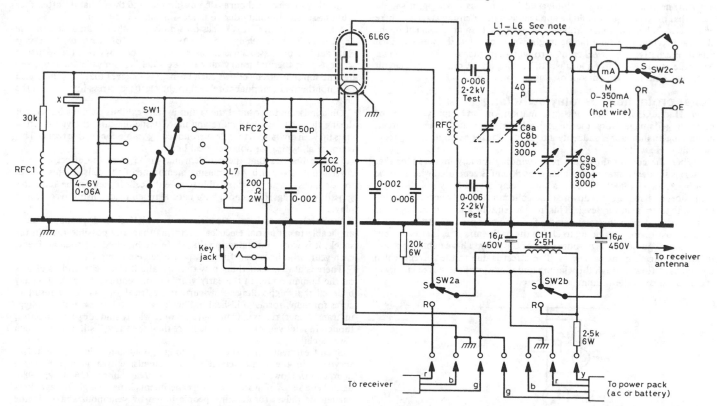

Fig 2. Circuit diagram of the single-stage 6L6G transmitter that formed part of SOE's 1941 Type 3 Mk1 ("B·1") suitcase transmitter-receiver designed by John Brown, G3EUR, and believed to be the first time that a pi-network was used as a transmitter tank circuit rather than as an antenna coupler. Operated from a 400V psu it provided an output on the crystal fundamental frequency of 14 to 18W and 12 to 14W harmonic in the tritet configuration. Plug-in tank coils with a coil reversing arrangement covered 3·5 to 16MHz. Switch 1 was for 3·5 to 4·4MHz crystals in position 1. Harmonic output in position 2. 4·4 to 5·8MHz fundamentals in position 3; harmonic output in position 4; 5·8 to 8MHz crystals in position 5; and harmonic output in position 6. C8b/C9b are brought in on the lower bands by reversing the coil. Component values were those used before the days of "preferred" values

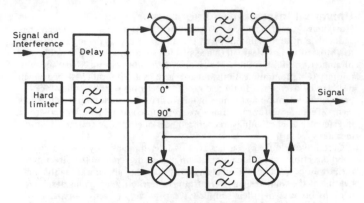

Fig 3. Universal interference suppressor as outlined by J H Roberts of Plessey at the recent IERE Radio Receivers Conference

At the recent Bangor radio receivers conference (see *TT* September), J H Roberts of Plessey presented a paper "A survey of receiver designs for interference suppression". In this he outlined, among other techniques, a "universal interference suppressor" technique that looks very promising. It was claimed that, under favourable circumstances, the system can reduce the unwanted components of the *stronger* of two incoming signals by as much as 50 to 60dB, permitting the weaker wanted signal to be received.

Fig 3 shows the basic idea. The incoming "signal plus interference" is directed along two paths (at i.f), one of which includes a hard limiter. This has the effect (as for the well-known "capture effect" of FM) of greatly suppressing the weaker (wanted) signal. We then have two paths; one still carrying "signal plus interference", the other virtually "interference only". It is then possible in this arrangement to notch out the interference components by combining the two signals in such a manner that they are of similar amplitude and 180° out-of-phase. The unwanted interference components cancel out and we are left with the wanted signal, previously many decibels under the interference! It sounds almost too good to be true. I suspect that in practice it may not be as easy as might appear from Fig 3.

The system is intended for such applications as eccm for military vhf and uhf (fm) networks, but if the "universal" tag means anything, it should mean that the technique should be applicable in other circumstances. There would clearly be additional problems in using such an arrangement for hf sky-wave reception, where fading might well mean that the wanted signal might alternatively be weaker or stronger than the interference signal. Nevertheless, it all seems an idea worth keeping an eye on, since the circuit elements could probably be put on one or two chips.

Zener protection for relay switching

Peter Hart, G3SJX, provides information on an improved way of preventing damage from the large back-emf generated when a circuit containing an inductor is suddenly interrupted, as for example during relay switching. He writes:

"When the current through a relay winding (or any inductor for that matter) is suddenly interrupted, a large back-emf is generated which can be well in excess of 1,000V for even a small relay. For a relay switched by a transistor, avalanche breakdown at the collector normally occurs, limiting the voltage to a lower level. This is undesirable and can damage the transistor (and even the relay winding). A common cure is to connect a diode across the relay winding to clamp the back-emf. This is effective but noticeably degrades the drop-out speed of the relay. This can be important in such applications as cw keyers. The effect is due to the current which continues to flow through the winding and diode until the stored energy in the inductance of the winding is dissipated.

"Alternatively, a capacitor can be placed across the winding to limit the peaks to a lower level, but this can degrade the pull-in time of the relay where the driver transistor is unable to supply the high peak charging current of the capacitor.

"A simple solution is to limit the back emf to a suitably low level but not to clip completely. This can be done by adding a zener diode as shown in Fig 4. An ordinary diode is required to prevent forward conduction of the zener when the relay is energized. Experiments conducted on a commonly-used small Varley plug-in relay with four-pole changeover contacts and 12V 185Ω winding gave the following results when used with a 12V supply:

Damping	Peak volts	Pull-in time	Drop-out time
None	800V	7ms	2ms
Diode only	12V	7ms	10ms
Diode + 10V zener	22V	7ms	4ms
Diode + 22V zener	34V	7ms	3ms
Diode + 33V zener	45V	7ms	2·5ms
1μF capacitor	45V	8ms	3ms

"In circumstances where switching speed is important, it is vital to ensure that the drive voltage does not drop below the rated voltage of the relay winding. For the Varley relay, reducing the voltage from 12 to 9V doubled the pull-in time to 14msc. However, increasing the voltage to 16V reduced the pull-in time by only a small amount to 5ms."

Electricity, burns and snake bites

In previous items on safety in the shack, I have recalled the old adage that "it's volts that jolts but mils (mA) that kills". In *TT* (January 1985, pp32–3) it was noted that the risk of death by electrocution relates largely to the current passing through the body in the region of the heart and whether this is over a period long enough to cause "fibrillation". This condition is where the heart is caused to malfunction, reducing or stopping the circulation of the blood. Such a condition very quickly causes permanent brain damage, if not death. Removal of the current does not automatically cause the heart to return to its normal rhythm, and sophisticated medical attention is required quickly. It was noted that the IEC has attempted to relate the danger to the current and time, and defined five "zones" of increasing danger (Fig 3 in *TT* January 1985).

However, there is another type of fatal or near-fatal accident involving heavy currents not passing through the cardiac region but resulting in severe burns. It has been noted in the USA that many of those admitted to hospitals with electrical burns do not survive, and those that do often face a life of severe disability due to the loss of one or more limbs.

Martin Atherton, G3ZAY, has drawn my attention to an article in *The MIT Report* (June 1986, pp5–6). As the result of work by Professor Raphael Lee of Massachusetts Institute of Technology (MIT) the article suggests that thermal injury may not be solely responsible for the tissue destruction that often follows such burns. He believes that there may also be a nonthermal component related to the electrical stress imposed on the cells.

On admission to hospital the victim usually exhibits obvious burns, but during the next few days more and more tissue dies and the victim often ends up with divitalized muscle surrounded by viable connective tissue. This is not at all typical of non-electrical burns.

Dr Lee believes that the problem may arise from the effect of large current pulses rupturing the plasma membrane of the cells. If this proves to be the case, it might be possible to save the cells if they can be kept alive (possibly by drugs) long enough for natural repair mechanisms to come into play.

While this is still to some extent speculative, and probably more applicable to industrial electrical accidents than any possible risks in the shack, it is worth remembering that there are hundreds of such accidents each year, with linesmen, firemen, policemen etc at most risk.

There is always something new to learn about electricity and its effects on the human body. In the early years of the century, it was still widely believed that high-voltage, low-current electrical shocks could result in cures for many forms of ill-health. Shocking coils (vibrator unit with step-up transformer) running from batteries were widely sold for such purposes, though in later years became little more than the "toys" still around when I was a child.

Such treatment fell into disrepute long-ago although, in extreme form, surviving in the controversial electro-convulsive treatment for severe depression. However, a recent report in *The Lancet* (26 July, 1986) describes a series of most successful experiments in using high-voltage, low-current dc pulses for treating people bitten by venomous snakes in the eastern Amazon jungle of Ecuador, where some four per cent of all deaths are due to snakebite and where more than half of all adult males have been bitten more than once.

In 34 cases dc pulses of 20–25kV at under 1mA were applied to the site of snake bites within 30min of the bite; in 10–15min after such treatment

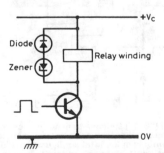

Fig 4. The use of a zener plus diode to reduce back-emf during relay switching results in faster drop-out times than when only a diode is used

all pain had gone and none of the usual after-effects developed. Most of the patients, all of whom survived, were able to go home after an hour. Seven people who refused the electric shock treatment showed the classic complications, and two required life-saving amputations. A small portable unit operating from a 9V battery is now being developed.

While there are not many dxpeditions to the Amazon jungle, an interesting sideline is that this form of electrical treatment appears to be equally effective in dealing with bee stings and insect bites. Indeed, the work followed a report in a local American newspaper that an Illinois farmer who was hyperallergic to bee stings had found that applying such dc pulses to the site of his bee stings prevented his usually severe reactions from developing. The international medical team that worked in South America included a member of the London School of Hygiene & Tropical Medicine.

Hands-free mobile microphone

The warning in the July *TT* that the next edition of the *Highway Code* is likely to include a specific recommendation that handheld microphones should not be used in vehicles while driving, has prompted Derek Haden, G4WXN, to send along some details of a low-cost but effective mobile microphone.

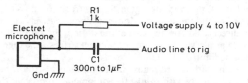

Fig 5. Basic arrangement of electret mobile microphone used by G4WXN

Heart of the system is an electret microphone module available in the Tandy stores at less than £1. Only a few other components are required: R1 and C1 as shown in Fig 5. These are soldered onto a small piece of Veroboard and mounted in a small plastic box together with a switch for ptt operation (and battery if necessary). About 2m of audio coaxial cable is used to connect the microphone insert to the Veroboard via a small hole in the box (alternatively plugs and sockets to choice could be used). The connections to the back of the microphone should be made carefully to avoid damaging it. The connections can then be covered and made to look neat and professional by the use of the outer case of a phone plug (preferably a plastic one as this will have some flexibility). The microphone will be found to be virtually the same size as the open end of the plug cover, providing a good push fit. Connections out of the box to the rig can be soldered to the Veroboard, and then taken out of the box to a suitable microphone plug. As can be seen from Fig 5, the electret microphone requires a suitable voltage to be applied, from about 4 to 10V. Many mobile transceivers provide a stabilized voltage output for accessories. The Yaesu FT77 has 8V available at the rear of the rig; the FT290R has 5·5V on one pin of the microphone socket. Should such a supply not be available, a small PP3 battery can be used, and in view of the low current requirement should last for a reasonable time. Nominal impedance is about 1,000Ω, which in the vast majority of cases will not require additional impedance matching circuitry.

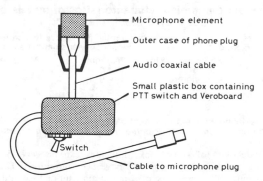

Fig 6. Physical arrangement of the mobile microphone

The microphone can then be attached to the operator via a tie clip or attached to the seat belt of the car or on a boom attached to headphones.

In his own case, G4WXN uses a short length of 5mm plastic hydraulic pipe which is firm but not rigid and can be moulded to shape using a hair dryer so that it forms a halter arrangement which slips loosely around the neck and is fairly inconspicuous. (If suitable pipe cannot be found locally you can contact G4WXN on 0953 607068, evenings).

He has used this microphone arrangement on both an FT290R and FT77

with excellent reports. The microphone is sensitive but does not seem to pick up excessive amounts of background noise.

Non-ionizing radiation levels

The long-standing debate over "safe levels" of human exposure to non-ionizing radiation from transmitting antennas has taken another turn with the issuing during July of new draft proposals by the National Radiological Protection Board (NRPB) in a consultative document. Although their recommendations differ in a number of respects from the now-current American (ANSI) standards, the NRBP follows ANSI practice in recommending lower levels at vhf (30 to 300MHz) where the body tends to act as a half-wave dipole.

In the draft proposals, a distinction is made between "occupational" levels and those to which the general public should be exposed. Both sets of limits are related to a maximum exposure of an average of 5h/day. The recommended public level at vhf is a maximum of 4W/m².

John Rhind, G6JR, in drawing my attention to the new proposals, notes that the public safe limit could be exceeded several metres away from legal-limit high-gain 430 and 144MHz antennas. Since the NRPB now considers that excessive non-ionizing radiation can result not only in thermal effects but also "disruption of behaviour effects", G6JR wonders whether this could account for some of the behaviour noted during high-power contests!

It has been pointed out on a number of occasions that it is not a simple matter to determine the intensity of near-field radiation from vhf, or even more so from hf antennas since these are not by any means the "point sources" used for far-field calculations.

A paper written by a staff member of the FCC in *IEEE Transactions on Broadcasting* Vol BC-31, No 4, December 1985, pages 81–7, shows how the current ANSI limits affect radio broadcasters using medium-wave a.m or vhf/fm transmitters: see Tables 1 and 2. It includes tables showing for vhf/fm the minimum height above ground for omnidirectional antennas radiating effective radiated powers (erp) from 0·5 to 200kW. For a vhf single dipole antenna and 0·5kW erp there can be a worst-case need for a minimum height of 4·1m. For 3kW erp the worst case height increases to 10m.

For medium waves, the normal broadcast practice is to use a monopole (vertical) antenna with maximum current at ground level. In this case the ANSI safe level is reached, with a 500W transmitter, rather less than 2m from the base of the antenna. At 1kW this becomes 3m; at 2·5kW around 4m; and at 50kW some 12m.

Table 1. ANSI Radio Frequency Protection Guides

Frequency range (MHz)	Electric field strength E^2 (V²/m²)	Magnetic field strength H^2 (A²/m²)	Power density (mW/cm²)
0·3–3	400,000	2·5	100
3–30	4,000 (900/f²)	0·025 (900/f²)	900/f²
30–300	4,000	0·025	1·0
300–1,500	4,000 (f/300)	0·035 (f/300)	f/300
1,500–100,000	20,000	0·125	5·0

Note
f = frequency in megahertz
E^2 = electric field squared
H^2 = magnetic field squared
V²/m² = volts squared per metre squared
A²/m² = amperes squared per metre squared
mW/cm² = milliwatts per centimetre squared

Table 2. Distances (in metres) at which fields from medium-wave stations with monopole antennas are predicted to fall below various electric field strengths

Electric field strength (V/m)	Magnetic field strength (A/m)	Transmitter power (kW) 1·00	0·50	0·25	0·10
25	0·06	27	22	18	13
50	0·13	18	14	11	8
75	0·19	13	11	8	6
100	0·25	11	9	7	5
150	0·38	8	6	5	4
200	0·50	7	5	4	3
300	0·75	5	4	3	<2
400	1·00	4	3	<2	<2
500	1·25	3	3	<2	<2
632 (ANSI)	1·58 (ANSI)	3	<2	<2	<2
750	1·88	3	<2	<2	<2
1,000	2·50	<2	<2	<2	<2

Notes: (1) This table can be used for any medium frequency or electrical height. Note that ANSI safe limits decrease between 3 and 30MHz.

(2) The entries in this table apply to *both* electric field strength and the corresponding magnetic field strength (assuming impedance of free-space equals 400Ω).

Tests carried out near broadcasting stations in Honolulu and Seattle showed that at some points accessible to the public, the ANSI levels were exceeded. ANSI makes no distinction between "occupational" and "public" levels.

High levels of electric field strength (V/m) and magnetic field strength (A/m) near transmitting antennas are clearly unavoidable, though in most cases the effects are confined to domestic appliances in the form of emc problems. I suspect that the years ahead will see increasing concern worldwide about non-ionizing radiation levels in residential areas, with signs that emc problems far from being solved are still exploding.

Frank Harris, G4IEY, draws attention to an item that appeared in some Japanese newspapers last June. Headlined "Electronic smog hangs over society" it reported the imminent establishment by the Japanese Ministry of Posts & Telecommunications of a "council on problems of unnecessary radio waves" that was expected to propose "regulation standards" within the next year. While most of us are anxious to see the UK introduce regulations limiting radio-frequency interference from home computers and similar generators of "electronic smog", it has to be recorded that the Japanese newspaper—in noting a number of accidents and problems that have arisen from lack of emc precautions—included several involving amateur radio transmissions which they appear to include in the category of "unnecessary radio waves". I suspect that the days of "Californian kilowatts" may be drawing to a close.

Low-cost rf switching

I must confess that I have never owned or used a coaxial rf switch, either manual or relay operated, though that has never stopped me from switching coaxial cable feedlines between receiver and transmitter or switching between alternative antennas. The reason is simply that on hf it is not necessary to avoid impedance discontinuities over a few inches (or even feet on the lower frequency bands).

As in so many aspects of current amateur practice, there is a strong tendency, particularly among newcomers, always to do things "by the book". The books rightly stress the importance of avoiding impedance discontinuities at uhf and even more so in the microwave region, but seldom mention that below 30MHz there is virtually no likelihood of any swr problems arising in a switch unit. More important than any question of impedance discontinuities is that any switch used in a high-power feedline should be adequately rated for the heavy currents found in 75Ω or 52Ω coaxial cable, even though it is most advisable never to switch rf while power is actually being delivered to the antenna, because of the high-voltage transients generated.

Paul Follini, VE1CZX, in *QST* (August 1986, pp25–7) shows clearly that standard domestic wall-toggle change-over switches, rated at about 15A in North America, when mounted in a standard metal enclosure fitted with three SO-239 sockets make perfectly satisfactory rf switches. This is true both for switching an antenna from transmitter to receiver or for selecting one of two antennas, on all bands up to 30MHz, so saving "some bucks" when compared to a pukka coaxial rf switch. His article includes detailed measurements of reflection coefficient and swr versus return loss made on his low-cost switches. These show that any losses or increase in swr are so small as to be quite insignificant.

I must admit to having once run into problems by using switches of relatively low-current rating (1 or 2A) due to accidentally switching with the line carrying rf power. My reason for using these, rather than standard wall switches, is that they are fitted with much longer paddles than most wall switches and this facilitates rapid and easy switching from transmit to receive when using a separate receiver/transmitter; a question that does not arise with transceivers where rf switching is more likely to be used externally only for selecting antennas. This seldom needs to be done frequently or rapidly. Toggle switches are better than rotary switches for this type of application.

A letter from David Jones, N4JED, in *QST* (July 1986, p 43) warns against using coaxial switches as a lightning protection switch. He writes:

"Not only is it not a lightning protector, it can create a direct path for lightning through your ham gear into the house electrical wiring. I personally know of people who had lightning enter their house through the coaxial cable lead-in from a grounded tower/antenna. In such a system the two-position coaxial switch introduced by MFJ Enterprises would shunt the current to the rig. A grounding coaxial switch is not a substitute for disconnecting your antenna from the rig. Any time there is the slightest chance of a storm, disconnect the antenna, ground and power leads. Don't just turn the coaxial switch. Do not use a coaxial switch as a lightning arrestor. This is not what they are designed for. Keep your rig disconnected from the antenna system when not using it. It is also a good idea for all of us periodically to check our antenna ground system and its connections."

In the UK, where lightning is much less frequent than in some parts of the USA, I suspect there are few of us who keep the rig disconnected when not in use, and the main requirement is to prevent static build up from discharging through the rig; for such purposes spark gaps and the old style of external knife switch is often regarded as adequate.

Lightning hazards

While static discharge is regarded as adequate for modest antenna installations, it cannot be assumed that this is sufficient in the case of major installations, particularly those with high towers in exposed locations. To judge from the illustrations in the journals and from the way in which choice 14MHz dx has become so much more difficult to work in recent years with simple antennas, there is an increasing number of installations where the antenna system is far from modest.

Come a thunderstorm and I feel decidedly less sorry that there is no really high metal tower at my QTH. This has been reinforced by dipping into a large 127-page (A4 format) book published by the European Broadcasting Union: *The protection of broadcasting installations against damage by lightning*. This stresses that protection of transmitting stations "requires a large number of precautions against the effects of direct and indirect lightning strikes and these precautions must be effectively co-ordinated. In the case of direct strikes on any part of the station, the lightning energy must be dispersed harmlessly; in the case of indirect strikes . . . dangerous voltage surges must be limited to tolerable levels".

Few amateur stations are really protected against strikes, but it is most advisable, particularly with solidstate equipment, to prevent the effects of indirect strikes from getting into the equipment. No system can guarantee absolute security. Lightning discharges result in thermal, electrodynamic, electrochemical and electromagnetic-field effects. Massive peak currents with steep wavefronts result in potential differences of several millions of volts and very high electromagnetic field strengths. Towers need to be really effectively earthed when attempting to do more than just provide leakage paths for static build-up, static-charged rain etc. But even static build-up can damage receiver front-ends and solidstate transmitters. Even valve receivers can have their first-stage coils burnt out, and indeed this used to be a common problem with both HRO and AR88 receivers (sometimes from static, sometimes from rf induced from local transmitters at the same site).

The EBU book describes the very formidable requirements for earthing high towers and the associated problem of providing protection against corrosion arising from metals in direct contact with damp or acidic soil; in effect, galvanic cells are formed, resulting in parasitic currents that hasten corrosion. It suggests that this constitutes a serious factor that significantly reduces the long-term effectiveness of earth-electrodes. For direct burial in soil, a solid conductor is less subject to corrosion and more resistant to mechanical stress than a stranded conductor of similar gauge.

Because of the electro-chemical characteristics of different metals, earth-electrodes of copper or steel with copper sheathing should not be bonded to earth-electrodes of more electro-negative materials such as galvanized steel or to other buried steel objects such as pipe work and tanks: see Table 1.

Table 1. Electro-chemical characteristics of metals used for buried electrodes

	Electrode	Potential (V) relative to a saturated copper/copper-sulphate electrode	
Metal	Embedded in	Minimum	Maximum
Copper	Soil	0	−0·1
Steel	Concrete*	−0·1	−0·3
Lead	Soil	−0·4	−0·5
Steel	Soil	−0·5	−0·7
Zinc	Soil	−0·9	−1·1

*For example, foundation reinforcement bars
(Source: *The protection of broadcasting installations against damage by lightning*)

Earth conductivity of some rocky hill sites can be very low, and techniques of "earthing improvement" have been developed. The EBU book points out: "The resistance of a mountain cannot be modified by technical means; it is determined by the natural properties of the substratum and by the weather. Contact and bedding resistance, on the contrary, can be reduced by appropriate measures, termed *earthing improvement,* such as increasing the soil conductivity by injecting highly-conducting solutions and thereby reducing the contact and bedding resistance. Formerly, use was made of saline solutions, although they were very conducive to corrosion. More recently, hygroscopic emulsions have been developed for this purpose. In order to facilitate the penetration of the emulsion into the rock, blasting is sometimes necessary. In the case of high-altitude transmitting stations, where rock of very high resistivity is often found, earthing improvement is in most cases essential. By emulsion injection, lower earthing resistances are obtained, independent of fluctuations in the air temperature and humidity, even where the soil-conductivity is exceptionally low. In very acidic soil, the application of this method will, moreover, provide adequate corrosion protection.

"Care must also be taken that the earth-electrodes are buried below the frost line. The freezing of the soil considerably increases its resistivity; an earthing installation for a power-supply system can have an entirely satisfactory propagation resistance during the warm season, but an unacceptably high one during the winter. For lightning protection earthing systems this is, however, not so important, because the lightning current is impulsive, and in icy ground the surge impedance of an earth-electrode is less than its propagation resistance."

I am not suggesting that amateurs on hill-top sites should start blasting operations or emulsion injection, but the fact remains that if amateurs insist on setting up installations akin to local broadcasting installations, they should be aware of the lengths to which the professionals go to earth their towers. There is also the point that for monopole verticals, where the earth is part of the antenna system, good earthing (or earth radials) is essential to reduce rf power losses.

An isokeraunic contour chart of the world in the EBU book gives the average number of "thunderstorm days" per annum in the various regions. This shows that the Shetland and Orkney Islands have only 1 to 5 such days; Scotland, Ireland and the north of England between 5 and 10. This compares to between 40 to 60 in parts of the mid-west of the USA, up to 100 in the Australian outback, and over 140 thunderstorm-days in some tropical countries. The variation is thus very large, but even in the Shetlands, if you believe in Murphy's Law, there is just a faint possibility that your impressively-high tower may be struck when the rare thunderstorm occurs!

In *QST* (August 1986), Dennis Bodson, W4PWF, begins a series of articles on "Electromagnetic pulses and the radio amateur" condensed from an official National Communications Report. This covers the extremely difficult problem of protecting radio installations from the effects of electromagnetic pulses produced by deliberately or accidentally exploding nuclear devices at high altitudes—a possibility that would seem to have been increased by the work on sdi ('star wars').

NEMP has an even steeper wavefront than lightning, and the survival of all forms of telecommunications equipment, computers etc would be in jeopardy. While nemp protection measures would also serve to provide lightning protection, I cannot help feeling that in a small country like the UK, survival of our gear in a nuclear war or after a nuclear accident is likely to be the least of our worries! For those who think otherwise, a useful start would be to switch back to valves rather than solidstate equipment, but there is little chance of that advice being taken.

The valve that changed everything

Dean Manley, KH6B (*TT* February 1986), in initiating "Project 6L6" reminded us that 1986 is the 50th anniversary of the introduction of the 6L6 beam tetrode by RCA Radiotron. I added that this soon led to the 807 top-cap version for rf as well as af applications and the host of later single and double rf beam tetrodes.

Bill Orr, W6SAI (*Ham Radio*, August 1986, pp43–5), follows up this theme by recalling in detail the evolution of "the tube that changed everything". In doing this he brings to light the reasons why the pre-war 807 was usually a stable valve *without* neutralization. Later this was seldom the case.

It was in 1935 that General Electric (US) developed the idea of "metal"

receiving valves that needed no external screening and granted RCA a manufacturing licence. A team under Otto Schade was already developing a new valve technique that they believed would overcome the relatively poor performance of power valves in terms of low-gain and low-efficiency when used for other than small-signal applications. The electrode structure comprised a tetrode valve using aligned grid and screen electrodes and beam-confining plates connected to the cathode, Fig 7.

The aligned grids and the beam-confining plates had much the same effect as a pentode's suppressor grid in removing the awkward "kink" in the characteristics of the screen-grid tetrode. The kink is caused by the fact that when an electron travelling at considerable velocity strikes the anode, the force of the impact dislodges other electrons into the inter-electrode space and will be attracted to a positively-charged screen electrode during those periods when the anode voltage swings below the screen voltage. This causes a reverse current known as secondary emission to flow between anode and screen. This can be largely overcome by the use of a suppressor grid (pentode) or by the insertion of beam-forming plates whereby electrons emitted by the cathode are directed to those parts of the anode which are at a critical distance from the other electrodes.

So was born the metal 6L6 with its possibility of producing up to about 35W rf (more if unduly punished) as a crystal oscillator. A pair of 6L6s could equally well provide some 25W of audio power with just 400V ht.

The metal valve was rather costly to manufacture, and late in 1936 came the alternative glass 6L6G providing, as has been noted in *TT*, improved rf performance. At the same time the electrodes of the 6L6G were slightly re-arranged and a top-cap anode connection added to form the 807 (6·3V heater) and 1625 (12·6V heater). These early 807s had additional internal insulation to give a maximum voltage rating of 600V, and small shields were added around the base of the stem to reduce internal feedback paths. Amateurs adopted the 6L6 and 807 valves as suitable for power amplification *without* neutralization. A 6L6G—807pa transmitter was described in a number of handbooks in this form. The idea was also adopted for the SCU "Mark 3" transmitter (6V6 co—807 pa) used for many years from about 1938 onwards. The 6V6 was a low-power 6L6.

But after about 1941, when the USA entered the second world war, production of the 807 had to be increased dramatically. As a result the special insulators and internal base stem shields were eliminated to reduce costs and facilitate production. The 807 thus became virtually a "topcap" 6L6G. When amateur activity re-started in 1946, many 807 rf power amplifiers were built to the pre-war designs, intended for the pre-war 807. As a result the 807 was soon found to be unstable above about 10MHz (sometimes with poor layout at much lower frequencies).

I recall an article "Beam tetrodes used as rf amplifiers" by Charles Bryant, G3SB (*RSGB Bulletin*, October 1950, pp135–6) which began:

"When the beam tetrode was introduced some years before the war, it was thought that at last an amplifier was available which did not require to be neutralized. Most amateurs who employed these valves in their transmitters soon found this was not so."

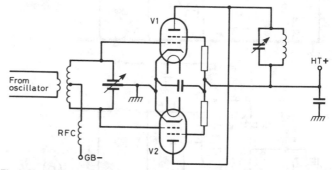

Fig 8. **Neutralized beam-tetrode amplifier arrangement occasionally used in the late 'forties and early 'fifties to overcome the unexpected stability problems brought about to some extent by the cost-cutting design of 807s for wartime mass production. When V2's heater is unpowered, the valve acts as a neutralizing capacitor. When powered, the stage becomes a push-push doubler**

The anode-to-grid capacitance of the 807 was given as 0·2pF and the 6L6 as 0·7pF. G3SB showed a technique culled from *QST* whereby a second 807 (unpowered) formed a neutralizing capacitance: Fig 8. With the heater of V2 powered, the stage converts into an efficient push-push frequency doubler. However, as he pointed out, although 807s were then plentiful and cheap, this arrangement took up quite a bit of space without providing any more rf output in the amplifier mode. Neutralizing an 0·2pF capacitance is not easy. G3SB suggested, as an alternative, the use of a cathode-follower driver, at least for low-power transmitters.

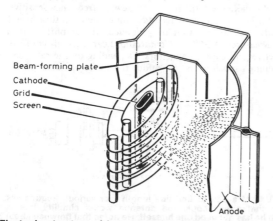

Fig 7. **Electrode structure of beam tetrode with aligned grid and screen electrodes and beam-confining plates connected to the cathode**

Beam-forming plate
Cathode
Grid
Screen
Anode

In the USA and later in Europe the 807 began to fade out and was replaced by the 6146 and the use of capacitance divider neutralization. However, the 6L6G was adapted as a sweep-tube in many early American tv sets with later versions 6LQ6 and 6MJ6 (both of which found considerable use in hf linear amplifiers) and for hi-fi audio amplifiers as the 6L6GC/6L6GB.

Despite the gradual swing to solidstate rf power amplifiers, the majority of hf transmitters in use today continue to use beam tetrodes either in transceivers or in external linear amplifiers or both. An understanding of the ills of valve rf amplifiers remains essential for most radio amateurs—though you would not think so from the RAE syllabus!

Neutralization of rf amplifiers

The notes on parasitic and tptg oscillation and other ills that valve and solidstate rf amplifiers often suffer (*TT*, August, pp570–2) have prompted "Jakey" Gould, G3JKY, to add some further useful advice on neutralization and grounded-grid amplifiers. He writes:

"First of all, I feel Fig 3 of the August *TT* could be a bit misleading. For the makeshift 'capacitor' shown in (b) to work, the grid circuit would have to be balanced, not the anode as shown in (a). (Agreed, I should have made it clear that these two diagrams were not linked in P R Keller's book—*G3VA*.)

"One of the nastiest problems with neutralization of tetrode and pentode valves is how to adjust the capacitor without either: (*a*) finding the presence of the trimming tool affects the neutralization; or (*b*) drawing sparks off the capacitor due to its being connected to dc. For instance, the neutralization capacitor in the FT100 transceiver has one end at 600V and the other at 300V. Shorting the latter to chassis burns out the driver rf choke quite rapidly.

"A better scheme involves a fixed 'feedback' capacitor and variable capacitance to earth, forming a capacitive potential divider as in Fig 9(a)." (I have added as Fig 9(b) a basically similar form of capacitive potential divider for unbalanced circuits that has been widely used at hf—*G3VA*.)

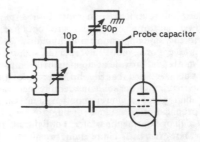

Fig 10. G3JKY points out that adding a third capacitor can provide a convenient form of neutralization up to about 200MHz with such valves as the 4CX250B. The small-value "probe capacitor" can be similar to that shown in Fig 3(b) of the August *TT*, cut or bent to bring neutralization within the range of the 50pF trimmer

"For the least inter-action between tuning and neutralization a third capacitor can be added as in Fig 10. I have used this arrangement up to 200MHz with 4CX250B valves with fairly conventional tuning capacitors and coils. It still worked at 300MHz when using coaxial grid and anode lines, the grid-line 'probe' capacitor being between the end of the half-wave line remote from the valve and the voltage-minimum point near the valve to obtain anti-phase feedback as in Fig 11.

"Above about 350MHz this seemed even easier mechanically, as the grid probe could be right at the grid terminal. This is because at higher frequencies the voltage minimum point on the line disappears 'inside'. This can be shown by clamping the valve in its holder to a sheet of metal, and attaching various lengths of rod or tube to the grid to form an open line as in Fig 12. A gdo may then be used to find the lengths of line corresponding to various frequencies.

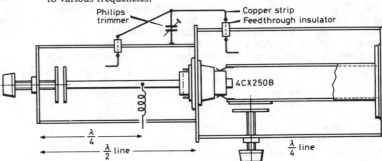

Fig 11. The arrangement of Fig 5 adapted for use with coaxial grid and anode lines. G3JKY believes that side discs as shown in the anode line are preferable to end-disc capacitors. With this (and many other neutralizing arrangements) beware of high rf voltages (and often high dc voltages) on the neutralizing capacitor. He also warns that typical fans running at 1,400–1,500rpm do not build up enough pressure to cool a 4CX250B in a coaxial line amplifier

"On vhf, I am not sure that the so-called 'series-resonant' screen neutralization is (or was) just that. I suspect that the capacitances between anode and screen and screen and grid, together with the inductance between screen and ground, combine to form a 'notch filter' between anode and grid. Transforming the 'star' into a 'delta' would effectively put an inductance across the anode-grid capacitance—unless you know better. This would make the arrangement somewhat frequency sensitive. I recall some published circuits actually added an inductor in the screen lead.

"Finally, on the question of grounded-grid amplifiers as raised by Richard Measures, AG6K, in *Ham Radio*. I can certainly confirm the need for effective grid bypass capacitors. Depending on the ratio between the anode tuning capacitor and the anode to grid capacitance of the valve, a

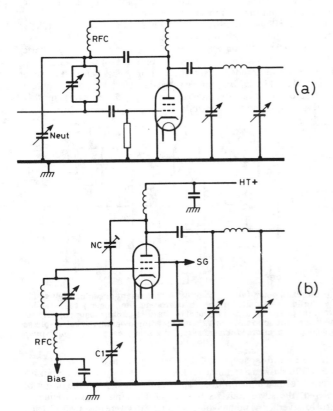

Fig 9(a). Use of a capacitive potential divider to facilitate neutralization of beam tetrodes. (b) Popular form of bridge neutralizing circuit when there is no balanced input or output tuned circuit. In practice NC is often fixed and C1 made variable to about 500pF (this is a safer arrangement as it removes ht from the adjustable capacitor)

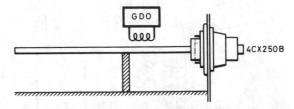

Fig 12. Use of a gdo to find line lengths for various frequencies. G3JKY believes that a telescopic rod antenna would simplify this operation, although he has not used one himself. He notes that between about 300 and 350MHz resonance usually occurs with the line a physical quarter-wave, indicating that the valve appears as a series-resonant circuit

proportion of the anode tank circuit current flows through the grid bypass capacitors! At some frequency this seems almost certain to cause the amplifier to go (to quote the immortal words of the late John Campbell, W2ZGU) 'whee-whoo, but good!'

"After much fun-and-games with a pair of 830s, which have a hefty anode-grid capacitance, I am resigned to either earthing the grid directly and providing a floating negative line, or returning to the push-pull neutralized arrangement I had before I became greedy and wanted to work more than one band!

"Another curious phenomenon with a g-g amplifier was with a TY-125 on 144MHz. With this circuit, all the anode tank current went through the grid capacitors. Tuning the anode circuit produced a very encouraging dip in anode current. The snag was that the amplifier showed no inclination to 'draw' and gave very little output. The explanation seems to be that the current in the bypass capacitors produced negative feedback (for a change) and effectively reduced the drive. Presumably, the valve did not have enough gain to go unstable at higher frequencies where the feedback became positive. Again, shorting the grid to chassis and floating the filament at bias voltage solved the problem."

The *Ham Radio* article by AG6K has also provoked supportive correspondence in that journal from NJ0G and W2YW. W2YW relates a horrific story of how he has had *three dozen* 572 valves fail in the manner described even though the amplifier was grid-driven, neutralized and had parasitic suppressors in both anode and filament leads. The big bangs that accompanied each incident were of sufficient current to blow 30A fuses in the 234V line feeding the power supply. He believes the trouble dates from around 1981 when the manufacturer changed the amplification factor of the 572 from 160 to 200.

NJ0G, on the other hand, mentions production experience with several hundred hf linear amplifiers using Eimac 8874 and 8877 valves without seeing a single case of parasitic oscillation or instability of any kind. He believes the key factor is the use of Eimac's recommended valve sockets (8874 E F Johnson socket as specified; for 8877 the Eimac SK-2210 socket). The need to use the correct sockets for the 4CX250-series of valves has been emphasised many times in the past by G4FRX. Incidentally, a major problem these days with valve equipment is finding good sockets for the various bases (there can also be a problem with some rarer types of finding the pin connections even if you have kept your valve data books).

Open-wire feeder spacers

I thought that *TT* had about exhausted the topic of feeder spacers over the past year or so. Certainly, there is a deservedly increasing popularity of multiband centre-fed dipoles or doublet antennas, call them what you will. With a suitable atu providing balanced output over a range of impedances, such antennas can be made to work well on any hf band regardless of the precise dimensions of the "top" unless this is absurdly short in terms of wavelength.

A long letter from A R Johnston, G4OGP, who designed and now markets the SPC300 etc series of atus, draws attention to his spacers (2·5in, 64mm spacing) designed to be attached very easily to any wire up to 1·5mm diameter (preferably multistrand pvc-covered wire). With 1·4mm multistrand this has a 580Ω impedance, making it suitable for either 600Ω non-resonant or resonant lines. The basic material is ultra-violet stabilized dark (black) polypropylene to a design he patented about 1981. He recommends spreaders spaced at about 4ft intervals with two thin nylon cords or fishing line around the ends of the last downward-running spacer to keep the line taut.

His own 130ft line to a 580ft doublet (there must be more room up in Lancashire than in south London!) has been up for over four years without problems, despite wind gusts exceeding 90mph. He suggests such feeders can be used from 1 to 150MHz, though I am not sure that his very simple way of fixing wires to spreaders by half looping the wire round notches might not prove rather inductive at 150MHz (thinking of the way telephone lines are inductively loaded, perhaps this would be no bad thing). His address is 63 Hallcroft, Birch Green, Skelmersdale, Lancs WN8 6QB.

In *QST* (August 1986, p38) two further suggestions appear. WA8MLV uses "120"-size plastic film spools. W0TOY claims that up to 15 2in spacers can be cut from coat hangers made of ⅜in diameter plastic. But don't bank on these materials being ultra-violet stabilized!

Tips and topics

The American semiconductor firm Signetics is, like Mullard Ltd in the UK, part of the large Philips group of companies. One result of this is that Mullard have recently published a series of product specifications and application notes on two extremely interesting ic devices originally developed by Signetics but now being marketed in the UK by Mullard. These are the NE602 mixer/oscillator and the SA/NE604 low power fm i.f

system. Both devices seem well suited to amateur radio applications, and the notes include work by Bob Zavrel, W7SX.

For example, the Mullard AN1981 publication *New low power single sideband circuits* (8pp) lets W7SX take a new look at Weaver "third method" ssb generators and ssb detectors, including the use of two NE602 mixers in a phasing-type direct-conversion receiver which gets rid of the "audio-image" problem; W7SX also shows how crystal filter methods are inherently more expensive and tend to restrict the use of ssb in some applications. Other publications (available from Technical Publications Dept, Mullard Ltd, New Road, Mitcham, Surrey CR4 4XY) include: AN1982 *Applying the oscillator of the NE602 in low power mixer applications;* AN1991 *Audio decibel level detector with meter driver* (by W7SX). AN199 *Designing with the SA/NE604;* SA/NE604 *Low power fm i.f system* (product specification); AN198 *Designing with the SA/NE602;* SA/NE602 *Double-balanced mixer and oscillator* (product specification).

Attention is also drawn to two recent papers by Peter Chadwick, G3RZP, of Plessey Semiconductors: *Advances in single chip frequency synthesisers* and *Phase noise, intermodulation and dynamic range.*

Although the proposal of using a musical "reed" as the diaphragm of an earphone to provide a fixed-tuned filter for cw reception (*TT* January 1986, p39) was published first in *QST* as an "April fool" joke, I continue to receive reports that not only can the system be made to work, but work well. Bill Craig, G6JJ, comments: "The late Bill Bailey, G2QB, demonstrated his 'phones modified in this way with mouth-organ reeds and they worked very well, though unsuitable for high-speed morse because, as in any other narrowband system, speed is limited. I think the difference was that the Australian device used aluminium or other non-magnetic material for the main part of the diaphragm, whereas G2QB used normal magnetic diaphragms and had a residual effect from them, although the main audio note was generated by the mouth-organ reed mounted in the slot in the centre. He was a superb model engineer, and I believe he used 12BA screws for mounting the reeds."

G6JJ believes that details were published, but has failed to trace where. He did, however, come across G2QB's description in *QST*'s "Hints & Kinks" (November 1962) of a "finger key" based on two straight keys mounted at a slight angle to one another and provided with extensions. One key is connected to the electronic keyer dot contact and the right-hand key to the dash contact. Keying is then with two fingers in similar fashion to piano playing. After a little practice the mental and muscular reactions quickly drop into place. The actuator and keyer were built in a single box, making the whole unit self-contained. □

BOOK REVIEW

GCHQ—The Secret Wireless War 1900–86, Nigel West. Weidenfeld & Nicolson, 1986. 294 + xviii pages. Hard covers £12.95.

Ever since Paul Wright, G3SEM, researched and helped produce the BBC television programme "The Secret Listeners" (VHS copy available to clubs from the RSGB Tape Library) and his subsequent *Radio Communication* article (December 1980, pp1299–1301) there has been an increasing interest, even among those born long after the second world war ended, in the secret role of the 1,500 or so pre-war British radio amateurs who were enrolled by Lord Sandhurst as Voluntary Interceptors in the Radio Security Service (initially part of MI5, later MI8c) or the many who served in the Special Communication Units, the Special Wireless Groups or in the main Inter-Service interception organization (Y-Service). It was not until the 'seventies that it became possible to reveal the extent to which high-grade enemy ciphers, including the Enigma machine cipher, were consistently "read" for many of the war years at Bletchley Park (known as "BP" or Station X) and the contents largely distributed over a special SLU/SCU hf radio network as "Ultra" or "Pearl" information.

The VIs and SCU3 were concerned primarily with monitoring the extensive radio networks of the Abwehr (German Military Intelligence) and the RSHA (German security police), whereas the Y-Service concentrated on the mass of transmissions of the German army, navy and air force. British signals intelligence had first got under way as part of Naval Intelligence in the first world war with code breaking done at "Room 40". Bletchley Park entered the second world war as the innocuously-named Government Code & Cipher School (GC&CS) answering to "C", head of MI6 (SIS). It emerged under Foreign Office control as GCHQ, subsequently moving first to Eastcote and then to Cheltenham.

In this new book, Nigel West brings together a mass of detail relating to British signals intelligence, and gives much credit to the work of radio amateurs (perhaps too little to the Y-Service on which BP depended for most of its intercepts, or the "traffic analysis" work carried out at Barnet). It is also not surprising that a significant number of minor, but decidedly off-putting, errors have crept into the book. These are unlikely to be spotted by those who were not directly involved and will not reduce the interest of such readers. But as far as the VI/SCU story is concerned, a much shorter but more reliable account remains the December 1980 *Radio Communication* article.

G3VA

Technical Topics
by Pat Hawker, G3VA

IT HAS LONG BEEN a requirement of the ITU's Radio Regulations (which have the status of a formal international treaty) that all transmitting stations should radiate only as much power as is necessary to ensure a satisfactory service; that transmissions should be such as to cause minimum interference and ensure efficient spectrum utilization; and that there should be no unnecessary transmissions or transmissions without identification.

One has to admit that the good intentions of the Radio Regulations are not always adhered to in practice—neither by amateur nor professional users of the crowded radio spectrum. In mitigation, it could be suggested that deciding what constitutes "a satisfactory service" is a bit like debating how many angels can be accommodated on the head of a pin. Coverage of broadcast transmitters on mf, vhf and uhf is now as often interference-limited as signal-strength limited. Whereas hf broadcast transmitters in the 'thirties were usually rated at about 10 to 15kW output, today they commonly exhale 250, 500 or more kW into large antenna arrays that result in effective radiated powers well up into the megawatt region.

Such powers are not to overcome the problems of hf propagation but primarily to drown out co-channel interference from other broadcast stations or to overcome the major problem of man-made jamming (itself a breach of the Radio Regulations when the effects impinge on areas beyond your own frontiers). On hf no feasible power could overcome the basic limitations imposed by the ever-changing muf, the absorption in the day-time D-layer etc, and guarantee a sufficient fade-margin to overcome the distortion produced by selective-fading of double-sideband am signals.

The highly-competitive nature of so much present-day amateur radio operation has encouraged many UK amateurs to run up to, and sometimes well beyond, the legal power limits. It is little use pointing out that if everyone in Europe were limited to a maximum of, say, 50W rf output and relatively modest antenna arrays, there would be remarkably little difference, except perhaps on eme, in overall results. The trouble with 50W or less to a dipole or monopole is that your signals lose out to the high-power crowd unless you can operate at times when they are too busy earning the shekels needed to put a TH6 up to 100-ft, or you are content (as many of us become) to seek out the stations bearing less exotic call-signs.

The dead zone boundary
Recently, to check further on the activity, or lack of it, on the 10·1MHz band (much increased since the appearance of Soviet amateurs) and also for my own enjoyment, I have been running about 15 to 20W rf output from the 5B/254M (miniature 807) power amplifier of a paramilitary Mk 123 transmitter-receiver and home-built vfo to what is virtually a random length of wire, about 37m long, fed through a pi-network atu.

This unambitious set-up provides satisfactory signals in the first-hop area beyond the "dead zone" only about one or two S-points below what could be expected from the usual 100W black box with resonant dipole.

Operating in this way has brought home to me not only the large skip or dead zone on this band at the present period of sunspot minimum (seldom under about 5–600 miles radius) but also the considerable depth of fading on signals arriving from close to the edge of the zone: much deeper and more pronounced than on the long-distance signals that come in when conditions are favourable. Signals from Japan, Australia etc seem to remain remarkably consistent for long periods whereas those from under about 700 miles can be S9-plus one minute and down to S2-3 the next.

In *IEEE Transactions on Antennas and Propagation* (September 1986, pp 1163–1170) a well-known American expert on radio propagation, Charles M Rush, provides a "mini-review" of ionospheric radio propagation models and predictions. This includes a clear description of the basic structure of the ionosphere that forms the basis of the "models" used to predict hf propagation. But it also includes a diagram that helps to explain why signals near the boundary of the hf dead zone can vary so much in signal strength and why the nearer signals are often much weaker than those a few hundred miles further away.

Many of the simplified diagrams on hf propagation still found in amateur radio handbooks not only ignore the existence of chordal hop modes but also seem to indicate that signals immediately beyond the dead zone arrive at full strength. In practice this can be misleading. What happens is that the edge of the skip is far from being sharply defined but is represented by a quite large area of gradually increasing field strength. This means that incoming signals can increase from zero to S9 or S9-plus as they come from transmitters increasingly far away—and can fade away with any change in the skip. There can be a large coverage area of strong signals before reaching another area of declining signals with increasing distance.

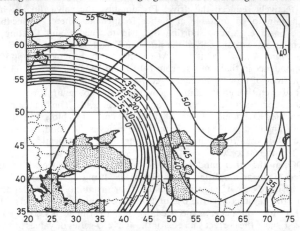

Fig 1. Calculated contours of the field strength (in dBu) for a high-power Voice of America transmission from Kavalla, Greece on 11·855MHz at 2000gmt for March 1985. Calculations assumed a 250kW transmitter and a curtain antenna. The diagram shows clearly that at the boundary of the skip (dead zone) the signal strength increases progressively as the distance from the transmitter increases. The close spacing of the contours in this region suggest that deep fading can occur rapidly with any change of ionospheric conditions, a phenomena that characterises operation on the amateur 10·1MHz band (*Source* C M Rush)

This is evident from Fig 1, taken from Charles Rush's paper, showing calculated contours of field strength (in decibels relative to 1μV) for a very high-power (250kW) Voice of America transmitter located at Kavalla, Greece and targeted on the USSR, on a frequency of 11·855MHz at 2000gmt for March 1985, with a curtain antenna array. The point to note is the way in which field strength increases from 0dBu to 50dBu over some hundreds of miles and indeed only reaches 55dBu at the very top of the map. The same general pattern, though not the same dBu!, would apply to stations using 25 or 250W rather than 250kW, although the shape of the coverage area is, of course, partly determined by the antenna array.

Getting to grips with the ionosphere
Although the ever-changing structure and state of the ionosphere has a direct bearing on virtually all operation below about 60MHz, most of us have only a hazy idea of what happens "up there" between the transmitting and receiving antennas. The vhf operator soon realises that his signals travel much further in certain weather conditions, but his signals (except in conditions of Sporadic E that remain only vaguely predictable) tend to pass straight through the upper atmosphere, the region that has most effect on mf and hf signals.

So it seems worth quoting in some detail from the introductory passages of Charles Rush's mini-review which describes succinctly present thinking on the ionosphere. He writes (US Goverment work not protected by US copyright):

"The ionosphere is that region of the earth's atmosphere in which free ions and electrons exist in sufficient abundance to affect the properties of electromagnetic waves that are propagated within and through it. For practical purposes, the ionosphere can usually be assumed to extend from about 50 to roughly 2000km above the earth's surface. The structure of the ionosphere is highly variable and this variability is imparted onto the performance of telecommunication systems whose signals are propagated via the ionosphere. The prediction of the ionosphere and the prediction of the performance of ionospheric-dependent radio systems is often assumed to be identical. Ionospheric predictions are generally made using models that are either physically, statistically, or empirically based. Predictions of the performance of ionospheric-dependent radio systems are generally made by using the ionospheric predictions in conjunction with other elements (models, formulas, equations, etc.) that permit the determination of system characteristics. Historically, the D region of the ionosphere is treated as the lowest ionospheric region. It has an altitude range from 50 to 90km and the electron density increases rapidly with altitude. The D region is under strong influence of the sun with the maximum values of the electron density occurring near local noon during summer. The ionization in the D region between 70 and 90km is caused primarily by solar X rays; below 70km, cosmic ray-produced ionization dominates. The high collision frequency between the electrons and neutral particles in the D region gives rise to substantial absorption of radio waves that are propagated into it.

"The E region is the next highest ionospheric region. It spans the altitude range from about 90 to 130km. The normal E layer closely resembles a "Chapman" layer with a maximum density near noon and a seasonal maximum in summer. The maximum density occurs near 100km, although this height varies with local time. During the night, the ionization in the E region approaches small residual levels. The normal E layer is formed by ultraviolet radiation ionizing atomic oxygen. Collisions between electrons and neutral particles, while important in the E region, are not as numerous as in the D region. The electron-neutral collision frequency generally decreases exponentially with altitude throughout the E region.

"Embedded within the E region is the so-called sporadic-E layer. This layer is an anomalous ionization layer that assumes different forms—irregular and patchy, smooth and disc like—and has little direct bearing to solar radiation. The properties of the sporadic-E layer vary substantially with location and are markedly different at equatorial, temperate, and high latitudes.

"The highest ionospheric region is termed the F region. The lower part of the F region (130 to 200km) displays different variations than the upper part, and for this reason the terms F1 and F2 (region above 200km) are applied. The F1 region, like the E region, is under strong solar control. It reaches a maximum ionization level about one hour after local noon and its presence is generally only obvious during the summer. At night the F1 and F2 regions merge and are termed simply the F region.

"The F2 region is the highest ionospheric region. It is also the most variable in time and in space. The maximum values of electron density in the F2 region can be as large as $2-5 \times 10^{12}/m^3$. The maximum value generally occurs well after noon, sometimes in the evening hours. The height of the maximum ranges from 250 to 350km at mid-latitudes to 350 to 500km at equatorial latitudes. At mid-latitudes, the height of the maximum electron density is higher at night than in the daytime. At equatorial latitudes, the opposite behaviour occurs.

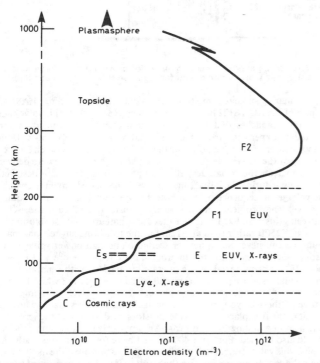

Fig 2. A simplified representation of the vertical distribution of electron density. In practice the vertical distribution will differ in different geographical regions

"The F2 region is strongly influenced by neutral-air winds, electrodynamic drift, and ambipolar diffusion that compete along with ionization processes to control the ionization distribution. The relationship between the direction of the geomagnetic field and the direction of the neutral winds and electrodynamic drifts plays a major role in the resulting F2 region structure. It is the plasma response to the dynamic processes in the presence of the geomagnetic field that gives rise to the observed variations in the F2 region.

"Within the F region, the collision frequency between electrons and neutral particles decreases markedly. However, collisions between electrons and ions, being Coulomb-type collisions, can give rise to relatively high effective collision frequencies. Substantial absorption of hf radio waves can occur, for example, near the peak of the F region.

"The F region extends upward into the topside ionosphere. The topside ionosphere is as variable, if not more so, as the F region. The variations become increasingly larger with altitude. Because the electron density continuously decreases in the topside ionosphere, the ionization in the topside becomes less and less important in terms of affecting most radio propagation systems.

"Fig 2 provides a rather simplistic example of the vertical distribution of electrons in the ionosphere. This particular distribution is characteristic of mid-latitudes at summer noon, solar maximum conditions. At any location on the earth, the vertical distribution can be expected to differ in detail from that of Fig 2. Many of the ionospheric models that have been developed over the years are limited to specific geographical regions because the mechanisms that lead to the formation and changes of the ionosphere tend to vary in their dominance of the overall distribution in specific geographical regions. This is particularly true for the ionosphere in the equatorial latitudes and at the high latitudes."

It is very noticeable how the muf is higher at any given time in southern Europe than in the UK—and, as is well known, north–south paths are frequently open at times when the east–west paths are firmly closed.

High-energy radiation dx

A note from Jack Darby, G4TVC raises an interesting question about the levels of x-ray radiation that may sometimes penetrate through the Earth's atmosphere from solar flares. He writes:

"I am employed by MEL in Crawley, Sussex as a system test engineer, working on high energy linear accelerators for medical use that can generate high levels of x-ray radiation. On the morning of October 16, a junior engineer working with me was being cautious and checking for induced activity with a G-M radiation monitor. He was surprised to find the level well above the usual 1 to 2 counts per second. The monitor was in fact showing between 12 and 20 counts! There was no apparent reason for this level. We checked with several other monitors and also at a distance of 50 yards from any possible local source of radioactivity. The monitors continued to read 12 to 20 per second.

"The following weekend was JOTA and the Crawley Amateur Radio Club were operating two stations on behalf of the local Scouts. We found the hf bands in a very active state and worked dx in many directions on most bands. 21MHz was open to the USA for most of the daylight hours.

"Could it be that these two incidents were connected? Can a sunspot-type flare cause such an increase in the 'natural' level of radioactivity? If so, we need only purchase one of the surplus pocket monitors for a couple of pounds in order to keep an eye on the dx conditions."

This incident is another confirmation that we have now crossed over from sunspot Cycle 21 to the new Cycle 22.

Renewed interest in valves?

It may well be technically incorrect to suggest that there has been a noticeable revival of interest in the use of valves in transmitters. Many readers would point out that in practice valves have never disappeared from a significant proportion of amateur stations. This includes the vast majority of those using anything like full legal power, the many who are happy to keep on the air with older but often entirely satisfactory equipment and a lot of those who prefer to keep at least some element of home construction. After all, 10 or 100W of rf power performs equally well or badly whether generated by thermionic or solidstate devices, the only difference is that for ssb operation a valve usually provides better linearity and hence fewer spurious signals or intermodulation products! Nevertheless, there must by now be many of the younger generation of amateurs to whom the thermionic valve is virtually an unknown device on which no questions have been asked for many years in the RAE.

It was therefore interesting to note in *Ham Radio Today* (November 1986, pp21–5) a long article by Brian Kendal, G3GDU on "Roll your own valve rig" covering the basic circuitry of valve oscillators, buffer and power amplifiers (though regrettably with no mention of the advisability of neutralization or parasitic suppression etc). I would also take issue with his

Table 1. Valve base connections

Valve base		1	2	3	4	5	6	7	8	9	TC
EC90	B7G	A		H	H	A	G	K			
EF80	B9A	K	G1	K	H	H	S	A	G2	G3	
EF91	B7G	G1	K	H	H	A	G3	G2			
EF92	B7G	G1	K	H	H	A	G3	G2			
EF93	B7G	G1	G3	H	H	A	G2	K			
EL90	B7G	G1	K	H	H	A	G2	G1			
EL91	B7G	G1	K	H	H	A	G3	G2			
6C5	IO			H	A		G1		H	K	
6F6	IO			H	A	G2	G1		H	K	
6J5	IO			H	A		G1		H	K	
6K7	IO			H	A	G2			H	K	G
6L6	IO			H	A	G2	G1		H	K	
6V6	IO			H	A	G2	G1		H	K	
6BW6	B9A	G1	K	H	H			A	G2	BP	
12AT7	B9A	A2	G2	K2	H	H	A1	G1	K1		HCT
12AU7	B9A	A2	G2	K2	H	H	A1	G1	K1		HCT
807	UX5	H	G2	H	G1	K	H				A
5763	B9A	A		BP	H	H	G2	K	G1	G1	
6146	IO	H		G2	K	G1	K	H	B		A

Legend: A-anode; B-base shell; G or G1-control grid; G2-screen grid; H-heater; HCT-heater centre tap; K-cathode; TC-top cap.
Note the 12AT7 and 12AU7 are double valves thus G1 corresponds to the grid of the first triode and G2 to that of the second etc.

(Source G3GDU in *Ham Radio Today*)

---

statement that there are no books covering valve techniques in amateur radio transmitters currently in print: both *Radio Communication Handbook* (5th edition) and *A Guide to Amateur Radio* (19th edition) provide valve as well as solidstate circuitry—but perhaps what G3GDU has in mind is the difficulty of finding detailed information on valve characteristics and valve base diagrams which I admit *can* be a problem (even my extensive technical library lacks information, for example, on the once popular TT11).

G3GDU does include some useful suggestions on valve types (though not their detailed characteristics) together with their pin connections (see Table 1) and has at least reassured me that I am not the last surviving member of the valve fan club!

Grounded-grid amplifiers

Recent references in *TT* (August and November) to stability and flash-over problems in high-power hf and vhf linear amplifiers are to some extent echoed in W6SAI's *Ham Radio Techniques* (*Ham Radio*, September 1986, pp 42–46). Bill Orr, W6SA1 who works for Varian-Eimac, one of the remaining major suppliers of high power thermionic devices, is well-placed to describe the good and bad points of linear amplifiers. He notes, incidentally, that despite the virtual disappearance of valves from current factory-built receivers, exciters and transceivers, it is a different story when it comes to high-power amplifiers where the vacuum-tube remains supreme, in spite of several attempts to market solid-state "kilowatt" amplifiers. "Such a device simply isn't cost-effective; I doubt that a practical 2kW (so-called) solid-state linear amplifier will be available at a modest cost in the near future." He considers that the cathode-driven, grounded-grid amplifier configuration is "admirably suited to the amateur-radio service in the hf and vhf regions. The circuit performs well in a properly designed and operated amplifier". For such an amplifier the valve is often a high-μ triode whch can result in good power gain and is difficult to overdrive. Since the drive power adds to the output power, it is a deservedly popular arrangement when using the typical 100W transceiver as an exciter.

W6SAI notes that such an amplifier seldom requires neutralization in the hf region since the feedback path from anode to cathode is small but that neutralization may be necessary above 30MHz. He also suggests that "In the better-designed cathode-driven amplifiers, a tuned circuit is used in the cathode to improve the regulation of the driver, to provide proper termination of the driver over the operating cycle, and to complete the anode-circuit rf return path. If the tuned cathode circuit is omitted the various tasks fall upon the output circuit of the exciter. Many solid-state exciters cannot stand this set of operating conditions and may exhibit instability and undesired oscillation. The operator may jump to the conclusion that the amplifier is oscillating even though the problem is really in the exciter."

W6SAI stresses that generally speaking the cathode-driven amplifier is a docile beast, with relatively low power gain (compared with a grid-driven tetrode amplifier) when triode valves are used and shielding is adequate. He writes: "Amplifier instability at the operating frequency can often be cured by careful attention to feedback paths external to the amplifier (proper bypassing of primary power leads) and by ensuring that the exciter and amplifier are operating at the same earth potential. An extra-short, heavy earth strap between exciter and amplifier will often cure an unstable amplifier."

On amplifier parasitics W6SAI takes a pragmatic view; "Much has been written about amplifier parasitics. Some of it is true . . . parasitics, when they occur, are usually mild and commonly above the self-neutralizing frequency of the valve.

"A sure-fire cure for a parasitic is to load the circuit at the parasitic frequency until the amplifier refuses to oscillate. The valve lead common to all parasitic circuits is the anode; this is where parasitic suppression should take place. A simple resistor-inductor circuit will do the job." But he notes that too many turns round the resistor will cause it to overheat; too few turns and the parasitic will not be suppressed.

On "flash-over" in this configuration, W6SAI recommends the insertion of a small series resistor in the anode supply line to limit the sudden discharge of the high-energy psu filter capacitors: "In most cases a 50Ω, 20W resistor in the ht + lead after the filter capacitor (either in the amplifier or psu) should provide adequate protection . . . to a power valve that may be worth many hundreds of dollars." He also notes the use of a small amount of rf negative feedback which can absorb some excess drive power, tends to make the amplifier more stable, and improves the intermodulation distortion (imd) figure slightly. The feedback circuit makes use of the anode-to-grid capacitance and is often arranged to provide about 2 to 3dB feedback. This is set by the value of the grid by-pass capacitance which may be say 600pF in an amplifier using two 3–500Z high-μ power triodes. Decreasing the grid capacitance increases the feedback but tends to degrade the grid-filament isolation at the operating frequency.

All of which underline a point made a number of times in *TT*, that high-power amplifiers may use very simple circuitry but require the application of good engineeering practices—and of course adequate safety precautions.

Valve failures

It was noted in the November *TT*, under "neutralization of rf amplifiers", that W2YW had reported in *Ham Radio* experiencing some three dozen big-bang failures of high-power 572 valves in grid-driven linear amplifiers despite the incorporation of neutralization and parasitic suppressors. He ascribed the problem to a manufacturing change in about 1981 that had raised the amplification factor of the 572 from 160 to 200, presumably by reducing the inter-electrode spacing.

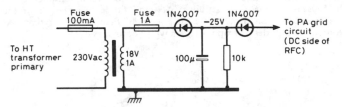

Fig 3. LA8AK's suggested arrangement for providing a minimum grid bias voltage as a protection circuit for high power linear valve amplifiers

A similar report has come to me from Jan Martin Noeding, LA8AK in respect of the RCA 8122 high-power tetrode. He writes: "This valve causes so many headaches that I consider that it should be avoided by radio amateurs. Experience from Farsund Radio (LGR/LGZ) and a Danish manufacturer of coast station transmitters suggests that between 30 and 50 per cent of the valves have become defective by the time they are delivered in Europe! Of the remainder, 20 to 30 per cent experience a destructive break-down during the initial tune-up, even when care is taken to switch on the voltages in sequence over an hour before applying a small amount of rf drive. The problem almost invariably turns out to be a short-circuit between grids 1 and 2. I consider that for amateurs the best solution is to use a 4CX250B rather than an 8122, but the following suggestions may be found useful: never buy a new or second-hand high-power valve without testing whether there are any internal short-circuits before you leave the shop. If two or more valves are operated in parallel with separate screen-grid regulators, use a protection circuit such as that in Fig 3 which keeps the control grid voltage at a minimum of –25V (relatively low impedance source). Otherwise you are likely to burn out those valves that had no short-circuit in the first place. Zinc-oxide varistors used to protect the screen-grid may help in avoiding break-downs. An input drive voltage control circuit should also be used. For the 4-400 valves I have found that it is inadvisable to push this valve straight down into its socket as you are quite likely to bend down the socket connectors with the result that with the passage of time the valve pin may no longer make contact with the socket, resulting in the possible break-down of the valve."

Instability in small-signal transistor amplifiers

The August *TT* (pp 571–2) included an item on instability in solidstate power amplifiers that listed a number of practical safeguards when using solidstate rf power devices near their maximum ratings. This recognized that it is still all too easy to destroy expensive devices. However, as Henry Higgins, G4ZVL points out it is well worth considering how to prevent spurious transistor oscillation even for small-signal amplifiers and other circuit arrangements. He writes: "It is not often appreciated that a bipolar transistor with reactive loads on its emitter and/or collector may exhibit instability. A reactive load may simply be a length of print-circuit trace or wire and not necessarily in the form of lumped component-elements such as inductors and capacitors, at the frequency in question.

"The effect is to generate at the base a negative resistance and reactive components. If the base input is such that it will cancel out these components and its resistance is equal in magnitude, but positive, then the transistor will oscillate.

"So if the base has a negative resistance and the input network is its 'mirror image' then it will cause problems. The base input does not, in effect, consist only of the capacitors, resistors, etc, but—as the frequency increases—trace lengths and wire length also contributes. (Remember that even a straight 1in length of 23 swg wire has an inductive reactance of about 16Ω at 100MHz—G3VA). In such circumstances the transistor may well oscillate at a high frequency, likely to be at vhf or uhf where the 'mirror image' occurs.

"The cure for this is fairly straight-forward and comprises inserting a 100Ω resistor in the base lead as close to the pin as possible to be effective, preferably within 2mm of it. It is of little use inserting such a resistor 50mm down a trace, it may even make things worse. It is good practice to include this in all small signal transistor amplifiers, and any other design where a reasonably low base current is used; exceptions include high current power regulators where the beta and the Ft of the device are both low.

"Also remember the oscillation will usually occur at a very high frequency and so may not be visible on a 100MHz scope, for example, and if a digitizing instrument is available—even less chance; it should be possible to see the oscillation with a good spectrum analyzer! If a transistor is oscillating it can have several effects; first it will generate a high frequency which may well cause problems with other parts of the circuit; or it may cause rfi and the transistor itself will have reduced gain where it is needed. One final point, assuming the amateur has the appropriate test equipment, it is still not easy to find out which transistor is oscillating as the additional capacitance of the probe, even at another part of the circuit, may stop the oscillation. So fit the base resistors as standard."

Magnetic (loop) antennas

The description of magnetic (small loop) antennas (*TT*, October, pp 705–7) was intended primarily to show the practical advantages and disadvantages of the compact loop transmitting antenna formed from large-diameter copper tubing or similar materials of very low ohmic loss, necessary to achieve reasonable efficiency in spite of the very low radiation resistance. However, Dr Andrew Smith, G4OEP is rightly concerned that some of the comments could inadvertently give rise to misconceptions as to the fundamental principles governing all transmitting antennas. As he puts it:

"*TT* occasionally reminds us about the mystic fog which surrounds the vswr fetish, but it is possible now that you might be in process of creating a myth around loop antennas.

"Possibly, the term 'magnetic antenna' has become established as a generic term for loops, ferrite rods etc in which, during reception, the device generates an emf in response to the magnetic field vector component of an incident electromagnetic wave. If the term has become established, there is little one can expect to do to influence its usage. But it is less than ideal when applied to transmitting antennas, which have the dual task of creating E and H fields in strict proportion (E/H = c) if they are to act as em radiators. If a magnetic antenna creates an H field in excess of E/c then the excess magnetic field cannot result in the radiation of em energy, and so is accidental to the operation of the device as an antenna. As *TT* suggested, this can be a source of inefficiency in such aerials.

"This is fairly obvious, but should be borne in mind when discussing the operation of these antennas. The statement ' . . . the system is no longer a true magnetic antenna, and electric fields develop in the neighbourhood of the antenna' . . . suggests that a purely magnetic transmitting antenna might in some way be possible. It would be unfortunate if *TT* were to be caught in the act of perpetrating an antenna mythology!

"I also feel uneasy about the discussion of coupling a loop antenna to a receiver. Surely the idea suggested by ' . . . the first-stage tuned circuit needs to be high-Q so that its losses, coupled back to the antenna, do not reduce efficiency' could be more accurately stated by something such as 'the source resistance of the antenna is unusually low, and so must be appropriately coupled to the first stage of the receiver'. Losses in the input circuit of a receiver must always be low in order to avoid inefficiency, but allowing the input resistance of the amplifier (and source resistance of the aerial) to lower the Q of the input filter is one way of avoiding losses! I think your point is really one about impedance matching and power transfer. "Finally, could a loop antenna radiate if it were enclosed in an electrostatic screen as most df receiving loops are?"

To the best of my knowledge, the term "magnetic antenna" originated in Germany and is widely used there. Incidentally, I was interested recently to have a 10·1MHz contact with a German amateur (DL8WR near Darmstadt) who was using a 1·4-metre diameter loop antenna mounted on his balcony—and putting excellent signals into the UK.

Breakover diodes for transient protection

In the early days of silicon power diodes, when most of these devices were rated to withstand only 400 peak inverse volts (piv), a good deal of attention had to be paid to making sure that equipment could cope with the momentary voltage surges which occur at irregular intervals on the electric supply mains; overvoltages that are usually much too short in duration to affect ordinary electric appliances or lamps.

As noted many years ago in *TT* and *ART* transient overvoltages often arise during power supply switching operations or from the indirect effects of lightning strikes and by induction, even where the conventional electricity supply lightning arrester has functioned correctly. Because of the greater use of overhead lines in rural areas, such areas tend to suffer from more and longer lightning transients than urban areas. One investigation showed that at Dudley in Worcestershire during a period of six weeks the following substantial overvoltages were recorded: 35 of 20 to 40 per cent above normal; 7 of 40 to 70 per cent above normal; and one of over 100 per cent above normal. At Cheam, Surrey in a period of 12½ weeks, there were 27 of 20 to 40 per cent above normal; four of 40 to 70 per cent; and eight of 70 to 100 per cent. Since a 100 per cent overvoltage on a 240 volt supply is equivalent to 480 volts rms or almost 700 volts peak it can be appreciated that although lasting only a few microseconds, silicon diode rectifiers need to be protected against such transients unless they have a high piv rating. Modern diodes are usually rated at 1000 piv and the problem has become less severe.

Nevertheless, quite a lot of equipments, including home computers etc, are not happy with mains supplies having high overvoltages and there are, for example, sockets now being marketed that give a "clean" supply, eliminating overvoltages and peaks of electrical interference etc.

Mullard have recently announced a range of "breakover diodes" (bod) developed specifically to provide fast transient over-voltage protection for data transmission equipment but which are also suitable for electronic equipment requiring transient impulse protection. The bod's are available in voltages between 100 and 280V in 20V steps. Being bi-directional they protect against transients of either polarity. Based on thyristor technology, in their normal high resistance state they pass less than 50μA of current at 85 per cent of breakover voltage. Within 5ns of a transient exceeding the breakover voltage the device switches to a low resistance "on-state", but switches back to "off" when the current through the bod falls to less than its holding value. It is claimed that the bod provides a faster, more stable form of protection than voltage-dependent resistors (vdr) often used for transient protection and can also replace zener diodes in some applications. This information comes from a Mullard press announcement and I have no practical experience of their application but it does seem to be a useful development for situations where equipment is known to be sensitive or vulnerable to short duration impulses. The possibility of using such devices to reduce the risk of valve flash-over might also be worth considering.

Folded-back dipoles

One of the lessons that can perhaps be learned from the work on small loop transmitting antennas, which could be expected to have a radiation resistance of less than 1Ω, is that this is not necessarily a bar to achieving a reasonably effective antenna system. This is always provided that we recognise the problems and limitations that stem from the low radiation resistance (which must not, of course, be confused with the feed point impedance).

In *HF antennas for all locations*, Les Moxon, G6XN rightly does not recommend the use of dipoles physically shortened by folding back the ends to a central insulator, since he believes that there are more efficient ways of end loading. He shows that in the folded back arrangement significant current flows in both directions, thereby decreasing the radiation resistance by a factor of about four when compared with some other forms of end-loaded elements which he describes (pages 148–9).

Dr Constantino Feruglio, IV3VS, recognizes the force of this argument, but nevertheless believes that such a system when designed for 1·8MHz (or

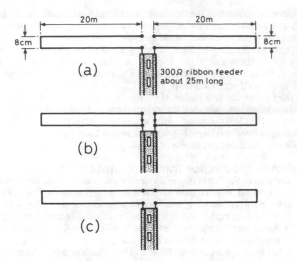

(a)

(b)

(c)

Fig 4. (a) The folded-back dipole as used on 1·8MHz by IV3VS. (b) Switched into the "double zepp" configuration (c) Switched into the "folded dipole" configuration for 3·5MHz operation

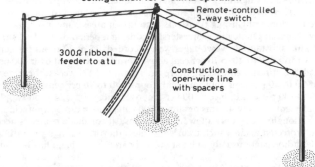

Fig 5. Implementation of IV3VS's multiband folded-back dipole antenna. As usual, performance is improved when the antenna is as high up as possible

possibly 3·5MHz) with a top span of 40m (or 20m) can form the basis of a useful multiband antenna since, when used in conjunction with a remotely-controlled switch it can work not only on 1·8MHz but also on 3·5, 7, 14, 21 and 28MHz (and with suitable atus on 10, 18 and 24MHz —G3VA). IV3VS uses the K8ANG balanced-output atu circuit shown in the June *TT*, Fig 9(b), page 420.

With the folded-back top of Fig 4(a), IV3VS achieves good 1·8MHz contacts throughout Europe. Switched into the arrangement of Fig 4(b), the system becomes a "double Zepp" antenna for 3·5, 7, 14, 21 and 28MHz etc. Alternatively it can be switched as in Fig 4(c) to provide a 3·5MHz half-wave folded dipole with useful broad-band characteristics. Length of the balanced feeder (slotted 300Ω ribbon line or open-wire feeder) is not critical since the entire system can be resonated on virtually any frequency by means of the atu, permitting operation also on 10, 18 or 24MHz. For limited spaces, the "top" could be reduced to 20m overall in which case the folded dipole configuration would be for 7MHz and efficiency on 1·8MHz would be lower. With a two-way rather than three-way remote-controlled switch the folded-dipole configuration could be omitted. Fig 5 shows the system as used by IV3VS.

Real zero ssb transceivers

Richard Lambley, G8LAM has drawn attention to an interesting concept described by three Japanese engineers working for NTT in *IEEE Transactions on Vehicular Technology* (February 1986, pp22–28): "A real zero ssb transceiver for land mobile radio: a simple method of demodulating ssb signals without an envelope" by Kazuhiro Daikoku, Shigeaki Ogase and Hitoshi Ohdate. I must confess that I find their theoretical explanations of "real zero ssb" a little daunting. But what it seems to imply is simply a form of single sideband transmission that uses a full level carrier yet occupies no more bandwidth than its band-limited audio modulation, ie 3kHz speech, and is entirely suitable for the 5kHz vhf mobile channelling that has long been an objective for the professional two-way mobile radio services.

A major difficulty with conventional suppressed-carrier or pilot-carrier ssb systems when used for mobile operation is the problem of coping with the pronounced multipath fading that is virtually always experienced when working mobile on vhf/uhf (see *TT*, November 1985, page 866). With

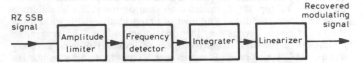

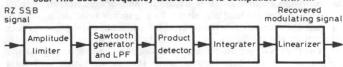

Fig 6. A simplified block diagram of one method of demodulating real zero ssb. This uses a frequency detector and is compatible with fm

Fig 7. Alternative method of recovering modulation from an rzssb signal using a product detector but requiring a sawtooth generator and low pass filter

conventional fm (nbfm) the ability to put received signals through an amplitude limiter provides an effective form of agc so long as the signal remains above the threshold.

Suppressed-carrier ssb requires that the signal is processed linearly and its "envelope" restored by injecting a local carrier. An advantage of rzssb is that it can be demodulated in much the same way as an fm signal (Fig 6) the essential functions being an amplitude limiter, frequency detector, integrator and linearizer. Alternatively, it is possible (Fig 7) to use product detection as normally used for ssb provided that the amplitude lost at the limiter is recovered; the most essential component of this approach being a sawtooth generator and low-pass filter.

For rzssb transmission the signals can be amplified using highly efficient polar-loop transmitters as developed by V Petrovic at the University of Bath (drawing on earlier work by the American L R Kahn), described on several occasions in *TT*, a technique that permits power amplifiers to be operated in the high-efficiency Class C.

No detailed circuitry is provided in the Japanese paper (their experimental transmitter was of the phasing rather than filter type). The authors conclude: "An rzssb transceiver has been theoretically and experimentally proven to be a viable spectrum-efficient technology. The attractive features of such a transceiver are:

(1) With the rzssb transceiver, signals can be transmitted in a bandwidth comparable to the information bandwidth.

(2) In the rzssb transceiver, an amplitude limiter can be used to remove amplitude degradation caused, for example, by fading.

(3) Frequency discriminators can be used to demodulate rzssb signals. A cumbersome carrier recovery operation is not necessary even though rzssb signals belong to linear modulation systems. Therefore, the rzssb receiver is compatible with fm receivers."

It remains to be seen whether rzssb is taken up widely either by professionals or amateurs. There are alternative forms of amplitude-compandored ssb, including a system developed in the UK at the University of Bristol, that have been shown to be effective for mobile operation with 5kHz channelling though such transceivers tend to be significantly more expensive than the commonly used fm mobile systems with 25kHz or 12·5kHz channelling. Nevertheless, rzssb seems atractive and it claimed that it is a method which can be easily implemented.

Morsum Magnificat

The October *TT* item on "Clutter clunk" (page 708) had N7ESJ suggesting that hi-tech, high-speed data and machine telegraphy could herald the disappearance of the "cultured and civilized tones of the radiotelegraph signal". Tony Smith, G4FAI seems to share these sentiments on an international level. In sending along the first issue of the English-language edition of *Morsum Magnificat*, a quarterly magazine that first saw the light of day in Holland, he writes: "We want to encourage an interest in morse beyond the practice of operating a key (although *that* will never be overlooked). Morse has a history, a culture, a technology of its own. We want to enlarge the horizons of the world of morse for today's operators, who sometime seem unaware of their rich heritage!" As one who has never regretted the time spent in gaining familiarity with the code as a teenager in the 'thirties, I would go along with his sentiments except that I believe that the international code we use, based on letter frequency in English (ie the single dit for the most used letter-E), owes more to the unremembered Alfred Vail, who worked with Morse, than to Samuel himself. Alfred was the practical engineer, Samuel the artist turned advocate of telegraphy. But life is like that—few would recognize ourselves as Vail operators! (*Morsum Magnificat* No 1, Autumn 1986, edited by Tony Smith, G4FAI, 1 Tash Place, London N11 1PA, telephone 01-368 4588, annual subscription £6).

Technical Topics
by Pat Hawker, G3VA

ONE PHRASE that has crept into common usage is "state-of-the-art". Applied to amateur radio it conjures up visions of the latest all-singing, all-dancing hf and vhf transceivers, automated computer-controlled "packet" networks, digital control of voice synthesizers and the like. As someone who struggles to keep abreast of what is going on not only in our field but also in the wider world of professional and defence electronics, communications and broadcasting, I would not wish to suggest that technological progress, in general, is other than a good thing. But increasingly it is becoming clear that the trend of development does pose problems for those of us who have been attracted by and have thoroughly enjoyed the traditional concept of amateur radio as a unique and friendly hobby that brings together both technical and operating practices and skills producing that now rare animal who can, if only crudely, design, build, maintain and operate a radio communications station.

Open at your own risk
The modern miniaturized factory-made transceiver with its many built-in facilities is a wonder to behold. But unfortunately it is now way beyond the understanding of most of us and requiring specialized skills to modify or repair. In his recent article on a hands-free microphone, G1SJU (December 1986, page 847) wrote: "The second (method of connecting the microphone to a mobile transceiver) is more complicated and involves opening up your rig. **This should not be attempted unless you have the knowledge and the skill to carry out the modification. Blowing up your rig may be a very expensive exercise.**" Sound and excellent advice but it must make some of us wonder where the hobby is heading when we are cautioned against even opening our rig!

Les Moxon, G6XN, licensed for 58 years yet still developing new antennas (see later) and other innovative work, has been a confirmed "home brewer" for most of that time. He admits to having built, for example, at least 15 ssb transmitters but was always so eager to incorporate new ideas and second thoughts that few passed beyond the prototype stage. But he found that he was spending a lot of time on construction once it became accepted that transmitters should always incorporate band-change switching. He stresses the great difference in building a monoband equipment with only the barest essentials and equipment that has the facilities and extras now found in even the least ambitious of current factory rigs—particularly in terms of the time involved in construction.

One result was that he finally succumbed to the black boxes. Yet he confesses that the experience has left him somewhat disillusioned. His main problem has been getting factory equipment put right when inevitably something goes wrong, while knowing that if he gets going inside the box its secondhand value will rapidly drop to zero.

His experiences with having others doing the servicing has a familiar ring. A black box taken back to the suppliers with two faults was deemed beyond their ability, and the rig was returned to the importers. It took nine weeks to get it back, allegedly cured, but in reality with the faults persisting. One subsequently turned out to be a recognized design fault in early production, curable—as G6XN had already discovered—by the use of an external high-pass filter. An earlier fault, intermittent vfo instability, took some three years before it was finally corrected.

Nor are these exceptional cases. His mobile rig, subjected to the usual rough life and accidental damage, was twice deemed "not repairable"; once because of "no spares" and in the second case because of the estimate of what the repairs would cost. In practice, d-i-y heavy-handed methods have kept it going, though modified to the extent that even the manufacturers might have difficulty in recognizing their offspring!

Nor is it clear that all operators really want or need some of the features now built into rigs, although many would like features that are seldom provided. Do we really need a costly tuning dial *plus* frequency readout? Is a good slow-motion drive essential when there is "bandspread" in the form of a speech clarifier? Not everybody wants to store frequencies in large memories. Do we have to be able to switch bands in a matter of microseconds?

When will it be recognised that some have no wish to participate in contests or spend their entire "hobby-time" in chasing squares or exotic dx? A simple monoband rig can teach one far more about hf or vhf propagation than is likely to be learned from constantly jumping from band to band. Why have we not taken advantage of the simplified home-construction potential of integrated-circuit devices (or for that matter thermionic devices)?

But then, it needs to be asked, have we as a body ceased to be interested in using amateur radio, in the phrase beloved by British broadcasting organizations, to educate, inform and entertain ourselves?

More on zener protection for relay switching
The November 1986 *TT* (page 779) included information from Peter Hart, G3SJX on the use of a zener diode in series with the usual protection diode that provides protection from the high back-emf transients generated when a circuit containing an inductor is suddenly switched. In practice the inductor often takes the form of a relay solenoid. G3SJX showed how the use of an extra zener diode can significantly reduce the pull-in time of a protective circuit; an important consideration when the relay is used, for example, as a keying relay.

Richard Golding, G3VZG suggests that G3SJX's circuit can be usefully improved by connecting the zener diode across the switching transistor's base-collector as shown in Fig 1.

In this arrangement the transistor then clamps the relay back-emf to a voltage equal to $V_{zener} + V_{be} - V_{supply}$ volts, G3VZG points out that this has two advantages:
(a) It saves a diode (conforming to the 'kiss' principle of keeping it simple).
(b) The switching transistor takes the strain, thus reducing the zener wattage requirement.

This arrangement is apparently standard practice in automotive electronics in order to achieve the fast "switch-off" of ignition coils and fuel-injector solenoids, etc.

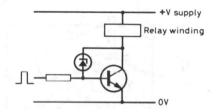

Fig 1. Zener protection for relay switching as used in automotive electronics, as reported by G3VZG

Compact multiband delta loop
Alasdair Fraser, GM3AXX, is pleased with the performance of a compact four-band delta loop antenna that can be fed directly from coaxial cable without an atu yet fits into a small garden. Since inductive loading is required only on 10MHz the efficiency is reasonably good and the only snag would appear to be the need to pop out to the switch box when changing bands, though even that could be overcome with the aid of a high-voltage remote-controlled three-position switch.

The theory is extremely simple; a full-wave on 14MHz is approximately the same physical length as a half-wave on 7MHz or 1·5λ on 21MHz: Fig 2. Originally, when 10MHz was released, GM3AXX fitted a small loading coil to his 14MHz delta loop antenna and found this to work remarkably well. Since then he has modified the loop as shown in Fig. 3 to include also 7 and 21 MHz operation. This arrangement has been used successfully by a number of local and English amateurs who report it to be ideal for small gardens. If the 10MHz facility is not required it would be possible to use a larger loading coil for 3·5MHz operation although inevitably this would have the effect of greatly lowering the radiation resistance, increasing the Q (thus narrowing the bandwidth) and significantly lowering the efficiency on that band; 1·8MHz loading is not recommended, but might put you on the band.

GM3AXX describes construction and adjustment as follows:
(1) Make up a 14MHz delta loop using two 33ft lengths of wire. Suspend the loop at its apex about 20 to 25ft above ground. Connect coaxial cable to apex (with or without balun) and run the cable (any length) to an swr bridge/transceiver. The base corners are connected via insulators to a

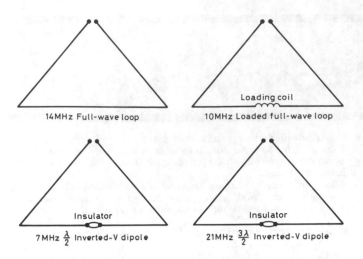

Fig 2. How a 66ft delta loop antenna can be configured for 14, 10, 7 and 21MHz to form the basis of GM3AXX's four-band antenna

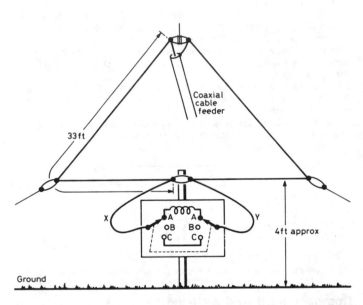

Fig 3. Practical construction of the GM3AXX's four-band antenna but note that having the base wire only 4ft above ground would breach safety recommendations except when used for very low power transmissions

convenient garden fence, etc, so that the base section is about 4ft above ground (*Note:* it needs to be higher if there is any risk of people touching wires at high rf—*G3VA*).

(2) Make up a ground post with insulator at the top and the switch box near the top. The insulator separates the two sections of the loop.

(3) With switch in position 'C' adjust lengths of stubs X, Y until loop resonates (ie shows low swr) at 14,050kHz (cw operation), 14,250kHz (ssb), or 14,200kHz (both).

(4) Then, and only then, with switch in position A, adjust the loading coil until loop resonates (low swr) at 10,125kHz. It is important that operation (3) is carried out before attempting (4). GM3AXX's coil is 20 turns on a 2in diameter former but a start should be made with 30 turns, then remove turns one at a time until the loop resonates.

The switch box should be waterproof and contains the two-pole, three-way switch (which needs to withstand high rf voltages except for really low-power operation). Switch positions are A for 10MHz, B for 7 and 21MHz and C for 14MHz.

I feel that it should be stressed that, except on very low power, the wires X and Y connected to the switch will be at high rf voltage, particularly on 7 and 21MHz, and that this needs to be taken fully into account where there is any possibility of anyone else, especially young children, having access to these wires.

The "Claw Mark 4" antenna

TT (March 1985, pp180-1 and a brief note in February 1986, page 107) provided information on a new form of loaded folded-dipole element for use in multiband arrays that has been under development over the past two years by Les Moxon, G6XN. The innovatory design, while remaining basically the same, has progressed through various detail changes in an effort to retain the advantages while eliminating problems in achieving repeatability and equally good performance on different bands, etc.

This has led to a Mk4 version, Fig 4, and G6XN has recently outlined the background to this development. He writes: "I remarked previously (*TT* March 1985) that the Mk3 version appeared to have no vices. However I later realized that on 10·1 MHz, whereas the Mk2 elements had been undercoupled, those of the Mk3 were seriously overcoupled. The neutralizing capacitances became so large that it became virtually a driven array. As indicated in my *HF Antennas for All Locations* book this meant that tuning and matching became difficult on this band, although with patience reasonable performance could be obtained.

"For Mk4 I have reverted to the earlier Mk2 arrangement in which the bent-over ends of the multi-wire section are brought down the expanding arms. Although the elements are shorter, the radiation resistance is not reduced and the effective height is increased. Coupling is satisfactory at 10MHz and current distribution in the loop is improved at 28MHz, removing any tendency for the radiation pattern to break up as well as providing a better match to 600Ω line. Planar loading has been discarded in favour of conventional helical (inductive) loading; replacement of metal by fibreglass has allowed the helices to be wound on 1in diameter tube at the lower end of the fishing rods. The number of wires in parallel has been reduced to two, simplifying construction.

"Another development is the discovery that for three-band operation it is not essential to use resonant feeder lines. For 14/28MHz a 50Ω feeder can be connected directly through a 4:1 balun. For 21MHz it is necessary to switch in another quarter-wave impedance transformer using a relay (a typical small relay proved successful) though no linear amplifier was used on 21MHz. Coaxial feeders, however, reduce the flexibility of the 'poor man's log periodic' feature."

Developed initially as a two-element multiband antenna G6XN has also tried it as a three-element array. While performance was improved on 28MHz, it is difficult to justify the extra complexity on other bands, and G6XN continues to stress that a two-element array can often be raised higher above ground than a heavier three-element antenna. He does not recommend using the extra element.

A small version of the "Mk4 Claw" has also been tested. The two outer elements (18ft span) from the three-element array were used. Arm lengths were increased to 16ft by means of 3ft 6in alloy extensions (for 28MHz this amount of metal should not be exceeded) and spacing reduced to 8ft to improve performance on 28MHz. Although not intended for 10MHz, this proved successful despite a calculated loss of 3dB relative to full size monoband performance. Feeders were short enough (about 40ft) to permit all tuning, matching and coupling adjustments to be carried out from the operating position, the loops being resonated only roughly prior to erection. Helical loading was distributed along the lower halves of the elements in contrast to the central loading of the basic Mk4.

Constructional notes for the Claw Mk4

Reference should be made to the notes on the earlier "Claw" elements in *TT*, March 1985 and February 1986. The "example" dimensions shown in Fig 4 refer to a simulated loop laid out horizontally six feet above a lawn for investigation of current distribution, etc. The lower dipole (BGE) may be helically wound along the entire length or end-loaded as shown with short helices (10ft of wire in helix is roughly equal to 6ft straight). The stub dimensions for 600Ω line or other feeder systems could be calculated from the figures given, though these are intended only as rough guide-lines. An atu in the shack is usually all that is needed (ie *no* stubs) with 600Ω line except on 10MHz and, if long feeders are used, on 21MHz. To match on 21MHz (at ground level) feed with 600Ω line and find point of "zero" current. Insert 10pF capacitors in series with each wire at a point 3ft closer to the antenna. In two cases this met the requirements for 21MHz also (about 17pF at 5ft should give approximate match to 50 ohms via 4:1 balun). Antenna resonances checked with gdo should be in-band if feeder is shorted on the transmitter side of the capacitors.

For a two-element beam, a loop spacing of 12ft at top (lower ends at mast head) is recommended if 10MHz facility is required; otherwise 8ft spacing is sufficient. The semicircular shape shown in Fig 4 is believed to be optimum. This shape is readily achieved with glassfibre fishing rods tapering down to about ⅛in diameter and suitably angled. Metal extensions at the lower ends of fishing rods may be used but a total horizontal metal dimension of one-fifth wavelength at the highest frequency band should not be exceeded. Helices may be wound on the fishing rods or on any glass-fibre struts but *not* on the metal extensions.

The use of two feeders in order to allow beam reversal from the shack (see previous notes in *TT* etc) is very strongly recommended by G6XN. It is highly desirable to make the elements and especially the electrical length of the feeders *identical* (use gdo) so that nulling for one direction holds for the other and there is no need to readjust the atu. It is easy to provide reflector tuning at the operating position. Reflectors need to be tuned only slightly lower (typically 1 per cent) than the operating frequency. Tune for signal nulls. Should the nulls not be reasonably deep, coupling needs adjusting (eg by fixed capacitors, in or out of phase) between feed lines; see Fig 4 (b). Two element arrays as described tend to provide deep nulls on most bands but with the Mk4 element G6XN obtained only about 10dB on 21MHz. In such cases the coupling needs adjusting, for example, by capacitors between points on the feeders where there is significant rf voltage. The correct phase can be determined by observing the current in the reflector relative to the driven element, or more easily by trial and error. Points such as Y-Y on the diagram are ideal for a coupling adjustment (in-phase connection to increase coupling). In practice, a single small trimmer just inside the shack sufficed to give an "infinite" null depth.

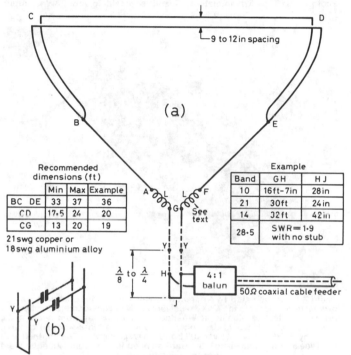

Fig 4. G6XN's improved Mark 4 element for "The Claw" multiband beam array. (b) Use of small capacitors to vary the coupling and so to improve the depth of the nulls on some bands

Anchoring towers to stay up

TT (November 1984, pp 965-6) drew attention to the safety problem of power-cables, gas mains and possible damage to other utility services including drains buried in the ground. At that time David J Reynolds, G3ZPF also gave advice on the preparation of mast and tower bases in order to ensure that the pressure that spreads downwards from underneath the base does not surcharge any drains, manholes or other surfaces. He noted that even a small lightweight mast should not be set up above a facility service since this involves the risk that you could be saddled with the blame for any subsequent damage; "Even if your base pressure does not, in fact, cause any damage, subsequent 'natural' faults of any kind will tend to be attributed to its presence by local authorities etc who will gleefully present you with the bill for repairs—and they may need to dig up your base in order to carry them out."

Rather different aspects of installing "anchors" for towers are touched upon by James H Hayes, W4XS, in a letter to *QST* (September 1986, pp49, 50); "More towers fail because of improperly installed anchors than for all other reasons combined. The most common sin involves a complete misunderstanding of the concrete anchor.

"Most amateurs use a posthole digger to sink a round hole for the tower anchor rod. They then fill the hole with concrete. Thus, the concrete takes the form of the hole—a cylindrical plug aligned with the axis of the guy. When guy tension is applied to the rod, it tends to remove the plug and all

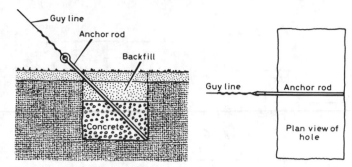

Fig 5. A cross-section of the form of secure anchor for antenna towers recommended by W4XS

too often succeeds. The unhappy amateur laments because he was sure he had enough concrete in the hole.

"The holding quality of a tower anchor is more dependent on the shape and position of the concrete than most of us realize. Here are a few hints for safe anchors:

The anchor hole should be dug in a rectangular shape and oriented perpendicular to the plane of the guy wires (see Fig 5). A backhole with a small (12in) bucket makes an ideal hole. The end of the guy rod should rest on the floor of the hole and touch the rear wall.

The anchor-rod eye should rest on the top lip of the hole, in line with the guy wire and exit the hole at about 45°. In order to assure the rod-eye position during the pour, drive a small wooden stake in the earth near the eye and securely wire the eye to the stake. The rod should not be bent. The tower manufacturer should specify the amount of concrete for each anchor. Be sure the rod remains in position during the pour and that part of the rod is covered with concrete.

In most installations, it is neither necessary nor wise to completely fill the hole with concrete. A 1- or 2ft block around the rod foot is usually specified. After the pour, backfill the hole and allow the concrete to cure before applying tension to the rod.

"After understanding this method, you can easily imagine how strong the anchor is. Any forces tending to pull the anchor from the ground must drag a small wall of concrete through undisturbed soil. When the rod is not bent or covered with concrete near the top of the hole, it is free to flex and not likely to fracture.

"The only anchor worse than a round concrete anchor is an earth anchor—and the only thing worse than an earth anchor is no anchor at all."

Early use of pi-networks

It is often forgotten that every circuit idea that today we accept as standard practice had to be thought of and implemented by one or more engineers. Hartley, Colpitts, Clapp, Gouriet, Vackar were/are all real people and similarly for the hundreds of circuit ideas that have never been called by the name of their originators.

At the recent 'History of Television' conference at the IEE, Dr Eric White (one of the early Marconi-EMI team that developed the 405-line system) described some of the many electronic circuits that were introduced in the 'thirties during the development of electronic tv in the UK and the USA. Today they are used (often in the form of integrated circuits) in all branches of electronics. But he confessed that he has never been able to track down the origin of the cathode-follower (emitter-follower) configuration although he recalls that the arrangement was much used in EMI research laboratories by 1933, especially as an amplifier output stage able to handle the stray capacitance of a length of screened cable connecting to the next panel, or to form a matched termination to such cable.

There is often considerable difficulty in pin-pointing the first use of a particular circuit configuration, particularly since, as in the case of the Clapp-Gouriet oscillator, two different engineers may develop the same circuit quite independently of each other. In the November *TT* I was rash enough to state: "To the best of my knowledge the first person to conceive and put into practice the idea of using the pi-network as an unbalanced output circuit for the final stage of a transmitter was John Brown, G3EUR for the 3 Mk1 ("B-1") suitcase transmitter-receiver of 1941-42."

This has resulted in a letter from S F Brown, G4LU showing that this technique dates back well before WW2. His letter has also enabled me to track down pi-networks used in this way in a 90/100W rf output transmitter for 7 and 14 MHz and in a 600W amplifier. G4LU writes: "Readers will be interested to know that the single-ended pi-network, as a tank circuit, was shown on page 82 of the 1938 edition of *Radio Handbook* as 'a simplified pi antenna coupling system' but strange to say it did not figure in any of the constructional equipments described later in the book (but see below).

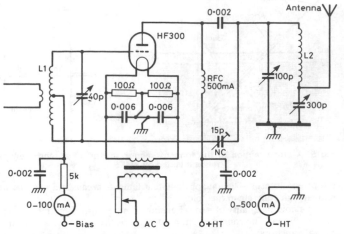

Fig 6. Grid-neutralized high-power amplifier using a shunt-fed pi-network tank circuit as published in the 1936 edition of *Radio Handbook*. Amplifier designs with this configuration had however virtually disappeared from the 1938 edition!

Photo 1. The Type 51/1 miniature transmitter providing about 3W rf output, introduced during 1945

"As a matter of history, the circuit in its push-pull form goes back much further in time. It was used in a STC 60kW transmitter installed at Rugby Radio Station in 1929 for the telephone service to the USA and also in a Post Office-built transmitter of the same period for the South American service. In the PO transmitter the output capacitance was variable but the input capacitance, made up of the grid-anode capacitances and the associated cross-connected neutralizing capacitors. Tuning was accomplished by varying the reactance of the inductive branches by means of series capacitances which, in some conditions, could flash-over on the dsb modulation peaks. This could mean panic stations all round to restore the transmitter to traffic!

"Another interesting feature of the circuit was that ht was fed to the valves by tapping into the coil at the nodal voltage point; this was found by using a "stick voltmeter" which in one tragic case proved to be lethal. This instrument was simply an insulated rod with a metal stud in the end. The stud would pull an arc from points at high rf potential; no arc no volts!"

G4LU's reference to the pre-war *Radio Handbook*, resulted in my checking the even earlier 1936 edition in the IBA Library. Pages 122–3 describe and illustrate two versions of a "90W cw transmitter" for 7 or 14MHz using two of the then popular "210" power triodes in the power amplifier. The first version has a "grid-neutralized final amplifier" in which the choke-coupled tank circuit indisputably forms a pi-network coupler.

The same basic grid-neutralized, shunt-fed pi-network circuit is also shown on page 95 of the 1936 *Radio Handbook* for a 600W cw amplifier based on the HF-300 power triode; Fig 6. This emphasized that shunt-fed tank circuits call for efficient rf chokes which have no resonances near any of the bands on which the amplifier is to be operated. This important piece of advice was often overlooked in the first post-war decade when pi-network tank circuits came back into favour. *Radio Handbook* pointed out that many types of rf chokes could fail in service when used on 3·5MHz but

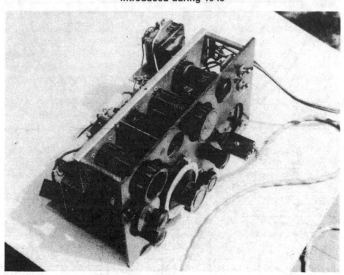

Photo 2. Mains-operated 1-v-1 hf receiver. This appears to be an early version of what developed into the MkXV receivers made in considerable numbers for British Intelligence Signals at Whaddon near Bletchley from about 1939. Almost certainly it would have originally been fitted in a wooden cabinet. Photo by G4HHZ. The receiver still brings in weak signals. The contrast with the Type 51/1 unit shows how the wartime need for very compact equipment speeded miniaturization

stood up satisfactorily when used on 7 and 14MHz, adding: "If the rf choke becomes quite warm after a few minutes of operation, it is proof that power is being lost in the choke and a replacement should be made by a more suitable type. The plate-blocking capacitor should be mounted at least 1in from the metal panel in order to minimize the capacitance to ground." Still extremely useful advice 50 years on!

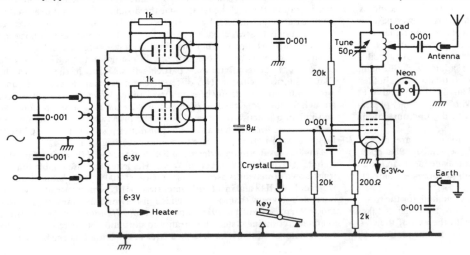

Fig 7. Circuit diagram of the 3W SOE "pocket transmitter" as introduced in 1945 and possibly the smallest hf transmitter of WW2. Three similar valves type CV136 (EL91 etc) were used as power oscillator and full-wave rectifier. The outer case measured only $5\frac{1}{2}$ by $4\frac{1}{2}$ by $1\frac{1}{4}$ inches and weighed about 1lb 11oz. Component values include some modern replacements in the example held by John Lawrence, GW3JGA

It is curious that amateurs were using the pi-network tank in the mid-'thirties but the idea then dropped out of sight until G3EUR resurrected it for some of the wartime suitcase sets. The American OSS organization based their SSTR-1 suitcase radio on G3EUR's B-2 so it may well be that the idea went back to the States as an SOE export!

Every time I mention the portable wartime clandestine radios there are always readers anxious to identify sets they have acquired (Pierre Lorain's *Secret Warfare* book is an excellent source of information). Photo 1 and Fig 7 show SOE's 51/1 pocket transmitter that was used on a limited scale in the final months of the war. This had an associated pocket "straight" receiver (53/1) using three 1T4 miniature valves. Photo 2 shows an early (and comparatively heavy) mains-operated 1-V-1 regenerative "straight" receiver with three metal 6SK7 valves built for the British Intelligence Service at Whaddon. I recently had a chance to try out this very lively receiver which belongs to an IBA colleague Tony Harwood, G4HHZ. It still brings in plenty of signals (unfortunately not always one at a time) on 3·5, 7 and rather less effectively on 14MHz. The old valve "straight" sets were much better than many younger readers might suspect, with sensitivity often better than early superhets and (at least on cw) with the selectivity improved by regeneration and sometimes by an audio filter.

Safe operations

In September 1984, *TT* sadly reported the deaths of two professional broadcast engineers (using an ob vehicle) and two citizen's band operators all of whom were electrocuted while attempting to erect antennas close to overhead power lines. It was stressed that the risk of a metal pole or antenna coming into contact with high-voltage power lines is "undoubtedly the single greatest potential hazard in field operation and antenna erection". Since there is always a risk that a metal pole may bend or become out of control during its installation or erection, a very wide berth indeed should always be given to power lines. As a correspondent later pointed out this is advisable not only on grounds of safety but also due to radiation of interference from high-voltage overhead power lines.

Sadly, the American magazines have reported the death during the 1986 Field Day of Mike Mankey, WB0TEE, an ARRL section manager. Apparently the group were using an unfamiliar site and failed to spot power lines hidden behind trees. A tragic reminder of the ever-present danger from power lines whether high voltage, 480V three-phase, or standard 240V or (in North America) 117V.

TT has previously re-printed the RSGB safety code; for a change here is the ARRL code as published in *QST* (September 1986, pp88–9):

"There are reasons for accidents involving radio gear, but never *good* reasons. Take no chances with electricity. Even a low-voltage shock can be serious—sometimes fatal.

"Heed the ARRL safety code; While there's no reason for you to be involved in a ham-related accident, that possibility always exists if you are not thinking safety. Following the ARRL safety code will make your ham experience more enjoyable. Read it and practice it.

(1) Kill all power circuits completely before touching behind the panel or inside the chassis or the enclosure.

(2) Never allow anyone else to switch the power on and off for you while you're working on equipment.

(3) Don't troubleshoot in a transmitter when you're tired or sleepy.

(4) Never adjust internal components by hand. Use special care when checking energized circuits.

(5) Avoid bodily contact with grounded metal (racks, radiators) or damp floors when working on the transmitter.

(6) Never wear headphones while working on gear.

(7) Follow the rule of keeping one hand in your pocket.

(8) Instruct members of your household how to turn the power off and how to apply artificial respiration. (Instruction sheets on the latest approved method can be obtained from your local Red Cross office).

(9) If you must climb a tower to adjust an antenna, use a safety harness. Never work alone.

(10) Do not install antennas at levels that permit humans or animals to come in contact with them. Not only might the victim sustain a severe rf burn, he or she could run into the antenna and be injured.

(11) Do not operate high-power uhf or microwave gear that has inadequate shielding against radiation. Similarly, do not look into or stand near microwave antennas when transmitter power is being fed to them.

(12) Do not install antennas near electrical power lines.

(13) Don't drink alcoholic beverages when working on equipment or installing antennas.

Take time to be careful. Death is permanent."

Parallel resistance nomograph

In these days of home computers and pocket calculators the use of nomographs, a form of analogue computer, has greatly diminished, yet for many purposes they remain simple and convenient, often providing entirely adequate accuracy. A nomograph that is new to me appears in *QST* (September 1986, page 50) republished from an item by James V Smith, KD4YD in the Manalee ARC bulletin.

This provides an easy way of finding the resistance of two resistors in parallel or alternatively convenient resistor values to provide a required value when connected in parallel. It simply consists of three intersecting lines, the outer two at 120° bisected at 60° with a third line all linearly calibrated to the same scale; see Fig 8.

To find the combined value of two resistors, plot the value of one on line R1, the second on line R2. Then the value of them in parallel is represented where a line joining the two points intersect. To find a combination yielding a given value, then, if that point is plotted on RT, any line passing through that and crossing R1 and R2 will show a possible combination.

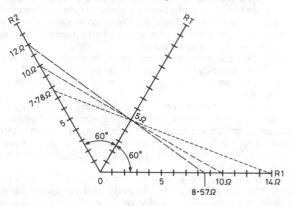

Fig 8 KD4YD's simple nomograph for two resistors in parallel

Lightning protection

In the November issue (page 781) I quoted the letter from David Jones, N4JED, originally published in *QST*, in which he warned against using coaxial switches as a lightning protection switch. It is only fair to note that Don Tyrrell, W8AD of Alpha Delta Communications, has commented (*QST* October 1986, page 50) as follows: "With regard to the letter from David Jones, I believe a clarification is in order since Mr Jones made his assumption based on only one type of station configuration. His letter describes a ground at the antenna and another at either the rig or through the ac line.

"If a coaxial switch is inserted exactly as he described, with no other grounds installed, his assumption is correct. In that case, the lightning surge current would be shunted from the coaxial centre conductor to the shield through the switch and to the rig. However, an internally grounded coaxial switch is a mechanical crowbar when in the grounded position, and can serve as an effective lightning surge protector (for near misses, not direct hits) when the station arrangement is changed as follows:

1. Attach a separate, external ground wire to the switch itself and run the wire to the station ground system (not the chassis).

2. Ground the coaxial cable shield to an external ground where the cable enters the building. Since our line of Transi-Trap coaxial surge protectors and our DELTA-4 gas-tube-protected coaxial switches are electronic crowbar devices, we list the same precautions in our installation sheets. It is true that *no* protector or switch should be tied back to the equipment chassis or depend on the chassis ground wire only to provide a proper surge-current return path. In so doing, a chassis can be raised many hundreds of volts above ground, causing serious component and equipment damage.

"Most equipment damage comes from lightning-generated surge voltages from distant, out-of-sight storms, so a good protector has a definite place in a communications station. (Italics added). During nearby thunderstorms, however, it is always good practice to disconnect all cables."

In the November *TT* I mentioned the problem with the unprotected front-ends of AR88 and HRO receivers of the antenna coils being burnt out by static or local rf pick-up. This has prompted Jack Maling, G5JL, to comment that some time ago his old Dynatron vhf/fm broadcast receiver, connected to a fairly high outside antenna mounted on the chimney, twice, in about two years, lost its front-end coil, presumably due to static. Since the total cost of repair amounted to some £50, he claimed on his "house contents" insurance policy that covers lightning damage. On each occasion the company paid up without comment. It is, however, questionable whether claims would be successful for transceivers etc which might not be considered as "domestic" equipment unless separately covered. There might also be difficulty in proving that the damage was due to lightning and not your own tranmissions!

As George Jessop, G6JP, indicated a few years ago (*Radio Communications*, December 1982, pp1042–46) gas discharge tubes (gdt) can provide useful protection; these are often called "gas filled surge arrestors".

AC mains transient protection

As noted by W8AD above and in the December *TT*, surge voltages can be generated on the ac supply lines both from distant lightning and from switching operations. Such voltage transients can induce costly faults in radio communications equipment and consumer-electronics appliances. Jerry Hinshaw, N6JH, in "AC line transient protection" (*Ham Radio* April 1986, pp59–61) describes how he put his video cassette recorder out of action with his lawnmower. "One day as I was trimming the weeds in my front lawn, my electric lawnmower blew a motor field rectifier and began to draw a heavy current from the ac line. The situation was quickly, but not instantaneously, corrected by the house circuit breaker tripping and breaking the circuit, as it should do.

"The electric fields in the motor collapsed, producing a large back emf on the now open-circuit ac supply cord. Unfortunately this cord connected the mower to the house circuit on which my vcr was awaiting the start of a tv programme.

"The vcr, like much modern equipment, including most transceivers and home computers, does not like high voltage spikes coupled into relatively fragile cmos ic devices. On a computer, line spikes or transients can cause data drop-outs, "soft" errors in the ram memory etc. In my vcr (luckily still under warranty) the unusually hefty transient fried some component on the microprocessor board."

N6JH notes that in the USA a number of "clean" outlet boxes are marketed that have built-in protection against voltage spikes. These units normally fit one or more small metal oxide varistor (mov) devices to provide transient suppression. The mov is a form of fast-acting voltage dependent resistor that is rather like a pair of back-to-back zener diodes. For this type of domestic application an mov is effective and tends to cost less than the "breakover diode" (form of back-to-back thyristor) described in the December *TT*.

A mov device can absorb, for its modest size, a surprisingly high energy transient lasting a matter of microseconds.

In the UK there are various "clean" sockets usually fitted with mov devices on sale; there are also rather lower cost 13A plugs fitted with presumably similar surge suppressors. N6JH however notes that in the USA the special outlet boxes cost at least $25 whereas on a diy basis he reduces the cost to about $5 per outlet box, using General Electric (US) metal oxide varistors type V130LA10A. GE devices are available in the UK, though I cannot find any listed in the latest trade catalogue of RS Components. But remember that you cannot use a V130 device on 240 mains (USA 117V) and

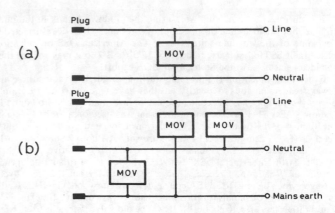

Fig 9. Schematic diagram show how metal oxide varistors (mov) can be installed to protect equipment from power line transients. (a) Two-wire system with single mov. (b) Use of three mov devices to protect fully a three-wire system

you would need a V250 or V260 type of device. The V number indicates the voltage at which the resistance of the device begins to fall rapidly.

Fig 9(a) shows a single mov used to protect a two-wire appliance, but for the more usual (and recommended) three-wire equipment and appliances it is advisable to use three devices as in Fig 9(b). But, of course, make sure that the outlet box or plug is put together so that there is no possibility of any hazard to you, your family or your pets!

The break-over-diode is intended primarily to protect telecommunications equipment where present practice is to use gas discharge tubes (gdt) at the interface to the outside world. The use of a gdt alone is not considered satisfactory as the residual voltage resulting from the relatively slow switch-on and high firing voltage can damage semiconductor devices. BT have been adopting a distributed two-stage protection strategy to protect against (a) surges due to lightning, (b) induction from adjacent power lines, and (c) accidental direct contact between power lines and telephone cables. It seems likely that the bod may become established in this area.

Tips and topics

Brian Bower, G3COJ adds to the 6L6 saga by recalling a story told to him by J B Gunn, the Englishman who was later to give his name to the Gunn-diode oscillator while working for IBM in Switzerland. As a schoolboy he was evacuated to the USA during WW2 and later became a member of the Cambridge University Wireless Society where G3COJ knew him. While in the USA he came across an American amateur who ran no less than 250W input to a pair of 6L6 valves. This involved soldering two large tin cans to the metal valves and filling them with water! With the aid of this improvised heat-exchanger, heat-sink, water-cooling system, call it what you will, it proved possible to run two 6L6s in a quarter-kilowatt transmitter. □

Technical Topics
by Pat Hawker, G3VA

MOST AMATEURS ACCEPT the inevitability of some degree of unreliability in their radio equipment. Even the best suffer from the so-called "bath-tub reliability curve"—initial high rate of failures, reducing to a more or less flat period of low failures, then rising once again as the equipment reaches the end of its useful life.

Frustrating though it is when a transceiver goes on the blink, it is fortunately not a matter of life or death. A minor personal tragedy perhaps for individuals or groups who may have gone to much trouble and expense, only to experience the frustrations of Murphy's Law that if anything can go wrong it will do so at the most inconvenient moment.

Where reliability really matters

But there are many professional and defence applications of radio communications, radar, broadcasting, speech and data telecommunications where reliability over many months or years is by far the single most important performance characteristic. Even with modern equipment, whether or not entirely dependent upon solidstate technology, the provision of redundancy and fall-back systems is regarded as essential. Even so it would be a rash or stupid engineer who would claim any system as 100 per cent reliable: 99 per cent, even 99.9 per cent or 99.99 perhaps, but never 100 per cent.

I once heard John Glenn, the astronaut, when asked what he thought about during his space trip, reply that he looked critically at the equipment on which his life depended and remembered that NASA always bought on the basis of accepting the lowest of three tenders!

Recently, the IEEE's *Spectrum* monthly journal (November 1986) ran a special feature "Our burdened skies" devoted to a critical examination of the American domestic air transportation system which is under great stress due in part to the increasing burdens placed on its air traffic control system. The journal emphasized that this is still an essentially safe system since "when crises do arise, the great majority are resolved without mishap".

But, it would seem, an increasing number of problems are arising, "The radios, radars and computers that help controllers do their job—some 23,000 pieces of equipment operating 24 hours a day, seven days a week—are not the latest available. Breakdowns occur. Failures in radio communications are not uncommon. Radars can be troublesome; some sets date to the second world war and still use vacuum tubes. Computers tend to become overloaded with data and are forced to throw away critically useful information. The air traffic control computers are not even as good in some respects as the IBM PC-XT personal computer."

Failures of the atc ground transmitters, despite the installation of back-up transmitters on the same channel, are by no means rare. This can be due to semiconductor, valve or component failures, failures of the control systems for switching in the reserve transmitters, failures in the telecommunications links connecting the controllers to the transmitters, power supply failures, problems with electromechanical relays and presumably to a lesser degree any of the various problems that arise with antennas, feeder cables, receivers and interconnecting links.

While the aviation industry, not unnaturally, claims that "outages" could be greatly reduced by installing the latest all-solidstate radio, radar and information-processing equipment, it should not be forgotten that semiconductors are vulnerable not only to transient overvoltages etc (from which they need to be protected) but also to long-term chemical and corrosion failure mechanisms that can affect a very small percentage of chips and components over a matter of years.

Spectrum reports that: "The information that is provided to the controller by computers and radars is transmitted to the pilots by radios. Along with the phone lines and switching equipment that carry signals to and from transmitters and receivers, radios are cited by controllers as the least reliable part of the atc system."

Loss of mains power at remote transmitter/receiver sites—a problem that also plagues broadcasters in all countries—may be due to accidental cutting of cables, lightning, snow and ice, failure of stand-by and "no-break" diesel generators, etc.

My own feeling is that more important than any calculated "mean time between faults" (mtbf) for amateur equipment is their "mean time to repair" (mttr). It is here that the older valve equipment scores heavily, provided the user maintains a stock of replacement valves. The other most common faults on older equipment, in my experience, are open-circuited high-wattage resistors, defective electrolytic capacitors, defective valve sockets and open-circuit lower frequency transformers due to "green-spot" corrosion. The most annoying faults are faulty band-change switches and slow-motion tuning drives.

Solidstate and the future

The December *TT* (pp853 to 854) included an item on the continued relevance of thermionic devices to amateur-radio transceivers, transmitters and linear amplifiers at other than low-power and/or portable and mobile operation. This was not to imply that in some areas, including uhf and microwave receivers, the conventional valve can match solidstate devices in performance; though we should not forget that satellite communications by and large still depend on the travelling-wave-tube-amplifier (twta). In the laboratories, the latest marvel is the modfet, a new class of Group 3 high-electron-mobility-transistor (hemt). Modfet stands for "modulation-doped GaAs (Al, Ga). As heterojunction field-effect transistor". At room temperature the experimental devices have achieved under 1dB noise figure up to 10GHz, under 2dB to 20GHz, under 3dB well above 30GHz at 300K (ie room temperature). Under cooled conditions, a modfet amplifier is capable of providing a noise figure of 0·4dB with 14dB gain at 10GHz at 77K. It is being claimed that these devices should prove inherently superior to all other fet technologies in operating or switching frequency, power dissipation and noise. But low-cost modfets may still be some way away.

A valid reason for the trend in amateur equipment towards all-solidstate power amplifiers is not performance but the fact that so many valve makers have virtually ceased production with the result that prices of *new* valves and high-voltage components, including mains-transformers, have risen at a rate much faster than inflation, whereas increasing production of semiconductors has had the opposite effect. But valves can still be found, not only in junk boxes, though this is not always true of valve bases.

Alan Williams, G3KSU draws attention to "The last days of the vacuum tube" by Joseph H Johnson, president of Microwave Modules & Devices (*Microwave Systems News*, September 1986, page 58). This argues the case for consigning valves not to the junk box but to the dustbins—a view that I find difficult to accept but one that needs to be examined. He poses provocative questions:

"Is the time approaching when vacuum tubes will no longer be required? . . . How long will it be before we see the last days of the vacuum tube? . . . Over the next two decades, dramatic changes will occur in high-power, high-frequency transmitters used in applications from weather radar, commercial broadcast or military communications to medical nmr equipment, linacs and industrial heating. Businesses dealing with high-power rf or microwave that fail to foresee this change are doomed to stagnation or failure. The wave of the future in the solidstate world is integrating device, circuit and cooling technology to achieve impressive performance improvements. *Once the transistor package with all its parasitics is discarded* (added italics) and the transistor chip is integrated directly into a thick- or thin-film hybrid module, decade-wide bandwidths or kilowatts of power become possible . . . Another innovation of the last few years is to use a building block approach to combine many amplifiers or modules to achieve very high power . . . Today a building block of 500kW is being developed . . . In the medium-wave broadcast band the transmitter of choice today is a 50kW all-solid-state unit. A 5kW vhf/fm (broadcast) transmitter can be sold for the same price as a tube unit, but operating and maintenance costs decline dramatically . . . Ultra-high-power solid-state and microwave amplifiers are a reality. Increases in both the power level and the frequency are constantly pushing many high-power tubes into the history books. Make sure you are part of the change."

Although there is more than a touch of jam tomorrow about this article, it illustrates well the strong pressures on the diminishing areas of valve technology still found in professional equipment. Yet I for one would continue to argue that *for amateur equipment* at medium or high-power, at the present time and possibly for some time to come, there remain valid reasons for resisting commercial pressures to write-off valves. There is still a place for them in our shacks as well as in the history books.

The valve/solidstate debate

Peter Chadwick, G3RZP, chairman of the RSGB's Technical & Publications Committee, enters the debate with a useful list of pros and cons. He writes:

The case against valves

(1) *Cost*—Look at the prices being asked even for small-signal receiving valves (although as an effective scrounger who came back from a recent business trip to the States with a load of metal octal valves who am I to complain?).
(2) *No valves in the RAE*—This really means that articles to be useful to newly licensed amateurs need basing diagrams, wiring diagrams etc.
(3) *High voltages are dangerous*—Many of today's amateurs may well only have high voltages in the power amplifier; as a result they forget about the danger.

The case for valves

(1) Power amplifier stages are more linear and less likely to have parasitics or, if they do, it is easier to find and cure them. Solidstate power amplifiers can have lots of spurs—and you will never know without a spectrum analyzer.
(2) For pa stages, the cost is comparable, especially if you consider the cost of the power supply unit.
(3) Linear amplifiers providing reasonable power efficiency, cost and ruggedness are much easier to build with valves.
(4) Valve circuits tend to be simpler.
(5) High voltages only kill if you touch them!

G3RZP continues: "It isn't a clear cut case by any means. Listening to some of the homebrew (solidstate) QRP transmissions on 3·5MHz, I think an EF91-EL91-5763 valve rig would give a signal with less drift, chirps, T7 notes and spurs than some of the solidstate rigs I hear! Homebrewing a solidstate pa is *not* easy if you are going to avoid parasitics; using a 2N3866 on frequencies as low as 3·5MHz is not a good idea, use a BFY50. The F, is lower and so are the chances of parasitics. Within the professional field, nobody now knows how they ever managed in the days before the spectrum analyser. In my view, the older valve circuits were tamer and possibly engineers (and amateurs) were technically more experienced!" At one time it was argued that nobody should use ssb without a good oscilloscope; the trend today is that to build a solidstate transmitter you need to have, or have access to, a good spectrum analyzer that can cost thousands of pounds. A powerful argument for sticking to "old-fashioned" valve technology.

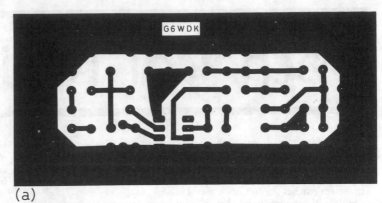

(a)

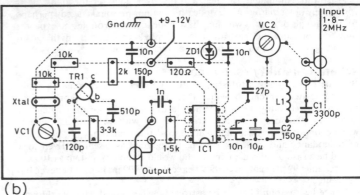

(b)

Fig 2 Printed circuit board and component layout for top-band converter

receiver. The SL1640C has a low-impedance emitter-follower output (pin 6). Since the makers do not recommend this pin being used to drive capacitive loads, G6WDK includes a 1·5KΩ load resistor. To reduce the voltage across the SL1640C (rated at 9V), the supply is regulated by a zener diode to a safe 6·2V. The converter is accommodated on a small (1¾in by 3¾in) pcb (Fig 2). Since the current drain is low, a PP3 battery could be used.

No alignment is necessary and, as G6WDK puts it, the converter should work on completion of the final solder joint. While not claimed as a high-performance system (a tunable pre-amplifier or rf stage might prove desirable for dx), it brought in 120 stations in 22 countries in a few weeks of operation using a 100ft random-length wire at only about 15ft above ground.

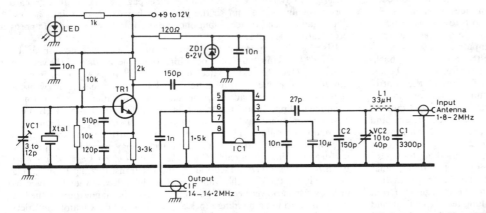

Fig 1. Top-band converter by F/G6WDK for use with any 14MHz receiver. Crystal 16·000MHz (fundamental), HC18U or HC25. IC Plessey SL1640C. TR1 any general-purpose small-signal npn silicon transistor with T018 case such as BSX51, 2N2222, 2N2369, 2N708, 2N914 etc. Capacitors ceramic unless shown otherwise. VC1 and VC2 small trimmer capacitors about 3–12pF. Resistors miniature 0·25W. L1 miniature 33μH rfc. ZD1 6·2V (0·25W) zener diode. Typical voltages (positive) to ground with 9V battery: IC pin 2, 3V; 3, 3V; 4, 6·5V; 5, 5·5V; 6, 5V; 7, 3V

Top band converter for hf receivers

There are still many receivers/transceivers in use that do not cover the 1·8MHz band. Michel Monteil, F/G6WDK, Egletons, France (one time G5MZC and who also operates G6WDK/P from the Isles of Scilly) built a 1·8HMz converter to use with a 1967 SR700A that would be equally suitable for any hf receiver lacking this band (Fig 1). This is based on a crystal-controlled oscillator and Plessey SL1640C double balanced mixer. Using a 16MHz crystal the converter spreads the 1·8MHz band over the i.f range 14 to 14·2MHz. Crystal frequency can be trimmed over a small range by means of the trimmer VC1. The antenna input circuit forms a broad-band, low-pass filter with a cut-off frequency of about 2MHz and its primary function is to attenuate strong hf signals ahead of the mixer, particularly 14MHz signals to minimize break-through into the main

Valves and the 807

Recent items in *TT* on the use of valves in medium and high-power transmitters have brought in a good deal of comment—plus an embarrassing number of base connections/characteristics of the old TT11 including the bitter sweet information that these were given in at least one book in my collection. A useful reminder that it is not sufficient to have a large number of ancient and modern books and brochures unless you can remember what's in them! I rule out the use of home computers as a memory since the amount of data needing indexing is too large for anything much less than a main-frame computer. My policy is just to hoard all the paperwork that comes my way and then try to remember what I should have somewhere!

Charles Wells, G4ZZG returned to amateur radio as a retirement hobby

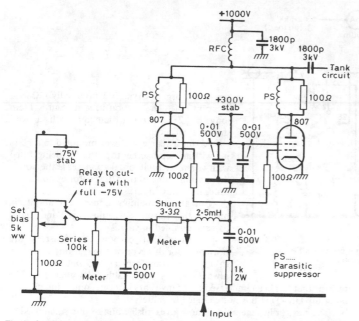

Fig 3. G4ZZG's linear amplifier using a pair of 807 valves with passive grid input. 1mA meter arranged to read grid volts and current (which should be nil)

Table 2 Valve base connections

Valve	Base	1	2	3	4	5	6	7	8	9	TC
6K7 (corr)	IO	S	H	A	G2	G3		H	K		G1
TT11	IO	H	BP	G1	G2			H	K		A
6SN7	IO	1G1	1A	1K	2G1	2A	2K	H	H		
813	7-pin L	F		G2	G1	BP		F			A
12BY7	B9A	K	G1	H	HCT	A	H	H	G2	G3	
2E26	IO	K,BP	H	G2	K,BP	G1	K,BP	H	BS		A
829	7-pin X	H	2G1	G2	K,G3	HCT	1G1	H			1A, 2A
6AG7	IO	G3,H	IS	G1	K	G2	H	A			
6SK7	IO	S	H	GS	K	K	G2	H	A		
6AQ5	B7G	G1	K,BP	H	H	A	2	G1			

BP Beam plates, BS Base sleeve, S Shield, L Large, X Special

arrangement; initially he had a tuned grid input circuit but changed to passive grid. With his 10W (TS120V) input he tried 50, 100, 200, 500 and his present 1000Ω (2W) input loading. He uses anti-parasitic devices in both anode and grid circuits (resistors-only in grid circuits) and single-point earthing for everything, including the tank circuit. Because of antenna restrictions, the rig is used only on 14, 21 and 28MHz, chiefly cw with some ssb. The new 807s perform well with 1000V and 120mA total current on cw providing 120W dc input and about 60W rf output. Bias voltage on the grids is −30V and standing anode current about 55mA; both grid and screen voltages are stabilized.

It is perhaps worth reminding some readers that the anode dissipation of a valve relates, not surprisingly, to the power dissipated (ie wasted) in the valve. A valve rated at 30W anode dissipation can be run with a dc input that depends on the amplifier efficiency; for example with say 70 per cent efficiency of a Class C sine-wave amplifier, the dc input could safely be about three times the anode dissipation, say 90 to 100W maximum dc input and around 70W rf output. Since more linears are run in Class AB2, with significant standing current and a maximum efficiency of around 50 per cent, you need a pair of valves (as in the G4ZZG amplifier) to achieve the same order of power output as a single valve in Class C. The older valve types were also designed for operation at full power only to a specified frequency, often 30MHz. Although usually still useful above this frequency, they need to be derated to a lower maximum power. Table 1 shows some examples of transmitting valves when used in Class C telegraphy service or narrow-band fm. Table 2 adds a few more base connections to G3GDU's list in the December '86 TT. As noted from time to time, the older valve types were often capable of surviving with the anode voltage well above the recommended figure—but not always!

after a break of 35 years. Remembering fondly the days of plentiful 6V6, 6L6, 807 valves, he acquired a TS120V (10W/26W p.e.p output) and set about adding on a valve linear amplifier. After the initial trauma of finding out current valve prices (actually, I see adverts for the 807 at £2 which is still not bad for a device that can run at a good 75W dc input in Class C telegraphy). Having long ago thrown away his old *WW Valve Guide* and the contents of his junk boxes he is now steadily compiling his own reference book of valve "pin-outs". He would welcome pin numbers on diagrams and similarly would like to see an RSGB publication on transmitting valves along the lines of Chas Miller's *Handbook of Valve Radio Repairs* which includes receiving valve information.

G4ZZG has acquired some UX5 valve sockets (still around but quite difficult to find) and has built a linear with two 807 valves and a psu providing a good 1000V (yes it is more than they are rated for but you can often get away with it). Unfortunately the first pair of 807s, obtained from a surplus dealer Sylvania JAN-type (that is to US Joint Army Navy specification) proved the exception; one glowed red and quickly gave up the ghost. He obtained a second pair from a Kent dealer who advertises valves in several journals and these appear to be of recent manufacture, with the brand name Selectron on the envelopes but supplied in plain white boxes (this usually means they come from Poland, the USSR or other East European countries which are still manufacturing valves in large numbers —*G3VA*).

Initially G4ZZG neutralized his 807 linear but found this unnecessary even on 28MHz when using passive grid input. Fig 3 shows his present

Table 1 Typical valves as Class C amplifiers

Valve	Anode Diss (W)	Max ht (v)	Max dc input (W)	Max freq full power	Heater V/A
6AG7	9	375	11·5	10	6·3/0·65
5763	13·5	375	15	175	6·3/0·75
6V6	8	350	16·5	10	6·3/0·45
6AQ5	8	350	16·5	54	6·3/0·45
6L6	21	400	40	10	6·3/0·9
6146	25	750	90	60	6·3/1·25
6146B		750	120	60	6·3
807	30	750	75	60	6·3/0·9
TT11	7·5	300	10	100	6·3/0·8
TT21	45	1,250	160	30	6·3
813	125	2,500	500	30	10/5

Notes: Figures are based on published ratings and are mostly conservative ICAS ratings. Figures for dc input apply to a single valve. Valves designed for television line-output (sweep) service not included (PL509, 6HF5, 6KD6, 6LF6 etc). Note that Class C (biased well beyond cut-off) is not suitable for linear service for which the lower efficiency Class AB2 is normally used.
Typical efficiencies (ie rf watts output/dc watts input):

Tripler stage	20–25%
Doubler stage	30–40%
Class A amplifier	10–50%
Class AB amplifier	50–60%
Class B amplifier	55–70%
Class C amplifier	65–80%

An 813 linear amplifier

A new 813 is a costly beast but there are still quite a lot around as surplus or hidden away in junk boxes if you can prevail upon their owners to part with them. W M Frost, G3OHE writes:

"Having experimented over the years with 813s and PL509s in various modes, I have finally come up with the basic arrangement shown in Fig 4. It is a development of the G2DAF design but with significant detail differences which considerably enhance the efficiency. Using a cheap, non-branded 813, this circuit, properly assembled, will provide a comfortable 400 watts at 28MHz, rising to 600W at 3·5MHz, without exceeding 250–260 mA anode current. Some of the modifications may be considered contentious by purist designers but signal reports confirm a clean signal with excellent audio quality; in fact, as good as comes from the driver unit.

"The main points of difference from the G2DAF arrangement are:

Input: This is through a trifilar balun connected to give a 3:1 voltage step-up from the 50Ω line. Input impedance is thus transformed to about 450Ω and ten 4·7k (2W) resistors in parallel give a close match under resting conditions. The arrangement makes the linear much easier to drive.

Quadrupler and 10K in 813 grid line: While the G2DAF amplifier is an excellent arrangement it has the disadvantage that 180–200V on the screen is not sufficient to give good AB2 efficiency. The change to a quadrupler alone is not an answer because the absence of bias causes the screen to draw very high currents, so depressing output from the four rectifiers to 250V maximum. The 10kΩ resistor allows bias to rise as drive increases. The result is that bias may rise at maximum output to 100V, allowing screen voltage to reach about 400V. At that level the valve can really perform efficiently.

Anti-parasitic arrangements: The 813 simply devours any device placed in its anode line. A choke in the grid circuit, plus a 10Ω screen stopper appear to provide sufficient safeguard against parasites.

Pi-tank capacitor: This is a 120pF component with the stator bars sawn through. Instead of switching in the extra 70pF section on 7 and 3·5MHz, it is connected to the 14MHz tap on the pi-coil. On 28, 21 and 14MHz, it forms an extra section to the pi-output capacitor. On 7 and 3·5MHz it helps to tune the tank circuit.

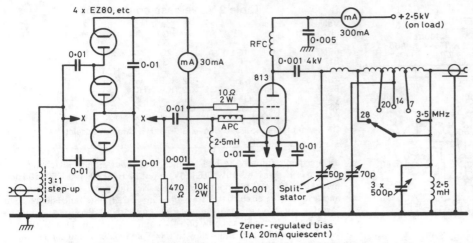

Fig 4. G3OHE's high-power 813 linear amplifier capable of providing a comfortable 400W (p.e.p) output at 28MHz and more on lower-frequency bands

The pi-tank values can be taken from the amplifier circuit for two 4–125A valves in the *Radio Communications Handbook*, the operating conditions being much the same.

It should go without saying that any amplifier and associated power supply unit operating with voltages in the kilovolt range should be constructed and treated with great care and full regard to personal safety. For example in Fig 4 omitting the 2·5mH rf choke shown across the rf output connection makes no difference to the *performance* of the amplifier as an amplifier, but can make a tragic difference in the event of a failure of the 0·001μF 4kV coupling capacitor since, in the absence of an rfc sufficiently rugged to ensure that an ht fuse blows, it would put a lethal 2·5kV dc voltage on the antenna.

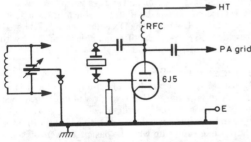

Fig 5. Untuned Pierce crystal oscillator readily doubling as a variable tuned oscillator—a once popular circuit on the lower-frequency hf bands (G3GDU)

Apart from the once ubiquitous 807 and 813, a number of correspondents have written in praise of other large transmitting valves. G4QK claims to have one of the few surviving 814 valves in captivity. G3KI mentions "the lovely 808". G3GDU, whose excellent article in *Ham Radio Today* on valves I may have appeared too critical of, writes "The demise of valve power amplifiers in professional 1kW transmitters has not been welcomed by all manufacturers. A friend who is managing director of a firm manufacturing 1 to 10kW hf transmitters maintains that the use of solidstate amplifiers is primarily due to customer requirement. Another manufacturer of vhf transmitters comments that his equipment is fully solid state for this same reason and that he could think of no more horrible device in a vhf power amplifier than a transistor." G3GDU adds that although interested in Project 6L6 single-stage transmitters he has always preferred, even in the simplest rigs, to use two stages and remembers the popular combination of a 6J5 Pierce crystal oscillator (Fig 5) which could double as a vfo in conjunction with 6V6, 6L6 or TT11 pa. Although it was not always appreciated at the time the oscillator split-stator capacitor should be of a reasonably large value to prevent excessive frequency drift as the 6J5 warms up or when the load on the oscillator is varied. Perhaps not to be recommended in this form above 7MHz.

Oil-immersed resistor mystery
Louis Varney, G5RV/CX5RV, writing from Uruguay, poses an interesting question on the effect of vegetable oil on carbon resistors. This may appear a rather esoteric question but it stems from a very practical problem. He writes: "I have encountered a curious problem with a carbon tubular DL

resistor, Morganite type 702, nominally 72Ω with a tap at 60Ω. The carbon tube measures 14cm long by 2·5cm outer-diameter with a wall thickness of 5mm.

"About a year ago it was mounted in a glass jar with a metal screw top, the jar being filled with *vegetable oil* in order to increase the power dissipation rating of the DL resistor by about 7–8 times its rating in air.

"But after remaining unused for about six months the resistance was measured and found to have doubled in value!

"I realize that carbon DL resistors are normally, for this type of application, immersed in *mineral* (transformer) oil, but this is not always readily obtainable. Another DL 72Ω resistor that has been immersed for many years in a can containing mineral oil at my UK QTH has not changed in value.

"The resistor in vegetable oil now gives misleading results when used as a dummy load. It would seem advisable for anyone using oil immersed DL resistors to check their resistance from time to time.

"But I wonder if any reader can explain *why* the resistance has been changed so dramatically by vegetable oil? Is this possibly a known chemical action between the two substances?"

Whither amateur radio?
With so much high-tech telecommunications and information technology on the horizon, one wonders sometimes what can be the future role of amateur radio. For instance, a paper "Telecommunications services in the next decade" by W E Falconer and J A Hooke of Bell Laboratories (*Proc IEEE*, September 1986) paints the following domestic scene. This, it is stressed, may seem futuristic, but is based on what is possible today. What separates it from reality is not lack of technology but cost, availability and compatibility:

"Mary Jones, mother of three, walks into the study of her modern, suburban home . . . After pressing a button to actuate the raising of a decorative wooden panel, she sits down in front of a built-in colorgraphics terminal. An electronic voice greets her with the words, 'Good afternoon, Mary. Today is Tuesday, September 28, 1994. It is 3.07 pm and the current temperature is 62 degrees. Skies will be clear the remainder of today with an overnight low of 44 degrees. What can we do for you today?' A menu appears on the screen offering electronic news, catalogue shopping, electronic banking, travel and entertainment listings. Mary presses 'talk to office' and, after entering her security codes, she downloads a copy of the 'sales results' database from the mainframe computer at the corporation for which she works. Then, accessing a statistical analysis package resident on a university computer, she attempts to verify a hypothesis concerning the impact of fluctuations in interest rates on the regional sales for which she is responsible.

"Her 17 year old son, Jimmy, sits in front of another terminal and responds to inquiries from an interactive calculus lesson, then pauses to call his girl friend, Cindy. Cindy is out playing basketball, but the call is automatically transferred to a portable phone she carries when away from home. To the accompaniment of razzing from her friends, Cindy explains she cannot talk now but will call back later.

"Cindy's father is at his office involved in a three-way multi-media teleconference call with a colleague in New York and a stockbroker in London.

"Because it is 10pm in London, the broker is not on 'live' but his recorded talk includes a chart showing hour-by-hour fluctuations of the London Stock Exchange . . . Usually on Tuesday Cindy's father, too, works at home via his remote terminal."

It is interesting to note that the UK has already established the teletext service much more firmly than the USA, has fast-growing cellular radio networks, pocket radiopagers, is planning a "radio data service" and "radio teletext". The old aim that anyone should be able to speak to anyone at anytime is becoming a real possibility. All of this surely means that we need carefully to re-think just what we want and expect out of amateur radio—and that may not include attempting to compete with hi-tech telecommunications services!

□

TECHNICAL TOPICS February 1987

Technical Topics
by Pat Hawker, G3VA

CHAMBERS DICTIONARY defines "neophobia" as a "dread of novelty" and it is, I fear, a condition that to some degree afflicts us all with advancing years. We look back nostalgically to a time when radio seemed more understandable and the technology could be seen in terms of good or bad, with today's circuits and components clearly better than yesterday's, just as some people see "digital" as superior in all respects to "analogue".

In preparing *TT* I sometimes suspect that I am in danger of being considered a severe case of neophobia. Perhaps so. Yet my post suggests that many readers are finding themselves looking back to the days before the dominance of the black boxes not just with nostalgia but with the conviction that we are in danger of losing some of the elements that made amateur radio a truly unique hobby and turning it into just another branch of telecommunications, little more exciting than the humble telephone.

We should, we must, welcome new technologies where these truly serve us better; yet it is surely necessary to examine new ideas carefully and critically before accepting them as the greatest thing since sliced bread. What *is* important is that we give them a fair trial and not just reject them out-of-hand from dread of novelty.

Carrier shift data transmission

Bob Redding, G3VMR (September House, Cox Green Lane, Maidenhead, Berks SL6 3EL) has recently drawn attention (*Radio & Electronics World*, December 1986) to the possibilities of very narrow band data transmission on vhf using the technique of coherent direct carrier shift. He is anxious to encourage experimental use of this technique and is ready and willing to transmit data at 1200baud or more within a 2kHz channel bandwidth "if I can find someone to receive it".

He regrets that the reaction of many people, including professional engineers, to new ideas tends to be negative since he feels it essential for us to update our thinking to accommodate the new components and techniques that won't go away, adding: "this is where I think our hobby is so beneficial in fostering an open mind and providing a chance to try something new or see what else it might do. For example, a power or traditional electronics background can get in the way of semiconductor appreciation until we realize the significance of switching at the zero crossing point of a wave . . . we should be able to send data better on a (linear) radio circuit than on a telephone line."

G3VMR is clearly the reverse of a neophobe. I must admit to some personal reservations about high speed data transmission as a routine or widespread part of our hobby, but fully agree that there is every reason to encourage experimentation and the development of new modes, if only to justify our continued existence as authorized users of the valuable radio spectrum. Whether direct carrier shift transmission, decoded by means of a phase-lock-loop in the receiver (Fig 1), rather than the use of modulated tones on ssb or fm transmission is, or is not, the better approach (it could be argued that with 25kHz channelling still accepted at vhf there would be only a limited practical advantage in reducing transmission bandwidth to 2kHz), is open to question, though G3VMR is convinced that this is the case. Many years ago, in *TT*, I attempted to put the case for moving away from fsk for standard hf rtty and using two tone or multi-tone systems which have been shown to produce much better copy in the absence of diversity reception. The impact was virtually nil.

I agree with G3VMR that it would be a pity if we confine ourselves entirely to "tried and tested" approaches.

Sound advice?

Brian Davies, G3OYU, after reading the recent *TT* items on the effect of loud noises on hearing (*TT* June, October 1986 etc) writes: "I was born profoundly (by today's standards) deaf. I could hear after a fashion but was 15 years old before my disability was accepted by the medical profession. Three major ear operations and six on my nose have given me back a great deal of hearing. At best my hearing is 25dB down, at worst, eg when I have a bad cold, 39dB down. My problem is conduction deafness which is a mechanical fault in the conduction of sound from the ear drum to the cochlea. More common is perception deafness, a fault in the electrics of the hearing system, usually deterioration of the cochlea itself.

"Strangely enough, I have been fascinated by sound and reproduction since a small boy and for some 45 years have been constructing audio amplifiers and ancillary equipment. I have taken several courses concerned with acoustics and sound reproduction. Then, 14 years ago, I professionally entered the field of the high power music market, mostly in discotheques. During this time I have been involved in a number of seminars to do with the health hazard of entertainment noise including discos, pop and classical concerts. It is evident that there is a lot of emotional feeling against the high power music environment much of which cannot be substantiated. In this connection I have found a great deal of misunderstanding of the problem and my conclusions are extremely relevant to the amateur using headphones ("cans" in the music profession).

"Regarding the problem of noise-induced tinnitus, in a person with normal hearing it is often only a temporary effect which goes away after a period of time, usually overnight. The cumulative effect, however, over a period of years invariably results in noise-induced deafness. It is instructive to consider the spectra of sounds which are known to cause tinnitus and noise-induced deafness; ie gunshots, steam hammers, metal-working shops etc. Without exception the wavefront is extremely steep. In other words it is impulse sound which causes the trouble. The only way to get these kinds of sounds from audio amplifiers is with distortion and probably the quickest way to get this kind of distortion is to use a peak limiter circuit of two back-to-back diodes. A far superior way to avoid the problem, although much more complex, is to utilize one of the attenuator (agc) ic devices which reduce volume rapidly but without attendant distortion.

"However, I am not convinced that it is necessary to limit the level of sound steep wavefronts. It is better to use an amplifier with very low distortion characteristics and with plenty of headroom to avoid over

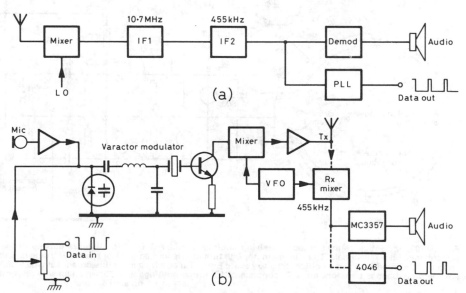

Fig 1. Bob Redding, G3VMR advocates direct carrier shift rather than audio tones from a modem for high-speed data transmission on vhf on the grounds of the much narrower channel bandwidth as well as its economic advantages. (a) A phase-lock-loop (eg 4046 cmos ic) is used in the receiver after the second i.f but ahead of the fm detector to provide suitable output levels of the data signal. (b) Modification of a typical fm transceiver for carrier shift data

loading. For cw a further refinement can assist both the distortion problem as well as the ability to read weak signals is to use a circuit which effectively rings and hence producing a near sine wave which by definition has no distortion products.

"There is evidence that distorted sounds will cause noise-induced deafness whereas undistorted sound probably will not. Until this is finally proved my recommendation is always only have sound levels at a level you can only just comfortably hear. Use audio amplifiers which have very low distortion products and enjoy what you are doing since the flow of blood around the cochlea is greater in the person enjoying what he is doing and this greater flow is in some way protective."

I must apologise to G3OYU for having edited down his very long letter but trust that I have retained the gist of his remarks. Personally I cannot entirely accept his advice not to use back-to-back diodes as peak limiters since the noises that I protect my ears against are invariably the loud switching clicks which I feel must have a steep wavefront and which would in fact be quite unbearable if there were even more headroom in my receiver af stage! In 1984 the BBC Designs Department announced, primarily for BBC staff, mono and stereo headphone protectors which took the form of small passive limiter circuits to protect the wearer against harmful sound levels from low impedance headphones such as the Pioneer SE550 and Beyer DT220. The limiting level can be preset to within the range 95 to 110dBA, though I gather that these ear protectors have never been widely used. For programme sound it may well be that G3OYU is right in warning against the use of peak limiters, but I still feel a need to soften those crashes and clicks that come out of my old receiver!

Small loop antennas

In December *TT*, Dr Andrew Smith, G4OEP, in taking exception to the term "magnetic antenna" when applied to compact transmitting loops, raised several interesting, if provocative, questions.

Tony Harwood, G4HHZ, agrees that in the *far field* of an electromagnetic field the E and H fields are in strict proportion (ie E/H is a constant, though not *c* in the usual sense of this being the velocity of light but 120π). However this does not apply to the *near field* of a transmitting loop where the magnetic field can predominate and perhaps justify the German term 'magnetic antenna'. He also, in answer to G4OEP's question "could a loop antenna radiate if it were enclosed in an electrostatic screen as most df receiving loops are?" says that the answer is undoubtedly "yes, it could and would". He points in confirmation to the classic text book on antennas: *Antennas theory and practice* by S Schelkunoff and the review of Lorentz's classic theory of reciprocity formulated in 1895 and derived from Clerk Maxwell's equations as described in last year's IERE's 11th Clerk Maxwell Memorial lecture by Professor A L Cullen.

The attraction of compact electrostatically screened loop receiving antennas in being much less susceptible to the electric fields of local electrical interference and, by dint of their directional properties, able to minimize co-channel interference from distant stations should not be overlooked by 1·8MHz and mf/dx enthusiasts. Following the recent items on transmitting loops two practical receiving designs have come from G3OUC and G8YZW.

Pat Painting, G3OUC writes: "For many years I have used kite-supported antennas for 1·8MHz field operation. Results have been well worth-while as far as transmission is concerned but severe problems have resulted on weak-signal reception from the pick-up of atmospheric and man-made noise. The same problem is also experienced when using my roachpole vertical antenna. At times rain-static can make it impossible to use 1·8MHz due to the receiver being swamped by noise.

"Various frame, loop and ferrite-rod active antennas have been constructed and all have worked quite well. However the shielded loop system shown in Fig 3 seems to give maximum noise reduction. All previous active antennas have picked up noise from the main station transmitting antenna if this is left connected. The shielded loop system works very well indoors and in suitable conditions provides reception of American and Russian stations; its directional properties can also be used to minimize noise and interference.

Mast guying

Bob Butcher, G3UDI presents a mast guying problem that has very practical implications. The question is; "If a mast is free to rotate about its base (ie masts not planted firmly in the ground) what is the minimum number of guy lines that should be used?". His answer (which came originally from a friend in the medical profession) is depicted in Fig 2.

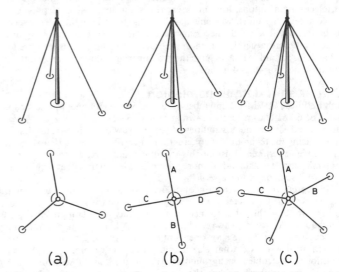

Fig 2. Minimum guying of masts that are not planted firmly in the ground needs not less than five guys to ensure stability in the event of one guy breaking (G3UDI)

(a) With only three guys the mast is unstable if one is broken.

(b) With four guys, the mast is still unstable if one breaks. This may not be obvious. Consider what happens if guy A breaks. The mast will start to

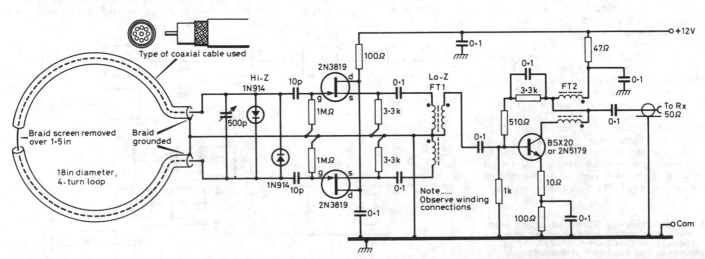

Fig 3. 1·8MHz "active" shielded loop receiving antenna used by G3OUC to minimize pick-up of local electrical impulse noise etc while providing good performance on weak signals. The 18in diameter four turn loop is formed from air spaced 75Ω coaxial cable. 1·5in of copper braid is removed at centre of cable. Loop is then taped with pvc electrical tape to secure turns. Tuned with a miniature broadcast type variable capacitor. Note that the loop is mounted vertically. For the broadband rf transformers, FT1 consists of 15t trifilar windings with 28swg enam wire on Amidon FT37–61 ferrite core. FT2 has 15t bifilar windings on similar core

move in the direction of B. Sideways guys C,D have *no* restraining effect as can be seen most easily if the *plane of the earth* is imagined to counter-rotate.

(c) Five guys thus seem to be the minimum number to ensure stability should one guy break. Suppose that A breaks, then B,C will still restrain the mast.

Passive 1·8MHz shielded loop

Mike Shepherd, G8YZW similarly writes: "I listen to several nets on 1·8MHz but have to contend with the background noises from electric motors and other sources of impulse interference which tend to be too fast to permit useful reduction by means of conventional noise limiters and often with several different electric motors being received at the same time from nearby woodyard, builders, launderette and vehicle coachwork rebuilders. Some of the nets use a.m which, when the signals are weak, is badly affected by the strong electrical interference.

"The *TT* item on loops prompted me to construct a Mark 1 version based on the impedance matching loop arrangement shown in Fig 3(e) page 706 of the October 1986 issue and the shielded "Indoor loop aerial for short waves" by S Mukherjee in *Electronics & Wireless World*, April 1985, pages 38 to 39, which describes receiving loops for 4–9MHz, 8–18MHz and 18–26MHz found to give more protection than a rod antenna against noise from electrical appliances. I scaled up the 4–9MHz version (700mm main loop diameter, 500pF tuning capacitor) to 1000mm main loop, 200mm coupling loop. But, possibly due to using H100 stiff coaxial cable (double screened) to provide some rigidity of the loop, found that the self-inductance and capacitance of the 10ft 4in length (including connecting ends) of the main loop required 750pF postage trimmer plus a 350pF sm fixed capacitor across the twin-gang variable capacitor (over 2000pF of which 1000pF is variable) as currently set to tune 1·85 to 2MHz. It could probably be converted to cover both 1·8 and 3·5MHz by switching in or out the extra capacitance. The 10ft version (Fig 4) results in a loop 42-inches wide. My next version will use 15–16ft of "ordinary" thick TV coaxial feeder cable to reduce the value of capacitance as well as improving performance generally.

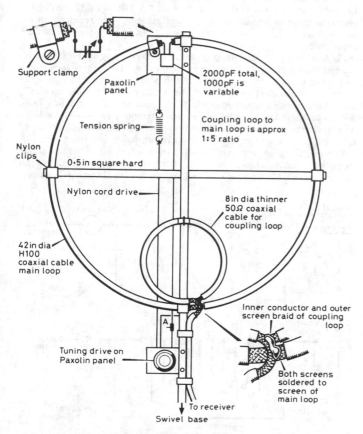

Fig 4. Prototype 1·8MHz shielded loop receiving antenna as built as a prototype by G8YZW. "Plastic" drive drum fitted to tuning capacitor. Aluminium drum to drive shaft and knob with small pulley wheel fitted close to cage to keep cord drive in line with "drums". At "A" a small calibration scale is fitted on wood shaft. Pointer fitted on inner cord with "card" scale fitted to take frequencies and/or stations for reference on removal

Labels in Fig 4:
Support clamp
Paxolin panel
2000pF total, 1000pF is variable
Tension spring
Coupling loop to main loop is approx 1:5 ratio
Nylon clips
0·5in square hard
Nylon cord drive
8in dia thinner 50Ω coaxial cable for coupling loop
42in dia H100 coaxial cable main loop
Inner conductor and outer screen braid of coupling loop
A
Tuning drive on Paxolin panel
Both screens soldered to screen of main loop
To receiver
Swivel base

"Tests so far show it to be far 'quieter' with relatively little loss of wanted signal strength compared with a 50ft check antenna used with an atu."

Refurbishing valve receivers

Receivers such as the HRO, AR88, Super Pro, HQ129, CR100 etc built over 40 years ago, often for professional or military users, can still give an entirely adequate performance, particularly as hf cw receivers. Admittedly, there will be significant switch-on frequency drift and the shape factor of single 455kHz crystal filters may look poor on paper in comparison with those fitted in modern high-performance receivers, but the "nose" selectively and mechanical construction are excellent—or can usually be made excellent by touching up the alignment.

Of course, the rubber insulation on the heater wiring may have perished; emission of one or more of the valves may have fallen resulting in low gain. But the old style of chassis construction and "ugly" wiring makes refurbishing or modification a relatively straightforward job.

A likely problem with any receiver built before, say, 1955 is leakage of capacitors, particularly with old tubular foil and paper fixed capacitors. Capacitors with solid impregnants are generally unsuitable for use where ac or high dc voltages were concerned. Insulation resistance, particularly of cardboard-cased units, falls to relatively low value, of the order of at most a few megohms; phenolic-resin moulded capacitors were a little better but insulation resistance tends to fall in humid environments. Electrolytic capacitors have always been among the least reliable of components particularly when sited near to hot-running valves such as rectifiers or audio output valves.

Special care is needed when attempting to put any equipment back into use after it has been in store for months or years. All electrolytic capacitors tend to have a normal leakage current. When not used for a considerable time, such leakage will initially be very high and it will take about half-an-hour or so for the capacitor to "re-form". When first switched on the very high leakage current may seriously overheat the device with the possibility of its complete break-down and consequent damage to the rectifier, mains transformer etc. The answer is always to "re-form" any high-voltage electrolytic capacitor that has not been used for say one year, and after an even shorter time in hot or humid climates. The technique is to apply across the capacitor its normal working voltage in series with a resistor of sufficient value and wattage to limit the initial leakage current to a safe value. For example in the case of an 8μF, 450V working electrolytic capacitor a high-wattage resistor of, say, 10,000Ω would be suitable. This could comprise a couple of 15W electric-light bulbs in series. The applied voltage must be dc although not necessarily smoothed dc. Unless the capacitor has deteriorated beyond repair, after about one hour of "re-forming" leakage current should reduce to not more than about 0·5mA for an 8μF capacitor or, say, 2mA for a 32μF capacitor. It is easy to check initial leakage, using a series resistor, when replacing electrolytic capacitors; a little more difficult, but still reasonable easy to arrange to do this with the suspect capacitor *in situ*. Failure to re-form capacitors can lead to major damage to the equipment, including the messy business of having a capacitor explode.

Still a common fault, even with modern equipment, is failure of the dial (pilot) bulbs. Replacement is usually a simple matter but there are some designs where this can prove quite tricky; the same may be said of the dial cords that so often broke in the days before nylon cord was generally adopted.

Robert B Kerr, GM4FDT in "Valved receivers—further thoughts" (*Practical Wireless*, January 1987, pp26-7) offers tips on restoring older receivers. He notes that loss of emission of now-rare (or expensive) valve rectifiers can be overcome very simply by substitution of silicon power diodes, but that if this is done some precautions are most advisable. One

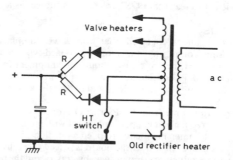

Labels in Fig 5:
Valve heaters
ac
R
R
HT switch
Old rectifier heater

Fig 5. There is a need to take precaution with replacing valve rectifiers with silicon diodes to avoid the initial switch-on and high running ht problems. Add an ht switch and suitable resistors

is that the silicon diodes apply full ht across the electrolytic-filter components and the receiver valves, etc immediately on switching on; an ht delay device is thus advisable. This can be a manual ht switch as shown in Fig 5 although some form of delay mechanism that functions automatically overcomes the problem of remembering to have the delay switch "off" whenever the receiver is turned on. He also reminds us that with silicon diodes the ht line is likely to be some tens of volts higher than with the usual valve rectifier (with significant internal resistance) unless series resistors are added. To satisfy peak-inverse-voltage (Piv) requirements he advocates the BY127 diode with its 1250 Vrrm, 1·5A rating.

Unless such precautions are taken, the fast switch-on and high off-load voltage can prove fatal for the electrolytics, even if these have been re-formed. It is often stated that a 450V electrolytic capacitor if used over a long period at a working voltage of say 300V or 250V tends to "memorize" the lower voltage and is likely to blow if say 400V is applied.

As mentioned earlier, leakage through older style fixed capacitors can be a problem and all old bypass and intervalve coupling capacitors may need replacing as they may easily affect the performance of the receiver. Intervalve coupling capacitor leakage results in positive bias being applied to the control grid of the following stage; dried out electrolytic cathode bias capacitors may reduce gain due to negative feedback, open-circuit reservoir capacitors are more likely to reduce ht than to cause hum; hum may be induced by leakage between cathode and heater within one or more valves. This may all sound like calling for major overhauls but in practice the open, reasonably spacious layout of many of the better old models makes such refurbishing well within the capabilities of most amateurs, even when equipped only with a multitest meter and a few tools. Re-alignment of a good communications receiver does require more care and the availability of a signal source (not necessarily a pukka signal generator although this helps).

The above comments, it should be noted, apply to those who wish to restore receivers in order to *use* them. Collectors of vintage models, on the other hand, seek to restore models without altering their appearance and using, if possible, genuine components of the appropriate period. But even so there are some tricks of the trade such as fitting new capacitors in the larger cases of the original components (see some tips by G4XWD on restoring ex-WD equipment in *TT*, June 1986, p420).

Resonant reed headphones

Among the correspondence arising from various mentions in *TT* of the use of small tuned reeds in headphones was a letter from F P Hughes, VE3DOB, editor of the *Canadian Amateur Radio Magazine*. He wrote:

"Your remarks (*TT*, March 1986) on reed headphones as an April Fool joke rather took me back since I recall reed headphones were once made commercially. To make sure that this was not my imagination I built a reed headphone. I soldered (acid core solder) a one inch length of clockspring to one pole of a cheap headphone, leaving a minimal gap between the spring and the other pole.

"It works well. I have not yet been able to measure its response, but by ear, there is a doubling in signal strength by a change of a whole tone up, and a halving by a further tone up. That is, if doh is 0dB, re is 3dB, mi is 0dB.

"I was able to follow cw at 30wpm (my maximum, not the phone's). The background 'noise' is a tone. Voice transmissions are unintelligible. The vibrations of the reed are swiftly damped by the magnetic field.

"It is interesting to tune through closely spaced cw signals. Several are heard at once, faintly. On tuning slowly, first one and then another 'pops up' into prominence. Tuning on 14MHz is critical, as you may guess.

"A usable pair of reed headphones would need controls for gap, at least one of the pair would have to operate a diaphragm. The 0·25 by 1in reed is not loud to the ear—like an o-v-o, but cw is perfectly intelligible. A diaphragm would increase both the volume and the damping.

"I was saddened to learn that *QST* treated this subject as a joke."

More pcb tips

While it needs to be recognized that for valve equipment "ugly" construction using connecting wires or Veroboard-type panels is still perhaps to be preferred, there is a vast amount of equipment for which the printed-circuit board is dominant, with the prospect of an increasing amount of surface mounting technology and hybrid thick-film or thin-film modules.

Two more pcb tips come from Dr Patrick O'Horan:

"(1) Having prepared a clean copper clad board with etch resistant pen or transfer, instead of immersing the board in etchant, float the board copper side down using surface tension. If the board is placed carefully with no air bubbles, the waste products are drawn away by gravity and the board etches much cleaner and much quicker. There is also less chance of transfers lifting as can be the case with constant aggitation of the fluid.

"(2) There are solutions available for 'silvering' pcbs to give that professional and protective finish. Indeed the process of silvering can turn a tarnished but well made board into a professional durable board. The solutions available are expensive and produce few boards for a considerable expense! I clean my boards well with a cream cleaner such as used in most homes (Vim or Ajax) after etching. I then thinly spread 'Pryolux' solder paste over the entire face of the board. This solder paste is widely available at plumber's merchants and is used for 'wipe' jointing lead pipes, a small tub is about £5 and will silver tens of boards if used sparingly.

"Having applied the paste, a hot air blower (paint stripper) is played on the surface until the solder flows evenly. If a blower is used do not be afraid to apply the heat for the time required for a smooth even finish. When cool merely wash in water and the water soluble flux will dissolve away taking the solder globules not attached to copper with it. If a hot air blower is not available then a blow lamp may be used but be careful not to scorch the board. As with commercial boards, fibreglass based board gives better results because of its better heat tolerance. I have found it better to dull and de-burr the board before starting to silver rather than dulling afterwards but this is possible. I have made many boards in this way and have even soldered up complete boards with the components in dry position but this is fiddling and not really of value to the amateur. I hope these notes have been of use."

Pi-network antenna tuner

While there continues to be a debate over the merits of the various "ultimate transmatch" configurations, it should not be forgotten that transmitters intended to feed directly resistive 50Ω coaxial feeders can be matched to end-fed multiband long-wire antennas, including the so-called "AoG" (Act of God) random length types, using either the simple two-element L-network or the long-established three-element pi-network.

Back in a 1960 issue of *GE Ham News* (in the heyday of the valve era both RCA and GE issued regular amateur-radio technical bulletins), S E Johnson, W2FBS, attempted to revive interest in the pi-network as an effective method of matching the low-impedance output of a transmitter to antenna feedpoint impedances of the order of 100 to 2,400Ω of long-wire multiband antennas. He provided constructional details of an atu suitable for use at powers up to 1kW on bands from 3·5MHz to 28MHz. With the restricted range of impedance ratios specified there is no requirement for high-voltage variable capacitors of more than about 350pF maximum capacitance.

Fig 6 (a) and (b) shows the two versions described by W2FBS; (b) with the coil tapped every two turns permits a more accurate impedance match and would be more suited for use with solidstate amplifiers than (a). Even more precise matching could be achieved with a variable ("roller coaster") inductance, though this would add to the cost unless a junk-box item. Special care should always be taken when attempting to use end-fed long-wire antennas with solidstate amplifiers unless these are well protected against looking, even temporarily, into a transmission line with a high swr.

There is still some controversy about how much or how little harmonic-suppression can be achieved in practice from any low-pass filter unless this incorporates a cross-over network and dummy load to absorb the harmonic

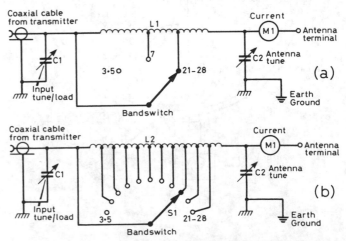

Fig 6. Pi-network antenna matching units as described by W2FBS in 1960 for feeding long-wire end-fed antennas. C1 30 to 350pF. C2 high-voltage 20 to 200pF. (a) L1 15μH, 20t, No 10 tinned wire, 3in diameter, 3·75in long with 10t wound 4 turns per inch and 10t wound 8tpi (1·25in long). M1 0·4A fsd rf thermocouple-type meter (but see text for low cost substitute). S1, 4- or 11-position heavy duty ceramic insulated switch for tap selection

power (absorptive tvi filters as described in past issues of *ART* and *TT*). But at least the pi-networks of Fig 6 are in the form of 1pf filters and should not enhance the harmonic content! Preferably a standard multi-section 50Ω 1pf tvi filter should be interposed between transmitter and the pi-atu unless filters are built into the transmitter.

W2FBS recommends that capacitor C1, on the low impedance side of the network, should have an air gap of about 0·03 inches when used with power amplifiers having up to 1·5kV ht, with C2 having a larger air gap of about 0·07-inches per 1000V on the amplifier. In practice, for typical 100W hf transceivers C1 can usually be a salvaged broadcast valve-receiver tuning gang which can provide some 1000pF (two-gang) or 1500pF (three-gang) capacitance thus extending downwards the impedance range of the atu.

It is worth remembering that, even with an exactly resonate end-fed antenna with its high-impedance, high-voltage feedpoint there will always be current fed to the antenna. Adjustment of an atu for maximum current or maximum voltage or both is thus an effective way of "tuning-up" a pi-network in the absence of an swr meter.

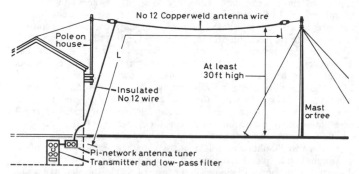

Fig 7. 243ft end-fed antenna as used by W2FBS (134ft is perhaps more typical for residential gardens) preferably with horizontal section 30ft or more above ground. A short heavy lead should connect the tuner to a good earth, although a counterpoise wire may be more effective for shacks above ground level

Since it is all too easy to burn out rf current meters, particularly on the higher hf bands, a satisfactory substitute can take the form of a torch bulb shunted by a few inches loop of wire. With a little trial and error the length of the shunt can usually be adjusted so that the bulb lights to some degree on all bands, though with low power it may be necessary to disconnect the shunt on the lower frequency bands. For his unit, W2FBS specified an 0·4A fsd thermocouple type rf ammeter, but I cannot believe this would always cope with 1kW amplifiers on the higher bands. I have to confess that many years ago I burnt out several thermocouple rf meters (they were then converted into dc meters) and decided that an occasional burnt out torch bulb was altogether more acceptable.

The W2FBS unit was intended for use with a 243ft wire on 3·5, 7 and 21MHz with a short, direct earth lead as in Fig 7. He pointed out that an swr meter in the coaxial cable link between the transmitter is handy (but not essential) for initially determining the correct settings for C1, C2 and S1 for each band.

Valves in transmitters

For umpteen years, the thermionic valve or American "tube" has enjoyed a deserved reputation for ruggedness and reliability over a reasonable operational lifetime when used in hf and vhf transmitters. The types introduced in the 'thirties and 'forties for hf, before the days of high-gain, closely-spaced electrodes and high-perveance cathodes often seemed to soldier on for ever, even when the manufacturers' published ratings were exceeded — though there was often a marked difference in the permissible degree of over-running between valves of the same type but stemming from different manufacturers. A couple of years ago I quoted, I think it was Brian Kendal, G3GDU, as suggesting that the only way you could be sure of killing an 807 was by hitting it with a shovel. Past experience suggests that, alternatively, lack of ventilation and consequent very hot glass envelopes can result in "gassy" ionized 807s or loss of vacuum due to cracked glass envelopes without resorting to the use of a shovel, but at least there was no need to protect them from high swr etc! I do recall an 813 physically breaking but that was due to it jumping out of its socket in the course of being taken in a signals vehicle along cobbled roads in France.

Valves introduced since about the mid-fifties and the use for rf linear power amplifiers of valves designed for television line-output ("sweep") applications did bring about the need for more care. Ceramic valves such as 4CX250-series also introduced the need for forced air-cooling and precautions against flash-over, though extending frequency range to vhf/uhf.

In the December *TT*, LA8AK warned of the problems experienced in Scandinavia by both professional and amateur users of the RCA 8122, with its proneness for short-circuited electrodes.

LA8AK's remarks have been endorsed by John Matthews, G3WZT who writes: "Some time ago I obtained three 8122 power tetrodes, brand new and boxed. On paper, these looked to be an excellent choice as a single-valve 144MHz pa. The valve has a very short grid-base and inspection of the constant current curves seemed to show it to be an excellent choice for linearity.

"I duly designed and constructed an amplifier using a single 8122 on 144MHz. All of the manufacturer's recommendations were followed including impedance-limited ht supply, stabilized screen-grid supply with overcurrent trip. After many hours slaving over a hot soldering iron, it was ready to go. Everything had been pre-tuned and neutralised; three minutes allowed for cathode warm-up prior to applying anode/screen volts. After a few seconds of rf, there was the sort of noise nobody likes to hear and the pa 'died'. Just as LA8AK described, G1 and G2 had short-circuited. After thoroughly checking power-supply sequences and voltages, a second 8122 was put in. Once again the same sequence of events and inspection showed G1/G2 s/c.

"Consultation with the manufacturer (RCA) proved no help (I am not a 'professional' customer!). Inspection of the tubes-insides, showed that large lumps of the cathode had 'vaporized' for no apparent reason. Later I changed the bias and socket to suit 'a good old 4CX250B'. The amplifier performed faultlessly and has been doing so for the past four years. I wonder how many others have trodden this same path with the 8122 and wondered why? I *still* wonder why; maybe RCA know!"

Lightning protection

J Lambert, G3FNZ noted the various comments in *TT* on protection against the emp problems arising from local lightning. He draws attention to an SMC leaflet on (a) a coaxial lightning arrestor in the form of a gas discharge model LAI; and (b) various static discharge devices, type DDL 14A/1 line transformer and type 2DLO1 high pass filter marketed by SMC. Of the coaxial arrestor for low power operations he writes:

"This unit has been used in the Far East, where lightning is prevalent, for several years with great success but unfortunately calls for a very tight vswr situation (1·5:1 between 1 and 20MHz) and are decidedly expensive (about £75). These devices are made in the USA".

The LA-1 is a surge arrestor designed for insertion in 50 and 75Ω coaxial rf transmission lines and designed to prevent significant static build-up on the antenna and transmission line thus reducing the incident probability of direct lightning strokes. It is claimed safely to by-pass to ground 10 or more direct or secondary strokes of lightning without damage to transmitting or receiving equipment.

Tips and topics

The Vackar oscillator turned up again in *Electronics & Wireless World*, June 1986, page 52 where P Hall describes it as a "reliable lc oscillator" commenting "lc oscillators can be temperamental. Either they require experimentation with circuit values to make them oscillate or they are complicated. This one (Fig 8) is guaranteed to work, tunes from 2 to 10MHz, is stable and has low harmonic output . . . ideal as the vfo for a transmitter or receiver."

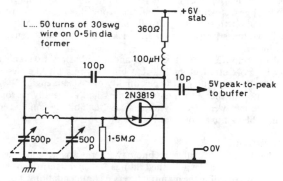

Fig 8. General-purpose stable Vackar vfo covering about 2 to 10MHz with component values shown

Francis Rose, G2DRT mentions that Heathkit no longer stock their time delay relay (as used on the SB230 linear amplifier) part number 69–74 RY2 but that Colomor (Electronics) Ltd will make one up in a base ready to plug into the SB230.

Technical Topics
by Pat Hawker, G3VA

BOB RALPH, G4KSG, a founder-member of the Collins Owners Club, writes in support of the view expressed in *TT* that the ability to understand, to maintain and, where necessary, to modify the equipment we use should be considered an essential or at least a highly desirable part of the enjoyment of amateur radio as a hobby. Yet, increasingly, none of these requirements is met with the complex, computer-aided, surface-mounted, integrated technologies now dominating the black-box market. He writes: "Obviously, I and my fellow club members wish to stay in the past. We take pride in the fact that we do understand the design of our equipment and can maintain it easily without sophisticated equipment. We do not desire to exchange these attributes for the glossy razzamatazz of 'do-it-all', computer aided design, computer aided maintenance, computer aided everything else equipment, all totally unnecessary to the enjoyment of our hobby.

"The licence is issued for the purpose of self-training as a radio station operator. This surely implies one should be in a position to maintain one's whole station in any eventuality.

'It is my personal opinion that the Society should take the responsibility of arranging for a HW100-type kit to be available together with the associated training/instructions/literature/parts etc. Construction and training could become part of local club and society activities if adequate training back-up to instructors were provided."

Valves for audio?

Neville Williams, VK2XV in his *Forum* column in *Electronics Australia* has recently been drawing attention to the way in which some of the current generation of hi-fi enthusiasts are being persuaded to buy expensive "super-quality" audio cables for which the claims being made vary from the modest to the preposterous and for which there is no shred of objective supporting evidence. He also knocks those who claim that the older-type valve af amplifiers had some special quality of reproduction denied to well-designed solid-state amplifiers. KT88 valves now sell at very high prices.

A few years ago, Peter Baxandall, a recognized UK authority on hi-fi, made a similar point in an article in *Wireless World*, stressing that both valve and solidstate amplifiers, if well engineered, contribute such a small percentage of distortion to the overall sound reproduction that any differences between them are undetectable, objectively and subjectively.

There is a very real danger that amateurs without reasonable technical understanding can become prey to myths—indeed some would claim that the long-standing swr fetish is an example of this. On the other hand, as suggested in recent *TT*s, soldistate versus valves *in transmitters* is still a debate in which it is logical to engage.

And even for audio, for the chap who likes to maintain his own equipment, the hankering back to ultra-linear valve amplifiers is not entirely a matter of nostalgia or myth. VK2XV reports an "enthusiast from way back" commenting: "Say what you like, the old valve amplifiers are friendly bits of gear. Switch 'em on and they come alive. You can trace the circuit from socket to socket by just looking at the wiring; and you can measure the voltages just as easily, and pick those that make sense from those that don't.

"Transistor amplifiers aren't like that and ic amplifiers are even worse. They may be more efficient and all that but they're a bit like diesel and electric trains, they don't have the personality of a steam engine."

Of course not all the old valve transmitters had a friendly personality —some I have met were decidely antisocial! But nobody could ever call them soulless black boxes, or unduly difficult to service.

Valve ratings

Even in the heyday of valve technology there was a good deal of misunderstanding about the published ratings and characteristics of valves, and the effect of exceeding the manufacturers recommendations. There was also the question of using television line-output valves in transmitter applications for which they were not designed.

As the ARRL's *Radio Amateur's Handbook* used to put it: "Vacuum tubes are designed to be operated within definite maximum (and minimum) ratings. These ratings are the maximum safe operating voltages and currents for the electrodes, based on inherent limiting factors such as permissible cathode temperature, emission and power dissipation in the electrodes." To this should also be added the important limiting factor for transmitting applications — the maximum temperature of the valve envelope.

American handbooks tend to show ratings in terms of "icas" (intermittent commercial and amateur service) which is defined to include the many applications where maximum power output under "operating" and "standby" conditions apply and where maximum power output is considered more important than very long life. Other publications, manufacturer's leaflets etc may be based on "ccs" ratings — ie continuous commercial service, applicable for example to am broadcast transmitters which have to run continuously for hours or even in 24-hour service. The American icas ratings are considered entirely suitable for amateur transmitters, though this may involve some shortening of valve life; this should be no handicap for normal amateur operation, particularly for Class C cw/or nbfm. Sensible valve ratings for ssb operation involve the question of the speech wave form: with no clipping (af or rf speech processing) the peak envelope power is delivered only over a small percentage of transmission time. On the other hand the quiescent "standing" current has to be 100 per cent dissipated by the anode electrode.

It is worth emphasizing, since many amateurs mistakenly confuse maximum anode (plate) dissipation with maximum dc input, that "plate dissipation is the power dissipated in the form of heat by the plate as a result of electron bombardment. It is the difference between the power supplied to the plate of the tube and the power delivered by the tube to the load." Thus, for example, the 807 had a plate dissipation of 30W, but in Class C cw service (say 66 per cent efficiency) it can run with icas ratings with say 800V on the anode, 100mA anode current, ie 80W dc input; but the anode would run cherry red and the valve quickly expire if one ran the tube with so little negative bias (Class A) that there was 80W dc standing input and no output. Fortunately, a transmitter power amplifier shows a deep "dip" in anode current when the tank circuit is resonated; this is the reason why a driven Class C power amplifier tank circuit must quickly be tuned to resonance whether or not a load is connected.

In case the impression is given of personal bias in favour of thermionic devices, I would stress that rectifier valves were a pain in the neck when used in transmitters. The need for high cathode current meant that valve rectifiers were (are) prone to loss of emission; most rectifiers required a separate isolated heater supply, and the voltage drop across a "hard" rectifier could be substantial (a voltage drop of 44V per anode with a 5U4 at 225mA); safe current depends on the type of ripple filter with a limitation on the value of the reservoir capacitor; mercury-vapour rectifiers were not only prone to radiate hash but needed careful storage in an upright position and a "delay" before the ht was applied.

The life of a rectifier valve operating near its maximum current rating is often seriously affected if the heater is under-run.

The introduction of high-slope, high-perveance (ie high peak cathode emission) transmitting valves in the 'fifties, including the 6146 (later 6146B), require more precautions than were usually considered necessary for the earlier beam-tetrodes (6L6, 807, 813, 814 etc.) RCA provided some useful hints. These include: check ac heater voltage directly at the valve sockets (under voltage often more damaging than slight over voltage); always provide adequate ventilation; do not have shiny surfaces positioned so that they reflect heat back into the valve (the unpainted aluminium valve shields are a major form of life-shortener for all valves, notoriously the miniature (B9A) receiving valves); use circuits with lowest possible resistance in grid and screen circuits; include overload protection in anode and screen circuits; check that the anode does not change colour at full load; reduce ht or insert a screen resistor for tuning under no-load conditions; do not overload valves tuning under no-load conditions; do not overload valves during tuning up; use adequate grid drive (too little drive can cause high anode dissipation); use flexible lead connection to anode caps to avoid strain, and finally, keep within manufacturer's recommended ratings.

So many readers kindly sent details of the TT11 that I feel embarrassed for having mentioned it. The particular attraction of that valve (anode dissipation 7·5W) was that it was designed for use at full ratings to 100MHz and at reduced ratings to 200MHz, making it useful for 144MHz. It was also popular for 1·8MHz, 10W a.m transmitters.

Solidstate hf linear amplifier

In recent months *TT* has stressed that, for high power linear amplifiers for the amateur service, the overall balance still comes down on the side of valve technology on both economic and performance grounds. Nevertheless there are situations which call for solidstate if only as a learning exercise.

The large Australian hobby firm of Dick Smith Electronics Pty Ltd has developed and is now marketing (Australian price about $A300, roughly £130) a kit for a solidstate amplifier designed to provide about 150W pep output from 15W input (about 50W from 10W drive on 28MHz). This is intended for use between 1·8 and 30MHz and incorporates switchable low-pass filters in the output. Harmonic output is given as at least 30dB down and the unit is claimed to provide a good clean signal. Greg Swann in describing this unit in detail in *Electronics Australia* (November and December, 1986) does not include any measurements on intermodulation products etc achieved with the two 2SC2290 devices with a 13·8V power source such as a car battery.

Fig 1 shows only the basic amplifier stage. The complete unit includes vswr, rf overdrive and excess-supply-voltage protection.

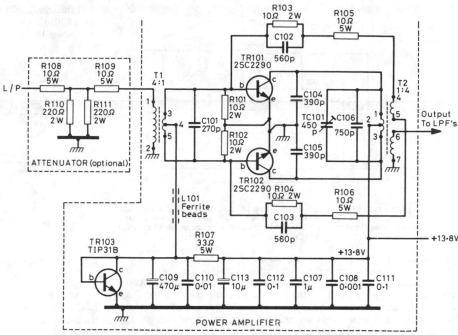

Fig 1. Solidstate amplifier stage of the Dick Smith Electronics 150W linear amplifier kit

Protective multiple earthing hazards

From time to time, *TT* items have drawn attention to the different domestic electricity-supply wiring systems used on the Continent to the traditional three-wire (phase, sometimes still called "line" or "live", neutral and earth) system used for many years in the UK. For example, in the standard UK system the neutral and earth conductors should always be kept isolated though this is not always the case with the Continental systems.

But, to add to the confusion, K A Jones, G8CZM has drawn attention to the increasing use in the UK of a system known as pme (protective multiple earth). Although this is by no means a new technique, it has only come into widespread use since about the mid 'seventies. It is now being applied to probably a majority of new properties and has been retrospectively applied to a number of older homes when there has been a change in the Electricity Board network. While pme systems are designed to meet normal safety requirements, they could, under fault conditions, impose a hazard to the radio amateur using equipment with its own earthing system. G8CZM provides a useful introduction to what is clearly an increasingly important topic (See also *News Bulletin* February). He writes: "In simple terms, a pme system is one in which the electricity supply authority uses a single conductor to act as both neutral and protective (mains) earth. In a cable system this is usually a single, pvc insulated, concentric sheath laid over the three-phase cores. The phase cores are paper or pvc insulated and there is no cable armour. At the incoming electricity supply position in the house, the neutral and protective (earth) conductors are split to provide the familiar three-wire (phase (line)/earth/neutral) domestic distribution system, defined in the 15th edition of the IEE Wiring Regulations as a type TN-C) system and shown in simplified form in Fig 2.

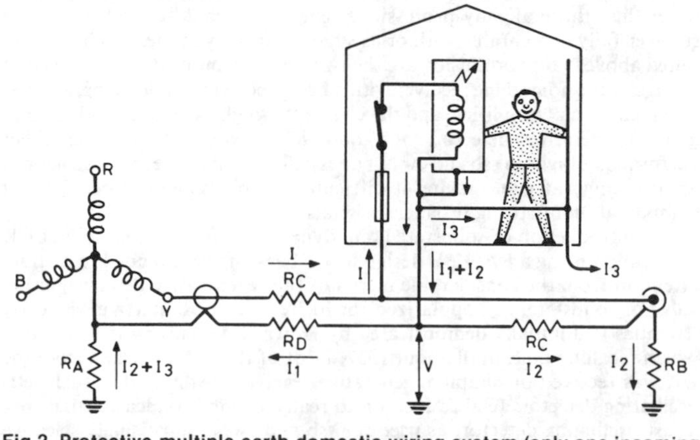

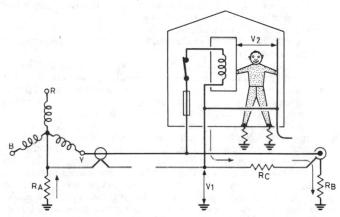

Fig 2. Protective multiple earth domestic wiring system (only one incoming phase shown for clarity)

"In the event of an internal fault in an appliance, the fault current is discharged safely as shown. However, because the neutral conductor carries return current, there will always be a potential difference on the metallic casing of any appliance with respect to local earth, although this is usually negligible.

Fig 3. Situation in the event of an electricity supply system fault where the neutral/earth conductor has become open-circuited. More likely on an overhead-fed network than with buried cables although not unknown with such systems

"Fig 3 shows return paths for normal current. The overall resistance to earth of the supply system neutral must not exceed 20Ω and the substation earth (RA) does not usually exceed 40Ω. In the case of radial feeders, the terminal earth, RB, might consist of only one unmeasured and unmonitored earth electrode, with a resistance from 20 to 3000Ω or so.

"Now take the case of an electricity supply system fault where the neutral/earth conductor has become open circuited. This is more likely to happen on an overhead-fed network but is not unknown on underground cable systems. Fig 4 indicates such a fault condition. The casing of an appliance can now reach a significantly higher voltage relative to local earth because it is connected through its common point with the neutral conductor and the load, to the live "phase" supply. This voltage is limited by the presence of alternative current paths, particularly through RB/RC and RA, but because the ohmic resistance values can be quite high, the voltage appearing on the metal casing of an appliance can, in the worst case, approach 240V.

"Fortunately, there is another requirement that has to be met when installing a pme system. This, put simply, is to ensure that any metalwork which might achieve a different potential from surrounding metalwork during fault conditions must be bonded together. Thus gas, water and oil

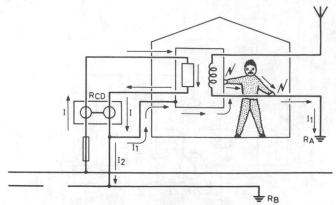

Fig 4. The possibility of a shock-hazard with a pme system where a separate signal earth lead has been brought into what is virtually the Faraday screened enclosure of a pme system. RA is more likely to be a better connection with "earth" than RB

pipes, central heating pipes and appliances etc are all bonded so that a person touching any of these appliances will detect no potential difference. It is possible to detect a pd because his feet will be in contact with an unbonded floor, but since domestic floors are usually carpeted and shoes are worn, this is unlikely to cause more than a slight tingle. Telecommunication-earths, however, are exempt from the bonding requirement.

"PME wiring presents no real hazard to the vast majority of people but the radio amateur and swl is likely to use a separate earth or counterpoise earth to their receiver, transmitter or transceiver; indeed this is essential with many antenna systems and may also form part of the safety precautions. It is widely recognized that the use, for this purpose, of a "mains earth" for signal purposes is likely to add to electric interference noise levels since this is a current carrying conductor. This is the reason why telecommunications earths are exempt from bonding.

"This means that under certain supply/fault conditions the casing of any metal or conductive cabinets in the shack can reach a dangerously high voltage above the separate earth.

"Furthermore, anyone touching the case of apparatus that is "live" in this way and simultaneously touching an unbonded conductor connected to another earth will not be protected by a residual current devices (rccd/elcb) since the current passing via the casing of appliances to earth passes both in and out of the elcb, thereby maintaining its balance; see Fig 4."

The T & P Committee is recommending a series of measures to reduce the hazard to a minumum. For his part, G8CZM feels that the first step is for the amateur to ascertain whether his electricity supply mains is of the pme type and, if so, to be aware that there will be a risk in bringing "earths" into a protective bonded enclosure. They should take precautions to avoid the possibility of simultaneously touching metalwork earthed to a local "signal" earth and any that is connected into the domestic protective-bonded enclosure. No exposed metalwork connected to the signal earth should be located within six feet or so of any metalwork bonded to the mains earth (radiators, portable electrical equipment etc).

When the rig is opened . . .

Dick Biddulph, G8DPS, comments on the "Open at your own risk" notes in the January *TT*. He writes: "My opinion is that commercial rigs have got so complex *and* so small that the average amateur with normal sized fingers cannot tackle them. Also the circuit diagrams are often very bad. I own two old commercial rigs, a Trio 7010 (ssb 144MHz) and a Yaesu FT2 auto (fm 144MHz) rig. Both are relatively simple and, by comparison with modern rigs, quite large. I have no great trouble in working on them. I use a bright light (a 60W sealed beam headlight which has a burned-out dipped beam), an angled mirror (Fig 5), and an array of simple tools such as tweezers, a soldering iron with a bent bit for working on the underside of a circuit board, etc.

Fig 5. An angled mirror can be a useful tool when servicing some of the older transceivers (G8DRS)

"I managed easily using these simple tools to replace the idiot diode in the TR7010. How do you blow an idiot diode? By being an idiot(!) and connecting the rig to a fully charged accumulator the wrong way round without a fuse!

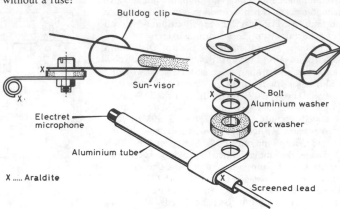

Fig 6. G8DPS's method of mounting a "hands-free" microphone for mobile operation

"With reference to mobile microphones I came to a similar conclusion to G1SJU about mobile operation but found a different solution. I fixed the microphone (same type, Tandy, 85p) to a short piece of aluminium tube (see Fig 6) to a large bulldog clip clipped to the sun visor. I put the T-R switch on the steering wheel spoke, near the right thumb position, and connected it to a small die-cast box on the fixed part of the steering column by a curly cable. The circuit I used was almost identical to that of G1SJU except that I put the l.e.d transmit indicator on a magnetic mount (old loudspeaker magnet covered with pvc tape) so that the light is visible directly *and* reflected in the windscreen so as to be visible without removing ones eyes from the road. The only snags so far are the pick-up of rather a lot of internal car noise and the curly cable squeaks as the steering wheel goes from lock to lock."

Regenerative "straight" receivers

New recruits to amateur radio are faced with the basic problem that the cost of a good, factory-built, general coverage hf receiver is tending to restrict the hobby to the well-heeled. CB equipment is still within the reach of many who now find it difficult to gain experience of the "short waves" by the traditional process of becoming first an enthusiastic swl and then a licensed radio amateur. The Yaesu FRG8800 costs more than £600, the Trio/Kenwood R5000 almost £900, the Icom IC R71 almost £800 and the welcome re-entry of a British designed communications receiver, in the form of the new Lowe HF-125 receiver, at £375 plus options, although significantly lower in cost than most of the Japanese competition, still represents an investment of several hundred pounds.

Secondhand receivers and transceivers, particularly those of fairly recent design with general coverage receive facilities, are not particularly cheap in the UK and there is always fear that the seller is anxious to dispose of a rogue piece of equipment. In terms of sheer value-for-money there is much to be said for some of the better, if bulky, receivers built 30, 40 or 45 years ago—but youngsters, not unnaturally, believe these to be virtually antiques.

What about home built receivers? Few would suggest that beginners, other than those already professional engineers, could expect to build a receiver fully comparable with or as small as factory models such as those noted above. More promising are the two basic forms of direct-conversion receivers: the homodyne receiver with a balanced product detector, af filter and high-gain af amplifier; and the classic "straight" receiver with a high-gain regenerative detector. A good homodyne can give excellent performance on both ssb and cw but does call for some care in construction, with the high af gain making it difficult to avoid some degree of direct demodulation of strong broadcast signals, particularly on 7MHz.

The introduction of solidstate homodyne dc receivers, with the first UK publication being a PA0KSB design in *TT* back in 1967, tended to distract attention from the considerable merits of the regenerative detector, either valve or solidstate, as popularized for hf by John L Reinartz in the early 'twenties and initially demonstrated by Howard Armstrong in 1913. It is worth recalling that, until about 1937, most of the hf dx worked from the UK was received on simple regenerative receivers. Admittedly, such self-oscillating detectors tend to lock on to really strong broadcast signals but a just-oscillating detector, as used for ssb and cw, is surprisingly selective when not overloaded.

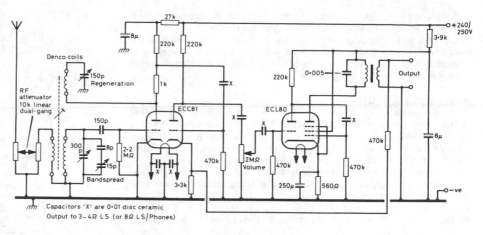

Fig 7. The simple but effective two-valve, four-stage (0-v-3) general-coverage receiver built by RS88565 for listening to broadcast and amateur signals (including ssb). The incorporation of the variable rf attenuator has proved a major aid in coping with strong signals. Straight receivers can still provide a valuable introduction to amateur radio.

It is worth considering the ideas and experiences of Alan Radmore, RS88565. "My hf listening, for various reasons, lapsed for several years during which I had no receiver other than a compact self-contained basic valve superhet I built in 1967. ECH42, EAF42, ECC81, BY100 rectifiers, plus bfo and with a useful psu output socket at the rear.

"A year ago my interest revived. I felt there was no hope of building a modern 'black box' so I bought my first factory-built set. I wanted something without too many 'knobs' and settled for a Trio R600 which is 'useful' but its 6kHz filter does not give me the 'entertainment-quality' audio that I like when listening to hf broadcast stations.

"With valves and components in the junk box and the psu in the old superhet receiver, I decided to build a general-purpose receiver. It needed to be simple, effective over all hf broadcast bands, and capable of checking through all the hf amateur bands. Simplicity ruled out the superhet. Good quality on broadcast stations ruled out the homodyne form of direct conversion. Logic dictated the 'straight' receiver. But it needed to be suitable for the 'eighties.

"Results? Well worth the effort! Audio quality is good and, with a large loudspeaker, of classic 'radiogram sound'. Sensitivity is excellent, 'reaction' (regeneration) is really smooth, as it should be, over all the ranges. There are no tuning dead spots. Plenty of audio output as needed for ssb on the speaker. Permits negative voltage feedback so that audio on ssb is superb.

"Selectivity? Those who have never used a regenerative receiver will claim that it can't be any good. There is, I agree, only one tuned circuit. Yet I find it gives me loudspeaker reception of broadcast and amateur signals from around the world. On the crowded 3·5 and 14MHz ssb segments, not even 2·7kHz guarantees interference-free reception.

"The secret, if there is one, is the incorporation of a variable attenuator culled from the receiver chapter of *Radio Communication Handbook* (This stemmed originally from *Electronics Australia* via *TT—G3VA*). Simple but the most effective of several that I tried. Most of the time it can be pre-set after evaluating band conditions, needing little subsequent movement one way or the other. It works well with a valve leaky-grid detector or a fet equivalent. The incorporation of an rf attenuator in a simple receiver would have been almost unthinkable in the old days. Today with so many strong signals it really is a case of being able to turn it down.

"I find it ironic that with this simple receiver (Fig 1) I can resolve weak top band signals during dark evenings when background noise often makes it impossible to do so with the R600 (and I'm not denigrating the Trio). On 3·5MHz ssb signals are often clearer during daytime on the simple set. Performance can be improved with a tuned rf stage (EF80) which was built externally for my prototype design and may be incorporated as a tuned/untuned stage in the final design, but again I have used an rf attenuator to avoid the need to vary voltages on the valve electrodes.

"I would stress that, at least for a listener, the classic trf receiver remains as useful as in the old days—with the ability of ssb to provide good signals adding to its value, both to beginners and others, both as a fun set or as a useful spare. It restores to the listener the vital wonderment of radio that comes from building a set that works. Plug-in coils (no complex band-switch), no need for a printed circuit board, something that often works at first go yet provides scope for bringing it gradually to near-perfection. And with firms now advertising factory sets as 'the ultimate' no need to wonder whether their next model will become 'more ultimate'."

Short antenna elements

Some 25 or 30 years ago, 1·8 and 3·5MHz mobile operation sparked interest in the use of radiating elements very short in terms of wavelength. It was soon discovered that inductively-loaded elements needed to be very accurately tuned (ie high Q, narrow bandwidth); base-loaded whips left a lot to be desired; moving the loading some way up the element improved performance but made the antenna top-heavy and liable to bend over alarmingly while the car was moving. Theoretically, the optimum position for a loading coil on a whip is at a height varying from about 0·4 to, with top capacitance loading, about 0·66 of the height.

An alternative to the loading coil is the helical-wound antenna that provides inductive loading continuously throughout its length. Although this provides a useful increase in the radiation resistance, it does mean that about 0·5λ of wire is needed to achieve 0·25λ resonance. This also implies that a metal whip cannot form a low-resistance antenna element so that, unless very thick, low-gauge wire is used, the rf ohmic losses will tend to be higher. Dielectric (eg ferrite) loaded whip elements are possibly the optimum approach for transmission but this technique has received little attention from amateurs.

It will be appreciated, at least by regular *TT* readers, that theoretically a short, well-matched radiator can be just as efficient and has the same radiation pattern as a full-length monopole or dipole. Unfortunately, this cannot be fully achieved in practice since the efficiency (E_f) of an antenna is $R_r/(R_r + R_{loss})$ where R_r is the radiation resistance of the element, the loading coil, and the ohmic losses in the matching network. If there were no R_{loss}, this would reduce to unity regardless of the shortness of the radiator and consequent very low radiation resistance. The practical problem is that as the radiation resistance becomes much lower, the ohmic losses assume proportionately more significance. The radiation resistance tends to decrease as the square of its length and may well be only of the order of an ohm or so on 1·8 or 3·5MHz.

A continuously loaded element does raise the radiation resistance significantly above that of a base-loaded element, and this can be further materially improved and the bandwidth increased by the use of a capacitance hat.

Since the transfer of most UK mobile operation to vhf/uhf, interest in very short and/or compact antennas has tended to be concentrated on balcony antennas, antenna arrays that need to rotate without extending over neighbours' gardens, and transmitting loops.

Ten years ago, Ronald Gorski, W9KYZ (*QST* April 1977) wrote a basic article, "Efficient short radiators" that provided some useful notes on helically-wound short elements, using wide copper ribbon tape, in conjunction with capacitance-hats.

He investigated these techniques on model antennas at about 100MHz showing that they can result in physically short but efficient two-element Yagi arrays providing some 4dB forward gain and about 15dB front/back ratio.

The vhf model comprised a 28in length of 0·75in cpvc tubing (plastic water pipe) wound with 38 equally spaced turns of 0·5in wide copper tape (resonance 104MHz). Then he added two 5·5in diameter, six-spoke, capacitance hats (resonance became 84MHz) and fed at low impedance via a C-match network (ie capacitors not inductors).

Translated to 14MHz, bandwidth would be 500kHz with element lengths slightly over 12ft and boom 10·5ft, diameter 1·5in or more.

W9KYZ's 1977 design pointers remain valid:

1. Make the element length no shorter than physically necessary for the particular location since both bandwidth and efficiency improve with longer elements.

2. Use large capacitance hats as these reduce the length of helical conductor for a given frequency and this minimizes R_{loss}.

3. Use large formers of good dielectric quality (eg fibreglass). The larger the form diameter (eg 1·5in), the greater the length reduction for a given number of turns and the greater can be the width of the conductor, so reducing R_{loss}.

4. Solder *all* joints and seal with silicone rubber. Do *not* rely on pressure joints.

5. For a good f/b ratio of a Yagi array with a split driven element fed from coaxial cable, some form of balun transformer is needed.

6. Use of a gdo is the only practical method of securing resonance with a fixed physical length. Construction requires cut and try. Proximity to surrounding objects affects resonance and should be minimized during tuning up.

Anchoring the big ones

David Reynolds, G3ZPF, who in *TT* (November 1984, pp 965–6) gave useful advice on mast foundations and other matters concerned with the stability of antenna masts and towers (and who has also written in *Short Wave Magazine* on such topics) was not convinced that the advice given by W4XS in *QST* and reproduced in *TT* (January 1987, p29) would result in a really secure anchor for some of the highest or heaviest towers. He writes:

"I was somewhat taken back at W4XS's 'recommended' secure guy-anchor for a number of reasons:

"Firstly, all that stops the rod from being pulled out of the concrete is the local bond between the curved surface of the rod and the surrounding

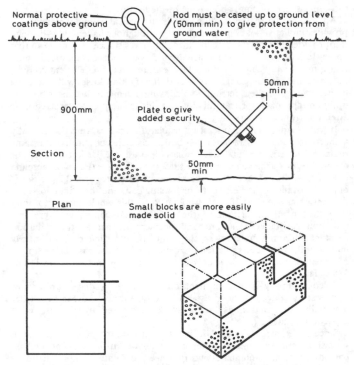

Fig 8. G3ZPF's recommended modifications to W4XS's guy anchor for high masts or towers as given in *TT*, January, Fig 5

concrete. With a light load *and* correctly compacted concrete there would probably be little to fear. But with really large towers, more common in the USA than in the UK, and with the likelihood of less than perfect mixing/compacting of the concrete with a diy project, a number of factors could contribute to local bond failure either instantly or over a number of years.

"Apart from fairly obvious corrosion of the bolt exposed to the air, there is the more insidious corrosion of the bolt where it is in contact with earth below ground. This would not be obvious until it failed. In Fig 5 of the January *TT*, the rod is shown passing right through to the lower face of the concrete. Again local corrosion from groundwater, plus ingress of water (especially through poorly compacted concrete *or* concrete of poor or

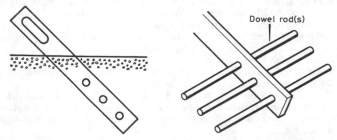

Fig 9. G3ZPF's alternative method of making the guy-anchor more secure. One or more dowel rods reduce any possibility of a "pull out"

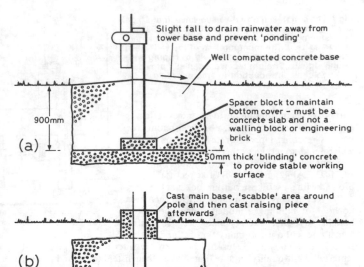

Fig 10. G3ZPF's recommendations for secure fixing the base of tower, tiltover mast etc. The base size will depend on the particular circumstances and professional advice is usually needed. (b) For situations where it is considered essential to hide the top of the concrete base

uneven mix proportions) would cause expansion and bursting of the concrete, thus reducing the local bond area available and/or exposing further areas to corrosion.

"Figs 8 and 9 show the alterations I would make to W4XS's design but there are some additional points worth driving home to anyone contemplating a diy job on a 'big league' antenna installation, apart from the obvious one of seeking competent professional advice:

"**1.** With bases of any size the amount of concrete needed becomes rather too large to be mixed by hand. It will save much heartache/backache if you obtain it ready mixed. The advice of the supplier can be sought on a suitable mix of concrete. Some soils require the use of sulphate-resistant concrete, for example.

"**2.** Good compaction of the concrete is *essential*. This *cannot* be obtained by 'stamping around' in wellies, whatever your friendly navvy may tell you. Poorly compacted concrete contains voids into which groundwater can and will percolate. Those voids near the surface can freeze up during the winter, spalling the upper surface of the concrete. Any metal encased in concrete is protected from corrosion by the strongly alkaline nature of concrete, but this protection is removed if water is held in voids in contact with the metal or if the concrete 'cover' is insufficient to withstand the test of time. A minimum of 50mm (2in) of cover is needed over metal near concrete faces exposed to earth, so aim for twice that and maybe you will end up with just enough once the swirling around of wet concrete being placed has moved things around in the hole.

"**3.** Compaction of concrete is made simple by the hire of a 'concrete-vibrator'. This consists of a mechanically vibrating tube usually powered by a compressor. Placed in the concrete it causes this to flow freely and ensures freedom from voids.

"**4.** *Never* pour in the whole of the concrete and then just push in an eyebolt afterwards. Always put any fixings in position *before* the concrete is poured and remember that concrete is heavy. As it swirls about in the hole any flimsy bracing intended to position the fixing will rapidly collapse/move about.

"**5.** The bottom surface of structural concrete in the ground should be at least 900mm below ground level in order to ensure freedom from 'frost heave' of the soil.

"**6.** Pouring concrete on to an earth base will stir up mud into the lower portions of the base and allow the fluid part of the matrix to leach into the soil, leaving cement-coated aggregate (ie the gravel). This void-filled area will give no protection to any metal fixings which extend into it. Always seal the base of the hole with a thin layer of 'blinding concrete' to provide a stable surface on to which to pour the remainder.

"Again I stress that these measures are significant only to 'big-league' antenna support installations. Nevertheless, the general principles (Fig 10) can be adapted to make even minor installations safer over longer periods of time than would otherwise be the case. With diy installations there will inevitably be corner cutting, but if these are from a 'Rolls-Royce' base rather than a 'flawed' plan, there is a far better chance of achieving a good result."

The transmitting receiver

In my youth, inspired by books and films such as Somerset Maugham's "Ashenden" stories, John Buchan's *Greenmantle* and *39 Steps* and Compton Mackenzie's real-life *Greek Memories*, I nourished ambitions, never fulfilled, of writing spy fiction, although at that time still lacking any practical experience of the murky if fascinating world of secret services. In my files I still have a small part of a typescript of a never-completed story that I sketched out in the very early days of the second world war.

This, for reasons that now escape my memory, involved my hero, Jack Davidson, being kidnapped in Stockholm and left by his Nazi captors in a room from which it was essential for him to escape. In the room, fortunately, was a shortwave receiver, in his pockets pliers and a screwdriver (yes, it was that type of story!): "At once he set to work. Dashing to the radio set he switched it on. It seemed ages before the valves heated up. He twirled the knobs, the set responded well. On the shortwaves station after station came bumping in. Scared of attracting the attention of his guards, Jack turned the volume down, satisfied by the sensitivity of the receiver that the aerial was a good one.

"With his tools, he soon had the back of the cabinet removed and the mass of wires, coils and condensers exposed to view . . . For the next three hours he worked as never before. He stripped a number of the components off the chassis, re-arranged the circuits until he had a receiver which, though inferior to the original, would still be capable of bringing in a number of signals. Turning his attention to the parts he had removed, he assembled a crude single-valve transmitter.

"This much was comparatively straightforward if time consuming. The hardest part was yet to come. It was minutes before careful handling of the receiver resulted in the faintest of buzzing which he recognized as the transmissions he sought. Then carefully he adjusted his flea-power transmitter until it was tuned to the same frequency. It remained only for him to couple the aerial to the makeshift station and to construct a crude morse key from his screwdriver and aluminium screening removed from the receiver . . . ."

Needless to say it all came right in the end. He successfully sent a message summoning help. There followed the exposure of Nazi intrigue in neutral Sweden and Jack's return to the welcoming arms of the unimaginatively named heroine, Jill Travers.

A few years later, I proved that a very simple tuned-plate, tuned-grid oscillator using one of the old 2V-filament battery valves could be tuned quite accurately to an incoming 7MHz signal received on an "all-wave" broadcast receiver and then loosely coupled to a 66ft antenna to establish a scheduled contact with a station several hundred miles away.

What I did not know then was that my fictional radio had actually already been successfully used in an emergency by Henry Jenkins, W7DIZ, in October 1934 or that a somewhat similar idea in the form of a plug in adaptor and standard radiogram was being used in real life by the German Military Intelligence (Abwehr) for clandestine (agentenfunk) radio communications.

The story of W7DIZ's exploits have been recalled by Bill Orr, W6SAI, in his *Ham Radio Techniques* column (*Ham Radio Magazine*, December 1986, pp 59–62). W7DIZ was one of the keepers of the Tillamook Rock lighthouse off the coast of Oregon when a gale damaged the building, cutting off the power generator which extinguished the light, silenced the foghorn and put shipping at great risk from the dangerous shoals. There was no means of warning the superintendent on shore except by radio— but at that time the lighthouse was still without an official radio transmitter.

All that was available was a collection of parts from an old Atwater-Kent broadcast set, a few dry batteries and scraps of tinfoil, copper and brass. On two pieces of wood, W7DIZ built from these parts a simple 3·5MHz transmitter and receiver. Lacking even valve sockets, he drilled holes in the breadboards to hold the valves and soldered wires directly to the pins (still a solution for those lacking sockets for transmitting valves?) using a gas torch. Coils were fashioned from wire taken from an audio transformer and wound on cardboard torch battery cases. A tuning capacitor for the transmitter was salvaged from the broadcast receiver; fixed capacitors made from tinfoil and wax paper taken from a loaf of bread. The transmitter was a simple tnt oscillator (ie tuned-anode, not-tuned grid) with no grid resistor or capacitor. The first morse key consisted of breaking the battery connection by hand, later improved by using a piece of spring brass. A 40ft antenna used wire salvaged from a broadcast coil. The receiver was just an oscillating detector, twisted wire forming an antenna coupling capacitor, a tinfoil unit as grid capacitor with no grid leak. The tuning capacitor comprised two brass plates separated by more waxed wrapping paper, and adjusted by moving one plate over the other with a pencil. But it worked! W7DIZ made a contact with another W7 station and passed his emergency message.

Another view on tinnitus

R E Parkes, P29PR/VS5RP/G3REP draws attention to the "alternative medicine" view that tinnitus (ringing in the ears) and nerve deafness tend to be aggravated by the consumption of refined sugar and flour products, salt, caffeine, tobacco, alcohol and drugs. In his own case, identifying an allergy to sugar brought about major relief. He sent along an article from *Healthy Living*, July 1986 by Paul Yanick of the US Hearing and Tinnitus Help Association. This claims that some hearing problems can be improved by changes in diet and lifestyle, and adds: "Protect your ears from loud noises, especially hearing aids that are too loud; exercise daily." The author advises us all to read the labels on supermarket food and wherever possible to eat natural foods; avoid soft drinks and tap water; and think positively. But remember this is alternative medicine and health-food philosophy which sometimes pushes a good idea to the extreme.

The *Healthy Living* article concludes: "For more information on how to overcome hearing and tinnitus problems, write to the Hearing and Tinnitus Help Association, PO Box 231, Iselin, NJ 08830, USA." But don't blame me if the association wants to change your lifestyle in ways that may prove as hard to accept as tinnitus or some loss of hearing!

P29PR in Papua, New Guinea has found that living with open windows rather than double glazing has also been beneficial. The note on the danger of overloud hearing-aids does, of course, apply also to any listening on headphones.

Tips and topics

Mark Rogers, G4RGB, apropos my remarks on metal oxide varistors in the January *TT*, points out that a range of these components suitable for 240V mains (275V limiting on ac, 350V with dc) *is* included in the RS Components trade list (Stock nos 238–609, 615, 621 sold in packets of five and priced according to their energy absorption rating but less than £3 per packet for the highest rated devices). My apologies for not spotting these devices in the suppressors/filters section of the massive RS 700-page catalogue.

Feedback on the 813 linear

G3OHE apologises for the omission from Fig 4 (*TT* February) of a vital component. This can be a 25KΩ 10 or 5W (or, say, two 22KΩ 2W resistors in series) wire-wound resistor across the output of the screen voltage quadrupler tying the 813 screen to ground in the absence of drive.

BOOK REVIEW

RADIO! RADIO! by Jonathan Hill (1st edition 1986). Published by Sunrise Press (2–4 Brook Street, Bampton, Devon, EX16 9LY). 244 large pages (A4 format). De luxe signed and numbered hardback edition: £18 plus £2 p&p. Softback: £12.95 plus £2 p&p.

This new and diligently researched book traces in pictures and words the development of the domestic "broadcast receiver" and of "broadcasting" from the earliest experimental days in which amateur experimenters played a prominent role, the start of regular broadcasting in the early 'twenties right through to the early transistor sets in the 'fifties and 'sixties. There will be few amateurs, even among the younger generation, who will not find an illustration and brief description of the radio on which they first "listened-in-to" in their youth. It needs to be stressed that Jonathan Hill is primarily interested in cabinet design—and there have been some weird and wonderful designs—rather than circuit developments. But it is fascinating to see, for example, some 90 illustrations in a section on "The Golden Age of Loudspeakers 1922–30" with all the variations on horn and moving-iron speakers, or the 40 or so valves, "Westector", magic-eyes etc from the "R" (Captain Round) valve of 1922 up to the introduction of the B8A base in the UK in 1953. For collectors of "vintage" broadcast receivers this is an essential handbook. My personal regret is that unlike the rather similar but less comprehensive American paperback *A flick of the switch* by Morgan McMahor, there is no attempt to cover the development of amateur radio communication receivers; although a few of the early short-wave receivers and converters, including the 1928 Marconiphone "Short Wave Receiver Model 34", and the 1933 Eddystone "short wave converter", are among the 800 UK models illustrated.

For readers interested primarily in circuit design, attention is drawn to an excellent 50-year anniversary paper in *The Journal of the Institution of Electronic and Radio Engineers* (*J.IERE*), October/December 1986, pp 325–341, by Keith Thrower of Racal-Chubb: "Evolution of circuit design for a.m broadcast receivers: 1900–1935". There is a lesson to be learned from his introductory remarks: "This paper traces the development of the a.m, broadcast receiver from the early attempts at wireless telephony by Fessenden in 1900, through to the near perfection of the superheterodyne receiver by 1935, with its high sensitivity, good selectivity, bandpass tuning and automatic gain control. Very little in the way of improvements to valve receivers came after this time, although the valves were made smaller, more robust and with a higher mutual conductance. The major post-war developments have been the semiconductor revolution, fm stereo broadcasting and true high-fidelity. It is interesting to note, however, that the performance of the average low-cost domestic radio of today is little better than the table models of 1935, and in some respects is worse, particularly with regard to bass response and ease of tuning." *G3VA*

Technical Topics
by Pat Hawker, G3VA

AS *TT* (BORN APRIL 1958) staggers into its 30th year of publication, it is interesting to speculate on the degree to which all the new technology we have witnessed has actually changed the hobby. Some would argue that home-construction, home-maintenance and ham-ingenuity have vanished together with the profound sense of wonderment that used to come from discovering that a simple receiver and simple transmitter could span the oceans. Today, in the UK, it is possible to lift a telephone handset and dial-direct to subscribers in 173 countries, and the young seem often more fascinated by the artificial intelligence of a personal computer than the marvels of Marconi.

Allan Taylor, G3JMO, worries that the factory-built, all-band transceivers, whose owners are often unwilling to risk using them with simple diy wire antennas, are opening the way to a breed of "systems co-ordinating consultants" as part of the marketing scene. They will arrive, measure your garden, advise on decorating and furnishing the shack; and their firm will then install and check out the equipment—and leave the newly-licensed amateur with naught to do but watch the visual display units and pay the instalments. How different, he suggests, from the days of the 0-v-1, the tri-tet, the Zepp and the human skills needed to copy a weak, drifting, chirpy dx signal. He foresees a long, slow decline of the hobby as it was for so many years.

I am less pessimistic. The mere fact that *TT* has chalked up around 1·5 million words, around 2,000 diagrams, all largely devoted to diy "kiss" forms of amateur radio, with a continuing problem of finding space for the many ingenious ideas that crop up, is surely proof that the hobby continues to flourish and is far from having entered into a terminal decline.

Ralph Taylor, GW2HCJ, and Urban Smith, GW3UTI, preparing to launch a series of instructional videotapes they have made themselves, remind us that the "kiss" principle is of long-standing, an unchanging truth: "Simplicity in the construction of machines cannot be too warmly recommended to the young engineer; for complexity increases the friction and expense, and endangers the chance of success from the de-arrangement of the parts", *The Mechanic's Calculator* by William Grier, 19th edition, 1862, p312. In amateur radio, "friction" refers perhaps to band behaviour!

An "ultra mini-beam" from VK2ABQ
For many years the various low-cost "wire" two-element antennas (and bow-tie dipoles) developed by Fred Caton, VK2ABQ/G3ONC, and introduced initially in *TT* and *Electronics Australia,* have become well-established as a logical and technically-justifiable approach for those with small gardens and/or limited budgets. The basic VK2ABQ wire array gained the cachet of being included, with some further suggestions, in *HF Antennas for all locations* by Les Moxon, G6XN. This design maintains its

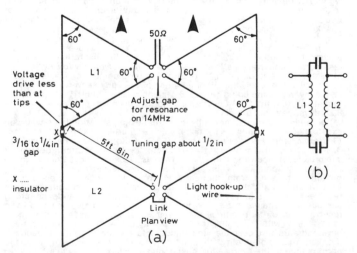

Fig 1. (a) Bird's eye view of the VK2ABQ "Ultra Mini Beam" for 14MHz. (b) Equivalent lumped circuit with inherent phase shift between L1 and L2.

popularity and, for example, turns up again in *Practical Wireless* (February 1987).

Recently VK2ABQ has sent along one of his annotated sketches outlining a new 14MHz "double triangle dipole" array (Fig 1(a)) suitable for very small gardens etc. It uses no loading coils or traps, and he believes it to be more efficient than an array with capacitively end-loaded elements. He stresses that being a fairly high-Q structure, the bandwidth is restricted and that its main attraction is that it provides a unidirectional antenna with good side rejection and some gain in spite of its small size. Size, rather than the overall performance of a full size beam, is the main attraction.

Both the dipole and the reflector consist of two open-ended loops in the form of equilateral triangles, each of the four triangles being formed from about 17ft of light hook-up wire. It provides a unidirectional cardioid radiation pattern, and can also work well on 21MHz in the form of extended dipoles, although the feedpoint impedance (about 40Ω on 14MHz) increases; presumably it could be scaled down as a 21/28MHz array.

It is necessary to adjust the loops using a grid dip oscillator, first adjusting the driven element and then making the "voltage-driven" reflector identical. Good insulation is needed, particularly at the central voltage nodes.

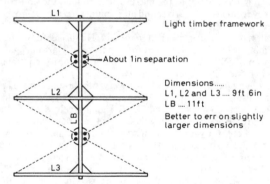

Fig 2. Light timber framework for the VK2ABQ array

VK2ABQ suggests mounting the array on a light timber frame (Fig 2). He points out that the antenna is not a close-spaced Yagi, since the reflector is voltage-driven with an inherent quarter-cycle phase shift. An equivalent lumped circuit (Fig 1(b)) may help to explain the principle. He adds that maximum gain will be achieved only when L1 and L2 are identical and in the form of equilateral triangles, although those experimentally inclined may wish to use a small stub at the reflector in lieu of the "link" shown.

I trust this is an accurate and understandable interpretation of Fred's rather cryptic notes.

Safety and mast guying
In the March *TT* (p180), Bob Butcher, G3UDI, showed clearly that it needs a minimum of five guys to protect a mast that is free to move about its base in the event of the loss of one guy. Since this type of installation is commonly a lightweight mast used for field-day or similar operation, the question of why a guy may fail was not considered. Experience suggests that cows have a penchant for entangling themselves in the guy ropes of masts and tents. But for more substantial or permanent installations the question of guys breaking under wind-strain etc becomes very important.

In this connection, David Row, G0EUE, offers an important rider, affecting safety. He writes: "Consider again Fig 2(c) of the March *TT*. For simplicity, assume that the wind is in the direction of Guy A and is towards the mast. Let the tension in A arising from the wind at the moment of failure be T_A. As soon as A breaks or parts, T_A is shared equally by B and C.

"Now consider Guy B (or C, which would be the same because they are symmetrical with respect to A). The tension to which it is subjected because A has parted is increased in inverse proportion to the cosine of its angle with

A, seen in plan. For the five-guy arrangement, this angle is 360/5 which is equal to 72°, and the tension in B, namely T_B, is increased thus:

$$T_B = \frac{1}{2} \cdot \frac{T_A}{\cos 72°} = 1 \cdot 6 T_A$$

"Since A, B and C are presumably all of the same strength material, it is unreasonable to expect B and C each to stand up to over 1·5 times the tension which caused A to part. In short, if wind (other than a gust of shortest duration and which does not repeat) causes the failure of one guy, the mast will come down.

"A five-guy arrangement is, as G3UDI explained, the minimum which will ensure stability when setting up the mast in *no-wind conditions*. This is a useful characteristic of antennas like the K1WA (*ARRL Antenna Handbook,* 14th edition, pp8–12 *et seq*) because it allows single-handed repair and adjustment of the accessible end of the dipoles with the mast still standing and stable.

"In practice, the calculation above over-simplifies the problem. For example, it takes no account of the effect of elasticity in the guys, and it assumes perfect symmetry. Generally the complications which occur in the real world worsen the result. In particular, bear in mind that the cosine function is not linear, and 72° is the region where it begins to take off; suppose obstructions in your garden lead to one of the angles being increased by only 4°, then T_B increases from $1 \cdot 6 T_A$ to $2 T_A$. At 80° it approaches $3 T_A$.

"As an old sailor who, as a young man, set sail in the square-rigger *Cutty Sark*, may I offer a sailor's solution: namely, to fit *preventers*—a system of ropes which, from the point of view of engineering design, are redundant structures. Preventers are rigged to prevent catastrophic failure by taking the load if the designed system fails. For example, in the K1WA "wigwam" a useful preventer would be three stout guys, not necessarily from the top of the mast, quite independent of the five-dipole self-staying main system. Belt-and-braces? Yes, and a good night's sleep through the roughest weather!"

As I read it, G0EUO's valuable contribution applies generally to mast guying strains, whether or not the base is free to rotate, and deserves careful consideration. Tall radio and tv broadcast masts are customarily stayed at several heights, partly I imagine to minimize flexing and oscillation. It was once my task to prepare a long non-technical explanation of the little understood problem of "vortex shedding". It was largely due to this phenomenon, which can occur at quite low steady wind speeds and which can cause a mast to go into violent, resonant oscillation, that the 1,265ft Emley Moor mast came crashing to the ground in March 1969. One result was that two other similar masts were equipped with heavy counterweights suspended inside the cylindrical steel structure to damp out oscillations. Perhaps fortunately mast oscillation frequencies are not usually a problem with amateur radio masts! Vortex-shedding, incidentally, is often the cause of the loud hum that can come from overhead telephone wires.

A less shocking keyer

From Bill Sterling, GM4DGT, a long-time advocate of touch keyers, come some tips relating to switching and keyers. He writes:

"Last year I purchased a well-used FT200 with the intention of using it to transvert on to 50 and 70MHz. I soon found that it exhibited the same annoying feature I had experienced on an old FT101. This was that the relay contacts would stick together, requiring much thumping of the keyer to release them. I have found that the addition of a 300Ω resistor in series with the keying lines alleviates the problem although it does not effect a complete cure.

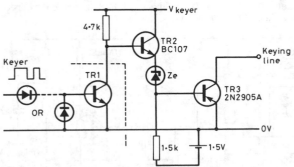

Fig 3. GM4DGT's "shockproof" keying arrangements. TR1 is either the original npn keying transistor or the relay contacts. TR3 2N2905A has withstood the bias voltage but an MJE350 might prove more reliable. An extra diode has been connected between TR1 base and earth. In normal positive keying GM4DGT uses a series diode in the base of TR1 to guard against collector/base breakdown and the transmitter bias etc

"I have also noted that a number of the factory and home designs for solid-state switching of the keying line use an npn transistor (or pnp device in a strange configuration). For a bias-keyed rig this means that the negative (earth) rail of the keyer floats at the open-circuit potential of the bias supply. With a metal-enclosed keyer or, in my case, a touch-keyer (*TT*, May 1977), an unpleasant 40V to 60V 'dirl'* may be felt if in contact with the keyer while making adjustments to the rig.

"The circuit of Fig 3 circumvents this 'shocking' state of affairs. I have used this arrangement since 1974 and wonder why so simple a solution appears not to be more widely used. The battery life is very long; the original was still working, although oozing, in 1983.

"TR1 may be the existing keying transistor in the keyer (or the relay). TR2 is a small-signal device (eg BC107) which, in conjunction with the zener diode, holds off the keying transistor, TR3, by nullifying the −1·5V from the single-cell battery. The zener diode is selected to be equal to the keyer supply voltage less the 1·5V (ie for a 9V keyer supply the zener diode would be a 7·5V type).

"For those who do not want to delve into the innards of the keyer, the whole unit (TR2, TR3) could be housed in a box with an input socket and key lead fitted. The supply could then be derived from a separate 9V battery."

*The word "dirl" is used as in the Scottish bagpipes "skirl". You get just as big a "fleg" (fright) and jump just as high when they start up unexpectedly!—GM4DGT

Feedback on 1·8MHz shielded loop and G4UAZ vfo

No matter how hard everyone along the publishing chain from original letter-writer to the printer tries, errors do creep into published material.

John Hawes, G4UAZ, draws attention to the vital caption of Fig 2 (*TT* June 1986, p417) giving the component values of his stable bipolar-assisted mosfet vfo. An obtrusive "k" crept unnoticed into the values of the emitter and collector resistors (R4, R5) for TR2. The value of each should have been 270Ω not 270k. G4UAZ mentions that there has been considerable interest in this vfo, suggesting that home-construction is not dead. He still has "no reason to doubt this is the 'ultimate' vfo circuit for stability". At least, until someone comes up with a "more ultimate" arrangement.

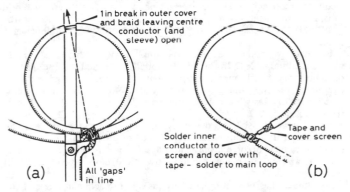

Fig 4. (a) Correction to the passive loop antenna shown in *TT* March indicating the 1in break in the outer braid of the small coupling togs opposite the feedpoint. (b) A possible alternative method of forming a Faraday type coupling loop.

More recently the 1·8MHz shielded loop receiving antenna developed by Mike Shepherd, G8YZW, from a *Wireless World* article (*TT* March, Fig 4, p181), unfortunately omitted the essential "gap" near the top of the small coupling loop where the outer covering and screening braid of the cable has to be removed over about 1in (see Fig 4(a)). Alternatively it might well prove possible to re-arrange the connections at the base of this coupling loop so that it forms a Faraday loop as used in some atus and tvi screen-breaker filters (Fig 4 (b)).

The April *TT* item on PME had Figs 2 and 3 transposed.

The trf receiver—still useful?

The April *TT* included details of a simple regenerative, general-coverage hf receiver based on two twin-valves (ECC81, ECL82) which Alan Radmore, RS88565 built primarily to listen to hf broadcast stations but also to serve as a back-up set for monitoring the hf amateur bands. By adding a simple rf attenuator ahead of just a single tuning circuit he found that his simple set could cope surprisingly well with the strong signals that come these days from 100, 250, 500kW or more transmitters used for external broadcasting. Selectivity of such receivers depends almost entirely on the Q-multiplier effect of a regenerative detector when adjusted just below or just above the point of oscillation, plus the possiblity of further enhancement, particularly on cw, by using a peaked audio filter or resonant headphones etc.

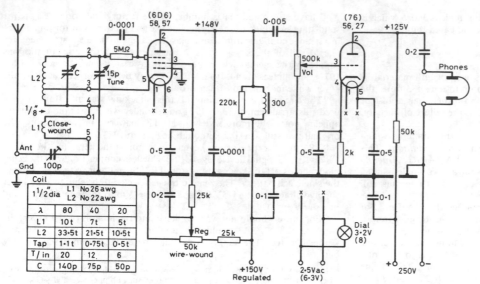

Fig 5. Circuit diagram of ZL2JJ's replica of a 'thirties "blooper" 0-v-1 receiver based on an early American design. Measured sensitivity at 7MHz compares well with a modern superhet receiver

Coil 1½" dia	L1 No 26 awg L2 No 22 awg		
λ	80	40	20
L1	10t	7t	5t
L2	33·5t	21·5t	10·5t
Tap	1·1t	0·75t	0·5t
T/in	20	12.	6
C	140p	75p	50p

Nobody would claim that such a receiver can achieve true single-sideband or single-signal reception but in virtually all other respects the performance can, with care, be made surprisingly good, coping well with the reception of cw, ssb and a.m (and nbfm). I still look back with pleasure to pre-second world war contacts with Australia, Southern Rhodesia (as then was), Newfoundland, Brazil, Argentina and the USA made with about 10W dc input and an 0-v-1 receiver using two of the old 2V-filament battery valves.

The development and implementation of the regenerative detector form of direct-conversion receiver reached its peak in a number of the excellent German military communications receivers such as the Lorentz FuG10, designed in 1937 as an aircraft receiver or the Torn Eb tuned radio frequency receiver (2-v-1) with an eight-band turret (see "German World War 2 communications receivers—Technical perfection from a nearby past" Part 1, by Dick Rollema, PA0SE CQ August 1980), and three-gang tuning.

But just how good (or bad) were the simple amateur "bloopers" as they were sometimes called? In the thirties nobody subjected them to the type of laboratory bench measurements that we expect to find today in equipment reviews—though one should always be careful in accepting that laboratory tests are a certain guide to the operational "feel" of a receiver.

Baz Kirkwood, ZL1BN, disclaims any intention of disposing of his modern Icom IC751, but nevertheless is one of the increasing number of people who have become keenly interested in "vintage gear" of the early 'thirties, and has been busy building 0-v-1 and more recently 1-v-1 trf receivers.

His interest has been stimulated by making the acquaintance of Peter Byam, ZL2JJ. ZL1BN writes: "One rainy afternoon I heard a musical 3·5MHz cw signal wobbling a little within the passband of my IC751 and so made the acquaintance of ZL2JJ. He was using a one-valve tnt power oscillator based on a design in an ARRL Radio Amateurs Handbook of about 1931 vintage. As a receiver he was using an 0-v-1 design of about the same era: Fig 5. Later I visited his farm in Taranaki and was utterly amazed at how serviceable his old-time gear was, and what fun it was to use. He builds immaculate replicas of early 'thirties designs, even turning brass terminals on his lathe. I returned home and lashed up an 0-v-1 receiver

which performed well but suffered from a few cross-modulation problems due mainly to the long earth lead to an upstairs shack. I have since progressed to a 1-v-1 receiver which is now the apple of my eye and I am collecting bits for a companion transmitter."

A disadvantage of a regenerative detector in an 0-v-1 arrangement is that it responds to strong signals on harmonic frequencies when oscillating. "On 3·5MHz I can hear local stations working on 14MHz but have increased the screening and the rf gain-controlled stage helps; also extremely careful decoupling and a top-cap grid valve," he writes.

Peter Byam, ZL2JJ, described and illustrated his 1931 replica receiver in the "Old Timers Club" feature in Break-in, July 1986. He introduced it as follows: "It's simple, easy to build and works astonishingly well. Even today the venerable 'blooper' deserves careful consideration. It makes an ideal companion to a homebrew cw transmitter and parts are not hard to find . . . . Like the self-excited power oscillator (seo) transmitter, a regenerative receiver, when coupled directly to an antenna, can be a bit tricky. The receiving antenna should be non-resonant and should not sway in the wind. Mine is about 30ft of wire hung around the shack. The real problem is body-capacity affecting the tuning. A very short earth connection helps as otherwise the receiver chassis and panel may be 'hot' to rf."

Many of the problems of a straight regenerative receiver are reduced by using a tuned or aperiodic rf stage. For example, it reduces the radiation from an oscillating detector directly coupled to an antenna which can otherwise be a source of interference to receivers in the locality. An oscillating detector needs to be made as stable as possible, with good electrical bandspread tuning. The one-time Eddystone click-stop band-set tuning system (as used in their 'thirties "All-World Two" etc but also marketed in component form) was an excellent arrangement, but there can be relatively few of these left in junk boxes. Resonant antennas connected directly to a regenerative detector tend to produce dead spots, due to suck out, etc.

Just in case readers may get the impression that TT, in pursuit of home-built 'kiss' equipment, is in danger of turning into an "old-timers column" it is worth emphasizing that well-designed solidstate regenerative-detector receivers can give good results, although the homodyne form of direct conversion is the more usual approach. Fig 6 shows a 14MHz triple-gang-tuned regenerative receiver designed specifically for operation on 14MHz. This was by F9GY and appeared initially in Radio-REF, with the circuit diagram reproduced in ART. Japanese 3SK88 dual-gate-mosfets could be used in lieu of the 40673 devices.

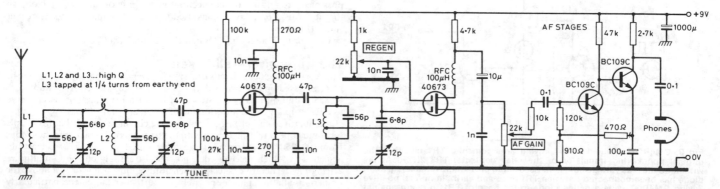

Fig 6. Solidstate 14MHz trf "straight" receiver originally described by F9GY in Radio-REF in the 'seventies and intended primarily as a monoband cw receiver

Measured performance of "bloopers"

The receipt of information on ZL2JJ's replica receiver led Don Sutherland, ZL2AJL (who conducts the New Zealand "Old Timers Club" column) to present himself at ZL2JJ's farm with a wagon load of test equipment. The aim was to establish an objective comparison between the sensitivity of modern receivers/transceivers with those used in the early and mid-'thirties. The results were illuminating.

In a series of tests he found that on about 7MHz this old-style 0-v-1 had a sensitivity virtually limited by noise: (1) with a signal input of 1μV (emf in 50Ω cable, ie -113dBm) the $(s + n)/n$ ratio was 30dB. (2) With the input from the signal generator reduced to give an $(s + n)/n = 12$dB, the input level was $0\cdot12\mu$V (-129dBm). (3) With the receiver "just oscillating" blocking began to occur with an input level of 200μV, representing a dynamic range (from 12dB snr) of 62dB. (4) By advancing the regeneration (reduced sensitivity), the dynamic range could be extended by another 20dB. (5) Measurement of the noise figure resulted in a double-sideband value of 12dB (15dB ssb).

As ZL2JL puts it: "It is clear that such a receiver of elementary design is able to match closely the performance in some of the important areas of many of the most modern, sophisticated receivers and transceivers. We see that claims of excellent performance made on behalf of these simple sets by 'old timers', based on their recollections of half a century ago and more, are fully substantiated. Only in the 'blocking' performance does it leave much to be desired."

This not only bears out the claims made by Alan Radmore in the April *TT* but suggests that the incorporation of a simple rf attenuator as he suggested can be an effective means of reducing the blocking problem and so giving back to the regenerative-detector approach to direct-conversion receivers a credible role even on today's crowded bands. With careful construction and use, a regenerative receiver could not only give that vital "pre-licensing" swl experience that many believe essential, but could also provide an operational receiver, for cw and possibly ssb, at least below about 10MHz. Similarly, with modern improvements in stability, there seems no reason to doubt that such simple-to-build receivers can work well on 50, 70 and possibly even 144MHz. Above this, the super-regenerative approach remains a possibility.

Ignition interference suppression

Back in 1976, D W Morris, G3AYJ, of Lucas wrote a virtually definitive article on "Suppression of vehicle interference for mobile radio operation" (*Radio Communication*, May 1976, pp336–343). There have also been various useful manufacturers' brochures on rfi suppression (eg *Giving two-way radio its voice* publication No 7R, 1978 by the Champion Spark Plug Company of Ohio, USA). More recently, pulse suppression ic devices built into some vhf/fm car radios have helped reduce the problem for broadcast reception on in-car entertainment systems.

Yet many amateurs still experience problems when installing mobile equipment. It is also well-proven that some vehicles tend to generate much more vicious electrical interference than others.

V Heaton, G3JIS, experienced a high level of pulse interference on 144MHz when he acquired a new car. His first reaction was that this could be because the car bonnet was made of plastic, partly but not entirely covered on the underside with an earthed metallic material. He writes: "A recent change of car caused me to re-investigate the problem of suppressing ignition interference on 144MHz. The new vehicle was claimed to be ready to take in-car entertainment equipment but has a plastic bonnet top and fuel injection equipment. The ignition coil had no fitted suppressor capacitor.

"When the car engine was run, both 144MHz equipment and a portable tv set in the house were adversely affected.

"Previous experiments on hf had shown that the lead length of the suppressor capacitors has a considerable influence on their effectiveness at high frequencies. The shorter the lead length, the more effective the suppression. This is due to the inductance of the lead lowering the series resonance of the capacitor and lead combination. Above the resonant frequency the impedance of the lead inductance effectively disconnects the capacitor from the circuit.

"To enable a direct A–B comparison with and without suppression, an inductance and capacitor low-pass network was constructed using Lucar connectors: Fig 7. Capacitor lead length is reduced to approximately $0\cdot25$in (about 6mm).

"The difference in the level of interference was very noticeable. The suppressor systems completely removed all pulse noise on reasonable 144MHz signals and almost completely removed noise on threshold-strength signals. On even the weakest receivable signals ignition noise was barely perceptible.

"It is interesting to note that while the car manufacturers had used very effective suppressor high-tension spark-plug leads, they had allowed the

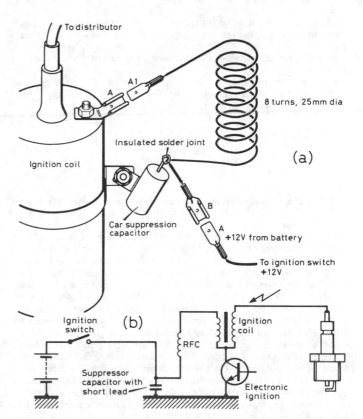

Fig 7. G3JIS's method of investigating and improving ignition interference suppression on 144MHz

low-tension return path to the battery to run through the whole of the wiring harness and dashboard area. Additional suppression provided at the source, by allowing a return path for the ignition current pulse at the coil and by blocking the higher frequency components with the series inductor, removed all pulses from the wiring harness, thus eliminating many metres of potential antenna path.

"Fig 7 shows Lucar connector A, which normally connects into the coil socket at A, ready to be connected into connector B of the coil return path filter. The capacitor is a normal car-type suppressor capacitor and the inductor consists of eight turns of 25mm diameter of 7–10A self-supporting flexible car wiring. Each turn is spaced the thickness of the wire from its neighbour."

Tracing mobile interference

The 16-page brochure "Giving two-way radio its voice" (Champion Spark Plug Company, Publication No 7R, 1978) provides a useful compilation of rfi suppression hints specifically in connection with two-way radio communication rather than the more usual hints on fitting in-car entertainment equipment. It notes at the outset that, while the suppression techniques and devices fitted by US vehicle manufacturers are usually adequate for standard broadcast reception. "Amateur radio, citizen band, police and fire services and marine communication systems may require additional measures beyond the basic suppression methods used by the vehicle manufacturer."

One section covers advice on locating sources of elusive interference, including the need to check reception with any squelch circuit taken out of operation. Where additional suppression is found necessary, the first step is to identify the source(s) of the interference.

On a weak incoming signal, *ignition interference* produces a popping sound that changes with engine speed and stops immediately the ignition key is switched off at fast idle. *Generator* or *alternator* noise appears as a high-pitched musical whine increasing in pitch as the engine speed increases. It does not stop instantly when the ignition key is switched off at fast idle. *Voltage regulators* (electromechanical) produce irregular, ragged, rasping sounds, often in conjunction with generator whine and similarly not stopping instantly when the ignition key is turned. Solid state regulators do not produce this form of interference. Instruments can produce various hissing, crackling, clicking sounds when the gauges operate and tend to be worse on rough roads (verify by jarring the dash).

A loud intermittent hash (sometimes more pronounced when the dash is jarred) can be caused by the voltage limiter used with fuel and temperature gauges mounted behind the instrument cluster. The brochure suggests: "Disconnect the gauges or their sender units one at a time . . . the rfi should disappear. Bounce the vehicle to actuate the fuel gauge sender unit." *Accessories* should be initially checked with all turned off, then turned on one at a time.

Wheels and *tyres* (static electricity) can produce an irregular popping or rushing sound but normally only in dry weather while travelling at speed and it usually disappears when the brakes are lightly applied.

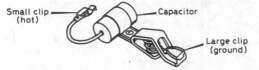

Fig 8. Use of a capacitor "touched" in turn to "hot" electrical points in order to trace sources of interference

The brochure suggests that where the source of interference proves particularly elusive, it may be possible to locate it with the aid of either: (1) a grounded capacitor touched to "hot" electrical connections in turn (Fig 8); and/or (2) a sniffer coil (Fig 9). To make and use a sniffer coil, disconnect the antenna from the transceiver. Wrap 50 turns of insulated wire (eg bell wire) into a coil 2in in diameter. Mount it on a wooden pole. Then, using a few feet of electric lamp cord, connect one side of the coil to the receiver antenna input, the other side to ground: "start the engine, turn on the radio, and probe around the engine and wiring with the coil. Bounce or shake the vehicle during probing. Maximum interference will be heard when the probe is near the source." I cannot help feeling that the details of the sniffer coil may stem from checking for rfi to medium wave broadcast reception (a near optimum frequency for electrical interference). If you are concerned only with 144MHz operation it might, I suspect, be advisable to use just a one- or two-turn loop and a coaxial cable connector rather than lamp cord. Alternatively check on a mf/lf car radio.

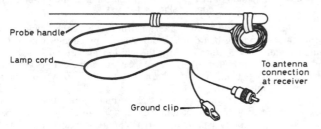

Fig 9. Sniffer coil for tracing sources of vehicle interference

TT has referred a number of times to the potential hazard and repair-costs that can result from emc problems in vehicles increasingly fitted with vulnerable electronic systems. For amateurs, rfi problems can arise not only from their own transmitter or that of a passing vehicle with powerful two-way radio but in extreme cases from radio and tv broadcast transmitters, communication centres, radar installations and the like.

R P Hope, GW8TVX, draws attention to an article "TV puts car electronics at risk" in the *New Scientist* (26 February 1987). This notes that "Car and component makers are reluctant to admit that their customers may be at risk from anti-lock braking systems or electronic transmission systems driven haywire by television and radio transmitters. But there is anecdotal evidence that some are powerful enough to stop engines and send instruments into a spin."

The magazine welcomes the news that Gaydon Technology, part of the Rover Group, has opened an £800,000 test chamber in which their engineers can study vehicle emc problems. It notes that in West Germany, it has been necessary for the authorities to install a giant Faraday cage over a stretch of autobahn that runs by a defence establishment. Amateurs contemplating operating mobile in a bright new "electronic" car should make sure that cmos devices, microprocessors etc are sufficiently resistant or shielded from local rf fields, as not to be affected by a near-by transmitter, including their own.

Biological effects of non-ionizing radiation

The possibility that there may be athermal biological effects (ie effects other than those due to rf heating of tissue or organs) resulting from the non-ionizing radiation of radio transmitters, high-voltage power lines or even deliberate malevolent "zapping" continues to excite the media, despite the continued absence of reproducible evidence from scientifically controlled experiments. I think that few experts now entirely discount the possibility

that low-level radiation *does* have some biological effects, the argument now being whether these are *harmful* effects.

A long article "The waves we all live in" by Cynthia Kee in *The Observer* (March 8, 1987, page 51) reviews in layman's language the "evidence" that has been advanced over the years to support the belief there are athermal effects. Much of this will be familiar to anyone who has attempted to follow this debate since the publication in 1977 of the book *The Zapping of America*. Many of the claims made in that book, including the suggestion that the Russian over-the-horizon radars were intended to brainwash the Americans, have long been discounted but it did concentrate attention on this subject, helped to bring about a revision of the American safety standards and has stimulated much research into this subject. However, one sometimes gets the impression that British research is more often aimed at simply disproving that there are any harmful athermal effects.

After a 1985 London conference "Electric and Magnetic Fields in Medicine and Biology" (IEE Conference Publication No 257), I wrote in *Electronics & Wireless World* (March 1986): "The effects of electric and magnetic fields on the human body remain in dispute. With the exception of thermal effects, directly related to power, everything else still seems to be open to question . . . for every claim there seemed to be a counterclaim. For example, Dr A T Barker of Sheffield University accepts that many thousands of difficult bone fractures have been cured, particularly in the USA, by treatments involving the use of low-energy, low-frequency pulsed waveforms 'to stimulate bone growth' but he provided experimental evidence that suggests the pulsed waveforms do not actually contribute significantly to the healing process, since he claimed that similar success can be achieved with the generator switched off. Similarly, a double-blind clinical trial at Sheffield of pulsed 27MHz energy in the treatment of soft tissue injuries failed to show a statistically significant difference between those so treated and control groups on whom 'dummy' machines were used. On the other hand, the Sheffield group speak highly of magnetic stimulators, and many of the 33 papers seem to show useful applications of magnetic or electric fields or currents in medicine, without any clear idea of how this comes about.

"A study at Manchester University sought to answer the question 'Can induced 50Hz body currents affect mental functions?' The experimental results seemed open to more than one interpretation, though the technique was also tested against the amount of alcohol drunk the previous night and it was found that subjects responded faster in syntactic-reasoning tests when they had had a longer night's sleep, a not unexpected result . . . Similar uncertainty was reflected also in papers on leukemia and electromagnetic fields, overhead power lines and childhood cancers. Absolute certainty was little in evidence."

In *The Observer* article, Dr John Dennis of NRPB, the organization charged with radiological protection, is quoted as saying: "We're on the dividing line between what is socially acceptable and caution. The public seem quite happy living with a risk factor of one in a thousand. We feel successful when both sides attack us equally. Nobody loves us."

I must admit, that where radiation hazards are concerned, I feel less confident than Dr Dennis that the public would happily live with a risk factor of one in a thousand. Some of us would like to see a little more certainty about the risks, or lack of risks, involved with low levels of electromagnetic radiation, a matter of some importance to radio amateurs, their families and their neighbours. The now-current American standards may be about right. If so, the risks from amateur radio are very small if normal precautions are taken; but it would be nice to be certain!

Tips and topics

Charles Wells, G4ZZG, in describing his 807 amplifier (*TT*, February) mentioned that he was compiling information on valves and valve bases. As a result he received many letters and much useful information, duly acknowledged except for the anonymous "Bert" (postmark Scotland) who sent a much appreciated 36 pages of valve data from an old American handbook. G4ZZG adds: "such actions prove that the old cameraderie and helpfulness of amateur radio is not dead and forgotten and contradicts the popular impression that amateur-spirit has got lost on the way to digitalization, packet radio and gigahertz frequencies."

Some brief hints and kinks from *QST*:

K0JFN: "An old trick for soldering to aluminium is to place a drop of oil on the aluminium and then scratch the metal with a knife or other sharp instrument until the area to be soldered is shiny. After the solder has taken wipe the oil from the surface."

WN9RIJ: "When soldering wire to an SO-239 female chassis connector, insert the head of a pair of chain or round-nose pliers into the contact sleeve on the front of the connector. The pliers act as a heat sink and will prevent the plastic insulation between the inner and outer conductor from melting."

Technical Topics
by Pat Hawker, G3VA

EVER SINCE broadcasting began in the early 'twenties, radio amateurs have faced problems of electromagnetic compatiblity (emc) and electromagnetic interference (emi or rfi), first in the form of bci, then as tvi and more recently the possibility of upsetting almost anything electronic, especially systems using cmos devices.

Yet it is only in the past few years that electronic engineers, as a whole, have been forced to wake up to the way in which so many of their cherished electronic systems have become vulnerable to strong local rf fields—and still do not recognise that almost any low-cost digital system itself generates and radiates hash. Because rf shielding and/or filtering add to the cost of consumer electronics, many manufacturers have tended to shut their eyes and ears to emc problems, most of which are far better solved at the design stage than by having to add on extra filters, screens etc.

At a recent IEETE symposium on "Electromagnetic interference: practical design and construction techniques" Professor Mike Darnell of Hull University made a strong plea for more emphasis to be placed on emc during engineering training. Emi and emc, he pointed out, were still largely neglected as academic disciplines by institutions of higher education. In fact, he stressed, many advanced electronic/electrical courses ignore the area completely. He suggested that the importance of emc is still not fully appreciated in the academic sphere; is not recognized as a true academic discipline; and no specialist emc engineers are being produced within the higher educational system.

My own feeling is that all electronic engineering training should include some awareness of emc/rfi etc and that this field of expertise should not be left only to specialist engineers. But then, as we have stressed before, training in electronics engineering is more and more being concentrated on fashionable "digital", with "analogue" and "rf design" largely ignored.

Broadbanding the dipole

A perennial topic is the Q, and hence the effective resonant bandwidth, of an antenna. The higher the element Q, as in any resonant circuit, the narrower the bandwidth, the more critical the tuning, and the greater the detuning influence of nearby objects. For amateur radio, and for many professional communications applications, it is usually a significant advantage for an antenna to have a low Q structure. This implies either a wire at least a full wavelength long or some form of "fat" dipole which may use large diameter tubing (as for most hf and vhf arrays), wide copper or aluminium foil, or multiple wires which can range from the separate twin wires of a folded dipole to the classic multi-wires of a "caged dipole" or the various forms of discones, biconical monopoles, etc. Such structures radiate much the same power as a simple half-wave resonant wire dipole, but over a greater span of frequencies.

In practice, a simple wire dipole has a bandwidth to its $-3\mathrm{dB}$ points of something like $\pm 2 \cdot 5$ per cent of its resonant frequency. This is adequate for most amateur bands, with the exception of the North American $3 \cdot 5\mathrm{MHz}$ band (3,500 to 4,000kHz) *provided* that the antenna stays accurately trimmed to mid-band frequency when elevated. Short elements inductively-loaded have very high Q; "stretched" dipoles capacitively-loaded have low Q and are much less affected by nearby wires or trees etc, but need a good deal more space.

The classic folded-dipole with twin wires of equal diameter remains an extremely useful single-band antenna. There is still considerable room for experiment in the use of different diameter conductors to provide any desired feedpoint impedance (Arch Doty, K8CFU, has just completed an extensive and very interesting study of the impedance transformation characteristics of folded monopoles which I hope to refer to soon). With equal diameters, folding a dipole raises its feedpoint impedance by a factor of four (ie nominally 300Ω for a single-element antenna).

However, many years ago it was shown that a folded dipole in which the element itself is largely formed from coaxial cable does not exhibit this "times four" factor and can be fed directly from similar cable: Fig 1(a). A variation on this antenna (but including a 1:1 balun) was patented a few years ago in the USA (R D Synder "Broadband antennae employing coaxial transmission line sections" US Patent 4,479,130 October 23, 1984) and has been marketed for professional or amateur radio use, with rather extravagent claims as to its performance, as the Synder dipole: Fig 1(b).

This antenna has recently been analysed by a well-known American antenna engineer ("Evaluation of the Synder Dipole" by Robert C Hansen, *IEEE Trans on Ant & Prop,* February 1987, pages 207–10). Although Hansen is critical of the claims made for the Synder dipole and points out that the bandwidth is roughly equal to that of a dipole of the same fatness, with a lumped resonant circuit at the feedpoint terminals, or to that of a conventional folded dipole, he does show that these coaxial-type elements do not raise the impedance by the factor of four. This would seem to me to indicate that the original version (Fig 1(a)) can still be an effective single-band antenna, fed by coaxial cable without a balun, without infringing the Synder patent.

A rather different technique for increasing the bandwidth of a fat dipole element is *resistive loading.* Correctly applied, this can result in a really broadband dipole, capable of being used over virtually the entire hf spectrum. The best-known example is the so-called "Australian dipole" with 300Ω feed, due to Guertler and Collyer and described in *TT* June 1974

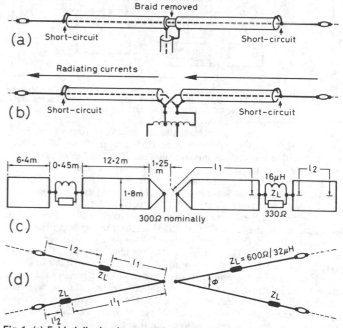

Fig 1. (a) Folded-dipole element suitable for feeding directly from coaxial cable. Overall length of the element is an electrical half-wave with the coaxial section also an electrical half-wave taking into account the reduced velocity ratio of the cable. (b) The Synder dipole with 1:1 balun. (c) The "Australian dipole" as described in *TT* June 1974 and September 1984. (d) Broadband resistive-loaded antenna reported by Austin and Fourie in *Electronics Letters* covering 3 to 30MHz with good efficiency when fed from 500Ω line

and September 1984, and in "sloper" or monopole form in *TT* September 1984: Fig 1(c). It could be argued that the T2FD antenna (*TT* July 1986) is a much earlier though less sophisticated form of a resistive-loaded antenna.

Dr Brian Austin (ZS6BKW and now also G0GSF) whose detailed computer studies of the G5RV-type antenna (*TT* May 1982 and *Rad Com* August 1985, pp 614–7, 624) attracted considerable attention, has more recently become intrigued with the possibilities of resistive loading ("Wire antennas for tactical hf communication" Part 1, *Elektron* June 1986 Part 2, July 1986). Together with A P C Fourie he has recently described an "Improved hf broadband wire antenna" (*Electronics Letters,* 12 March 1987, pp 276–7). In this he reports an inverted-V form of "fat" (diverging wires) resistive/inductive loaded dipole (Fig 1(d)) which can result in an antenna covering the entire range 3–30MHz with an swr not exceeding $2 \cdot 5:1$ and a radiation efficiency better than 40 per cent even at the low-frequency end (40 per cent may not seem high but in fact it is very much higher than with most broadband antennas!) when fed from 500Ω transmission line. This seems a highly promising development of the Australian dipole, and with Dr

Austin now based at Liverpool University it is to be hoped that he will find time to describe some of his recent work in *Radio Communication*.

In-channel-select fm threshold extension

Erwin David, G4LQI/VE2UQ and ex-PA0CG, draws attention to a short piece he wrote for the East Kent Radio Society's *Carrier* newsletter, based on an item by PA0SE in *Electron* November 1986. This describes a new "in-channel-select" (ics) technique that can significantly improve the sensitivity and selectivity of vhf/uhf fm receivers. A commercial "black box" adapter is being made and marketed by the German firm H&C Electronik Hansen & Co of Berlin, which is claimed to improve the s:n ratio of weak fm signals by 6dB and rejection of in-channel splatter from stronger adjacent-channel signals by some 20dB.

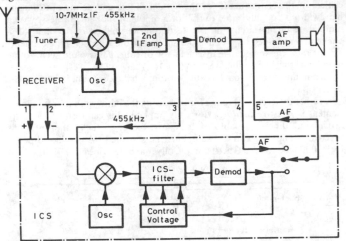

Fig 2. "In-channel-select" unit as marketed by a German firm to enhance intelligibility of weak fm signals and improve adjacent channel selectivity. The 1,800Hz filter tracks the signal

As far as I can judge, the ics technique appears to be a form of threshold-extension demodulation, as originally developed for professional reception of weak satellite signals, but implemented in a form suitable for use with typical amateur radio fm transceivers. The German unit, shown in outline in Fig 2, features a very narrow voltage-controlled filter that automatically tracks the fm signal. For 145MHz (25kHz channelling) the filter bandwidth is only 1,800Hz, ie about one-tenth of the usual i.f filter bandwidth. The receiver's fm detector output voltage, proportional to the instantaneous deviation, steers the ics filter so that it tracks the incoming signal. In demonstrations at a Dutch/German hamfest last year, PA0SE reports that audibility of weak signals was improved by the unit from Q1 to Q4, though never completely to Q5. For strong signals it is usually advisable to switch threshold-extension demodulators out of circuit. The German hardware is being offered primarily as an external unit for base-station receivers, although the principle can be applied to mobile receivers. A threshold extension demodulator does not, of course, improve the front-end noise factor of a receiver, but there is no doubt that the technique does make it possible to copy signals that would otherwise be unintelligible. It certainly seems a development worth keeping in mind.

R-C-L parallel impedance bridge

From Jan-Martin Noeding, LA8AK, comes a simple form of antenna impedance-measuring bridge. He believes that there are still many amateurs who are puzzled about the nature of antenna impedance and who believe it is possible to assess this as though it is always a pure resistance. Others use elaborate circuits to measure the reactance, yet arrive at results that have little bearing on reality, since they often discover that the measured capacitive or inductive reading of the antenna or transmission line varies with the impedance.

After examining and building a number of bridges, LA8AK has settled on the Wheatstone arrangement shown in Fig 3. He writes:

"This bridge is very easy to build and calibrate. It has no coils, and the circuit is theoretically independent of frequency. In practice the critical factor is the lay-out. I built the unit in a box, 155mm wide, 75mm deep and 50mm high. Within the 1 to 18MHz range of my signal generator, the reading shows very little variation.

"Inductance is measured with a capacitive representation, from the formula $L = 25,300/(f^2 \times C1)$, assuming that C1 and C2 are calibrated for equal minimum capacitance. The complete impedance or admittance is calculated from the measured values. The device uses a sensitive form of

quasi-logarithmic amplifier (IC1) to compensate for the non-linear diode characteristic. While values as low as 10pF are easily measured in parallel with 50Ω (less at 3MHz), the available accuracy is dependent upon the gain of the dc amplifier. However, the user should recognize that it makes little sense to measure 10pF in parallel with 10Ω at 3MHz since the equivalent inductance would be 281μH!

"To calibrate the bridge, connect a 100Ω resistor across the input, and then use a series of fixed capacitors of known value across the variable capacitor *not* being calibrated (ie across C2 while calibrating C1). For example, with C1 at minimum and a fixed 10pF across it, then C2 must be increased by 10pF to achieve balance, and so on.

"Since it is difficult to obtain potentiometers having good performance at rf, I used somewhat larger than usual trimming potmeters, screened from

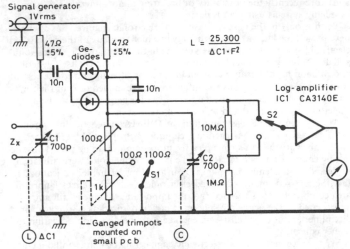

Fig 3. LA8AK's Wheatstone bridge for R-C-L measurements between about 1 and 20MHz

each other by a piece of aluminium sheet between them, with the potmeters ganged by a plastic shaft cut from another potentiometer.

"An excellent explanation about parallel to series impedance conversion will be found in the article "A single-stage linear amplifier for 50MHz" by John Matthews, G3WZT (*Rad Com* June 1986, pp404-8).

"A noise-bridge version of this instrument may also be considered. However, it is rather impractical to operate a receiver in the garden when adjusting a 1·8MHz antenna. With the bridge as shown, one needs only a coaxial cable from a signal generator located in the shack. On the other hand, a noise bridge has the important advantage that it does not produce unwanted signals on the bands, though it may be difficult to use when a band is crowded. The basic bridge arrangement, however, is suitable for both versions."

Receiver circuit ideas

Dave Parnell of Pickering, North Yorkshire, has sent along some novel ideas that he has used in home-built hf receivers; suggestions that could be adapted to suit specific requirements, rather than intended for precise duplication.

Variable-bandwidth crystal ladder filter. The bandwidth of a crystal ladder i.f filter can be made variable over a useful range simply by making the middle capacitor variable. This can be done conveniently by using a varicap diode or, in his case, a 1W zener diode acting as a variable-capacitance diode: Fig 4. With 8MHz crystals, he finds that the −6dB points can be varied continuously from 1·1kHz to 2·8kHz by varying the control voltage from 0 to 8V. The bandwidth variation is not symmetrical about the centre frequency but is entirely on the high-frequency side of the passband response. Clearly, this simple form of bandwidth control must

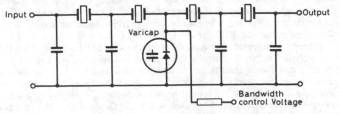

Fig 4. Simple technique for varying the bandwidth of an 8MHz crystal ladder filter from about 2·8kHz down to 1·1kHz

result in a slightly sub-optimum stop-band response, but in practice this seems to be insignificant.

2nd i.f amplifier with agc. Dave Parnell has used the Plessey SL6270 "vogad" ic device at a second i.f of 140kHz: Fig 5. This is very effective provided that suitable reductions are made in the value of the capacitors which determine response timings. The agc characteristics are excellent. The time constant can be changed by switching in different capacitors. It is also possible to change the gain manually by applying a control voltage to the agc time-constant capacitor.

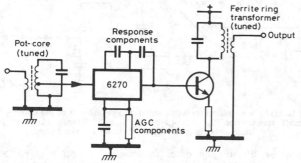

Fig 5. Use of an SL6270 vogad ic at a second i.f of 140kHz

Multi-band transmission line oscillator. Dave Parnell writes: "I use a transmission line oscillator with a quarter-wavelength of miniature coaxial cable (as previously described in *TT*) *but* I switch in binary lengths of cable to provide 32 frequency bands with the aid of five miniature toggle switches: Fig 6. This covers 14 to 36MHz in 32 overlapping bands. The highest band is 2·3MHz wide, the lowest 580kHz. I follow this with a buffer amplifier and a switchable divide-by-two flip-flop which gives me another 32 bands from 7 to 18MHz. Used in a receiver with an 8MHz i.f, this form of local oscillator provides a frequency range of 10kHz to 28MHz (with a small gap at the i.f)."

Ring mixer drive: The advantages of using a near square-wave drive to a ring mixer, in order to achieve optimum dynamic range, are well documented. Dave Parnell uses bus-driver chips, of the type normally used to drive microcomputer data buses, in order to provide square-wave drive to a Schottky-ring front-end mixer. He uses 8T26 chips which are high-current Schottky-clamped bus drivers. This gives fast edges and plenty of drive power. Other types may be suitable. A terminating resistor must be used: Fig 7.

Re-forming electrolytic capacitors

In the item "Refurbishing valve receivers" (*TT* March 1987, page 181) mention was made of the need to "re-form" any high-voltage electrolytic capacitor, as used in valve equipments, when it has been out of use for more than about a year, or even less in tropical climates. Otherwise the initial leakage current may be high enough to damage other psu components, or even result in an exploding capacitor. It was pointed out that the usual technique is to run the electrolytic capacitor for about half-an-hour or more through a high-wattage series resistor of the order of about 8,000 to 10,000Ω. Two useful comments have been made on this topic.

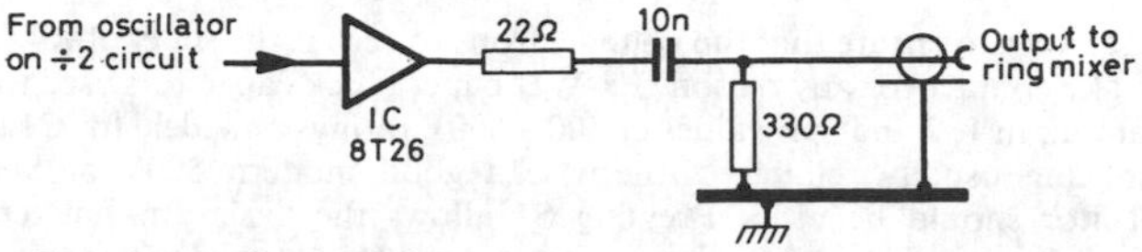

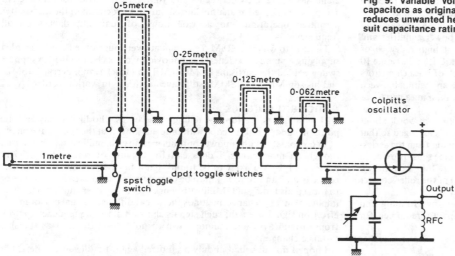

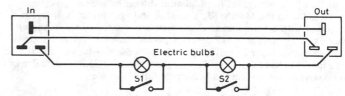

Fig 7. Method of providing near square-wave drive to a ring mixer

Douglas Byrne, G3KPO, writes: "While agreeing that high-voltage electrolytic capacitors should be 'reformed' in any valve receiver which has not been used for some months, this is easier said than done! Removing the chassis and feeding voltage through a resistor to each capacitor is a time-consuming task. It is much easier simply to apply the mains supply through a Variac variable-voltage transformer which is 'wound up' slowly over several hours, albeit keeping an eye on the colour of the rectifier anodes and watchful for any undue heating of the transformer. For those without a Variac, the receiver can be operated with a small light bulb in series with the mains lead, or even using a small board constructed especially for the purpose. This can have a couple of bulb-holders and two switches plus an output socket and a lead to the input plug: see Fig 8.

Fig 8. Use of electric lamp bulbs to reform electrolytic capacitors in situ

Mike Shepperd, G8YZW, also develops this theme by sending along the circuit diagram (Fig 9) of a variable voltage dc psu, originally published in *Radio Constructor* November 1953, intended specifically for the purpose of re-forming electrolytic capacitors. He writes:

"This unit covers the range 40 to 400V when a 200 − 0 − 200V transformer is used. Valves such as the 807, 1625, 6Y6 etc, will stand the piv applied to the electrodes and can often be recovered from the junk box or obtained at reasonable cost. R4 controls the voltage, with R3 connected

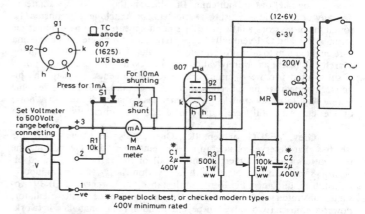

Fig 9. Variable voltage power supply unit for re-forming electrolytic capacitors as originally described in *Radio Constructor* November 1953. R1 reduces unwanted heating of the capacitor. Use a series external resistor to suit capacitance rating. R4 varies the output voltage over the range of about 40 to 400V

Fig 6. Multi-band transmission-line oscillator

to the slider to ensure that the voltage drops to zero if the slider of R4 fails to make contact for any reason. Ex-WD paper block capacitors used to be common, in 1, 2 and 4µF values at 400–600V ratings and ideal for C1 and C2, being usually reliable. Otherwise a good modern 500V or better capacitor should be used. Pressing S1 allows the basic 1mA meter to indicate low currents, otherwise the meter should be shunted with a suitable resistor to about 10mA fsd. The capacitor to be re-formed should be connected to terminals 1 and 2, with a voltmeter set to the 500V range to terminals 1 and 3.

"Set R4 to the lowest voltage position and switch on. Allow the 807 to warm up, then slowly advance the voltage control to the working voltage of the capacitor, watching for excessive current indication, and/or heating of the capacitor. Should this occur reduce the voltage and allow the capacitor time to cool down. Check again at low voltage to see if it begins to re-form, indicated by a gradually decreasing current; then gradually increasing voltage. If it again shows a tendency for the leakage to rise, throw it away! A couple of hours soaking at its rated working voltage will usually reduce the leakage current to an acceptable level, but an extended period will ensure that the component is as well re-formed as it can be. Make sure that R4 is *always* set for minimum voltage before switching on."

As noted in the March *TT*, a modest leakage current is always to be expected with a high-voltage electrolytic capacitor. The values suggested were, say, 0·5mA for an 8µF capacitor, about 2mA for 32µF etc. A variable voltage psu dedicated specifically to this purpose may be regarded as a bit of a luxury unless this is a regular task; however, the G3KPO external mains bulb series-resistor seems an easy makeshift substitute.

The pi-network and the variometer

The history and development of the pi-network (*TT* November 1986, January 1987) continues to attract interest and to turn up some new ideas. By coincidence two letters have come in from Canadian amateurs on this topic. L Herrington, VE4QL (one-time G5QL) of Winnipeg, recalls that the pi-network, as a universal matching network, was first brought to the notice of radio amateurs by Arthur Collins, W0CXX, founder of Collins Radio, about 1931, in *QST* or one of the other American amateur radio magazines of that period.

He recalls ruefully that he used one with an end-fed wire, forming a half-wave or aog (Act of God) antenna. But since, in those days, few amateurs had any appreciation of using swr meters for matching adjustments, he found the pi-network a little puzzling since it appeared to tune at numerous settings of *L* and *C*. Eventually he found that an rf ammeter in the antenna wire enabled him to adjust for optimum results. This, as I mentioned in the March *TT,* is still an entirely valid technique even when a small torch bulb is substituted for the rf ammeter. VE4QL comments: "Today, the pi-network appears to have become an exercise in mathematics. We've come a long way in radio knowledge of antennas, what with atus, swr, noise bridges etc, yet I still have more confidence in rf ammeters and/or neon bulbs!"

Kurt Grey, VE2UG, of Sept Iles, Quebec, also has memories of the 'thirties that deserve consideration. He remembers that German marine transmitters (both commercial and naval) of the early 'thirties used pi-networks extensively, often with a "variometer" as a continuously adjustable inductance: Fig 10(b). For instance, the Lorentz LO4OK39 two-stage transmitter used three variometers, one each in the master-oscillator, power-amplifier (two valves in parallel) and antenna matching network. VE2UG also points out that the Collins ART13 aircraft transmitter (813 pa) similarly used a variometer in a pi-network arrangement: Fig 10(a).

VE2UG writes: "The basic difference between the American and German versions was the coupling used between the power amplifier and the antenna tuning. The German version provides a higher degree of attenuation of unwanted harmonics. The value of each *C* is in the range 10 to 50nF. Such capacitors were made in one large block of mica capacitors with terminals sticking out on one side, so eliminating any wiring between the individual capacitors. The block formed, so to speak, a mica capacitor with taps.

"This brings me to an interesting point. But first a word about 'variometers'. These comprised two series-connected coils arranged so that one section can be turned through 180° rotation, changing from the series-aiding to the series-opposing condition. They could thus provide a continuously-variable inductance without incurring the well-known problems of the rubbing contacts (or the unused turns) of the roller-coaster form of variable inductance.

"The book *Radio operating questions and answers* by Hornung and McKenzie, a standard manual for marine and aeronautic radiomen for many years, stated:

'*Question:* Why do many marine transmitters employ variometers rather than variable capacitors as the tuning adjustments?'

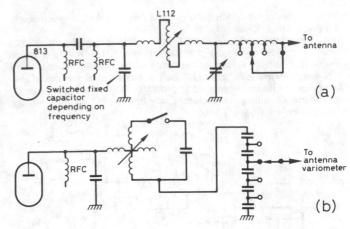

Fig 10. (a) How a variometer was used in the pi-network of the Collins ART13 aircraft transmitter. (b) Arrangement used in German Lorentz marine transmitter in which three variometers were used

'*Answer:* Because, in order to maintain a proper *Q* for various frequencies, the inductance rather than the capacitance of the oscillatory circuit must be varied. The use of variometers also permits constant *LC* ratio.' "

VE2UG adds: "It is a pity that the variometer has lost it's place in amateur radio equipment, Admittedly, they are rather expensive to fabricate. Some time ago, in correspondence with an hf engineer working for a well-known amateur radio organization, he maintained that the variometer was an historic oddity used for receiving purposes only in the early years of this century. He was clearly unaware of the fact that a very large variometer is currently used in a 2MW vlf transmitter in Massachusetts!

"Finally, I would like to mention that in contrast to the American-made ART13 variometer, fabricated from silver-plated copper wire unsupported by any former, the German-made variometers utilized silver windings plated on to a ceramic former and had a temperature coefficient of only a few parts per million. Thus, with a selected capacitor network of appropriate temperature coefficients, the stability of the master oscillators was very close to that of a non-ovened crystal oscillator."

A further recollection of how a pi-network was used in the Collins 18M-5 transmitter-receiver, developed originally for one of Admiral Byrd's Antarctic expeditions, comes from Colonel Jerry Parker whose recent callsign, G1SML, belies a long and distinguished career as a professional radio communications engineer with the Post Office and also wartime involvement with clandestine radio links in the Middle East and Western Europe.

He recalls that in Cairo in 1941 or 1942 he bought from special funds a number of the 18M-5 equipments which had a 6V6G as a crystal oscillator or vfo, an 807 pa, a pair of 6V6G as high-level audio modulator (a.m) and a five-valve superhet receiver with a tuned rf stage (12SK7, 12SA7, 12SK7, 12SQ7, 6G6G). This was, for its time, a well-designed, compact, transportable radio station (14·25in high 9·6in wide, 9·75in deep, weight 25lb 10oz plus psu). It provided (provides) an rf output of 15W cw between 2 and 8MHz, 12W cw between 8 and 16MHz, 5W carrier for a.m speech. The pi-network used as an unbalanced output tank circuit of the transmitter permitted operation into a wide range of load impedances on all frequencies.

The uses to which the 18M-5 equipments were put by the British included supplying a number to General Mihailovic's Cetniks before British support swung behind the partisans of Marshal Tito (Josef Broz). Jerry, G1SML, and his son Micky, G1SMM, still have an 18M-5 in working order.

A modern paraset

QRP enthusiasts are fond of telling those of us who like to have a little power in hand, if only to cope with fade margins, that they can make plenty of hf cw contacts with rf power outputs measured in milliwatts. This is true, though on most bands it does call for the use of reasonably-efficient antennas; it is also likely to be found that a fair percentage of minipower contacts on 7 and 10MHz fail to be completed either due to interference or to the signals fading out. Milliwatts work best along near-muf paths, which implies that any change in ionospheric conditions can have a dramatic effect on signal strength; such signals show an alarming tendency to drop from around S7-8 one minute down to noise level the next as the skip distance changes.

I hope I do not sound unduly prejudiced against milliwatt exhalers, but in excuse I recall having to struggle to copy cipher traffic from dry-battery valve transmitters using crude antennas during the second world war. On the other hand, transmitters providing around 3 to 5W rf output, even with an aog throw-out antenna, usually had enough in hand to cope with normal fading as experienced on signals near the optimum working frequency (ie about 15 per cent lower than the muf for the specific path).

One of the simplest transmitter-receivers used for clandestine radio from 1939 to 1944 was the so-called Mark 7 or Mark 7/B made by Special Communications but also used for a short period by SOE as the "paraset". A circuit diagram and panel layout of the Mark 7/B was given in *TT* (November 1982, p961) showing that the 0-v-1 receiver used two metal 6SK7 valves, and the crystal-controlled transmitter a single 6V6.

A letter from S Pauwe of Mijdrecht, Holland (callsign not given), describes how he has drawn upon the basic Mark 7 arrangement, although he has never seen an actual model (I recall seeing many of them stacked up in a room in Paris in October 1944 after they were recovered from the French Resistance operators, but I fear they must all have been destroyed later). He writes:

"I have never seen a Mk7 except on a slide at a lecture by John Brown, G3EUR, and the diagram you gave in *Wireless World* (January/February 1982). But having gained some experience by constructing breadboard models, I set out to construct an improved version, having a suitable box on hand and digging out parts from my junkbox. Basically, my receiver follows the original circuit arrangement except that it is arranged to tune just the cw segments of the 3·5 and 7MHz bands and uses 6SH7 valves rather than 6SK7 variable-mu valves, since I consider a regenerative detector should use a sharp rather than a remote-cut-off valve.

"The transmitter uses a 6V6 or 6L6, but with pi-network output switchable for 3·5 and 7MHz. My first addition was a side-tone oscillator, but to avoid using transistors I adopted an old favourite microphone/speaker howl-round oscillator with a carbon microphone. However, I did experience trouble where least expected: due to stray hf, the particles in the microphone stuck together, with the resistance dropping to a very low value. It could be restored by tapping the microphone (shades of the coherer) but would again fail after a few symbols. A little rf suppression has cured this problem.

"The next step was to provide automatic changeover from transmit to receive. My first intention was to use the cathode current of the 6V6 to operate a relay, but I found that this could be eliminated thus making possible full break-in. To achieve this I had to depart from my original intention of not using any parts that were not available 45 years ago. In practice I use a zener diode permitting the receiver to operate between symbols. There are some clicks (reduced by back-to-back diodes across the af output) but the receiver stays on frequency well enough to make break-in a most useful facility.

"Tuning is very simple. The transmitter is adjusted using a dummy load. After switching to the antenna, the atu is adjusted to provide the same

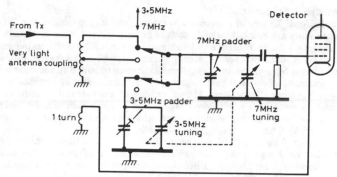

Fig 12. Improved tuning arrangement for bandspread on 3·5 and 7MHz (range 140kHz)

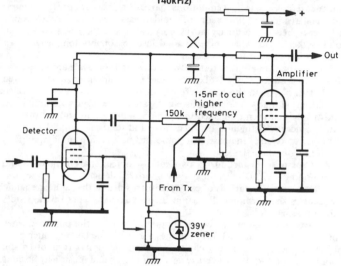

Fig 13. Circuit used to maintain more constant ht on regenerative detector while transmitter is being keyed

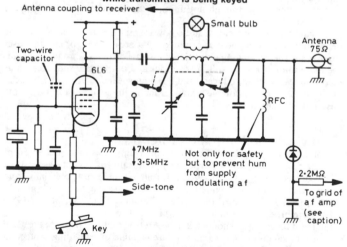

Fig 14. Transmitter based on 6L6 with pi-network tank

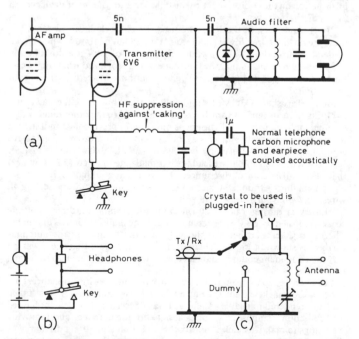

Fig 11. Circuit arrangements used to improve the basic Mark 7/Paraset transmitter receiver to provide sidetone, audio limiting, audio filtering etc

brilliance of the bulb. The receiver is adjusted to the crystal frequency by simply putting the crystal to be used in the transmitter in series with the lead between the transmitter and atu. Passing the crystal frequency on the receiver tuning gives an audible plop in the headphones, permitting near zero-beat netting." Figs 11, 12, 13 and 14 show some of his ideas.

"Operation with this simple rig is limited at the moment by lack of suitable crystals as I have only one that I can use, but in due course more will turn up in the flea markets."

None of the original suitcase sets was intended to be used on the same frequency as the base station, since this would have made interception and detection of the clandestine station easier. But with the modifications suggested there is little doubt that this type of compact, attache-case, rig could still prove effective and provide a stronger signal than many of the solidstate miniwatt rigs when used with a mains psu or a dc–dc inverter with a car battery capable of providing both heater and ht power.

Audio and solidstate

In the April *TT* a brief reference was made to the way in which some hi-fi enthusiasts are being persuaded to buy expensive "super-quality" audio cables, and the belief generated by some writers that KT88 valve amplifiers have some inherently better "sound" than even well-engineered solidstate amplifiers. My purpose in raising these topics was to underline the fact that we all need to be on our guard against the creation of technical myths as a sales technique. Fortunately, the advertising of amateur radio equipment and accessories has, with some usually minor exceptions, been rather more restrained in advancing technical hype, although the old advice of *caveat emptor* (let the buyer beware) remains valid.

Maurice Whatton, G8FUR, who, until he retired, was responsible for the production-design of high-quality BBC monitoring loudspeakers, has been provoked to comment in rather more detail on the question of audio mythology. He writes:

"Some years ago, I helped to organize and take part in a listening test, under carefully-controlled conditions. None of a panel of very experienced listeners, recognized possessors of 'golden ears', was able to detect any difference between ordinary heavy duty cable and the so-called 'special loudspeaker cable' when this was used in a reasonably long length as a connection cable for loudspeakers.

"Similarly, the definitive test between valve and solidstate amplifiers was that carried out by Peter Walker of Quad using amplifiers manufactured by that firm. Again the tests were conducted under carefully controlled conditions with an experienced listening panel. The results were analyzed statistically and then published in *Wireless World*. This showed that the panel could not distinguish between valve and solidstate amplifiers.

"It is, of course, the case that some early transistor audio amplifiers suffered from three defects:

(1) Crossover distortion, a particularly objectional form of audio distortion now virtually eliminated by improved design.

(2) Frequency limitations of early transistors meant that at higher audio frequencies the harmonic distortion increased. New types of transistors solved that problem.

(3) Overloaded stabilized power supplies. The hard clip produced when amplifiers with stabilized power supplies are overloaded is very much more objectionable than the soft clip of unstabilized units. It is often not appreciated that while the average power of speech and music may be quite small, the peak output may be very high and the amplifier must deliver this peak output without distortion. (This is particularly the case with high-fidelity reproduction, though not unimportant even for processed speech on ssb transmitters—*G3VA*).

"Finally the current trend to audio power amplifiers using power mosfets means that designs can now be produced that are as good, or in some cases better than, the preceeding amplifiers in the recording or broadcast chain. The main limitations are still in the input and output transducers such as microphones, disc reproducers and the loudspeakers. Even the highest-quality loudspeaker available produces many times the distortion of any reasonable amplifier."

More views on lightning protection

Recent references to the difficulty of providing adequate protection of amateur radio equipment—particularly solidstate equipment—against the effects of electromagnetic pulses (emp) from lightning and potentially from the even more devastating emp that would result from high-altitude nuclear explosions (*TT* November 1986, p781, January 1987, p31, March 1987, p183) have brought in a number of additional comments.

First and foremost, it should again be stressed that few if any of the usual precautions taken by radio amateurs are capable of providing protection against direct strikes, or even strikes in very close proximity to the shack or mast/tower. The November 1986 *TT* showed that for professional broadcast installations designed to sustain direct strikes on high masts, it is recognized that it is *essential* to have extremely good earthing systems, even to the extent of undertaking blasting operations at rocky sites to facilitate the injection of highly-conductive solutions in pursuit of "earthing improvement". But it was also noted that isokeraunic charts indicate that, at least in those northern areas beyond the Watford Gap, the number of thunderstorms experienced in any year is relatively small.

E McFarland, G3GMM, recognizes that many UK amateurs tend to be almost indifferent to the question of lightning protection "but, come a long, hot summer, we all have second thoughts about our protection and feel apprehension at the first rumble of thunder breaking out in the middle of the night.

"Even the operator with a modest wire or vertical antenna at not more than about 30ft lays in bed and vows to do something better than a crocodile clip to a simple earth stake.

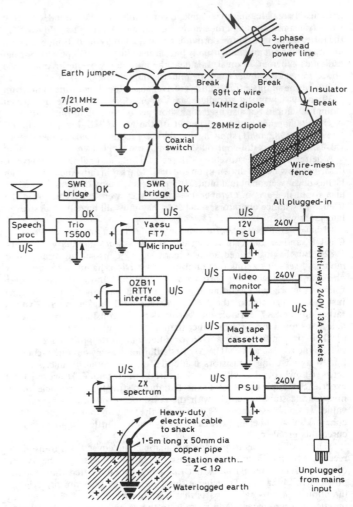

Fig 15. Z21AB's installation showing the results of the lightning strike that "took out" virtually all the solidstate equipment although the valved Trio TS500 remained in good trim. The culprit was probably the earth connection

"The first-class article by George Jessop, G6JP (*Rad Com* December 1982, pp1042–46) gave positive advice but there is still a need for more information on the choice, practical installation and sources of devices such as gas discharge tubes.

"In the old days, in the RAF, we used the old-style knife switches but these are no longer readily available and not well-suited for use with coaxial feeders. I must admit to seeing unmarked boxes of gdts at a mobile rally priced about 60p each but at the time none of us recognized what they were. Later, re-reading G6JP's article, I fell to gnashing of teeth at the missed opportunity!"

Many of us share G3GMM's midnight qualms, but come the dawn and lightning hazards tend to vanish from our minds. On the other hand, radio amateurs in regions where lightning is much more prevalent cannot afford to overlook this problem, as may be evident from a story of extensive equipment damage suffered by A E Skipper (Z21AB/G4JUO/ZS6AES). His experiences in Zimbabwe lead him to challenge the view (*TT,* January) that it is sufficient to disconnect the antenna and mains lead from equipment during thunderstorms unless this also includes disconnecting *all* wires, *including earth wires.* He writes:

"Last year during a heavy storm my house sustained a direct multiple strike. Transient energy was present through the mains leads and antennas. The radio shack had been unplugged from the mains and the antennas earthed as shown in Fig 15. Theoretically it might seem that there was no way my equipment could be damaged with all items duly taken to the shack earth.

"In practice, apart from serious damage to house wiring appliances, my entire radio shack, except the valved Trio TS500 transceiver, was 'taken out' and rendered unusable. As far as I was concerned this incident has led me to discount established theories about earthing antennas and removing wall plugs to make a shack safe. My theory is that a lightning discharge of this nature causes the earth potential to be raised at the point of discharge, taking time to discharge or dissipate. The result is a high static charge sufficient to break down most semiconductor junctions, causing irreversible damage to solidstate electronic equipment.

"Examination of the wiring and burnt-out components shows beyond doubt that the equipment was damaged through the earth connection. In addition, on my 69ft of antenna wire, it shattered two egg insulators, welded a multistrand copper wire into a single strand and caused the supporting wire at the fence end to disappear. I no longer believe that you can prevent lightning damage by earthing! Zimbabwe is a country in which violent thunderstorms occur every season. I would suggest to those who operate in similar circumstances that they should disconnect everything, *including the earth*. This is the best form of lightning protection. Incidentally my insurance claim was Z$5,500 but fortunately there was no problem with the payment."

While one can understand his feeling that he was let down by the traditional advice, I must, in fairness, emphasize that the advice given in *TT* and *Radio Communication* has indicated quite clearly that there is no simple way of protecting equipment against direct or even near strikes, particularly where the earth conductivity is less than near perfect. As noted above and last November, protection of solidstate broadcast transmitters requires extremely good earthing, far better than found in most amateur installations. Even so, it is known for lightning to "take out" mf solidstate amplifiers. Valve equipment is far less vulnerable to emp.

Fortunately the chances of a direct strike or a near miss on the average UK amateur radio installation is little or no greater than on the house of a non-amateur. On the other hand if you are thinking of duplicating WD8RXP's *180ft* tower (see "Mid-Michigan Skyhook" *QST*, January 1987, pp15–17) then I suggest you give careful consideration to lightning hazards. But then I seriously question whether amateurs *should* be thinking of such monstrous installations, even if they have a local authority prepared to approve one. Envy? Not entirely.

The transmitting gramophones

In 1936, the Abwehr and the later Amtsgruppe Abwehr (German military intelligence) as an organization within the high command of the German armed forces (OKW)—not to be confused with the notorious Nazi police organizations that became grouped together as the RSHA and which in 1944 succeeded in taking over control of the Abwehr—began building up a "Geheimen Funkmeldedienst" (secret radio reporting service). A pre-war German radio amateur and professional radio engineer, Technical Superintendent Black, was appointed to form a centralized unit for the development and production of portable hf radio equipment for intelligence radio networks, including those for communicating with secret agents. This was established at Berlin-Stannsdorf where a design centre, workshops and assembly line were located together with the main Berlin base station, under the cover name of "Heeresneubauamt" (Office of new building for the armed forces).

Detailed information on the large number of hf receivers and transmitters built at Berlin-Stannsdorf, where many pre-war German amateurs came to

be employed, and also "suitcase" equipment built in the UK, USSR, USA, Finland etc has been diligently compiled and collated by Dipl-Ing Rudi Staritz, DL3CS with the assistance of many amateur collectors and others interested in a type of equipment that was largely based on amateur radio concepts. These have included Gerhard Stroessner, DJ2VN, a member of RSGB, who has kindly passed to me booklets and photographs compiled and collated by DL3CS. Virtually all of the Stannsdorf receivers were "straight" regenerative-detector designs although the main intelligence offices were often equipped with communications receivers, such as the Siemens R4, closely patterned on the HRO. In the first year of the war, Stannsdorf continued to acquire HRO "PW" tuning drives (and also British Hivac miniature valves) through neutral countries.

One of the "Agentenfunkgerate" (agents radio equipment) developed in the early days comprised a plug-in "adapter" transmitter for use with an existing receiver such as the popular "all-wave" broadcast sets. The transmitter obtained its heater and ht power when the adapter was plugged into the output stage of the receiver. Adapter transmitters using various valve types (AL4, AL5, 6V6, 6L6) were produced. Fig 16 and the photograph show a 6V6 version of the "Senderanfertigung Grammo" for use with large, old-style cabinet gramophones. This particular version had an associated 350Vdc/180Vdc/6·3Vac psu and a four-valve receiver (1-v-2) using two miniature 4695 pentodes (untuned rf stage) and two 4671 af triodes. Other versions were simply plug-in transmitter units, for use with broadcast or communication receivers.

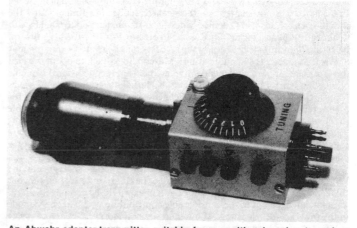

An Abwehr adapter-transmitter suitable for use with a broadcast receiver fitted with an EL12 audio output valve (*Photo from DL3CS collection*)

Tips and topics

Alan Williams, G3KSU, felt sure that he had seen the nomograph for two resistors in parallel (*TT* January). Sure enough he traced a similar idea in *Wireless World*. The issue was that of 3 October *1928*. Ah, well, there's nothing new under the sun, even in electronics.

More hints and kinks from *QST*:

WA0KKC: "If you use a typical self-supported tower without the top section, the structural pipes are open-ended at the top. Corks in the top of each pipe will prevent moisture building up and wind whistle."

W4FXE: "When erecting dipoles, a bit of pruning is usually necessary and it is not easy to correct if in the process the antenna is cut too short, I cut the antenna short of the calculated length and then solder on an additional length of rigid no 12 copper wire at each end. It is then a simple matter to prune a little at a time, and I usually finish up with the desired resonance and a trimming wire between 1 and 5in long that is self-supporting and can be left in place (Fig 17)."

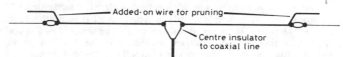

Fig 17. W4FXE's suggestion on how to prune a dipole without the tears of cutting it too short

WD9DID "I was worried about the guy lines in my yard: difficult to see and could injure someone walking into them. I went to the local hardware store, bought three foam-rubber insulating sleeves intended for lagging 0·5in water pipes. Each sleeve is 4ft long and silver in colour. They slip easily onto the guys. To make them even more visible in the dark they can be sprayed with fluorescent yellow paint, applied very lightly since paint solvents can melt the foam."

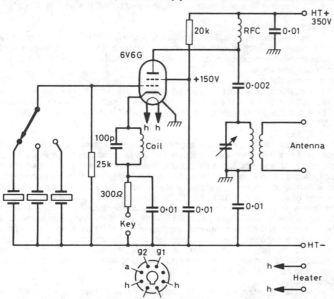

Fig 16. Circuit diagram of one version of the Abwehr "Senderanfertigung Grammo" adapter-transmitter produced at Berlin-Stannsdorf from about 1937 onwards. This version, apparently for concealment in large cabinet gramophones, was used with its own receiver and psu

Technical Topics
by Pat Hawker, G3VA

A RECENT international conference on antennas and propagation (ICAP87, IEE Conference Book No 274) included a noteworthy paper by Prof A D Olver (Queen Mary College, University of London) on "A century of antenna development", reminding us that it is now 100 years since Heinrich Hertz began a series of experiments to verify the existence of the electromagnetic waves which had been postulated by the Scot James Clerk Maxwell. This brilliant mathematician predicted that all changes in electric and magnetic fields cause waves to be propagated in space and that visible light is just one form of such electromagnetic waves. Maxwell published his ideas in 1862, although what are now known as the basic Maxwell Equations are the later simplified versions of Hertz and Oliver Heaviside.

Hertz's early experiments involved generating radio waves at vhf and uhf and, as the paper notes, the early "microwave-optics period" that came between the work of Hertz and Marconi included the development of the first microwave horn antennas (then called "collecting funnels") by the Indian scientist Bose, in Calcutta, working at frequencies up to 60GHz with a laboratory bench set up. In Russia, Professor Popoff, for his work on detecting lightning discharges, was the first to use elevated wire antennas at low frequencies (1896 publication). Marconi was quick to adopt the idea (or possibly arrived independently at the same conclusions) for his pioneering work on exploiting the use of Hertzian electromagnetic waves for practical communications. By 1899 he was commenting on the need for high antennas when he claimed that "the distance over which it was possible to signal with a given amount of energy varies approximately with the square of the height of the vertical wire and with the square root of the capacity of the plate, drum or other form of capacity area which may be placed at the top of the wire".

In his paper, Dr Olver pays tribute to the role of radio amateurs and the Wireless Society of London (which became the RSGB in 1922) pointing out that "no story of the development of antennas would be complete without an acknowledgement to the considerable contribution which has been made in the practical development of antennas by amateurs".

For 100 years, antennas have remained the key to progress in radio communications. In recent years the computer has had an enormous impact on design theory although virtually all the basic designs stem from pre-computer days. In professional design, as Dr Olvey shows, a major advance has stemmed from the "Moment Method" using computers that enable the current distribution in small antennas to be predicted with much better accuracy than was practicable in the years bc (before computers). But it is worth stressing that the validity of the results obtained from computer calculations depends on both the quality of the software "modelling" and the quality of the information fed to the machine. Given half-a-chance, a computer will respond to slipshod work with silly and misleading answers; by no means all of the published computer predictions of antenna parameters stand up to the cold light of practical application.

Yet, as Dr Ambrose Fleming put it in 1909, and quoted in 1987 by Dr Olver: "The antenna is, so to speak, the mouth or ear of the (radio) station, by which it speaks through the ether, or by which it hears the etherial whispers coming from other stations."

Antenna basics

In compiling *TT*, in order to provide members with information that will be fresh and interesting to the majority, it is necessary to assume that most readers will already have absorbed and understood the basics of established technology, either as the result of studying for the RAE or (more importantly) as part of their practical activities, using the basic handbooks and manuals such as the long-established *A Guide to Amateur Radio*. It would be tedious in the extreme if every *TT* item had to be based on the idea that readers had little or no practical or theoretical knowledge of radio communication engineering!

However, one becomes increasingly aware that the practice of absorbing technical information from books appears to have declined, possibly due to the pervasive influence of other media; including television, which in general does not lend itself to serious study unless accompanied by note-taking, revision and practical projects. The value of amateur radio as an enjoyable form of self-training has always pre-supposed the combination of book-study with do-it-yourself projects.

Antennas and transmission lines are prime examples of areas of radio technology where some knowledge of fundamentals beyond that required for the RAE is necessary. AC theory has never been a requirement of the RAE, yet some understanding of terms such as reactance, impedance, radiation resistance etc is vital to understanding antennas. So this month we include a very brief rundown on just a few of the basic terms that so often seem to give rise to misunderstandings. If you find such definitions tough going, this may be an indication that you need to refer back to one of the established handbooks. Familiarity with these terms is essential to understanding articles on antennas at other than the most elementary level.

Radiation

Energy is conveyed away from a conductor carrying a periodically varying current by means of the electromagnetic field which is set up in the surrounding space. This field has two components: an electric wave with vectors in the same plane as the conductor; and a magnetic wave having vectors at right-angles to the electric wave. Both sets of vectors are perpendicular to the direction in which the energy travels.

If two conductors are placed close together and carry equal "go and return" currents, the electric and magnetic fields are cancelled at all distant points by the fields due to the reverse current in the other conductor. Thus no energy is conveyed away (radiated) from the pair which constitute a transmission line; all the energy remains in the electric and magnetic fields in the space between the conductors. But if the conductors are moved apart and placed end-to-end the fields no longer cancel at distant points in space. Energy is conveyed out of the conductors by the electric and magnetic fields; and these two fields form the electromagnetic field.

When the conductors are in series or parallel resonance at the frequency of the generator—that is, of an electrical length one-half of c/f (where c is the velocity of propagation of electromagnetic waves, and f is the frequency of the generator, so that c/f is the wavelength), a standing wave of current is set up on the conductors. In these circumstances, the input impedance is purely resistive, and all the input power, apart from any rf ohmic losses, is radiated. In the series resonant form the magnitude of this resistance is called the *radiation resistance*, or perhaps more correctly as "the radiation resistance referred to the loop current I_o" so that: R_r equals $P/I_o{}^2$ where the term I_o is the maximum value of the standing wave of current on the conductors and R_r is assumed to be located at the point where I_o is flowing. Two conductors in series resonance form what is termed a "half-wave dipole". This is the fundamental form of resonant antenna comprising a single conductor with an electrical length equal to half the wavelength of the working field.

Radiation intensity

The power per unit area in the field of an antenna is termed the power density. If this power density is multiplied by the square of the radial distance from the antenna, the product is the power per unit solid angle, and is called the **radiation intensity.**

Free space fields

In the equatorial plane of a half-wave dipole, the field in free space is $7\cdot02$ $\sqrt{(P)}/d$ V/m, where P is the transmitted power in watts out of the dipole and d is the distance in metres. With an output of 1,000W (1kW) the field is $222/d$ V/m.

Polarization

The polarization of an electromagnetic wave is defined in relation to the electric field; thus a vertically-polarized antenna is one that radiates a vertical electric field, and a horizontal magnetic field. A vertically-polarized wave will be radiated when a generator is connected between a vertical wire and earth, in which case the field strength of the wave will be due to the combined effects of the wire and its image in the surface of the ground (earth) plane. Antennas with either vertical or horizontal polarization, or at some angle between, are termed **linearly-polarized antennas**. If the antenna responds to two orthogonal field components (ie components at 90° to each other) having time phase between these components, the antenna is termed elliptically polarized. In the one particular case where the magnitudes of the two orthogonal components are equal and the phase angle is ±90°, the antenna is said to be **circularly polarized.**

Reciprocity

In reference to antennas, the term reciprocity means that the directivity and characteristics of an antenna are the same for receiving as for transmitting.

Gain

The gain of an antenna is the ratio of power required at the input of a reference antenna to the input of the given antenna needed to produce, in a given direction, the same field at the same distance. It is usually given in the logarithmic representation in decibels (dB). Basically the gain equals (maximum radiation intensity)/(maximum radiation intensity from a reference antenna with the same power input). Normally such gain is along the main lobe of radiation. It should be noted that the gain of an antenna may be specified in decibels with reference to an isotropic antenna (dBi), or to a half-wave loss-free dipole isolated in space and the equatorial plane of which contains the given direction (dBd), or to a perfect vertical antenna, much shorter than $\lambda/4$ placed on the surface of a perfectly conducting earthplane (dBv).

Isotropic radiator
An imaginary (hypothetical) antenna which is assumed to radiate equally in all directions. Compared with an isotropic antenna, a half-wave dipole has a gain of 1·64 times (2·15dBi); an elementary dipole (an imaginary point source much shorter than a half-wave dipole) has a gain of 1·5 times (1·76dBi); a short vertical has a gain of three times (4·76dBi); a quarter-wave monopole has a gain of 3·28 times (5·15dBi): see Table 1.

Effective radiated power (erp)
This is the power supplied to the antenna multiplied by the relative gain of the antenna in a given direction. For "omnidirectional" vertical antennas the more common term is ermp (effective rdiated monopole radiated power). The term eirp (effective isotropic radiated power) is also used.

Beamwidth
The beamwidth of a directional antenna is generally specified as the angle subtended by the major lobe between the points at which the power has fallen to one-half of its peak value. At these points, field intensity is 0·707 (−3dB) of its maximum value.

Array
A group of radiating elements spaced some distance apart and with the current in each element having a particular amplitude and phase is termed an array. An array of several dipole elements will, in some direction, produce a maximum field strength K times that of a single dipole carrying the same current at its centre as each dipole in the array. The term K is used to denote the array factor.

Front-to-back ratio
The ratio of power radiated in the forward direction of an antenna to that radiated in the opposite direction.

Endfire antenna
An endfire source has maximum radiation along the linear axis; a representive endfire array is the Yagi-Uda antenna.

Broadside array
A broadside source has maximum radiation normal to its axis. A representative broadside array is the horizontal array of dipoles as used for hf broadcasting or, say, a colinear array of dipoles.

Driven element
An element which is connected to the transmitter/receiver via a transmission line. A driven array is one in which all the elements are driven elements.

Parasitic element
An element which is not connected directly to the transmitter/receiver via a transmission line, but receives its energy by the coupling due to the proximity of other elements. In any parasitic array (eg Yagi-Uda antenna) there will be one or more parasitic elements, but at least one element must be a driven element.

Radiation resistance
An antenna has distributed inductance, capacitance and resistance. When the inductance is very much greater than resistance per unit length, the current along the radiation portion varies sinusoidally and the radiation resistance is considered as lumped at the position of maximum current. Where an antenna is less than $\lambda/4$, radiation resistance is considered as being located at the feedpoint. For a resonant half-wave dipole, the radiation resistance is at the centrepoint, and since it is purely resistive it is *in this case* the same as the antenna input impedance and feedpoint impedance. In free space the radiation resistance of a half-wave dipole is approximately 73Ω, neglecting losses and assuming that the dipole length is infinitely greater than its width. In these circumstances radiated power equals the square of the feed current times the radiation resistance.

In practice the centrepoint impedance of a half-wave dipole will be affected by its height above earth, being roughly 73Ω at $\lambda/4$, $\lambda/2$ and $3\lambda/4$ etc, but rising to about 100Ω at 3·5λ/10 and falling to about 60Ω at 6·7λ/10. The presence of additional parasitic or driven elements will tend to reduce the impedance significantly; a reflector placed 1·5λ/10 behind a dipole will reduce its impedance to roughly 25Ω; a three-element close-spaced Yagi array may have a feedpoint impedance of only about 10Ω. The impedance of points equidistant on either side of the centrepoint of a dipole rises with the electrical distance from the centre and, theoretically, at the ends would be infinity; in practice, the ends may have resistive impedance of the order of 2,000 to 5,000Ω, the actual value depending on the losses.

In non-resonant antennas, the input impedance is the vector sum of the effective radiation resistance and the resultant reactance. $Z = \sqrt{(R^2 + X^2)}$, where R is the effective radiation resistance (ie, radiation resistance plus loss resistance) and X is the resultant reactance (ie, the difference between the inductive and capacitive reactances).

Bandwidth
The current taken by a resonant antenna, and hence the radiation, falls off as the frequency is varied away from resonance. There will be two frequencies, one above and one below resonance, at which the power will be reduced by half. The difference between these frequencies is termed the **bandwidth** of the antenna. For example, a half-wave dipole having a length/diameter ratio of 10,000 will have a bandwidth, expressed as a percentage of the resonant frequency, of the order of eight per cent. With a length/diameter ratio of 100 this increases to about 15 per cent. Bandwidth of multi-element Yagi arrays may well be less than five per cent, unless the designer has taken steps to increase this figure.

Folded dipole
A dipole antenna may be made in the form of one or more narrow loops so that, although the overall length is still an electrical half-wave, the antenna current flows through two or more paths. If the conductors are identical, equal and in-phase currents will flow, and the total radiation will be the same as from a simple dipole. But since the currents have been divided equally between the two conductors, the centre feedpoint impedance will be four times as great although the radiation resistance remains the same; thus 4 × 73Ω, nominally taken as 300Ω. As the number of wires in which the current flows increases, the feedpoint impedance increases by the square of the number.

Thus a two-wire folded dipole has four times, a three-wire dipole nine times, and a four-wire dipole 16 times the feedpoint impedance of the single wire dipole. This assumes that the currents divide equally between the wires; in practice a wide range of impedance transformations can be obtained by varying the ratio of diameters and spacings. For example, in practice a two-wire folded dipole using different diameter conductors may have a feedpoint impedance from roughly 2 to 12 times that of the single-wire dipole. It is thus possible to arrange for, say, a multi-element Yagi array with a folded driven element to match accurately a 52Ω coaxial or, preferably, a balanced transmission line.

An important characteristic of the folded dipole is that it will have a bandwidth significantly greater than that of a simple dipole.

Table 1. Maximum (theoretical) gains of lossless basic antennas

Type	Location	Max gain (dBi)	Max gain (dBd)	Direction of max gain
$\lambda/2$ dipole	Free space	2·15	0	Plane perpendicular to axis
$\lambda/4$ vertical monopole	Over perfect ground	5·15	3	On horizon
$\lambda/2$ vertical dipole	Centre $\lambda/2$ above perfect ground	8·2	6.05	On horizon
$\lambda/2$ horizontal dipole	Immediately above perfect ground	9·1	6.95	Straight up
$\lambda/2$ horizontal dipole	$\lambda/4$ above perfect ground	7·4	5.25	Straight up
$\lambda/2$ horizontal dipole	$\lambda/2$ above perfect ground	8·2	6.05	Plane perpendicular to axis, 30° above horizontal
$\lambda/2$ horizontal dipole	$3\lambda/5$ above perfect ground	9·2	7.05	Plane perpendicular to axis, 24·6° above horizontal

(Adapted from *HF Communications Data Book*, Rockwell-Collins)

Notes. In practice, the gain and direction of maximum gain of vertical antennas are affected very much more by ground losses than are horizontal antennas. A power gain of about 5 to 6dBd is usually the most that can be achieved in practice with an hf three-element close-spaced Yagi beam (theoretical 7·5 to 8·5dBd). About 4 to 5dBd (theoretical maximum 5·2dBd) can, with care, be obtained from two elements. Better overall results may often be achieved by raising a (lightweight) two-element Yagi than by increasing the number of elements at a lower height. Field strengths over a long, low-angle path when compared to an antenna at $\lambda/5$ height are roughly × 2 at 2λ/5, × 3 at 3λ/5, × 4 at 4λ/5 and × 5 at 1λ. 1λ loops give roughly a 1dB gain over dipole elements (ie gain of two-el quad can be up to about 6dBd). At vhf, height gain in the range 3 to 10m can amount to about 5·5 to 6·5dB for each doubling of the height in rural areas, 8 to 9dB in urban areas on paths up to 50km, and about half these gains for distances exceeding 100km (source ICAP87). +1dB = × 1·4 the power, +3dB = × 2, +4dB = 2·5, 5dB = × 3·2, 6dB = × 4, 7dB = × 5, 8dB = × 6·3, 9dB = × 7·9, and 10dB = × 10.

The folded dipole and monopole
The notes above underline the very useful features of using folded elements, though this form of antenna seems to be less commonly used than a few decades ago. Like so many other important developments, the folded dipole came from the fertile brain of Dr John D Kraus, W8JK, whose work has spanned and influenced both professional and amateur radio communications over several decades.

The folded dipole provides roughly twice the bandwidth and, for a given weight of copper, only half the rf ohmic losses of a single-wire dipole. Multi-wire dipoles are, in effect, narrow loop elements and can be implemented with an overall span of $\lambda/2$ or alternatively $3\lambda/4$ or $3\lambda/8$ as shown in Fig 1. In each case the antenna current flows through two or more paths, and the nominal feedpoint impedance shown is that for equal wire conductors. A remote high-voltage switch can be used to provide a two-band antenna: Fig 2.

As noted below, recent interest has been centred on folded monopoles but, before reporting this work, it may be worth drawing attention to a

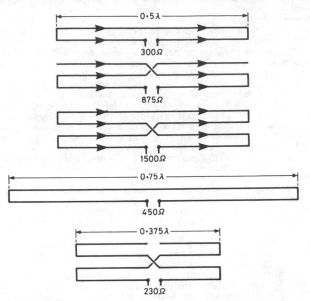

Fig 1. Basic folded twin and multi-wire dipole antennas showing nominal feedpoint impedances (resistive) when used as a single element with equal-diameter wires forming the folded elements

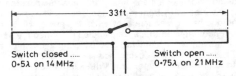

Fig 2. Two-band folded dipole for 14 and 21MHz. Could be scaled for 21/28MHz operation. Best used with open-wire transmission line and atu to accommodate feedpoint impedances of about 300Ω on 14MHz and about 450Ω on 21MHz

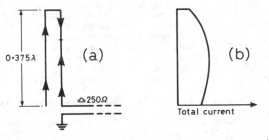

Fig 3. The 3λ/8 vertical folded antenna working against earth. Feed impedance about 250Ω. Current distribution is similar to that of a vertical top-loaded single-conductor antenna

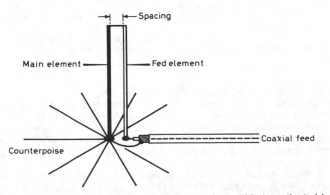

Fig 4. Form of the folded monopole antennas thoroughly investigated by K8CFU and his team. A selection of just six of the 13 variations used on 14MHz is listed in Table 2. Similar exhaustive investigations were carried out on all pre-WARC hf bands from 1·8 to 28MHz. The final detailed report has not yet been published.

Table 2—Provisional dimensions for 14·2MHz folded monopole as in Fig 4

Base impedance	Height of elements	Main element diameter	Fed element diameter	Spacing
50Ω	15·1ft	0·25in	1·75in	3·0in
			2·75in	4·0in
			4·0in	6·0in
75Ω	15·1ft	0·25in	1·25in	14·25in
			1·75in	16·25in
			2·75in	22·5in

relatively little-known 3λ/8 vertical folded antenna working against ground. Fig 3 shows this arrangement together with the total current distribution (vector sum of currents in both wires). The terminal feedpoint impedance is about 250Ω. As W8JK puts it in *Electronics Manual for Radio Engineers:* "An interesting property of this antenna is that due to the multi-wire construction, a current distribution is produced which is similar to that of a vertical top-loaded single-conductor antenna." It can also be assumed that the higher feedpoint impedance, not at the current node, means that earth losses would be less than for a conventional vertical monopole.

Quarter-wave folded monopoles

Arch Doty, K8CFU, a retired professional engineer, recently kindly sent me a long, detailed report of an extensive study made by himself; John Frey, W3ESU; and Harry Mills, K4HU, and with an input from Dr George Brown, made during 1985–6. This covers the characteristics of λ/4 folded monopole antennas used in conjunction with a 64-radial counterpoise (Fig 4). This work followed on previous investigations into the use of counterpoise and ground-screen "artificial ground" systems as originally reported in *TT* (February 1983).

The final report runs to some 48 pages and includes suggested dimensions of 50Ω and 75Ω folded-monopole antennas for the 1·8, 3·5, 7, 14, 21 and 28MHz bands (the 1·8MHz monopole calls for elements up to 115ft high!) The feedpoint impedance, by using different diameter elements, is designed to match directly into 50Ω and 75Ω coaxial cables without any requirement for an antenna tuning unit. An unexpected, but potentially important, finding was the discovery of the existence of "capacitance bottom loading".

As with the counterpoise study (which involved making some 20,000 measurements) this new study has involved taking thousands of measurements. The detailed report is not intended for publication and has resulted in a patent for land mobile antennas based on these principles. While K8CFU sent his report to prove that not all of the older amateurs are afflicted with neophobia (*TT* March 1987), I have abstracted (Table 2) just a tiny part of the massive amount of data collected by K8CFU.

It is interesting to note that early on in this investigation, the three doughty experimenters (whose combined ages come to 215 years) found that the base impedance of a groundplane monopole is much lower than the oft-published figure of 35Ω. It may be recalled that attention was drawn to this point by G6CJ in *TT* where it was shown that 19 to 21Ω is a typical range, with a few raised horizontal radials. The American team measured the base resistance of λ/4 vertical antennas over a 64-radial counterpoise at between 21 and 33·5Ω, the value decreasing with larger-diameter unipole elements.

Folded normal-mode helix vertical

Iain Morris, ZC4IM, has been using some limited spare time to investigate a novel form of folded monopole that shows considerable promise, though it still calls for the type of thorough investigation undertaken by K8CFU and his team of "Old men of the mountains". ZC4IM writes:

"I have been playing about with an antenna idea which looks very promising but I am being beaten by the fact that I have to work! I wonder if those with the time and/or test equipment could take it a stage or two further.

"It concerns the normal-mode helix short elements which, as noted in the April *TT*, have a lot of potential. They also have at least three disadvantages. The first two, restricted bandwidth and low radiation resistance, are common to all loaded antennas. The third, and the reason why the helix element has never really taken off, is the pain and strain of winding the beast, particularly if you want a tapered pitch. That's my opinion, anyway.

"One way of raising the radiation resistance of an antenna is to fold it. But a folded helix sounds as though it would be even more strain and pain to wind. That was my reaction, too, when the idea first crossed my mind. My limited technical library did not mention such a process. So, I folded a vertical helix with four radials and tuned it for 28·5MHz. The reflectometer revealed that not much power was being reflected when fed with 75Ω coaxial cable. The bandwidth between the 2:1 vswr points was

400kHz. Drooping the radials raised the vswr so they were left horizontal. A Chinese copy was made and installed at ZC4AB, the local 28MHz expert. His pet HB9CV antenna had obviously suffered during the winter, and signal reports on the folded helix were about two S-points up. The HB9CV was given a good going over and then showed about an S-point-and-a-bit up on the vertical helix; the trial continues.

"The fuss was taken out of winding the helix elements by using 300Ω ribbon shorted at the top. Just over a λ/2 of ribbon was wound single-spaced by using two lengths of ribbon and then taking one away. The former was a plastic water pipe (32·5mm pvc) and the ribbon was anchored using pvc tape. In the tuning process one of the good points of this format showed itself. Naturally enough, in pruning the ribbon I took a little too much off. It was easy just to uncoil a little of the helix and this put matters right. In fact *The ARRL Handbook* recommends a linear portion at the end to lower the Q. The size reduction factor was 0·4 using single spacing.

"The system clearly works. But there are at least two avenues to be explored. The first is the use of this principle for shortened verticals for the lower hf bands. At 7 and 3·5MHz, there should be an increase in radiation efficiency as it would put more power into the antenna and less into the earth resistance. A 7MHz groundplane antenna would be only about 13ft in height. It would be nice to raise this into more-open space, although the 28MHz prototype clearly did not like drooped radials so they must remain horizontal. This is a limitation because, while the radiator has shrunk, the radials remain full size. The next step might be the use of a single radial folded back on itself in a circle. (Or possibly the G6XN form of inductance and capacitively-loaded counterpoise?—*G3VA*.) The radius of such a circle would be close to ⅙th wavelength and such a compact radial could probably be mounted above head height, allowing the lawn to be mowed and stopping anyone from coming into contact with points at high rf. With ribbon helix elements one might need to think of the current capabilities of the ribbon, but since the current would be shared they would be lower than the traditional loaded vertical. Certainly there was no sign of ZC4AB's antenna melting.

"The other use for such helix-wound elements might be for shortened beams, which is how this project started. Believe it or not, I was looking for a beam that would have no forward gain (I am a confirmed 1W QRP man with 90 countries worked) but a good front-to-back ratio. A folded helical dipole works and gives me the required 'no-radiation-off-the-ends and no-real-directivity-anywhere-else' characteristics so I never progressed to an array. I can now work Africa and Japan without attracting the attention of large numbers of strong-signal European stations!

"There are still a number of questions. Can the turns be touching? Could I run two or three different-length ribbons in parallel, just like the old three vertical wires taped to one bamboo? I have a modern version of this on the aforementioned pvc pipe on top of a lightweight aluminium mast and it works a treat. If such a three-band vertical was erected at any height, the horizontal radial system might be three concentric circles. Variation of radiation resistance with spacing and/or diameter could do with looking at. There's plenty of scope for further experimentation. But if I go down in history as the man who folded the helix (rather than squaring the circle) I will try not to let it go to my head!"

Anyone with queries or results could write to Major J Morris, ZC4IM, c/o the ZC4 QSL Bureau.

Simple nanofarad meter

If an instrument for measuring resistance is called an ohmmeter it would seem logical to call a "capacitance meter" a picofarad or nanofarad meter. It's just a thought that comes from seeing the description by Gabriel Rivat, F6DQM (*Radio-REF* April 1987, pp32,34) of a simple analogue capacitance meter capable of measuring, at least roughly, all those unmarked or indecipherable capacitors with values from about 2·5pF to 3µF. F6DQM points out that the high accuracy provided by expensive digital capacitance meters is seldom required in practice. His unit (Fig 5) is based on a design that appeared in *Ham Radio* (March 1980) though I have not been able to check back to compare the two designs.

His unit comprises two 555 ic devices, IC1 forming an astable multivibrator running at about 1kHz, while IC2 is a triggered monostable whereby the mark/space ratio and hence the average height of the pulse train is varied to suit the capacitance range required. In effect, the principle consists of measuring the average voltage of a train of pulses of fixed frequency

where the average height of the pulse is a function of the unknown capacitor connected across X. For such a measurement to be possible the monostable pulse height must always remain less than the rate at which the monostable is triggered, if I have correctly understood the French text.

Because F6DQM used a 1mA fsd meter calibrated 0 to 30, he made his ranges suit. However, he provides alternative component values for a more typical 0 to 1 calibration.

PIN diode rf attenuator

The use of an rf attenuator in front of any receiver having limited dynamic range has become established practice. This can vary from the simple ganged-potentiometers as used for the two-valve regenerative-detector receiver, *TT* April 1987, to quite elaborate arrangements. There are also now many transceivers in which the signal-frequency amplifier can be switched out to reduce the signal applied to the front-end mixer.

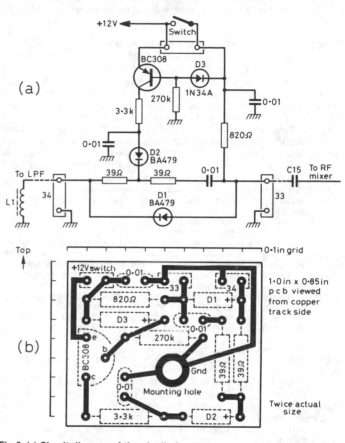

Fig 6. (a) Circuit diagram of the pin-diode attenuator used by G0FAH on his Ten-Tec Argosy rig but suitable for most receivers that are overloaded by strong signals. Designed to avoid the need for permanent modifications of the Argosy. (b) The pcb layout. On the Argosy, L1 is on the lowpass filter board, C15 is on the rf mixer board. Switch is on the af gain control. Mount board with screw through "hole"

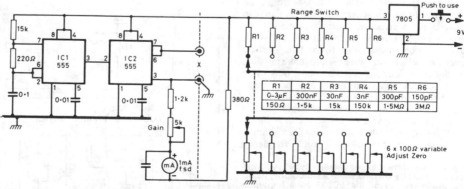

Fig 5. Simple wide-range capacitance meter described by F6DQM in *Radio-REF*. For ranges of 10µF, 1µF–100pF, R1–6, progresses from 47Ω, 470Ω.....4·7MΩ

Bill Wright, G0FAH, a QRP enthusiast, recently prepared an article for the G-QRP Club magazine *Sprat*, describing a pin diode attenuator arrangement he uses for his Ten-Tec Argosy transceiver but equally applicable to other equipments. He considers the Argosy a very fine transceiver, especially for cw, but he finds that the first mixer can be overloaded by the strong signals found at night on 3·5 and 7MHz. He was anxious to use an attenuator that would not require any enclosure drilling for potentiometers or switches. His modification avoids working on the pcb boards or hole drilling, since pin diodes need not be located near the switch that controls the attenuator.

In practice, the existing push-pull switch on the af gain control is used to place a 20dB attenuator between the lpf unit and the rf mixer board. This switch is normally used with the Ten-Tec for power on/off, but for this purpose the switch located on the psu may be used instead, since the two switches are simply wired in series.

Fig 6 shows his circuit arrangement, with two BA479 pin diodes and a BC308 series voltage regulator. Constructional details are given in the *Sprat* article.

Electrostatic discharge can kill cmos

David Hollander, N7RK, in an article "The hidden dangers of electrostatic discharge—esd" (*QST* March 1987), reminds us that one of the major problems plaguing modern electronic components is damage from static electricity, more correctly known as electrostatic discharge or esd. It is important that anyone building or modifying or servicing electronic equipment using mosfets, cmos and similar devices, either in discrete or integrated form, should appreciate that esd can cause not only complete component failure (particularly when the components are not safely wired into equipment) but may also result in performance degradation that is difficult if not impossible to detect without detailed laboratory tests. ESD continues to be a major concern to the semiconductor industry.

N7RK lists a number of ways in which to combat esd:

(1) Use a workbench with an earthed metal top or an earthed sheet of metal as the work surface.
(2) Earth all soldering irons or solder/desolder stations.
(3) Use an earthed wrist strap in contact with the skin.
(4) Place all mos devices on an earthed bench surface *prior* to handling them as you may be electrostatically charged with respect to the bench surface.
(5) Check all power supplies for voltage transients. Connect low-impedance equipment to mos devices only after the equipment is powered up and disconnect before power is turned off.
(6) Never insert or remove a mos device from a circuit with power applied.
(7) Use anti-static bags for storing or transporting assemblies.
(8) Never exceed the device maximum ratings as shown in the data sheet.
(9) Keep the workbench free of objects such as paper, cigarette ash, plastics etc.
(10) Never use brush or spray cleaners to remove flux from a pcb.
(11) Observe all the above precautions when replacing a mos device during repair.

Remember that in low humidity, static electricity up to about 35,000V can be generated just by walking across a carpet; in conditions of high humidity this may still amount to some 1,500V. Static electricity is produced when any two non-conductive materials are rubbed together. A power mosfet may be susceptible to as little as 100–200V esd; cmos devices to 250–2,500V.

The super-gainer receivers

Recent *TT*s (April, May) have described the merits, and some demerits, of the high-gain regenerative detector. But so far it has been assumed that this is for use in direct-conversion trf receivers such as the classic detector/af amplifier (0-v-1) and rf amplifier/detector/af amplifier (1-v-1) "straight" receivers. However, it should not be forgotten that a fixed-tuned regenerative detector can also make a most effective "second detector" for simple superhet receivers, as an alternative to diode or product detectors. In the late 'thirties, regenerative detectors were used to make possible the design of superhet receivers using only three valves; the later arrival of dual triode-pentode af valves reduced this to "two-valve" designs.

I first became conscious of this "super-gainer" technique in the pages of *The Radio Handbook* (9th edition, 1942) where it was used for "a simple three-tube superheterodyne" (6K8 frequency

converter, 6SJ7 regenerative detector, 6V6 audio output) and also for an "economical five-tube superheterodyne (6K7/6K8/6SK7/6SJ7/6F6). Both designs used 1,500kHz i.f transformers with a few-turn "tickler" coil wound between the windings to provide regeneration. Soon afterwards, I had an opportunity of trying a three-valve super-gainer built by Roy Wilkins, G2ALM. The use of 1·5MHz rather than 455kHz for the i.f significantly reduced the problem of "image" reception, even on a design having no tuned signal-frequency amplifier.

I was so impressed that in 1946 I adopted the technique, although this time with 465kHz i.f, for a receiver based on the pre-war Tobe-Deutschmann tuner and triple-tuned i.f transformers; this had a tuned rf amplifier but, even so, on 14MHz needed an additional tuned-input/tuned-output preamplifier to reduce image reception to an acceptable level. Later I added three 465kHz crystals, one in each of the two i.f stages and one in the regenerative detector stage, to provide sharp cw-only selectivity. The high-gain detector meant that up to this stage the gain of earlier stages could be kept low. This receiver remained in operational use for some 25 years, finally being retired because the Tobe tuner covered nothing higher than 14MHz so that external converters were needed for 21/28MHz.

Malcolm Healy, G3TNO, recalls that, as a schoolboy, he built a very simple superhet receiver using only two valves from a design that he believes appeared in *Practical Wireless* possibly in the 'fifties. He writes:

"From Fig 7 you can see it uses only two valves. The first is a conventional ECH81 frequency changer with an output at 455kHz. The second is an ECL82 with the triode section forming a regenerative detector and the pentode as audio output stage. L1 and L2 were Denco plug-in coils selected to cover the required frequency ranges (mine was bandspread for 3·5, 7 and 14MHz). L3 and L5 are the primary and secondary of an intervalve i.f transformer (455kHz). L4 is an additional winding on the same former as L3 and L5 to provide 'reaction' (regeneration) which is controlled by VC1 (500pF). The 'sense' of L4 has to be correct for positive feedback. (One used a rule-of-thumb that a winding ht/anode should be in the same sense as grid/filament—*G3VA*.)

"In operation, VC1 is adjusted so that the detector is just oscillating and provides Q-multiplication and also bfo action. I remember hearing a lot of dx using this very simple superhet receiver, both on cw and eventually, when people began using it, ssb."

As the earlier *Radio* design showed, for amateur-band reception there is really no need to gang together the tuning of L1 and L2, simply bandspread tuning the oscillator only. I remain convinced, however, that "image" reception could be usefully reduced by raising the i.f at least to 1·6MHz if you can find or make a suitable ift. Whether there is any useful role for regenerative detectors for solidstate receivers is a question that might be worth exploring. It has been pointed out by Wes Hayward, W7ZOI, in *TT* that "simple" in this context does not necessarily meaning using a minimum number of transistors.

Rewelding broken valve filaments

Berj N Ensanian, KI3U, in *QST* (January 1987, pp34–5) contributes a timely item on rewelding broken filaments of high power transmitting valves. This is based on his experience with 100TH triodes, but similar techniques might well prove successful for other expensive (directly-heated) high power valves; and if the technique fails, well the valve was already unserviceable and "beyond repair". The technique is suitable in cases where the filament has broken or fused in just one spot, rather than shattered, and where emission is still good.

First, an ohmmeter is connected across the broken filament pins, and the envelope lightly tapped at various points with the plastic handle of a screwdriver while watching the meter. It is likely that the needle will flick

Fig 7. Two-valve "super-gainer" type superhet receiver built by G3TNO while a schoolboy, using the triode-section of the ECL82 as a high-gain regenerative detector. Image reception could be reduced by using a higher i.f (eg 1·6MHz)

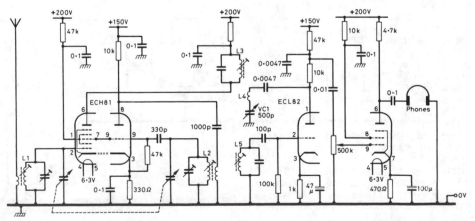

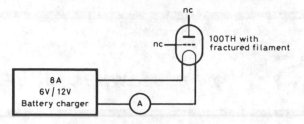

Fig 8. KI3U's set up for repair of broken high-power valve filaments such as those of the 100TH high-power triode

up occasionally denoting that the vibration is bringing the broken ends of the filament into contact. KI3U then marks the spot where the tapping has proved most effective with a felt marker.

Then he uses the arrangement shown in Fig 8 to effect the actual repair. A switchable 12/6V battery charger and ammeter is connected across the heater and the tapping resumed: "As I began tapping the tube envelope with the screwdriver handle, bluish-white sparks appeared at the top of the filament. With increased tapping frequency, the filament suddenly lit brilliantly, drawing more than 8A. I immediately switched the charger to 6V and the current dropped to a steady 5·75A. After a few seconds, 12V was again applied for about one second, then I switched again to 6V and about 5·75A. After 35mins, I replaced the charger polarity (current had stabilized at 5·6A). *In reversing the polarity the filament experienced its first shutdown since the reweld.* Power was removed after five minutes at reverse polarity. Using a variable ac transformer, I applied power until the filament drew its rated current of 6·3A when rms ac voltage across the filament was 4·0V. Nine minutes after applying power, I raised the voltage to 5·0Vrms, the rated value. The current then read 7·0A (rated 6·3A)."

For the next 30 days, KI3U ran the filament at 6·3A for 1·5h daily. The measured inter-electrode capacitances were slightly up, but the 100TH had been restored to life as an effective high-power valve.

While some readers may question whether it is worth attempting to reweld a broken filament in this way, it is worth noting that the 100TH is still manufactured but costs around $200 in the USA. KI3U also believes that the filaments of some modern directly-heated valves experience similar premature breaks. The technique of short over-voltage "flashing" can also sometimes prove effective where the filament or heater of a valve has not broken but emission has fallen due to the cathode or filament becoming poisoned.

If only someone could come up with a way of similarly restoring rf power transistors, the world's fastest-acting fuses!

No bulldog clips on sun visors!
C Edwards, RS27222, writes from bitter personal experience to warn against using bulldog clips on sun visors as a means of mounting "hands-free" microphones for mobile operation (G8DPS's method in the April *TT*). Such clips can prove very dangerous in the event of an accident. He writes: "I was taken from the scene of an accident by ambulance for *just that*—an injury caused by a bulldog clip on my sun visor used to hold notes. Modern sun visors are designed not to cause injury in an accident situation." Perhaps I should have remembered that *TT* (July 1984, p579) drew attention to the EEC regulations on car radio installations "intended to ensure that a driver will not be cut by any part of a radio, will not get his hands stuck nor receive any electric shocks. Equipment must be easy to operate and with rounded, recessed controls. . . ."

That dummy load resistor mystery
Dr A F Webb, G4LYF, has come up with an intriguing, if complex, explanation of G5RV's oil-immersed dummy-load resistor mystery (*TT* February, p112). This is based on the possibility that the current flow between the individual particles of "carbon black", separated by only a few atomic diameters, may involve the wave-mechanical "tunnelling" effect, and that polymerisation by the vegetable oil could result in the oil being chemically bonded to the carbon surfaces, thus increasing the resistance. G4LYF adds the suggestion that if indeed the tunnelling effect is involved in current flowing in composition resistors, there may exist the possibility of producing a "negative resistance" effect under certain conditions, as in the Esaki tunnel diode, thus conceivably opening the way to an oscillating resistor.

Louis Varney, G5RV, who posed the original query, reports a further development. He writes:

"In August 1986, a new 50Ω dummy load was constructed using four 50Ω 3W carbon resistors connected in series-parallel and immersed in vegetable oil. However, these ex-junk-box resistors are completely covered by the original green body paint (with black tip and dot indicating 50Ω value). On

completion, the dc resistance was measured as 50Ω, and the vswr on 14MHz measured as 1:1. In October 1986, the oil was removed from the glass jar and the dummy load packed ready for my annual visit to Uruguay where, in early November, it was re-filled with vegetable oil. Resistance and vswr were measured and found correct. Monthly checks were made and no change in resistance or vswr found. Now (April 1987) shortly before returning to the UK, further checks show *no change* after eight months. It would appear to be necessary, if unpainted carbon resistors are to be used for a *vegetable* oil-immersed dummy load, to give the resistors a coat or two of paint or clear varnish before immersing them in the oil."

The Telefunken "B-2" and British Mk123
Recently, while using a British Mk123 on 10·1MHz (as mentioned in the December *TT*) I had a couple of cw contacts with OZ5MA who was using a genuine B-2 at the Danish War Museum in Copenhagen. The Mk123, possibly the last of the series of paramilitary/clandestine *valve* models to be designed and produced in the UK for some years from about 1956, remains a notable example of the degree of miniaturization possible with valve technology (the only transistors were an OC71 as a side-tone oscillator and a separate ac/dc converter unit for operation from 12V batteries). The two-stage (5A/163K, 5B/254M) transmitter, for which a simplified circuit diagram was given in *TT*, June 1983, page 513, runs at up to 40W input (about 20W rf output) and the receiver (Fig 9) is based on sub-miniature (B₉D base) valves, types EF72 and EF73. The complete unit, including the

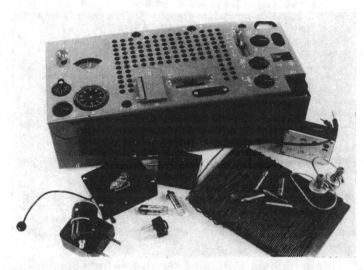

The British Mk123 transmitter-receiver with built-in mains psu which was originally developed about 1956 and which remained in service for paramilitary operations for nearly 20 years. Still provides a usable cw rig on 3·5/7/10/14MHz amateur bands. Shown here with some of the associated accessories including spare EF92/EF93 sub-miniature valves, mains-plug and crystal-holder adaptors, "reel" antenna as well as 100ft of antenna wire, neon-tester to indicate whether 110 or 220V mains, ac or dc. There is a built-in morse-key (right-hand bottom corner) but also a socket for use with an external manual or high-speed auto-keyer. *Photo: Wendy Gilles, IBA*

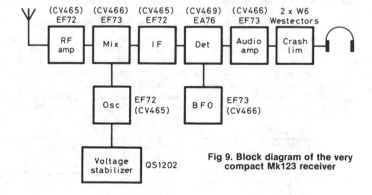

Fig 9. Block diagram of the very compact Mk123 receiver

mains psu, and built-in key, weighs under 8lb (3·5kg) and measures 11·38 by 3·3 by 5·38in (29·9 by 8·5 by 13·6cm). It covers 2·5 to 20MHz in three wavebands. Apart from the lack of a crystal filter and electrical bandspread needed for amateur radio applications, it is an excellent and very stable receiver.

Technical Topics
by Pat Hawker, G3VA

RECENTLY there has been a spate of items in *TT* recalling the days of simple, all-valve transmitters and receivers, and stressing the relative ease with which these could be built on the kitchen table and, when necessary, serviced in the shack. From 1935 onwards, the better receivers were capable of excellent performance on hf, particularly for cw, though often suffering from an annoyingly long period of warm-up drift. Receivers for many years used a "single-crystal" filter with phase-adjustment and less than ideal shape factors, but usually with variable selectivity that can still be highly effective on cw; and when used with a stenode-type rising af characteristic can give reasonably satisfactory ssb reception.

The old sets were, admittedly, often physically bulky and very heavy (the AR88 weighs over 100lb, the ex-Navy B-40 even more). With a separate transmitter and receiver, it is necessary to "net" the two together before calling a station, a process that takes a few seconds longer than the change-over with a transceiver. A few of us still stick to separate units, but the vast majority of the present generation of amateurs has almost certainly never operated "separates" either on hf or vhf.

Why, one can hear some readers muttering, drag up the past? Amateur communication has moved on since the days when many UK homes were still on dc mains and the most popular antenna was a Zepp! But I doubt if even such readers would want *TT* to be only about vlsi, GaAs, modfets, electronic memory, digital techniques, working eme on 10GHz or just saying which of the latest new wonders are "best buys".

For, perhaps paradoxically, readers show much more interest in simple, often seemingly antiquated techniques, but which still show promising developments, than in the latest marvels. Could it be that once an amateur has bought the ultimate in transceivers there is little you can do with it except operate and send it back for expert servicing when something goes wrong?

Amateur radio *operating* is fine and I am not decrying the black-box "appliance operator". But how much more satisfying is the hobby when accompanied by some understanding of, and interest in, the technical side of radio communication—and the proud feeling that comes from having made at least some part of the equipment, even if only an atu or wire antenna, yourself.

A simple high-performance receiver—the super-dc-gainer

The July *TT* included a discussion on the 50-year-old concept of "super-gainer" receivers: simple superhets in which the need for i.f amplifying stages is eliminated by using a high-gain regenerative detector, as in the simple "two-valve" superhet receiver built by Malcolm Healy, G3TNO, while a schoolboy. Clearly, in the form shown, the super-gainer could not provide the performance, particularly in terms of selectivity, associated with modern communications receivers, although far from negligible as a stand-by general-coverage or beginner's receiver.

However, by a strange coincidence a letter from Dennis Unwin, G0FMT, arrived before the publication of the July issue, but after it had gone to press, outlining a most interesting variation of the super-gainer technique that retains most of the simplicity but is capable of extremely good performance. In place of the regenerative-detector plus medium-gain af amplifier of the classic "super-gainer", G0FMT substitutes the homodyne form of direct-conversion receiver with its low-gain "synchronous" (product) detector and high-gain af amplifier. He writes:

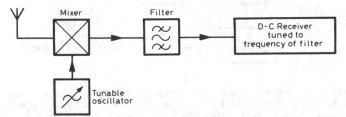

Fig 1. Outline of G0FMT's "super-dc-gainer" receiver technique combining the advantages of the superhet with the simplicity of direct-conversion receivers to provide a high-performance receiver

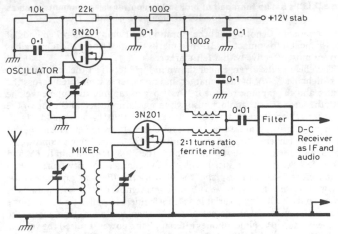

Fig 2. Circuit diagram of a suitable mosfet "front-end" for a "super-dc-gainer" receiver

"I have been following, with great interest, the comments in *TT* on the problems of home-construction of amateur equipment in this era of expensive and sophisticated 'black boxes'. I suspect that I have tendencies to 'neophobia' both in relation to amateur equipment, and in my professional world of biological instrumentation. This tendency has led me to experiment, over the last few years, with the problem of designing simple receivers which nevertheless have good performance.

"I have made direct-conversion receivers, and although they work surprisingly well, their performance does not satisfy me. What I am looking for is a simple receiver that has the performance of commercial equipment, although it may be less convenient to use. Such a receiver really has to be a superhet. However, I believe that the expertise that has developed around the direct-conversion receiver is valuable, and should be used if possible. So my idea is to use a direct-conversion receiver as the i.f and output stages of a superhet receiver. I think of this as a kind of 'intermediate technology' approach. The arrangement is outlined in Fig 1.

"I have now built three receivers of this type and have been delighted by the performance. The approach has several advantages over the conventional superhet:

1. You don't have to build an i.f amplifier, with its specialized components and problems of stability.

2. The alternative direct-conversion techniques are well developed, and are available in kit form.

3. The single 'block filter' does not have to be all that good. As long as the sides are reasonably steep, not much else matters, since the bandwidth will be determined by af filtering in the dc receiver section. The main function of the i.f filter is to remove the unwanted sideband (audio image on cw).

"I have compared my latest receiver with my FT77, which is not a bad performer. I have not been able to find a signal on the FT77 that cannot be copied equally well on the home-made receiver. Fig 2 shows the simplest 'front-end' that I have been able to devise. Many professional communications engineers will, doubtless, turn up their noses at the use of a dual-gate mosfet as a mixer (just as years ago they used to at the almost universal triode-hexode valve mixer). I have used a hot-carrier diode ring mixer, but the problems of low impedance, high drive requirements and harmonic mixing inevitably demand a considerable increase in complexity over the mosfet design. Furthermore, the high input impedance of the mosfet makes it easy to provide good input selectivity, which of itself reduces the dynamic range requirements when compared with commercial receivers which nowadays usually have octave-wide input filters. Surely the essence of good design is a compromise between the many conflicting requirements, which must include the facilities available for construction. It would indeed be surprising if a design optimized for amateur home construction would suit the commercial radio market.

"It would also seem unlikely that commercial techniques would be ideal for amateur home construction! So we should stop trying to copy equipment that is designed for a different environment and think for ourselves. The important question with regard to the mosfet mixer is 'is it good enough?'. In practice, with a selective input circuit, no rf input attenuator is required on any hf amateur band at any time of day, which is more than can be said of many of the factory-built receivers. The sensitivity of the receiver is such that the 'background noise' of all bands is audible. This suggests to me that the performance is adequate, even if another type of mixer might theoretically be better.

"One final point on receivers: the volume control of a direct-conversion receiver has to cover a large range, and with a log-law type potentiometer the control is usually a bit 'sudden'. To get over this, I use a two-gang (stereo) 25kΩ log pot with the two halves cascaded. This provides a very smooth control.

"When I was first licensed (as G8CKU), the only way of getting on to 144MHz was to build your own equipment, and I can still remember the excitement of my first QSO (with G2XV). I feel quite sorry for new licensees who have their first contacts on a black box. I suspect that many of them would like to build equipment if only the task did not seem so enormous. I think that helping them to do so is about the most important challenge in amateur radio today."

Clearly, G0FMT has left many options open to implementing this most interesting form of high-performance receiver. He does not indicate what types of i.f filters or their centre frequencies that he has used, other than that these must be within the tuning range of the d-c receiver section. With the tuned bandpass rf input filter shown in Fig 2, a wide range of ceramic, crystal and crystal ladder filters should give a good image performance. A ceramic or home-built ladder filter using colour tv crystals could keep costs low.

This seems an excellent approach to home-construction of receivers that stand comparison with the best modern "black boxes". Surely, more will be heard of this super-dc-gainer technique!

Stable pll oscillator for mf/hf converter

Many amateurs have good amateur-bands-only receivers which may or may not include the WARC bands (10, 18 and 24MHz) but would like to extend the range to that of a general-coverage receiver of comparable performance. Austin Parker, G3AQY writes:

"Still fully operational here in my workshop is an almost 30-year-old station, including a much-cherished Racal RA17 which I shall never forget collecting, new from the factory, in 1948. In my shack, however, I have a modern solidstate transceiver, the Heathkit HW5400. I chose this because I could not be happy using equipment which I could not attempt to service myself. It functions very well indeed but has no general-coverage facility on the receive side. Many other amateurs must be in the same situation, but there has been little published on the construction of a suitable converter to receive from, say, 1 to 27MHz in bands of 1MHz tuned by the 'amateur-bands dedicated transceiver' tuning, in receive mode, from 28 to 29MHz.

"Because such a converter should preferably have frequency stability as

good as that of the transceiver into which it is to be fed, I searched for a 'constructor-friendly' phase-lock-loop (pll) circuit that would lock a vfo to the harmonics of a 1MHz crystal. Ultimately, I found one in the 1983 edition of the ARRL *Radio Amateurs Handbook* (Chapter 6.9) with additional information in the original constructional article by W1KNI in *QST* (January 1982).

"Fig 3 shows my slightly simplified version of this circuit. It was great fun to build, and with the addition of a Plessey double-balanced mixer and small power supply stage I now have an ultra-stable converter giving me the required general coverage and permitting the use of the HW5400's filters etc, including the two memories normally available for the 28MHz band.

"Components do not seem to be critical. I used a BCY71 for the oscillator transistor, TR3, a couple of junk-box 1N270 diodes for D4 and D5, and the varicap diode D3 finished up composed of two nondescript 'surplus' diodes in parallel. The meter is needed only initially, to set the bias adjustment for 0·5mA. The tuned circuit for the oscillator, L3/C2, has to comprise several coils and a two-pole switch to cover the required range.

"At first I arranged for the vco to be on the 'high side', tuning from 29 to 57MHz. Not only would this have been preferable for the usual reasons, but it was also then much easier to arrange for the vco to cover the required frequency range with the minimum number of switched coils and with small changes in amplitude. Unfortunately, I had failed to remember that the signal frequency would then decrease as the 'tuned i.f' (ie HW5400 tuning on 28MHz) increased. This was felt to be an intolerable state of affairs when using a transceiver with a digital frequency readout! In some cases, however, it might prove an acceptable simplification."

Hazards of non-ionizing radiation

The May *TT* item "Biological effects of non-ionizing radiation" included references to a rather sensational article by Cynthia Kee *(The Observer, 8 March, 1987, p51)* in which Dr John Dennis of NRPB was quoted as saying: "We're on the dividing line between what is socially acceptable and caution. The public seem quite happy living with a risk factor of one in a thousand. We feel successful when both sides attack us equally . . ."

Dr Dennis, who is NRPB's Assistant Director (Physical Sciences), has asked us to make it clear that Mrs Kee quoted his remarks out of the context of several hours of discussion ranging over the whole problem of setting limits for exposure to electromagnetic fields. He is naturally unhappy with the implication that he believes the public are content to accept high levels of risk in this area. He writes:

"The actual context of my remarks to Mrs Kee was in relation to road accidents. The annual risk of a fatal road acident is about 1 in 10,000, with about 6,000 people being killed every year; over an average life-time of about 70 years the risk may be stated in a rather over-simplified fashion as about 7 in 1,000. By any standards this is a significant risk, nevertheless there is a degree of public acceptance of this risk which is not accorded to the risk of about one in a million arising from the radiation dose to the average member of the British public from the Chernobyl nuclear reactor disaster. Obviously, risk acceptance is not a simple question of numbers;

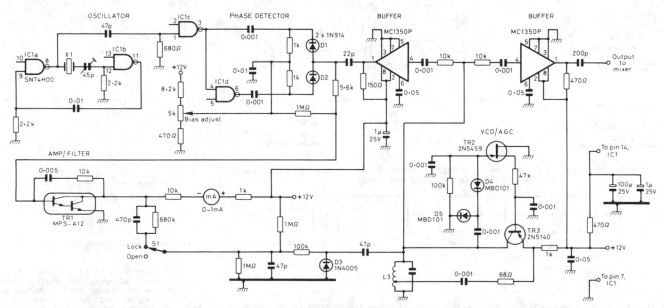

Fig 3. High-stability general-coverage pll oscillator used by G3AQY for a general-coverage converter to enable an amateur-bands-only transceiver to tune 1 to 28MHz in 27 1MHz bands. Based on an *ARRL Handbook* design originally described by W1KNI

the origin and nature of the risk and the perceived benefits or otherwise of the source also play a part in public acceptance.

"In the case of exposure to electromagnetic fields there is some rather unsatisfactory epidemiological evidence that suggests that exposures may be associated with an increased risk of leukaemia (see *TT* August and September, 1985—*G3VA*). Unfortunately, if this risk is real, it is impossible to quantify, and if it could be quantified I have no way of deciding what would be the level of risk from this source that the public would find acceptable. However, I suspect that there would be orders of magnitude difference between what *Rad Com* readers might accept and what would be accepted by Greenpeace. The National Radiological Protection Board has in the past regarded annual fatal risks of between 1 and 10 in a million as acceptable to the public, and between 10 and 100 in a million as acceptable at work; this is based on the observed risks which seem to exist from a variety of sources.

"I would dearly like to obtain firm evidence for the leukaemia risks from electromagnetic radiation. Appropriate animal experiments to obtain this evidence would take between 5 and 10 years to complete and cost between £500,000 and £10-million to carry out. NRPB simply does not have the resources to perform such experiments. In any case, it seems to me that those with a vested interest in the use and production of electromagnetic fields should pay for such investigations; ie, the electrical and electronic industries, the power generation and broadcasting interests, and the readers of *Rad Com*."

Audio cw bandpass filter using "kiss" approach

Leigh Harrison, VK6WA/G4CLP, writing from Padbury, Western Australia, has come up with a simple cw audio bandpass filter using the "kiss" approach: Fig 4. This filter is designed to be inserted in-line with the headphone socket of the receiver, and is used with a lightweight set of miniature headphones of the "Walkman" type providing adequate level for comfortable listening.

The filter comprises a six-pole multiple-feedback arrangement of the Butterworth type. The bandpass response is substantially flat between 570 and 1,000Hz but about 35dB down at 300Hz and at 1700Hz, and about 45dB down at 2·8kHz. It uses a single TLO74 quad bifet op-amp integrated circuit and a BC548 emitter-follower headphone amplifier. Three of the op-amps form the filter while IC1d provides a Vcc/2 reference voltage, allowing a single-rail power supply to be used. Power consumption is about 60mA from a 10V supply; however, any voltage rail from 9 to 25V may be used provided that the value of R12 is adjusted to keep TR1 within its rated dissipation (625mW).

FM threshold extension

Dr R C V Macario, GW8SRW, of the University College of Wales, noted the June *TT* item (page 407) on the "in-channel-select" (ics) fm threshold-extension unit being marketed for use with amateur vhf transceivers by H&C Electronik Hansen of Berlin. He feels that this system is, in effect, very similar to the "tracking n-path filter" of the type developed in his laboratory at the University of College of Swansea some 17 years ago. This was described in *Electronics Letters* (5 March, 1970) as a "Method of reducing the fm threshold using a tracking n-path filter" by R C V Macario and S Patel: Fig 5. He even believes the original detector unit is still in existence somewhere and confirms the threshold extension possible with this type of dynamic tracking filter. His model used a self-synchronized filter with a typical (stationary) bandwidth of 100Hz at an i.f centre frequency of 100kHz in conjunction with a conventional pulse-counting fm discriminator. It was capable (Fig 6) of reducing the fm threshold from an input carrier/noise ratio of about 11dB to about 6dB. The fm extension was demonstrable on both speech and music, but was limited to use of carrier frequencies (i.f) of under about 500kHz due to the limitations of the then available switching circuit modules required for the n-path filter.

Two-element hf beams

Attention is drawn to the long, chapter-length article by Les Moxon, G6XN, "Two-element hf beams" in *Ham Radio* (May 1987, pp 8–12, 14, 17, 19, 21–2, 25–7, 29–32) introduced as follows:

"Physically small beam antennas that represent the least compromise in gain and directivity have been discussed in the literature. Large antennas, for those for whom size is no problem, have received widespread coverage . . . Yet the topic of medium-sized antennas—which includes the majority of amateur beams—remains an area of uncertainty, about which many have sought, without success, for more information. The quad-versus-Yagi controversy continues unabated; conflicting claims are made for what might appear to be bewildering variety of different beams; and an imperfect grasp of essentials has turned an inherently simple situation into one of needless complexity, with two-element beams deprived of their rightful status."

TT on a number of occasions has espoused G6XN's belief that it is better to have a lightweight two-element array at a good height than a heavier three-element array nearer the ground; and that the maximum theoretical gain of a two-element array (often dismissed in many texts as 3dB) rises with close-spacing to above 5dBd, only about 1db less than what is likely to be achieved in practice with a 3-element array.

In *Ham Radio* G6XN shows that for two elements the directive pattern —and therefore the gain—depend only upon the phase shift ratio $0/0_0$ and are independent of the size, shape or spacing of elements, provided the dimensions are not excessive. This, he points out, is in flat contradiction of widely-published figures: "Those figures derived mathematically

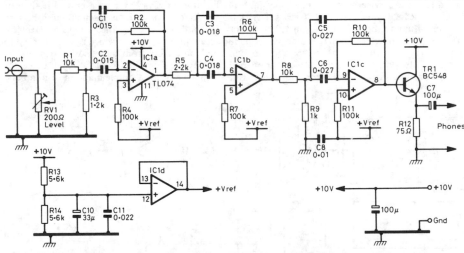

Fig 4. VK6WA's audio cw bandpass filter using an active Butterworth filter based on three sections of a TL074 quad bifet op-amp integrated circuit

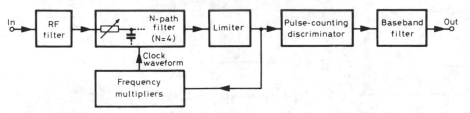

Fig 5. Outline of N-path dynamic tracking filter threshold extension demodulator as developed at Swansea in 1969–70 and seemingly basically similar in principle to the German "ICS" system noted in the June *TT*

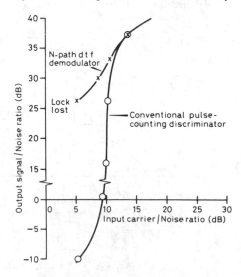

Fig 6. Performance of Dr Macario's dynamic tracking filter showing the much improved performance compared with a conventional system for carrier/noise ratios between about 6 and 11dB. Measurements with 1kHz modulating tone, modulation index of 5, rf bandwidth of 30kHz and baseband filter bandwidth of 5kHz

for parasitic arrays show gain and directivity to be *critically* dependent upon spacing and whether an element is tuned as a director or reflector . . . although the calculations are correct they happen to be the wrong ones! . . . normally performance is sacrificed if the elements are straight . . . this is the worst possible shape because it minimizes coupling, consequently precluding the possibility of the presence of equal currents except with very close spacing of the order of 0·05λ.''

G6XN outlines a number of designs of two-element horizontal beams with reduced length and enhanced coupling, as well as the application of enhanced coupling to conventionally-shaped beams. A number of his recommended designs should already be familiar to readers of his *HF Antennas for all locations* book and his later ''Claw-type'' designs, VK5HA planar loading techniques etc as described in *TT*, though with some further developments such as a form of vertical VK2ABQ array suitable for mounting on fence posts.

G6XN concludes by pointing out that his 16-page article is intended to provide guidance, rather than blueprints, for the construction of antennas tailored to suit individual needs. ''The Claw designs will be useful even if the best mast available is only a garden post, and I hope that some who have decided that beams are 'not for them' will have second thoughts . . . Claw elements are particularly suitable for use as top-loaded verticals for the lower-frequency bands.''

For *TT* items on some of the recent G6XN designs see *TT* August 1983, April 1984, March 1985 and January 1987.

The rhombic—Queen of antennas

In the 'thirties, E Bruce, of Bell Telephone Laboratories, described (*Proc IRE*, August 1931 and January 1935) a then novel highly-directive, long-wire hf antenna in the form of a rhombus (a squashed square): Fig 7. Terminated correctly at the far end, this high-gain antenna provides unidirectional characteristics; unterminated it works as a bidirectional array shooting both forwards and backwards. Within a few years, the rhombic antenna became firmly established for fixed point-to-point commercial and military strategic communications as well as for signals-intelligence interception. Despite limited sidelobe suppression, hf gains of about 8 to over 15dBd could be achieved with broadband characteristics that could extend over several octaves, and gave very desirable low vertical angle performance even when suspended from four relatively low masts (low in terms of professional communications). It rapidly came to dominate the hf point-to-point scene.

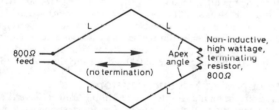

Fig 7. The classic rhombic antenna array providing a unidirectional beam when terminated or bidirectional when there is no terminating resistor. L is normally at least one-wavelength long at the lowest operating frequency

The foreword to a book *Rhombic Antenna Design* by A E Harper of BTL (published by Van Nostrand in 1941) recalled that ''When there was built in 1929 at Lawrenceville, New Jersey, a radio telephone station for initiating overseas short-wave service, the most pictured feature of the new establishment was a gigantic wire fence or net, a mile long, stretched across the landscape on a row of 185ft towers. This comprised the transmitting antenna complement for the three telephone circuits to Europe.

''A year ago the nets were taken down, the towers dismantled and sold for junk. Near them had arisen a number of telephone poles carrying at odd-looking angles a few almost invisible wires . . . the most spectacular conquest of the rhombic antenna.''

Unfortunately for amateur radio, there were two major drawbacks to the rhombic: it needed a lot of space and the directivity could not be easily changed. The result was that amateurs developed instead the compact rotary close-spaced Yagi and W8JK arrays despite the usually lower gain. But amateurs who have ever had access to rhombics for professional applications tend always to cherish a dream that one day they may retire into the countryside and acquire, or get permission to erect poles in, a large flat field and have envied those Australians, ARRL headquarters staff etc with space to erect hf rhombics.

Curiously, few amateurs have shown much interest in using long-wire or rhombic antennas for vhf or uhf where they can be fitted into a suburban garden or even a loft-space, and where an ''antenna-farm'' of several rhombics pointing in different directions is by no means out of the question.

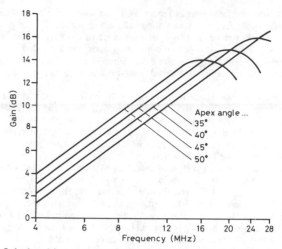

Fig 8. Calculated free-space gain for rhombic in which L is 100m for various apex angles, showing that bandwidth of the array can be used as a design parameter. Note that gain above ground is up to 6dB greater at some elevation angles

Years ago G6CJ demonstrated table-top rhombics working in the microwave region.

Joe Ellis, VK4GL *(Amateur Radio (VK)*, March 1986, pp 10–11) is fortunate enough to be a farmer with access to a rather rough field, about 300 by 140ft, sufficient for an hf rhombic. He notes that ''the rhombic antenna is the ultimate in simple wire arrays, where maximum gain is required in a given direction. Many amateurs have aspired to a rhombic only to be deterred by space considerations. To be effective, this antenna needs to be big (in terms of wavelength). Apart from space the requirements are simple: some poles, lots of wire, and a good antenna tuner . . . my rhombic is near and over the tops of trees at an average height of 45ft, which is too low. Nevertheless it works superbly . . . if I could discover how to turn the farm around, I would dispense with my Yagi antennas.''

With a history dating back more than 50 years, it might be supposed that there is little need for more research and development of this antenna. So it was interesting to find in the ICAP87 *IEE Conference Book No 274* (pp 79–80) a paper by A G P Boswell, of the Marconi Research Centre, on ''Wideband rhombic antennas for hf'' in which the design of rhombics is approached on the basis of achieving performance over a desired frequency range, using modern electromagnetic-computing design techniques. The parameters are the leg length (L) and the apex angle at the feeder/terminating ends; lesser design parameters are the wire diameter, the terminating impedance and the height above ground which affects the elevation angle of the beam.

It is noted that with single-wire rhombics, the characteristic impedance (feed and terminating) is often assumed to be 600Ω but in practice is usually about 800Ω. The paper shows that varying the apex angle results in sub-optimum gain but changes the bandwidth of the antenna. This is illustrated in Table 1. From this it can be seen that a rhombic covering 4 to 16MHz could be constructed with an apex angle of 48° and a leg length of 107m to provide a 10dB gain (4dB free-space gain) at the lowest frequency of 4MHz. With the same apex angle, an antenna with legs 20m long would be usable up to beyond 56MHz whereas if the apex angle was reduced to about 38° the bandwidth would extend to beyond 70MHz band. Conversely it should be possible to achieve 10dB gain at 50MHz on a rhombic covering the 50, 70 and 144MHz bands with legs only about 6.8m long and an apex angle of around 50°. Fig 8 from the ICAP paper shows the calculated free-space gain for a rhombic with 100m legs for various apex angles plotted against

Table 1. Bandwidth of rhombic antennas versus apex angle

Apex angle	f_{max}/f_{min}	L/λ for 10dB gain at f_{min}
36°	5·3	1·82
38°	5·1	1·73
40°	4·9	1·67
42°	4·7	1·60
44°	4·5	1·53
46°	4·3	1·48
48°	4·0	1·42
50°	3·7	1·36

Note: Minimum operating frequency is arbitrarily defined as the frequency at which the free-space gain is 4dB (ie the gain over ground is up to 10dB). Maximum operating frequency is defined as the frequency of maximum gain.

(Source: A G P Boswell, ICAP87)

frequency, showing how gain increases with frequency up to a fairly clearly defined maximum frequency and then falls off quite rapidly. In practice gain is further increased by 6dB by the presence of the earth plane, as for all practical antennas, to a degree depending upon earth conductivity and the required elevation angle of the main lobe. Theoretically, gain rises at 6dB/octave above an arbitrarily chosen minimum gain of 10dB over ground.

A G P Boswell notes that rhombics fail at the high frequency end of their operating range when the individual radiation patterns of the four radiating wires align themselves so closely with the directions of the wires that the azimuth radiation pattern of the antenna splits into two. This effect is more marked with the wider-angle designs, which also show rather worse sidelobe suppression at the higher frequency.

In his *HF antennas for all locations,* Les Moxon, G6XN, sets out the attractions and the drawbacks of large arrays such as rhombics, and shows that the theoretical gain of a terminated rhombic with the appropriate apex angle increases from about 5dBd with legs one-wavelength long to about 12dB for 5λ legs. He also notes that "with some manipulation of ropes, terminating resistors and feed points, a rhombic can be switched to provide a choice of four directions with a good chance of being able to put a useful sidelobe in most of the other directions that may be needed." The natural level for the pair of first sidelobes is -6dB so that this can still provide a powerful dx signal.

More thoughts on up-dating Drake R4 receivers

It has long been the policy in compiling *TT* to avoid publishing too many items on modifying specific equipments unless the suggestions are of relevance also to other models. There seem to me to be a number of good reasons for this: quite often manufacturers correct problems that may be experienced on early production, so that modifications may apply only to a limited number of equipments; in some cases the modifications may themselves introduce unexpected problems; modifications normally invalidate any guarantees and reduce resale values; it takes skill and experience plus considerable courage to implement circuit changes on the densely packed pcbs of modern equipment; it would be wrong to encourage *TT* readers who may lack both experience and the test equipment needed for other than the simplest changes; nor is *TT* in a position to check out readers' modifications with the equipment manufacturers before publication.

Nevertheless, with relatively little home construction these days except in East Europe, useful technical insights can often be obtained from consideration of suggested modifications provided that they illustrate basic design principles. A good example was the various comments on up-dating the once highly-regarded but now ageing Drake R4-series of general-coverage valve receivers. Some years ago WB0JGP and K8RRH of Sherwood Engineering showed clearly that by fitting an additional high-performance cw crystal filter to an R4C the close-in dynamic range measured with signals spaced at 2kHz could be increased to 85dB, significantly better than any of the solidstate amateur receivers and transceivers then (and possibly now) available, see *TT* August and October 1984. With many modern receivers having frequency-synthesizers, it is often not even possible to make meaningful measurements of dynamic range with 2 or even 20kHz spacing due to the high phase-noise resulting in severe reciprocal mixing, oscillator noise etc.

The 1984 items were followed up last year by Dave Johnstone, G4EVS, who reported on a number of additional front-end modifications to an R4B (*TT* July 1986) and his contribution provided a good insight into the whole area of receiver performance. One of those who read G4EVS's comments with great interest was the energetic Jan-Martin Noeding, LA8AK, who has an R4C with a late serial number. He writes:

"I have for some years wondered why there should be a 10mV vfo signal in the first i.f stage. With the aid of a spectrum analyzer connected to the pre-mixer output the reason becomes clear: see Fig 9. Two strong signals

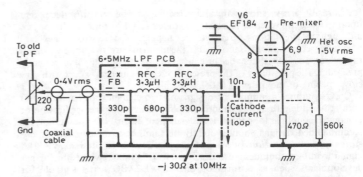

Fig 10. LA8AK's modified pre-mixer circuit for his R4-C (serial number 22073). The new lowpass filter is mounted at the side of the valve socket

are present at the mixer output, they are envelope-demodulated in the receiver's first mixer and produce the difference product which is the vfo frequency. The output from the heterodyne crystal oscillator represents all possible series resonances, in odd order; the crystal oscillator frequencies are 'pumped' from cathode of the pre-mixer to the 1pF mounted in the opposite side of the receiver and grounded via the capacitors. It is no wonder that heterodyne tones are a serious problem in this receiver.

"To avoid spreading the cathode current field through the receiver it is necessary to connect a pi-type 1pF close to the valve. This filter has the following functions:

1. It attenuates harmonics from the oscillator.
2. It isolates the heterodyne frequency signal in the cathode circuit from the rest of the receiver.
3. It provides sufficiently low earth-return impedance at the heterodyne frequency.

"The use of ferrite beads and resistance in the coaxial cable going to the old 1pF will also help to remove spurious frequency products. The addition of the extra 300pF capacitor, as noted by G4EVS, does not help very much since the cathode has a 30cm 'tuned coaxial cable' to the 1pF.

"After making these modifications, several heterodyne tones disappeared although some are still left. The use of a potentiometer to adjust the vfo level to set the correct local-oscillator level reduced the product $f_x = f_{vfo}$ by 10dB, while the other remained. I tried to use IE-500 and MC1496 as mixer with an EF184 as amplifier but the results were much worse. The only possibility for further improvement may be to correct the defects of the original compromise circuit. But the harmonic which used to fall into the 145MHz band is removed. I believe this modification is valid for R4C models with serial numbers above 22,000 and possibly those above 16,000."

Ferrite beads and rfi suppression

For many years the humble ferrite bead and its big brother the ferrite toroid have been among the most effective techniques for rfi suppression, not only for your own domestic equipment but also when tackling complaints from the neighbours since such devices can often be installed without the possible risk involved in taking a soldering iron to sort out a high-cost stereo hi-fi unit.

Jack Althouse, K6NY (Palomar Engineers, PO Box 455, Escondido, California, USA) is convinced (aren't we all!) that rfi has once again become a serious problem. He has sent along a most useful "RFI tip sheet" on "Using ferrite beads to keep rf out of tv sets, telephones, vcrs, burglar alarms and other electronic equipment". While the tip sheet relates directly to the ferrite beads marketed, together with a wide-range of toroid ferrite cores, by Palomar Engineers, much of the advice in the tip sheet is of general interest.

The attraction of the ferrite bead is that just slipping one or more on to any wires conveying unwanted rf into equipment stops or reduces the entry of rf. This can be via an antenna lead, loudspeaker cables, pick-up leads, mains cable etc, or multi-wire cables, without having to make any other modification to the equipment. To quote the tip sheet:

"Ferrite beads are made of the same materials as the toroid cores used in broadband transformers but are used at much higher frequencies. For example, ferrite Mix 43 is used for tuned circuits in the range 0·01 to 1MHz. It is efficient and losses are low. But if it is used in the 40 to 200MHz range it is lossy. So when you slip a bead of Mix 43 over a wire and there is rf in the vhf range going through the wire, it is just as though you put a resistor in the wire. But you did not have to cut the wire to insert a resistor; you just slipped a bead over the wire. If the resistance of one bead is not enough you can add more beads or add longer beads to get more resistance. The beads, unlike a resistor, do not affect the wire at low frequencies, so

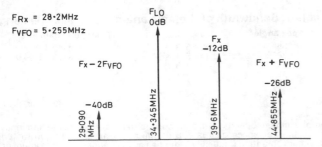

$F_{Rx} = 28·2MHz$
$F_{VFO} = 5·255MHz$

FLO
0dB

Fx
−12dB

Fx − 2F$_{VFO}$

Fx + F$_{VFO}$

−26dB

29·090 MHz
−40dB

34·345MHz

39·6MHz

44·855MHz

Fig 9. Spectrum from the original pre-mixer of the R4-C before modification

Table 2. Impedance in ohms of FB-18 size ferrite beads versus frequency

Bead material	Frequency (MHz)				
	1	10	40	100	1,000
Mix 73	45	110	110	110	120
Mix 43	15	70	110	150	160
Mix 64	6	40	110	160	400

that audio, dc etc pass through the wire just as though the bead were not there. There are three bead materials in general use: Mix 73, Mix 43 and Mix 64. The impedance in ohms of size FB-18 beads versus frequency is shown in Table 2. This shows that beads of the three materials all work about the same at 40MHz, but below 40MHz Mix 73 is best. Above 40MHz Mix 64 is best. For overall performance from 1 to 1,000MHz, Mix 43 is the best choice.

"It is important to remember that the frequencies in Table 2 are those of the interfering signals to be eliminated; not the operating frequencies of the equipment being protected. For example: to protect a telephone at audio frequencies use type 43 or 73 beads to keep out 14MHz rf. When you buy beads it is necessary to specify the physical size (FB-3, FB-8 etc) and the bead material (Mix 73, Mix 43 etc) depending on the frequency of the rf interference. FB-1, FB-3 and FB-7 have 0·05in holes that will slip over bare No 18 awg wire; FB-8 has a 0·09in hole and will slip over the insulation of No 22 awg wire; FB-24 and FB-63 have 0·2in holes for larger wire or cable."

The tip sheet points out that when a multi-wire cable is passed through a bead it has the effect of suppressing rf transmission through all of the wires and is much easier than putting beads on each wire. Balanced twin-lead cable (as widely used with American tv receivers) is a special case; a bead on each of the wires would kill the tv signal as well as the unwanted rf signal, but if the whole of the twinlead goes through a single bead, the tv signal is not impeded but rfi will be suppressed. Similarly with coaxial cable: "The signal going through the cable is confined to the inside of the braid, but the outside of the braid acts just like any other wire; it can pick up unwanted rf which then reaches the tv set or video monitor; a suitable 'bead' placed over the cable suppresses the outer-braid rf without affecting the signal." For such purposes it is necessary to use a core with a large-diameter hole; the Palomar range includes toroid cores with hole diameters up to 1·4in but with some differences in the materials: Mix 77 is the best below 40MHz; Mix 43 is the best between 30 and 150MHz, but can be used from 1MHz to 1GHz; and Mix 61 is the best above 200MHz.

With toroid cores it is often possible to pass the cable more than once through the hole. It is advisable to do this as many times as possible since each turn is the equivalent of adding another toroid. Palomar also now supply "split beads" that solve the problem of putting beads or toroids over cables that have plugs that will not go through the holes. These are beads that have been cut in half, the two halves are put over the cable and then wrapped with tape to hold the two halves together. The mating edges are polished so that the two halves mate very closely, and are available with centre holes of 0·25 and 0·5in diameter and also for flat computer cable 2·5 or 3in wide. Since it is important that the two halves of a split bead fit exactly together, never attempt to use a 0·25in split bead for a cable of more than 0·25in diameter. The split beads are in the Mix 43 material.

For use in tuned circuits and wideband transformers etc, the advantages include the high permeability which means that you get a high inductance with few turns, with little leakage of the magnetic field; however, it is always important to remember that ferrites are easily saturated and should be used only in low power (receiving) applications unless you are certain that the cores will not reach saturation point.

John Greenwell, G3AEZ, draws attention to another solution to rfi that may or may not involve some form of ferrite loading. He has sent along a glossy brochure from W L Gore & Associates (UK) Ltd (Pitreavie Business Park, Dunfermline, Fife KY11 5PU; tel 0383 733380) on their range of "lowpass cables". It is claimed that these cables (single conductor, twisted pair or multi-core) and an associated range of filter assemblies will pass low-frequency signals up to a specified (-3dB) frequency (normally 5MHz for cables but selectable from 50kHz to 200MHz for the filter assemblies) but attenuate higher frequency hash and rfi with a more than 25dB/octave characteristic. The cables and filters absorb the interference rather than reflecting it back along the system. The brochure, however, gives no indication of the cost of these useful-looking products.

Tracing valve pin-outs

Frank Hughes, VE3DQB, noting the recent items about the problem of tracing valve pin-outs when no valve data books are available, writes to chide me for forgetting a useful chapter in the long-out-of-print 160pp *Radio Handbook Supplement* published by the RSGB during the second

world war at the staggering price of 2s 6d (12½p) as a companion to the *Amateur Radio Handbook* which was being used as an RAF training textbook. The supplement included a 15-page chapter "A service operator's vade mecum" by B W F Mainprise, G5MP, full of practical advice on how a signals operator could make improvised repairs in the field using substitute components "in a manner which need never enter the mind of a depot engineer".

"Surely," writes VE3DQB, "so useful a text is always within your reach and by now you will have snatched down your copy". Yes, indeed. Fortunately my copy, although now water-stained from a disastrous frozen-pipe burst that sadly reduced my library last winter, is still to hand.

VE3DQB points out that a section on page 115 headed "Enemy equipment" was intended to help the service operator presented with captured valves of unknown type to trace the base connections. For the benefit of the many readers deprived of a copy of that 1941 book, he has paraphrased and up-dated G5MP's advice as follows:

1. Locate the two or three pins with a little resistance between them; these are the heater pins. No resistance means an internal connection.

2. Apply a low voltage to the heater and slowly increase it until the heater glows cherry red. Nowadays, long odds on this being 6·3 or 12·6V.

3. A clip lead connected to a 9V battery and milliammeter in series is clipped to one of the active pins, and the other pins tried in sequence. When the meter shows current flowing, the negative side of the battery is connected to the cathode of the valve.

4. Leaving the negative connection to the cathode in place, and the positive connection to another pin, connect a second 9V battery to the cathode (positive this time) and connect the negative terminal in turn to all other pins. Those that affect the meter reading are connected to grids between the cathode and the pin connected to the meter.

5. Repeat 4 until the pins of all grids and the anode are known.

6. Scrutiny of the electrodes through the glass envelope (assuming that it is not a metal valve or a metallized coating) should identify multi-section valves, and alert the investigator to look for two cathodes etc.

Happily thumbing through the other pages of the *Supplement* with its chapters on fundamentals, radio mathematics, direction-finding, cro technique, mathematical tables and formulae etc, one is reminded of the days when even though equipment was relatively simple and understandable (and serviceable), amateurs in uniform took the acquisition of technical knowledge very seriously—and this was all years before the introduction of the compulsory RAE!

Kurt Grey, VE2UG, while far from being anti-solidstate, considers that mechanical design has become mediocre and makes servicing more difficult than it need be: "Unlike a valve, which could be simply pulled out and replaced, the removal of a transistor can be a nightmare. Very often the pcb is damaged in the process. Coils, resistors, capacitors may have to be removed just to get at the transistor. Designers seem to have been brainwashed into believing that transistors never fail. And then, when at last the new transistor is in place, power 'on' and output restored what happens? The tv monitor shows breakthrough. A $20,000-plus spectrum analyser is needed (as Peter Chadwick, G3RZP, noted recently in *TT*) to trace and cure the parasitic spurii resulting from the minor changes in layout that came about in reinstating all the components that had to be removed to reach the transistor!"

Tips and topics

For those interested in packet radio, attention is drawn to a special issue of *Proc IEEE* (January 1987) which devotes more than 150 large pages to a series of papers on "Packet radio networks". Many stem from the current investigations into using packet radio for military mobile networks, including a paper by B H Davies and T R Davies of the UK Royal Signals & Radar Establishment: "The application of packet switching techniques to combat net radio." The guest editors regret that so many of the papers stem from efforts sponsored by military organizations, adding: "This is due to the unfortunate lack of success that we experienced in including a paper on the application of this technology to the commercial and amateur sectors." A paper on "Issues in packet radio network design" points out that much of the present work is concerned with "broadcasting" messages to mobile users over a single channel on a store and forward basis, but that some of the amateur and commercial applications "de-emphasize this capability", by which I assume is meant that most amateur packet operation is between fixed sites.

"PIN-diode rf attenuator", TT July p498, Fig 6(a). Please note, polarity of D3 should be the reverse of that shown: cathode joins base of the BC308. Shown correctly in layout diagram Fig 6(b). Note also transistor must be silicon pnp type and D3 a germanium type so that base is held off when D3 conducts via the 270kΩ resistor.

Technical Topics
Pat Hawker, G3VA

THE APRIL ISSUE of *QST* devoted a couple of pages to a first "1987 Messy Shack Photo Contest" providing illustrations of a memorable collection of shacks crowded jam-tight with equipment, and workbenches littered with masses (or messes?) of leads, tools and instruments of all types. WA4HXZ was named owner of "the most functional messy shack"; W1AN "most creative use of space"; W2JMU "messiest workbench". The only European shack featured was that of Torfinn Horn, LA4OFA, credited as having a "messy shack with most potential". I should have entered!

All good fun and a space filler not to be taken seriously, you may be thinking. Yet the June issue reported that "the response to this article was overwhelming. The Messy Shack Contest generated more letters to the correspondence editor than any other feature in years".

Why should these photographs, so different from the tidied-up and neat displays of black boxes that one sees pictured in the amateur magazines these days have struck such a responsive chord? Was it mere nostalgia for the days when most amateur shacks looked like the furious efforts of a mad spider to spin a web of wires over open breadboard gear that somehow always remained prototypes? Or perhaps a reaction against those neat little transceivers smaller and less exciting than the family hi-fi? Or a heartwarming proof that there are still some shacks so overflowing with bits and pieces that it is only just possible for an operator to squeeze in?

There is plenty of evidence that many of those who knew and enjoyed amateur radio in days past regret the gradual phasing out of the old idea that an amateur was essentially an experimenter; the shack a place in which you gingerly touched bare wires to see if they were carrying 240V ac, harmless 6·3V or finger-burning rf. And gear was operated manually, *not* under microprocessor control.

Phil Horwood, G3FRB, is one of those who admits to increasing despondency about the way amateur radio is progressing. "How can a youngster get started these days with the ridiculous cost of commercially-made gear?" he asks. The answer surely depends on the extent to which youngsters can be persuaded that you do not need an all-singing, all-dancing black box to enjoy amateur radio. G3FRB believes the rot set in when the 144MHz Class B licence (the original Class B was for 420MHz upwards for which no commercial units were marketed) led to the black-box syndrome by forcing the beginner on to vhf rather than the traditional initiation with simple, often home-built but always "understandable" and "serviceable" equipment on 1·8, 3·5 or 7MHz. He would favour the introduction of an hf/cw "Novice" licence instead of Class B licences, but one can imagine the number of indignant letters to the editor if anyone attempted to say that no more Class B licences would be issued! And the Americans grumble that 5,000 of their "novices" drop out each year without, in many cases, ever getting on the air—and, messy shack contests apart, the black-box syndrome is not unknown in the USA!

But certainly the growing interest in "replica" equipment of the 'thirties reflects some disenchantment with current practices, aptly summed up in some doggerel verse from *Radio-ZS* by A Buchan, ZS5NZ, which I have taken the liberty of shortening and slightly modifying:

> *The old-timer awoke with a tear in his eye*
> *He'd been dreaming again of the days long gone by,*
> *Of racks and of panels of regular size*
> *And calls reaching out to some foreign skies*
> *The heat and the glow of the bright 813,*
> *And the open-wire feeder outside he could see*
> *The dx a'plenty the sunspots would bring*
> *And all that was needed — a piece of wet string,*
> *On the key of bright brass a CQ he'd send*
> *And back would come China and dx no end.*
>
> *Then he looked at his new transistorised set*
> *With its miniature dials so easy to net,*
> *Who wants all this black new-fangled gear?*
> *Where are the homebrews of yesteryear?*

Professor Cyril Northcote Parkinson, author of Parkinson's Law, has warned of the effects of the growing automation and computerisation of our lives (and shacks?). He has formulated a new law: "The chief product of a highly-automated society is a widespread and deepening sense of boredom.

People should be forbidden by law to work more than three days a week at computers or other kinds of automated equipment."

Variometers ancient and modern

The reminder by Kurt Grey, VE2UG, of the use by Lorenz and Collins Radio of variometers for hf marine and aeronautical transmitters and their continued use at vlf (*TT* June 1987, p409) stirred some memories of the advantages, particularly in terms of trouble-free service, that these components had over the "roller-coaster" variable inductors that succeeded them on hf.

Both George Cripps, G3DWW, and Phil Horwood, G3FRB, point out that an hf variometer was used in the No 19 set, the standard British Army vehicle set of the second world war. G3DWW writes: "I have for many years made use of a No 19 set variometer as a most convenient variable loading coil. These were designed for use in the 2 to 8MHz range, and can certainly load up these frequencies effectively on to an 8ft whip antenna . . . *Marine Radio Manual* by Danielson and Mayoh (George Newnes, 1966) shows a number of marine transmitters using variometers for antenna loading in the 500kHz mf band. At the Rugby Radio (GBR) vlf (16kHz) transmitter the variometers are 16ft diameter hexagonal spiders wound with Litz cable, and the antenna current is 900A with 270kV rf at the antenna feedthrough point! Roller-coasters in a marine environment and salty atmosphere might prove dodgy."

Checking my copy of *Marine Radio Manual*, I note that among the transmitters using mf variometers were the Marconi Oceanspan, Marconi Salvor 2, Redifon G47B and G80, IMR 62. Apart from the question of a vulnerable sliding contact, one could imagine that the construction of a "roller-coaster" with sufficient turns to cope with 500kHz whip antennas would not be easy, and variometers may still be standard practice for this application.

Phil Horwod, G3FRB, also puts in a good word for the variometers used in the No 19 tank sets. He cannot recall one ever going wrong, something that could not be said of other components in the early production of the No 19 which had an altogether less happy record. Like other one-time members of REME, he says: "I would like a pound for every 19-set I repaired or for every Sherman or Churchill tank I climbed out of." He still feels cross that few people associate the Army with radio. There were, he points out, as many radio people in REME as in the RAF and RN combined. I must admit that my only wartime encounter with REME was once trying unsuccessfully to get them to repair a 150W Onan petrol-electric generator belonging to Special Communications. Perhaps if I had taken them a No 19 set I would have been better served!

The linear variable inductor—a modern variometer?

An alternative form of continuously-variable inductor, more suited to small-signal applications than high-power antenna matching, is permeability tuning in which dust-iron cores are physically moved in and out of the inductors, a technique used very successfully by Collins Radio for receivers and vfos.

A new form of "quasi-linear controllable inductor" has been described by A S Kislovski of Hasler Ltd (Switzerland) in the prestigious *Proc IEEE* (February 1987, pp267–9). This is a "linear variable inductor (lvi)" for which is forecast an extremely wide spectrum of potential applications, though I have no idea as to whether this is likely to include radio communication engineering. A S Kislovski writes: "It is obvious that the new component will prove an extremely versatile tool in the hands of electronic power engineers. At the same time, it is felt that it also represents a sort of challenge to all creative electronic engineers—to explore the new horizons which it has opened." Unusually emotive words to find in *Proc IEEE!* It is claimed that the lvi "fills the gap which has existed among the components featuring electronically variable fundamental electric properties: resistance, capacitance and inductance."

Basically the lvi is a magnetic component using ferromagnetic core material, its permeability being externally controlled by a bias field produced by an additional winding. A S Kislovski writes: "A bias field colinear with the signal field has until now not been considered as a suitable means for the obtaining of a linear variable inductance. The reasons are two-fold. First, a

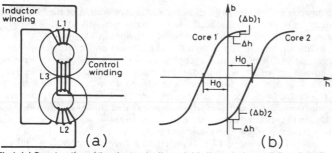

Fig 1. (a) Construction of the electronically-variable linear inductor (lvi) as described by A S Kislovski of Hasler Ltd. (b) Operating points of the two tooidal cores under the influence of the control bias current in L3

strong coupling between the bias and the signal fields seems to be inevitable; second, the linearity range of the inductance is severely limited."

The arrangement shown in Fig 1(a) virtually eliminates the first of these problems and greatly reduces the second. Windings L1 and L2 are identical and wound on separate, preferably toroidal cores of ferromagnetic material. Winding L3, the control winding, is wound over both cores. Windings L1 and L2 are connected in series but produce opposing fluxes in L3, so that there is no or very little coupling between the inductance L1 + L2 and L3. When there is no current in L3, the total inductance of the component is thus L1 + L2, but as current in L3 is increased, the biasing current displaces the operating point of the cores along their hysteresis curves (Fig 1(b)) and the effective inductance of L1 and L2 becomes increasingly series-opposing in a linearly-controllable fashion, so that their effective inductance falls. It is claimed that the linear variation of inductance can extend to a range as high as 1 to more than 100. The Swiss experiments were carried out with two 13mm toroidal cores of 3E1 material, with L1 and L2 each comprising 30 turns and L3 10 turns, the bias current in L3 being adjusted from zero to several amperes.

I remain curious as to the extent to which this technique could be applied to practical rf applications at hf or vhf, using suitable dust-iron toroids, and at what power levels or perhaps only for small-signal applications? It would be interesting to have reports from anyone investigating this concept, which appears to offer the possibility of emerging as a modern form of electronically-controllable variometer. It could be that the system is intended for use only where there is dc flowing in L1/L2 as well as L3, or alternatively where all windings are fed wth rf at the same frequency. It would be worth finding out.

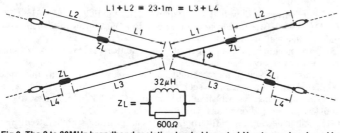

Fig 2. The 3 to 30MHz broadband resistive-loaded inverted-V antenna developed by Dr Brian Austin (G0GSF/ZS6BKW) and Andre Fourie, providing high radiation efficiency and low swr at frequencies down to 3MHz. Feedpoint impedance about 500Ω

Resistive-loaded broadband antennas

TT (June 1987, p406) in discussing techniques for broadbanding dipole antennas, made brief reference to the recent work of Dr Brian Austin (G0GSF/ZS6BKW) and Andre Fourie on resistive-loaded antennas, including a new high-efficiency design covering the entire hf band 3 to 30MHz: Fig 2. This uses parallel inductive/resistive loading in much the same way as the "Australian dipole" but as an inverted-V type of "fat dipole" with diverging wires that would, incidentally, be easier to implement than the Australian dipole with its 1·8m spreaders. However, I omitted to include any information on the actual dimensions of this antenna.

G0GSF, noting the omission, writes: "The homebrew community will be pulling their hair out now that you have whetted their appetites by quoting its performance characteristics without giving the key dimensions! They are as follows:

L1 + L2 = L3 + L4 = 23·1m
L1 = 13·5m (hence L2 = 9·6m)
L3 = 17m (hence L4 = 6·1m)

"Whereas the included angle φ does not markedly affect the vswr, the characteristic impedance of the feedline is dependent upon it to some extent. When φ = 5°, Z_o (opt) = 500Ω, whereas φ = 0° requires Z_o (opt) = 400Ω.

The change is so slight that it is probably not really worth worrying about in practice."

With an overall element span of 2 × 23·1 = 46·2m, it could prove difficult to fit such a useful antenna into a back garden, though the inverted-V bow-tie form of construction allows the centre support to be on a roof in order to make use of both front and back gardens.

In my June *TT* comments I noted that the T2FD was an early form of an antenna loaded resistively to increase bandwidth. Although some amateurs consider that (with a suitable atu) the T2FD does form an effective multi-band design, it was noted many years ago that the T2FD originally stemmed from a US Navy design intended only to broaden the bandwidth of a dipole by a relatively modest degree. Dr Austin comments:

"We certainly did examine the so-called T2FD configuration: both with the computer and experimentally (at least in measuring vswr). Our conclusions were that it is not an effective broadband configuration, and your term 'aperiodic multi-band' is probably far more accurate. Its vswr is certainly very peaky and nowhere near as flat as one American manufacturer would have his customers believe. This was confirmed by both the measured results and the computer prediction. However, when one examines radiation efficiency as well (as we clearly must) then its performance — or lack of it! — becomes really evident. At the 3MHz end it performs about as well as a resistor, rising thereafter in a series of sawtooth-like oscillations to about 70 per cent at 18MHz, but with deep notches down to about 20 per cent around 12 and 24MHz. These figures apply to an antenna 27·4m long and 0·46m between conductors, with nominally an 800Ω load, as would be given by the equations quoted in *TT* September 1986 for a low-frequency cut-off of 1·8MHz. Scaling dimensions to operate from 3·5MHz would produce the more usual T2FD geometry. This research brought to light a number of important aspects and some of these will be published soon."

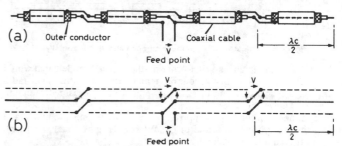

Fig 3. Basic geometry of the "coco" (coaxial colinear) antenna formed from a series of electrical quarter-wave sections of coaxial cable taking into account the velocity factor of the cable

"Coco"—the coaxial colinear array

Some 15 years ago, *TT* (September and November 1972) drew attention to the way in which coaxial colinear ("coco") antenna arrays (Fig 3) were being used professionally; not only for the comparatively well-known vertical vhf antennas having an omnidirectional horizontal radiation pattern and narrow vertical radiation pattern, but also as a transportable 26-element horizontally-polarised centre-fed array on 49·8MHz (Fig 4) described in *IEEE Trans on Ant & Prop* July 1972, pp513–6. The November 1972 *TT* included an example of a more conventional 144MHz vertical coco design by W6PIV (Fig 5), and a note from Dud Charman, G6CJ, who recalled that the famous tv pioneer Alan Blumlein of EMI had tried, unsuccessfully, to make such a system work as early as 1935. Although 144MHz designs regularly turn up in amateur radio magazines, there is in my mind a question-mark over this approach. One could not guarantee 100 per cent success.

Recently, however, a detailed theoretical model together with computer simulations of its current distribution and measured performance characteristics have been published for 24- and 26-element coco antennas at 50MHz and for six- and eight-element coco antennas at 915MHz in a short paper by Thiery J Judasz (University of Colorado) and Warner L Ecklund and Ben B Balsey (US National Oceanic and Atmospheric Administration) in *IEEE Trans on Ant & Prop* (March 1987, pp327–31). Warner Ecklund was one of the authors of the 1972 paper noted above.

The paper recalls that large coco antenna arrays along the lines outlined in 1972 have been used successfully for many years. The mesosphere-stratosphere-troposphere radar at Poker Flat, Arkansas, has an antenna made of 256 separate coco antennas constructed from coaxial cable. The Jicamarc radar observatory in Peru has a 50MHz array of 1,536 separate coco antennas, in this case constructed from aluminium tubing. Commercial vertically-polarised coco communication antennas—for example, for two-way mobile radio—are available in the range 400 to 520MHz. Yet, in spite of its relatively wide usage, no thorough theoretical description has previously been published.

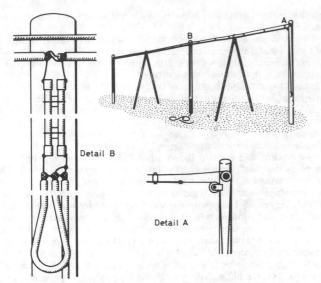

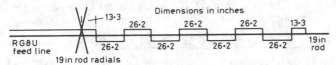

Fig 4. The 26-element portable coco array for 50MHz described in 1972 for mounting on three poles. The nylon messenger line and polyethylene slip rings used to connect to the antenna are shown in detail A and B shows feed arrangement consisting of balun and quarter-wave matching transformer. All electrical connections should be waterproofed

Fig 5. The vertical 144MHz colinear antenna shown horizontally

The IEEE paper includes a first-order mathematical "model" that would be of interest mainly to professional antenna engineers rather than radio amateurs. Nevertheless, the fact that computed and measured radiation patterns of the various coco arrays are in close agreement does at least give more confidence in this design approach. It is also interesting to note that a modification akin to that found in the W6PIV design (Fig 5) was found beneficial. To quote the paper:

"A modification of the 26-element 50MHz antenna yields a much smoother current and phase distribution. In this instance, the last element on both ends of the array has been replaced by a shorted section (λc/4 in length) followed by a section of cable (λair/4 in length) as discussed by Wheeler in 1956 and by Branner and Williams of RSRE in 1981. For short antennas, both model and measurements show that the final section should be somewhat shorter than λair/4 (0·21 λ air) for a modified eight-element antenna at 915MHz . . . the result of the end treatment is to sharply reduce the sidelobe levels."

More ideas on "straight" receivers

R B Kerr, GM4FDT, has been following recent *TT* items on regenerative detectors and direct-conversion receivers with interest since this is an area where he has achieved considerable success with some novel designs, including the application of regenerative Q-multipliers to direct-conversion receivers, the use of sub-miniature (EF73/CV466) valves with low ht rails and

dc powering of heaters, as well as ingenious exploitation of the "harmonic mixer" as originally introduced into d-c receivers by RA3AAE in the early 'seventies and described on a number of occasions in *TT* and *ART*.

It has also been noted that the Q-multiplication characteristic of a regenerative detector can be applied to virtually any type of receiver front-end in order to improve pre-mixer or pre-detector selectivity. GM4FDT uses this technique in conjunction with a homodyne-type direct-conversion receiver comprising front-end Q-multiplier, balanced product detector, af amplifier with response shaping for cw and ssb (Fig 6); in addition the vfo can be switched off for a.m reception with the Q-multiplier used to provide regenerative gain and selectivity.

This receiver uses 10 EF73 subminiature (wire-ended) valves and one BC170 pnp transistor. The vfo normally operates at half the received frequency, but by switching the product detector from push-push (2Fo) to push-pull (Fo), where Fo is the vfo frequency, reception at a signal frequency of Fo is possible. Plug-in coils are used.

The Q-multiplier (Fig 7) has proved very effective and applies a negative resistance across the antenna tuned circuit, no extra feedback windings or taps are required. It could be applied to almost any receiver, perhaps with the addition of a series antenna capacitor to vary coupling and to avoid dead spots. The receiver can also operate at × 3Fo (push-pull detector) or × 4Fo (push-push); ie with the vfo at 3·33MHz one receives 10MHz signals or with vfo at 3·5MHz one receives 14MHz signals. A wide range of controllable af gain is achieved by adjusting the negative bias on the suppressor grids of three af stages.

GM4FDT finds that most of the problems peculiar to d-c receivers, such as microphony, modulation hum and vfo pulling, disappear when receiving on multiples of the vfo frequency at a slight reduction of gain, easily compensated for in the af stages. For headphone reception the entire receiver operates with an ht of 24 to 30V, for loudspeaker listening the ht for the final af stage is increased to 100V. As a result of considerable experimentation, he offers the following conclusions applicable to the construction of direct-conversion receivers:

(1) TRF receivers work "as advertised" if well built and skillfully operated.
(2) Valve heaters are best run on dc for "that silent background." GM4FDT runs his in series from a constant-current nicad charger. This makes it possible to cope with the odd heater voltages of tv-type valves still readily available (often at no charge) such as the EF80, EF183, EF184, PCC189, PCC84, PC86 and PC88. The PC88 and PC86 (as used in the old valve uhf tv tuners) are grounded-grid triodes useful to 430MHz.
(3) Homodyne d-c receivers operate best with harmonic mixers such as the RA3AAE product detector with anti-parallel diodes or push-pull valves, fets etc.
(4) Many valves work well at low ht, particularly the ECC82, 6J4, 6J5, 6C5, EF73 (CV466), EF80 at 24V and some down to 12V. Acorn valves such as the 955 and 956 will oscillate at 5V!
(5) Variable antenna coupling and rf attenuators are very useful with virtually any receiver.
(6) In any trf receiver there should be always one rf stage to minimise oscillator radiation, antenna "suck-out" etc.
(7) Audio response for ssb should be about 300 to 2,300Hz. For cw about 400Hz wide centred on your favourite cw tone.
(8) Excellent decoupling, rf filtering and screening all help stability. Reducing the grid capacitor in a regenerative detector from the usual 100pF to about 10pF often improves ssb reception. It is also worth adjusting the value of the grid resistor for optimum results.
(9) Plug-in coils and electrical bandspread tuning are highly recommended.

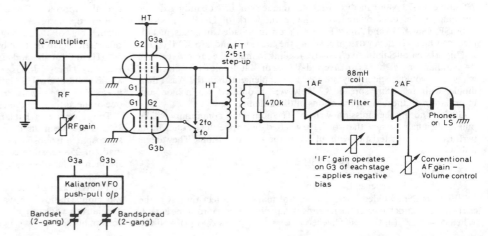

Fig 6. Basic outline of the versatile direct-conversion receiver developed by GM4FDT using 10 sub-miniature valves and one pnp transistor

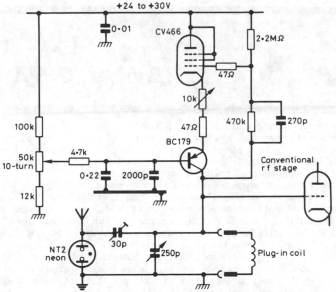

Fig 7. Negative-resistance Q-multiplier as used by GM4FDT but suitable for use with other types of receivers to increase pre-mixer rf selectivity

Apart from simplification, it is easy to wind more coils to cope with new bands etc.

(10) Finally, build it like a battleship!

In connection with **(10)**, GM4FDT recalls that he once had a German military trf receiver made by Philips (1-v-2) that was later handed back to the makers who now have it in their museum in Eindhoven. The chassis was a die-cast box 0·25in thick, the massive coil turret with ceramic coil formers covered 15kHz to 18MHz and operated by a handwheel through two spur gears suitable for a lathe! The 220V ac psu provided 100V ht and 4V dc with the lt supply smoothed with 1,000µF capacitors and lf choke. It also had a beautifully-made ganged capacitor and dial for tuning.

Certainly the mechanical construction and performance of the German military radios remains vividly in the minds of all of us who ever had an opportunity to use them. Personally, I recall a transmitter-receiver with a trf receiver fitted with a magnificent turret that I used occasionally in 1945–6. Admittedly some of the small passive components, such as capacitors, were less reliable than the mechanical parts.

Vegetable oil and the resistor mystery

Bill Craig, G6JJ, believes there is a much simpler solution to G5RV's dummy-load resistor mystery (*TT* February, July) than that suggested by G4LYF. He writes:

"The resistors concerned are of carbon in a clay matrix. Like other ceramic materials they withstand chemical attack well. Mineral oils, which are paraffins, have good chemical stability. Vegetable oils, on the other hand, are glycerides of fatty acids which yield acid products over a period of time due to hydrolysis and oxidation. The reactions are accentuated at high ambient temperatures.

"When I discussed the matter with Dr Harold Emblem, G1ANY, he was quick to point out that corrosion of the end connections was almost certainly the reason for the increased resistance of the dummy load. Such resistors usually have metallised ends around which are clamped metal bands through which the connections to the resistor are made.

"If 'good' connections are made to the ends of a resistor that has apparently increased in value, it will probably be found that the resistance of the element itself is unchanged."

Without getting into an argument between chemists, it would seem sensible when applying the coat of paint or clear varnish as suggested by G5RV (July) to make sure that you cover all the metallic parts as well.

Tips and topics

With reference to recent items on linear and other high-power rf amplifiers using valves, P Carver, GW4WWE writes: "In view of the scarcity these days of high-voltage compact variable capacitors, readers may be interested to know that Jackson Brothers (a firm still making a large range of variable capacitors) make a variant of the 804-series capacitor (up to 220pF) capable of withstanding 1·5kV and having ptfe interleaves fitted between the plates. Also available is a range of ptfe tubular trimmers rated up to 2·5kV. Although the firm does not supply direct, Maplin Electronic Supplies of Rayleigh, Essex, will take special orders of required items. Incidentally, the Jackson Bros catalogue makes good reading for those who may have been making a long and frustrating search for such components. They also have separate catalogues covering stand-off insulators, slow-motion drives, dials and gearing systems."

On a different but related topic, GW4WWE writes: "In regard to burned-out anode parasitic-suppression resistors, may I suggest that the problem is often caused by the use of carbon film resistors which, despite claims to the contrary, are sufficiently inductive to go up in smoke, particularly on 21 and 28MHz. The solution is to use carbon composition types which unfortunately are rapidly disappearing off the market. If anybody knows a source of composition resistors at a reasonable price perhaps they would let the rest of us know." □

Technical Topics
Pat Hawker, G3VA

FOR AMATEUR RADIO to survive meaningfully into the 21st century, it is surely not enough just to recruit youngsters showing a passing interest in the concept of being able to talk or type to like-minded individuals at a distance; we must be able to show that there are still good reasons for becoming interested over a long period in the technology and the human skills of radio operating without relying solely on machine intelligence. For one thing is certain: the future will see the disappearance of the last vestiges of the idea that there is something special and elitist about using electromagnetic waves as a communications medium.

Universal radio

Already telecommunications people are thinking beyond the concepts of mobile cellular radio and the cordless telephone to an era of "universal digital portable radio communications" (see for example the 42-page article by Donald C Cox of Bell Communications Research in *Proc IEEE*, April 1987) in which 900MHz, 10mW handheld digital transceivers are seen as forming the final 1,000ft "connection" into the public telephone system. On the same lines, British Telecom are soon to introduce their CT2 digital 900MHz cordless telephones, and cordless PABXs have already been marketed. Everybody will use compact handheld transceivers and inevitably the pressures on vhf and uhf spectrum will continue to grow, with the possibility, currently being considered, of deregulation of the radio spectrum whereby users will "buy" channels from new profit-making "frequency planning organisations".

At the same time, the hf spectrum, which at one time looked like being largely written off by professional communicators in favour of satellite systems, is undergoing a major revival, particularly by the Services, both for jam-resistant communications and for high-power monostatic and bistatic over-the-horizon radar. For hf communications, much thought is being directed at designing fully-automated systems capable of providing reliable links over hundreds or thousands of miles yet "as simple to operate as a car radio telephone" to quote a presentation by Dr J N Hopkinson of Plessey at the 1987 URSI National Colloquium at Sheffield University.

The Plessey work is aimed at further de-skilling hf operation on the grounds that experienced hf radio operators are a vanishing race and that: "The successful operation of a present-day (professional) hf link demands a considerable degree of operator skill and experience if not to say black art. Ships' radio operators require several years of intense training, followed by many years of actual experience before they can become proficient . . . the thrust of the research at Plessey Roke Manor has been to employ the increasing availability of low-cost computing power to extend the facility to unskilled users. The computer first provides its preferred frequencies from pre-programmed knowledge of the sunspot conditions, time of day, location

of the desired recipient station etc. It then controls the communications receiver to operate as a sensor to test its predictions. By doing so, the frequencies can be iterated so that a free channel close to the optimum can be located. The computer then initiates and controls the communications process, identifying and linking up with its opposite number."

An automated system of this type has been operating 24 hours per day five days per week between Roke Manor and Caswell, near Northampton, with a menu of 80 spot frequencies between 2 and 25MHz, and has achieved an average throughput of 32,800 characters per hour with better than 36kch/h for 49·1 per cent of the time and less than 12kch/h for only 11·8 per cent of the time. The skill is entirely that of the systems designer.

This is fair enough for military and civil professional purposes but is hardly the way which some of us would wish to see hf amateur radio developing: it is precisely the need to develop operating skills, with that dash of the "black art", that makes the hobby one of lasting interest. No human challenge—no hobby!

Des Vance, GI3XZM has gone on record (*Members' Mailbag,* July 1987) as advocating a concerted move to encourage the use of *simple* gear, regardless of power. Because he feels that the oft used "kiss" does not lend itself to such a movement, he has come up with the acronym "TRUMPS" standing for "Transmitters and Receivers Using Minimum Parts". He would like to see TRUMPS receiving the sort of promotional effort that is devoted to QRP, rtty, data communications etc.

Transistorised bloopers: a novel approach

As part of his interest in simplicity, GI3XZM has built several simple regenerative blooper-type receivers but with solidstate devices rather than valves, using a FET as an infinite impedance detector in conjunction with a bipolar Q-multiplier. Results have been encouraging enough to pass along some of his circuit arrangements. He writes: "I reasoned that by separating the detector and reaction duties neither need compromise the other. Reaction (regeneration) smooth beyond belief is achieved. With the feedback transistor loosely coupled to the tuned circuit as in vfo practice the good selectivity associated with an infinite impedance detector is further improved and stability is certainly better. Fig 1 shows some typical arrangements.

"The first such receiver I built was for a young swl and covered 9 to 16MHz (three broadcast bands and 14MHz). With a 10m 'throwout' antenna it brought in all the dx he could want. More recently my son built an mf (medium wave) version as his first constructional project, using a frame antenna. Selectivity was such that on weaker stations there was an obvious loss of treble as sidebands were cut as the reaction control was advanced. When he was finished with it, I took turns off the frame antenna to see how far up in frequency it would work, also reducing the value of the associated

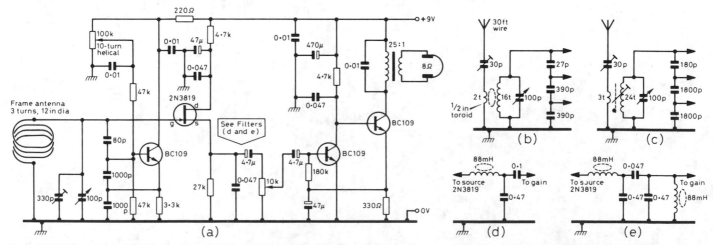

Fig 1. GI3XZM's solid-state regenerative "blooper" receivers. (a) 3·5MHz version with frame antenna mounted about 12in above chassis with miniature coaxial-cable "download". (b) Input circuit for 9 to 16MHz version. (c) Conventional input circuit for 3·5MHz receiver using wire antenna (coil 26swg close-wound on 0·5-in slug-tuned former). (d) Audio filter that replaces the 4·7μF capacitor shown in (a). (e) CW filter for 14MHz "Mark 2" version.

capacitors. On 3·5MHz in daytime it made a perfectly servicable swl receiver. Even on 7MHz, with a two-turn frame antenna, ssb was clearly resolved despite the presence of the high-power broadcast stations, although at this frequency, the use of a frame antenna affects frequency stability due to body capacitance etc. I am currently constructing a Mk 2 version for 14MHz with an rf stage to provide antenna isolation and gain control."

GI3XZM admits that at nightime with a frame antenna the sensitivity of the 3·5MHz receiver is not sufficient for resolving weak ssb, but this can be overcome by using a coil tuned input circuit with a conventional antenna when it has adequate sensitivity and receives ssb with a pleasing clarity.

Is there sporadic-F propagation?

An extremely interesting result of the availability to UK amateurs of the 50MHz allocation has been the transatlantic contacts made each year since 1985 in June/July despite the sunspot minimum. It is quite clear that these contacts have been made at times related to the summer peak of sporadic-E conditions, but over distances considerably greater than could be expected from a single reflection from the E-region of the ionosphere (about 90 to 130km above earth). One possibility might be some form of layer entrapment or chordal hop but there is little evidence for this. Some amateurs have attributed these contacts to "double-hop sporadic-E" but in view of the restricted areas of intense ionisation associated with sporadic-E the chances of working stations in various parts of the USA on the same day by such paths seems inherently unlikely, at least as an annual occurrence.

To me it seems far more likely that the explanation is to be found in the possibility (for which there is some evidence) that there can be sporadic-F sheets of intense ionisation brought about by the same mechanism as sporadic-E. The F region of the ionosphere spans heights from 130km to over 500km (F1 130 to 200km, F2 above 200km).

TT February 1985, pp112-2 noted the generally accepted explanation of how sporadic-E occurs, as described by Dr E B Dorling in a letter to *Wireless World* in April 1978, as follows: "Sporadic-E was first seen to occur in the way it does, that is as very thin intense layers of ionisation, by a British Skylark rocket flown from Woomera, Australia, in 1958. By 1966 an association between these layers and sharp reversals in wind direction at high altitude had become recognised. Wind measurements in the very rarified atmosphere up to 150km or so revealed that a surprising pattern of wind reversals with height can occur; what is more the measurements showed that the pattern often descends slowly over a period of hours, with, for example, a sharp wind shear first appearing *above 150km height* (italics added), then moving downwards to below 100km before fading. The cause of this rather unexpected wind structure appears to be the propagation of atmospheric waves horizontally over great distances.

"The sharp wind shears are at the root of the sporadic-E layers, though in rather a complicated way. The winds, tenuous though they are at such heights, act to move the ions and electrons in the ionosphere in such a way as to displace the plasma vertically. Where strong wind shears of the appropriate sense exist, the plasma is squeezed into a thin concentrated layer, being moved downwards from above, upwards from below. As the wind pattern descends, the layer descends into an ever denser atmosphere, until finally at a height of about 100km it is brought to a halt . . .

"Sporadic-E then owes its transient character to interactions between atmospheric waves, the ionospheric E layer, and magnetic and electric fields. All but the magnetic field are constantly changing, so that the right conditions for layer formation occur—well, sporadically . . . Were the sporadic-E layers to be composed simply of ionised atmospheric gases, they wouldn't persist. They are, in fact, composed of *ionised metallic atoms*, mainly magnesium, silicon and iron, probably the remains of burned-up meteorites. The descending wind shears sweep up the metallic ions and bring them down as sporadic-E layers out of the thermosphere into the lower regions where atmospheric turbulence then churns them away into oblivion. sporadic-E layers seem to be the product of Nature's vacuum cleaning!"

Sporadic-E, in being composed of metallic atoms (ions), thus differs inherently from the normal D, E, F1 and F2 ionospheric gaseous layers. At the recent URSI national colloquium, Dr L Kersley and Dr P J S Williams described some of the current work that is being carried out at the University College of Wales—Aberystwyth on sporadic-E propagation. The aims of this research are to be able to predict the strength of backscatter at the lower end of the vhf spectrum (46 and 93MHz) and further investigation of the mechanisms whereby these interesting irregularities are generated in the E region. My ears pricked up when a fleeting reference was made to the fact that some evidence has been found of *particle reflection* from patches of ionisation in the F region correlated to sporadic-E propagation. Such sporadic-F patches would account very neatly for the annual June/July 50MHz transatlantic contacts and for some of the other anomalous propagation between about 20 and 100MHz.

The useful 4–65A valve

Percy Greenwood, G2BUJ, draws attention to the Eimac 4–65A valve (European equivalent QY3–65). He finds this a useful valve for home-built high-power linears for use at hf or up to 144MHz. With 2,000V on the anode and 400V on the screen-grid he obtains a measured 300W p.e.p on all hf bands from a single valve.

The 4–65A, introduced in the mid-'fifties by Eimac, is a small radiation-cooled, radial-beam power-tetrode with a maximum anode-dissipation of 65W. Short, heavy internal leads and low inter-electrode capacitances (grid/anode 0·08pF, input 8pF, output 2·1pF) contribute, according to the data sheet, to stable, efficient operation at high frequencies. It is suitable for use at maximum ratings up to 150MHz, 15 times higher than the older 813.

The valve is an interesting example of the post-war range of power tetrodes, though later largely superseded for professional applications by the ceramic forced-air cooled devices such as the 4CX250 series. Capable of withstanding anode voltages up to 3kV in some applications, it can deliver relatively high power output at much lower anode voltages. The thoriated tungsten filament is rated at 6·0V, 3·5A, and care should be taken to ensure that the voltage measured at the heater pins really is close to 6·0V. It has five base pins (seven-pin type socket) fitting National HX–29 or Johnson 122–101 sockets (Fig 2). The quick-heating features of these thoriated tungsten filaments may otherwise not prove conducive to long-life. Table 1 shows typical characteristics.

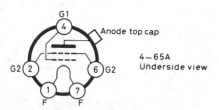

Fig 2. Base diagram of the high-power 4–65A rf power tetrode that can provide 300W p.e.p as an ssb linear, and can run at full ratings up to 150MHz

Table 1. Typical operating data for 4–65A valves

For Class C cw, fsk or fm telephony

DC anode voltage (V)	1,000	1,500	2,000	3,000
DC screen voltage (V)	250	250	250	250
DC grid voltage (V)	−80	−85	−90	−100
DC anode current (mA)	150	150	140	115
DC screen current (mA)*	40	40	40	22
DC grid current (mA)*	17	18	11	10
Drive input power (W)*	3·0	3·2	2·1	1·7
Screen dissipation (W)*	10	10	10	5·5
Anode power input (W)	120	180	240	275
Anode dissipation (W)	30	40	45	45
Output power (W)	90	140	195	230

*Approximate values

For Class AB2 ssb linear amplifiers

DC anode voltage (V)	1,500	2,000	2,500
DC screen voltage (V)	300	400	500
DC grid voltage (V)*	−55	−80	−105
Zero-sig anode current (mA)	35	25	20
Zero-sig anode current (mA)	35	25	20
Max-sig anode current (mA)	200	270	230
Max-sig screen current (mA)†	45	65	45
Max-sig peak rf grid voltage (V)	150	190	165
Max-sig dc grid current (mA)†	15	20	8
Max-sig driving power (W)†	2·3	3·8	1·3
Max-sig anode power input (W)	300	540	575
Max-sig anode dissipation (W)	105	190	225
Average anode dissipation (W)	60	65	65
Max-sig useful output (W p.e.p)	150	300	325

*Adjust to stated zero-signal anode current
†Approximate values

Owing to the intermittent nature of the speech waveform, average dissipation is much less than max-signal dissipation. However, if the amplifier is to be tested with a sine-wave signal source (or if a high degree of speech compression and peak limiting is to be used—*G3VA*), arrangements must be made to lower the duty cycle to ensure average anode dissipation does not exceed 65W.

At maximum anode-dissipation the anode operates (correctly) at a cherry red colour. As G2BUJ puts it: "The colour of the anode through the side screen makes it look good!" New, branded 4–65A valves are still available, though not particularly cheap: a current advertiser in *Electronics & Wireless World* quotes £65, though this is less than some comparable types. For anyone unfamiliar with valve characteristics and rf power amplification, a study of Table 1 will show clearly the differences between anode dissipation and the rf output on cw/fm (Class C) and p.e.p output on *unprocessed* speech on ssb (Class AB2).

Coaxial stub filters reduce rfi from 50MHz transmitters

TT (September 1985) devoted several pages to discussing some of the many reasons why the 50MHz band represents a valuable acquisition and the wide variety of propagation modes and antennas that can be used. But attention was also drawn to two potentially difficult problems. 50MHz remains in use for European television channels E-2, E-2A and East European R-1, and also in Eire, with little or no likelihood that European countries other than the UK will ever abandon vhf television (there is even talk of a new UK vhf channel though possibly not in the old Band 1 part of the spectrum). The second problem is bci and the consequent need to ensure that any 50 to 52MHz transmitters have extremely low harmonic output. The second harmonic falls entirely within the broadcast Band 2 which will eventually extend from 88 to 108MHz. The section 100 to 102MHz currently continues to be used by the public emergency services, but will later be used for a fifth national vhf/fm service. The section 102 to 104MHz is part of the segment forming the "upper local radio sub-band"; there are already a number of BBC and ILR transmitters in this band, and your next-door neighbour may be listening to one of these only a party-wall away from your 50MHz transmitter!

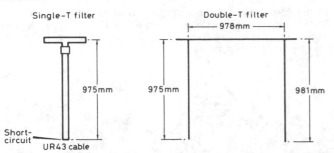

Fig 3. Single and double 100MHz quarter-wave coaxial stub filters for use with 50MHz transmitters to suppress harmonic interference to Band 2 broadcast or emergency mobile services. Dimensions suitable for cables with a velocity factor of 0·67

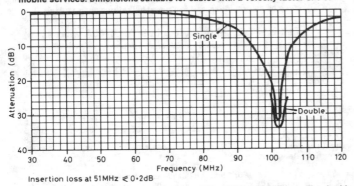

Fig 4. Measured attenuation characteristics of the 100MHz stub filters. The double filter is stagger-tuned to increase notch bandwidth rather than to increase attenuation

Paul Boyd, G4TUZ, writes: "With the likely upsurge in 50MHz activity following the extension of the band and with Class B operators already moving in, the problem of second harmonic suppression is once again with us. Some measurements I have made recently using shorted quarter-wave coaxial cable stub filters (Fig 3) may be of interest, especially as many newer amateurs seem to have difficulty in believing just how effective they can be. As may be seen from Fig 4, I find a single quarter-wave stub provides up to about 31dB rejection of the second harmonic, with a similar level achieved at the fourth and subsequent even harmonics. The stubs used UR44 cable fitted to BNC plugs and 'T' pieces. Additional rejection or a wider notch can be achieved using two stubs. These can be stagger-tuned and separated by a quarter-wavelength. The dimensions indicated are for total distance from the centre of the 'T' piece to the shorted end of the cable, and should be valid for any cable with a velocity factor of 0·67. The 'T' piece is an integral part of the stub and must always be present when the stub is used. For anyone

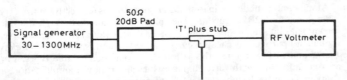

Fig 5. Measurement set-up used by G4TUZ to produce the response curves shown in Fig 9

contemplating 50MHz operation this must surely be one of the cheapest and most effective ways of preventing or reducing interference to the broadcast Band 2. The measurements were made using the set-up shown in Fig 5."

The construction, adjustment and use of single and double open and shorted coaxial cable stub filters have been discussed on several occasions in *TT*, and details appear in *ART* (currently out of print but with a new edition planned).

Pocket power

W H Jarvis, G8APX, writes: "The largest (and most expensive) nicad pack for a range of handheld transceivers allows barely 20min transmitting on high power. A pack of dry cells lasts longer but works out far more expensive. A remarkably simple and cheap solution is a new 12V, 1·1Ah, lead-acid battery sold under the brand name of 'Dryfit' and currently avalable from many retailers at around £12.

"I attach a metre of twin flex with a 'power jack' ready to plug straight into the handheld. This way the separate extra battery can easily go into my pocket during /P operation. The easiest way of keeping the Dryfit accumulator charged and ready for immediate use is to keep it wired in parallel with your car battery: Fig 6. I have a 3W 'festoon' lamp in series. You can see a glimmer while driving, confirming the Dryfit unit is charging. When starting the car the festoon lamp lights, showing that the accumulator is trying to help power the starter motor. And if you drop the flylead, so that it short-circuits to earth, the bulb comes on full brightness as a warning.

"These sealed Dryfit batteries are claimed to be maintenance free, do not leak in any position, and never need 'topping up' with distilled water."

While on the subject of handheld transceivers, and noting that there are now units providing up to about 5W rf on 430MHz to stubby "rubber-duck" antennas that tend to be held only a matter of inches from the user's eyes, a reminder seems needed about the sensitivity of the eyes to rf fields. A few years ago, the USA firm of Motorola investigated this problem using simulated tissue and came to the conclusion that on vhf a potential hazard exists when the power output rises to about 7W; 5W output on uhf, with the field concentrated by the miniature antenna, must be getting rather near to the hazard threshold. Safe enough perhaps if you recognise the need for care, but getting a little too close for comfort of mind!

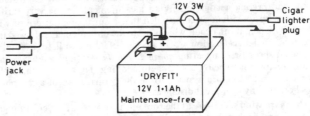

Fig 6. How G8APX keeps his sealed 12V 1·1Ah "Dryfit" lead-acid battery charged ready for use with his handheld transceiver

An alternative type of rechargeable cell to lead-acid and nickle-cadmium is emerging with the marketing of the first commercially-available, high-energy rechargeable lithium cells by Moli Energy Ltd, 3958 Myrtle Street, Burnaby, British Columbia, V5C 4GE, Canada. An article in *QST* June 1987 sings their praises (the authors are linked with Moli Energy Ltd) with a *QST* sub-heading suggesting that "*properly applied* Moli Energy's rechargeable lithium cell is superior to its nicad counterpats (for handheld transceivers)". I have stressed "properly applied" since one of the problems surrounding the application of lithium batteries (which have, for example, a much longer shelf life than nicad, more energy per unit of weight etc), both disposable and rechargeable, is the risk of explosion unless there is effective current limiting etc. Even small lithium cells used as non-volatile memory systems have been known to explode and damage equipment and, potentially, the user.

A Moli rechargeable lithium battery pack suitable for a handheld transceiver is not cheap; *QST* gives a figure of $99 for a pack.

Traveller's radio

Five years ago I wrote a two-part article for *Wireless World* in which I ascribed the beginnings of portable hf communications equipment largely to the wartime development of clandestine mains-operated transmitter-receivers compact enough to be carried, with all necessary accessories, in an attaché case or suitcase. These in turn had drawn, in most countries, on ideas tried out by radio amateurs in the 'twenties and 'thirties.

For instance, I noted that in the mid-'thirties, Ted Cook, ZS6BT but then ZT6AQ, had travelled around South Africa with a 30W hf transmitter (double-triode co 6A6 driving an LS5, later B12, power amplifier) built into a Burndept portable-radio receiver case about 18 by 18 by 8in, with an 0-v-2 receiver (ie regenerative detector and two af stages for those who have never used this once-universal short-hand) in a second, similar case. As described at the time in *The T & R Bulletin* (January 1937, p305) he contacted many amateurs over long distances from temporary locations, including his seventh-floor flat in the centre of Johannesburg. One of his main problems was to avoid causing "key clicks" to an estimated 400 broadcast receivers within a radius of 1,000ft of his makeshift antenna; a problem that later affected clandestine operations in western Europe!

A modern high-performance solidstate "CW Travelradio" capable of providing a useful 12 to 15W rf output between 14·0 and 14·1MHz has been described by Rick Littlefield, K1BQT, in *Ham Radio Magazine* (June 1987). This is far more compact and of much higher performance than ZS6BT's pioneering efforts, with the transceiver unit a compact 1·5 by 4·5 by 6in and weighing only

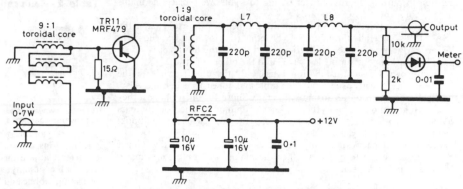

Fig 7. K1BQT's 12W output stage for his 14MHz "CW Travelradio"

1·5lb, making it possible, as K1BQT puts it, to "pack a private dxpedition in a very small bag". Unlike the usual QRP rig, this includes a high-performance superhet receiver (9MHz i.f) with crystal filter rather than direct-conversion, and has an MRF479 transistor as a broadband Class C power amplifier (Fig 7) which with 0·7W drive provides up to about 15W rf output on 14MHz, sufficient power to give good dx results with simple antennas.

K1BQT indicates that he runs this rig from a 13·8V psu capable of providing 2·5A intermittently, but does not indicate the size or weight of this unit. In practice, for transmitters of more than about 3W output, whether solidstate or valve, it is virtually always the psu or battery that constitutes the heaviest part of a portable rig, despite such improvements as toroidal mains transformers etc. To the best of my knowledge one of the lightest transmitter-receivers capable of more than 10W output, weighing only about 1·5kg complete with psu, remains the Danish wartime "Telebogen" clandestine set designed by L Duus Hansen, OZ7DU, as noted in *TT* October 1985, p786.

In an accompanying article (*HR* June 1987) K1BQT describes the 0·5λ dipole with an overall span of 21ft 4in, inductively loaded in the centre of each section with air-spaced coils of 4·85μH, that he uses with his "CW Travelradio". He provides some useful advice on achieving good performance from simple antennas at temporary sites, as follows:

(1) Look for a high and open location. Get above the rooftop if you can but keep directivity and take-off angle in mind.

(2) Keep the antenna at least 5 or 6ft from the building surface. Proximity to electrical wiring, foil insulation and structural metal can detune it. Bending elements outwards may help to decouple the ends from a metal structure.

(3) When you side-mount to a building, try to locate the antenna on the side facing the desired direction of transmission. Better to use the structure as a reflector than as a shield.

(4) If there are horizontal wires close by, vertical polarisation works better (conversely, in or near trees or vertical metal structures, use horizontal polarisation or slope the antenna downwards towards the desired direction —*G3VA*). When using vertical polarisation for a dipole make sure the bottom end is at least 6ft above ground. Also make sure the antenna is clear of people and pets. Even QRP signals can develop enough rf potential at element tips to cause painful burns and injury.

The rccb—an IEE safety warning

Back in 1981, in the course of some discussions and explanations of the role of the residual current contact breaker (rccb), then usually still known as an elcb (earth leakage circuit breaker), *TT* included a note of warning from Llyr Gruffydd, GW4CFC, that this device is not the complete answer to all mains-safety problems. He felt its value was limited partly because it offers

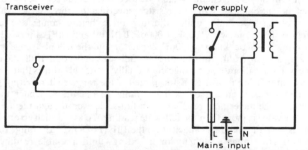

Fig 8. The mains-input arrangement that G3NKS found on his "Corsair" transceiver and which he considers hazardous.

radio amateurs no protection against shocks from the secondary side of a double-wound mains transformer, but especially because introducing an rccb into a shack can lead to a false feeling of immunity to shock. This conclusion was based on his experiences of a laboratory with many water taps and much electricity. He had found that installing rccbs, rather than adding to staff safety, induced a state of euphoric carelessness among at least some of the occupants.

Again, in *Members' Mailbag* (November 1984, p 953), H Du V Ashcroft, G4CCM, also expressed misgivings on reports that seemed to imply ample safety in the use of 30mA rccbs in radio shacks and at field day sites. G4CCM's letter was criticised on a number of grounds by several correspondents, so I suspect that he felt some satisfaction in finding in *IEE News* (June 1987, p8) an item emphasising that while the additional protection of an rccb is desirable for all domestic installations, proper care in the use of electricity is the only true safeguard. The writer noted concern over the use by the trade of various names for these devices such as "safety trip" and "safety switch", then adding:

"While fully recognising the important part played by these devices in contributing to electrical safety, those who hold a balanced view are increasingly concerned at some claims which appear to suggest that these devices provide complete safety from electric shock. No device can do this—the aim is always that the shock experienced will not lead to serious physiological effects. The danger arising from such claims is that people may believe that, by using such devices, they can 'take chances'—that there is no need to be concerned about worn or damaged flexible cords and that they can put off to another day the replacement of suspect plugs or other equipment."

Mains safety and imported transceivers

Derek Thom, G3NKS, has uncovered two mains-input hazards in his Ten-Tec "Corsair", or, more specifically, in the Model 260 power supply unit. First, the mains input cable enters the rear of the cabinet and "live" (phase, line L) wire is taken straight to the fuse holder mounted adjacent to the entry point. In his unit the wire is connected to the cap end of the fuse holder; hence, when the cap is removed along with the captive fuse, the live cap contact ring is exposed and could easily be touched accidentally.

Second, the "live" (L) wire is routed from the fuse-holder (tip or end connection) to the Corsair transceiver cabinet via connectors and a multiway cable where it connects to the "power on/off" switch mounted on the front panel (part of the rf gain control). The L wire returns from this switch to the psu via the same multiway cable, where it connects to the "power on/off" switch mounted on the psu: see Fig 8. Thus switching "off" at the psu does *not* remove the mains supply routed to and from the transceiver cabinet. In his view one might reasonably expect that after switching off at the psu, all voltages would be removed from the transceiver cabinet. Clearly this does not happen, and an unwary operator could easily come into contact with mains voltages when working on the transceiver with the covers removed (especially as there are unprotected, ie unsleeved/unshrouded, terminals at mains potential within the transceiver cabinet).

He adds: "I have overcome both hazards by changing over the connections to the fuse holder, so that the incoming live conductor goes to the tip or end connection, and by linking out of the circuit the live conductors to/from the transceiver cabinet (this is no loss because the 'power on/off' switch on the transceiver cabinet seems to me to be redundant) "

Since the above notes were written, Rowley Shears, G8KW, managing director of KW Ten Tec Ltd, has written to G3NKS as follows:

"Your Corsair Mk1 must have been quite an early one. We became aware of the mains wiring arrangements, and this has been rectified in a similar way to the action you have taken. We have been receiving Corsairs from Ten-Tec with the parts which are exposed to stray fingers covered with protective sleeves. In the psus which are supplied from Ten-Tec USA stock, we have to change the wiring from 115V to 230/240V so we decided to go one further: in addition to putting the fuse holder wiring to rights, we replace the mains cable to conform to EEC standards.

"When we first made enquiries about this problem, we were told that in the USA, 115V is generally thought not to be lethal (this is why it was chosen in the very early days of domestic electricity) and even to this day no provision is made for marking one supply leg "live" and the other "neutral".

"In my own Corsair installation I use only the on/off switch in the transceiver because my psu is under the table and not easily accessible. Also, the 'field' from the psu transformers affect my Shure 444 microphone if they are close together on the table. It is, we know, common practice for amateurs to have the psu under the table to keep the top clear for log-book, microphone, morse key etc."

It seems worth checking on any imported equipment (ie virtually 100 per cent of transceivers) to check whether the mains wiring etc conforms to British and European standards.

Tune-up protection

With solid-state power amplifiers, it is well-recognised that most rf power devices will not sustain, even temporarily, a serious mismatch or no-load conditions at anywhere near full ratings. Most rigs therefore incorporate protection circuits which automatically reduce power output when the output load has a vswr of more than about 2:1. Even so, many amateurs retain, with some reason, a fear of connecting up long-wire and voltage-fed antennas that require the correct adjustment of an antenna matching unit in order to avoid an extreme mismatch; nor is the adjustment of an atu made easier by the action of the transmitter protection circuit.

Fred Piesse, VK3BYW ("A tune-up protection device", *Amateur Radio* (VK) May 1987, pp6–7) became convinced of the need for tune-up protection some years ago when he lost the final rf transistors of his early-model IC701 transceiver while attempting to match a random length of antenna wire at a camping site. Later he replaced this model with an IC751 but his fear of tune-up damage returned when he read in the instruction book: "As the output is quite high, avoid connecting the antenna connector to open lines and do not transmit under mismatched conditions. Otherwise the final stage could be overloaded and cause a malfunction of the unit" and "The final transistors used in the IC-751 are of good design and are protected to a reasonable extent by circuits incorporated in the set . . . When in doubt about antenna systems, use the lowest power settings to achieve meaningful readings. Use a good tuner or transmatch when necessary. Always use caution and exercise judgement when testing rf power generators."

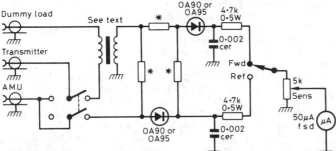

Fig 9. VK3BYWs tune-up protection unit.

This need to exercise caution is not specific to the IC-751 and sums up the present state-of-the-art: reliable operation of solidstate devices *is* to be expected when you use antennas that present a reasonable match, but does not encourage those who like to experiment with a variety of antennas. To set his fears at rest, VK3BYW has developed a simple but ingenious unit. This places a matched dummy load across the output of his transmitter during tune-up but at the same time provides a small amount of rf to actuate a QRP-type swr bridge to determine when his antenna is reasonably well matched. Once this has been achieved output power is cut temporarily, the dummy load and swr bridge are switched out of circuit and any final adjustments made. If for any reason the antenna cannot be matched quickly, damage to the transmitter will not occur with it operating into a matched dummy load. Nor will the in-built transmitter protection circuits make it difficult to adjust the antenna matching unit. Other band users will be thankful for the absence of strong signals during tune-up. It is also usable with valve transmitters as the atu can be adjusted independently of the transmitter controls.

The broadband rf transformer is wound on a half-inch (12mm) diameter toroid (Amidon T50-6) with primary two turns of 20swg enamel-covered wire, secondary ten turns of 24swg. This is mounted on a small piece of matrix board through which the pigtails can be threaded and coated with epoxy resin to keep the windings in place. Keep rf leads short.

198

Table 2—Calibration of tune-up protection unit with 50μA fsd meter

Scale reading	VSWR value	Scale reading	VSWR value
0	1·0	12·96	1·7
2·38	1·1	14·28	1·8
4·55	1·2	15·5	1·9
6·52	1·3	16·67	2·0
8·33	1·4	21·4	2·5
10·0	1·5	25	3·0
11·54	1·6		

Note: For swr values exceeding three use formula: vswr = (50 + X)/(50 − X) where X is the reverse scale reading.

Accuracy of the swr meter depends on a good match of the 50Ω resistors. VK3BYW used two 100Ω resistors in parallel selected with the aid of a good ohmeter. Calibration of the meter is not linear see Table 2. VK3BYW used a detachable dummy load to save carrying his heavy station unit when operating mobile and houses his unit in a home-made box measuring 160 by 90 by 75 mm (wdh) finished in Auto-Spray touch-up paint. He considers it easy build, low in cost and dispells any fear of damage to his equipment. Where the swr bridge is used only for initial tune-up, accuracy of calibration is probably unimportant.

More on the simple capacitance meter

The July *TT* (page 498) showed a simple capacitance meter culled from an item by Gabriel Rivat, F6DQM, in *Radio-REF*. Unfortunately Fig 5 omitted the essential connections to the range-switch rotors and gave only a brief description of the background to this attractive, low-cost device. Thanks to Dave Plumridge, G3KMG, who sent me a copy of the earlier article by Courtney Hall, WA5SNZ; in *Ham Radio* November 1978 on which F6DQM based his design this in turn led me back to WA5SNZ's original version (*Ham Radio* April 1975) which used a not readily available programmable unijunction transistor plus transistor inverter-amplifier as the trigger source. There was nothing particularly critical about this form of trigger source and WA5SNZ in 1978 simply substituted the 555 device.

In Fig 5 (*TT* July p498) the top rotor of the range switch should be connected to the higher of the two test terminals (ie the one connected to pins 6, 7 of IC2). The lower rotor (switching the zero adjustment resistors) goes to the junction of the 380Ω resistor and the 1mA meter.

The 1975 version using a type AT6028 "put" as the trigger source used only a single, panel-mounted zero adjustment control which required setting each time the range switch was set to a different range *before* the capacitor to be measured was connected to the test terminals. The need for the zero adjustment (particularly for lower capacitance ranges) arises from the input capacitance of pins 6 and 7 of the 555 and stray capacitance amounting to about 25pF. This results in an output pulse even when there is no capacitor connected to the test terminals. Without a zero adjustment to null out the voltage from this pulse, the meter would read, on a 100pF range, about 25 per cent of full scale even with no capacitor connected.

The basis of this type of unit is that the average dc value of a pulse waveform has a direct linear relationship to the duty cycle (ratio of off-time to pulse-time) of the waveform. The system functions roughly as follows:

The trigger source is simply a free-running pulse generator which has a constant frequency, about 500Hz, and produces a narrow negative output pulse. Each time a trigger pulse occurs, the one-shot multivibrator (IC2) initiates an output pulse whose width is determined by the capacitor-under-test. The larger the value of the capacitor, the wider the pulse. Since a dc meter reads the average value of the pulse waveform, the meter may be calibrated directly to read capacitance. Care must be taken, however, that the pulse width does not exceed the time between trigger pulses and the frequency of the trigger source must be high enough to prevent jitter of the meter needle. The pulses must be of constant-voltage and this is achieved by using a regulated psu (12V regulated to 5V) delivering up to 60mA. Because of the relatively high power consumption and the need for constant-voltage pulses, a battery supply is not advisable. If field operation is needed use alkaline batteries. In the 1978 version, WA5SNZ used three 500Ω zero-adjustment pre-set potentiometers with one resistor covering the three larger value ranges of his five-range unit, adjusting these before connecting any capacitors (his ranges were 100pF, 1,000pF, 0·01, 0·1 and 1μF) calibrated by connecting a single known 100pF capacitor on the 100pF range and adjusting the gain (calibration) control for full-scale deflection. It should not be necessary to calibrate each range individually. WA5SNZ warns that when the capacitor being measured is too large for the range-switch setting the circuit may be driven out of its linear range of operation. Under these conditions, the meter may read less than full-scale even though the actual capacitor value is more than the full-scale reading. To avoid such erroneous readings, test an unknown capacitor on the 1μF (F6DQM 3μF) range first, then move the range switch to lower settings until a usable reading is obtained. Keep the original calibration capacitor handy for occasional calibration checks. □

Technical Topics

Pat Hawker, G3VA

THE JUNE *TT* drew attention to the need for professional engineers to receive more training in electromagnetic compatibility (emc) as part of the general electronic and electrical engineering courses in higher education. David Lauder, G1OSC, senior lecturer and Peter Jackson, head of electronics group, of Hatfield Polytechnic School of Engineering report that: "At the Hatfield Polytechnic we have already identified the need for emc teaching and have included an introduction to emc as part of the revised syllabus for the BEng/BEng (Hons) degree courses in Electrical and Electronic Engineering which is currently being submitted for re-validation. The introduction to emc forms part of a proposed 'advanced digital techniques' course to be taken by all electrical and electronic engineering degree students in their third year. We also run courses for graduate engineers in industry. Our two week 'digital systems design' course includes an introduction to emc and we are planning a new one week course on emc and reliability, with approximately 50 per cent devoted to emc."

Ron Taylor, G3AVQ points out that the concept of the "super-dc-gainer" (solid-state superhet without i.f stages by using a mixer in front of a fixed-tuned direct-conversion receiver), as described by G0FMT in the August *TT*, is not as new as I suggested. He points out that a form of this technique is used in the Century 21 and Century 22 transceivers where it is curiously described as a "double direct conversion" technique. My memory has also been jogged into recalling that *TT,* December 1977 included the front-end of a "3·5MHz dx receiver" republished from an article by E J R Hubach, PA0FIN/OH1ZAA using exactly this principle (*Electron* No 6, 1977). I should have remembered this since I also included this design, with its almost ideal form of gain-distribution, in a paper: "Keep it simple: direct-conversion receivers" presented at an IERE "Conference on Radio Receivers and Associated Systems" (*IERE Conference Proceedings No 40,* 1978) together with the even earlier idea of using a crystal-controlled converter in front of a tunable dc receiver.

As G3AVQ points out there is very little new under the sun and you can't keep good ideas from re-emerging. He notes from reviews of the Century 22 (*SWM,* February 1986, *Ham Radio Today,* July 1986) that G0FMT's remarks on the advantages of this intermediate technology over conventional superhets (or d-c receivers) are well justified. G3AVQ adds: "I too have tried a basic d-c receiver and like G0FMT find the performance does not satisfy me, being, in my view, inferior to a *good* trf (regenerative detector) receiver with really smooth regeneration". In this connection, Harvey Collett, G3KI recalls a trf design by the late Jerry Walker, G5JU: "A modern selective receiver featuring Mullard Red E valves" (EF8EF6/EL3) in the *T&R Bulletin* (March, April, May 1939) with built-in monitor/frequency meter which he says was a "truly magnificent straight receiver for its day."

Batteries, portable and emergency power

Until the emergence of the handheld transceiver, the vast majority of amateur radio operation depended upon mains-electricity or 12V lead-acid car batteries. It was often only for the field-day operations that "emergency" and battery systems came into their own, unless one goes all the way back to the two- or three-valve straight receivers of the 'thirties for which the combination of a 90V or 120V ht dry battery and a rechargeable 2V lead-acid "accumulator" provided a silent background refreshingly free from intrusive mains-hum.

Operation of a modern high-performance solidstate receiver from disposable batteries is not a particularly cost-effective operation, and even with rechargeables the interval between charges, particularly where frequency-synthesisers are used, tends to be short. Listening recently to one of the reviews of broadcast hf receivers that are a feature of the weekly BBC World Service "Waveguide" programme, I was shaken to learn that, for the model under discussion, a standard set of carbon-zinc batteries would provide only about 2h continuous listening, the significantly more expensive alkaline-manganese batteries rather longer. For such receivers, either a mains power unit or a rechargeable battery is virtually essential.

As noted in the October *TT* by G8APX, there are some useful sealed (maintenance-free) lead-acid 12V 1·2Ah units selling for around £12 as a cost-effective alternative to nicads. Where low-weight with a very high energy content are needed, there are now the Moli rechargeable lithium battery packs being marketed in Canada but at the off-putting price of $99 a pack.

Other developments, both disposables and rechargeables, are available or in the pipeline. In the USA, Duracell began marketing high-power consumer lithium batteries in 1985, directed primarily at the flash-camera market ("High power consumer replaceable lithium manganese dioxide batteries" by H Taylor *IEEE Transactions on Consumer Electronics,* August 1986, pp694–9). These 6V, 1·30Ah batteries (Fig 6) are claimed to be suitable for loads up to 200mA, have a shelf life of five years and incorporate no less than three safety mechanisms to overcome the danger of explosion that has delayed the development of lithium batteries for general use (see the letter by G4GNQ, *Rad Com* September 1987). A safety mechanism in the top of the cell incorporates a positive temperature coefficient device (ptc) that presents a very low resistance at room temperatures but switches to very high resistance at about 95°C. An external short-circuit which can result in currents of the order of 10A will quickly raise the temperature of the cell to the ptc switching temperature and limits the current. On removing the short-circuit, the ptc reverts to its low-resistance state and the battery continues working. Should the cell temperature be raised by external heat rather than current discharge, there is a vent mechanism to prevent pressure build up. As a third safety precaution, the separator is heat sensitive and effectively closes its pores to prevent the internal flow of ions between anode and cathode should both the other mechanisms fail.

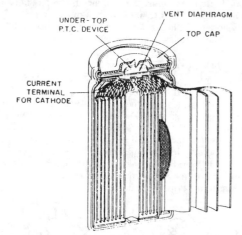

Fig 6. Schematic of a high-power lithium manganese dioxide (Li/MnO$_2$) cell developed by Duracell for consumer applications showing safety arrangements to minimise risk of explosion

A novel form of "wraparound" plastic polymer rechargeable lithium battery is being developed by Varta in conjunction with BASF in West Germany (*Electronics* 9 July 1987, p41). This takes the form of a thin postcard-sized package (4mm thick) when placed flat but since they are as flexible as cardboard they can be wrapped around components or bent to fit the shape of the equipment enclosure. The Varta-BASF cell uses polpyrole for the positive electrode and lithium for the cathode; output is nominally 3·6V dropping during discharge under load to about 2V with an energy density matching 1·2V nicad cells. It is claimed that at the present state of development the polymer cell can go through about 500 charge/discharge cycles, but the companies are aiming to double the energy density and raise the recharging cycles to about 1,000 before marketing them. Polymer cells were originally proposed in 1977 by Professor Alan MacDiarmid (University of Pennsylvania) and Hitachi and Toyota are also working on them.

The search for batteries that could power electric vehicles or provide emergency lighting is also continuing. The latest entrant appears to be aluminium-air batteries (*New Scientist* 23 July 1987). The US firm Alupower is marketing a dry aluminium-air battery for emergency lighting. The battery is stored in its dry state and actuated by adding salt water. An Al-air battery size 5 by 5 by 10cm is stated to be capable of supplying 1A at 2·2V for 24h, a larger version for 240h. A problem with either zinc-air or aluminium-air batteries is that once activated they discharge continuously (although slowly) when no load is being drawn.

Wendell Tulencik, K8OIP, in "A few thoughts on emergency power" (*QST* May 1987, pp30–2) is concerned with generating enough power to meet virtually any domestic requirement in the event of, for example, winter storm-damage that could result in loss of mains-power for several days. Fortunately this is rare in the UK although it can happen, and my own emergency fall-back system (box of matches and candle) does occasionally get called into use, but then I do not have to worry about any food stocks in a deep freezer. *This was before 16 October!*

K8OIP is better equipped. He has a 5kW alternator with fan-cooled 12hp engine in an acoustically-treated shed, and advises those who suffer frequent power outages to consider 10kW alternators driven by two-or three-cylinder diesels with automatic starting from a 12V battery. Engine noise is a major problem with generators and alternators, whether the installation is 100W with a two-stroke petrol engine or 10kW and a diesel. Television OB support vehicles often have trailer-mounted diesel-alternators that show that it is possible, but not easy, to achieve virtually silent running. K8OIP also stresses the need to provide safe storage of fuel, warns of dangers of fumes and engine heat, and points out that the exhaust fumes of petrol, diesel, natural gas or propane engineers are all lethal and must be properly vented out of any enclosure without relying on natural ventilation.

His 10 commandments for operating such an emergency or field-day installation are:

(1) Use only the fuel recommended by the manufacturer.

(2) Pour fuel through a large-mouth funnel with a fine screen to filter out dirt and other contaminants.

(3) Keep waste cloth or paper towelling handy for blotting spills. Store properly in a covered metal waste bin.

(4) Keep a supply of lubricating oil handy.

(5) Have some 50 or 100ft extension cords available.

(6) Keep at least one CO_2 or dry-powder fire extinguisher ready for instant use when handling fuel.

(7) A torch with good batteries is a must. Two torches are better than one!

(8) Check fluid levels and start the alternator at least once a week.

(9) If you have trees close to the house, keep a small chain-saw handy.

(10) Use a small trickle charge to keep the (starting) battery charged.

12V equipment on 24V supplies

Heavy-duty vehicles etc often have 24V electrical systems. Most 12V transceivers draw far more current on transmit than receive and would be damaged if any attempt were made to use them on a 24V supply by using a conventional voltage-dropping resistor. J Dehoog in *Electronics Australia* (May 1987, p50) points out that the answer is to utilise the constant voltage drop of about 0·7V across the junction of a silicon power rectifier. If nine bridge rectifiers, bolted to a suitable heat-sink, are connected in series (Fig 5) the output will be 12 to 13V largely independent of the load being drawn. Each bridge should be derated to about 75 per cent of its ac current rating. The ac input connections to the bridges are not used.

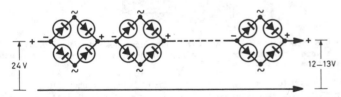

Fig 5. Use of nine silicon bridge rectifiers in series and mounted on heat sink to permit a 12V transceiver to be used from a 24V supply

Watch radiation risks?

For several years there has been a seemingly interminable controversy about whether there are any significant hazards facing those who sit in front of visual display units (vdus) for many hours a day. Much of the argument has centred around the tiny amount of ionised radiation (X-rays) that can come from high-voltage cathode-ray tubes etc, although repeated measurements have shown this to be extremely small. My own theory, for what it is worth, is that a far more likely cause of stress, migraine headaches, nausea etc stems from the visible flicker of 50Hz and even 60Hz vdus and television sets. A small percentage of the population is now known to be particularly sensitive to flicker (photo-sensitivity), though the effects are much reduced in the case of television viewers by the fact that the optimum viewing distance is of the order of 5 to 6 times the screen height. The screens of picture tubes are relatively dim compared with sunlight or disco lighting (driving along tree-lined roads can result in very pronounced flicker at a rate of a few hertz). The vdu operator, however, does sit close to a high-contrast screen.

Photo-sensitivity flicker is known to act as a trigger for about five per cent of those who suffer from epilepsy and is thought also to trigger some migraine headache attacks. The US television field rate of 60Hz results in much less large-area flicker and interlace-twitter than the European 50Hz field rate and it does appear that this results in fewer reports of television-induced epileptic attacks.

My reason for bringing this up in *TT* is that some medical researchers in the USA and the UK are reported (*New Scientist* July 23 1987) to believe that some individuals suffer "allergies" triggered by extremely weak electromagnetic fields (allergies are one of the most controversial subjects in medical research). The danger is that if this suggestion were to gain acceptance either by the medical profession or by the public it would clearly have repercussions on the operation of radio transmitters in residential areas. Apparently it is claimed that specific frequencies (within the range 1Hz to 2GHz) can induce nausea, fatigue, hyperactivity and headaches in some individuals—symptoms that sound suspiciously like those associated with photo-sensitivity. It is even claimed that some individuals are affected by the radiation from digital watches. I find it entirely possible to accept that flicker, detected by our eyes, can have medical effects, but it hardly seems credible that the rfi from a digital watch on the wrist could induce an allergy.

Antennas—theory or practice?

There is an old joke about the newly-licensed amateur who complained that he had standing waves on his antenna. But before joining in the laughter at his expense, one should not forget that there is an important class of antennas which does not (or should not) have any standing-waves on their radiating element—the so-called travelling-wave or transmission-line antennas, including the terminated long-wire, vee-beams and rhombics.

In *HF communications—a systems approach*, Dr Nicholas Maslin provides a grouping of antennas into three main classes to which I have attempted to add some examples from amateur practice:

(1) Self-resonant antennas. In this class fall all types that are based on the half-wave dipole or quarter-wave monopole. While basically single-band systems, there is also a class of multi-band antennas arranged to resonate at a number of frequencies, such as the G5RV, the W3DZZ trap-dipole, multi-wire dipoles etc.

(2) Resonated antennas. These comprise the antennas that use an antenna tuning or matching unit to transform widely varying input impedances to a specific value such as 50Ω, and can be used over a number of bands provided that the atu is adjusted correctly at the different frequencies; examples include Marconi antennas, centre-fed doublets, whip antennas, random-length wires etc.

(3) Broadband antennas. These include antennas designed to present an impedance which remains near-constant over a wide band of frequencies, and are often of the travelling-wave type. Examples include fat dipoles (caged, fan and bow-tie), Beverage and terminated long-wires, rhombics, log-periodics and some Yagi and monopole antennas using special techniques such as discones etc.

The amateur approach to antennas has always tended to be largely pragmatic, often drawing on professional designs but then making modifications and changes until satisfied with the performance by using a gdo, noise bridge etc to make final adjustments rather than attempting to analyse the design mathematically. There is a lot to be said for amateur pragmatism which avoids the complex mathematical procedures that arise from the need to take into account the many variations in siting, element/wire diameter in terms of length/diameter ratios, earth conductivity, effect of nearby objects.

But there is the danger that myths can be created by the absence of objective measurements. It is usually enormously difficult for an amateur to measure, except in the crudest terms, the efficiency or the precise radiation pattern (particularly the vertical radiation pattern) of his or her antenna. Put up a new hf antenna during a spell of good propagation conditions and even the most inefficient "piece of wet string" will span the world. Again, the logarithmic nature of the decibel makes it largely pointless to strive for small increases in efficiency; remember that a terminated rhombic antenna, hailed in the August *TT* as the "queen of antennas" has a maximum "efficiency" of around 50 per cent, compared with the near 100 per cent of a good dipole, with almost half of the transmitter power dissipated in the 800Ω terminating resistor. In the case of the rhombic this matters not at all because that power, had it not been "wasted" in the resistor would have been radiated in the opposite direction to the target area. For sky-wave contacts, it is usually only the tiny fraction of the total power that is radiated at the appropriate vertical elevation in the right direction that travels to the distant station.

In practice some antennas of extremely low efficiency have to be tolerated. Dr Maslin points out that with some of the electrically-small hf antennas used on aircraft, the radiation efficiency at 2MHz can approach − 50dB; that is to say, only 10mW radiated from an antenna fed from a 100W output transmitter.

The author of the ICAP87 paper on rhombics, featured in the August *TT*, A G P Boswell of the Marconi Research Centre, is, in *alter ego*, G3NOQ. He writes: "I was pleased to see the *TT* references to my ICAP paper and

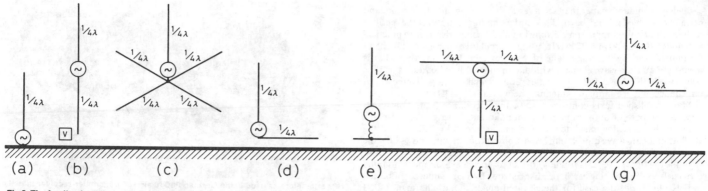

Fig 3. The family of verticals. (a) Standard monopole (unipole) antenna fed against earth. Any significant resistance in the earth connection will dissipate a substantial amount of the transmitter power so that good earthing systems (stakes, radials, mats etc) are most important. (b) The λ/2 vertical dipole requires no direct earth connection but has both high and low angle lobes of radiation. As for all vertical antennas the earth conductivity is important because of the large induced currents. Without very extensive earth mats only limited improvement is likely from any buried radials etc. The antenna can be voltage-fed at V with the current feed-point short-circuited. (c) Conventional four radial ground plane (radials usually slope downwards to facilitate impedance matching). The artificial earth formed by the four radials does not prevent large currents being induced in the real earth. (d) The "bent" dipole (ie single-radial ground plane) results in mixed polarisation and is unlikely to provide true omnidirectional horizontal radiation pattern. Nevertheless it can form an effective general purpose antenna, particularly if the earth conductivity is good. (e) G6XN's inductively loaded counterpoise form of monopole/dipole (March 1981). In practice the "coil" can be in the form of distributed inductance. (f) G3VA's 1970 "inverted ground plane" or "λ/4 T" raises the current maximum in cluttered sites. It can be voltage-fed at V if the current feed-point is short circuited. (g) The "original" two radial ground plane as developed by Dr George Brown of RCA (additional radials added later to meet customers' wishes!)

interested in your suggestions for using these antennas for the low-vhf amateur bands. This had not occured to me, but I would expect them to be equally good at frequencies above 30MHz. At really high frequencies they might benefit from an earth mat to reduce the effects of resistive losses in the ground under the antenna, but I have not done any work to determine at what frequency this effect becomes significant.

"The gain figures I quoted are related to an isotropic radiator and the gain shown in Fig 8 (free space) should be reduced by 2dB to give values relative to a dipole (dBd).

"The usual resistive termination at the unfed end of a rhombic can be replaced by a short-circuit. This does not affect the forward radiation but adds an equal lobe in the reverse direction, although the impedance match might suffer a bit. Another common technique is to run a feeder to both ends of the antenna so that either end can be fed, the other being resistively terminated."

The groundplane dissected

Professional engineers have always been far more concerned than amateurs in detailed analyses of the electrical characteristics of antennas. Computer software based, for example, on the "Method of Moments" has opened new possibilities and is encouraging antenna specialists to take a new look at some long-established designs. One antenna that has come under new scrutiny is the humble groundplane.

In a series of *TT* items in 1981 and 1983 an attempt was made to sort out some of the factors affecting the performance of the popular elevated "groundplane" with wire radials and the vertical quarter-wave monopole, with the real earth often assisted by buried radials forming the groundplane (Fig 3). *TT* also told the story (July 1981, page 626) of how Dr George Brown of RCA first used an elevated groundplane antenna with just two wire radials for American police radio operating between about 30 to 45MHz in the 'thirties. It was only when customers refused to believe that an antenna having two quarter-wave radials looking like a half-wave horizontal dipole could provide an omnidirectional radiation pattern that he simply added two more radials on the classic principle that the customer is always right. Later, for hf, amateurs found they could obtain a better match to a coaxial feeder by drooping the radials downwards, with the added convenience that these could be extended beyond the insulators to form additional guy wires.

While there is no doubt in my mind that the practical development of the elevated ground-plane antenna in the form we know it was one of the many fundamental contributions to antenna development made by Dr George Brown, and that it was from the RCA work that it reached radio amateurs, Alois Krische, DJØTR/OE8AK (letter in *Ham Radio*, June 1987, page 6) has traced an earlier description of this antenna in a series of patents taken out by Dr Maurice Ponté of CSF (French patent No 764,473 of 1933, US patent No 2,026,652 applied for in 1933, UK patent No 414,296 applied for in 1934) covering all the significant features such as elevated feedpoint, coaxial feeder and radials. Alois Krische points out that this does not diminish the role of Dr George Brown as a great American inventor and antenna specialist.

A check of the Patent Office summary of 414,296 confirms that part of a patent for "Aerials: directive wireless signalling" indisputably includes the outline of a groundplane antenna and the note: "To reduce losses in the

feedline to a short-wave aerial mounted at a considerable height above the ground, a conductor which may be shaped as a disc or square, or as a series of radiating wires, is mounted at the foot of the aerial and connected to one of the feedlines". A diagram shows a current distribution with both element and groundplane a quarter-wavelength. And if you are wondering how an "omni-directional" gpa could form part of a directive system, the answer is that a series of vertical reflectors were mounted at the extremity of part of the solid ground-plane which was rotatable!

Melvin M Weiner of The Mitre Corporation (an American research organisation that specialises in R&D for the US Services) in "Monopole element at the center of a circular groundplane whose radius is small or comparable to a wavelength" (*IEEE Trans on Ant & Prop* May 1987, pp488 to 495) takes an in-depth look at elevated monopole antennas above circular thin-copper groundplanes. To quote the abstract: "The input impedance and directive gain of a monopole element at the centre of a circular groundplane in free space are summarised for arbitrary element length and element radius with groundplane radii of zero to more than two wavelengths. Numerical results are obtained by utilising various models and are compared with measurements. The models include a groundplane of zero extent, the integral equation method, method of moments, combined with the geometric theory of diffraction (gtd)."

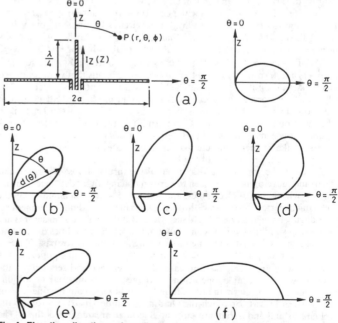

Fig 4. Elevation directive gain patterns, for any azimuthal direction, of a thin quarterwave element mounted on a ground plane of radius a. The patterns are polar graphs on the same linear scale. (a) $2\pi a = \emptyset$ ie wire radial(s) in free space. (b) $2\pi a/\lambda = 3$, (c) $2\pi a/\lambda = 4$, (d) $2\pi a/h = 5$, (e) $2\pi a/\lambda = \sqrt{(42)}$, (f) $2\pi a/\lambda = $ infinity (ie monopole over perfect "ground" such as sea water)

Such a formidable paper may seem far removed from amateur radio, and certainly much of it is far beyond my understanding, but it has the merit of including not only computer modelling but direct comparisons with practical antennas between 30 and 254MHz, using a circular copper ground plane of 4ft radius. And by a groundplane of "zero-extent" I assume that what is meant is a quarter-wave element with one or more thin-wire radials. It thus helps to settle those 1981–3 debates about such matters as the input impedance of a groundplane antenna (theoretically 19·43Ω).

Many published texts continue to give the impedance (radiation resistance) at the base of both grounded monopoles and elevated ground-plane antennas having a few insulated wire radials as about 35–36Ω (half of the 70–73Ω of a half-wave dipole, half-wave above ground), and shows how the diameter of a solid ground plane affects the vertical radiation pattern: Fig 4.

While the figure of 35Ω is roughly correct for the ideal monopole mounted on a perfectly conducting earth, or earth assisted by a large number of buried radials, this is **not** the case for the elevated gpa, as Dud Charman, G6CJ pointed out in *TT*, many years ago. He reported having measured the radiation resistance of an elevated resistance as "less than 20Ω" (the figure given in *Radio Communication Handbook*). To provide a good match to 50Ω coaxial cable it is necessary to use either a folded radiating element (*TT*, July 1987) or to slope the radials downwards by about 40°. G6CJ gave the simple formula $R = 18 (1 + \sin \theta)^2$ as a useful guide. If θ is 90° the antenna becomes a vertical half-wave dipole, with an R of 72Ω; the solution for 50Ω gives θ as 42°.

Variometers and German military equipments

The discussion on variometers, launched by Kurt Grey, VE2UG with his recollection of well-constructed German marine hf variometers (*TT* June and see also *TT* September) has brought in a most interesting letter from Dr Ing Hans L Rath, DL6KG. As a member of the German Air Force Signal Corps during the second world war he recalls that Lorenz variometers were used in the standard German aircraft equipment (FuG10). The FuG10 was originally designed in 1937 by Lorenz, which incidentally was a firm within the American ITT group of international companies including STC, although subsequently also manufactured by a number of other companies, including some in occupied countries. The hf variometers used had powder-iron cores and were a popular acquisition by post-war German amateurs who often removed the iron cores for use on the higher frequency bands.

DL6KG still has two of these variometers in his junk box and has provided photographs showing their construction. He has also measured the range of inductance provided by these variometers: without core 4 to 17µH; with core 6 to 38µH, clearly a most useful component for such applications as hf pi-network tank circuits or antenna matching units.

There is in fact much that can still be learned in the art of mechanical design from those remarkable German military equipments, and I have been re-reading the articles by Dick Rollema, PA0SE "German World War 2 Communications Receivers—technical perfection from a nearby past" (Part 1, *CQ* August 1980) and "German Army Wireless Equipment" by W Farrar, G3ESP. (*The Royal Signals Quarterly Journal*, April 1947, later reprinted in *Mercury*, the journal of the Royal Signals Amateur Radio Society).

PA0SE described the FuG10 as: "consisting of beautifully-made separate receivers and transmitters for different frequency bands that were combined in a rack . . . the antenna was matched by a remote-controlled tuner . . . The superiority of Lorenz was especially evident in the mechanical engineering of their equipment. In the following years the dividing line between Telefunken (the traditional manufacturer of German military radios) became less clear as equipment was manufactured under mutual licensing contracts. Also other big firms like Siemens and companies in countries occupied by Germany took part in the production of the FuG10."

It needs to be appreciated that much of the thrust of post-war radio and electronics development has been towards replacing high-cost "mechanical" systems with low-cost electronics, and that if we were to demand today the mechanical perfection of some 'thirties designs in factory-built equipment we would truly have to pay Rolls-Royce prices. But the home constructor is not necessarily so inhibited if he can draw upon workshop facilities or can find and refurbish salvaged components surviving from the nearby past. There is also much to be learnt from the way in which the German equipment was designed with great emphasis on ease of maintenance and servicing in the field as well as reliable operation in rugged environmental conditions (although even the German radios found it hard to keep out the fine sand of the Western Desert for which they had not been designed). Visitors to the Kelham Island industrial museum at Sheffield are reminded that "The measure of the skill of any craftsman is ability in the use of the simplest of tools to create perfection."

An outstanding feature of most German military equipment was the use of a special lightweight alloy "Elektron" metal (about 90 per cent magnesium, 8

HF variometers as used in the German FuG10 aircraft transmitter-receiver initially designed and built by Lorenz from 1937. Normally these units had powder iron cores as shown in the unit on the left. When the core was removed for post-war amateur equipment as in the unit on the right it reduced the maximum inductance from 38 to 17µH. Mechanical construction made such units suitable for high-stability variable frequency oscillators. (*Photograph courtesy DL6KG*)

per cent aluminium, 2 per cent other metals). The main frameworks used thick, intricate castings, screens and cover plates cut and pressed from sheet Elektron, with the whole assembly bolted together. The result was a modular form of equipment, appreciably more rigid than the British pressed steel chassis, although, because of the thicker sections, no lighter in weight.

Multi-band receivers had well-constructed turrets from which the tuning units could be easily removed and were operated from a handle on the panel through a train of gears and sometimes levers. These were very positive in action, often with the fixed contacts lifted before the turret was rotated to avoid rubbing contacts that would have worn off the contact material. The tuning drives had precision gearing with spring-loaded split gears to reduce backlash. Tuning scales were large and clearly calibrated with up to 270° rotation and with accurate pre-settable mechanisms which had a setting accuracy of the order of 1 in 10⁴. Virtually all transmitters were vfo rather than crystal controlled but the lavish use of temperature-compensated capacitors, stable inductors and extreme mechanical rigidity provided excellent frequency stability and ease of netting. Many of the transmitter coils had silver turns burned into ceramic formers, a technique that could reduce the temperature coefficient by a factor of 200 compared with conventional coils. Receiver controls were often arranged so that an operator needed to use only his left hand to adjust tuning, bandwidth, volume and audio-filter while leaving his right hand free to copy the incoming cw signals. Receivers were, as far as possible, designed to use one specific type of general-purpose pentode valve in all stages, using often the special RV2 range of miniature valves with side pins that fitted top first into fully enclosed sockets with a knob on the base of the valve by which they could be easily removed.

Almost all equipment had switched meters so that an immediate check could be made on selected voltages, some incorporating additional operational performance checks. Generous bypassing and decoupling made for stable stages. Equipment truly deserved the description "built like a battleship" or, as PA0SE has put it: "The moving parts such as gears, tuning capacitors and switches are masterpieces of mechanical engineering." Detailed and well-presented manuals facilitated servicing in the field. Army sets were often designed only for use up to about 7MHz; artillery units used 3 to 7·5MHz for communications, 25 to 27MHz for gun sound ranging; tank-to-tank communications were between 27 and 33MHz with vehicle equipment often between 20 and 25MHz. Front-line infantry used vhf, around 100 and 150MHz. Ground-to-air co-operation was around 42 to 48MHz with a tendency for vhf to be used near the front to make interception more difficult. The Germans were acutely aware of the possibilities of interception (I still have one of their *"Feinde hoert mit!"* ("The enemy also listens") plaques stuck on to my LG300 transmitter). They used many intercept receivers covering frequencies as low as 10kHz and as high as about 305MHz in their army intercept units.

Because many of their main equipments were designed and standardised about 1937–8, the circuit arrangements were ingenious rather than electrically advanced, with many receivers using "straight" rather than superhet circuitry. W Farrar has summarised the German army equipment as "from the mechanical viewpoint very well built, due to the rigid light-alloy castings, anti-backlash gearing and accurate construction methods; electrically, the equipment was good and efficient, but not modern when judged by British wartime standards, although it was in some cases quite ingenious."

Since writing the above, I have received from DL6KG a number of books published by AEG-Telefunken on German radar, radio-navigation, radio-guidance, radio-controlled missiles, df and intercept equipment of the second world war. A truly remarkable range of equipment.

Linear loading of short elements

A note from Dr Constantino Feruglio, IV3VS expresses satisfaction with the technique of "linear loading" elements for a 1·8MHz dipole antenna with an overall span of 54m. He based his design on the notes by Bill Orr, W6SAI in his *Antenna Handbook* which in turn drew upon the Hy-Gain linear loaded elements for their 7MHz beam. He simply multiplied the dimensions shown in Fig 5 by four. W6SAI points out that loading coils, unless of exceptionally high-Q construction, add considerable rf ohmic resistance loss. While the Hy-gain elements are made of aluminium tubing with the folded portions of 12 gauge hard-drawn copper wire, the version built by IV3VS for 1·8MHz uses only copper wire of 2·5mm diameter. Feed impedance will be affected by the folding and also, of course, by the height above ground which on 1·8MHz is likely to be only a small fraction of a wavelength. This is no problem if a balanced feeder (open wire, slotted 300Ω ribbon etc) is used with a suitable atu. IV3VS points out that if switched into the arrangement of Fig 4(b) of *TT*, December 1986, ("folded back dipoles") the system becomes a random "double zepp" working well on 3·5, 7, 14, 21 and 28MHz. But in the version shown here it will work without switching on the same bands. He adds: "Even shortening the span to 40m and increasing the folded lower portion, the antenna will still work satisfactorily on 1·8MHz." My own feeling is that with open-wire balanced feeder one could dispense with the linear loading altogether provided that the atu can cope with the impedances which will then be governed by the overall length of element plus feeder wire, in a conventional "doublet" arrangement.

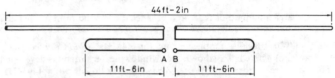

Fig 5. "Linear loading" of a short half-wave element as used in 7MHz array (W6SAI's *Antenna Handbook*)

Simple transistor tester

A simple arrangement for use with a multimeter that checks whether a transistor is "good" and can identify the emitter and collector leads has been reported by A Corben in *Electronics Australia*, June 1987, p85.

He notes that most stand-alone transistor testers do little more than can be achieved with a conventional multimeter. To use the device shown in Fig 6 the base lead must be known and connected correctly. Connections to the other two transistor leads and to the ohmmeter are unimportant (assuming, that the internal battery on the multimeter is limited to less than 3V).

First is to check that the two junctions are operating correctly as diodes in showing a low forward and high reverse resistance using the polarity switch. When this has been done, the pushbutton is pressed and the new reading noted. If the resistance increases by about 12–20 per cent, the selector switch will be in the position indicating that the lead is an emitter; if the change is only of the order of 2–5 per cent, the selector indicates a collector. Abnormal readings will usually indicate a defunct transistor.

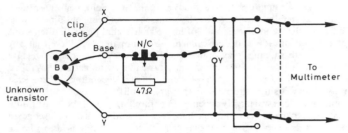

Fig 6. Transistor tester for use with conventional multitestmeter (*Electronics Australia*)

Tips and topics

Brian Castle, G4DYF noting the reference in July *TT* to the use of wrist straps to reduce the chances of zapping cmos ic devices from static electricity warns that "If you put on an earthed wrist strap it should *not* be a direct earth connection. For safety it should have a high-value resistor (eg 1MΩ) in the earth lead.

Peter Chadwick, G3RZP notes that carbon composition resistors (see *TT*, September) are still made by Allen Bradley and are available from their distributors (but possibly only in large numbers), though he is not convinced that the reason why some carbon film resistors tend to burn up when used as parasitic suppressors is due to any excess internal inductance but could indicate that either the choke has too many turns, or the dissipation of the resistor is too low. □

Technical Topics

Pat Hawker, G3VA

WRITERS AND COLUMNISTS can neither expect to, nor in my opinion should they attempt to, please everybody all of the time. Some new-time readers resent being reminded of what they have missed by not being old-timers; some like, some dislike to be reminded of how classic techniques still offer scope for experimentation and development; some apparently believe that any reference to thermionic devices immediately marks one out as a non-progressive despite the fact that 99·999 per cent watch tv on thermionic cathode-ray tubes, with well over 90 per cent of viewers and listeners depending on broadcast transmitters using thermionic power amplifiers, and with space communications still largely dependent on travelling-wave-tubes and up-link klystrons. No matter; anything that happened before the 1980s is of no concern to those who do not ascribe to the view that "science without its history is like a man without a memory". Journalists and technical writers, in the view of some, should be concerned only with "oooh" and "aaah" reporting of discovery, promise, prediction and progress of new superstitions, taken in by shrewd public relations fashioned to sell technology on behalf of government departments, universities, professional societies, industry, broadcasters, health groups and publicity-seekers. I am old-fashioned enough to believe that writers and advertisers and publicists should stay at arms' length. Public relations, it has been said, is organized lying.

Near the mark was that innovative engineer/amateur, J P Costas, W2CRR when he wrote: "We may be far better off to improve what we now have rather than to seek a cure for our present problems by discarding completely the old and accepting something entirely different. This statement may draw the accusation that the writer is not of a progressive frame of mind. I would deny this by stating that progress and increased complexity are not necessarily synonymous. True progress is achieved when improvements are obtained without a significant increase in complexity."

During the 30 years of *TT*, the vast majority of space and encouragement has been given to solidstate electronics and I can think of very few major developments that have not been outlined in *TT* in advance of other UK publications on amateur radio. But current trends in professional communications technology, such as surface-mounted devices, application-specific integrated circuits, 64K memory chips, millimetric-wave GaAs integrated circuits, computer-integrated-manufacture etc are not advances that can readily be taken on board by amateur experimenters. But for some readers, mention of valves, variometers or vintage receivers or anything less than state-of-the-art seems to act like a red rag to a bull.

Mark David, G4MEM, for example, complains that he has become more and more frustrated by *TT* which he claims indicates that I would like to see everyone using HROs and No 19 sets, *(wrong!)*. He and I agree that early transistor sets may have been poor compared with the valve equipment of the 1960s. He continues "But the modern sets really do perform well, and rather than knock microprocessor technology, why not see it as an aid for operation which is what this modern technology is supposed to be? Having been professionally involved with valve, transistor and microprocessor equipment, I know which I prefer to work with. The impression given by the column to new amateurs may not be one reflecting the pioneer spirit of our hobby. Perhaps it is time for an author with a more modern outlook, reflecting amateur radio as it is now."

That's a put down and no mistake! Yet virtually by the same post there arrived (from an overseas amateur) a letter that began: "First of all I must thank and congratulate you on Technical Topics. There is always something new to me and I do find it makes Rad Com the finest radio amateur magazine of all."

Perhaps the time is coming for *TT* to be wound up, if only to make more space for all those non-technical topics that seem to obsess so many RSGB members these days! For I still believe that amateur radio should not be confused with amateur information technology, useful as the micro can be for some applications in the shack.

Using car-radio antennas on 144MHz

Back in February 1981 (*TT*, page 140), details were given showing how a 144MHz antenna could, with the aid of a simple filter, double-up as a standard am/fm broadcast antenna (Fig 1). In *TT* (September 1986, p637) and in more detail in the full-length article by David Last GW3MZY and Trevor Goddard,

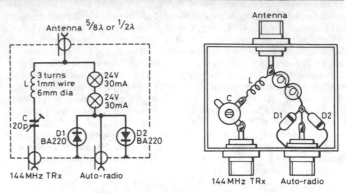

Fig 1. PA0GWF's method of feeding a broadcast car radio from his 144MHz transceiver antenna as described in *TT*, February 1981

GW6RYH "The 'Backlite' mobile antenna for 144MHz" *(Rad Com,* February 1987, pp106-8) where it was shown that window-heater antennas developed for broadcast reception could be used for two-way radio, including 144MHz, operation.

It is an obvious advantage, even at the risk of a slight reduction in 144MHz performance, to have only a single, ordinary-looking antenna on your vehicle. No extra holes need be drilled but even more important is that there is nothing to suggest to the potential thief or vandal that there is a two-way radio waiting to be torn out. It is claimed that in the UK alone one in-car entertainment (ice) unit is stolen on average each minute of the day, often accompanied by damage to the vehicle. Various techniques to make such equipment less attractive to thieves, including sophisticated security coding, are increasingly being incorporated into the more expensive ice systems but not yet, apparently, in amateur mobile transceivers.

Dick Rollema, PA0SE, has added to the single, unobtrusive antenna approach by developing and describing a filter separating 144MHz signals from those destined for the broadcast receiver. He writes: "All designs I came across in the past were meant for use with a 144MHz antenna doubling for car-radio use. I did it the other way round. My car came with an antenna mounted on

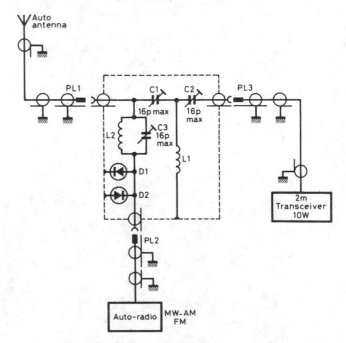

Fig 2. PA0SE's matching-filter permitting the use of a standard car-radio antenna on a 144MHz transceiver while retaining its use for broadcast reception

the front side of the roof, immediately above the windscreen. The position seemed acceptable for my 144MHz rig so I decided to give it a try. The filter unit now has the additional task of matching the car-radio antenna to the 50Ω output socket of the transceiver. I use a T-network in high-pass configuration as shown in Fig 2 (L1, C1 and C2). The broadcast receiver is protected by the parallel-tuned circuit L2, C3, resonating at 145MHz. For extra safety, diodes D1 and D2 are added. However, when properly tuned the residual rf on PL2 is of the order of 50mV or less when running 10W rf output from the transceiver, so that the diodes do not conduct. When the broadcast receiver is tuned to a reasonably strong or not-too-weak signal, broadcast reception is undisturbed when transmitting. Only on a weak broadcast station is some blocking noticeable. This can, in fact, be used for fine tuning of C3 which can be set for minimum disturbance of broadcast reception while transmitting.

"When setting up the filter, the car radio is replaced by a resistor (eg a 50Ω dummy load). C1 and C2 are tuned for minimum swr at the transceiver output and C3 for minimum rf voltage at PL2. It is useful to prune L1 in such a way that proper matching is achieved using minimum capacitance at C1 and C2 since this improves the filtering action. Similarly for L2 and C3. Not having a separate reflectometer for vhf, I used the built-in reflectometer that most if not all 144MHz transceivers include for protection of the power amplifier. I fitted a banana socket on the back panel of the radio and connected it to the output of the internal swr-bridge. With a multimeter between this socket and chassis, C1 and C2 were adjusted for minimum voltage.

"The filter has been in use for about 2½ years and no retuning whatsoever has been necessary. Theoretically the car radio antenna can be expected to perform rather worse than 5/8th-wave whip used previously but, in practice, in view of the wide fluctuations in fieldstrength in mobile operation, this is virtually unnoticeable.

"L1 and L2 are made from 1.8mm copper wire (electricians' wire with insulation stripped). L1 has two and a half turns on 10mm internal diameter. L2 has five turns, 10mm internal diameter. This data to be used as a guideline only. As noted above the coils should be so dimensioned that C1, C2 and C3 are near their minimum value. The filter is mounted in a metal box with lid that happened to be available, dimensions are 10cm wide, 5·5cm deep and 5·8cm high. The unit fits behind the car radio in its recess and is kept in position with some sponge rubber."

Constant-current charging from 12V batteries

K G Pollard with the "initialised callsign G4KGP" has an FT290 which has eight nicad cells in its battery pack. On camping holidays with his family, the only power source available for recharging the cells is the car battery. The car is little used on these occasions so that the battery is not being recharged for much of the time. In a tent it is not convenient to take out the cells of the FT290.

The nicad cells have an operating voltage of 9·6V but, when charging, a battery pack terminal voltage of about 12V is required to provide the 14-hour or one-tenth charge current. The car battery, in its quiescent state, ie not being charged, has a terminal voltage of about 12·6V. This raises the problem that it is necessary to make the car battery a constant-current source, providing the FT290 battery pack with 120mA at a terminal voltage of 12V, from a power source which varies from 12·6V to 14·5V.

G4KGP uses the simple arrangement shown in Fig 3 comprising just two transistors and two resistors. He writes: "It couldn't be much simpler. It works as follows: the BD132 transistor is turned on by the 3·5kΩ resistor. The current to the battery under charge flows through the 1Ω resistor which thus develops 120mV across it. This 120mV turns on the AC128 transistor, draining away the drive to the BD132. The circuit stabilises at a current of 120mA, so forming a constant current source. Employing a germanium transistor as the current sensing element reduces the voltage loss of this section of the circuit; a silicon device would require about 0·6V to turn it on.

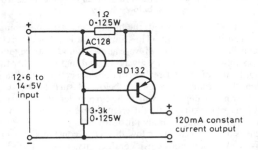

Fig 3. Simple constant-current charging system for re-charging nicad batteries from 12V car batteries

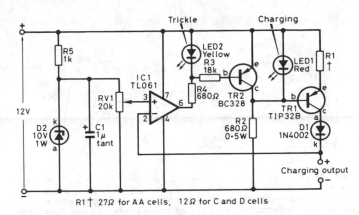

Fig 4. More elaborate nicad charger incorporating automatic float charge for use with AA cells (50mA charging rate) and larger C and D cells (120mA charging rate), as described by P Boyle in Electronics Australia

"The circuit has been arranged so that the negative terminal of the charger is at car ground potential for negative earth cars because the FT290 case is then at the same potential, so avoiding possible short-circuits. For positive earth cars the transistors could be replaced with an AC127 and a BD131. As the maximum applied voltage, when the car engine is running, is about 14·5V, the maximum power dissipation in the BD132 is only about 300mW, 14·5V-12V x 120mA, so no heat sinking is required. I soldered the case of the AC128 to the metal backing of the BD132 (do the soldering very quickly!) to provide thermal feedback. If the BD132 heats up then the AC128 turns on at a lower voltage than 120mV, so limiting the current flow. This makes the circuit thermally stable."

A rather more elaborate nicad charger incorporating automatic float charge is described by P Boyle in Electronics Australia (April 1987): Fig 4. This is similarly intended to operate from a 12V car or boat battery, charging up to six cells in series. When charging is complete, a trickle charge prevents the cells from self-discharging. Operation of this charger is as follows: Initially, with the 12V battery connected but no nicads connected, the yellow: "trickle" light-emitting diode (l.e.d) will light. Once the nicads are inserted, the red "charge" l.e.d lights and remains on until the nicads are charged. The red light then goes off and the yellow light comes on, TR1, R1 and LED1 form a constant current source. LED1 is lit via the current through R2 providing a 2V drop. The voltage across the base-emitter junction of TR2 is 0·6V leaving 1·4V across R1. When R1 is 27Ω, the current through TR1 is 1·4/27=52mA. When R1 is 12Ω the current is 116mA. These currents correspond to the 14-hour charge rate for AA cells and the larger C and D cells respectively.

IC1 is used as a voltage sensitive switch to turn off the charger. It monitors the nicad voltage set by the 10V zener D2 and trimpot RV1 which is set to the correct fully-charged potential of the cells. When this voltage is reached the output of IC1 goes low and switches on LED2. The resulting 2V across it turns on transistor TR2 via R3 and turns off LED2; this in turn reduces the voltage across R1 to 60 per cent of normal, representing the trickle charge. To adjust RV1, initally turn it fully in the direction of the zener diode cathode. Charge the nicads for 14 hours and turn RV1 back until the yellow and red l.e.ds are both just alight. With RV1 left in this position the red l.e.d will extinguish after several minutes. Note that RV1 would need readjustment if a battery with more or less cells is to be charged.

Vertical arrival angles of dx signals

Most amateurs interested in long-distance communication by means of ionospheric propagation (ie medium frequency, hf and lower vhf) soon come to recognise that results depend to a large extent upon the vertical radiation pattern of their antennas. Power radiated outside the optimum range of arrival (departure) angles is virtually wasted power. With real earths of finite conductivity it is extremely difficult on hf to achieve vertical radiation patterns effective below about 5° above the horizon, difficult enough to radiate much power below 10°. On the other hand, high angles of elevation, associated with horizontal wires at heights above ground significantly less than a half-wavelength, can put very strong signals from F2 or F1 layer reflections into locations less than about 1,000 miles away.

This much, of course, is common knowledge. Yet few of us have any clear idea when we are working a dx station what is the vertical angle of arrival of the signals, or the appreciation that this can vary with the frequency, height of the reflective layer, mode of propagation (chordal hop/grey-line propagation etc) or appreciate that even an antenna with little low-angle radiation can still give good dx performance for limited periods of the time that the path is "open".

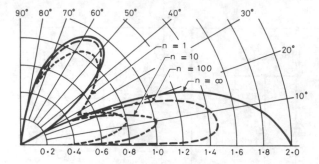

Fig 5. Vertical radiation pattern of a vertical dipole located one-half wavelength above earth of finite conductivity (n=1 represents very poor conductivity, n=infinity represents salt water). Note how at low elevation angles radiated power varies enormously with ground conductivity. (Source Collins' *HF Communications Data Book*)

In 1937, RCA mounted a successful operation designed to receive in the USA the early 405-line television signals from Alexandra Palace. As part of this work they used an interferometer technique to measure arrival angles not only of the 45MHz transatlantic signals but also (on March 4, 1937) of a number of 28MHz signals from amateur stations dotted around the USA.

The 45MHz signals were found normally to arrive at an angle of only 7·5° above the horizon. The 28MHz signals varied with distance and direction from 8·1° (2,720km, layer height 353km) to 17·2° (1,800km, layer height 360km) and also, in a more southerly direction, 1,960km, layer height 402km). Typical arrival angles were around 12–14°.

In 1960-1 a more extensive set of measurements were made on frequencies around 14MHz by the Post Office (now BT) Engineering Department in the course of an investigation into the cost-effectiveness of raising their point-to-point rhombic antennas from 150ft to 300ft (a project left unfinished). More than 30,000 measurements were made at Bearley and Canewdon on signals from Poona, India; Sydney, Australia; and New York. Arrival angles were found to be largely dependent on the ratio of the operating frequency to the muf, and there was evidence that at times arrival angles were as low as 1° while at other times signals from the same location arrived at angles above about 18°, again 12±2° was typical for F2 modes. What this implies is that with a transmitting and receiving antenna effective down to very low elevation angles, signals will be received for longer periods of time, even in disturbed ionospheric conditions and at times on frequencies well above the nominal muf. On the other hand it shows that even if your antenna puts only a tiny percentage of your total power below about 15° elevation you should still be able to work dx occasionally. There was little difference in normal arrival angles from New York, Poona and the much longer path from Sydney.

A casual inspection of the vertical radiation patterns (vrp) of antennas tends to fuel the age-old debate on vertical versus horizontal polariasation. It is important to appreciate that this argument cannot be decided on the basis of "free-space" patterns or patterns with "ideal" earth. The effect of the height of a horizontal antenna above "real earth" and for vertical antennas the conductivity of the earth surrounding the antenna out to a distance of up to 100 wavelengths are the determining factors.

A valuable article "Some reflections on vertical antennas" by C J Michaels,

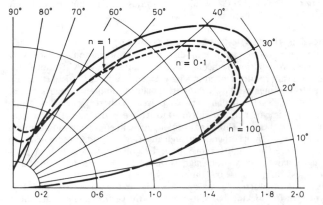

Fig 6. Vertical radiation pattern in the plane perpendicular to the axis of a horizontal dipole one-half wavelength above earth of finite conductivity. Note that earth conductivity has little effect on vrp and only slight effect on efficiency. (Source and details as for Fig 5)

Table 1. Measured vertical angles at which signals from England arrived in New Jersey

Frequency (MHz)	Angle below which signals arrived 99% of the time (Degrees)	Angle below which signals arrived 50% of the time (Degrees)	Angle above which signals arrived 90% of the time (Degrees)
7	35	22	10
14	17	11	6
21	12	7	4
28	9	5	3

W7XC in *QST*, July 1987, pp15-18 carries the highly-relevant note: "Many amateurs have observed that on a dxpedition a simple vertical antenna on an ocean beach performs beautifully, while their own vertical radiates equally poorly in all directions."

The author provides useful data to back up his explanation of why a salt-water ground-plane "earth" is very desirable with vertical polarisation, but has only a marginal effect on a horizontal antenna. He gives a useful table of vertical arrival angles (Table 1) that agrees well with the 1960 Post Office measurements but shows, also, how this tends to vary from band to band.

He also warns of the common fallacy that the use of an extensive network of buried or surface radials (up to 120 are commonly used by medium frequency broadcast stations), completely overcomes the disadvantage of a site having poor ground conductivity. He writes: "A ground radial system is often used to reduce the losses in the near field of a vertical antenna. The radial system does just that—unfortunately this has little to do with the low-angle radiation characteristics of the antenna, because the area of ground reflection (Brewster angle) lies quite a bit farther out from the antenna than any practical ground screen, earth mat, radial system (that could be installed by amateurs)." Enormous earth mats have been installed for example in Australia, to permit the reception of signals down to below 1° elevation for signal-interception purposes. He adds: "In selecting a location for a vertical the best sites are marshy areas and those overlooking (salt) water, although radiation towards the inland side will not be as good as the over-water path. Small islands are ideal, especially ones that do not rise above the water to any great elevation."

For horizontally polarised antennas, ground conductivity has far less effect:

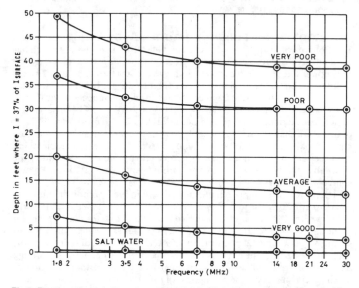

Fig 7. Depths at which the current density is 37 per cent of that at the surface for different qualities of earth over the 1·8MHz to 30MHz range (W7XC, QST, July 1987). Depth for fresh water (not shown) is 156ft almost independent of frequency below 30MHz

Table 2. For low angle radiation, the higher the better. A sloping wire or a sloping site can also provide good low angle radiation. It is often claimed that a horizontal dipole less than a half-wave above ground is not suitable for long-distance operation. While I have always argued that the higher the better, it should not be forgotten that real earth does not reflect hf signals from the surface but often from quite a few feet below the surface. W7XC provides a diagram showing the depths at which the current density of an rf signal is 37 per cent of that at the surface for different earth charcteristics over the range 1·8MHz. The rf gets surprisingly far down.

Real earth may have high or low dielectric constants and high or low conductivity. With very poor earth conductivity, such as a sandy desert (or fresh water) an antenna wire laid directly on the surface or even buried a couple of feet below the surface, will still radiate quite effectively, at least at high vertical angles.

Table 2. Gain of ½λ. Dipole as function of height and ground parameters, using lowest lobe

Height	Approx gain, db/isotropic			Direction of gain, above horizontal		
	A	B	C	A	B	C
¼	8·14	6·28	5·14	90°	90°	90°
½	8·14	7·16	6·60	30°	29°	29°
1	8·14	7·64	7·30	15°	14·5°	14·5°
2	8·14	7·90	7·72	7·5°	7°	7°
4	8·14	8·03	7·94	3·75°	3·5°	3·5°

A—perfect ground; B—moist soil; C—dry soil

One of the most effective ways of lowering the radiation angle of a horizontally polarised antenna of limited height is to use an array which sharpens the vrp in much the same way as it does the hrp. Such an array is not necessarily the usual Yagi or quad. Long-wire and rhombic antennas etc also show the same effect. A good rhombic, for example, may have maximum radiation at around 11-12° with its −6dB angles about 5° and 16°, just the range needed for consistent dx operation!

Long-wire antennas on 50MHz

In the August *TT* I wrote: "Curiously, few amateurs have shown much interest in using long-wire or rhombic antennas for vhf or uhf where they can be fitted into a surburban garden or even a loft-space..". Mike Parkin, G8NDJ is an exception and confirms that a simple long-wire antenna can put out a potent signal on 50MHz. He writes: "Having built a 50/144MHz transverting system. I was naturally keen to test it out. I did not have a 50MHz antenna so I decided to try my long-wire antenna used for listening on the hf spectrum. Rather to my surprise the antenna loaded after using a length of 75Ω coaxial cable as a matching transformer. The system worked well and I was constantly asked by the amateurs contacted for the details. It was suggested that I send along the information for possible publication.

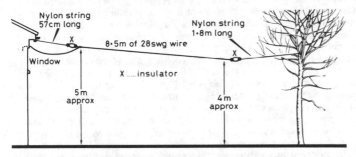

Fig 8. Basic 50MHz "long-wire" antenna used by G8NDJ

"Basically the antenna is 8·5m of 28swg copper wire suspended between the house and a tree at the bottom of the garden using insulators and nylon cord. At the house end is attached 1·8m of copper wire to act as feeder between the 75Ω matching transformer and the horizontal span of the antenna. There is 9cm of this inside the house, the rest (1.71m) attached (by soldering) to the antenna and passed through the wooden window frame.

"Initally the coaxial cable was 4m long and I chopped it back 5−10cm at a time until the swr meter reading dropped to near unity. In practice 3.9m of cable resulted in a match of 1·1:1.

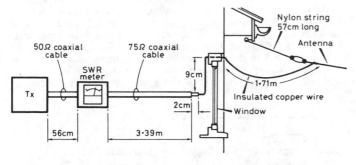

Fig 9. Details of matching arrangement used by G8NDJ

"I have been very pleased with the performance. Local contacts fall off beyond about 20 miles but it has resulted in cross-band contacts (via Sporadic-E?) with Norway, Spain, Switzerland, Italy, Germany and Portugal in a few weeks of operation. It provides a simple and cheap antenna and one that would be well suited to portable operation."

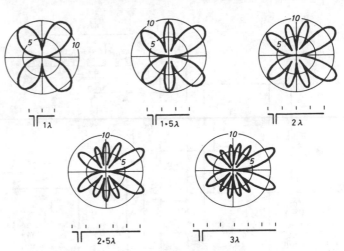

Fig 10. Horizontal radiation patterns of "long-wire" antennas fed at one-quarter wavelength from one end. Note increasing asymmetry with length of resonant long wire antennas

The ususal way of feeding a vhf long-wire with coaxial cable is simply to connect the coaxial cable to a resonant long-wire, a quarter-wave in from one-end. The possibility of using "stretched" long-wire antennas using capacitors at the appropriate intervals should not be overlooked.

Negative-line and universal keying circuits

The May *TT* included GM4DGT's keying arrangements designed to avoid electric shocks from a floating negative rail. More recently, R B Kerr, GM4FDT has sent along an alternative negative-line keying arrangement that he uses with his CQ110E transceiver: Fig 11. In this I_1 should be greater than the key down current I_2. The voltage rating (Vcbo) of TR1 must be greater than the key-up voltage. No batteries are required. Logic 1 (ie usually = 5V) represents key down. Resistor R (330Ω for the CQ110E) can be determined from I_1 = (ttl level—0.7)/R to make I_1 sightly greater than I_2 for reliable operation.

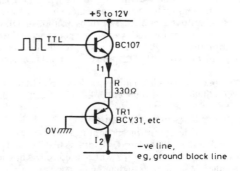

Fig 11. GM4FDT's negative-line keying arrangement

Steve Cook, G4ANA ran up against the problem that his key, a magnificent cmos version of the "Ultimatic" had a relayless output circuit which was fine for positive keying, but, on switching to negative keying as used for example for grid-block transmitters, connected the transmitter chassis to the keyer's positive rail, leaving the paddle metalwork connected to the negative rail. He writes: "Several sets of exploding nicad batteries later, I devised a "kiss" single ic arrangement (Fig 12) which not only enables me to bond all the metalwork together but has also incidentally much simplified the polarity switching and provides a 'universal' design.

"The circuit relies on the same 'same-or-different' switching characteristic of an exor gate, and clears polarity problems completely. Polarity selection is now achieved by connecting the keyer case to one or other of its power rails, leaving nothing 'floating'. IC1a inverts 'case' potential (also brought out on pin C) to provide 'anti-case' (on pin A): the input is protected against static damage by the inclusion of R3. The 'anticase' potential is used to provide the 'pullups' on the paddle inputs via R1, R2, with C1, C2 providing the usual 5ms scratch filtering. IC1b and c then compare paddle potential with that on pin B: by linking this pin A or C, the ouputs from these gates may be made active high (positive) or low as required by the main keyer pcb.

"IC1d similarly provides output polarity selection. The logic ouput of the keyer pcb (which may be of either polarity) is here compared with pin D, which is linked to A or C such that IC1d output is active high on positive keying, active

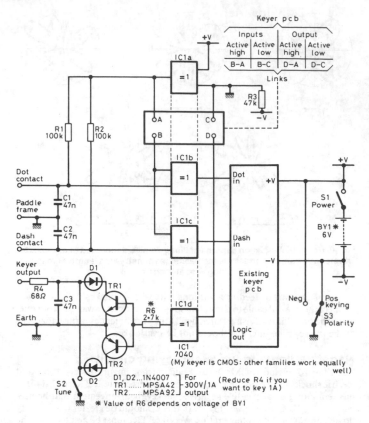

Keyer pcb			
Inputs		Output	
Active high	Active low	Active high	Active low
B–A	B–C	D–A	D–C
Links			

Fig 12. Dual polarity relayless keyer interface with all metal work bonded to earth (G4ANA)

low on negative. This output drives the bases of TR1, TR2, the high-voltage keying transistors, the emitters of which are connected to the case. If the case is negative and IC1d output goes high, TR1 turns on and, via D1, so does the transmitter. If the case is positive and IC1d output goes low, TR2 turns on and energises the transmitter through D2. R4 and C3 provide the usual click filter. Usefully, the b–e junctions of TR1, TR2 protect one another against excessive reverse polarity.

"Result—Nirvana! My nicads no longer explode no matter what touches what. I commend the idea to anyone with a keyer with a 'floating' paddle."

Valves in the museum or shack?

The recent revival of interest (by no means confined to *TT*) in valve technology is not apparently shared by all readers. G Orford, G4FRO complains bitterly that his heart sinks when he looks at *TT* which he considers has degenerated to tedious nostalgia, for those less than sixty, concerning vintage radio, countless valve items, and no longer providing readers with useful or relevant or "where's-the-soldering iron" items. Well, well—luckily for my morale this view does not seem to be shared by other correspondents, not all of whom are "senior citizens".

Geoff Lomas, G4SYC although admitting to belonging to this apparently "past it" category writes: "Like yourself, I am still fond of using valve equipment, despite having spent well over thirty years at the sharp end of computer and military electronics design. The hf rig is the old Heath SB101 and for general coverage the even older AR77. Both are still in fine condition and seem to work as well on cw as any modern and much more expensive gear. The AR77 has been usefully augmented with a digital read out I described in *Wireless World* in the days when there was only limited choice of integrated circuits. A valve I do not like much is the 6146B which I find subject to internal catastrophe; these have been replaced in the SB101 by 6293 valves, a development of the 6146B designed for pulse modulator service and far more robust, although almost identical electrically and physically. When I first acquired the SB101, it suffered from appalling drift. This was tracked down to a six-inch length of coaxial cable joining the vfo to the first mixer. The braid was corroded and varied in capacitance as the rig warmed up. Not one of the more obvious faults!"

Graham Maynard, a keen and experienced listener to medium-wave dx, in the course of a long report on this aspect of the hobby, in *M W News*, writes: "I was brought up in the blue spot, red spot and white world of the early germanium transistors, buying my first OC72 at the age of twelve... during the past twenty years I've tried bipolar, fet, integrated circuit devices and battery valve designs with inductive, crystal, ceramic and mechanical filters, balanced mixers, differential stages, etc, but for serious dxing I use an 'old-fashioned' valve set, a 1953 Marconi Mercury, type 1017 marine receiver. Indeed, it was the power, size, weight (and later cost) disadvantages that started the thermionic decline and not failings in attainable performance... until I can afford a modern solidstate receiver capable of *good* medium-wave performance my choice remains with secondhand professional valve gear." One of the disadvantages of much modern solidstate equipment is the use of electronic (diode) tuning in place of the much higher-Q variable tuning capacitor. It is primarily above 100MHz that the low-noise characteristics of modern solidstate devices become important.

Peter Chadwick, G3RZP warns that builders of "replica" transmitters need to ensure that they meet modern band-requirements in respect of chirp and clicks, etc. The need for a T9 and low drift however does not usually present any problem with crystal control. And of course some valve equipment of the 1950s and 60s were first-class performers (eg Collins equipment). But with 'thirties designs emc, tvi and rfi can be virulent unless adequate precautions are taken. G3RZP does not believe we can afford to indulge in the luxury of nostalgic gear with nostalgic performance! He confirms, however, that considerable use was made both in US wartime equipment and for marine emergency receivers right up to the mid-1960s of a low-voltage (12, 24, 28V) ht bus, sometimes using two pentodes (eg 2 x PL84) in parallel to provide sufficient audio output. On the use of Q-multipliers at the front-end of receivers, either valve or solidstate, he warns of oscillator radiation.

Variometers and the linear variable inductor

The recent *TT* notes on old-style mechanical variometers and the proposed linear variable inductor (lvi) outlined by A S Kislovski of Hastler Ltd in *Proc IEEE* (February 1987, see *TT* September p661) have continued to attract comment. Tim Wright G1BCR/G9BZW reports that what appears to be an identical technique has been used for a decade in the Marconi Instruments fm signal generator type 1066B as a means of controlling the sweep range. A number or readers have pointed out that, in principle, the lvi, although based on the use of two linked toroidal cores, is similar to the long established magnetic amplifiers and saturable reactors widely employed in 50 and 60Hz lighting and other control systems, using conventional E and I laminated cores.

For example, Peter Chadwick, G3RPZ, after being finally convinced that the Proc IEEE piece was not an April Fool joke warns that any core near saturation would result in horrific intermodulation when used with high-power rf signals for, say, a pa tank circuit or an atu. He also points out there is a problem with mechanical variometers. The inductance is $L1 + L2 \pm 2M$ where M is the mutual inductance. With "opposing" values of M the Q inevitably goes down, since the rf ohmic resistance is constant and thus at higher frequencies is appreciably greater than would be in the case for a conventional inductance. He adds: "This is why most marine (500kHz) transmitters only used the variometer for relatively small increments of inductance, providing tapped inductors for the wider changes in inductance". Despite this problem there is still a lot to be said for hf variometers such as those made by Lorenz etc.

Relay driver

C E Rowley, G6KVU sends along a circuit for a relay driver that he originally designed for controlling a set of bandpass-filter switching relays in a portable transmitter-receiver but which could clearly have many other applications. He writes: "A disadvantage of using low-voltage relays is that they usually have a low coil resistance and hence draw a correspondingly high operating current. For applications where a number of relays may be required to operate from a standby battery supply, it is clearly desirable to use a relay driver circuit that will maintain the holding current of a relay at as low a value as possible, without impairing its ability to energise it reliably. The arrangment of Fig 13 was designed for this purpose and for a 50-ohm 5V relay, results in a current reduction from 100mA at rated voltage, to a reliable holding current of 25mA.

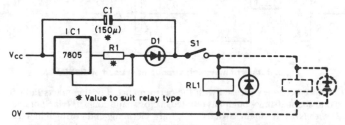

Fig 13. G6KVU's relay driver circuit can cut battery consumption during the hold-in of low-voltage relays by about a factor of four

"With S1 open, the output from D1 will be close to Vcc and C1 discharged. When S1 is closed, C1 charges through the relay coil, the resulting current pulse through RL1 energising the relay. As the capacitor charging current decays, the relay is held energised by the constant current supplied by the IC1 7805 voltage regulator ic. The value of R1 is determined by the expression 5/IR where IR is 1·2 times the minimum holding current of the relay. Note that R1 and D1 carry the full output current and should be rated accordingly. The use of an led for D1 provides an indication that the relay is energised. Capacitor C1 should be a good quality electrolytic, suitably rated for the supply voltage. When S1 is opened, the relay de-energises and C1 rapidly discharges.

"The arrangement requires the input voltage to be as least 2V greater than the rated voltage of the relay coil. By increasing this value to twice the rated voltage of the relays, the corresponding overdrive transient, generated when S1 closes, significantly improves the pull-in time. It also permits relays of different coil voltages to be energised from a common supply (Vcc). Since it is essentially a constant-current arrangement, and an added advantage is that the relay supply is protected against a short circuit.

15W 12/240V inverter

In the past couple of years, *Electronics Australia* has published several designs for solidstate inverters transforming 12V dc into 240V ac in order to permit the operation of domestic appliances etc from 12V car batteries. One of these, for 300W output published in *EA* in September 1985, was briefly mentioned in *TT*, February 1986, page 110.

In the April 1987 issue of *Electronics Australia,* John Clarke describes a "12/240V inverter for portable compact disc players" intended for powering compact-disc players in a car but which could equally well be used for other mains-type equipments that consume 15W or less: Fig 14. The output waveform is basically a stepped square wave (duobinary) suitable for most appliances designed for mains sine-wave operation. Although only a low-power unit, the claimed line regulation is impressive: for an input voltage range of 11V dc to 15V dc, the output voltage changes only from 240V ac to 249V ac. Load regulation at 12V input is also good, changing from 242V ac at no load to 241V ac at 15W load. Efficiency at full load (15W) is 82 per cent with the current drain approximately 1·5A dc. Standby current at no load is 120mA.

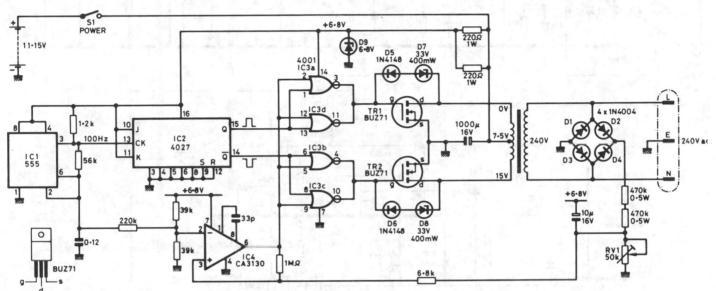

Fig 14. 15W 12-to-240W inverter as published in *Electronics Australia*

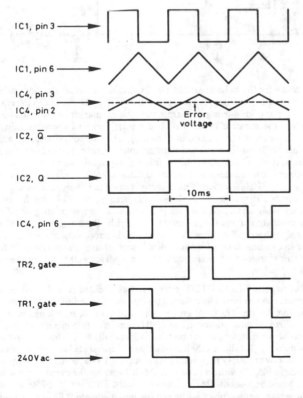

Fig 15. Waveforms at various points in the 15W inverter

The two fet switching devices (BUZ71) are heatsinked and are sipmos devices (Siemens power metal oxide semi-conductors). Several safeguards have been incorporated in order not to impair the audio quality and "to provide protection from the voltage transients common in a car electrical system" (a fact not always appreciated by mobile operators used to battery operation for handhelds etc). The negative return of the dc supply is isolated from the signal output ground to eliminate the possiblity of a current loop that can give rise to noise and distortion. The unit is based on a standard 15V centre-tapped mains transformer. Four integrated circuit devices drive push-pull switching transformers at 50Hz. The 555 in a stable mode produces a 100Hz square wave with 1:1 duty cycle. The output of IC1 goes to a 4027 J-K flipflop which in effect divides the clock input by two, with IC3 providing buffers. Waveforms at the device pins are shown in Fig 15. Output voltage is adjusted by RV1 to read 240V ac with a 12V dc input.

The EA article provides full constructional details including pcb layout etc but most of the essential detail is given in Figs 14 and 15.

A hybrid ultimate receiver

Ray Howgego, G4DTC, has been keeping the flag of experimental development flying in Caterham in a quest to develop the ultimate amateur hf communication receiver. In the course of this he has cunningly combined both traditional and novel ideas, some of which (including a novel crystal ladder filter) will have to be held over for another month.

He sets the scene as follows: "I have three factory-produced receivers, each representing different design philosophies: an FRG7, an FT200 transceiver and an Eddystone 940 general coverage receiver of the mid-1960s. **(a) The FRG7:** Yaesu seem to have been so enraptured with their implementation of a solidstate Wadley triple-mix system that other aspects of receiver performance were ignored. Seven transistors, all prone to cross-modulation, precede the filter. The attenuator reduces this problem but does not reduce the noise level. There are some unexpected spurii. In my experience this receiver is improved beyond belief by fitting an i.f gain control (eg by manually controlling the agc line)

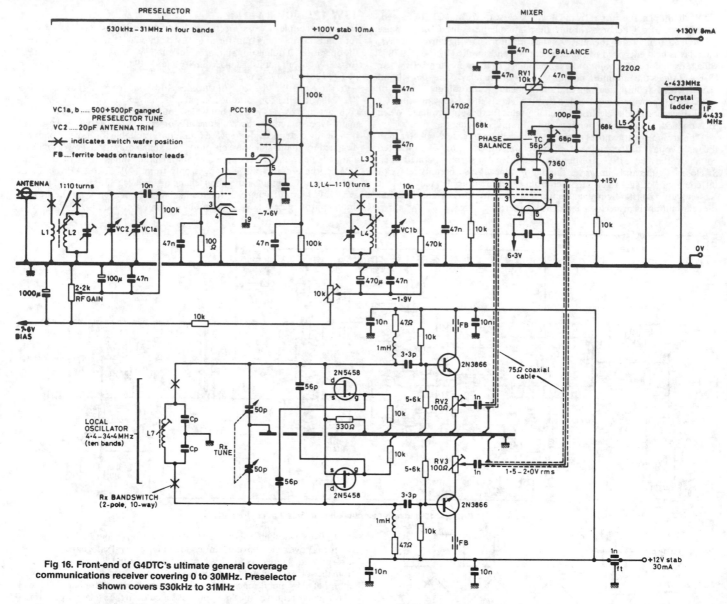

Fig 16. Front-end of G4DTC's ultimate general coverage communications receiver covering 0 to 30MHz. Preselector shown covers 530kHz to 31MHz

revealing the extreme importance of using just the right amount of gain in the i.f stages. **(b) The FT200:** The receiver section far outperforms the FRG7 but lacks sensitivity at the higher frequencies. Has just the correct gain in the i.f stages. In operation, the af gain should be held high, and volume controlled by the rf gain. **(c) Eddystone 940:** This general coverage valved receiver far outperforms the FT200 even on the amateur bands. The 940 seems to have been sadly overlooked as one of the great receivers. Whoever designed it knew what he was doing. Signals inaudible on the FRG7 stand out against a quiet background. Unfortunately it has three disadvantages: single-conversion to 450kHz (claimed image rejection at 20MHz only 40dB); the use of an easily overloaded 6BE6 for ssb detection; and combined rf/if gain control. This control unfortunately reduces the signal more rapidly than the receiver noise. The problem can be eliminated by removing the gain control line from the ECC189 cascode first rf amplifier. (This receiver has two rf amplifying stages with the front end comprising an ECC189 cascode, 6BA6 second rf amplifier, 6AJ8 mixer, 6C4 local oscillator and two 6BA6 i.f stages with a single vacuum-mounted crystal providing a 6dB bandwidth of 400Hz, and a four-gang tuning capacitor with the large Eddystone 140:1 slow motion drive and tuning scale. The five bands covered from 480kHz to 30MHz with a vernier scale – *G3VA*).

"The point I am making is that although all three receivers have similar sensitivity specifications, and all should produce a noise level below that of cosmic noise, their actual performance is noticeably different. Having heard several other recent receivers it is evident that those using the final generation of valve designs produce a much cleaner sound that those using transistors, provided the gain distribution is correct."

In publishing G4DTC's comparisons, I feel it should be underlined that the Yaesu FRG7 and FT200 models were relatively low-cost equipment built expressly for the swl and amateur-radio markets whereas the Eddystone 940 was a general-purpose professional receiver built by Eddystone in the era when the company was moving away from the amateur market (for which it was then making the amateur-bands EA12 receiver). Some of the later Eddystone receivers were made for, and marketed by, The Marconi Company which in the late 1960s took over the company completely and pulled out of the amateur market, though Eddystone have continued to produce some fine professional communications receivers. Modern solidstate professional models can cost up to over £20,000 which is not exactly a price tag likely to appeal to many newcomers. To my way of thinking, it has been a retrograde step for amateur factory designers to follow the professionals' footsteps in going for up-conversion to vhf and frequency synthesis with all the attendant problems of excessive phase-noise (jitter), reciprocal mixing and consequent reduction of near-in dynamic range. I wonder how many solidstate receivers built for the amateur market have a performance better in all respects than, say, the Collins 75A4?

But to return to G4DTC's letter: "It was decided therefore to build my ultimate receiver based on a design philosophy that embraced both valve and solidstate devices. The front-end has emerged as in Fig 16, taking into account the following considerations: The 7360 beam-deflection mixer was considered essential, nothing within an amateur budget really outperforms it. Although now quite costly (about £15) it probably still represents best performance per pound. Power supply requirements are modest. The receiver was required to tune dc to 30MHz with an i.f of 4·433MHz to permit the use of a crystal ladder filter based on low-cost PAL colour tv crystals. The use of the 7360 allows one to tune right across the i.f without a trace of a whistle. The i.f rejection is of

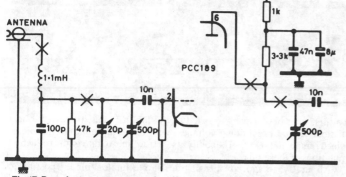

Fig 17. Preselector arrangement for vlf reception (0 to 550kHz) used by G4DTC

the order of 50-60dB while the 7360 provides about 25dB of conversion gain.

"The equivalent noise resistance of the 7360, at 1,500 ohms, is usually claimed as making it suitable for use as the first stage of an hf receiver. However this implies the use of a good antenna and for amateur applications it is useful above about 14MHz to have a stage of rf amplification. A PCC189 (more readily available than the ECC189) in a cascode circuit, with its enr only about 200 ohms, represents the ultimate in signal-to-noise performance. The gain of this stage is controlled by varying the grid bias, I find this better than the usual variable resistor in the cathode circuit since it reduces valve noise and signal in the same proportion, which cathode biasing does not. To reduce the valve to cut-off, it is run at only 100V anode potential instead of the usual 180V; this barely affects the gain. In operation, the gain of this stage is held at or below unity over most of the spectrum but can be increased to 30dB if required. The antenna trim control is essential to compensate for different antennas and ensures adjustable tracking.

Both valves have dc heater supplies through small dropper resistors from a rectified and smoothed 6.3V winding. The 7360 requires −1·9V bias supply for both valves to be absolutely free of ripple; hence the use of high-value electrolytics. For tuning below 500kHz the alternative circuit (Fig 17) is switched in with R-C coupling between the two stages. The input arrangement of the PCC189 combines a tunable circuit over 500 to 300kHz with a low-pass filter below 300kHz. This arrangement permits signals at frequencies down to a few kHz to be received at good strength.

"The deflecting electrodes of the 7360 are supplied from a balanced solidstate Kaliatron oscillator tuning 4·4 to 34MHz in ten switched bands, each 3MHz wide. In my view, synthesised oscillators, with all their problems, should be avoided like the plague. On hf who needs them? The oscillator in Fig 16, after drifitng about 4kHz in the first ten minutes then settles down to within 20Hz for an indefinite period (measured at 30MHz); after two hours I became bored with watching for a change in the final digit on the counter. The Kaliatron oscillator has proved exceptionally reliable and provides a very high output, independent of L-C ratio; output is almost as high as its supply voltage. A high degree of buffering can then be employed. It is however intolerant of any inbalance in layout or component tolerances.

"The deflecting anodes of the 7360 show a fairly high capacitance (about 10pF) and it proved necessary to supply them from a low impedance souce. This also allowed the local oscillator to be situated remotely from the mixer. Hence the 2N3866s which get quite warm. The base circuitry of these devices forms a filter with a steady roll off towards low frequencies and ensures an rms input to the 7360 of 1·5 to 2V at all frequencies. RV1 and TC are set for optimum i.f rejection. RV2 and RV3 allow equalisation of the antiphase oscillator outputs but are probably unnecessary since these outputs are within 2% of balance. Component values for the 7360 mixer were taken from previously published materials and were found to have been carefully optimised." ☐

Technical Topics
Pat Hawker, G3VA

ALTHOUGH RECOGNISING that many amateurs and professionals are convinced that the future of radio communications and broadcasting equipment is firmly in the direction of all-solid-state – see, for example, the view of Joseph H Johnson of Microwave Modules & Devices that the time is rapidly approaching, when vacuum tubes will no longer be required. (*TT* February 1987) – I remain convinced that amateurs should not be in any hurry to phase-out completely thermionic devices for such applications as rf power amplification. Unfortunately, marketing people, as noted later, have convinced many "customers" that thermionic devices are unreliable and obsolete, or virtually so, even at powers in the kilowatt range.

High-power solidstate – to be or not to be?

A few months ago, Kurt Grey, VE2UG, noted the comment of K Weiner, DJ9HO, on page A.l.l. of the *UHF Compendium* that "due to financial considerations valves will remain with us in uhf power amplifiers for quite some time". But it is not only from financial considerations that we need to recognise that *for amateur applications* there are other positive advantages. VE2UG puts it bluntly:

"The amateur fraternity and some other users should recognise the true price-tag attached to some of the super-duper, hi-tech gear. Maintenance free? Who is kidding who? Recognise the need for transient protection to be applied to power lines; this can be complex and costly.

"Then something goes wrong. The solidstate output module(s) is knocked out. Was this due to power transients, lightning, failure of mismatch protection? One can seldom be certain as to the cause. Unlike the pull-out, plug-in of valve replacement, the solidstate transceiver usually has to be returned to the supplier. Transistor replacements thus involve not only the high-cost devices but also transportation cost, servicing costs and loss of the use of the equipment over extended periods."

Broadcasters tend to be attracted to solidstate for reasons that have little bearing on amateur operation. Few amateurs, for example, are concerned about the energy-consumption costs of operating a high-power transmitter over many hours daily. A year or two back, the Canadian CBC organisation installed and brought into use the world's first 50kW solidstate mf/a.m broadcast transmitter and achieved an energy-cost saving of $12,300 (energy cost $0.05/kWh) in a period of nine months. CBC regard their experience with this type of technology as "quite favorable, both in terms of performance and maintenance". But they note that in 12 months of operation eight power fets and two or three fuses have been replaced. Major problems were encountered when the prototype transmitter was switched on for the first time: six toroid pot cores and about 40 power fets had to be replaced. The failure of the fets was traced to the weakness of the isolation seal pad washers, later replaced by washers containing glassfibre to increase the stiffness. Sporadic failures of some pa modules occurred because of over-heating at a time when the building's ventilation system was incomplete.

Customer education

At a recent IEE international conference, Radar-87, the keynote address, given by David Barton of ANRO Engineering Consultants, USA, noted that 90 per cent of major radar research and development projects have been ending in failure to deliver a usable product. He put much of the blame on the customers (military and civil) demanding only the latest technology. He stressed that:

"The role of consumer education in radar is just as important as in matters of household safety, diet and health. But who is to perform this service? Medicine in this past century had more than its share of snake-oil salesmen. As professionals we must make sure that we are not performing the same dubious role for our users. The user must be assisted in selecting and specifying radar functions which are appropriate to his system requirements." For radar, I would suggest one could simply substitute amateur radio!

David Barton also expressed some pertinent opinions in respect of rf power generation: "Throughout this (postwar) period, the attempt was made to get as much power as possible out of a single tube, and to use multiple tubes only when absolutely necessary. Presumably this was the result of cost considerations... As a result of the pressure for high output

powers, tube designs were pushed to the limit of emission density, heat dissipation and breakdown voltages, with resulting reliability problems which remain today. Low reliability also is traceable to the small production quantities of these tubes.

"About 10 years ago, advances in transistor technology made it possible to consider development of solidstate radar transmitters. Even with advanced devices, power levels were (and are today) pitifully low in microwave bands. But the solidstate industry was not discouraged, and their marketing efforts found assistance from the reliability engineer. The deficiency in power output was presented as a fundamental advantage: many sources would have to be combined, giving great redundancy and reliability. Radar customers who previously would not accept dual-tube transmitters, now began to insist on modular transmitters having hundreds or thousands of solidstate sources in the name of reliability. Even with its multiplicity of modules, the usual solidstate design cannot compete economically with tubes unless the radar waveform is changed to permit use of very high duty factors. As a result there are radar systems being designed today in which the high-energy pulse, needed for maximum detection range, consumes almost half of that range as dead time..."

While these considerations mostly apply specifically to radar, there are, I would suggest, lessons to be learned. For instance, it shows the reasons why some of the older ('fifties) valves are less vulnerable to flash-over, inter-electrode shorts etc than the later ceramic tetrodes. The note from Percy Greenwood, G2BUJ, on the 4-65A (QY3-65) power tetrode in the October *TT*, has prompted John Roscoe, G4QK, to comment: "I preferred the more powerful QY3-125A (4-125A). I had a pair in 1953, used one at a time, and they remain enshrined in my memory as the best valves I ever handled. I paid £5 each for them, slightly used, and later sold them to Rowley Shears, G8KW, probably for the same price."

Electronically variable attenuator

Arising out of the recent discussion on variometers (presumably one of the backward-looking topics that have upset some readers) I included in the September *TT* an item on a forward-looking linear variable inductor as proposed by A S Kislovski of Hasler Ltd. This in turn prompted several accounts of how similar or related techniques are being used successfully in existing solidstate equipment.

Mike Perks, ZS6BIM, of the South African firm Grinaker Electronics, writes to point out that in the late seventies he used a similar technique in the design of an electronically-variable attenuator to control the drive to a solidstate 500W hf linear amplifier, including its use in the automatic level control (alc) system. With the permission of Grinaker Electronics, ZS6BIM has sent circuit details of the drive system from which I have extracted only the part appertaining to the variable attenuator: Fig 1. ZS6BIM writes: "The attenuator circuit provides about 30dB control over 1·6 to 30MHz with low distortion at an operating input of 5 to 20W and with the power applied to the variable inductor first attenuated by R126, R127 and R129. The circuit operates by increasing the transmission loss with the variable series inductor. The fixed input attenuator optimises the source impedance for the variable attenuator and provides a well-defined input impendance for the driving source. The additional components

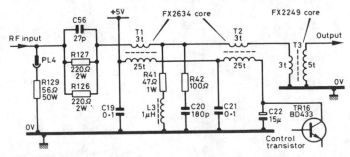

Fig 1. Electronically variable attenuator developed by ZS6BIM for use in a solidstate 500W hf linear amplifier built by Grinaker Electronics

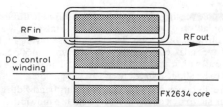

RF in → [balun core] → RF out

DC control winding

FX2634 core

Fig 2. Balun core winding method. Note that the rf winding is wound through the one balun core aperture only

R41, L3 and R42, C20 compensate for performance roll-off at the low and high end of the band.

"Using a 25-turn control winding, full attenuation would occur with a current of 400mA at 30MHz, falling to less than 100mA at 1·6MHz. As maximum control current corresponds to maximum attenuation, in practice only a small current flows. The problem of preventing coupling of the rf and control windings is solved by winding the balun core of T1 and T2 as shown in Fig 2."

QRP power boosters

Listen around 3,540kHz and one soon discovers that a few hundred milliwatts of rf can provide a reasonably-steady signal when band conditions are stable. But those signals tend to be terribly vulnerable to fading conditions that often take them below the high noise level of electrical interference seemingly inevitable in urban and suburban areas on this band.

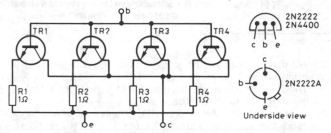

Fig 3. Use of four transistors connected in parallel. R1 to R4 serve as equalizing resistors to form a ballasted power block (QST)

As Doug De Maw, W1FB, puts it in "Low-cost QRP power boosters" (QST July 1987, pp30-4): "If you're working QRP, a signal gain of 10 to 13dB can mean the difference between being copied and having your signal lost in the mud." His article shows how on 3·5 and 7MHz, numbers of low-cost transistors can be used in parallel to raise the output from a milliwatt rig. For example, four 2N4400 or 2N2222A transistors can be connected in parallel for rf power amplification provided that low-value equalising ballast resistors are connected in the emitter leads to form, in effect, a ballasted power block. Four 2N4400 devices connected as in Fig 3 can deliver 1·5W of 7MHz power in Class C with a 50 per cent duty cycle. Some semiconductor firms, such as Motorola, market such power blocks as ballasted transistors or b.e.t (balanced-emitter-devices). The low-value emitter resistors not only tend to balance the power in the transistors but also prevent thermal runaway – the phenomenon that affects bipolar rf power transistors due to excessive junction heating which, once started, continues to increase the current until the junction is burned out. Thermal runaway can be induced by operating a transistor

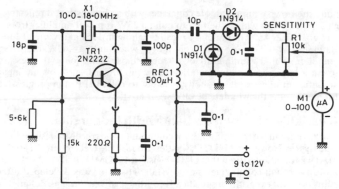

Fig 4. Tester used when matching transistors for use as in Fig 3. Use a transistor socket to facilitate plugging various transistors into circuit. R1 is 10K linear carbon composition control. RFC1 can be a small rf choke of any value from 500μH to 2·5mH. M1 could be 50, 100 or 200μ φσδ

power amplifier into an inadequately matched load. A b.e.t device has the emitter resistors formed directly on the silicon chip together with the multiple transistors, but there is no reason why the same technique cannot be used with discrete devices. Matched transistors can be selected using the test jig shown in Fig 4.

Fig 5, taken from W1FB's article, shows how up to eight devices can be used in parallel/push-pull configuration to provide a useful 3W output from 150mW drive, useful either for QRP or as part of a higher-power exciter. Alternatively, a single Motorola MRF475 or roughly equivalent Japanese 2SC2092, as widely used in cb rigs, can provide 5W rf output from 250mW drive in the arrangement shown in Fig 6. In his QST article W1FB provides constructional details, including pcb lay-outs, although stressing that it is meant primarily as an ideas source for those who like to

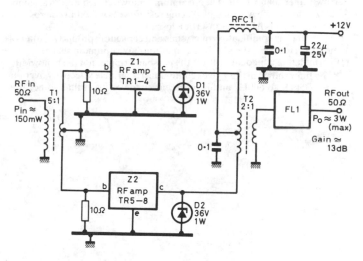

Fig 5. How two power blocks may be combined to form a push-pull 3W amplifier. Zener diodes D1 and D2 may be used instead of the ballasting resistors if matched transformers are used

Fig 6. 5W amplifier using cb type transistor. C5 and C8 are disc ceramic. C6 and C7 are tantalum or electrolytic. R1, R2 and R3 are 0·25W carbon composition resistors. Silver-mica capacitors may be substituted for polystyrene (P) types. Impedance transformation ratios are shown above T1 and T2. L1-0.22μH inductor. Small rf choke or 8 of No 24 enam wire on an Amidon T-37-6 toroid. L2, L4-0.8μH inductor. 12t of No 24 enam wire on an Amidon T-50-2 toroid. L3-1.67μH inductor. 18t of No 24 enam wire on an Amidon T-50-2 toroid. RFC1-2.8μH choke, 24t of No 26 enam wire on a Amidon T-50-2 toroid. RFC2-42μH choke. 10t of No 26 enam wire on an Amidon FT-37-43 toroid. T1-Primary has 16t of No 26 enam wire on an Amidon FT-37-43 toroid. Secondary has 6t of No 26 enam wire. T2-Primary (Q1 side) has 9t of No 24 enam wire on an Amidon FT-50-43 toroid. Secondary has 15t of No 24 enam wire (W1FB, QST)

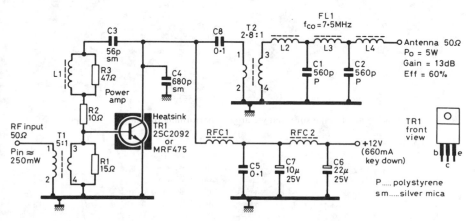

build their own equipment. He concludes with an interesting, if reflective, challenge: "Who will be the first to build a 25W rf power amplifier from a bag of 2N2222As? To that end I recall laughing in 1952 at my friend John Baumler, W8UUN (now a silent key), who built a 400W p.e.p ssb amplifier around six miniature 6CL6 tubes in parallel. I found it necessary to eat a large serving of crow after I saw (and heard) his 4 by 4in linear amplifier in operation!" Nobody is likely to call W1FB non-progressive for mentioning the wonders of valves – or are they?

A variable wide/narrow bandwidth ladder filter

The "front-end" of the "ultimate" hf communications receiver designed and built by Ray Howgego, G4DTC, was described in the December *TT* (pp915-7). It was mentioned then that G4DTC uses a 4·433MHz ladder filter based on low-cost Pal colour television crystals. His filter was developed after many hours of experiment specifically for this receiver, since no designs for "wideband" ladder filters suitable for the reception of a.m signals appeared to have been published. The filter that has resulted would, however, be suitable for any receiver intended for a.m/ssb/cw/rtty reception, since the 3dB points can be varied from 4·35kHz down to 600Hz. The work has also brought out several points of interrest about ladder filter techniques generally. The nine-crystal filter is shown in Fig 75. G4DTC writes:

basically a six-pole roofing filter followed by a variable three-pole filter. It should prove reliably reproducible. When the crystals were swapped around there was no obvious difference. The crystals used were Philips HC18-U units supplied by Sendz Components of Shoeburyness at 50p each. In a batch of 10 they were all within a range of 80Hz. Crystals in the large case style (eg HC6-U) tend to be about 200Hz lower.

"This filter really does work well. The maximum bandwidth gives pleasant a.m with 'razor-sharp' selectivity. Set at a 2·2kHz bandwidth for ssb, it gives total suppression of the opposite sideband."

G4DTC provides the following details of the filter and its performance: C1, C2 is a 60 + 142pF miniature tuning capacitor as found in most cheap portable broadcast receivers, or Maplin FT78K. Set integral trimmers for maximum bandwidth when capacitor plates are fully unmeshed. Set R1 for best compromise between insertion lose and shape factor, 2·5kΩ nominal. Set R2 for best compromise between minimum bandwidth and insertion loss, 1·2kΩ nominal.

The following specification should be achievable: C1, C2 plates unmeshed: 3dB points at 4,437·25kHz and 4,432·90kHz, bandwidth 4·35kHz. C1, C2 plates half-meshed: 3dB points at 4,434·0kHz and 4,432·90kHz bandwidth 1·10kHz.

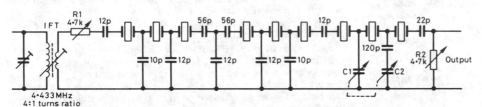

Fig 7. Variable selectivity ladder filter using low-cost Pal colour television crystals developed by G4DTC for his "ultimate" receiver

"(1) The bandwidth is determined entirely by the "vertical" capacitors. If, however, these are reduced below about 10pF, the bandwidth begins to narrow rather than widen. The maximum bandwidth achieved was about 4·5kHz. This can be widened by placing resistors (1kΩ to 10kΩ) across the capacitors but this increases insertion loss.
(2) Virtually any combination of crystals and capacitors produces a filter of some sort. However, the published equations give optimum shape.
(3) Terminating impedances affect the passband ripple, not the bandwidth.

"The filter shown in Fig 7 gives continuously-variable selectivity over the range 4·35kHz to 600Hz and is much easier to construct than some. It is

C1, C2 plates meshed: 3dB points at 4,433·5kHz and 4,432·90kHz bandwidth 600Hz. Insertion loss in passband: Maximum (R1 2·5kΩ, R2 1·2kΩ) 10dB. Minimum (R1 0Ω, R2 1·2kΩ) 6dB. Passband ripple 1–3dB (dependent on R1). Ripple reduces with bandwidth. Stopband attenuation: beyond range of measurement (better than 60dB). −20dB bandwidth typically 1,000Hz wider than the −3dB bandwidth.

Details of G4DTC's i.f amplifier, detector, agc and S-meter circuitry, based on Plessey integrated circuits and discrete semiconductors, and also the bfo/carrier injection oscillator, will be given another month. □

Technical Topics

Pat Hawker, G3VA

THE MULTIPLICATION of electronics products in homes is adding to the problems of operating transmitters, even of low power, in residential areas; at the same time, the cmos microprocessors and other electronic systems fitted in so many vehicles underline the safety risks involved in emc problems. At one time, the amateur needed to worry only about interfering with his neighbours' television and radio receivers, but today the list of vulnerable equipment has grown long, including such items as video cassette recorders, electronic telephones, smoke detectors, security alarms, domestic-appliance controls etc. At the same time, radiation from domestic appliances, personal computers, switched-mode television sets, electronic light dimmers etc, makes weak-signal reception increasingly difficult. Many of us feel that, for too long, the UK authorities have lagged behind other countries in legislating against excessive radiated interference and poor immunity of consumer products to strong rf fields — though one has to recognise that such legislation may not always be to the advantage of the amateur.

Recently, there have been signs that renewed efforts are being made to persuade the authorities and industry of the increasing range and importance of emc problems. A number of UK universities where emc research has been carried out in recent years — including the universities of Bradford, Bristol, Hull, Nottingham and York, plus City University, London, have joined together in a loose consortium in an attempt to increase the awareness of Government departments, research establishments, industry and broadcasters of the importance of emc — and actively to seek more sponsored research into various little understood or unquantified aspects of emc. In late-November about 70 people were given an outline of what has been done already and an opportunity to discuss how they viewed emc topics. It was clear, for example, that there is considerable support in industry for the view that I have expressed in *TT* and elsewhere that it would be helpful if all training courses in electronic engineering included at least some grounding in the importance of good emc design. I took the opportunity of contrasting the long delays in introducing UK legislation on levels of permitted radiation from personal computers with the position in the USA where the FCC imposed tight regulations several years ago. Mr A Nieduszynski, the divisional head of the DTI's Radiocommunications Division, gave an assurance that he expected the draft EEC directive on emc to be implemented within about 18 months. It is clear, however, that, in the past, many design engineers have felt that matters such as emc and overall thermal regulation problems were of little concern to the designer and could be left to be put right later, if necessary.

It is much to be hoped that this group of academics, of whom the leading lights appear to be Dr Andy Marvin (York University) and Dr Peter Excell (Bradford University), is successful in creating more interest at the highest levels in this subject, though my feeling is that the inclusion of this topic in degree and HNC courses is every bit as important as the award of more sponsored research grants.

John Worsnip, G2BAQ, who wrote the article on reducing rf breakthrough from microcomputers in the December issue of *Rad Com*, is a senior lecturer at the Cambridgeshire College of Arts and Technology (CCAT). He has mentioned that they have a unit in the computer technology option of their HNC electronic engineering course which covers emc topics, and intend to include similar units in their BEng degree course in the near future. A number of their student projects have also been concerned with aspects of emc. There is hope yet!

Rejuvenating Dryfit and nicad batteries

In *TT* October 1987, p750, G8APX drew attention to the range of sealed, maintenance-free rechargeable lead-acid (gel-electrolyte) batteries, sold under the brand name of "Dryfit", for the operation of hand-held transceivers. Compact units with a capacity of, for example, 12V 1·1Ah or 6V, 2·6Ah, are widely available. Treated well, these units provide many charge-discharge cycles while retaining their normal ampere/hour capacity.

Although they are "sealed" units, eliminating acid spillage, and with a "solid" electrolyte, for safety reasons they include pressure vents to deal with any excessive build-up of pressure due to over-loading or over-

charging. Reading G8APX's notes, Tim Harrowell, G3IMI, was reminded of an article he had filed away, from a German magazine, on the rejuvenation of Dryfit batteries that have lost their capability of holding a full charge due to excessive loss of moisture from the gell electrolyte through the vents. He points out that substandard batteries are often available cheaply at rallies, having served their working lives in operating burglar alarms.

My dictionary-aided translation of the article ("Regenerierung von Dryfit-Akkus") may be a little crude but the gist of the procedure is as follows: First carefully drill into the top cover of the battery (just clear of the cell vents) with a 2–3mm-diameter drill. There will be three cells and thus three pressure vents in 6V batteries, six in 12V batteries. Then, with the aid of a syringe, inject into each cell some distilled water, approximately 1·5ml/Ah of normal capacity. Leave the battery for some hours and then re-seal the holes with an adhesive such as Uhu-plus. After a couple of charge/discharge cycles the capacity of the battery should then be restored to nearly its original value, though one cannot guarantee success.

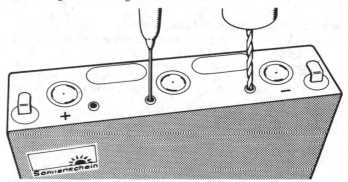

Fig 1. Rejuvenating the three cells of a 6V Dryfit rechargable accumulator by drilling a hole into each cell and injecting a little distilled water by means of a syringe and later sealing the holes with Uhu-plus adhesive

The German author seems well satisfied with the results he achieves with defective batteries which he claims are often restored to 90–95 per cent of their original capacity.

The article reminded me of an item on "rejuvenation of nicads" contributed to *TT* (combined June/July 1980 issue, p636) by David Foster, G3KQR, in which he used a hypodermic needle and syringe to inject distilled water into nicad cells that had lost weight. As there must be many readers not having access to 1980 issues of *Rad Com* it seems worth repeating this item:

G3KQR wrote: "The most important finding (of my experiments) was that old nicad cells had lost weight. For the HP11 size, 45 by 25mm, in some cases the weight loss was as much as 40g. This appeared to be due to gassing and loss of fluid. It was reasoned that the weight loss was most probably due to loss of water, and not so much due to loss of hydroxide. These 'sealed' cells are provided with a pressure-gassing vent, which seems to allow blow-off at a pressure of about two atmospheres.

"The gassing vent in these cells is under the positive terminal, sometimes obscured by a brass soldering terminal which can be drilled by shallow penetration with, say, a No 55 drill. Pressurised venting is made possible by the synthetic rubber plug that is trapped during the manufacturing process between the 'Top Hat' of the positive terminal and the top disc; the two metal portions are spot-welded together.

"Access to the cell can be gained with a hypodermic needle and syringe thrust vertically through the top, through the rubber into the cell (the needle 'track' will 'self-heal' on withdrawal of the needle).

"Alternate suction and pressure will allow topping up to be done, using distilled water. Old cells were found to need about 3ml of water. The procedure is simple and safe and there is no contact with the hydroxide. Hundreds of cells seem successfully to have been given a new lease of life... in view of their condition they were acquired very cheaply." No attempt should be made to replace hydroxide as the handling of potassium hydroxide is extremely dangerous."

Previous *TT* items have shown that it is sometimes possible to remove short-circuiting "whiskers" in nicad cells and also to overcome sulphation in lead-acid batteries.

Also as noted before in *TT,* some dry cells (carbon-zinc etc), if not left fully discharged for too long, can often be given a new lease of life when "charged" at a very low rate (a few milliamps) preferably using "dirty dc" (ie rectified ac without filtering out any of the ripple). Care must be taken to avoid the risk of overheating and so causing an explosion that can occur from attempting to "charge" sealed dry cells too rapidly. A less effective, but sometimes worthwhile, trick is to gently heat a dry battery for a couple of hours when it is nearly discharged. This can tone up the depolarizer and tends to be most effective on batteries that have been discharged continuously into a load for long periods.

B D Tipper, G3WWL, has discovered a useful (and often free) source of flat (just a few millimetres thick) 6V batteries suitable for use with small transistor devices. He writes:

"I have occasion at my place of work to use a large quantity of Polaroid Image film. Each film pack when exhausted still contains a quite respectable 6V (nominal) dry battery, and it takes but a second to remove the battery from the plastic pack. These batteries are thus free, robust and, being flat, can be fitted into equipment where it may be difficult to install a conventional battery. I have found various uses for these batteries, eg powering the p.e.p circuitry in a power meter where one has now lasted at least six months. Contact to the battery can be made conveniently via fanned out multistrand wire held with Sellotape. Maybe others will also be in a position to make use of this tip."

More on the tune-up protection device

The tune-up protection device for use with hf tranceivers described by Fred Piese, VK3BYW, in *Amateur Radio (VK)* May 1987, and reproduced in *TT* (October 1987, p782) has rightly attracted considerable interest. André Saunders, GM3VLB (ex-5Z4KL), after completing one the night before the CQWW contest, found it invaluable in loading his 135ft end-fed antenna through a single-L, single-C homebrew atu. He comments: "I was able to do this quickly and in complete confidence and without fear of damaging my FT707. Definitely one of the most useful and simple 'gadgets' in a long time."

Unfortunately, as constructors soon found out, VK3BYW's circuit diagram (Fig 9 of the October *TT*) contained errors in respect of the bridge-type swr indicator section. As shown, it will not work properly and may give a false impression. Fortunately, most constructors were able to make the necessary corrections by comparing this part of the circuit with those published in the standard handbooks. Corrections have also been published in *Amateur Radio (VK)* September issue, and by Steve Hart, VK5HA, in the Australian South Coast Amateur Radio Club newsletter *Scarchat* (brought to my notice by John Gill, VK5AJG) although it would appear that VK5HA's diagram still contains an error. Spenny, G6NA, points out that this type of device is not a true swr meter, only a bridge. When the null is zero, then 1:1 swr. At readings other than zero one can assume swr from the table given by VK3BYW (October *TT*). The actual indications are (R) the voltage across the bridge in the classic Wheatstone method, and (F) voltage across a standard resistor. Actual swr can only be measured by reflectometer-type devices which are usually derived from Maxwell's bridge.

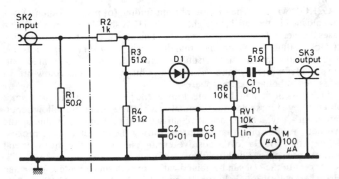

Fig 2. The tune-up gimmick for a low-power (FT7) transceiver as described by G4HHB in 1981

Both G6NA and GM3VLB have provided notes on the modifications they made to produce effective working models, and I feel it is worth showing both versions. More information on this type of swr indicator can be found, for example, in *The ARRL Antenna Handbook,* 14th edition, page 15-4, as "Resistance bridge for swr measurement".

Spenny, G6NA, writes: "I was very interested in VK3BYW's tune-up unit. I have been using a resistive bridge similar to the one described by Les Mays, G4HAS, in *Rad Com* (August 1981, p715) in his article "Safe tune-up with the FT7": Fig 2. This is perfectly ok but does not give any indication of swr, so I find the ability of the new device to read a ratio most attractive.

"I first made up the VK3BYW version as shown on a piece of Veroboard, and it appeared to work reasonably well, albeit insensitively, just about ok on a 50μA meter. This is easily remedied by changing the core of the broadband transformer for a ferrite of about 100μ.

"I then tidied it up may making a small pcb to mount on the tune-send switch. Putting this unit between my atu (with its resistive bridge) and the transmitter I found quite a discrepancy between the tuning demanded by the two bridges. I puzzled over this for a time after I had done all the clever things like matching the diodes at rf and checking to see if stray capacitances were affecting the readings. Then I thought of a drawing error, could not think of a simple one, so rigged it all up again with a 500Ω carbon pot in the antenna position. Sure enough it balanced all right – at minimum ohms, actually 8·29! Another look at the VK3BYW circuit and it became obvious. So back to square one, a couple of circuit changes (see Fig 3) and it works like a charm."

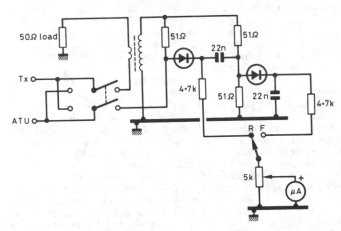

Fig 3. G6NA's modified quiet and safe tune-up device as described by VK3BYW in the October *TT*. Transformer primary two turns, secondary 10 turns on ferrite (μ about 100) core. All resistors two per cent

G6NA adds the comment that he would like to see this and similar devices widely used, not only from the viewpoint of protecting solidstate transmitters but also because of the reduction of on-air tuning squarks. He adds: "Dave Tong can take the squawk out of an in-band tuner, but nothing can reduce desensitising when agc is in use. With the 50μA meter at full sensitivity the antenna should receive only 8mW which ought not to affect wanted signals. Even with a 500μA meter it is 60mW, again a reasonable value. With this little unit no 'final adjustments' will effect any improvement and must be discouraged."

GM3VLB's modifications led to instant success after repeated failures with the circuit as published in October. He writes:

"A search through the literature produced the circuit of a resistance bridge for swr measurements (*ARRL Antenna Handbook* as above) almost, but not quite identical to VK3BYW's circuit. In Fig 4 the circuit to the left of and including the toroidal transformer works flawlessly, and is omitted for the sake of clarity."

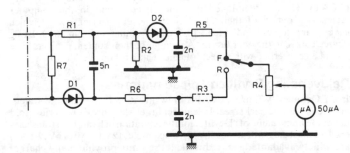

Fig 4. GM3VLB's modification to the resistance-bridge section of VK3BYW's tune-up device. R1, R2 47Ω (0·5W) should be equal in value but the exact value is not critical. R3 approximately 1kΩ but select (see text). R4 47kΩ variable. R5, R6 47kΩ, R7 50Ω (1W), D1, D2 OA90 or OA95

"Some additional notes may be helpful. R5 should be selected to be as close a match to the line impedance as possible. R1 and R2 should be equal but their exact value is not critical. R3 is needed to compensate for slight differences in the arms of the bridge. I found a 1kΩ resistor suitable but a small preset might be convenient. R3 is selected by applying some rf to the transmitter input terminal with no dummy load connected, and then adjusting R3 to give equal meter deflections in the forward and reverse positions."

The Australian tune-up protection gimmick is, in effect, a form of implementation of a silent-tuning principle developed initially at Philips Research Laboratories for military and professional communications systems by Professor Mike Underhill, G3LHZ: see, for example, his article "Simple quiet tuning and matching of antennas", in *Rad Com* May 1981, pp420-2. This system was based on the use of a crystal calibrator/receiver to provide the means of tuning for match. It was developed to permit tuning/matching of Service transmitters under strict "radio silence" conditions. The less rigorous VK3BYW technique seems more suited to the less-demanding amateur radio situation. If widely adopted it would allow amateurs to experiment with antennas without risk of blowing their power amplifier modules and at the same time bring a welcome relief from those loud tuning squawks.

Stable oscillators and pll phase-noise

It has been said that "what we call progress is the exchange of one nuisance for another nuisance". Or, as Oscar Wilde put it: "We are all learning new ways of making old mistakes... success is not having the same problem as last year... experience is the name we give our mistakes." This seems apposite to the low-cost form of pll (phase-locked-loop) frequency synthesisers found in most current hf transceivers and general-coverage receivers. The synthesiser is undoubtedly a convenient and effective form of stable oscillator, and excellent for some applications such as handheld vhf transceivers and general-purpose hf broadcast receivers in permitting users to press-button tune to a desired channel or frequency. High-grade, high-cost professional synthesisers are capable of very high performance. Problems arise, however, when a low-cost pll vfo is used in what would otherwise be high-performance equipment with a good dynamic range.

I recall at the dawn of the professional synthesiser era in the early sixties a heated debate between Marconi engineers who favoured the (very high cost) mixer-type synthesiser and Racal engineers who considered pll-type synthesisers more cost-effective in spite of their inherently greater phase-noise and jitter. Since then enormous research and development effort has been expanded on improving the characteristics of professional pll synthesisers, and the synthesisers fitted in *some* of the currently available amateur equipment have improved significantly, but most still severely limit the near-in dynamic range of receivers, as a study of Peter Hart's equipment reviews will indicate.

For really high performance, as G4DTC put it in the December *TT*: "synthesised oscillators with all their problems should be avoided like the plague. And who needs them (with high-stability vfos)?" To add to the information already given on his Kalitron tunable local oscillator and applicable to all oscillators tuned with variable capacitors: "One of the major sources of drift in LC oscillators is caused by convection currents changing the permittivity of the air between the plates of the variable capacitor. Considerable improvement is effected by placing the capacitor in a draught-proof enclosure." Another technique that was occasionally used for transmitter vfos in the days before the one-unit transceiver was to locate the vfo LC circuit in a separate enclosure well away from any heat-generating devices and then to connect the tuned circuit to the active oscillator device via coaxial cables which formed part of the fixed capacitance.

G4DTC has also queried whether "Kalitron" is the correct spelling for the form of push-pull oscillator used in his "ultimate" receiver. I have never come across the origin of this oscillator which first started to be used in amateur vhf equipment in the 'fifties. It is not mentioned in the comprehensive *Theory and design of valve oscillators* by Dr H A Thomas (first published in 1939) although this includes a push-pull vhff (50MHz) oscillator stabilised by resonant "long lines" (which could take the form of a resonant length of miniature coaxial cable): Fig 6. It is mentioned that "such schemes have been in operation at commercial transmitters and it has been found that the degree of frequency stability attainable is sufficient for most practical purposes. The greatest single factor causing frequency variation is change of temperature; the temperature coefficient of frequency is of the order of 40 parts in 1-million/°C at frequencies in the neighbourhood of 50MHz."

In the "Technical Correspondence" column of *QST* (September 1987, p43), David Newkirk, AK7M, of ARRL, complains that poor choice of terminology can lead to misunderstanding of circuit function and design. His example of this is the phrase "dual digital vfos" applied to synthesised-tuned

amateur transceivers and receivers. He comments: "... nearly every new amateur transceiver these days sports these characteristics: (1) microprocessor frequency control; (2) phase-locked-loop (pll) frequency synthesis; and (3) digital (that is, direct numeric) frequency readout. But this does *not* make such a vfo 'digital'! Far from it, in fact. The non-digital nature of pll vfos is the main reason for the spectre we're coming to know all too well as phase noise. High receiver dynamic range is more or less accepted as important by amateur equipment manufacturers. Now, we must increase their understanding of the fact that noisy oscillators can and do offset improvements in dynamic range. If you've noticed in some receiver/transceiver reviews that a given dynamic-range measurement was said to be 'noise limited' you've seen the result of phase-noisy pll vfos."

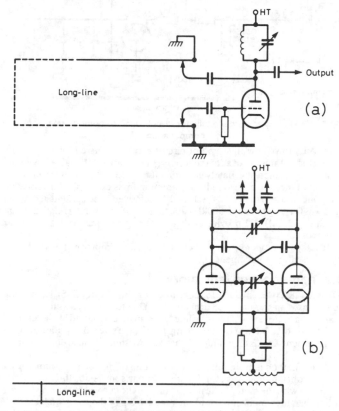

Fig 5. Stabilisation of vhf valve oscillators by means of transmission-line (Lecher lines) section or by coaxial cable section. A solidstate multiband transmission-line oscillator, using quarter-wave sections of miniature coaxial cable and covering 14 to 36MHz in 32 bands was briefly described by Dave Parnell in *TT* June 1987, p408

"What does this have to do with whether or not a vfo is pll or digital? If it's commanded and displayed digitally, it's digital, right? Not necessarily. At the heart of almost all of our pll vfos are phase-locked LC (inductor/capacitor) or vxo (variable crystal oscillator) circuits. Phase locking is simply a method of forcing a vfo or vxo to a desired frequency and holding it there by negative feedback. (Oscillators tuned in this way are almost always controlled by varying the tuning voltage of one or more varactor diodes; such a vfo is thus called a vco; a voltage-controlled crystal oscillator is a vcxo). Because it's possible to use microprocessors to monitor and control pll circuitry, and because microprocessors 'speak digital', many of us feel safe in referring to such microprocessor-controlled pll vcos and vcxos as 'digital'... Yes, there are truly digital vfos, vfos in which the output signal is fabricated piece by piece in digital circuitry. Because such circuits do not use phase-locked loops to achieve good frequency stability, they can, in theory, provide an output very low in phase noise. But the vfos in most of our 'digital vfo' rigs aren't digital at all... Here's my vote for better terminology where microprocessor-controlled vfos are neither dual nor digital: 'dual vfo command registers'. It almost sounds like something new."

The 1939 book on oscillators by Dr Thomas, referred to above, includes many ingenious compensation techniques to improve the stability of oscillators against voltage changes, including resistance (reactance) stabilisation, phase-compensation and the German Dow electron-coupled tetrode/pentode oscillator (the origin of the once extremely popular "eco") as well as amplitude-limited techniques by Arguimbau and Groszkowski. Two-valve oscillators include the classic two-valve Franklin master oscillator and the Ross-Gunn oscillator which is basically similar to the Kalitron except that it used two tuned circuits, one in each anode circuit.

Although all these oscillator circuits were originally developed for use with valves, most of them can and have been successfully implemented in solidstate form. Walter Glazar, W3WI, in *QST* revives, in modern guise, F Llewellyn's 1931 reactance-compensated oscillator which can be implemented by the simple expedient of adjusting the reactance of a strategically-located bypass or coupling capacitor to minimise frequency variations due to changes in supply voltage which cannot be entirely eliminated by the use of conventional ic regulators.

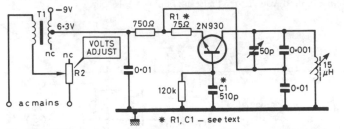

Fig 6. W3WI's experimental oscillator circuit used to demonstrate reactance compensation

W3WI shows how this type of circuit can be adjusted by temporarily adding a small amount of ac to the supply (Fig 7) until a detectable fm wobble is on the note, then alternately adjusting the value of C1 and R1 to improve the tone. Once the adjustment for minimum fm is established, fixed-valve components are installed (C1, R1) and T1 removed. The oscillator shown in Fig 6 was for use at about 1,500kHz and C1 (510pF) presents a relatively high reactance (230Ω). R1 provides a degree of negative feedback and further improves stability.

Reactance compensation can even be used to improve the stability of crystal oscillators in demanding situations.

Star hf resonance indicator

TT June 1985, p455, included a short note from Ian White, G3SEK, showing how he uses an swr meter to trim coaxial cable to length so as to form, for example, a half-wave vhf phasing line. This, in turn, resulted in a letter from Bill McLeod, VK3MI, reporting further experiments leading to improvements in this technique. He has also written this up in detail in *Amateur Radio (VK)* July 1987, pp26-7. His experiences have shown that this modified method is more suitable for low or high-impedance sections using the appropriate load resistor for the comparison. Also, the accuracy is improved with the meter indicating a "dip" in the current to the resistive leg rather than maximum current to the reactive leg of the two parallel paths.

In his *Amateur Radio* article he points to some shortcomings in using gdos or hf noise bridges when an accurate resonance indication is required. On the other hand, he suggests that a toroid transformer-type swr meter can be used very effectively as an indicator for a variety of antenna adjustments:

"These instruments compare the phase and amplitude of the voltage and current indication sections. Like the noise bridge, they are calibrated and compensated for 50Ω or 75Ω transmission lines. Below 10Ω, the current meter section still indicates but the voltmeter is starved; over 250Ω the opposite effect occurs, with voltage indicated but insufficient current. These characteristics can be used as an indicator for transmission line tests using suitable comparison terminations and a buffer pad for a power signal generator which can be the station vfo, a low-power driver stage or a QRP transmitter (Or possibly the VK3BYW transformer plus dummy load technique? – G3VA).

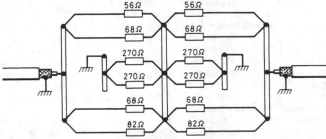

Fig 7. 6dB, 50Ω attenuator pad for VK3MI's Star hf resonance indicator. Series resistors 2W metal oxide: 1 by 56Ω, 2 by 68Ω, 1 by 82Ω. Shunt resistors (2W metal oxide) 4 by 270Ω (or 1 by 66·9Ω). Common bars: multiblock inserts each drilled three ways transversly

"A 6dB attenuation pad is normally used to reduce the voltage and current each to half the input value for a 50Ω termination, ie it reduces the power by a quarter. When terminated by a non-reactive 50Ω resistor it can become a dummy load. More importantly it also has the property of only changing from 30Ω to 84Ω at the input port when the output is either shorted or left open. These are values well within the 2:1 capability of most solidstate equipment designed for 50Ω.

"It is essential to buffer equipment during initial tune-up or for antenna and transmission line testing. Also it is ideal to allow the use of 5Ω and 330Ω terminations in tests using the swr meter for a dip indicator, as it tends towards a current limited source when the load approaches zero and as a constant voltage device for high impedance loads.

"Power handling capacity of available non-reactive resistors is a difficulty but metal oxide types are obtainable in 2W rating. A pad capable of absorbing 10W of rf power with the output port open-circuit can be built using the T-configuration as in Fig 7.

"Then, for testing series tank circuits and quarter-wave stubs (inverting sections) to an open circuit at the remote end, and also half-wave lines (repeating sections) to a short-circuit, the output port of the 6dB pad can feed via a T-connector to both a 5Ω termination (two 10Ω resistors in parallel) and the test section in parallel, as in Fig 8(a). The swr meter in the resistive leg does *not* indicate swr, as insufficient voltage is developed across the load for that section materially to affect the reading. However, in-phase current to the resistive termination shows a dip when it is 'robbed' by the line section, falling to minimum value at resonance. As a check, disconnect the line section to permit the dip to rise to maximum reading, showing that the dip is not due to any other circuitry. Then substitute a non-reactive resistor, usually 1 to 10Ω, for the same dip reading. This value is the equivalent series loss of the test section; for example, RG58 cable will be about 2·5Ω for a quarter-wave section at 3·6MHz, increasing for poor quality or damaged cable; this measurement can be converted into a cable specification figure for loss per 100ft or per 100m.

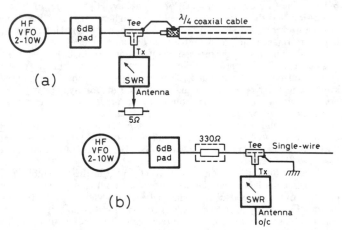

Fig 8. (a) Set-up for hf resonance indicator 1 to 20Ω; (b) for 200 to 1,000Ω

"The arrangement in Fig 9(b) can be used for higher impendances from 200Ω to 1,000Ω where a bridge with a suitable range is not available (the 'ant' port of the swr is left open). However, this is of less practical value and accuracy than the low impedance case, as the test sample is usually subject to other influences: for example, a half-wave wire must include the distance to effective earth from the T-coupler and the compacitance to earth (the same restrictions apply to other methods of measurement).

"The frequency accuracy of this dip method can be better than one per cent with a reasonable frequency-readout from the vfo... A complete instrument could be constructed. However, for occasional use, the station swr meter provides a readily-available indicator, while the 6dB pad limits and protects the source as well as its other uses."

Antenna installation tips

Peter Delaney, G8KZG, still overhears much discussion among amateurs on such antenna installation topics as the effective weatherproofing of cable joints, plugs/sockets etc.

Other aspects, such as the strains imposed on coaxial cable during and after installation, are often disregarded entirely. He considers that a publication, issued several years ago by Pye Telecommunications Ltd *HF, VHF and UHF Communication Antennas* (TSP220/5), contains practical tips that are worthy of wider distribution.

The introductory general section covers topics relating to the use of coaxial cable feeders, weatherproofing, baluns, wind velocity, pressure and wind/ice loading etc. I trust that I am not infringing any Pye Telecommunications copyright by paraphrasing some brief extracts from this useful section, interposed with some additional comments by G8KZG and myself.

Coaxial cable. Pye point out that a major source of losses in conventional braided cable, compared with the more expensive cables with solid copper sheathing, is the effects of moisture on the braid. Water can quickly oxidise copper braid and increase resistive losses without changing the nominal impedance of the cable. It is emphasised that any damage to the outer sheath, even a pin-hole, will allow in time a considerable amount of rain-water to reach the braid, yet will be almost impossible to detect. (**Note:** the test procedure outlined by VK3MI on page 109 should detect a change in cable resistance — G3VA.) It is believed that pvc-sheathed cables are more vulnerable in this respect than polythene-sheathed cables, and polythene sheathing is to be preferred. Cable with a solid outer rather than braiding is potentially the more reliable, and Pye suggest that this could repay in time the extra initial cost in some (exposed) installations.

Handling coaxial cable. Pye note that many antenna faults are brought about by the mishandling of the feeder cable during installation. Tension can cause either open- or short-circuits. Should the braid be pulled free of the clamping ring in the plug, one or more of the fine wires can short to the inner conductor. Alternatively, the inner conductor and polythene insulation can be caused to move inside the braid, causing the centre pin to lose contact with the socket and result in an open-circuit fault. During and after installation, cable should be treated with care and never subjected to tension. Cable runs should always be supported by the mast or a carrier wire. (Unfortunately, this is often a counsel of excellence rather than practical policy for hf wire dipoles other than the inverted-V types, but can usually be followed for beam arrays and most vhf/uhf antennas — G3VA.)

With 10mm (0·405in) cable, it is not advisable even to take a length up a mast and drop one end to the ground; nor to leave the coil on the ground and feed one end up the mast. Preferably, the coil of cable should be taken up the mast, the top secured and the feeder fastened to the mast (without undue tension on the cable) progressively as the coil is lowered. Pye stress that coaxial cable is not a homogeneous conductor: the outer covering, braid, polythene and inner conductor can all, under stress, move relative to one another; furthermore under stress any one of these layers could take the whole load. Note that, for example, 45m (150ft) of URM67 cable weighs a substantial 7kg, while the inner conductor comprises only seven strands of 0·77mm diameter copper wire. G8KZG feels that few amateurs ever pay much attention to the tensions resulting from the weight of coaxial cables when installing an antenna, or the possibility that the core could have to carry the full weight of the load.

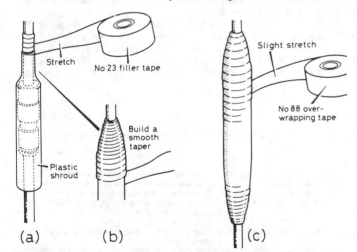

Fig 9. Waterproofing an external coaxial-cable socket and plug connection as recommended by Pye Telecommunications

Waterproofing connectors. Plug and socket connectors exposed to the elements always need additional protection; without it there will sooner or later be moisture ingress, possibly ruining the cable over a considerable length due to hygroscopic effects in foam or semi-air-spaced cable as well as braid corrosion. Pye warn that permanently-joined connectors for fixed installations, even inside a plastic shroud such as those supplied for pmr base stations, should be further protected by winding with suitable tapes: Fig 9. After extensive tests, Pye recommend the use of a combination of two 3M "Scotch" wrapping tapes, Nos 23 and 88.

Both are elastic filler tapes of the type described in 1985 (*TT* January, March and June) as "self-amalgamating" tape when a debate arose on the degree that such tapes are vulnerable to ultraviolet rays in sunlight. Pye recommend 3M No 23 to provide the basic weatherproofing and to build up the steps between the cable and the connectors. The No 88 tape then provides a tough over-wrapping which gives mechanical protection to the join. Pye state: "These self-bonding tapes, when applied correctly together, provide a sound waterproof covering suitable for all climates".

The recommended method of wrapping, shown in Fig 9, is described as follows: "Remove the paper backing from a length of No 23 tape and commence wrapping on the coaxial cable about 38mm (1·5in) from the connector, Fig 9 (a). The tape should be stretched to two/three times its natural length as the wrap is carried out, and each turn should overlap the previous one by about 50 per cent (ie half-lapping). When wrapping over a step, several turns are necessary in order to build up a comparatively even taper (Fig 9 (b)). The wrap should be finished on the coaxial cable at about 38mm (1·5in) beyond the second connector, and for the final turn the tape should be only slightly stretched. Applied in this manner the tape will easily fuse into an inseparable void-free mass. The over-wrapping with No 88 tape (Fig 9 (c)) should completely cover the previous wrap, starting slightly before the beginning of the filler tape. A full turn with 100 per cent overlap is recommended before winding on with a 50 per cent overlapping. The tape should be stretched slightly during winding but relaxed on the final turn which, like the first, should have a 100 per cent overlap and completely cover the end of the filler tape."

G8KZG uses a variation of the Pye technique. After applying the self-amalgamating tape as described, he adds a generous layer of "Hammerite" paint to cover the entire joint with a margin at either end as a protection against uv. He comments: "This *appears* to provide an effective and lasting seal, although, of course, I cannot enter into the type of testing that companies such as Pye can undertake." On the 3M "Scotch" tapes he adds: "No 88 is described as a 'flame retardant cold and weather resistant . . . for applications where superior cold-weather resistance is judged important'. It is basically a pvc insulating tape of superior grade. Tape No 33 would also seem suitable, it is also pvc and can be used down to −17·8°C and is specifically claimed to be 'highly resistant to physical abuse, chemical attack, and ultraviolet light'. It also seems rather easier to obtain (eg Farnell in Leeds)."

Checking antenna installations

The Pye Telecommunications publication *TSP220/5* also provides a useful reminder on some aspects of antenna checking with particular reference to the effect of feeder losses on vswr readings. As G8KZG comments, this is a hardy annual topic but, judging by comments overhead on the bands, is still frequently misunderstood.

Pye point out that a dc continuity check on an antenna installation can often reveal open-circuits or poor connections. (This is always true of folded dipole driven elements; with non-folded elements open-circuits in the feeder can be detected from the shack if a high-value, eg 100kΩ, resistor is wired across the centre-gap (feedpoint) of the element for this purpose — G3VA.) It is more difficult to recognise a short-circuit feeder or a moisture-ruined element even with the aid of a vswr check. Broadcasters often use a vswr "trip" to close down automatically a high-power transmitter in the event of an antenna/feeder fault, yet at least one four-channel uhf television antenna at a main station (Durris, near Aberdeen) caught fire and was damaged beyond repair when a trip re-set correctly because a fault had carbonized a short-circuited cable up the mast forming a matched dummy load. This deprived some millions of viewers in Scotland of all four programme channels for some days — and several thousands of viewers of acceptable signals for many months while a replacement antenna providing the same coverage as the original antenna was being built.

Pye point out that the accuracy of the match between the antenna and the transmission line when measured by a reflectometer depends on where the vswr meter is inserted in the system. If the point of measurement is remote from the discontinuity or change of impedance, then the vswr reading needs to be corrected to allow for the cable loss which has the effect of reducing the reflected power. Fig 10 shows this effect quantatively. For example, a vswr of 1·5:1 at the antenna junction will appear as 1·3:1 at the end of a cable having a loss of 2dB, as would be the case with 100ft (30m) of URM67 cable at 100MHz. It should be noted

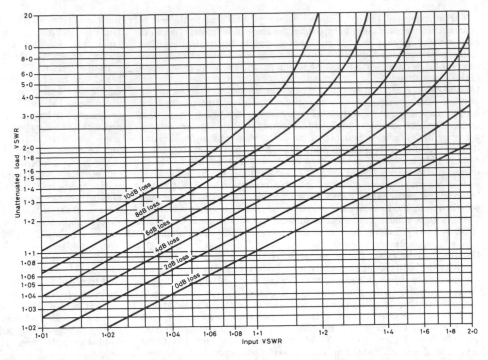

Fig 10. The effect of feeder attenuation on measured vswr. For example, an antenna with an unattenuated vswr of 10:1 and a feeder loss of 6dB would appear to have a vswr when measuured at the transmitter end of only 1·5:1

that *any* termination, including an open circuit, will produce a vswr not exceeding 1·25:1 at the end of a cable having a loss equal to or greater than 10dB as might well be the case for a cable ruined by moisture ingress.

Faulty, high loss, feeders will thus always show a low vswr, for example a feeder with badly-oxidised braiding. It is important always to investigate any *change* in the vswr of an antenna because, under certain conditions, an increase in feeder loss is likely to result in an *improvement* in the vswr measured at the equipment end of the feeder. Because comparison is the best guide to deterioration in the antenna system, it is thus essential that initial readings be made and recorded.

Pye recommended the following procedure:
(1) Before erecting an antenna, check and record: *(a)* the dc resistance of the feeder (centre conductor and outer connected together at one end); *(b)* insulation of feeder (between centre conductor and outer); and *(c)* vswr of antenna.
(2) When the antenna has been installed, check and record: *(a)* vswr of system; and *(b)* dc resistance of system read between centre conductor and outer.

Incidentally, for those who still set great store in achieving an extremely low vswr, just add a long length of lossy cable to your feeder. You, but not your contacts if any, will be delighted at the difference it makes to your vswr!

G6XN's end-fed Windom

Almost 60 years ago (*QST* September 1929), L Windom, W8GZ, described the use of a single-wire feeder for a half-wave dipole antenna. This soon became known worldwide as a "Windom antenna" although (as John D Kraus, W8JK, has pointed out) the principle of the single-wire feeder was originally conceived and developed by Bill Everitt and John Byrne at Ohio State University.

In effect, the single-wire feeder, when matched correctly to the correct point along the dipole element, is itself a transmission-line antenna so that some energy must always be radiated from such a feeder, unlike a twin-wire or coaxial transmission line. The traditional method of adjusting the tapping point is to aim at there being no standing waves on the feeder wire (in the early days by running a neon along the line). Nevertheless, even when correctly adjusted, a single-wire feeder always radiates some energy and is to some extent a lossy feeder and a source of moderate rf fields when brought into the shack.

Les Moxon, G6XN, in a recent letter, admits that in his book, *HF antennas for all locations* (RSGB), he gives the Windom antenna a rough time, including it in the section "feeder systems to be avoided" and emphasising its losses. However, this assumed a long feeder line, and he points our that for a feeder length of around λ/2 it can be shown that the power radiated from it is the same as from a dipole carrying, at its centre, the same relatively low current. It is thus equivalent to a loss of only

0·6dB; this would rise to a much more significant 3dB loss by radiation only for a very long straight single-wire feeder.

"In addition there is the earth loss which comes to 0·18dB for a quarter-wave 'artifical earth' which has the advantage of being easy to calculate, but could probably be eliminated (at least at the lower frequencies where it can be long enough to be out in the clear) by using a shorter wire or counterpoise with inductive loading.

"I have applied the idea to a full-wave inverted-V for 7MHz, erected as a temporary substitute for a beam lost in the October hurricane. This has yet to be evaluated for 7MHz dx but works as well as can be expected of a long-wire antenna on 14MHz where the swr is about 3·0, though on 7MHz it is less than 1·2! Perhaps more to the point, I set up a 'scale model' at 29MHz, comparing a half-wave dipole centre-fed (75Ω twin feeder) with the same dipole end-fed with about 1·5λ of single wire. Assuming a loss of 0·35dB in the twin feeder, the total loss for the single-wire feeder plus artificial earth came to 2dB (ie 1·65dB down) which seems reasonable but emphasises the need to keep the single-wire feeder lengths as short as possible (for 3·5MHz even a half-wavelength would represent a very long feeder!).

"Replacement of the centre feed by end-feeding, Zepp-fashion but with a G6CJ balancing stub, gave identical results but only after going to some length to reduce stub losses (heavy gauge and widespacing). Removal of the balancing stub then caused a loss of only 1dB, in line with experience that the conventional Zepp feed *sometimes* seem to work well enough."

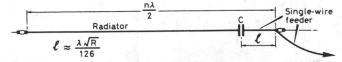

$$\ell \approx \frac{\lambda\sqrt{R}}{126}$$

Fig 11. G6XN's end-fed Windom antenna with single-wire feeder. λ is wavelength in feet. R is radiation resistance (referred to a current loop). A value of 500Ω is assumed for the impedance of the single-wire feeder. Reactance of capacitor C is 1/λ C approximately equal to 70λ/l.
Values found in practice:
At 7MHz, l = 12ft for n = 2 (C = 27pF).
At 29MHz, l = 2ft for n = 1 (C variable and not measured but estimated to be about 5pF).
Principle of operation: From a point of maximum rf voltage on the antenna one moves a short distance outwards to find an impedance (from a Smith Chart) equal to R + jx, where R matches the single wire feeder, X being tuned by the capacitor. Since l is short and current in it small, its virtual removal from the radiator has negligible effect on field strength

G6XN has developed further thoughts on Zepp antennas and or radials but these must be held over. So back to the end-fed Windom: Fig 11. G6XN writes: "The important thing is that it provides a much simpler method of end feeding, without the complication of the G6CJ balancing stub, the unpredictable losses of the conventional Zepp arrangement, or the mechanical and weatherproofing problems of remote tuners for voltage-fed antennas. Were it not for these problems, end-feeding would tend to be more attactive than centre feeding for non-rotatable antennas, since the ends are more likely to be within reach of or close to the shack. In addition the centre of the element no longer has to support the weight of the feeder.

"The matching principle used for the single-wire feed had previously been used in a two-wire version for matching the 'Claw' antenna at ground level (near the mast) on 10MHz, and for matching each of a pair of inverted-V elements at 7MHz. I have never come across it elsewhere and find it extremely useful; however, since it is more or less what the Smith Chart tells one to do, I can hardly claim it to be original.

"The single-wire feeder should be particularly useful for inverted groundplanes (see for example *TT* November 1987, Fig 3(f), p836). It may also be of interest to note that if R increases as f^2 and is small enough, one would have an ideal multiband system with nearly the same value of capacitance needed, in the same place, on the fundamental and all harmonics until l approaches one-eighth-wave. There is a tendency for this and, though it does not quite happen in practice, the fact that capacitors for different bands are nearly co-located and in many cases accessible does lead to interesting possibilities for multiband operation, without the loss of efficiency and the 'rf in the shack' problems sometimes associated with random-length wire antennas; but one is restricted by the need to keep the feeder short in terms of wavelength."

Passive frequency multipliers

Modern practice, stemming primarily from ssb requirements and the use of pll frequency synthesisers, has reduced the use of the one-popular Class C frequency doubler/multipliers of the valve era. Oscillator chains for uhf operation often use diode frequency multipliers, including varactor diode multipliers that are "passive" in the sense of not requiring to be powered other than by the rf input.

Chris Randall, G4RBR, and David Skinner, G3PVH, have both drawn attention to an item in the publication *News from Rohde & Schwarz* (No 118, 1987/3) on passive frequency multipliers. The article is based on a recent R&S patent (DE 3524 112C1) due to the work of Bernd Fritze. As mentioned several times *TT*, it is perfectly in order to use patent disclosures for experimental (ie home construction) purposes, but not for commercial products except under licence from the patentees.

R&S point out that frequency multipliers made up solely of passive components are simple in their design and afford reduced interference, but on the other hand they present the disadvantage that the forward voltage across the diodes, corresponding to the difference between input and output voltages, is reduced by the generated output voltage just when the diodes should pass the maximum current for the purpose of obtaining high efficiency especially for generating higher harmonics. Furthermore this output voltage increases the reverse voltage across the diodes just when minimal current should flow, ie the diodes should be cut off.

The article continues: "The invention based on replacing the diodes by common-base transistors makes the current, being an exponential value of the input voltage, virtually independent of the output voltage. A frequency multiplier of this type generates sufficient current even in the case of output circuits designed for higher harmonics, and the output

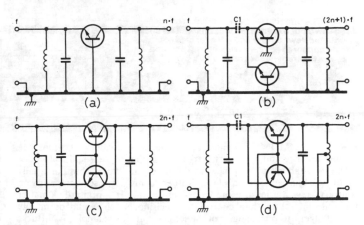

Fig 12. Passive frequency multipliers as described in the R&S patent using common-base transistors and complementary-pair transistors in various configurations

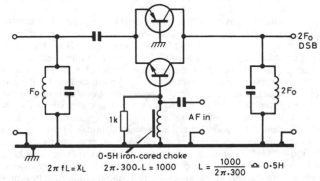

Fig 13. G3PVH's suggested balanced modulator with single-ended input and output tuned circuits based on the R&S passive frequency multiplier concept

circuit can therefore be excited to yield higher multiplication factors at greater efficiency. In addition, the minimum forward voltage of transistors is smaller than that of diodes, so efficiency is improved even more. The transistors work as purely passive components without an extra operating voltage."

R&S show four examples of passive frequency multipliers based on the use of common-base transistors (Fig 12), including the use of a single transistor, and complementary pairs (ie one npn and one pnp device of similar characteristics). In *(a)* the input circuit presents a low impedance at the desired harmonic frequency and the output tuned circuit filters the desired even or odd harmonics out of the generated spectrum; *(b)*, with the transistors in parallel, is for the generation of odd harmonics, while *(c)* produces even harmonics, the odd-numbered harmonics being suppressed with the input circuit configured as an unbalance-to-balance transformer; *(d)* has the output circuit in the form of a balance-to unbalance transformer and is for the production of even-numbered harmonics. It is noted that the suppression of unwanted harmonics is particularly effective with circuits using complementary transistors if the emitter currents are made symmetrical by C1.

G3PVH believes that this approach could also be used as a balanced modulator producing suppressed carrier double-sideband output at twice the input frequency. Fig 13 shows his suggested arrangement with single-ended input and output, though I do not think he had actually tried this idea at the time of writing. □

Technical Topics
Pat Hawker, G3VA

FIRST THIS MONTH, I must thank the many readers who took the trouble to write and express their conviction that there is still a place for *TT* in its established form in which both new and "old" (but potentially useful) technology finds a place. Rather to my surprise there were no contrary views, at least in the letters sent to me. It is primarily a matter for editorial rather than contributor decision and it would be unduly self-indulgent to quote many of the letters; but, for example, L N Buck, G0DLR, shares my concern over a too uncritical acceptance of micro-processors built into transceivers *for amateur radio,* no matter how useful they may be for commercial and military circuits where the criteria are different and the contacts are not made for the interest and enlightenment of the *operators.*

G0DLR writes: "That microprocessor-controlled equipment is easy to operate is undoubtedly true, especially with solidstate power amplifiers and linear amplifiers that automatically tune themselves. However, when tuning and loading my old-fashioned FT101ZD with its unprotected valve output stage, and my equally outdated homebrew linear with its incredibly ancient 813s, I am in control of the equipment and do have a fair idea of what goes on inside; unlike, I suspect, a lot of the owners of the latest 'automated' equipment which does practically everything except hold the QSO (The latest generation of adaptive automatic hf radio systems developed for commercial/military applications by Plessey and Rohde and Schwarz does even that in designing the operator right out of the system – *G3VA*). Making radio gear so easy to operate is without doubt brilliant technology, but puts its construction and design beyond the abilities and pockets of all but a very few, and if equipment becomes so 'clever' that its adjustment and maintenance by the operator becomes unnecessary, one might as well use the telephone, which can give worldwide communication at a fraction of the cost.

"One of the features of modern equipment that intrigues me is the proliferation of memories. Do people actually find uses for these? Some years ago I was able to acquire at bargain price a remote digital vfo for my FT101ZD, and this is festooned with memory buttons. I'd love to be able to justify them! The vfo is occasionally useful but most of its life is spent sitting alongside the rig with its display and l.e.ds glowing and looking impressive!"

In looking this month at some aspects of microprocessor-controlled transceivers and receivers I would also stress that such techniques require the use of synthesisers, which in the low-cost amateur-budget form place a finite limitation on performance in terms of near-in dynamic range, and often on the not so near-in. Purchasers need to balance the operational convenience against critical on-air performance.

Tomorrow's equipment

The recent items on the high-performance "ultimate" lf/mf/hf receiver developed by Ray Howgego, G4DTC, have indicated that current, factory-built equipment designed for the budget-limited amateur market still involves a number of significant compromises, some demanded by features that many (though not all) have come to accept as essential. G4DTC highlighted problems stemming from all-solidstate front-ends with broadband pre-mixer selectivity, pll frequency synthesis, digital noise arising from inappropriate lay-out/inadequate screening/filtering of digital frequency read-out etc. He solved these problems by not using a pll synthesiser, by the use of two thermionic devices (PCC189 cascode rf amplifier/7360 beam-deflection mixer) and free-running Kalitron hf local oscillator and *no* microprocessor control systems, while emphasising that it is not sufficient simply to use such configurations without very careful consideration of such traditional factors as gain-distribution, gain-control and premixer selectivity.

Coincidentally, the annual "receivers issue" of *Ham Radio Magazine* (November 1987) included two important articles on modern receiver design. Robert J Zavrel, W7SX, in "Tomorrow's receivers: what will the next 20 years bring?" refers to many of the same problems noted by G4DTC but forecasts that these may be gradually overcome in future by using new technology that has still to impact on amateur receivers and transceivers.

concentrating on increasing the dynamic range of mixers by the use of improved passive ring mixers in which a number of diodes are paralleled in order to improve their strong-signal performance. Such devices are costly and also require a great deal of local oscillator power. For example, to handle an rf signal of 100mW the oscillator output needs to be at least 1W, since a ring mixer needs roughly 10 times the rf signal power to achieve optimum results as a linear commutation (switching) mixer, preferably with the drive in the form of a near square-wave signal.

W7SX sees one solution to this problem in the use of the integrated passive fet ring mixer as exemplified by the Siliconix Si8901. This was described, following the receipt of information directly from Ed Oxner, KB6QJ, of Siliconix, for the very first time in any amateur radio journal in *TT* March 1986, and also in my contribution to IERE Conference Book No 64, July 1986 "Dynamic range: fact or fiction?" W7SX writes: "With this device, gate voltage rather than a forward-biasing current turns the switches 'on' and 'off'. Since the gates represent high impedances, voltage/power ratios can be increased, thus lowering the local oscillator power requirements dramatically. Indeed, to handle the same 100mW rf power of our diode ring example, the Si8901 requires about 25mW of local oscillator power instead of the 1W mandated by the diode rings. The other critical specification is the third-order intercept point, which is necessary for defining the useful dynamic range. Again, the Si8901 greatly surpasses the old diode ring mixer."

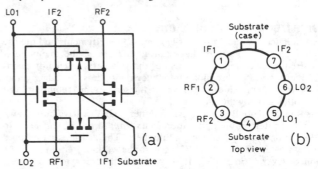

Fig 1. Siliconix Si8901 ring demodulator/balanced mixer: (a) Functional block diagram: (b) Pin configuration with Si8901A in TO-78 and Si8901Y as surface-mounted So14 configuration

In *TT* March 1986, KB6QJ reported his experimental Si8901 mixer with a resonate-drive transformer as achieving third-order intercept points of +39dBm (input) with only +17dBm of local oscillator power. Others had reported third-order intercept points of over 40dBm presumably with increase of oscillator power. Figs 1–3 are taken from the Siliconix publication "Designing a super-high dynamic range double-balanced mixer" which incorporates the Siliconix Application Note (AN85-2) on this device. As mentioned in *TT* August 1986, this is available from the Publicity Department, Siliconix Ltd, Morriston, Swansea AS6 6NE (tel 0792 74681). A recent enquiry indicates that this device is available both in a conventional can mounting as the Si8901a, and as a surface-mounted device. In small quantities the Si8901a costs just

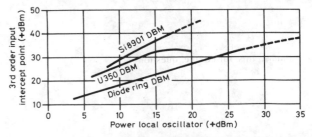

Fig 2. Performance comparison between Si8901 dbm, U350 fet active dbm and diode ring dbm

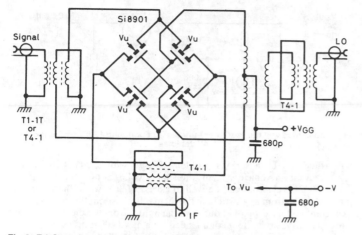

Fig 3. Ed Oxner's prototype commutation double-balanced mixer as described in the Siliconix application notes

under £13, which puts it in much the same price bracket as the 7360 mixer (you can't expect to be as lucky as G2AUB who admits to once buying three 7360 valves for three shillings!). W7SX believes that the Si8901 should also make an excellent active mixer, using the same concepts as for the old U350 jfet devices.

W7SX considers that synthesisers offer distinct advantages in that they can be directly controlled by microprocessors and do not require special mechanical rigidity or moving parts, but admits that at present it is difficult, if not impossible, to duplicate the permeability-tuned oscillators of the 'sixties with pll synthesis, given the constraints of typical amateur budgets. He notes, however, that another type of synthesiser – the "direct digital synthesiser" – holds great promise for the future. It is also possible that synchronous oscillators, as in the old-style synchrodyne receivers, may provide a solution.

Microprocessors in receivers

In the same "receiver" issue of *Ham Radio* (November 1987), another well-known designer of advanced military hf receivers, Professor Ulrich L Rohde, KA2WEU/DJ2LR, contributes an article "Designing a state-of-the-art receiver", sub-titled "Readily understood – though not greatly utilised – concepts mean better performance". In this he stresses: "The state of the art in hf receiver design using semiconductors has improved greatly. The use of either CATV-type transistors (ie transistors developed specifically for the distribution amplifiers in cable television networks) and double-balanced mixers using hot carrier diodes or double-balanced mixers with switch-type fets have eased the large-signal handling problem of just a decade ago."

But he adds: "One weak link in the chain, however, remains; this is the synthesiser, with its inherent noise contributions. To a large extent the overall architecture of the receiver and the synthesiser determines the performance, and even the best high-performance components – placed in the wrong sequence – can cause a good design to fail."

DJ2LR devotes much of his article to the use of microprocessors in receivers, although he carefully distinguishes between the *essentials* of high-performance receivers and the additional "bells and whistles" features made possible by microprocessor-controlled synthesisers: Fig 4. He notes that these features include improved user interfaces or computer interfaces for remote control. Since the commercial and amateur markets are price-sensitive and also very sensitive to proof of performance, any claims of lower capabilities are noticed: "Consequently, when on-the-air tests of some late-model receivers suggested poorer performance than previous models, this raised the question of why, despite the knowledge acquired in recent years, such an inconsistency should occur."

Fig 4. Architecture of the elaborate internal computer system found in modern professional fully-synthesised receiver (DJ2LR)

In effect, as I understand it, DJ2JR recognises that the inclusion of pll synthesisers in a high-performance, amateur-budget receiver, in order to provide "bells and whistles" features, still involves accepting some degradation of its basic performance as a receiver. It thus remains a matter for individual amateurs to decide which is the more important to them; the basic performance or the bells and whistles features.

DJ2LR notes that the sections of the synthesiser most vulnerable to picking up extraneous signals are the lines going into the output vco. Inexpensive solutions frequently lead to high-impedance feeding points which then become "antennas" collecting all the switching noise; another reason for noisy synthesisers is the use, in the synthesiser loops, of operational amplifiers that are too noisy. Either discrete low-noise amplifiers or Darlington stages should be used. Detailed analyses of the noise and jitter sources in pll synthesisers have been given in professional papers by such writers as Professor Mike Underhill, G3LHZ, and Peter Chadwick, G3RZP, in which they stress that on account of its basic simplicity the digital pll is likely to remain a major technique for frequency synthesisers in the years to come, while stressing that an acceptable compromise of low noise and good switching speed can be achieved *only by careful pll design*. For those who value near-in dynamic range etc, there is much to be said for G4DTC's advice that "synthesisers should be avoided like the plague" – at least in the highest-performance, hf receivers.

To do this would involve the omission of microprocessor control which, as DJ2LR points out, enables receivers to feature built-in clocks, frequency-scanning with variable scan rates, availability of at least 100 channels and channel scanning, plus a combination of receiver control functions such as the serial RS-232 or IEE-488 bus remote control capabilities. Because the bfo and the main oscillator are both synthesised, the combination of the two allows either passband tuning or variable bandwidth.

"Another area of interest in the use of microprocessors is the linearisation of the transfer characteristic of the tuning range of the oscillator and the linearisation of the S-meter. The microprocessor can also switch the tuning rates to correspond to the operating mode and select the appropriate bandwidth receiving crystal filters required for that same mode. Digital implementation of signal analysis allows demodulation of rtty and morse code. Many other novel approaches are possible . . . One of the frequent mistakes made in this context is the use of only one microprocessor, which gets overloaded, or the use of four-bit microprocessors. In better radios, eight-bit microprocessors, which can handle all these functions efficiently, are used. The best approach is parallel processing."

Automatic receivers

In *TT* October 1987, I noted the Plessey work aimed at further de-skilling hf operation by using the increasing availability of low-cost computer power to develop an adaptive, fully automatic, hf radio system that can run unattended by any operators. Alan Williams, G3KSU, has sent along further information on this system (Fig 5) as published in the autumn 1987 issue of Plessey's *New Technology*. It is introduced as follows: "Historically, in order to establish an hf skywave link between two points, a pre-arranged frequency-time calling schedule, or a lot of luck, has been required. Assuming that the intended receiving operator is monitoring the correct channels, at the correct time, or using a large bank of receivers

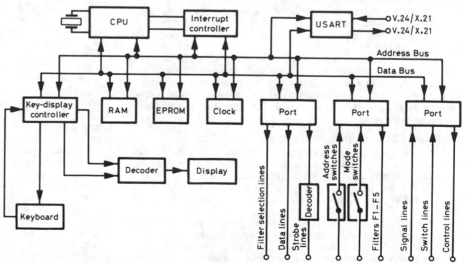

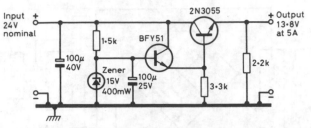

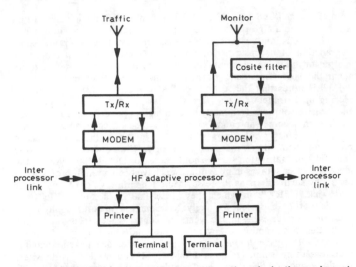

Fig 5. Station configuration of the Plessey automatic and adaptive equipment that finds and selects usable channels, makes contacts with other similar stations and passes traffic without requiring any operator to be in attendance

Fig 6. Stabilised voltage regulator suitable for supplying 13·8V equipment in 24V vehicles

simultaneously, then the initiating operator would call on different frequencies, in turn, until a reply is received. This method requires skilled operators, and often a great deal of time, to establish a link. The links often fail during natural ionospheric disturbance, even though predictions can be calculated. The establishment and maintenance of communications, using skywave propagation, either without skilled operators or when the ionosphere is highly disturbed, requires an adaptive system with a linking protocol. Plessey Military Communications has designed and supplied to MoD an adaptive system which is both simple to operate and requires a minimum of operator interaction to establish and maintain a network of links. Since each station in the network may be container mounted, if necessary, deployment is rapid and requires a minimum of setting up, prior to traffic transmission."

During 1987, Racal introduced a new range of "modular" receivers (types RA3701-4) for a wide range of professional and military applications that rely heavily on processors, three back-lit crystal display panels and a four-key menu system to control up to 24 special features. The user is instructed how to proceed by messages in the display panel, and provided with elaborate "bite" (built-in test-equipment) facilities. As equipment becomes more and more complex, the requirement for bite facilities becomes more and more important. The Racal system is claimed to operate at five levels:

(1) Automatically at power-up providing basic processor module and memory tests.

(2) Continuous monitoring of correct operation.

(3) Operator initiated confidence check, providing a complete automatic self-test of all modules.

(4) Fault finding, which calls up any of the automatic tests on request and includes signature analysis. Tests requiring manual intervention, such as remote control loop-back tests, are included at this level.

(5) Factory test. The receiver cycles continuously through its automatic self-test. Results of the tests are displayed and faults can be investigated further using the bite menu facilities, instructions being provided to the operator at each step.

So there we are, some of the wonders of new technology of digital electronics and microprocessors for those with very deep pockets. But take your choice as to whether all this adds much to the basic interest of amateur radio operating with understandable technology; or comes down to computer talking to computer, with the operator, if any, as an unnecessary passenger.

Powering 12V equipment from 24V supplies

TT (November 1987, p835) included an idea from a reader of *Electronic Australia* on the use of a series of bridge-rectifiers, producing a constant voltage drop for varying loads, to enable 12V equipment to be powered from a 24V vehicle system. Both Jack Wootton, G0AWP and Steve Damon, G8PYP, have expressed important reservations about the technique.

G0AWP writes: "Although this is a novel idea, it has one serious drawback. While admittedly, unlike a ballast resistor, it will provide a constant voltage drop, irrespective of current drawn, it will not provide a constant output voltage when used with a fluctuating input voltage. While

this would not be a serious problem if used with a 24V battery not connected into a vehicle system, the supply voltages on vehicles having nominally 24V electrics can be well in excess of 30V when the engine is running, apart from any switching transients. In these circumstances, with a constant voltage drop of about 12V, the output from the diodes could be more than 18V, not to be recommended for a new £400 transceiver!

"I service radio and audio equipments installed in coaches and commercial vehicles, and know of many instances where even well-designed 24V equipment has been damaged by excess voltages, both transient and prolonged overvoltages. Some 24V equipments are fitted with a zener clamp diode across the supply (after the fuse), typically rated at 33V, 6W in order to avoid such damage.

"A much more satisfactory technique is to use a series regulator. The traditional Darlington arrangement with zener stabilization as in Fig 6 is ideal, and is extensively used commercially. Such a voltage regulator need be no more costly to make than purchasing nine bridge rectifiers, and may even be cheaper; many junk boxes will yield a 2N3055 and BFY51 and on a suitable heatsink will easily provide 5A, enough for a typical 10W fm transceiver. The principal advantage is that it supplies a fixed voltage output irrespective of supply voltage fluctations as well as load variations. There is this not the hazard involved in using a diode chain to power rigs in 24V vehicles."

Steve Damon, G8PYP, raises a different objection to the use of a diode chain formed from bridge rectifiers. He writes: "The Australian writer has fallen into the 'age-old' trap of using bridge rectifiers rather than single diodes, presumably in an attempt to increase the current rating. Consider a bridge rectifier as used in this application: Fig 7. The rectifier consits of four diodes Da to Dd, with forward voltage drops V_{FA} to V_{FD}. In the real, non-ideal, world, each of the diodes will have slightly different forward voltage drops.

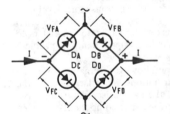

Fig 7. Diode bridge rectifiers have a maximum current rating when used as voltage droppers equal only to the rating of a single diode

"Then if, for example, we assume the voltages are: V_{FA} 0·58V, V_{FB} 0·59V, V_{FC} 0·60V and V_{FD} 0·61V, $v_{FA} + V_{FB}$ is 1·17V and $V_{FC} + V_{FD}$ is 1.21V. The result is that D_A and D_B will conduct, passing all the current, while the voltage across D_C and D_B will never be large enough for conduction to occur. Also, since D_A and D_B are connected in series, *each* will pass the full load current.

"The result is that the safe current rating of the complete rectifier block is reduced to that of *one* of the individual diodes. For a typical mobile application (3 to 4A load), it would be more economical to use, say, 18 MR750 (5A) diodes at 54p each, than nine KPC802 (8A) rectifier blocks at £1.37p each (prices taken from Farnell Electronic Components catalogue)."

It is perhaps worth noting that the use of either a series regulator or a diode chain represents an electrically inefficient system since one is drawing twice as much power (VA) from the 24V battery as is being used by the equipment, ie a maximum efficiency of only 50 per cent. This is not important in a vehicle in which the engine is running most of the time, but in circumstances where the recharging or float-charging of the battery presents a problem, a more efficient, though initially more costly, approach would be the use of a 24V/12V switched-mode dc/dc converter which can have an efficiency of the order of 75–80 per cent or so for a well-designed unit.

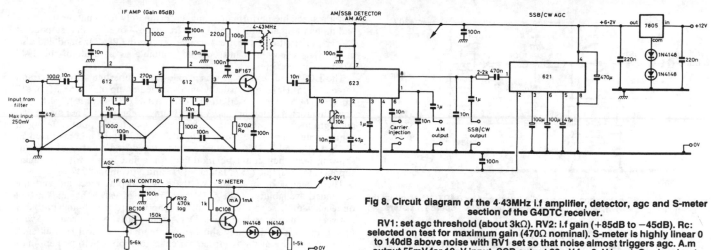

Fig 8. Circuit diagram of the 4·43MHz i.f amplifier, detector, agc and S-meter section of the G4DTC receiver.

RV1: set agc threshold (about 3kΩ). RV2: i.f gain (+85dB to −45dB). Rc: selected on test for maximum gain (470Ω nominal). S-meter is highly linear 0 to 140dB above noise with RV1 set so that noise almost triggers agc. A.m output 55mV for 10μV input. SSB output 30mV for 2μV input. Carrier about 200mV rms

More on G4DTC's ultimate receiver

TT (December 1987, January 1988) has outlined the front-end and variable-bandwidth crystal ladder filter developed by Ray Howego, G4DTC, for his "ultimate" high-performance, general-coverage (vlf/lf/mf/hf) receiver. While it is unlikely that many readers would wish to duplicate this design *in toto*, the philosophy and circuit details provide a useful guide for less ambitious receiver projects.

This month sees the completion of G4DTC's notes, covering the i.f strip, the usb/lsb carrier-injection/bfo circuitry, and some final thoughts. He writes:

"The i.f strip (Fig 8) was designed around the familiar Plessey 600-series of integrated-circuited chips. No doubt the cheaper 1600-series would do, although an equivalent of the SL623 appeared unobtainable. The i.f gain control gives manual control of the agc line, with the BF167 providing the extra gain required for optimum agc operation on a.m signals (if omitted, the agc voltage is insufficient and overloading occurs). The agc characteristics of the SL621 are superb for ssb reception. A point not stressed sufficiently by Plessey in their application notes is the importance of rf decoupling of the agc line. Three 100nF capacitors, evenly spaced along the line were found necessary. I feel certain that insufficient decoupling of this line accounts for the instability frequently encountered when using these devices.

"It should always be recognised that a broadband i.f amplifier produces broadband noise. A second narrowband (crystal) filter at the end of the i.f chain would be ideal. Plessey acknowledged this and suggest that some type of filter is necessary when the i.f gain exceeds about 68dB. However, the high-Q i.f transformer shown in Fig 8 was found to be quite satisfactory.

"The a.m detector in the SL623 is capable of very low distortion but demands a rather high signal voltage (a common defect in practically all envelope detectors!).

"A suitable bfo circuit is shown in Fig 9. Low-cost 4·433MHz PAL colour tv crystals can be easily pulled by series or parallel trimmers to provide suitable frequencies either side of the i.f carrier frequency so that specially selected crystals are not essential. The tuned BF167 buffer is essential to remove the second harmonic output which can otherwise cause distortion in the SL623 ssb detector.

"The audio and final af power amplifiers are worth mentioning. I have been horrified to see widespread use of the LM380 ic as a power amplifier. These devices are so noisy that they can provide the dominant noise contribution in receiver. (For example, my domestic 30W hi-fi amplifier gives less noise at maximum gain than an LM380 with its input grounded!). Several well-known designs even precede an LM380 by a 741 op-amp which is an even noiser chip. It is far better to use the LM383. This device provides up to 8W output, higher gain and virtually inaudible noise. A kit is available from Maplin for £5.60. The 741N is a low-noise op-amp but at many times the cost of the standard 741, but chips designed specifically for low-noise characteristics are readily available (eg HA12017, OP-27, ZN459).

Table 1. Filter response referred to 1kHz level

− 6dB at 3·2kHz	− 6dB at 380Hz
−12dB at 4·6kHz	−12dB at 240Hz
−18dB at 6 0kHz	−10dD at 160Hz
−24dB at 7·8kHz	−24dB at 110Hz
−30dB at 10kHz	

Input level 1V rms

"Most receivers (including this one) can be cleaned up beautifully by a well-designed active audio filter. In particular, I regard a filter as essential for a.m. Of the many active filter designs tried, that published in *Amateur Radio Techniques* (7th edition, p115, and several earlier editions) by ZL2APC and using two fet devices has proved the best of the simple circuits. However, the source resistors (quoted in ART as 33kΩ) produce such a low standing current through the fet devices that it is difficult to see that this circuit could operate effectively with any type of fet. I believe this was a misprint for 3·3kΩ. The circuit (amended version in Fig 9) will then take virtually any type of filter. ZL2APC provided the Table 1 details of filter response referred to a 1kHz level, from which it will be noted that unlike most published active af filters this was designed for speech reception rather than cw, and was suggested for use in receivers having only modest i.f selectivity in order to provide an

Fig 9. Circuit diagram of the carrier injection/bfo used by G4DTC. L1 80ft 36swg on 6mm former tapped at 15f. L2 10f 36swg over 15t of L1. Set output to 200mV (150mV) peak into 1kΩ. Crystal frequencies pulled: usb 4,435·5kHz, lsb 4,432·5kHz

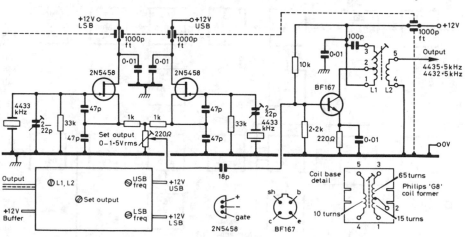

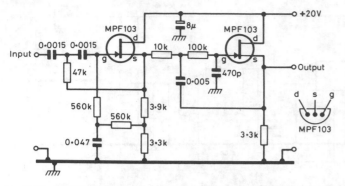

Fig 10. The ZL2APC active bandpass audio filter used by G4DTC to clean up the audio output, shown with amended values for the two source resistors

apparent increase in signal-to-noise ratio and improved readability of signals with high and low frequency heterodynes and audio chatter outside the filter passband noticeably attenuated making receiver operation a more pleasant task. If n-channel fets (eg 2N4360) are used, the polarity of the supply must be reversed.

"Digital frequency counters should be used with care in high-performance receivers. At worst, they can cover the entire spectrum with 'digital noise'. At best, they can produce some unexpected spurii. For example, the often used 7216A counter ic produces (in addition to its 10MHz reference oscillator) 500Hz harmonics (the display multiplex frequency) and harmonics of the 10MHz dividers (right down to 100Hz for the reference counter). Even if the counter is thoroughly screened, the display, clearly, *must* be visible somewhere! In addition, the counter will send its harmonics back down the lead which connects it to the receiver. Connecting a 7216 counter to an FRG7 receiver covered the entire spectrum with 100kHz markers! I note with concern that one *Rad Com* design has an unscreened 7216 chip on the receiver board only 3in from its rf wiring. Even when screened, low frequency, radiating eddy currents are induced in the screen!

"The resulting 'ultimate' receiver is capable of exceptional performance, particularly on the amateur bands even if operated with maximum gain. Broadcast-band reception requires backing off the gain controls as there is simply too much gain. The rf amplifier, as noted in the December *TT*, can be operated at high loss to attenuate very strong signals without impairing the snr. The entire receiver has been constructed on double-sided pcb (including the two front-end valves) and looks decidely 'state-of-the-art'."

Six-band QRP transmitter from BC348R receiver

During the second world war, many thousands of rugged, general-coverage communication receivers were manufactured for the US services. Of these the BC312, BC342 and BC348 were the best known and were among the most popular of the low-cost "war surplus" acquisitions by amateurs in the late 'forties. The BC312 was for operation from 12V dc supplies, the BC348 from 28V dc supplies. All three used 6.3V octal valves, mostly of the metal-octal type. With single-crystal i.f filters they

had a respectable performance but, unfortunately for amateur use, they had no bandspread tuning and had a frequency coverage that stopped at 18MHz, necessitating the use of converters on the 28MHz band and also on 21MHz when this band became available as a result of the 1947 Atlantic City conference.

The BC348, for example, was a nine-valve superhet with two rf and three i.f (915kHz) stages, usually with a valve line-up of 2 × 6K7 (rf), 6J7 (mixer), 6C5 (local oscillator), 6K7 (i.f), 6F7 (i.f/bfo), 6B8 (i.f/demodulator), 41 (output) and VR91 (voltage regulator). There were two main groups having the same performance specification but differing in some circuit details; one group suffixed J, N and Q; the other suffixed E, M, P, O, R and S. Both groups were featured in a number of journals showing how they could be modified for amateur use with ac mains supplies, for example *QST*, January 1947 and November 1947.

The mechanical ruggedness of these war-surplus receivers and the continued availability of the 6·3V octal range of valves has meant that quite a few of these receivers are still in working order, although probably not very often in operational use. Del Arthur, G0DLN, has come up with an ingenious idea that may shock those readers who feel that all such receivers should now be regarded as "collectors' pieces" to be kept in or restored to their original form. He writes:

"I feel that some of your readers would like to know that it is amazingly simple to convert many second world war receivers into effective cw transmitters or transceivers with minimal effort. I have done this with a BC348R, and the interest generated on the air with this rig is enormous. The normal BC348R block diagram is shown in Fig 11 (a). Most users of this receiver will have increased the bfo coupling to improve the reception of ssb. It takes less than half-an-hour to convert this receiver into a stable QRP cw transmitter covering six amateur bands (1·8, 3·5, 7, 10, 14 and 18MHz). The block diagram is then as shown in Fig 11 (b). Output from V2 (6K7) is at high impedance and is limited to about 100mW, so I use a compact external pa running about 10W. There is space inside the receiver for an internal driver and pa. To operate as a transceiver requires at least three relays to switch the signal path.

"It should be noted that adjustment of the bfo when receiving will shift the transmit frequency, so it is necessary to remember to return the knob to its original position when transmitting. One way round this is to cut out the bfo on transmit (another relay) and to turn V5 into a Miller oscillator on transmit (yet another relay). It would in theory be possible to use the existing audio output valve as the transmitter pa, but this is likely to increase the proliferation of relays to alarming proportions and I feel that a separate pa stage is simpler (unless possibly you have a separate receiver so that the BC348 or other surplus receiver can be hard-wired as a transmitter — G3VA).

"Harmonic rejection is excellent due to the use of the existing high Q tuned circuits into and out of V2. Birdies due to bfo harmonics are likewise rejected by the i.f transformers in the bfo signal path. The existing rf gain control effectively regulates the rf output power.

"Many amateurs would love to get airborne with their own contraptions but are deterred by the cost and difficulty of finding the necessary components etc. This modification is essentially a cheap and cheerful way of doing this — and is great fun. The more cowardly types could easily do the transmitter modification only, and use existing black boxes for receiving."

I feel it should be added that before adapting an old communication receiver for transmission, it would be advisable to check carefully the stability of the local oscillator on the higher frequency bands, if you wish to use these, particularly in respect of the mechanical vibration likely to arise from the use of a straight morse key on the same table. Local oscillators did not have the large swamping capacitance across the tuned circuit, as found in old transmitter vfos. A good test is to tune the receiver to a 14MHz cw or ssb signal and then try the "thumping test". The US BC-series receivers, many intended for airborne operation, will probably pass, but many less-rugged receivers are likely to fail on the higher frequency bands.

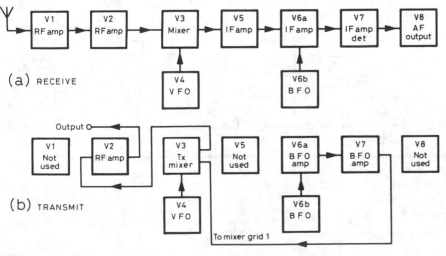

Fig 11. G0DLN's method of converting a BC348R receiver into a QRP transmitter in a matter of minutes. By incorporating switching relays, it can be used as a six-band transceiver provided that the local oscillator stability is sufficient

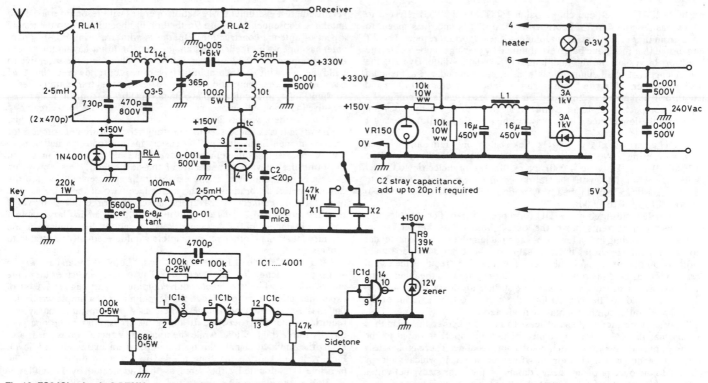

Fig 12. ZS6JC's simple 3·5/7MHz cw transmitter. L2 24t, No 24 wire or heavier wound on 30mm former and tapped as shown. L1 any choke greater than 1H at 75mA. RL1 relay dpdt with 15,000Ω coil or similar. Adjust working conditions with R9

Simple 3·5/7MHz cw transmitter

For the many readers who still feel that there is a place in amateur radio for very simple valve or hybrid valve/semiconductor transmitters capable of producing about 12W rf output, Fig 12 shows a rig described by John Lowmass, ZS6JC, in *Radio ZS* March 1987, brought to my notice by Dick Rollema, PA0SE. ZS6JC believes that there are still many young as well as older amateurs interested in getting on to the hf bands on cw at minimal cost while at the same time obtaining an insight into the simple valve technology not required for the RAE etc. Simple power crystal oscillators have the advantage of being very easy to construct and work surprisingly well with a minimum of constructional bugs and adjustments. His design, although based on those of the 'forties and 'fifties, does incorporate silicon diodes in the power supply, and uses a cmos sidetone generator giving an output adequate for a small loudspeaker, with an antenna relay operated directly from the 150V dc line to provide single switch operation between transmit and receive, switching being carried out by breaking the centre tap earth line of the 300-0-300V transformer. An alternative is to use a relay controlled by a Darlington-pair transistor operated from an rf pick-up loop taken from the output, but the system shown has the advantage of being able to kill the receive signal if required without actually transmitting. The transmitter should operate equally well on 3·5 and 7MHz with suitable crystals. Cost can be kept low by scrounging bits from old valve receivers etc. Almost any of the old tetrode or pentode rf valves could be used, including the 6146, 807, 6L6 etc. With a 6146, ZS6JC gets about 12W rf output from 20W dc input. Crystals are preferably the older, more robust type capable of rather more crystal current than the modern miniature packages.

Groundplanes of zero extent

In *TT* November 1987, pp836-7, in "The groundplane dissected", it was reported that in his analysis of the groundplane antenna, Melvin M Weiner (The Mitre Corporation) referred to a groundplane of "zero-extent" without explaining what this implied. The term was unfamiliar to me, and I assumed wrongly that the author meant a quarter-wave monopole element with one or more thin wire radials, as opposed to the solid groundplanes of the other groundplane antennas analysed in his paper.

However, Dr Brian Austin, G0GSF, of the University of Liverpool, has followed up the references listed in Weiner's paper and has obtained, for the university library, a copy of the book *Monopole Elements on Circular Elements on Circular Ground Planes* by M M Weiner, S P Cruze, Li Cho-Chou and W J Wilson (Artech House, 1987). This devotes a

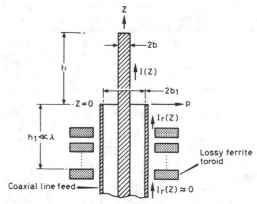

Fig 13. Zero-extent groundplane antenna as described by Melvin Weiner (Mitre Corporation)

special section to the concept of a groundplane of zero extent. It turns out to be precisely that: a quarter-wave elevated monopole with *no* radials. Such an antenna could be of practical value for some amateur radio as well as professional applications, as well as throwing fresh light on the role of radials. G0GSF writes:

"This antenna is effectively an electrically thin monopole element with no groundplane nor any semblance of one, even in the form of radials. What is interesting of course is how one feeds such a configuration, and Fig 13 from the book contains the answer. The use of the lossy ferrite toroids around the coaxial cable, providing a choke against the outer-braid current, does the trick. This is, in effect, the form of balun proposed by Walter Maxwell, W2DU, in *QST* March 1983.

"Weiner's experimental results (Table 2 in the IEEE paper) do not show this configuration though, so it leaves unanswered the question to some extent. What it does seem to suggest is that the usual horizontal radials are in effect playing no part other than acting as a shield which prevents (decreases?) the flow of current on the outer-braid of the coaxial feeder cable. Tilting the radials downwards through an angle does indeed (as G6CJ has shown) increase the feed point resistance. But is this effect though not just because more current can now flow on the braid because of a decrease in shielding effectiveness of the tilted radials, thereby bringing the 'other half' of the dipole into play? There is clearly scope for some careful measurements in this area!"

The W2DU ferrite-bead choke balun (*QST* March 1983) referred to above was described in *TT* February 1984, pp134-5, and does appear to differ from the zero-extent groundplane in one important respect. The *TT* item noted that the choke balun "is obtained by placing numbers of ferrite beads or sleeves around the final length of coaxial feedline. By using the added lengths of small diameter cable of the same impedance as the main feeder, numbers of ferrite beads having an inner diameter of 0·197in and length of 0·190in can be threaded on to the extra cable to produce 'a superb, compact, wide-band balun'. Note that such a balun does not transform the impedance and so may not be directly substituted for a 4:1 ratio balun."

W2DU described a 1·8 to 30MHz choke balun, only 12in long including connector, using 50 No 73 ferrite beads (Amidon FB-73-2401 or Fair-Rite 2673002401-0, μ 2,500 to 4,000) over 50Ω Teflon-dielectric RG303/U cable (or RG-141/U with the fabric covering removed). For 30 to 250MHz, use 25 No 43 beads (Amidon FB-43-2401, Fair-Rite No 2643002401, μ 950 to 3,000).

The ferrite beads used by W2DU form primarily an rf choke, blocking the flow of rf currents down the outer braid of the feeder, as an alternative to coiling into a few turns the final length of the coaxial feeder (for 14 to 30MHz several turns of cable of about 8in diameter should suffice). On the other hand, the Weiner groundplane requires the use of *lossy* ferrite, as used in tvi filters, to absorb the power on the outer of the cable braid. To quote the book: "For sufficiently lossy ferrite toroids along the outside of the coaxial line, the current on the exterior of the coaxial line's outer conductor may be neglected."

What is by no means clear, at least to me, is whether this technique means that the feedpoint impedance of the monopole is raised to the extent of permitting direct matching of a 50Ω feedline. There is obviously work to be done in evaluating this form of antenna, which could be likened to the once-popular "sleeve dipole" without the sleeve but with a considerable amount of power wasted in those lossy toroids.

Yet more on quiet tune-up/protection

Since writing the item on "More on the tune-up protection device" (*TT* February), an illuminating letter on the origins of this device has come in from Lad Kucera, N9AEG. He writes:

"The circuit published in the October *TT* appeared strikingly familiar. A bit of research turned up an article "Tune up swiftly, silently and safely" by William Vissers, K4KI (*QST* December 1979) of which the author assigned rights to SST Electronics. While the advertisements for SST Electronics faded away some years ago, I believe they commercially produced this product before their disappearance.

"The unit which I built in 1980 from the *QST* article, has proven to be a very useful test instrument. My station operates with resonant coaxial-fed antennas, consequently my use for the unit has been limited to the tuning aspect of antenna construction. Operators who are using non-resonant antennas, open-wire feeders and an atu, may find that having the unit in line continuously is the key to easy tune-up. There is some incentive to build the unit with a self-computing type of readout; however, thus far I have resisted the temptation to do so. Since the transmitter sees a constant load, the commonplace meter calibrate control is far less sensitive in response to impedance changes in the antenna load circuit.

"Those readers who are interested in constructing such a unit may like to know that it is not necessary to go through the procurement process for each component individually. The easiest method of construction is to obtain an existing reflectometer, discard the old rf sensing unit, and substitute the relevant components of the new circuit. This conversion process is rewarding in that the existing reflectometer will include the cabinet, meter, calibrations on the meter face, two of the controls, and two of the rf connectors. My personal choice for conversion was a Heathkit model AM-2. This long-obsolete model has a fairly large cabinet and is obtainable in USA fleamarkets for about five dollars. I am confident that many other reflectometers would be equally adaptable to conversion."

K4KI's *QST* article of 1979 was sub-titled: "Looking for an easy way to adjust your antenna-matching network? This tune-up indicator takes the guesswork out while it protects your equipment" and begins: "A bit of experimentation on my part led to the development of a simple swr bridge that has several real advantages when used with an antenna system requiring a matching network. It allows the transmitter to be operated directly into a dummy load while the antenna system is adjusted. It also keeps the radiated signal (during tune-up) at an extremely low level. Finally, it will shorten the time needed to get a rig on the air." The principle is undoubtedly the same as that advocated by Fred Piesse, VK3BYW: see Fig 14.

Coaxial fed multiband "Windom" long-wire antenna

Gian Moda, I7SWX, sends along details of a simple multiband antenna that works on all bands from 3·5 to 28MHz, including WARC bands other than 10·1MHz: Fig 15. It is in effect an adaptation of the twin-wire form of the 300Ω Windom antenna but fed with 75Ω coaxial cable by means of a 4:1 balun. He has used this antenna for nearly 10 years with powers up to 200W rf, and finds the swr at the transmitter is quite low, not more than 2:1 at the band edges. The 4:1 transformer is made of pvc wire (eg black and red wire used for connecting loudspeakers to hi-fi amplifiers) connected as shown. It does not saturate, I7SWX reports.

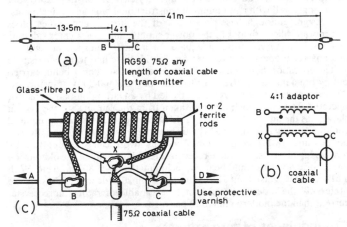

Fig 15. I7SWX's multiband antenna and 75/300Ω balun transformer

Hints and tips

Shaun P O'Sullivan, G8VPG, adds some useful information in respect of a tip that appeared many years ago in *TT*. He writes: "For many years I have searched for a dentist's inspection mirror to view the hidden parts of a radio chassis. Genuine dentists' tools are, however, difficult to find and also quite expensive. However, an excellent dental inspection mirror designed for home-use is available from larger branches of "Boots the Chemists", priced at only 89p. It is better for our purpose than a genuine professional tool since it has a plastic handle which will not cause any short-circuits. I have found this item to be an invaluable part of my tool box."

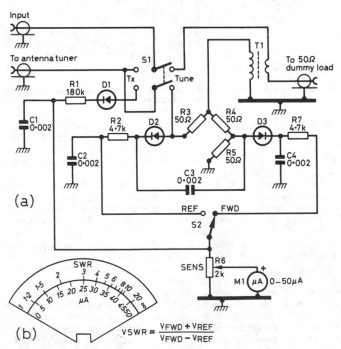

Fig 14. The original K4KI tune-up device (*QST* December 1979). T1 primary 2t No 20 insulated wire, secondary 10t No 24 insulated wire on Amidon T50-6 toroid core or equivalent. (b) Calibrated meter face, an advantage if direct swr readings are required

$$VSWR = \frac{V_{FWD} + V_{REF}}{V_{FWD} - V_{REF}}$$

Technical Topics

Pat Hawker, G3VA

A RECENT CORRESPONDENT in the letters section of *Practical Wireless* (January 1988) admits to having "caught the bug" of amateur radio, agrees that there should be a proper licensing test of operating procedures and the use of appropriate instruments to prevent interference, but "cannot really see the point of everyone having to learn basic electrics and electronics and how the insides of transceivers work . . . it is possible to pass a driving test without having the slightest knowledge of what happens under the bonnet . . . I feel that the present examination system is inappropriate in this respect, given that sets no longer need to be constructed at home from bits and pieces." The *PW* editor added the comment: "Wow! I think we're likely to need some fireproof paper to print the answers to this letter."

Yet, if one puts oneself in the position of a newcomer, there is a perverse logic in these views, heretical though they may seem. Seen through a newcomer's eyes, amateur radio today must seem, at least superficially, to consist almost entirely of blackbox operating in pursuit of awards, QSL cards, squares, prefixes, contests, social activities including conversation on air with known circles of friends. The "technical" interest must seem to be confined, except for a few professional engineers in our ranks, to little more than deciding whether Brand X offers more "goodies" than Brand Y. It is no good blaming cb, a disenchanted younger generation, or even the RSGB. The hobby today is what *we* have made of it. How can we expect newcomers to realise that awards, contests etc were introduced and promoted primarily to add a spice of competition and personal achievement to a hobby founded firmly on scientific and experimental interest in the technology of radio communication, both principles and practice. The fact that most of us today use factory-built equipment should not blind us to the need to have at least a reasonable understanding of the technology and some knowledge of those "bits and pieces" that go into the equipment if the hobby is to survive in a meaningful manner. And how can those interested only in operating be sure their black boxes really are working as their designers intended?

Admittedly we have to recognise that amateur radio and its technology are changing as we lose our links with the pioneering days. Sadly, an increasing number of those who have contributed so much to radio technology – both amateur and professional – are no longer with us. 1987 saw the passing of some great American engineers to whom as amateurs we owe much. Dr George Brown, whose classic work on antennas while with RCA has been featured often in *TT,* died on 11 December. I can personally vouch for the encouragement he gave to many of us. His 1937 paper provided the spur for the development of close-spaced rotary beams (both driven and parasitically excited); he showed the importance of reducing ground losses on monopoles by the use of up to 120 ground radials; he pioneered the elevated groundplane etc – not to mention his work as RCA director of research on the development of colour television.

Arthur Collins, W0CXX, founder of Collins Radio, died in February 1987. He not only popularised the pi-network matching technique among amateurs; his firm, initially founded to build transmitters for amateurs, came to be respected throughout the communications industry for the excellence of its equipment. It was Collins Radio that, with the KWM-1, became the first manufacturer of amateur hf ssb transceivers. Another 1987 loss was Harold Smith who, while with Bell Telephone Laboratories, devised the "Smith Chart" to help solve antenna and transmission line problems. Yet another was Walter Brittain, co-inventor of the transistor.

Home-built low-cost spectrum analyser

Last year (*TT* February 1987, p111), Peter Chadwick, G3RZP, in entering the debate "valve or solidstate" for rf power amplifiers noted that "Homebrewing a solidstate pa is *not* easy if you are going to avoid parasitics . . . Within the professional field nobody now knows how they ever managed in the days before the spectrum analyser". Similarly, Kurt Grey, VE2UG)*TT* August 1987, p586), emphasised that even replacing a transistor in a solidstate transmitter often calls for a $20,000-plus spectrum analyser to trace and cure the parasitic spurii resulting from the minor changes in layout that come about in reinstating all the components that have to be removed to reach the transistor. Even a second-hand professional spectrum analyser can cost far more than an entire factory-built hf amateur station including a rotary antenna array!

But for amateurs already having a reasonably good oscilloscope, the cost of a simple spectrum analyser suitable for a variety of purposes,

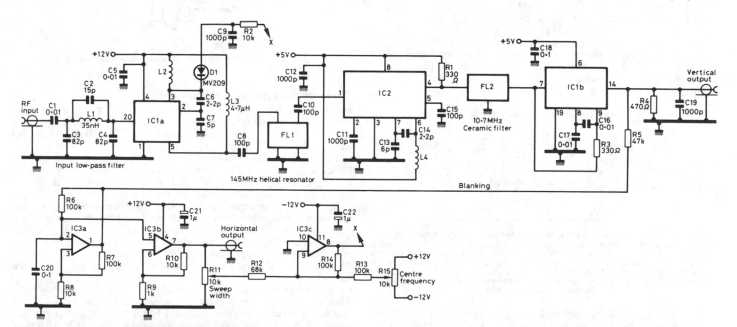

Fig 1. Circuit diagram of the *RF Design* low-cost spectrum analyser for use in conjunction with a general purpose oscilloscope. C1, C5, C16, C17: 0·01μF ceramic. C2: 15pF npo. C3, C4: 82pF npo. C6, C14: 2·2pF npo. C7, C13: 5pF npo. C8, C10, C15: 100pF ceramic. C9, C11, C1: 1,000pF ceramic. C18, C20: 0·1μF ceramic. C21, C22: 1μF electrolytic. FL1: 145MHz helical resonator (Toki CBT or home-made). FL2: 10·7MHz ceramic filter (Murata SFE 10·7). L1: 4·5t, ³⁄₁₆in id. L2: 3·5t ³⁄₁₆in id. L3: 4·7μH moulded choke. L4: 5·5t ³⁄₁₆in id. R11, R15: 10kΩ linear. R1, R2, R3, R4, R8, R10 0·25W

including the tuning and adjustment of solidstate transmitters etc, can be quite modest, even though the resolution and range may not compare with a $20,000 model. Giles Humpston, G4GYO, draws attention to an article in the "rfi/emc corner" of *RF Design* (January 1988): "A simple spectrum analyser – pocket-sized 0 to 100MHz unit uses only three ics", by Albert Helfrick (Doty RF Industries). It is introduced as follows: "here is one of our *RF Design Awards* contest entries, an extremely simple spectrum analyser usable with a general-purpose oscilloscope. It is a valuable tool, allowing detection of rf energy at low levels. In addition to the circuit design and equipment troubleshooting applications noted by the author, this unit should be extremely useful in locating leakage from shielded enclosures, pinpointing sources of radiation in digital circuits, and tracking down sources of interference." The author's suggestions include its use as a low-level signal searching tool for trouble-shooting and developing rf circuits: "Used with a one- or two-turn coil attached to a length of coaxial cable it can 'sniff out' the presence of rf signals . . . it can be used to tune oscillators and amplifiers by placing the pick-up coil near the circuit to be tuned . . . it is invaluable for tuning transmitters since parasitic oscillations often occur when a transmitter is poorly tuned".

The unit as described covers rf inputs from near zero to over 100MHz with a log display range of more than 60dB and a minimum detectable signal of −75dBm. It is claimed that the sweep linearity and the linearity of the log display are excellent. Since it has a first i.f of 145MHz (oscillator sweeps between 145 to 245MHz) it is clearly not intended for adjustment of 144MHz transmitters but should prove suitable for hf and possibly 50MHz equipment. A spectrum analyser needs to be able to detect parasitics at frequencies well above the transmitter frequency, as well as the low-frequency parasitics that occur with solidstate transmitters.

In effect, a spectrum analyser is a crude "receiver" which can be swept (scanned) rapidly and repeatedly across a wide frequency range, in synchronism with the horizontal ("X") axis of a crt display; with the strength of detected signals indicated by the vertical ("Y") trace at the frequency concerned. The *RF Design* article outlines the use and functioning of the unit, providing a circuit diagram (Fig 1) but leaves the construction, pcb layout etc to the reader.

ICIA is the converter section of a Motorola MC3356 fsk receiver chip with its oscillator frequency swept from 145 to 245MHz by the hyperabrupt varactor diode D1 (MV209) under the control of the IC3 (TL084) relaxation oscillator. The first i.f of 145MHz is tuned by the helical resonator (FL1). The author states that FL1 is the most expensive device in the unit if bought (such devices are often used in the front-ends of vhf receivers) but can be home-constructed without undue difficulty. It is not clear whether the resonator he used has only a single section, but it would be advantageous to use a multi-section helical resonator such as described in a number of publications. Fig 2 shows an agc-controlled helical filter as described many years ago in *TT* and *ART*, although agc would not be required in this application. A long, detailed paper on helical (resonator) filters has been published recently in *Journal IERE* (Sept/October 1987). With a second i.f of 10.7MHz it is important that FL1 should provide sufficient selectivity to eliminate (or at least greatly reduce) the "image" signal that will otherwise appear 21·4MHz from the real signal (2 × 10·7MHz), and other unwanted products. A two- or three-section filter would probably be adequate.

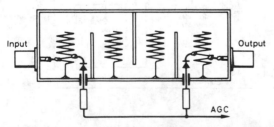

Fig 2. Typical arrangement of a four-section helical resonator filter. This 1972 design included pin-diodes as an agc-controlled attenuator and provided a passband of about ± 2MHz at 100MHz and some 50dB attenuation beyond 5MHz off tune. Attenuator (not needed in this application) had a control range of about 40dB (source "Radio Receivers 1972" conference book). A detailed design article on helical resonator filters appears in *Journal IERE*, September/October 1987

IC2 (Signetics NE602) is an oscillator/mixer chip, with the oscillator adjusted to 155·7MHz by deforming the coil L4. The bandwidth of the second mixer is governed by the 10·7MHz ceramic filter; a filter intended for the i.f amplifier of a standard fm broadcast receiver will provide a bandwidth of about 250kHz. This filter governs the resolution of the

analyser, but cannot be too sharp in view of the inherent phase noise etc of the oscillators. The 10·7MHz i.f amplifier uses part of the MC3356 fsk receiver chip (IC1B) and provides an output proportional to the log of the limiter input (the discriminator section of the MC3356 is not used). The buffer/summing amplifier of the time-base chip IC2 provides about ±10V peak output and results in a −2 to −22V bias across the varactor diode, with the negative-going voltage applied to the varactor diode and the opposite polarity applied to the X-axis of the oscilloscope to give the correct relationship between sweep voltage and analyser frequency. The square-wave output of the ramp generator is used as a blanking voltage, the trace being forced off-screen during retrace.

The author suggests that (in the USA) it should not be difficult to replicate the analyser (complete, power supply, case and all) for less than $50 if the helical resonator is home-made. He adds: "it's probably the best $50 tool an rf designer could own".

Universal polarity keyer

James Bryant, G4CLF, noted the dual-polarity relayless keyer arrangement described by Steve Cook, G4ANA, in the December *TT*. He writes: "I have built a relayless keyer which does not need to be switched but operates regardless of the polarity applied to the keyer output terminal.

"The output stage is shown in Fig 3. It uses two VN2222L N-channel vmos fets and a pnp bipolar transistor – almost any general-purpose type having a Vceo of 1·5 times the maximum negative keying voltage should do the job. TR1 may be replaced by a vmos device having a higher breakdown if the positive keying voltage is likely to exceed +50V (the rating of the VN2222L is +60V). R2 is chosen to restrict I_1 to 10 per cent more than the maximum negative key current.

"The logic drive signal is greater than 0·5V for logic 0 (key up) and between +3V and +15V for logic 1 (key down). The diodes must carry the key current and have a reverse breakdown of more than the maximum keying voltage."

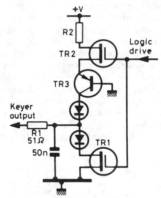

Fig 3. G4CLF's universal polarity relayless keyer arrangement

Thoughts on front-end design

In *TT* (November 1987, p834), in connection with the concept of the simple "super-dc-gainer" type of receiver, I made a fleeting reference to a 1977 "3·5MHz dx receiver" by Jan Hubach (PA0FIN/OH1ZAA and also ZF2KZ, NN0Y, FO0ZA etc) originally described in *Electron No 6, 1977*, and briefly in *TT*, December 1977. Having recently returned from his USA and ZF2KZ trips, OH1ZAA was surprised to find references to his 1977 design in both *Electron* and *Rad Com*, and this provided an ignition spark to provide some additional comments. He writes:

"In the early 'seventies, free-running vfos (combined with crystal-controlled pre-mixers) were still widely used, and the common problem was a lack of sufficient dynamic range before the i.f stages. When double-balanced mixers were introduced, several manufacturers tried to apply the new technology; however, still with poor to mediocre results. This was not at all surprising since their design assumptions were often incorrect:

(1) Still too much emphasis was given to receiver *absolute* sensitivity. Therefore applied amplification was unnecessarily large before the i.f stages; any matched antenna on the hf bands brings in sufficient noise power compared to a dummy load at a temperature of 300K. Therefore extreme sensitivity does not add to snr improvement on reception. Over-sensitivity is still a problem with 'modern' receivers, but is easily cured by inserting an appropriate attenuator.

(2) There was a fixation in thinking that the balanced mixers had to be terminated with a matching impedance for the desired received signal. However, also the driving sources had to represent a correct match to the mixer; in addition, *all* spectral components generated in the mixer (ie *any* frequency) had to see the correct match at *any* port of the device. The most common mistake was to match the mixer just at the intermediate frequency, while ignoring the fact that in real life there were at least a hundred other unmatched signals present at the output of the mixer. These were 'reflected back' into the device, producing a super soup of products (often by new reflection at the other unmatched ports).

(3) The third-order intercept point was only a theoretical value based on a two-tone measurement. Active devices, especially, exhibited very good intercept values but 'collapsed' at much lower levels than some passive devices. However, up to that point their performance was superb, particularly suitable for transmitter applications where only two signals occur at a time (low spurious). High-claimed intercept points encouraged dropping of rf-preselectors, thus allowing peak addition of wideband rf signals and saturation of dynamic range on receive. Any two signals with a frequency-difference equal to the i.f were invited to add to the garbage, especially where the mixer ports were not properly terminated.

(4) The non-linearity of crystal filters was generally severely underestimated, and still represents a limiting factor. Deterioration of performance starts well under 20dBm levels.

OH1ZZA's remarks underline a point made several times in *TT* that while strong-signal performance and a wide dynamic range have become recognised as the hallmarks of good vhf and hf receiver performance, the accepted methods of laboratory measurement usually fail to tell a truly realistic story, opening the way to a high degree of specmanship on the part of manufacturers and retailers. It is, for example, as OH1ZZA notes, conventional practice to make dynamic range measurements using two signal generators with frequencies spaced 20kHz apart or, with synthesisers, now often necessarily spaced 50 or 100kHz apart. This can result in impressive intercept points well above 0dBm and instantaneous dynamic ranges of 90 to over 100dB *on paper*. Yet such measurements are often far from representing the performance of the receiver when connected to a good antenna where, with the limited degree of pre-mixer selectivity found in most modern receivers, there may be dozens of strong signals crowding into the mixer, some much closer than 20, 50 or 100kHz away and having a cumulative effect.

Valve receiver performance

In his introduction to his hybrid "ultimate" front-end, Ray Howgego, G4DTC (*TT* December 1987) singled out the sixties Eddystone 940 as one of the "great" valve receivers. By coincidence, Tim Wright, G1BCR/G9BZW, had been preparing a full-length article on this receiver for

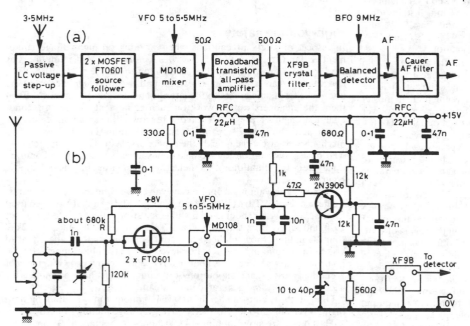

Fig 4. The high-performance 3·5MHz dx "super-dc-gainer" receiver front-end designed by OH1ZAA/PA0FIN in the mid-seventies

"The 3·5MHz dx front-end (Fig 4) was designed several years before its publication in 1977, based on the above viewpoints. Later versions had improvements, such as higher bias currents for improved dynamic range and higher level mixers. Note that emphasis is on near-perfect wide-band matching, passive amplification (using the input resonance), and streamlining for minimum component parasitics by matching circuit configuration to the given 'mainframe' (ie key components: mixer, filter).

"Today, in the 1988 situation, we can look back and realise that a couple of manufacturers have, to a considerable degree, applied correct design procedures for their latest front-ends. However, with the digital trend, frequency synthesisers have spoiled the opportunity for superior reception when they are used in conjunction with these improved front-ends. It is still hard to find equipment providing the ultimate quality in reception that modern technology could easily provide. Once this has been achieved, there is still the problem of having to cope with synthesiser-generated transmitted signals, but it will be an immeasurable pleasure to tune a clear signal, with the synthesised 'high-grass' at a respectable frequency separation. The most elegant solution is to use a variable crystal oscillator (vxo) to tune the dx-slot of an hf cw band. This would be quite easy on, for example, 3·5MHz, using a relatively high i.f (eg 21·4MHz) with the vxo covering 24·9 to 24·925MHz. With a 9MHz i.f, full 10kHz coverage can still be achieved by tuning 12·5 to 12·51MHz on the vxo. A good rule of thumb for a vxo is not to attempt to pull the crystal to provide more than a 0·01 per cent tuning range. At higher deviations the first practical problem is stability rather than phase noise."

Short Wave Magazine including detailed measurements and some modifications. Since such laboratory measurements (misleading or not) have been published only in recent years and usually only for solidstate receivers, it has been difficult to compare, except on-air, modern receivers with the old classics such as the AR88, 75A4 etc. It is thus interesting to see how the 940 measures up in a bench test.

For the record, and with acknowledgement to Dick Ganderton, editor of *Short Wave Magazine*, the following is a summary of G1BCR's findings:

Minimum detectable signal	−129dBm (0·9μV)
Minimum usable signal (12dB snr)	−117dBm
Noise figure	6 or 7DB
IMD instantaneous dynamic range	20kHz 79dB
	100kHz 98dB
	300kHz 117dB
Gain (1dB compression at 50kHz)	95dB
Selectivity	−6dB ±2kHz
	−60dB ±8kHz ±3kHz
Image	−70dB at 10MHz
	−40dB at 20MHz
	better than −110dB at 2MHz

The suggested modifications include: (1) Removal of i.f tertiary windings to improve i.f shape factor; (2) modify rf stage and local oscillator to reduce noise; (3) Modify agc (+ rf gain); (4) Fixed mixer bias to improve linearity and stability; (5) Stenode modification to improve af response when filter is in circuit. (Full details in the *SWM* article).

It seems worth emphasising the value of the pre-mixer selectivity as reflected in the increasing dynamic range of the receiver to signals off-frequency. Additional pre-mixer selectivity would improve image rejection on 14MHz and above, resulting from the low 450kHz i.f (single conversion).

High-power all-solidstate transmitters – progress report

Recently I spent a day at an IEE colloquium "Advances in solidstate technology for broadcast transmitters" that yielded a number of points of interest even to those of us who still prefer tetrode p.a valves in amateur radio transmitters. A series of papers described all-solidstate transmitters: for radio, up to 50kW (a.m) and about 5kW (vhf/fm); for television (vhf and uhf) up to about 30kW rating; bipolar and mosfet devices capable of rf outputs per device of about 100W and 200W; and detailed "cost of ownership" analyses by BBC and IBA engineers.

"Cost of ownership" analyses depend on such factors as initial capital cost and subsequent loss of the interest that would have been received if the money had simply been invested; depreciation of the assets over the estimated operational lifetime; energy-consumption costs (a major factor for high-power transmitters operating for up to 24h/day); maintenance and repair costs, including costs of mobile maintenance teams etc. The detailed "cost of ownership" analyses of both the BBC and IBA engineers showed clear advantages for all-solidstate television installations, compared with tetrode or klystron amplifiers, up to at least 5kW, and possibly even in the range 10 to 15kW, although with BBC and IBA tending to differ in this range, with the BBC urging caution.

A number of the points raised were relevant to amateur radio transmitters, although nothing I heard convinced me that it is time to throw out my 6146Bs or even my aged 813. Within the solidstate field we are still in a state of transition, with general agreement that mosfet devices are tending to replace bipolar devices for linear rf power amplification. At present this is possible only up to about 150MHz (eg Band 2 fm radio) although several speakers seemed convinced that uhf power mosfet devices at comparable power to bipolars will soon be available. Some engineers claim that mosfet devices should prove more reliable than bipolar; the fact that many of them are capable of operating from higher supply votages (50V to 80V) than bipolars (usually 28–32V) helps to ameliorate the problem of high currents. The device's lower sensitivity to supply voltage variation has reduced the need for complex power supply design for some applications; furthermore the major advantage of fet devices is higher gain at uhf. This is in the region of 10dB as opposed to the 6dB typically obtained at uhf from bipolars. As D Drury, of Varian TVT Ltd (formerly Pye TVT), pointed out, the higher gain enables a reduction to be made in the number of driver devices, reducing the total component count and effectively increasing the transmitter efficiency and reliability: "If output powers in excess of 100W are achieved with this level of gain, then solidstate tv transmitters with output powers in excess of 5kW become economically viable to manufacture".

A significant advance has been achieved in bipolar rf power devices by the use of gold metallisation of the internal connections which are subject to extremely high current densities, leading to metal migration and eventual fusing with conventional aluminium-based internal leads. SGS-Thomson Microelectronics, at its plant in the USA, has introduced a series of tv/radio linear gold-metallised high-power bipolar transistors with double and triple the output power of the highest power devices of a few years ago, stemming from development work on devices for solidstate L-band military radar transmitters. For example, a single SD1483 can provide 250W rf output at 100MHz in Class C (for fm radio transmitters) with a gain of 12dB, operating from a 28V rail. The SD1485 at 200MHz for television in Class AB with 32V rail, 11dB gain, two-tone imd −28dB, gives a peak sync rf output of 240W at 1dB compression. For uhf television (470 to 860MHz) the SD1492 in Class AB can give 150W output with a 7dB gain.

N Miki, of Toshiba, stressed that reliability and stability are the ultimate aims of solidstate technology, but achieving them depends on such factors as adequate protective circuits, including protection against lightning surges on the antenna and especially from the spikes and surges induced on mains supplies. Passive components such as resistors are preferably derated by some 50 per cent from their nominal rating at 85°C chassis temperature. Electrolytic capacitors still need to be recognised as having only a limited lifetime, with care needed if this is to exceed 10 years in a high-temperature environment. With many devices used in the modules and sub-modules of high-power transmitters, good dispersion control (ie ensuring equal current/power sharing between the devices) is required, and it is necessary to use combining systems of high efficiency.

For high-power solidstate transmitters, as with valves and klystrons, cooling is a major consideration. Large heatsinks by themselves are inadequate, and forced air cooling is often used in addition. NEC have developed a high-pressure jet air system from small nozzles directed at the transistors, dispensing with heatsinks. Air-cooling is much more attractive than the water or vapour cooling systems used in high-power broadcast transmitters using klystrons or large tetrodes; such cooling can introduce significant reliability problems.

Solidstate is also seen as attractive from the safety point of view, with an absence of high-voltage (hv) power supplies. Voltages up to 72V are classified internationally as "low-voltage" (lv) equipment. It is perhaps worth remembering that the safety regulations of the BBC and IBA do not permit work on hv transmitting equipment by an unaccompanied maintenance engineer, so that the mobile maintenance teams used to maintain the large networks of unattended transmitters must always consist of at least two engineers. I have commented before that it is just as well that amateurs are not obliged to abide by such rules, though it is most advisable that other people in the house know how to switch off all power and deal with any emergency. With valve equipment it is most advisable that all power can be removed by means of a single switch. One of the hazards of the present state of the hobby is that many amateurs have become used to dealing only with low-voltage equipment and forget the dangers of high-voltage valve amplifiers and their associated power supply units.

High-voltage safety

In respect of safety precautions when working on high-voltage equipment, Brian Clowes, GW4HBZ, writes as follows: "Valve amplifiers as used by radio amateurs would never be allowed for use by the BBC, IBA and other organisations on safety grounds. All hv supplies must be interlocked with any access to the interior and a solid earth applied. Even then, the engineers cannot work on such equipment without a second, qualified engineer present. I have a borrowed linear amplifier on the bench here, and there are not even any warning lables. There is no mechanism to discharge quickly the capacitors. With so many newcomers who have grown up on low-voltage solidstate I wonder what should be done about the situation. Should electrical standards similar to domestic equipment be applied?

"On a lighter vain regarding recent valve/semiconductor comparisons, we have at Moel y Parc (BBC North Wales) a klystron that has been used for more than 71,000 hours and is still going strong. It went into use about 1970 and, apart from short breaks, has been in use ever since in a 2kW sound amplifier (now reduced to about 800mW in view of the changed vision/sound ratio in the UK). I believe one klystron has topped 100,000 hours (15 years' service at 18 hours a day). With a conversion efficiency of around 25 per cent and vapour phase cooling, it must have accounted for a lot of electricity and generated much steam!"

One of the points made at the IEE colloquium was that modern high-power uhf tetrodes (formerly having average lifetimes of only about 7,000 hours) are now topping 14,000 hours in operation. Thomson in France have been producing very high power tetrodes using a patented Pyrobloc grid that seems to result in appreciably more rugged valves.

Misconceptions in linear valve amplifiers

Whatever may be the situation in a few years' time, there are still large numbers of valve power amplifiers in use in transceivers, linear amplifiers, and the diminishing number of separate transmitters. As Peter Chadwick, G3RZP, puts it: "High-power solidstate linears are not for the beginner – they are more of a major project than an auto-tune valve linear." But, as he points out, there are still a number of misconceptions about the optimum operation of linear valve amplifiers; one reason, perhaps, is that there is still a natural tendency to think of transmitter amplifiers in the Class C mode (biased well beyond cut-off in the absence of drive), suitable for cw, fm and rtty, but not for ssb.

G3RZP lists some of the common myths and misconceptions:
(1) "You'll get longer valve life if you wind back the bias." Actually, you'll splatter more! As the standing current is a small percentage of the peak current, it will make little, if any, difference to valve life.
(2) "You don't need matched pairs." Some advertisers advertise matched pairs with good reason. I tried 14 6146Bs, all new, of different ages, manufacturers and batches. Under a fixed set of screen, bias and anode voltages, anode current varied from 9 to 36mA with an average of 21mA and standard deviation of 7mA. The best way of avoiding the need to select matched valves is to use a separate bias potentiometer for each one. Alternatively, and possibly even better, is adjustable screen grid volts and common adjustable bias as recommended by Collins for the 4CX250

family. Television sweep (line output) valves show even more variation than 6146Bs. Separate bias pots give good life even with sweep valves.

(3) "Thermal runaway means new pa valves." Yaesu rigs incorporating an "anti flash-over diode" in series with the screen grid are prone to thermal runaway. What exactly this diode does is a bit of a mystery, but reverse screen current leads to runaway. By zener-stabilising screen and bias, providing a low-impedance shunt bias return (*not* a series regulator), you can stop it. I had a set of 6146Bs four years old in my FT102, well hammered in a number of major contests. Standing current would rise from 75mA to 200mA in 2min of operating. But after fitting the screen stabiliser, shorting out the series diode, stabilising the bias, the current creep is only about 25mA after 5min of key down and 100W output on 28MHz.

(4) "Don't tune up as heavily as the book says – if it says 'load to 200mA' only load to 150mA." The result of such misguided advice is to increase screen grid dissipation and splatter!

G3RZP advises to stabilise *both* screen and bias voltages – or neither. This is because anode current is affected by both. Stabilisation of only one of these voltages leads to the quiescent point wandering with mains supply variations.

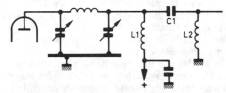

Fig 5. Possible means of avoiding the problem of choke resonances in amplifiers as suggested by G3RZP and based on the ssb textbook by Pappenfus

TT has, in the past, drawn attention to the problem of avoiding resonances on one or more bands of the rf chokes used in conjunction with pi-network output circuitry, a problem significantly intensified with the addition of the 10, 18 and 24MHz bands. G3RZP writes: "I notice several articles on linear amplifiers where problems occurred with rf choke resonance. This is likely to get worse when full power operation is possible on the WARC bands. I wonder if anyone has tried the scheme, outlined in the professional textbook on ssb by Pappenfus, of putting the rf choke at the output end of the pi-network as in Fig 5? By making L1, L2, C1 a highpass filter, L1 and L2 are only about 25µH. C1 is a well-rated capacitor of around 0·01µF capable of carrying several amperes of rf current. The variable capacitors have to be capable of withstanding more volts than in the conventional arrangement, but this could be taken care of by 0·01µF, 5kV series capacitors and two or three 10MΩ resistors in series across the variable capacitors. The highpass filter cut-off should be fairly low, say 500kHz."

VHF/UHF receiver noise figures

Joe Reisert, W1JR, in his regular "vhf/uhf world" column in the February 1988 issue of *Ham Radio*, includes an interesting section on factory-built receivers/transceivers. He writes: "Readers have asked about the noise figures of commercial rigs. The majority of transceivers I've measured were over two or three years' old and in the 6–8dB noise figure region; they often need an external preamplifier for serious dxing.

"Part of the reason for the higher noise figures is input switching, which often uses lossier solidstate switching instead of mechanical relays. Internal convenience switching and small diameter coaxial cable often add additional losses. Dynamic range is a consideration since (to achieve) low noise figures requires moderate-to-high gain ahead of the first stage of selectivity. Then there are those terrible uhf input connectors!

"A problem with many commercial transceivers is that, for economic reasons, they often employ a low first i.f such as 10·7MHz. Additional input filtering is required to effectively suppress images, and this often adds loss. The newer transceivers sport lower noise figures, typically 2–3dB.

"The subject of imd (intermodulation distortion) is seldom given enough attention. Receivers and the later stages must be protected from large signals, even those out of band. This is particularly troublesome where there are large rf emitters such as nearby fm or tv transmitters."

Later on transmitters he notes: "There still seems to be much interest in highpower transmitters. There aren't many to choose from and they are expensive. 8877s (linear amplifier valves) are now well over $500 and prices are rising. Older, more available tubes such as the 7213 and 4CX1000 are of interest, but straightforward designs are still scarce . . ."

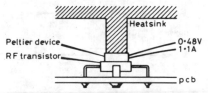

Fig 6. G1MFG's suggested use of a Peltier-device to cool the first stage of a low-noise vhf/uhf receiver. Note that direction of current flow is important. If reversed, it heats rather than cools the transistor. But make sure the device is suitable for use at low temperatures

In connection with vhf/uhf receiver noise figures, Giles Read, G1MFG, wonders if anyone has tried cooling their front-ends akin to the techniques used for many years in professional satellite terminals. Last year, G8VR quoted OH1ZAA as saying that Finnish winter temperatures down to −40°C made the noise figures of masthead preamps go "real low". G1MFG wonders if anyone in the amateur side of things has ever attempted to do this artificially? (Take care, many standard solidstate devices are not intended for low-temperature operation, although military types are often intended for operation down to −40°C – G3VA). He suggests using a Peltier-effect heat-pump directly attached to a preamp transistor, and notes that RS and Farnell both supply Peltier devices at reasonable prices (about £6). The RS device can maintain a temperature differential of around 60°C, which would suggest the transistor could be at, say, −30°C or so with ambient temperatures of around 10–20°C. Fig 6 shows his suggested arrangement, but G1MFG emphasises that he has not actually tried such a system. I know that some of the professional 12GHz satellite tvro terminals use Peltier devices to cool their front-end devices, though with modern low-noise semiconductors I suspect that the practical improvement would be limited at vhf, though possibly useful at uhf and shf. Has anybody tried it?

Minimising rfi from digital equipment

It is well recognised that the increasing amount of domestic and business digital equipment, particularly home computers, has become a major source of interference to weak-signal reception. By October 1983, the FCC was insisting that every computer manufacturer in the USA should comply with rules limiting the amount of permissible electromagnetic radiation from their products; but, almost five years later, in the UK we are still waiting for the introduction of enforceable regulations covering information technology equipment, although these are now promised before 1990 in response to the European Community EMC Directive which is expected to cover all electrical and electronic equipment, including information technology, telecommunications, radio, industrial and medical equipment.

Meanwhile many of the home computers sold in the UK would fail the FCC regulations. In this connection, I have been re-reading a 1983 article (*Electronics* 25 August, 1983, pp131-4) "Minimising emi at minimal cost in computing equipment", by Glen Dash (Dash, Straus & Goodhue Inc) which was aimed at showing that complying with FCC rules is not costly to the manufacturer if taken into account at the design stage.

The FCC regulations cover both radiated emissions between 30 to 1,000MHz and the signals fed back into the mains-supply lines between 0·45 and 30MHz. High-frequency current transients are produced when logic chips change state and form the basic source of radiated emission; the limited rise-time of ic devices concentrates most energy below 300MHz.

Mains-conducted emissions have two main sources. Above 10MHz the radiated emissions from the logic chips couple into the mains cables; lower-frequency noise tends to come from power rectifiers and switched-mode power supply units. To quote the *Electronics* article: "Rectifier noise comes from rectifier diodes that do not turn off quickly enough during zero crossings of the ac input. Switching supply noise shows up as harmonics of the switching frequencies. For large supplies, the amplitude can be quite high. By and large, computers that use switching supplies need line filters, most of which (for USA mains practice) comprise three capacitors and one two-winding inductor as in Fig 7.

"The line-to-line capacitor, typically 0·01 to 0·47µF value, cancels out differential noise by shorting the two main sides of the line at high frequencies. Bypassing each side, two other capacitors (together with the inductors) filter out common-mode signals. Leakage specs limit the size of these capacitors to between 0·001 and 0·01µF, so they are not large enough to filter out most common-mode noise signals, especially those from switching power supplies.

"The job calls for a series inductor, which generally ranges from 1 to

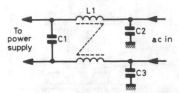

Fig 7. Typical mains filter to prevent noise from power rectifiers and switch-mode power supplies etc being injected into the ac power leads. An alternative form of filter is to wind the power cable around a suitable ferrite toroid

7mH. The bifilar-wound series inductor can operate only on common-mode signals, ignoring differential currents passing through the inductor and therefore avoiding saturation. So the inductor limits common-mode noise but avoids saturation by the 60Hz (USA) current."

The article stresses that it is more difficult to meet the FCC limits on radiated emission, and discusses such questions as radiation resulting from the clock driver's earthing pin which may excite the whole earthing system of the pcb so that common-mode noise appears on all points, including the I/O cables, whose earth return is often tied to logic earth so that any wire connected to this will tend to radiate. Capacitive bypassing, the shielding effect of metal or metallised cabinets and enclosures, as well as the finite rise time of the device, can combine to reduce radiation. Designers have, in effect, three main choices: "One is to lay out the pcb to cut the supply-line impedance, preferably to a value below 10Ω at 100MHz. Proper use of bypassing, multilayer boards, or bus-bars can help. If good layout does not achieve compliance (with the regulations), by shielding or filtering the 'antennas', the cabling attached to the pcb or back plate may have to be shielded, too. In some cases, even the pcb and the internal wiring may have to be shielded."

Proper layout, use of ferroceramic (ferrite) sleeves and filters etc, can all be put into effect by designers, though more difficult to introduce later into that confounded computer next door!

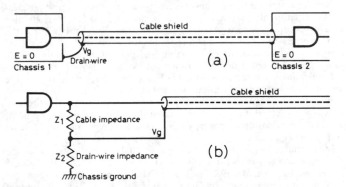

Fig 8. A screened cable can still radiate rfi when the cable-boot design is poor. The inductance of the drain wire can cause much of the rf noise to appear on the outside of the shield – a tip having wide application apart from its use in rfi problems. Equivalent circuit

Worrying flicker and over-investigated radiation hazards

In *TT* November 1987, p835, I was bold enough to advance as "my own theory for what it is worth" an opinion that the medical symptoms of stress, migraine headaches, nausea etc often ascribed to ionised or non-ionised radiation from visual display units, transmitters etc, were more likely to be caused by relatively high-frequency (25, 30, 50 or 60Hz) flicker in conjunction with the enhanced photo-sensitivity of the eye/brain system of a small but significant minority of the population. These views were based on dealing for over a decade with occasional complaints from viewers of tv-induced epileptic convulsions and migraine headaches.

It was thus interesting to read (*The Observer*, 10 January 1988) that Dr Arnold Wilkins of the Applied Psychology Unit, Cambridge, has found that even the imperceptible 100Hz flicker from fluorescent strip lighting (which does not have the thermal inertia of filament lamps) on 50Hz mains supplies appears to be a major cause of stress and illness among office workers. This has been observed and quantified by the Cambridge team with a detailed study due to be presented at a National Lighting Conference in Cambridge during March.

Dr Wilkins is quoted as follows: "Our results clearly show that normal fluorescent lighting has a detrimental effect on office workers' health. But not everyone is affected. Most of our cases were made up of a minority of

people who suffered considerably . . . A new non-flicker type of fluorescent lighting mimics daylight more exactly, which is why it seems to produce less illness". Some scientists suggest that flicker may cause nerve impulses from parts of the visual pathways to oscillate at the same rate, causing abnormal responses in the brain.

Independently of *The Observer* report, Jeff Jeffrey, VK6AJ, writes: "For many years I suffered from the odd migraine and headaches at work. I put it down to the stress of split-second timing and public exposure as I was a radio announcer and television newsreader. Studio areas are isolated from the outside world with air-conditioning and artificial lighting. Some years ago the lighting was changed in the duty supervisor's office where I spent many hours of the working day. Fluorescent tubes were taken out and filament bulbs installed. From then on I had no more migraine attacks, although I was still affected if I stayed for long in supermarkets where there was no daylight but scores of fluorescent tubes. If there is also daylight present the effect is delayed longer . . . The last time I went to my optician for reading glasses, she said she had heard of the effect from other clients."

The conventional fluorescent tube "strikes" twice in every cycle of the ac mains, ie "undetectable" 100Hz flicker on 50Hz mains supplies. Dr Arnold Wilkins points out, in *The Observer* report, that a new type of "non-flicker" fluorescent tube powered by switched-mode units at up to 15kHz (30kHz strikes) mimic daylight more exactly "which is why it seems to produce less illness." Visual display tubes with longer persistence phosphors similarly have less flicker and seem beneficial for those who suffer from photo-sensitivity effects.

B Carter, GW8AAG, on the other hand, points out that an attractive proposition for the shack, workshop or where lights may be left on for hours, is the Philips "SL" high luminous output lamps. For example, the Philips SL9 consumes only 9W of electricity yet provides the light output of a conventional 40W bulb. He points out that for safety reasons it is most advisable to change the lampholder, since this is likely to have been weakened by the heat of the incandescent bulb which weighs only a couple of ounces, whereas SL lamps weigh almost a pound (425g) of miscellaneous glassware, starter gear and plastic cap. I have no idea of the extent of flicker with these lamps but, since they are basically fluorescent lamps, they could provide a source of problems for anyone with enhanced photosensitivity, though economical for the majority.

Two American university scientists – Kenneth Foster and William Pickard – have written a trenchant article (*Nature* 10 December 1987) highlighting the need to establish guidelines for *halting* some of the protracted and inconclusive research into possible biological effects of low-level non-ionised radiation (at the sort of levels that would be found in the vicinity of amateur radio transmitting antennas). They claim that after 40 years of investigating the possible hazards, the field is still littered with inconclusive, ambiguous and controversial reports, impossible to evaluate fully. Many of the reports remain unconfirmed and have not proved repeatable.

The problem, it would seem, is not, as often suggested, that too little is known about the biological effects of microwave, uhf, vhf or lower-frequency energy. Many of the thousands of papers are concerned with heating of tissue, which, when excessive, is clearly hazardous. Yet, fundamental questions are still being raised about the very existence of hazards associated with low levels of exposure, and significant public concern remains.

The American authors do not argue that low-level radiation is hazardous, or take issues with the 1982 ANSI standard (discussed in *TT* November 1986), but rather they underline the difficulties involved in demonstrating the safety of environmental agents of all sorts, adding: "Granted, society must search for hazards of its technologies. But how to cope with the scientific noise that these studies produce? Such searches for hazards can go on too long, and guidelines for ending them must be established." They note that there is now an enormous literature on biological effects, some at energy levels below the ANSI standard, some of which might be considered harmful: "Many of these reports are too brief to evaluate, while others have obvious technical flaws. Much of the controversy surrounding microwave energy has arisen from different interpretations of them".

The authors discuss in detail three effects which have been reported to occur under exposure conditions permissible under the ANSI standard: the microwave auditory effect first reported in 1947 by an observer who, when standing in a beam of a pulsed radar antenna, could hear "clicks" at the repetition rate of the microwave pulses. This has been confirmed but is not now considered a hazard, being due to acoustic transients arising from thermal expansion in tissues subject to rapid microwave heating. Heart-rate effects of which there are conflicting reports and of which they conclude: "There the matter stands. Which of the reported effects were due to the experimental error and which of the negative follow-up studies were inadequate to have confirmed an earlier positive finding is still, in some quarters, a contentious issue."

Of blood-brain barrier effects they conclude: "Few investigators would now claim that the blood-brain barrier is greatly affected by microwave irradiation at levels anywhere near those allowed by past or present ANSI exposure standards. The effects illustrate how easy it is to collect evidence which neither demonstrates a hazard nor provides assurance that no hazard is present."

Crystal oscillators at uhf

For many years, piezo-electric quartz crystals based on mechanical lapping and polishing were restricted to fundamental modes below about 20MHz and overtone frequencies below about 150MHz. In 1986, STC announced a range of crystals operating in fundamental mode to 75MHz and in third-overtone mode to over 200MHz. Recently, in *Electronic Letters* 3 December 1987, G Gonzalez and B Avanic of Miami University described an oscillator design using a crystal with a fundamental frequency of 842·911MHz provided to them by Piezo Technology Inc. They note that "using chemical polishing methods for quartz has resulted in AT-cut crystal resonators with fundamental frequencies up to 1·6GHz . . . The manufacturing of these crystals is still in the infancy stage and production in large quantities is still years away. Yet the potential of this technology in the area of communications is immense. For example, these crystal oscillators can be used as reference oscillators in the microwave region and as voltage-controlled oscillators with excellent spectral characteristics".

Tips and topics

C J Chapman adds eleventh and twelfth commandments when using petrol-electric generators (*TT* November 1987): "When you *have* spilled fuel over the generator, allow it to dry thoroughly *before* starting it up! Petrol/oil mixtures take quite a while to dry thoroughly. The twelfth commandment is to check the output voltage *before* connecting your radio equipment. Governors have been known to go wrong."

On the question of operating 12V equipment from 24V vehicle supplies (*TT* November) he adds: "Use a zener and some power transistors, or an LM317HV adjustable ic regulator. They are designed for vehicle use with a maximum input of 57V and have 'safe area' operating characteristics. The data sheet gives circuits using bypass transistors for higher currents, and the device may also be used as a switching regulator. If you are using a couple of hundred pounds worth of radio, it doesn't make sense to risk blowing it to save a tenner."

B Carter, GW8AAG, notes that may circuit diagrams, including those in *TT*, often depict mains-connected apparatus having a double-pole single throw switch: "All good and proper – but the mains is shown connected to the moving contact. It is often proper and suitable to use a double-pole, double-throw switch if one is to hand. This means that if the circuit diagram is followed the mains is not 'switched off' but is switched to two exposed connection points. All circuit diagrams and wiring up should be on the principle of the moving contact being connected to the apparatus."

Harry Neff, W3JN (*QST* December 1987), draws attention to a useful source of those fast-vanishing air-dielectric variable capacitors – old, broken-down domestic radios, which also yield other still-useful components such as resistors, knobs etc. *QST*'s column editor, N1FB, adds "don't overlook old transmitters, surplus military gear etc at flea markets etc. Though the item may not be useable or worth repairing for its original purpose, the value of the components inside may far outweigh its apparent worth . . . but you may need some muscle to carry away heavy items."

Bob Baird, W7CSD in *QST* December 1987 writes: "Many cities and towns (in the USA) have an electric razor repair shop that replaces nicad batteries in rechargeable electric razors. The razors I've seen contain two nicad cells. Often, only one of these cells has failed, but both cells are replaced when repair time comes. I talked a razor repair person out of a box of such rejects and got 40 cells; 20 of these charged perfectly on the first try! Brief application of heavy overcharging current (safer to use a charged high-capacitance electrolytic capacitor – *G3VA*) to the rest of them netted another dozen useable cells. Free nicad cells? Check your friendly electric razor repair shop."

Gordon Crayford, VE6EI (*QST* December 1987), recalls an old tip when he writes: "You can find the resonant frequency of an inductor/capacitor combination (or an unknown crystal frequency – *G3VA*) if it falls within the tuning range of your receiver. Connect the components as a parallel tuned circuit in series with the antenna lead as shown in Fig 9.

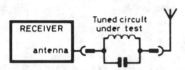

Fig 9. Simple method of determining the resonate frequency of a tuned circuit where a gdo is ineffective or not available. In effect the old-fashioned "wavetrap" of yesteryear

With the receiver tuned for minimum signal or noise response, the receiver frequency display shows the approximate resonant frequency of this tuned circuit. This technique can be used in situations where a dip meter is impractical, such as when the tuned circuit under test is inside a shield can or inaccessible because of its position. There is often no need to remove or otherwise isolate the tuned circuit from the associated circuitry."

Feedback

Last month's single 3·5/7MHz cw transmitter. Although *Radio ZF* gave the value of the cathode resistor connected to the keying jack as 220kΩ 1W (Fig 12, March *TT*) this must be an error for 220Ω 1W.   □

Technical Topics

Pat Hawker, G3VA

IT WOULD BE UNFORTUNATE if recent items in *TT* were interpreted by readers as implying that there is an unbridgeable gap between those who accept that there is a continuing and justifiable role for thermionic valves and those who regard anything less than all-solidstate as being far from state-of-the-art. As Ray Howgego, G4DTC, puts it: "I feel that the 'valve versus transistor' debate has been over-stated. As a physicist, I regard any electrical effect, whether naturally occurring or within a man-made device, as simply a phenomenon. When one applies physics to practical situations to produce a desired end result, one chooses the phenomenon which is the most suitable or most cost-effective in the circumstances. How easily the anti-thermionic lobby changes its opinion when valves are placed alongside solidstate devices on bright, shiny, double-sided printed circuit boards. What if Yaesu or Icom were suddenly to re-introduce valves into their receivers? On recently touring the radio rooms of a modern frigate in the Devonport dockyard, I was surprised to see a considerable quantity of valve equipment, receivers and transmitters."

Low-cost linears

G4DTC continues: "To add insult to injury, with what device can one obtain 180W p.e.p output on the hf bands for £5? Why, a valve of course! I have never understood why so many constructors of linear amplifiers search tirelessly, and often in vain, for cheap American 'sweep tubes' (6JS6, 6LQ6 etc) or even such transmitter tubes as 811s and 813s, when the excellent British (European) PL509 and PL519 are still in abundant supply, rarely cost more than £5 or £6 new, and are much tougher than their more expensive American/Japanese counterparts.

"Many happy hours have been spent here evaluating the performance of these valves as a grounded-grid linear amplifier using the test circuit of Fig 1. Associated component values were mostly cribbed from equivalent USA designs. The 40V heaters of the PL509 and PL519 have possibly put off prospective users but are really a blessing in disguise since 40V transformers are readily available and the relatively low heater current (0.3A) means that the mandatory heater choke (RFC2) becomes a far more modest component."

Using a two-tone test signal from an FT200, the results obtained for an undistorted two-tone test pattern are shown in Table 1.

G4DTC adds: "There was no discernable difference between the PL509 and PL519. However, the PL519 is mechanically a more substantial valve having a thicker glass envelope, higher permissible control-grid dissipation and improved electrode connections. The valves seemed almost indestructable and ultimately limited by envelope temperature. Hence, a draught of cold air was blown at them from a small fan on a gramophone motor. During tests, the valves were often run for 10 to 15min continuously at full power. One PL509, known to have given daily service for 10 years in a domestic television receiver, measured up as though it were new!

"A few notes for intending constructors:

(1) All tests *must* be carried out on a two-tone signal with an oscilloscope lightly coupled to the dummy load.
(2) The grid voltage must be adjusted to give zero cross-over distortion. Very little change was discernable up to 5V, and zero bias might prove acceptable.
(3) Both control grid pins (1 and 8) *must* be decoupled to ground.
(4) The input resistance was not measured but matched well into the driver transmitter with no adverse effects.

Table 1. PL509/PL519 with two-tone signal from FT200

The following results were obtained with an undistorted two-tone test pattern:

Test frequency	3·70MHz
Anode volts (Va)	710V
Anode current (Ia)	162mA (max signal)
Grid bias voltage (Vg)	Approximately 5V
Average output current (rf) into 70Ω load	1·15A
Peak envelope power output	185W
Peak evelope power drive	20W (estimated)
Anode load resistance (R_L)	1,900 – 2,100Ω (estimated)
Valve anode/ground capacitance	22pF
Grid current (maximum signal)	60mA
Zero signal (quiescent) current	30mA (PL509), 20mA (PL519) at Vg = 5V

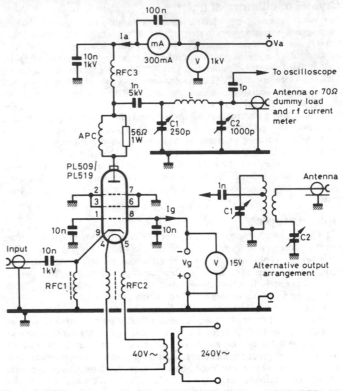

Fig 1. G4DTC's test circuit of the PL509/PL519 linear amplifier. RFC1 80t 20swg enam on ferrite rode. RFC2 two windings of 20swg wound bifilar for 10cm along ferrite rod. RFC3 113t, 24swg on 0·75in diameter former in four sections (16t, 25t, 30t, 42t from anode end). APC 8t 22swg on 56Ω resistor

(5) The pi-network at 3·7MHz comprised: C1, 145pF; C2, 425pF; L, 34 turns, 16swg, diameter 1·25in, length 3·5in (this is not ideal, but useful for starters).
(6) PL509 bases (B9D) are readily available from television service departments.

"Four of these valves in parallel would run at full legal output with plenty to spare. However, the low anode resistance (500Ω) and high capacitance (88pF) would make a pi-coupler difficult to implement above 7MHz, and the alternative output network shown in Fig 1 would be more attractive. A plug-in coil system would allow automatic selection of the best arrangement. I am hoping to carry out tests on such a parallel combination soon."

Audio filter/clipper

For many years I have used a simple crash-limiter using back-to-back diodes across the output to high (4,000Ω) or medium (300Ω) headphones using af transformers to raise (and where necessary then lower) the impedance when fed from a low-impedance socket on the receiver. Although this type of approach has been criticised (G3OYU, *TT* March 1987) I have always found it invaluable for cw reception, using it in conjunction with a passive filter (the old FL8).

Bill Wright, G0FAH, has designed and built a more elegant combined audio filter and clipper (Fig 2), for use with his Ten Tec Argosy 2 transceiver, but which should prove equally suitable for use with any receiver that provides about 0·5V p–p audio output. With the Argosy 2, only one soldered connection is made to the transceiver (to obtain the 8V supply). Construction of the unit is being described in detail in *Sprat* (G-QRP Club) but the following notes cover the principles. The circuit board is shown in Fig 3.

The unit is built around a dual-fet op-amp(TL072) and has an output

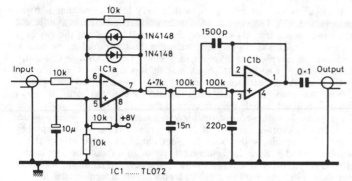

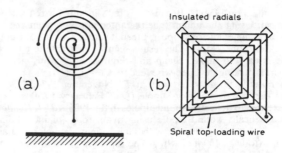

Fig 2. G0FAH's audio clipper/filter, designed initially for use with Ten Tec Argosy 2 but suitable for use with many rigs

Fig 3. Circuit board layout of the audio clipper/filter

Fig 4. (a) Basic configuration of the spiral top-loaded antenna (stla) designed initially for use at vlf but later investigated by the Canadian Broadcasting Corporation and shown to be effective at mf and hf. (b) Practical implementation as used by CBC

The long-established "T" and "inverted-L" form of top-loading, although requiring two supports, remains among the most effective vertically-polarised antenna where there is not sufficient height for a full quarter-wave monopole. Less recognised is the spiral top-loaded antenna (stla) which was described in *TT* November 1974, pp764-5: Fig 4. This is a more effective form of loading, provided that the turns are far enough apart, than the more usual top-loading coil plus capacitance hat of equivalent area. Another little-used arrangement is the folded umbrella arrangement (*TT* July 1974) which allows a mast radiator of only 0·1λ (or more) to be fed directly from coaxial cable: Fig 5.

The use of short linear or helical dipole elements with capacitance hats, however, is now quite widely used. Both Doug Harris, GW3NDR and Dr Constantino Feruglio, IV3VS, have recently reported good results from the use of this class of antenna.

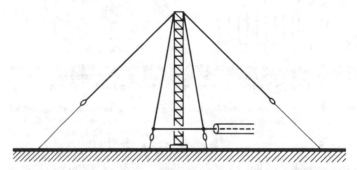

Fig 5. The folded umbrella antenna configuration which allows mast radiators of one-tenth-wavelength or more to be fed directly from low-impedance coaxial feeder cable as developed for mf broadcasting

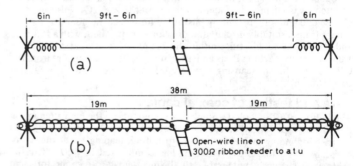

Fig 6. Shortened dipole antennas. (a) GW3NDR's 14MHz dipole with 20ft span using aluminium tubing with loading coils and capacitance hats. (b) IV3VS's multiband dipole for 1·8 to 30MHz using helically-wound wire element wound on nylon rope with capacitance hats that serve also as corona dischargers

limited by the diodes to about a maximum of 1V p–p. If germanium rather than silicon diodes are used, the device would clip at about 0·5V p–p. The clippper is quite "soft" and followed by a lowpass filter so that there should not be any steep wavefronts to harm the ears, and thus overcomes G3OYU's objections to the simple diode limiter.

The first op-amp (IC1a) functions as a soft clipper with a gain of unity. The af then passes through a three-pole lowpass active filter which removes any harmonics produced by the clipper together with high-frequency hiss. The filter is flat to 2·7kHz, 3dB down at 2·9kHz, −10dB at 4kHz and −20dB at 5·8kHz, with an output coupling capacitor chosen so that, with the Argosy's internal cw filter switched off, the output is −6dB at 100Hz. There is no dc isolating capacitor on the input as this is already provided by C27 on the Argosy's i.f-af board. For other equipments not having an isolating capacitor a 1μF capacitor should be fitted.

G0FAH reports that the performance of the clipper is very good, with no distortion on peaks while removing all the crashes. The filter removes hiss without reducing speech quality, which means that G0FAH finds that he can continue to use his hi-fi headphones which do not have the odd resonances and nulls of some cheaper headphones; he once tried a pair of well-known Japanese communication headphones which proved to have virtually no response at 750Hz; fine for speech but useless for cw.

Small antenna elements

While the vhf/uhf operator seldom needs to worry about the size of his dipole elements, this is by no means the case on hf, and even more so on our single mf band (1·8MHz). The restricted size of the average British garden and the limited scope for antennas for the flat-dweller has encouraged the use of electrically-short antennas: elements brought into half-wave or quarter-wave resonance by means of coils, capacitance hats or the various forms of linear loading, including the simple dropping down of the ends of a dipole element, zig-zag or meander or helical elements etc. Over the years, *TT* has included many novel forms of small antennas, many developed initially for professional applications.

Recently, skimming through a library copy of *Small Antennas* by K Fujimote, A Henderson, K Hirasawa and J R James (Research Studies Press), I was relieved to find that the majority of the loading techniques in this high-cost book have been featured in *TT*, though by no means all have subsequently received the attention that they perhaps deserve.

GW3NDR, with a span limited to about 20ft, uses the arrangement shown in Fig 6(a) on 14MHz with excellent results, the element being mounted 30ft above ground on a chimney. He writes: "The end-loading coils are wound with 18swg on 0·75in plastic waste water pipe. The capacitance hats were made from copper-plated mild-steel welding rods (from Halfords). The loading coils have spaced turns (about single wire diameter spacing) and consist of about twice the length of wire of the portion of the element missing from a full-size dipole (in this case each coil comprises about 13ft of wire). The element was checked with a gdo at ground level, and adjusted by means of the coils so that the antenna was roughly resonant on 14MHz. Because it is fed with open-wire feeders this is not critical. Using aluminium tube the antenna is very light and easily mounted on a single pole or support. I feed it with a Z-match atu and find it will work also on 21MHz. The results seem comparable to a full-sized dipole. It is easy to make, cheap and requires little adjustment. The hardest part is making the open-wire feeders."

IV3VS noted relevant references in *TT* November 1974; *QST* June 1971, and the Teletron Slinky Dipole (*QST* February 1974) as well as some references to helically-wound dipoles in the 1986 *ARRL Handbook*. He built a helically-wound dipole using nylon rope (diameter 10mm). Each arm is 19m long wound with 80m 1·6mm-diameter enamelled copper wire (total of 160m of wire). The turns are about 7/8mm spaced. The ends of the helical diple have capacitance hats, which prevent corona effect (three wire spokes, each wire 1m long) and which also lengthen the antenna electrically. The antenna is fed directly using 300Ω ribbon feeder and atu. This works well from 1·8 ro 28MHz (some peculiar radiation patterns). IV3VS considers this a really good multiband compromise for those without space for a full 1·8MHz dipole.

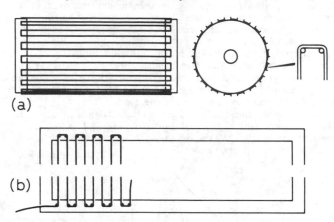

Fig 7. Non-inductive end loading for very short end-fed 1·8MHz antennas. (a) Coil-like construction suitable for external use. (b) A flat frame may be more suitable for indoor/attic antennas. As described by G2QM in 1958

It is not effective to end-load an antenna element with a close-wound coil unless this connects into a capacitance hat. However, as for the stla it *is* possible to end-load with a wire having relatively little mutual induct-ance between the turns. As long ago as 1958, Dr M J Heavyside, G2QM ("Aerials for confined spaces", *RSGB Bulletin* January 1958, pp318-9) showed how a loading "coil" comprising 37 wires each 3ft long (114ft in all) could be "wound" between two circular end pieces spaced 3ft apart, using insulated pegs, and winding as shown in Fig 7(a). With this amount of loading, a 14ft length of antenna wire, fed as a quarter-wave Marconi antenna, was claimed to radiate well on 1·8MHz. G2QM also used an end-loaded indoor antenna in his attic, for which he found a flat 3ft square frame, suitably insulated, more convenient. Then, with a 15ft wire and 8W input to his transmitter, he could work around the UK on 1·8MHz, even reaching Paris and attracting a letter of complaint from the GPO saying he was causing interference to marine traffic at a Danish coast station!

Care and testing of coaxial cables

The February *TT* included a number of comments on the high attenuation that can be experienced on coaxial feeder cables that have been subject to rough handling or ineffective weatherproofing, leading to the ingress of moisture. As Kurt Grey, VE2UG, has commented in *QST*: "Coaxial cable is particularly vulnerable to flexing damage at connectors and bulkheads. Protect it well, flex it minimally, keep bending radii as large as possible and take the action of weather into consideration".

The *TT* notes showed how a lossy cable has the effect of reducing the swr measured at the transmitter end (see Fig 10, February p111). It seems worth adding that this characteristic can be used to check the extent of cable loss in any odd piece of cable (old or new) before using it as a feeder. The procedure was described many years ago in the *RSGB Bulletin* (November 1961, p211) by O J Russell, G3BHJ, as the following extracts show:

"A common check upon a length of coaxial cable is to terminate it in a dummy load matching its impedance, and to measure the standing wave ratio (swr) when rf is applied. This test indicates very little, as the effect of cable loss is to ensure that the meter reads close to unity swr even if the cable is mismatched. It is not generally appreciated that such a test will

indicate unity swr, or nearly so, with a very lossy cable that is badly mismatched. . . . The swr test on a piece of matched cable is a futile and often misleading test. By reversing the test and measuring the swr on a completely mismatched cable, a sensitive indication of cable loss is obtained. A complete mismatch is most conveniently arranged by short-circuiting the far end of the cable, making this truly short in a physical sense since the inductance of some inches of wire at rf is sufficient to disturb the readings . . . the cable should be cut short and the outer braiding bridged sharply over to contact the stub of the inner connector. Fig 8 shows the values corresponding to a given cable loss. . . . In practice an indicated short-circuit swr of 20:1 or greater is perfectly acceptable, and 15:1 tolerable, with about 12:1 debatable. A figure of 8:1 or less would be good grounds for rejecting it, although it should be appreciated that cable attenuation increases with frequency so that at vhf it may be necessary to accept that there will be feeder losses exceeding 1dB."

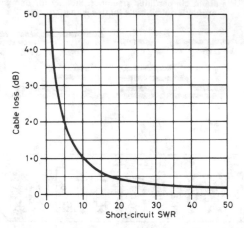

Fig 8. Attenuation plotted against swr of a short-circuited coaxial feeder cable

In 1961, it was possible to connect a transmitter to a short-circuited feeder without risk. Today, it would be necessary with solidstate amplifiers to use either a separate source of rf or, for example, the tune-up protection device featured in recent *TT*s.

Vehicle emc affects reliability and safety

The growing professional interest in the problems of electromagnetic compatibility (emc) that have long been of concern to radio amateurs, was strikingly reflected in a recent IEE colloquim on "vehicle electromag-netic compatibility". Two trends have transformed vehicle emc from being largely a question of suppressing ignition and accessory interference to in-car entertainment systems to one with important safety and reliability overtones: (a) the proliferation of car electronic systems based on cmos microprocessors; and (b) the increasing use of "composites" such as glass reinforced plastics (grp or "fibreglass") rather than metals in vehicle bodies, with rfi/emi and esd (electrostatic discharge) now recog-nised as "probably the most effective killers of electronic modules in cars". While car manufacturers have begun to take seriously the question of immunity against strong rf fields, including those from nearby radio, television, radar and carphones, it should not be forgotten that few manufacturers contemplate the possibility that a radio amateur may wish to install a high-power transmitter in the vehicle.

Dr Andy Marvin (University of York) defines emc thus: "Electomag-netic compatibility is attained when an electronic system consisting of two or more sub-systems operates in the manner defined in its specification, without the individual sub-systems, or other external electronic systems, suffering from, or being the cause of, electrical disruption". Two poss-ibilities for disruption arise; first, from unwanted interactions between sub-systems taking the form of cross-talk between cables, inductive pick-up from transformers or scan coils, or ground loop noise; the second is disruption or interference between electronic systems which would not normally be interactive, including interference from local high-power radio transmitters, or impulsive noise voltages introduced on mains cables by electric motors, power electronic devices, or ignition systems.

The problems of rfi/emi generated within a vehicle are seen as bound to rise as the electronic complexity of motor vehicles increases. M T Crowther (Jaguar Cars) put it thus: "There was a leap in the quantity and type of technology employed in motor vehicles which happened with the launch of such cars as the new BMW7 series, the new Jaguar XJ6 and the new Opel Senator. From cars with, perhaps, (electronic) engine management and a trip computer, our industry has jumped straight to cars routinely containing seven or more microprocessors. Since susceptibility to, and generation of, radio energy seems to be poorly understood by hardware engineers, it appears that this aspect of component design has been largely ignored. Understanding the mechanisms involved requires a knowledge of both antenna and transmission line engineering. Until recently, problems in this area have been rectified as they have manifested themselves at a stage in design too late to influence fundamentals such as pcb layout and logic design."

He added: "Most interference to date has proved to originate from clock harmonics, in some cases the emissions have been from the gate output, in others from the supply lines to the gate . . . In all instances of interference (to in-car radio receivers) emissions have been reduced to acceptable levels by decoupling ic devices and filtering of clock outputs or by reducing current rise time of the clocks by other means. Careful attention should be paid to the family of logic selected, the component layout, power supply bussing and signal trace layout . . . the use of 'slow' logic such as 4000 series cmos is recommended. If another logic family, such as the 74HC series, is used, far more care must be exercised in its implementation. It is not uncommon to see harmonics beyond the twentieth radiating from a module. In every case of interference it was found that the system clock was responsible for narrowband interference, while data busses were responsible for broadband interference. . . . Isolation of i/o from digital circuitry is important . . . isolated digital and analogue power supplies should be used when mixing digital and analogue circuitry on the same board. Good power supply bussing is characterised by low impedance and good decoupling over a wide bandwidth, which is achieved by maximising the capacitance between the power lines and minimising their self-inductance."

It will be appreciated that such advice applies equally when considering the incorporation of digital circuitry, microprocessors etc into fixed station design.

Keith Price (Jaguar Cars), in discussing the use of test chambers for checking the immunity of vehicle equipment to strong radio fields (to about 50V/m), drew attention to the curious phenomenon of "windowing": "Some components are susceptible at relatively low power levels, but revert to normal operation as the power level is increased. No satisfactory explanation for this phenomenon has yet been found. The effect is sometimes referred to as 'windowing' and has been found to be much more common than would at first be expected."

In describing the provision of "emc/esd protection in composites", K L Longmore (Lotus Engineering) commented that: "For both radiation of, and susceptibility to, rfi and protection against esd, behaviour of metal-bodied vehicles is now well known. The increasing use of composites in vehicle bodies and the existence of totally composite construction prototypes present a rather different picture, adding up to a step into the unknown, especially in light of tougher emc requirements, product liability etc."

Here again there is a parallel situation in regard to the use of plastics etc rather than metal for equipment enclosures such as personal computers. Mr Longmore suggested there are three main approaches to providing shielding/screening of composites: **fillers** (ie loading the resin with conductive particles); **meshes/weaves** ("since composites are based on casing a strong mat in a resin, clearly if the mat can be made conductive it could form an effective screen"); and **surface coatings**, for example by making the gel coating of grp conductive, applying a conductive paint (by spraying) or by sticking a metal foil on to the surface. For the low-volume production of Lotus cars, self-adhesive aluminium foil has proved effective. In the USA, for high-volume production, an alternative approach has been to enclose the vehicle engine in its own metal box.

As with all rf shielding problems, it is usually not sufficient to screen, no matter how effectively, the source of rf unless one also takes care to filter and isolate all leads emerging from the enclosure. In the case of vehicles, problems can arise due to radiation from, or cross-coupling within, the main wiring harness. Screening of individual or associated

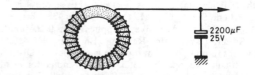

Fig 9. G3MEW's method of suppressing a difficult case of alternator whine for 144MHz mobile operation. A single layer winding of the power feed to his rig on ferrite toroid plus 2,200µF capacitor

wires depends on the effectiveness of the shielding. It has been pointed out (*TT* July 1984) that the percentage coverage of the outer conductor of standard coaxial cables now tends to be between 40 and 60 per cent. Such cables "leak" rf to a significant degree.

G E R Denman, G3MEW, has added a tip to the notes on vehicle interference suppression given in the May 1987 *TT*. He writes: "I find that the advice given in *Radio Communication Handbook* does not really help in the more difficult cases. I encountered a case of alternator whine on my FT290 (144MHz) although the *Handbook* considers this should not cause problems above 27MHz. Simply adding a suppressor to the alternator made no difference. I cured the problem by a single layer winding around a ferrite ring core with a 2200µF capacitor to earth on the rig side of the winding: Fig 9.

Building stable tunable oscillators

In the December 1987 *TT*, it was noted that the free-running "Kalitron" oscillator used, with good buffering, by Ray Howgego, G4DTC, for his "ultimate" receiver has proved "exceptionally reliable, providing a very high output, independent of LC ratio". The single-conversion approach contributes to the total absence of spurious carriers over the entire tuning range. Oscillator stability was measured as "after drifting about 4kHz in the first 10min, it then settles down to within 20Hz for an indefinite period (measured at 30MHz)".

I gather from G4DTC that some readers have questioned whether such stability could possibly be achieved over the entire tuning range of a band-switched oscillator. In this connection one must stress once again that the stability of any free-running LC oscillator cannot be guaranteed simply by selecting one "special" type of oscillator circuit, but depends on the care taken in the choice of components, the mechanical construction, and the precautions to overcome the main causes of drift in oscillators: heat, humidity and operating parameters. Particular emphasis needs to be given to such factors as the change in coil *inductance* with change of temperature. It is also important that the construction should be such as to render unimportant any flexing, expansion or movement of the chassis or pcb. Leads and components should be rigid but *not* under stress when secured in place.

G4DTC explains that he has adopted a "no compromise" technique: capacitors are mica type; he uses heavy gauge wiring with a reinforced double-sided pcb and liberal coatings of Araldite. The band-change switch was chosen with care: the wafer switch assemblies from RS proved excellent with the rotors Araldited to the shaft ("Makaswitch" units were *not* suitable for this application).

A single-range 5·8 to 6·3MHz Vackar fet oscillator built and described by Peter Martin, G3PDM, many years ago (see *ART* and *Radio Communication Handbook*) achieved ±2Hz/30min after a short warm-up period. This resulted from strict observance of some 15 points. These included use of a strong box (diecast or better); use of high-quality variable capacitor; use of air-spaced trimmer; very effective prior cleaning of variable capacitors (preferably using ultrasonic bath); adjustable temperature compensation (Oxley "Tempatrimmer" or lower-cost "Thermo Trimmer"); use of silver-mica capacitors Araldited to surrounding solid objects; use of 2W solid-carbon gate resistor for minimum heating and low inductance; use of buffer/isolating amplifier essential, preferably incorporating negative feedback to maintain low harmonic content; oscillator components with single earthing point; preferred use of ceramic coil former, avoiding use of ferrite cores; and short leads with stiff wires for interconnections in the oscillator tank circuit.

So far it has not proved possible to trace the origin of the "Kalitron" push-pull oscillator in spite of an extensive library search of likely journals etc. Its first appearance (called only a "push-pull oscillator") in the *RSGB Bulletin* (predecessor to *Rad Com*) was in January 1953 in an article "Mixer master oscillators" by Bert Allen, G2UJ, and based on a heterodyne-type vfo built by A E Livesey, G6LI, with the variable oscillator tuning over an mf range.

The next appearance, this time identified as the "Kalitron" (one *l*) was for "A 72MHz vfo for 144MHz drive" by "Oxo" (G5OX) (*RSGB Bulletin* September 1958) and included the note: "The writer is indebted to G W Slack, G5KG, for suggesting the basic circuit of an oscillator which is reputed to have a high degree of stability. It is a twin-triode (12AT7) push-pull circuit, very reminiscent of the multivibrator, and glories in the title Kalitron. It comprises very few components and is one of those delightful circuits which function not only in 'breadboard' form but repeats the performance when re-engineered for final use."

Don Napphin, G3MLS, has a 1931 reference to a two-valve circuit developed by an L B Turner "The Kallirotron, an aperiodic negative resistance triode combination" and notes that *Kalli* is a prefix derived from the Greek word *Kallos* meaning "beautiful". Neither G3MLS nor I have been able to check the original 1920 publication (*Radio Review*) but I have found a note on the Kallirotron in the classic *History of Radio Telegraphy and Telephony* by G G Blake (1926) from which it appears to have no connection with the Kalitron oscillator but was intended as a means of reducing static crashes: "In this circuit, two valves are connected with their filaments in parallel. Weak signals are amplified by this arrangement, while powerful atmospherics are actually reduced to a strength below that of the oridinary received signals". In other words an early form of noise limiter rather than an oscillator.

Rather worryingly, my dictionary defines "Kali" as "the Hindu goddess of destruction . . . Her cult characterised by savagery and cannibalism".

Nicad batteries – facts and fallacies

Rechargable nickel cadmium batteries have, with reason, become a popular source of power for portable and handportable equipment. They can provide reliable service over many years if due account is taken of their peculiarities. Yet it remains true that many amateurs are failing to appreciate not only the full capabilities but also the limitations of nicad cells used in battery packs.

J Fielding, ZS5JF, in "Nickel cadmium batteries for amateur radio equipment" (*Radio ZS* September 1987, pp4-5) provides a useful survey of the facts and foibles of nicads. The following extracts from his article attack some of the common myths and also provide some safety hints.

(1) "Rapid charging causes a decline in cell capacity."

Not true provided that the charge is always terminated at a safe point.

(2) "You should not charge only partially discharged cells as this causes a loss in capacity."

Not true. It is not necessary to discharge fully nicad batteries before recharging. In fact, *the opposite* is true. Repeated partial charging gives an increase in the number of charge/discharge cycles compared with full-discharged cells.

(3) "White crystals growing on the tops of nicad cells mean that the seal is faulty and the cell should be scrapped."

Not true. The electrolyte (potassium hydroxide) is extremely searching and can penetrate the seals used in minute quantities. These crystals are potassium carbonate, which is harmless and can be removed with soap and water. The action of the carbon dioxide in the atmosphere reacts with the electrolyte to form the crystals. After removing the crystals, it is recommended that a smear of silicon grease is applied to slow down regrowth of new crystals. The amount of electrolyte lost in this way is insignificant.

4. "I have a cell which appears to take a charge, but after the normal charging period the open circuit voltage is very low. I have been told I should throw it away."

Not true. The reason the cell won't take a charge is usually due to minute crystalline growth across the internal electrodes, caused by prolonged storage. A cure that nearly always works is to pass a very high current for a very short time through the affected cell. This fuses the internal "whisker". Discharging a large electrolytic capacitor is one method of doing this. But note that in a battery the faulty cell *must* be isolated from the other cells since zapping the complete bettery will not usually result in a cure. Charge the capacitor to about 30V and then discharge it through the faulty cell. Several attempts may be required to clear a stubborn cell.

(5) "A battery contains a cell with reserved polarity. The only cure is to replace it"

Not true. The reversed cell can usually be corrected by a similar technique to that given for (4). After re-polarising the cell, the complete battery can be charged in the normal way. Full capacity can be regained after about five cycles.

(6) "A nicad battery should be stored only in a discharged state".

Not true. It can be stored in any state of charge. Due to its inherent self-discharging characteristics it will eventually become fully discharged after a sufficiently long period of storage. To recharge the battery before returning it to service, a "conditioning" charge of 20h at the normal charging rate is recommended. Afterwards charge normally; full capacity can again be expected after about five cycles.

(7) "It is not advisable to keep a nicad battery on permanent trickle charge as this causes permanent degradation of the cells."

Not true. So long as the trickle charge current is adjusted correctly, the charge can continue indefinitely without loss in cell capacity. The safe current can usually be obtained from the manufacturer's data, but 0·025C is a reasonable guide (ie about 100mA for a 4Ah cell and *pro-rata*). This enables the battery to remain fully charged.

ZS5JF also lists seven safety points that should be considered by users:

(1) **Do not** short circuit a fully-charged battery. This, if prolonged, can cause excessive gas production with the danger of possible rupturing of the sealed case.

(2) Nicads contain a caustic electrolyte: this is perfectly safe as long as common sense is used in use and handling of the cells.

(3) A nicad can supply a very high current for a short period (a 4Ah cell can supply over 500A for a few seconds). Sufficient thought should be given to selecting a fuse between the battery and the equipment. The connecting wires should be capable of passing enough current to ensure the fuse blows quickly in the event of a short-circuit.

(4) **Do not** use partially-discharged cells with fully-charged ones to assemble a battery. Assemble the battery with all cells discharged and then charge them as a battery.

(5) **Do not** carry a fully- or partially-charged battery on an aircraft without taking proper safety precautions. A short-circuited battery pack can be a time bomb in such situations. Consult the relevant IATA regulations or ask at the airline check-in.

(6) **Do not** subject battery packs to very high or low temperatures. Never dispose of a battery pack in a fire or throw it out with domestic waste. If it cannot be disposed of properly it is probably best to bury it in the garden in a safe spot.

(7) **Do not** discharge battery packs below about 1V per cell, otherwise there is the possibility of cell reversal.

ZS5JF provides a good deal of other information on charging nicad batteries, and gives as a reference a Varta publication of 1982 *Sealed Nickel Cadmium Batteries* from which some of his notes may have been derived.

Tips and topics

Brian Smith, GW0IER, passes along two useful tips:

(1) A tip passed to him from G0GCM. Cheap (about £10) digital thermometers with a probe that can be taken to the pa compartment of a transceiver or linear amplifier enables the rig temperature to be monitored continuously and appropriate steps taken if this rises above, say, 100° or 90°: Fig 10.

Fig 10. GW0IER finds an inexpensive digital thermometer useful for monitoring the temperature of his transceiver pa compartment

(2) A component puller can be made from a bent paper clip: Fig 11. Simple, but proves invaluable in salvaging resistors, transistors, capacitors etc from surplus circuit boards.

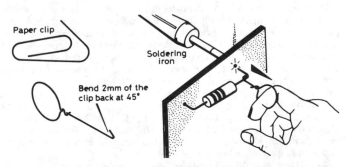

Fig 11. A handy component puller can be made from a bent paper clip. GW0IER cannot recall the origin of this idea but finds it very useful for salvaging components from surplus circuit boards

Ray Howgego, G4DTC, has received several enquiries from readers seeking pcb layout diagrams for his "ultimate" front-end. He is willing to supply these if a suitable sae is enclosed. His address is 31 Campbell Road, Caterham, Surrey CR3 5JP (tel Caterham 43838).

M J Gould of Self Adhesives Supplies Ltd, 9-10 Southview Park, Marsack Street, Caversham, Reading, Berkshire RG4 0AF (tel 0734 483833) writes to point out that the firm is a Preferred Distributor for 3M "Scotch" self-adhesive tapes No 23, 33 and 88 as noted for weatherproofing antenna external connections in *TT* February 1988. The firm will supply radio amateurs with single rolls (No 23 £4.83, No 33 £5.52, No 88 £3.77 or one roll of each for £12.67 including VAT). Quote your callsign when ordering.

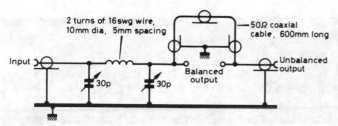

Fig 12. A 144MHz pi-network atu providing balanced and unbalanced output as described by G3UUS in a 1983 *Ham Radio Today*

Dave Ackrill, G0DJA, finds a 144MHz atu (Fig 12), described originally by G3UUS in a 1983 *Ham Radio Today,* useful when experimenting with vhf long-wire antennas along the lines of that described by G8NDJ (*TT* December 1987). He uses a 30m wire, with 94cm of 75Ω and a counterpoise 381cm long.

In the March 1988 *TT,* Del Arthur, G0DLN, showed how he had converted a wartime BC348R receiver (i.f 915kHz) into a six-band exciter for a QRP cw transmitter/transceiver, using the bfo and the local oscillator as a mixer (heterodyne) vfo. This has prompted John Roscoe, G4QK, to warn that problems of spurious radiation could arise, particularly with receivers having the more common wartime i.f of 455kHz. He writes: "If I follow G0DLN correctly, he is in danger of producing two frequencies on transmission, the unwanted one being the usual "second channel" spaced twice the i.f away (ie 1,830kHz) from the desired frequency. There may be sufficient post-mixer selectivity to reduce to an acceptable level the image frequency with the i.f used in the BC348R but this is unlikely to be the case with an i.f of 455kHz (second channel 910kHz spacing) with the limited attenuation likely to be produced in a single rf stage. This is a pity. In the HRO, for example, the first oscillator, running at enormous output (sufficient sometimes to cause tvi to vhf television) had the valve anode at zero rf potential. An output taken from that point had some buffering from the tuned circuit and could be used to drive a transmitter. I did just that – but only on 3·5MHz."

In the March 1988 *TT* I gave the old address for the Siliconix publicity department in connection with the application notes for the Si8901 mixer ic. The new address is: Marketing Services, Siliconix Ltd, 3 London Road, Newbury, Berks RG13 1JL (tel 0635 30905). □

Technical Topics

Pat Hawker, G3VA

FRANK HUGHES, VE3DQB takes issue with the description, from time to time in *TT* and elsewhere, of amateur radio as "a hobby". He draws attention to an editorial he wrote for *The Canadian Amateur Radio Magazine* of January 1987. In this he noted that VE7AHB, in an earlier issue, had stated that "the reason why we retain our immensely valuable spectrum, despite the enormous commercial and military pressure for ever more channels is set out in the ITU *Radio Regulations* as Resolution No 640, where the only reason for exclusive amateur bands is given as the service amateurs render during emergencies . . . the glorious fun available on our bands is to be paid for by readiness to help in emergencies . . . Our bands are not there just for us to collect pretty postcards, or to see how many stations we can briefly QSO during contests, or to talk to some fool who has risked his neck to set up shop on some worthless speck of rock in mid-ocean, or to ragchew by the hour on trivialities." VE3DQB, in his letter, adds: "Amateur radio is no more a hobby than other emergency services, like St John Ambulance for instance. The best word I can think of to describe either is 'avocation'".

As someone who sees nothing much wrong – or unduly frivolous – with "hobby" (dictionary definition: an activity pursued in spare time for relaxation) I fully recognise that at the next WARC which now seems likely to be in 1992, our hf and vhf bands may indeed be under considerable threat. In 1979, at the time of the last WARC concerned with the entire radio spectrum allocations, there was a belief among many professionals that hf was rapidly losing its importance for long-distance civil and defence communications.

Pressure on hf spectrum

But now the position has changed. As many of the papers at the recent "Fourth International Conference on hf radio systems and techniques" at the IEE, London *(IEE Conference Publication No 284)* stressed, there has been a resurgence of hf for medium-distance, low-cost communications and for an increasing number of bistatic and back-scatter and surface-wave hf radars now in use or under-development in many countries. New adaptive processors and real-time channel-evaluation (rtce) techniques can provide reliable data transmission at up to about 2400 bits/second (sufficient for a secure channel of encrypted digital vocoded speech) while frequency-hopping and other pseudo-noise techniques can make the traffic difficult if not impossible to intercept. Complex error detection and correction techniques can ensure accurate copy, without the need for skilled radio operators. At the same time the problems of satellite communications, with their risks of failures during launch or in orbit, tend to have stayed more costly than was predicted. Moreover, increasingly they are seen to be vulnerable to jamming and disruption, and need to be backed up by hf if only as a fallback system.

ITU Radio Regulations

While recognising the force of VE3DQB's concern, I feel that he has put a little too much emphasis on the "emergency" value of amateur radio. Perhaps I am a little jaundiced by having once been one of several amateurs who were taken in by contacts with a station which claimed to be a ship on fire in the Atlantic and requesting help. This Tony Hancock type situation resulted in an extensive air search mounted from Canada but proved to be all part of a stupid, carefully planned hoax.

I checked the ITU *Radio Regulations* and finally traced Resolution No 640 "Relating to the international use of radiocommunications in the event of national disasters in frequency bands allocated to the amateur service". In effect, this resolution, although recognising that "the stations of the amateur service, because of their widespread distribution and their capacity in such cases, can assist in meeting essential communications needs" makes it possible for *official* stations to move into and use the exclusive amateur frequencies during "natural disasters". Certainly, the existence of Resolution 640 affords some assurance that exclusive amateur allocations will continue to be recognised, if only as emergency reserve bands for the authorities.

Instead of "hobby" we should perhaps, wherever possible, use the term "the amateur radio *service*" and recognise that this is defined in *Radio Regulations* (which has the force of an international treaty) as "A radiocommunication service for the purpose of *self-training*, intercommunication and *technical investigations* carried out by amateurs, that is, by *duly authorised persons interested in radio technique* solely with a personal aim and without pecuniary interest" (added italics). There is no role in this definition for the dabbler without any interest in radio communication technology!

Doubly-balanced product detector

In the course of an article on "Product detector performance" (*RF Design*, March 1988), Fred Brown, W6HPH, draws attention to the use of discrete cross-coupled fet devices in the convenient configuration shown in Fig 1. While this technique has been mentioned before in *TT* as a useful mixer circuit, in both bipolar and integrated form, I cannot recall mentioning its usefulness as a fet product detector.

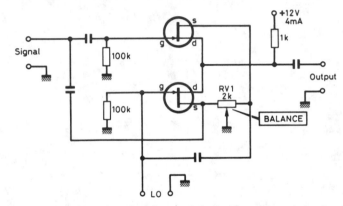

Fig 1. Doubly-balanced product detector (mixer) with unbalanced signal and oscillator drive connections based on cross-coupled fet devices (W6HPH in *RF Design*)

An advantage of this type of circuit configuration is that it has a doubly-balanced output yet does not require either a balanced input or balanced oscillator drive. Only about 1V (3mW) of local oscillator injection is needed. The signal and local oscillator impedances are 350 Ω. The output impedance is essentially that of the drain load resistor, in this case 1000Ω. W6HPH notes that the 2000Ω balance adjustment potentiometer, RV1, can be adjusted for minimum oscillator voltage at the output. The input coupling capacitor should be selected to have under 1000Ω reactance at the signal and oscillator frequencies. The value of the output capacitor depends on the lowest desired output frequency and the load impedance. Conversion voltage gain is about 2dB; a.m rejection ratio for a 100mV 90 per cent modulated signal is about 27dB.

50MHz receiver converter

The opening of 50MHz to amateurs in several continental European countries, including Holland, despite the continued use there of Band I for television, should further enhance interest in this most rewarding and valuable part of the radio spectrum. *Reflecties door PA0SE* (*Electron*, April 1988) includes information on a simple 50 to 28MHz receiver converter by PA0WFO (Fig 2) plus also some ideas for a 50MHz transverter suitable for use with a 144MHz transceiver.

The receiver-converter of Fig 2 has a noise factor of about 3dB and a total amplification of about 25dB. It should thus give excellent results when used with any reasonable 28MHz receiver. In the absence of strong local signals, for example from Band 2(88 to 108MHz) broadcast stations, it can use the simple high-pass input filter; where there are strong local signals the alternative LC bandpass filter should be substituted.

Coil and transistor information is given as: L1, L2 10 turns, 0.8mm wire 4mm diameter. L3, L4 12 turns, 0.8mm wire, 4mm diameter. The L3 tap is 2t from the earthy end. L5 is 7t, 0.8mm wire, 6mm diameter. L6 2t, 0.8mm wire, 6mm diameter. L7, L8 7t, on 5mm coil former with ▶

adjustable core. TR1 any of BFY90, BFR91, BFR90, BFW92. TR2 any of 2N200, BF905, BF900, BF960, BF981, 40673. TR3 any of 2N2222, 2N706, BC107, BC108, BC109, BF115, BF199, BF190, BF200, BF224. TR4 any of 2N2222, BC107, BC108, BC109, BF115, BF199, BF200, BF224. The oscillator section could also form part of a 28 to 50MHz transverter.

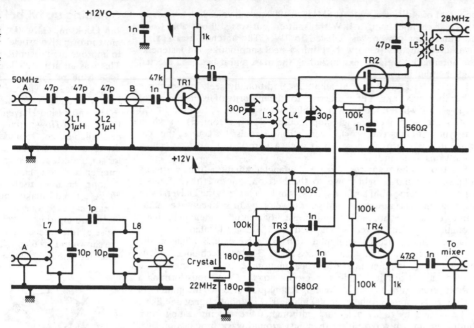

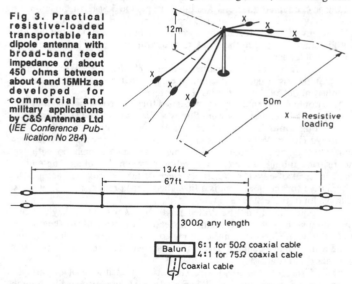

Fig 2. PA0WFO's 50MHz crystal-controlled receiver-converter with output at 28MHz. See text for coil details, etc (PA0SE, Electron)

Antennas for medium-haul paths

The changing role of hf for professional and military communications, with the emphasis now increasingly on its use for medium-distance links of under 2500km, has resulted in new thinking in relation to mobile, transportable and fixed antennas. The traditional whip is not suitable where maximum high-elevation radiation is required; adaptive frequency control and frequency-hoppers have similarly caused more emphasis to be given to broadband rather than sharply resonant systems. Mobility demands antennas that are easily erected.

Sky-wave radiation from a dipole only a few feet above ground is often far more suitable for distances of a few hundred miles than a 10m whip. Some broadcast antennas, particularly those for "tropical" broadcasting, have long recognised the need for antennas radiating skywards. Indeed this was once vividly described in a two-part article by Paul Sollom, G3BGL/VS7PS, "Skybeams, Moonbeams and Howitzers" (RSGB Bulletin, July, August 1952) where he reported his experimental work for a broadcast service from Ceylon (Sri Lanka) to Southern India with a target area some 300 to 700 miles distant. Even broadcasters aiming at world coverage are now concentrating more on "single-hop" coverage by making use of relay bases dotted around the globe, backed up by transmitters with powers climbing up to megawatt levels.

The April IEE HF Conference included a paper "Numerical modelling and design of loaded broadband wire antennas" by Dr Brian Austin (G0GSF) and Andre Fourie, describing in detail the broadband resistive-loaded antenna noted in TT (September 1987, p662) and also mentioned briefly in Electronics & Wireless World and Ham Radio. In the IEE paper, it is pointed out that "Radiation patterns are generally of secondary importance in applications where low-gain wire antennas are used. This is particularly so when the (transportable) antenna is frequently erected in close proximity to the ground with its orientation often somewhat irregular".

A term now being applied in professional communications is "nvis links", standing for "near-vertical incidence skywave links". A conference paper by B S Collins & B R Phillips of C&S Antennas Ltd gives the options for nvis as: compact loop antennas; horizontal low dipoles; fan dipoles; loaded dipoles; delta (half-rhombic) loops. The "most satisfactory" nvis antenna for fixed stations is given as the (sloping) log-periodic dipole array (1pda) but this is regarded as "too large and complex for transportable use."

The authors describe a new C&S professional antenna comprising a resistive-loaded broadband fan dipole supported (in the inverted-vee configuration) by a lightweight (8·2kg) 12m telescopic mast using carbon fibre reinforcement that is claimed to be capable of being erected by one person in 10min, and able to support an 8kg antenna in a wind of 100km/h. The antenna (Fig 3) is a three-wire fan dipole intended for use at any frequency between about 4MHz and about 15MHz, presenting an average and reasonably constant impedance of 450Ω. No details are given

of the resistive loading devices positioned towards the ends of the dipole arms but these presumably are basically similar to those of the Australian dipole and the improved Austin/Fourie design.

The paper notes that: "the absolute gain of the antenna was compared at the lower end of its working band (ie about 5MHz) with that of a half-wave dipole mounted 0·25λ over good flat ground, confirming that

Fig 3. Practical resistive-loaded transportable fan dipole antenna with broad-band feed impedance of about 450 ohms between about 4 and 15MHz as developed for commercial and military applications by C&S Antennas Ltd (IEE Conference Publication No 284)

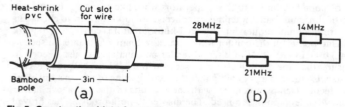

Fig 4. Dual (harmonic) band dipole. As shown it acts as folded half-wave dipole on 7MHz and as a T-matched dipole on 3·5MHz but dimensions can be scaled for 7/14 or 14/28MHz (VK1PM reported in W6SAI's Ham Radio Techniques)

Fig 5. Construction hints for quad antennas: (a) pvc heat shrink tubing as wire support. Glue wire to quad arm with pvc cement. Two-wire wraps will hold it securely after the glue has dried. Stagger the quad wire supports on each side of the arm to distribute the stress more equally; (b) it can be better to use two smaller booms spaced about 1ft apart as supports. The wire supports shown in (a) are staggered on quad arms to distribute wire stress.

the target of -4dBi was met. At 5MHz, a 1200km ssb voice link was set up in a clear channel using a 1kW transmitter, but was still operable when the transmitter power was reduced to 7W." The antenna uses kevlar-covered conductors fitted with stainless-steel snap-hooks and fasteners. The antenna kit weighs 16kg including the mast and it has been erected single-handed in 15min.

It could be argued that hf amateurs traditionally seek long-distance rather than nvis links. Yet in practice, for the majority of us, inspection of the log-book will tend to show most hf contacts on 3·5, 7, 10, even 14 and 21MHz are, in practice, single-hop medium-distance contacts for which nvis-type antennas can provide very strong signals. Of course, the real dx-fanatic will turn his nose up at such a heresy and insist on calling dx-only on a flat band!

For those who want to increase low-angle radiation from vertically polarised antennas, right down to the horizon, another hf conference paper "Launching of hf surface waves" was by a team at the University of Birmingham who are concerned with developing hf surface-wave radar. This discusses a technique for obtaining a 3-6dB improvement in hf signal strength at ground level, when used with a coast-located vertically-polarised dipole already equipped with extensive radials filling in the space between the antenna and the sea-plane. The new technique consists of using a very large number of vertical monopole rods connected to the ground mat to provide "inductive ground loading" and thus forming a "two-layered ground". An interesting technique but, since the number of vertical rods appears to be over 500 in the trial installation, not one likely to be copied by many amateurs, although there are interesting possibilities in surface-wave rather than just ground-wave propagation over sea paths.

On the other hand, one can imagine quite a lot of locations where the dual-band (harmonic bands) antenna shown in Fig 4 could be used. This system was spotted in *Ham Radio* (March 1988) and apparently stems from Ron May, VK1PM. With the dimensions shown the antenna is for 3·5 and 7MHz, but it could be scaled down for 7/14MHz or 14/28MHz. The central 67ft portion forms a 7MHz folded dipole with the end pieces acting as decoupled quarter-wave linear traps. On 3·5MHz it functions as a half-wave dipole with T-match feed. There is of course no technical reason why the 300Ω feeder should not be brought down to a suitable atu with balanced output in the shack to avoid the need for a balun to match to co-axial feeder.

Also in *Ham Radio Techniques* (April 1988) Bill Orr, W6SAI points out that the rising sun-spot count means that it is time again to think seriously about 28MHz antennas. He writes:

"It's not hard to build a quad, but it is difficult to construct one that will stay up in bad weather. They are floppy affairs at best, and you must put a lot of thought into the physical arrangement of the antenna.

"Lloyd Hosor, W9YCB, has some interesting ideas on quad construction. He says the best quad arms are made of 'Calcutta bamboo' with pvc heat shrink tubing slid over the bamboo between the joints. The end of the arm is also sealed with a short piece of heat shrink. An acceptable alternative for the quad arm is a fibreglass (grp) drapery pole. Lloyd has found a lot of these at garage sales.

"The poles should not be drilled for the quad wire after they've been protected with heat-shrink tubing. Instead, cut a piece of pvc lengthwise to fit the pole. Cut a slot in the tubing to hold the wire and glue it to the quad arm with pvc cement. Two-wire wraps will hold it securely after the glue has dried (Fig 5(a))

"Lloyd staggers the quad wire supports on each side of the arm to distribute the stress more equally (Fig 5 (b)). He uses two smaller booms spaced about one foot apart as supports because a single boom for a four element quad will not stand the gaff in bad weather."

John Levesley, G0HJL passes along what he refers to as "just a minor but I hope helpful tip to those operators who, like me, use a tapped coil vertical hf multiband antenna (or conceivably tap a 'sloper' to change its centre resonant frequency). It is well-known that it is convenient to mark the tap points on the coil for future quick retuning of an antenna such as my Hi-Gain 18V-2. With this particular antenna care is also needed to ensure that the feeder clamp is secured outwards at 90° to the coil, otherwise there is a possibility that the close spacing of the coils will allow the feeder clamp to connect with the sections of the coil above and/or below the feed point required. The answer to both problems has proved to be the little plastic pegs sold to hang Christmas Cards from. These mark the tap points clearly and permanently, and even have ridges on the outer surface which help lock the peg between the turns of the coil. An additional benefit is that they force the coil open that extra millimetre at the tap points, preventing unwanted taps above or below the feeder clamp."

Cleaning up tvi/bci

Jim Cookson, G4XWD, draws attention to what he feels is one of the most informative articles written on the subject of advising viewers how to improve their reception that has appeared in a non specialist magazine. This was an article "Clean-up campaign" by David Martin in the April 1988 issue of *Practical Householder*. It is a well-balanced article that makes it clear to viewers that in cases of tvi "often the fault lies in your own tv set and not the transmitter".

The impression I have is that the author has studied carefully the useful DTI booklet *How to improve television and radio reception* which should be available free, from main post offices. This booklet, was introduced at the time when DTI ruled that the Radio Investigation Service could no longer undertake to respond by personal investigations to tv and radio interference complaints without making a minimum charge of £21. Among the most useful appendices to Part 2 are details on: toroidal chokes; braid-breaker and high-pass filters; fitting of ferrites and rf bypass capacitors; characteristics of filters; and available filter types. There are informative "check charts" giving guidance on determining the cause of interference, etc. Braid-breaker and mains filters in the booklet are shown in Figs 6 and 7, but there is little reason to reproduce or digest much of this information in *TT*, when UK readers should be able to

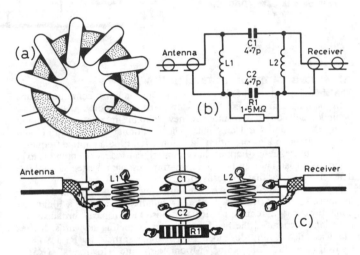

Fig 6. TVI suggestions from the DTI's booklet *How to improve television and radio reception*. (a) "Braid-breaker form of toroid choke for use on tv antenna feeder or as a mains filter. As a braid breaker the choke should be made using small diameter (standard) co-axial cable and the ring should not be wound more than two-thirds full to reduce capacitance between the ends of the coil. The assembly should then be taped to secure the turns, and a co-axial connector fitted at each end. The coil can then be readily interposed between the co-axial download and the television-set's antenna socket. As a mains filter it can be made in the same way by threading the mains cable through a ferrite ring. Again wind only two-thirds full. Ferrite rings of suitable material such as Mullard FX1588 (see also TT, August 1987). (b) Combined braid-breaker and high-pass filter. L1, L2 4 turns 20 swg 6mm i/d, 6mm long. Single-sided pcb 2in by 1in. Scrape grooves approx 1·5mm wide in copper to leave four areas as shown in (c).

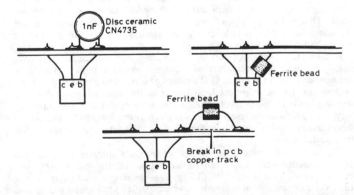

Fig 7. Fitting of ferrite beads and rf bypass capacitors as recommended in the DTI booklet. Capacitors should be disc ceramic and fitted with the shortest possible leads in order to minimise the lead inductance. The ferrite bead should preferably be fitted on the base lead of the transistor, but where this is not possible it should be fitted in the printed-circuit copper track as shown.

obtain a copy of this excellent 28-page (A4) booklet from any main Post Office. Even if the staff claim they have never heard of it, or that there is none in stock, it is worth pleading with them to get more from the DTI. Very large numbers have been printed – and every UK amateur should have his own copy.

G4XWD is one of those who agree that there is an obligation that all licensed amateurs should take seriously the need to "self-train" themselves to deal with technical matters. He writes: "As many are now appliance operators and openly profess no real technical interest or knowledge, how can the authorities, when they hear the inane conversations, continue to resist the pressure from legitimate business users, the military and the broadcasters etc for some of our frequencies. The sooner we all start the self-training and behave in ways which merit the retention of frequencies, the sooner our bands will be assured."

Second thoughts on G4DTC's i.f strip

Mike Grierson, G3TSO, was surprised to read in the March *TT,* in connection with the use of the Plessey SL621 agc device, the comment: "Plessey do not stress the point that it is important to decouple the agc line adequately". He points out that, on the contrary, the Plessey applications note states quite categorically that "the total decoupling on the agc line should not exceed 15nF or the impulse suppression will suffer". This means in effect that a total of three 4·7nF capacitors is the maximum practical decoupling capacitance. The total of 320nF used by G4DTC would have the effect of destroying the noise impulse suppression characteristics of the SL621. He writes: "I have constructed three separate transceivers using the SL600/1600 series of devices, all using the SL621 agc system, and none of them use more than 15nF decoupling on the agc line. Performance is excellent. All too often the SL621 is blamed for other circuit deficiencies which manifest themselves as low frequency oscillation of the agc system. The two major causes are: pick-up of local oscillator signals by the high gain i.f strip causing a residual agc bias under no-signal conditions, common on both the well-known G3ZVC and G4CLF boards, and a 6V supply to the SL621 that is high impedance. If the latter is in excess of 2Ω at lf, the 621 can be starved of current when a sudden input is made to pin one. It is also important in G4DTC's design to ensure that the local oscillator signals are removed from the SL623 during a.m reception if the agc system is to function correctly."

Ray Howgego, G4DTC, has commented: "I agree with all that G3TSO says, particularly the excessive decoupling of the agc line. This oversight, on my part, arose as follows: the prototype was constructed on separate pcbs on an open chassis and incorporated only two 10nF decoupling capacitors close to the 612 devices, in awareness of Plessey's recommendations. However, it was found that some instability appeared to be present, and was traced to the presence of local oscillator voltage on the agc line. At that point, totally forgetting Plessey's advice, an attempt was made to crush this voltage by heavy decoupling. My notes and circuits were prepared at this point. However, when the receiver was rebuilt as a permanent installation, the improved layout and screening did not necessitate the use of the extra capacitors and they were subsequently omitted, reverting to just 20nF of decoupling (even this could be reduced to advantage). Apologies to anyone who used the excessive decoupling, though constructors would probably not have noticed the difference in performance."

Components for home-brew projects

Recently, I received a letter from a Californian amateur who has visited England several times in recent years commenting how difficult it had become in the USA to obtain the parts for home-brew projects. He felt that, by comparison, UK amateurs are still well served. I was reminded of this lament by an article "Home-brewing equipment, from parts to metal work: helpful hints to get you started" by Paul Johnson, W7KBE (*Ham Radio,* March 1988, pp26-28). His introduction began: "Why are so few hams building electronic gear these days? To find out I conducted a survey among my friends. Three major reasons are: (1) Lack of parts and difficulty in finding the necessary materials at reasonable prices; (2) Choosing the wrong projects. Some pick projects that are of no use to their ham operations or that are too difficult for them to complete; and (3) The challenge of metal work can be overwhelming". He offered the following sources of inexpensive parts: (a) Local club sales and auctions. Heavy second world war equipment (often called boat anchors) usually sells at give away prices. Strip down for usable parts and hardware. Keep all screws, nuts, spacers, and small parts such as capacitors and resistors. (b) Garage and silent-key sales. Look for wire, solder, tools, coaxial fittings, connectors, etc. Store for future use.

(c) Hamfests (and mobile rallies), electronic surplus houses, junk yards, ham friends, on-the-air swap meets.

Start with useful projects like field strength meters and antenna tuners before tackling more complex projects such as linear amplifiers. Remember that the foundation of any project is a panel, a chassis and a cabinet.

In *Amateur Radio* (VK), Drew Diamond, VK3XU, offers some practical tips on vfo construction. He writes: "There is a puzzling tendency these days for some builders, especially manufacturers, to make a vfo using sloppy techniques, and then to tack on a phase-locked loop (pll) to stabilise the thing, so adding unnecessary complexity (and phase noise) and reducing the overall reliability of the device. If the amateur is prepared to put a little thought, effort and material into the job by following some pretty well established guidelines, the result will be a quality vfo without the need for the pll panacea." See the May *TT* for hints on building stable vfos.

QST (March 1988) carries Part 1 of an informative contribution by John Grebenkemper, KI6WX, "Phase noise and its effects on amateur communications". He points out the phase noise of oscillators is a subject that remains a mystery to many amateurs yet is an important performance parameter of our equipment. I recall attempting to introduce the subject of oscillator noise and its importance in amateur equipment as long ago as April 1968, based on some notes from Walter Schreuer, K1YZW/G3DCU, and the text-book *Vacuum Tube Oscillators* by Edson. KI6WX points out that hissy interference from off-frequency local signals is often the result of reciprocal mixing brought about by oscillator phase noise, and that on a transmitted signal it causes effects identical to phase noise generated in the receiver. Phase noise on an oscillator signal has exactly the same effect as frequency modulating the oscillator with noise.

He notes that there is no theoretical reason that prevents a phase-locked oscillator from having as good as or even better phase-noise characteristics as a free-running oscillator using an lc tuned circuit – although this is most unlikely to be achieved in practice with low-cost pll oscillators. He illustrates the significant difference in phase-noise between the IC751A, the TS-930S, and the FT-767GX.

Howarth Jones, GW3TMP, of TMP Electronic Supplies, Unit 27, Pinfold Workshops, Pinfold Lane, Buckley, Clwyd CH7 3PL (telephone Buckley (0244) 549563) noted the information in *TT,* August 1987 on the different ferrite core mixes and their uses for interference suppression. This was based on information from K6NY of Palomar Engineers of California. It seems opportune to repeat a note included many years ago, that TMP is a UK source for Amidon toroidal cores in the various mixes. GW3TMP mentions that although he has had small advertisements running for many years, he continues to be surprised at the number of letters he receives saying "I've been trying for years to find out where I can obtain a T50-2 core, etc". He feels that there must be many readers who wondered how to get hold of cores, split cores and beads similar to those mentioned last August without writing to the USA. Hint taken?

Tips and topics

Zack Lau, KH6CP, in the March issue of *QST* illustrates how a matched dummy load for those really high-power amplifiers (up to 1,500W) can be formed from four lower-power dummy loads by means of two quarter-wave coaxial matching sections: Fig 8. The only problem is that the load becomes frequency sensitive and suitable for use only on one band. On that band, however, it should be possible to obtain an almost perfect 1:1 vswr. The coaxial matching sections should be **electrical** not physical quarter waves and must be capable of handling the power.

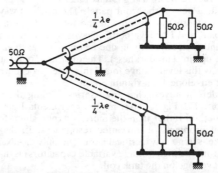

Fig 8. Forming a matched high-power dummy load from four lower-power dummy loads by the use of quarter-wave (electrical) matching sections of co-axial cable. But note that such a dummy load is effective on only one band (KH6CP)

Mobile installation check-list

In his "fm/rpt" column in *QST* (January, 1988, p67), Stan Horzepa, WA1LOU, includes a useful list of points to be taken into account when installing amateur-radio transceivers in vehicles. He writes:

1. Radio controls, microphone and tone pad should be located so that they can be reached by the driver without the need for changing position or detracting attention from the road.

2. For safer operation, leave both hands free for driving by using a headset microphone that can be activated by a ptt switch mounted on the steering wheel (Remember the UK's revised Highway Code – *G3VA*)

3. Cords and wires should be routed so that they will not entangle the driver's hands or feet or interfere with steering, braking or shifting gears.

4. Before taking a drill in hand to make holes for mounting the radio equipment or for routing cables, check to see what is on the other side of the drilling site; in today's compact vehicles, almost any spot that you pick to drill will have something on the other side of it.

5. Use a pair of heavy cables to supply sufficient current from the battery to the radio equipment.

6. Install a fuse near the point of connection to the battery or to your vehicle's electrical system.

7. Wherever a cable passes through a wall or partition in your vehicle, the cable should be protected by a grommet.

8. For best omnidirectional coverage, a mobile antenna should be located on the roof in the centre of your vehicle.

9. Use a magnetic-mount antenna if you shudder at the thought of drilling an antenna mounting hole through the exterior of your vehicle.

10. Eliminate spark plug noise by using (a) resistive spark plug suppressors, (b) resistive spark plugs and/or (c) resistive-wire cabling between the distributor and the ignition coil. (c) is the most effective method of suppressing this type of interference.

11. Today, many vehicles come off the assembly line with resistive-wire cabling already installed; however, after a few years, this cabling may deteriorate (as evidenced by cracked insulation) and should be replaced for continued effectiveness.

12. To protect your equipment against theft, use a sliding mobile mount that allows the radio to be quickly removed and stored out of sight or carried away with you when you leave your vehicle unattended.

While, as noted before in *TT*, difficult cases of electrical interference from accessories or digital electronics may require additional measures, the American list of do's and don'ts seems a useful starting guide.

Using the PL519 and other tv valves

By coincidence, Del Arthur, G0DLN, has come up with a number of points to consider when using PL519 and other television "sweep" (line-output) valves just in advance of the publication of the item in the May issue, provided by G4DTC, on using these valves in linear amplifiers. In effect, G0DLN's remarks were prompted by "misconceptions in linear valve amplifiers" by G3RZP in the April *TT*, p265 but can usefully be considered as adding to both items. G0DLN writes:

"I have recently built an hf amplifier using three PL519s and agree with G3RZP that it is essential to use separate bias potentiometers when using tv sweep valves. The constructor **must,** however, be cautious in the choice of such potentiometers. Most carbon-track pots are rated only 1W or less and the probable dissipation must be worked out beforehand, and a good safety margin allowed. **Never** use secondhand carbon pots or you may lose one of your valves in a matter of moments. If the bias supply voltage is high enough to cause problems with dissipation, the pots can usually be padded with external resistors using Ohms Law. I also use a wirewound 'master' bias control pot on the front panel. The obvious way to adjust these pots is to equalise the currents at the intended operating point. However, a simpler, and I believe better, way is to start with all pots set for low current and then adjust them one by one until each anode is just starting to cherry up (in semi-darkness). The operating point should turn out to be just below this level. I have found this latter procedure produces the best two-tone envelope at maximum power.

"G3RZP wonders if anyone has tried series feeding the pi-filter as shown in the April *TT,* Fig 5. After many experiments I have recently been using this method rather than the more common shunt-fed method with its attendant problems of unwanted resonances. In the series-fed circuit the rf choke is in no way a critical item. The only disadvantage that I can see (apart from the high-voltage variable capacitors) is that you end up with the full ht voltage on the tank coil.

"Anyone thinking of using sweep valves should be warned that owing to the very high input capacitance of these valves there will be a high vswr between the transceiver and the amplifier when a passive-grid input

arrangement is used. This can affect 14, 21 and 28MHz quite badly in the case of solid-state tranceivers. However the problem is easily overcome by shunting the dummy-load grid resistor with a parallel tuned circuit of low-L and high-C. The high-C will swamp out the input capacitance of the valves (which varies with temperature) and it is quite easy to adjust to the operating frequency. This has the useful by-product of acting as a harmonic trap.

"PL519s are plentiful, cheap, and altogether good news for those wishing to work ssb at high power. However, they do not like accepting a single tone at high power for any length of time. Tune-up should start at low-input levels and full-power tuning done in short bursts of only a few seconds duration."

Background to the Eddystone 940

The recent references to the 'sixties Eddystone Radio receiver type 940 has prompted Bill Cooke, now G0ION but for more than 50 years' successively chief engineer, managing director and chairman of Eddystone Radio, though recently retired, to fill in some details of how the 940 came to be born. He writes:

"Eddystone for many years had a very good market overseas for what was termed the discriminating swl but by the 'sixties were concentrating on professional models for Sweden, Germany, Canada, Australia and the USSR as well as the MoD in the UK. The success of that side of the business had left our agents without a really saleable receiver for the 'discriminating swl'.

"Lack of really volume business on some early designs had resulted in some considerable surplus of many items held in the Eddystone stores. At that time Harold Cox was technical director and he set me the task, as chief engineer, of designing a receiver using what we had in stock with only minimum additional purchasing. An inventory indicated that this should be possible; and a target of less than six months to the start of production was set. It was not the intention to consider this as a 'professional' Eddystone receiver since these were normally all designed to meet various government specifications and 'approvals'.

"Several hundred 940 receivers were manufactured initially for sale to agents throughout the world. Few if any problems arose during production and it was rare indeed to come across a faulty 940, though I feel sure that some of the other Eddystone valve receivers of that period could equally be considered as 'classic' designs."

Bill Cooke recently took the RAE and morse test and has now become an active amateur. But he looks back on his 50 years spent alongside many well-known amateurs, arguing and enjoying every minute spent discussing the design of receivers and transmitters, not to mention Eddystone's little-known approach to the television receiver market.

G0ION's letter reminded me of a pleasant day spent at the Eddystone factory in the 'sixties after which I wrote some notes on the early history of a firm that played a dominant role for many years as a UK manufacturer of high-grade communications receivers and components. Even now few of the many who have used Eddystone products know that it all started when women began to cut their hair short in the period following the end of the first world war.

The Eton crop, the bob and the shingle meant a dramatically falling demand for the once popular wire hair-pins. This was a disturbing trend for the Birmingham costume-jewellery firm of Jarrett, Rainsford and Loughton who had a factory turning out six tons of hair pins each week. In 1922, G Stratton Loughton took this part of the firm into the new "wireless" business as one of the companies associated with the original British Broadcasting Company.

The competition proved intense and some five years later Harold Cox and Arthur Edwards changed the emphasis from medium to high frequencies. This soon resulted in such models as the Eddystone "All-World Four" which in its "ant-proof" aluminium die-cast case brought the BBC Empire Service and other early short-wave broadcasts to many tea and rubber planters in the Far East, so helping to pioneer the concept of "tropicalised" radio equipment. For amateurs the modest "All-World Two" with its ingenious bandspread plus bandset tuning was an extremely popular "first model" in the late 'thirties – as many of us still remember.

Later Eddystone helped pioneer the use of vhf for police radio, providing an emergency communications network for the London police just a few weeks before the outbreak of the second world war in September 1939. The company suffered severely in the blitz and were finally forced to move into the old West Heath Lido swimming baths (known as "The Bath Tub") where it became the first radio company to operate from a swimming pool – still I believe their home as a subsidiary of GEC-Marconi.

TECHNICAL TOPICS

PAT HAWKER · G3VA

THE EDITORIAL IN *QST* of January 1948, just over 40 years ago, was headed "single-sideband" and the opening paragraph read as follows: "Several articles in this issue of our magazine point the way to the most significant development that has ever occurred in amateur radiotelephony: carrierless single-sideband emission. After years of fearing that our receivers weren't stable enough to permit the use of sssc – as we're calling it – the adventurous appearance on the air of an experimental station with this method of emission has shown that it isn't so difficult after all, and that its merits are waiting for all of us. And so immense are these advantages that we are convinced that a speedy revolution in our equipment and our operating practices is imminent and certain."

PIONEERS OF SSB

Although *QST* soon dropped "sssc" in favour of "ssb", seldom can an editorial forecast have been so perceptive and so quickly fulfilled. Within just a few years, a.m. (often unfairly dubbed "ancient modulation") had virtually vanished from the amateur hf bands. Single-sideband, of course, was not invented in 1947 by the amateurs. The theory had been proved mathematically by Carson as early as 1922; even the first transatlantic transmission of speech in 1915 depended on tuning the high-Q long-wave antenna to maximise one set of sidebands. Point-to-point transmission with one sideband and reduced carrier was implemented in the late 1920s on vlf and in the thirties on hf (a leading exponent was Alec Reeves who later invented pulse-code-modulation, which has become the basis of digital transmission systems). But remember that in 1947 hf ssb with fully suppressed carrier was not used – not by the military, in aviation nor the maritime services. The amateurs, initially in the USA but soon world-wide, truly blazed the way for the general adoption of the sssc form of ssb.

The very first amateur contact using ssb took place on September 21, 1947 between W6YX and W6VQD. W6YX was the experimental amateur station of the Department of Electrical Engineering, Stanford University, California. Trustee for this station, and the man behind this experimental ssb project, was Dr O G ("Mike") Villard, W6QYT. His account of those historic "single-sideband operating tests" was one of the articles in *QST* of January 1948.

I was reminded of this important revolution in amateur radio by meeting W6QYT in London at the recent hf conference where he presented a paper and – in true amateur practice – demonstrated his prototype "portable unidirectional hf receiving aerial for reducing co-channel multi-hop sky-wave interference" (see later). With him, also from SRI International (the research institute associated with Stanford University), was George Hagn who presented a companion paper on "the wide-strip horizontal loop antenna (hla): an effective solution for ground-wave interference to short-wave reception." George told me an interesting story about how he had encouraged the US "Special Forces" in

Vietnam in the 1960s to bypass normal military procurement procedures to acquire and use Collins KWM2 amateur-type ssb/cw transceivers. These, he had found, were able to perform better in the jungles of south-east Asia than the regulation military radios – yet another example of the way in which amateur radio has so often been shown to be in the forefront of radio communications.

I noted (*TT*, April) that Collins Radio, founded by the late Art Collins, W0CXX, developed and marketed the very first amateur hf/ssb transceivers (Model KWM1), designed primarily for hf/mobile operation. This prompted Bob Ralph, G4KSG of the Collins Owners Club to send along some information on this historically important model. G4KSG is proud to own a surviving KWM1 and knows of only two others in the UK (one of them in Lowe's display cabinet at Matlock). Only 1300 were made between 1965 and 1969, when the KWM2 was introduced. The power amplifier uses two 6146s, providing a respectable 100W pep (nominal) rf output from 175W pep input. The sideband filter comprises a Collins 455kHz mechanical filter requiring two mixers to reach signal frequency, and there are 24 valves, with the useful 6DC6 doubling as a receiver rf amplifier. Frequency range is limited to any ten 100kHz segments between 14.0 to 30.0MHz with a tunable i.f. between 3.9 to 4.0MHz. G4KSG writes: "At maximum gain, agc threshold is 1.5 µV. Antenna noise is detectable and signals are readable well below the 1.5µV level. Comparisons with modern equipment indicate that the sensitivity is marginally less, but audio is pure and noise-free."

In the 1970s, Art Collins sold his company to Rockwell International and much of the former glory of the company as a leading manufacturer in the amateur field has been subjugated to the group's work on military and aeronautical communications and information technology. But to Mike Villard, Art Collins and the Collins Radio engineers belongs much of the credit for setting the agenda for present-day amateur radio and for professional mobile hf communications.

BROADBAND FET AMPLIFIERS

The April *TT* included a progress report on the high-power devices and all-solidstate transmitters currently being developed for radio and television broadcasting. The report noted the increasing trend towards the use of mosfet rather than bipolar rf power devices and listed some of the reasons for their increasing popularity. Some engineers claim that mosfet devices will make more reliable transmitters, principally because they operate with higher supply voltages (50 to 80 volts, typically) compared with bipolars (28-32 volts for professional applications, and often only 12 to 15 volts for mobile and amateur transmitters). The higher voltage helps to ameliorate the problems caused by the very high currents in high-power bipolar transistors. The operating characteristics of mosfets tend to be less sensitive to supply voltage variations, reducing the need for

complex stabilisation circuits. Greater gain at vhf/uhf is usually achieved with mosfets, although input capacitance lowers the effective input impedance. Some engineers are still convinced that bipolars score for the linearity needed for ssb (though, for this mode, really good linearity remains easier to achieve by forgetting solid-state and using valves).

An interesting approach to high-power, professional, broadband transmitters becomes possible with the marketing of a new rf n-channel, enhancement mode tmos power field-effect transistor by Motorola. This is designated type MRF151G but is also known as the Gemini package. The device is a combination of two fets within a single package (see **Fig 1**). It has been designed for broadband commercial and military communications applications using push-pull circuits in the 2 – 175MHz band; also for vhf/fm or vhf television broadcast transmitters. With a

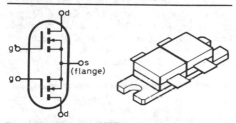

Fig 1. The Motorola MRF151G "Gemini" rf power field-effect transistor package designed for broadband push-pull amplifiers in the 2 to 175MHz frequency range

50V supply line, the MRF151G can provide 300-watts carrier output.

A 300W amplifier based on this device has been described by H O Granberg of Motorola in an article entitled: "Building push-pull, multi-octave, vhf power amplifiers" (*Microwaves & RF*, November 1987).

Reprints of this article are available from Motorola RF Semiconductor Product Marketing, 5005 East McDowell Road, Phoenix, Arizona 85036, USA, or possibly from the Motorola Literature Distribution Centre for Europe, 88 Tanners Drive, Blakelands, Milton Keynes MK145BP.

The article describes in detail a broadband amplifier (**Fig 2**) operating over the frequency range 10 to 175MHz (although it is noted that efficiency can be improved by reducing the frequency span). It notes that the recent development of high-power vhf/uhf power fets makes such amplifiers possible: "These fets have recently become available in a push-pull package configuration – commonly called the Gemini. A push-pull Gemini package is a flange-mounted transistor header capable of accommodating two individual transistors – either fets or bipolars. One of the three transistor electrodes is connected to the normally grounded flange.

"On first observation, it seems that a push-pull header would not be as advantageous as separate headers for each transistor. Separate headers provide better thermal distribution, improved circuit design and layout versatility, ▶

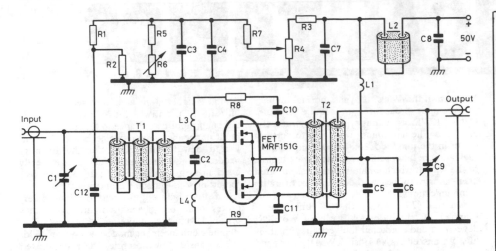

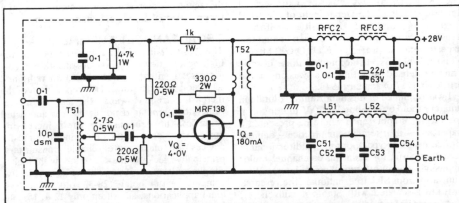

R₁ = 1 kΩ–1/2W
R₂ = 1·5 kΩ–1/2W
R₃ = 1·5 kΩ–2W
R₄ = 1-kΩ trimpot
R₅ = 6·8-8·2 kΩ–1/4W (depends on FET g_{FS})
R₆ = Thermistor–10 kΩ at 25°C; 2·5 kΩ at 75°C
R₇ = 2 kΩ–1/2W
R₈, R₉ = 50 Ω power resistor–EMC Technology type 5310, or KDI Pyrofilm type PPR 515-20-3
C₁, C₉ = 8–60 pF, ARCO 404 or the equivalent
C₂ = 130pF ceramic chip
C₃, C₁₀, C₁₁ = 0·1 μF ceramic chip
C₄, C₅, C₁₂ = 1000 pF ceramic chip
C₆, C₇, = 5000 pF ceramic chip
C₈ = 0·47μF ceramic chip, or lower values in parallel to reach the value indicated
L₁ = 10 turn, AWG #16 guage enamelled wire, 5-mm inside diameter
L₂ = Ferrite beads, 1·5μH total
L₃, L₄ = Lead lengths or R₈ and R₉, 20-mm total
T₁ = 9:1 RF transformer–25Ω, 0.062-in. outside diameter, semirigid coax
T₂ = 1:4 RF transformer–25Ω, 0·090in. outside diameter, semirigid coax
FET = MRF151G
Notes: For T₁, two type 75-26 E and I Micrometals powdered iron cores are required.
For T₂, three type 100-8 E and I Micrometals powdered iron cores are required.
All chip capacitors of 5000 pF or less are ATC type 100 or equivalent.

Fig 2. 300W broadband amplifier for operation in the range 10 to 175MHz as described by H O Gronberg of Motorola in "Microwaves & RF" November 1987. Heart of the amplifier is the Gemini push-pull transistor package.

and higher production yields. The result is lower cost-per-watt of output power. . . . But there are important advantages to the push-pull design. For example, the power gain performance of this design is difficult to duplicate in single-ended configurations because power gain is directly related to the emitter- or source-to-ground inductance. Also, in push-pull designs, the common-mode inductance is completely insignificant – mutual inductance between each emitter, or source, becomes the critical factor. This mutual inductance is much easier to control and minimize." The article describes design factors for both linear and cw operation.

It notes, however, that: "Stability is a concern with all solid-state amplifiers. It is easier to achieve with fets than bipolar transistors, mainly due to a higher ratio of feedback capacitance to input impedance. The 'half f₀ oscillation' phenomenon is unknown with fets, since the nonlinear diode junctions are not present. However, at low frequencies, the fet input impedance is almost a pure capacitance with high reactance, resulting in extremely high power gain. If the fet gate is not properly terminated due to input mismatches, low-frequency instabilities may take place – especially if the frequency response of the input circuit is low enough to sustain the activity. . . . Depending on the exact conditions and device type, relatively low-level parasitic oscillations can occur. In worst-case scenarios, a latching-type condition will destroy the fet instantly."

The article describes ways in which the risk of such instabilities can be minimized, including the use of input and output magnetic cores, heatsunk to the copper heat-spreader. I do not know the retail price of single MRF151G devices but this is most unlikely to be at a level at which any amateur could contemplate lightly the possibility of devices being destroyed instantly! Do-it-yourself high-power solid-state amplifiers, whether based on bipolars or fets, demand either a high-level of up-to-date engineering skills or a willingness to duplicate very carefully a proven design without introducing any of the customary "let's hope this will do" modifications.

A more modest, medium-power fet amplifier (**Fig 3**) capable of providing an output of 50 watts pep on any amateur hf band was described by Harold Hepburn VK3AFQ in Part 7 'of a series of articles entitled "Building blocks revisited" in the Australian *Amateur Radio*

(December 1987 issue). VK3AFQ notes that: "To a certain extent this amplifier breaks new ground in that the active device is a power fet (Motorola MRF138) and a 28-volt supply rail is used. This shift from the conventional 12-13-volt supply and bipolar transistors has been made primarily because the industry trend is towards higher supply voltages – with a consequent easing of matching problems – and the use of fets with their reduced drive requirements, absence of thermal runaway and, not least, their improved close-in noise characteristics".

Without the signal output filter (L51, L52, C51-54), the amplifier has a power output which is substantially flat between 1·5 and 30MHz but VK3AFQ comments: "However, the total harmonic content tends to be high at the lf end of this range, falling somewhat as the frequency increases, so that the real 'flatness' is less than the above statement might imply. Because of the inherent harmonic content, the amplifier must *never* be put on air without a filter appropriate to the frequency in use."

VK3AFQ provides details of layout (including pcb), construction of the broadband output transformer, T52, as well as the construction and

TABLE 1 FILTER DATA

	T51				
BAND	μH	No OF TURNS	AWG GAUGE	TOROID FORMER	C51-54 pF
160	3.76	27	26	T50/2	1500
80	2.05	20	26	T50/2	820
40	1.08	15	24	T50/2	430
30	0.75	13	24	T50/6	300
20	0.55	12	24	T50/6	220
17	0.40	10	22	T50/6	160
15	0.37	10	22	T50/6	150
12	0.30	9	22	T50/6	120
10	0.25	8	22	T50/6	100

NOTES
0.40mm enamelled wire can be used in place of 26 AWG wire.
0.50mm enamelled wire can be used in place of 24 AWG wire.
0.80mm enamelled wire can be used in place of 22 AWG wire.

Fig 3. Power fet hf linear amplifier described by VK3AFQ in *Amateur Radio* (VK) capable of about 40W pep output. Details of the signal filter component values for bands from 1·8 to 28MHz are shown in Table 1. Notes on the amplifier: T1 7t No26 awg enamel (0.4mm) on Amidon BN 73-202 Ferrite balun core. RFC1 15uH moulded rfc. RFC2, 3 2.5t on Ferrite bead – Philips No 4312-020-36700 or Amidon FB-43-5111. M is monolithic ceramic capacitor. Details of the construction of T52 given in the orginal article

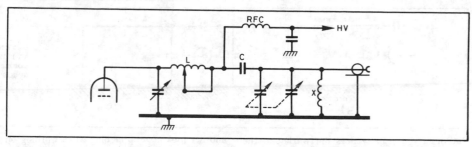

Fig 4. Arrangement used by GW3TKH to overcome the problem of rf choke resonances in a pi-network tank circuit

commissioning of the amplifier. This all appears quite straightforward but again I would emphasise that my notes are intended only to indicate the ways in which power fets are being used increasingly. Anyone attempting to duplicate either the 300W or the 50W pep (25W cw) amplifier really needs to consult the original, detailed articles. The "building block amplifier" is intended for use in conjunction with a low-power driver amplifier described in Part 6 of VK3AFQ's. In these circumstances the rf input to the driver amplifier, to achieve the 50 watts pep output from the power amplifier, is well under one milliwatt.

RF CHOKES IN PI-NETWORK TANK CIRCUITS

In the April *TT*, Peter Chadwick, G3RZP, drew attention to a possible method of overcoming the all-too-common problem of rf choke resonances on one or more hf bands – a problem made significantly more difficult to overcome by the addition of the WARC bands of 10, 18 and 24MHz. G3RZP noted the arrangement outlined by Pappenfus in his textbook on ssb of putting the rf choke at the output end of the pi-network (Fig 5, page 266, April issue) and wondered whether anybody had tried this scheme.

An answer came from Keith Winnard, GW3TKH who confirms the value of this approach and offers a further minor, but useful, modification, which removes the high dc voltage across the variable loading capacitors (formed from ganged variable capacitors of the type used for many years in broadcast receivers).

GW3TKH writes: "About two years ago, whilst finalising a QY4-400 grounded-grid amplifier (ie trying to get a quart into a pint pot), the anode rf choke in the conventional pi-network configuration would overheat or burn-out on one band or another. This was no doubt due to the much closer proximity of the screening compartment shifting the self-resonances of the choke. After some thought, it appeared that the choke specification would be less critical if designed to function at lower impedance. So a small, simple-to-make choke was knocked up and tried in the arrangement shown in **Fig 4** (basically similar to the April, Fig 5). No attempt was made to use variable diameter formers or complicated windings of the conventional high-impedance pi-network rf chokes. In practice, the simple choke has been in use ever since. The efficiency and docility on all bands from 3·5 to 28MHz equals that of the original, more spacious breadboard layout, although the amplifier is now contained safely in a small, rf-tight cabinet with its associated high-voltage power supply, making it domestically acceptable

"The position of the high-voltage, high-current coupling capacitor C was adopted in order to permit the use of a normal receiver-type ganged loading capacitor. The tuning capacitor, the coil, and associated band-switch must be capable of withstanding the combination of high dc and rf voltages. With a high-voltage supply at 2·75kV, C is rated at 6kV."

"So, to answer G3RZP, the Pappenfus arrangement has been tried and certainly, at this station, works!"

In **Fig 4** the rf·choke X is the indispensable safety precaution that prevents the high dc voltage reaching the output socket (and hence the antenna), should C fail. It needs to be of sufficient current rating to ensure that the high-voltage power supply fuse blows, rather than the choke burn out. I added this note, since realizing – too late – that no such safety choke was shown in the PL509 test amplifier (Fig 1 of the May *TT*), which was intended for operation into a dummy load rather than an antenna. But even for this application, a safety choke is advisable.

END-FEEDING AND THE ZEPP

In introducing the novel concept of an end-fed Windom (*TT*, February 1988, pp111-2) Les Moxon, G6XN, pointed out that "were it not for the problems, end-feeding would tend to be more attractive than centre feeding for non-rotatable antennas since the ends are more likely to be within reach of, or close to, the shack. In addition the centre of the element no longer has to support the weight of the feeder."

The end-fed Windom antenna provides a useful, if partial solution to this problem but is essentially confined to a specific band, for which both the capacitor and its position need to conform to the values and dimensions suggested by G6XN. Although, presumably, the antenna would function to some degree on other bands as a simple "random-length" long-wire antenna when tuned against earth or a counterpoise by means of a suitable pi-network matching unit. Alternatively, the 40m (134ft) long-wire is an effective end-fed antenna capable of working well on virtually any frequency, but is not without its problems. With an atu close to the operating position, the amount of rf floating around the shack is bound to be high. The antenna will also be susceptible to picking up electrical interference radiated from the mains, and at higher frequencies there will be pronounced nulls and lobes in directions governed by the site rather than the direction of the desired dx. Nevertheless, it is a simple, low-cost solution that has proved useful over a number of years at G3VA with the far end supported by trees.

But my first transmitting antenna, in common with many other amateurs of the day, was the then popular zepp with 66ft top and 32 or 16ft tuned feeders. This was in 1938-39. Again in 1946-47, a zepp antenna helped me achieve post-war DXCC Nr 321 worldwide, so I have always retained an interest in this type of antenna, even after it fell out of favour in the early 1950s.

The zepp, as noted in *TT*, January 1986, dates back to a German patent of 1908: **Fig 5(a)**. It was extremely popular for amateur operation in the 'twenties and 'thirties, before the availability of co-axial cable feeders, as a convenient end-fed arrangement, seemingly well suited to operation on harmonically-related bands. It was not until 1956 that serious doubts were cast on the efficiency of this form of antenna. Then, in discussing the use of baluns, Dud Charman, G6CJ (*RSGB Bulletin*, December 1955) noted that "simple connection of a resonant antenna to one side of a tuned line will not work – it is necessary to add the transformer winding in the form of the stub to tell the line it is balanced. *This is one reason why the old zepp antenna was so uncertain in its behaviour.*'

In his 1982 *HF antennas for all locations*, Les Moxon, G6XN, really put the boot in, explaining why, in his opinion "Despite its time-honoured status this (traditional form of end-fed zepp) is very uncertain in its behaviour. ▶

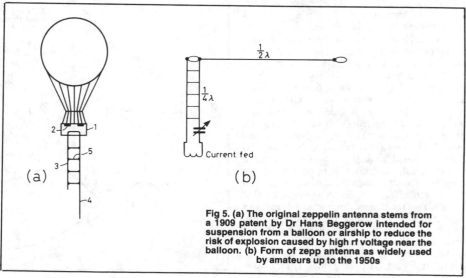

Fig 5. (a) The original zeppelin antenna stems from a 1909 patent by Dr Hans Beggerow intended for suspension from a balloon or airship to reduce the risk of explosion caused by high rf voltage near the balloon. (b) Form of zepp antenna as widely used by amateurs up to the 1950s

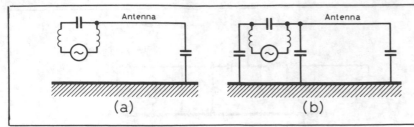

Fig 7. (a) How G6XN illustrates the problem posed by the conventional zepp arrangement. (b) Improved results without a G6CJ stub appear to be possible where the resonant feeder wires are well spaced and close to the ground: the equivalent circuit

Put bluntly it usually **does not work** and the reason is the same one that we have met before in a different guise. In going from a balanced to an unbalanced system or *vice-versa,* a balun is essential. Without one, there is no guarantee that the antenna will work better than a random length of wire. Nor, to be fair, any certainty that it will *not* work, but the zepp feed has been found particularly uncooperative in this respect." A suitable balun stub, as suggested by

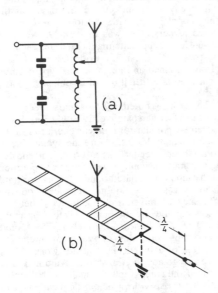

Fig 6. The unbalanced-antenna/balanced-line stub as suggested by G6CJ in 1955 together with its equivalent circuit

G6CJ, and endorsed by G6XN, is shown in **Fig 6**. However, the need to employ this stub, which may not be readily accessible, makes it more difficult to exploit efficiently the multiband properties inherent in this system.

G6XN added: "The reader may well be wondering how it is that if the zepp feed does not work it managed to avoid suspicion of its 'bonafides' for so many years, being ousted from popularity mainly by the swing of fashion, which currently favours low-impedance coaxial lines. . . . It has, in fact, been found by the author that in two cases the balancing stub was not essential, but in each of these cases the wires were spaced about 7in (18cm) and only some 2-3ft (0·6-0·9m) from the ground. Even so the system did seem to be less critical, particularly in respect of balance in the main feeder, when the stub was in use." In this section of *HFafal* G6XN emphasised that there is an urgent need for the end-feeding of some types of antenna, particularly vertical dipoles or inverted ground-planes which are often difficult for mechanical reasons to feed anywhere other than at their base.

It is thus not surprising that G6XN took

another look at zepp feeding while working on his end-fed Windom. To add to the notes in the February *TT*, G6XN wrote: "My experience is that the conventional zepp feed *sometimes* seems to work well enough. In this, and the one other case in my experience that leaves no margin for doubt, the feeders were widely spaced and close to ground so that the field at the ground produced by one conductor would not be completely cancelled by the other (ie the equivalent circuit is not as in **Fig 7(a)** but as in **Fig 7(b)**). In other words, there is capacitance from each wire to ground as well as between the wires, thus completing the circuit.

"I am sure that this is not the full story. With the dipole centre-fed, the zepp stubb (improved version) could be connected without noticeable loss, though the current flowing in them was large and there was no way it could be reduced. With a stub end-impedance possibly as high as 0.3MΩ, an out-of-balance capacitance of 0.03pF would be enough to energise it. To energise the antenna (say 5000Ω end-impedance) from the stub requires a lot more out-of-balance – but enough to cause significant feeder radiation? Even more doubtful, but it could be a useful field for further study, though I fear not by me. At my age, life is too short for tidying up all the loose ends, and one tends to have other priorities!"

Intrigued by these remarks and convinced that there is a real need for a reliable, reproducable form of multiband end-fed antenna, I temporarily lowered the long-wire antenna and replaced it with a 21MHz zepp that bore more relationship to the original zepp designs than to either of the ones suggested by G6CJ or G6XN.

I used some transmitter-type 300-ohm cable with the wires spaced about 0.75in (18mm) as the "open" feeder, in conjunction with a pi-network matching unit which provided balanced output. I struck the exceptionally good hf conditions at the end of April and had little difficulty in making plenty of contacts, including some reasonable dx. But I soon became uncertain. Was the antenna really functioning as a half-wave element or as a random-length long-wire antenna? I soon reverted to the end-fed long-wire of which a significant proportion runs through the roof space. So there still remains a real problem to solve in developing a genuine transmission-line, end-fed antenna that can be relied upon to work every time! But how do you prove an antenna is working as a zepp rather than as an inefficient long-wire with lots of power wasted in high circulating currents?

UNIDIRECTIONAL LOOP RECEIVING ANTENNA

The two simple loop receiving antennas developed by Mike Villard and George Hagn (plus a contribution by George's 13 year old daughter!) were designed primarily to meet the

Fig 8. Wiring and layour details of the Stanford Research Institute co-planar loop antenna described by W6QYT at the IEE's hf conference. Notes: (a) antenna connection. L1 23t, 1-in diameter wood core, No 18 GA insulated wire. C1 5-20pF. C2 350 to 600pF (eg medium-wave tuning capacitor) R1 250-ohm composition resistor for Q adjustment R2 attenuator to overcome agc action during initial tuneup. Receiver Panasonic RF9, Sony ICF4901 or similar

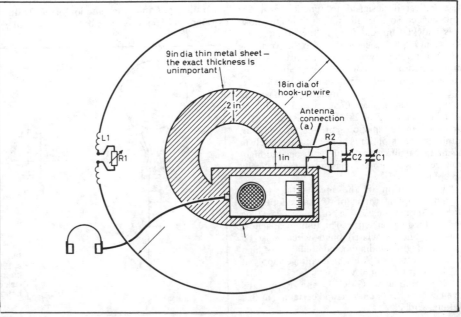

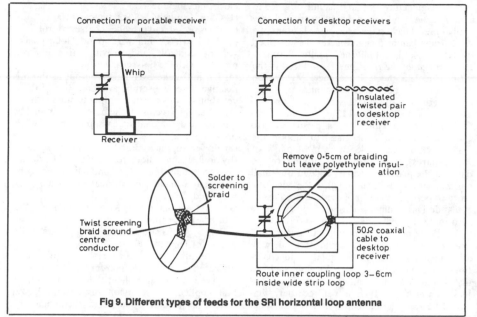

Fig 9. Different types of feeds for the SRI horizontal loop antenna

needs of those listening to high-power hf broadcast stations, particularly in areas still beset by ground-wave or sky-wave jamming.

The most novel is a co-planar twin loop (ctl) antenna which could well have useful applications for amateur-band reception or possibly for d/f hunts. It was developed to meet the following goals: (1) no active elements; (2) reasonable sensitivity (by broadcast-reception standards); (3) simplicity of construction; (4) use of commonly available materials; (5) ease of operation; and (6) satisfactory performance indoors if possible (in practice this can be achieved, although the 'direction' of signals indicated by the position of the loop may not be accurate).

The ctl comprises two loops, both loaded to resonance, with the inner loop made of a flat, foil element: see **Fig 8**. A third inner 'coupling' loop may be provided to permit a co-axial cable feed to a receiver located away from the loop.

The ctl exhibits unidirectional properties and, when correctly adjusted, shows a pronounced null on sky-wave as well as ground-wave signals. W6QYT describes this (*IEE Conference Publication No 284*, pages 141 to 144) as follows:

"In contrast with the conventional loop whose null is perpendicular to the plane of the structure, the ctl null is in the plane of the loop(s). Because of symmetry, when this is the case, both loops respond very similarly to variations in the angle of the elevation of the incoming signal over an appreciable range of angles."

W6QYT calls the inner loop, the R (receiver) loop and the outer loop is designated I (independent) loop. He explains: "To generate a unidirectional null, the side of the loops opposite to the tuning capacitors is pointed towards the distant station. When I-loop tuning is correct, current flowing in that loop generates a local H-field whose phase is opposite to that of the H-field of the incoming signal. The magnitude of this local field may be adjusted by altering the Q of the I-loop by means of a variable resistor when the Q is higher than necessary for the purpose. When the local H-field magnitude and phase are such as to cancel exactly the ambient H-field, the R-loop (located

inside the I-loop and designed to respond *only* to H-fields) finds itself in a null region, or 'shadow' and the receiver registers a greatly reduced output. In this situation, the effective coupling between loops is very small. If the signal direction changes (or the direction of the loops is changed relative to the signal), the phase, and to some extent the amplitude, of current in the I-loop changes. The cancellation is then no longer complete, and the signal reappears in the output of the R-loop".

He has found that "on average, a readily-attainable front-to-back ratio for the ctl in the case of skywave signals seems to be around 20dB. This is sufficient to attenuate co-channel interference in typical situations to an extent which gives the listener the choice of two independent programmes (on the same frequency), instead of an unacceptable mixture. The antenna also rejects ground-wave interference". Results are presented of antenna patterns relating to signals from 15MHz broadcast stations.

The alternative SRI horizontal loop antenna (hla) is a very simple single-turn, resonant loop constructed of a wide strip of metal or foil and brought to resonance by means of a variable capacitor. It can be implemented in any one of several versions (see **Fig 9**). It will effectively null out ground-wave interference in much the same way as the more usual vertical-plane loop. Nulls are unlikely to be observed on incoming sky-wave signals but it could be used by amateurs to reduce local electrical interference,

where this is radiated directly from information-technology, industrial, scientific or medical signals, or ground-wave signals from a nearby transmitter.

MORE ON THE LOW-COST SPECTRUM ANALYSER

The low-cost spectrum analyser for use with a general-purpose oscilloscope described by Albert Helfrick of Doty RFL Industries (and now also identified as K2BLA) in *RF Design* (January 1988) and included in *TT* (April, pp262-3) has attracted interest, with a number of readers determined to build one of these useful instruments. However, it seems possible that there may have been some errors in the original article, although I have yet to find a correction note in subsequent issues.

Roger Blackwell, G4PMK, writes: "I have so far built the rf section, and other constructors may like to note that there seems to be an error in the oscillator section of the NE602. With the capacitor values specified, it certainly does not oscillate around 155.7MHz. However, if you pick capacitors as specified in the NE602 data sheet: 22pF between pin 7 and ground; 5.6pF between pins 6 and 7, then it tunes perfectly using the specified coil. Incidentally, I use the easily available BB209 as the vco variable capacitance diode. Prospective constructors may also be interested in a more ambitious analyser which was described by the same author in *QST*, November 1985 as "An inexpensive spectrum analyser for the radio amateur" (the block diagram is shown in **Fig 10**). It has some ideas for the 'video' and sweep circuits, and a choice of i.f. bandwidths that might be applied to the simpler design described in *RF Design*."

Mike Horrocks, G8GTP, had noted the design in *RF Design* in advance of the *TT* notes but has also beeen experiencing problems, including that of finding a source of the by-no-means-common ic devices specified by the author. However, he was able to obtain them from: The Chip Shop (Semicons Ltd), 6 Bean Leach Drive, Afferton, Stockport, Cheshire (Telephone: 061-483 1989).

It would be interesting to learn if anybody has achieved entirely satisfactory results with this design, and if so, just what modifications, if any, they found necessary.

KILNER-JAR MAGNETOMETER

As G8KG has hinted, the progress of sunspot cycle 22 has clearly been proving unusually difficult for those whose task it is to predict hf propagation conditions months in advance. Several speakers at the recent IEE hf conference drew attention to the problems this poses to communicators and broadcasters attempting to rely on either published predictions or on the ▶

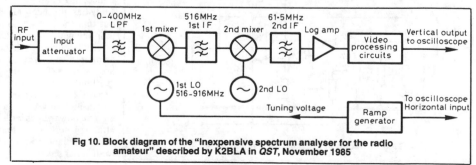

Fig 10. Block diagram of the "Inexpensive spectrum analyser for the radio amateur" described by K2BLA in *QST*, November 1985

use of computer programs such as "Minimuf" and similar alternative software. This is encouraging the professionals to make much greater use of various complex forms of "real time channel evaluation (rtce)", adaptive frequency selection and the like, as well as more use of ionospheric oblique sounders, etc. One result is that the professionals have become interested in using Sporadic E modes between about 20-30MHz.

For the radio amateur, however, it is usually a matter of regularly monitoring bands to find out what is happening that day, that time. It is then possible to predict pretty accurately what is likely to happen during the next few hours, taking into account the rotation of the Earth. One cannot help feeling that 21, 24 and 28MHz bands are often open in some directions, to some countries, far more often than the amateurs in the areas concerned (misled by published predictions?) realise! Anything that helps amateurs to become more aware of current ionospheric conditions is thus of interest.

Martin Vincent, G3UKV, was attracted to the concept of jam-jar magnetometers as do-it-yourself "A" or "K" index monitors by references in G8VR's *VHF/UHF* column of March 1987 (pp196-7), and also April 1988 (p289), where it was reported that nearly 100 readers had requested information on the home-brew jam-jar magnetometers of the type used by members of the Aurora Section of the British Astronomical Association. G3UKV writes:

"I tried the basic version using a beam of light, and its magnified reflection off a mirror glued to a bar magnet, but I found this awkward and very easily upset. I have since been passed details of a "Recording jamjar magnetometer" as described by H. R. Hatfield published in the February 1983 *Journal of the BAA* and reproduced in the form of a data sheet. It's a goer! My version differs in some details of mechanical construction but utilises the same sensor and op-amp electronics (see **Figs 11** and **12**).

"Using an old kilner jar, a plastic rod (to avoid having to drill the glass) to support the Hall-effect device (634SS2 from Maplin's or Radiospares), and ordinary cooking oil to dampen the magnet's swings, I glued the small bar magnet (about 25mm long) to the edge of a piece of perspex (instead of the lead used in the BAA design), immersed in the oil. A centre zero meter is ideal, since it can be zeroed and will indicate positive or negative magnetic-field changes. A normal meter could be used, with adjustments so that under 'quiet' field conditions, it reads centre-scale. Ideally, such an instrument is kept on all the time. For those lucky enough too own a pen-recorder, that would be even better than a meter. The small pcb/psu sits on top of the jar.

"The main application, at this time of rising solar activity in Cycle 22, is to observe changes in the earth's magnetic field, indicating the onset of a solar storm, and sometimes giving rise to radio auroras. It's a do-it-yourself 'A' or 'K' index monitor!"

Notes on the BAA data sheet relating to the electronics include:

(1) Gain is equal to R8/R3, typically 100.
(2) R6 is preset and provides coarse control.
(3) R5 is a 50 Ohm wirewound "loudspeaker volume control" and provides fine control, together with the fine setting arm.
(4) Do not make Sw1 unless output at Pin 6 is positive. Use fine setting arm and R6 and R7 to get about 2 volts-positive output to start with.
(5) When Sw1 is closed, the output is damped by C1. R8 and C1 control damping when Sw1 is open.
(6) Power supplies must be carefully regulated (by double zener-diode regulation?). The device needs less than 10mA total and batteries may be used. The voltage is not critical but must be well regulated.
(7) When setting up: (a) Measure voltage at Pin 2 of sensor. Adjust suspension until it is about +2V. (b) Adjust R6 so that −2V appears on R6 slider. (c) Then make fine adjustment.

Note also that all parts, except where indicated, should be non-ferrous. It is also observed on the data sheet that when torque is first applied to the nylon suspension, it will release itself again to some extent, and may well take several hours to settle.

SUNSPOT WEATHER

For many years there has been a scientific debate whether the sunspot cycle has any effect on climate – the so-called Maunder minimum of the eighteenth century is often mentioned as coinciding with a period of very cold winters.

American scientists have recently reported in *Nature* (April 28, 1988) on some results of the ACRM-1 (Active Cavity Radiometer Iradiance Monitor) satellite experiment which has provided a nearly continuous record of solar total irradiance variations since early 1980. The long-term variations have revealed a downward trend during the declining phase of solar cycle 21, a flat period between mid-1985 and mid-1987, and an upturn in late 1987. These measurements, they believe "suggest a direct correlation of luminosity and solar active region population. If the upturn continues into the active maximum of solar cycle 22, a relation between solar activity and luminosity of possible climatological significance could have been discovered."

No wonder it has always seemed that the sun shone more brightly on amateur radio during periods of sunspot maximum!

"RADIATION" DANGER TO RADIO AMATEURS?

A recent "Panorama" television programme alarmed some amateurs because of its reference to Dr Samuel Milham's study of the cause of death of 1,691 amateurs over many years in Washington state and California. A study which appears to indicate an increased risk to certain rare leukemias. This study was discussed soon after it appeared in The Lancet in *TT*, August 1985. It seems worth pointing out that Dr Milham's study has also been raised recently in the USA. *QST*, March 1985 points out that the study also suggested that radio amateurs had *fewer* deaths than the general population from certain other kinds of leukemia (it was myeloid leukemia that showed an increase over expected totals, 16 compared to 5·7). *QST* also notes that some professionals suggest there are "serious flaws" in Dr Milham's methodology and that his study "certainly did not establish a causal link between amateur radio and certain cancer incidences". In fact attention seems to have turned increasingly towards the possible hazards of 50Hz magnetic fields from electric power lines with the CEGB currently mounting an investigation – although here again many experts are convinced that the risks, if they exist, are likely to prove insignificant and not in any way to be compared to such risks as smoking. ☐

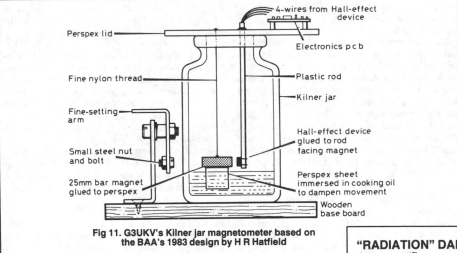

Fig 11. G3UKV's Kilner jar magnetometer based on the BAA's 1983 design by H R Hatfield

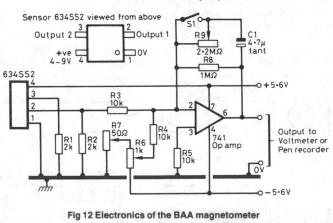

Fig 12 Electronics of the BAA magnetometer

TECHNICAL TOPICS

PAT HAWKER · G3VA

TELEPHONE INTERFERENCE

In *TT* (April 1984, pp313-4), I drew attention to the then rapidly increasing problem of 'eti – elelctronic telephone interference' writing: "The trend of semiconductor development seems inevitably to result in ever more vulnerable devices and equipment: very large scale integration is being accompanied by lower operating voltages and higher-speed operation . . . more and more cmos and lsi devices are finding their way into consumer appliances of all types." This section included a report on the problems and cures reported by Mike Grierson, G3TSO for his then newly-introduced 'Statesman' telephone instrument. It was evident that at least some of the new 'electronic' telephones had been introduced or approved by British Telecom with little investigation as to their vulnerability to strong local rf fields.

However, in *TT*, December 1984, I was able to report after visiting BT's research establishment at Martlesham that: "In view of the problems of rfi on the new generation of electronic telephones, it was pleasant to find a lively recognition of emc/rfi problems and to receive some assurance that telephone designs are being made more resistant to local rf fields." BTR had, in fact, been given the task of setting up a small unit to subject new equipment to rf immunity tests before it was put on the market. For several years the BT field engineers have been curing interference to (and sometimes from) telephone apparatus. For most amateurs any remaining problem of eti can be solved with goodwill all round.

BT field engineers have been provided with 'customer service information' covering the results of laboratory and field immunity tests on the various telephone instruments now in use. The tests have been carried out between about 100kHz to around 200MHz and do show that the newer models have been much improved. While such information is intended for use only within British Telecom, it seems to me to be information which should be available to amateurs. The following is a digest of a BT csi sheet dated July 1987 that has reached me in a plain brown envelope from somebody who clearly shares this view:

Statesman, models 9001, 9003, 9040 (early production): poor immunity throughout the radio spectrum.
Statesman, models 9005, 9003 or 9101 (modified): good immunity as tested between 100kHz and 200MHz.
Statesman, model 9040 (Gen 85/35 or later): good immunity.
Statesman, model 9101AR: good immunity.
Tremolo 9701 (early production): fairly good immunity below 10MHz, poor immunity 10 to 200MHz.
Tremolo 9701 (since summer 1986): fairly good immunity 100kHz to 150MHz.
Tribune (TMC): good immunity to 10MHz; fairly good to 200MHz.

Tribune (DFM): fairly good between 100kHz and 10MHz; poor from 10 to 200MHz.
Venue 24/24E: fairly good 100kHz to 200MHz.
Ambassador 8304/8401: fairly good immunity 100kHz to 200MHz.
Viscount (all models except 9511 Mk4/9515/9525): fairly good immunity to 10MHz, poor immunity from 10 to 200MHz.
Viscount 9511 (Mk 4) since July 1986 and 9515/9525: good immunity from 100kHz to 200MHz.
Tele 8746 with carbon microphone or MIC insert 21B: very good immunity throughout spectrum.
Note that the date of manufacture is shown on many BT telephones by an eleven digit serial number on the base: the first four digits show the year (two figures) and week (two figures).

It should be appreciated that the above information is intended only for guidance and individual apparatus may differ. Obviously, no attempt should be made to modify yourself any telephone instruments that are the property of British Telecom. Or even (at least theoretically) any connected to BT lines.

In the June *TT* (p423, Fig 7) I reproduced a diagram from the DTI booklet *How to improve television and radio reception* giving guidance on how to fit ferrite beads and rf bypass capacitors as a means of reducing direct breakthrough of rf into af amplifiers, etc. It seem worth adding some other tips from an article "How to deal with audio rfi problems" by Doug De Maw, W1FB (*QST*, May 1988, pp18-20). He emphasises that "rf energy can disrupt audio amplifiers and may render an amplified microphone useless. Simple fixes can cure these problems easily . . . it requires no special skills to install suppression components, and the art is by no means new". He points out that although the majority of problems are associated with rf entering the first stage of any af amplifier, this is not necessarily true when the rf energy enters a piece of equipment via the ac mains cord or along cables, including loudspeaker cables, that connect to external accessory units. W1FB admits that today the most difficult consumer appliance to cure of rfi problems is the video cassette recorder (the UK penetration of these devices is now almost two-thirds of all tv homes)

but claims that "there is no entertainment gadget or piece of ham gear that can't be rfi-suppressed if you have the patience to tackle the job."

A hint given by W1FB is that although a ferrite bead (mounted as in the DTI illustration) can be effective at vhf as a series impedance, it offers negligible help in holding back mf/hf energy: "a single bead of 850 permeability ferrite provides only about $1\mu H$ of inductance at hf and this is of no value for hf or mf operation". He found that the microphone input of his Kenwood transceiver includes a ferrite bead near the base of the first transistor stage; he replaced this with a miniature $390\mu H$ rf choke which offers fairly high impedance to rf but is not a signal barrier at audio frequencies. With high-impedance (fet or valve) input circuits the choke can be replaced by a resistance of about 2·7k. In fact the arrangements shown in Fig 1 date back to the earliest days of bci suppression, but are no worse for that.

One of the problems with vcr installations is the untuned, wideband pre-amplifier through which the incoming tv signals pass, even when the machine is not recording. In an article "A video recorder tvi case history" (*Amateur Radio* (VK), March 1988) an Australian amateur reports effecting a cure by fitting a high-pass filter very close to the vcr antenna socket. On the other hand, W1FB found it necessary to battle with his vcr for several days before he cleaned it up; he plans to tell the story in a further *QST* article.

In *Ham Radio Today* (July 1988, p8), John Mayall, G3VPH draws attention to another telephone problem brought about by insufficient immunity to rf fields. He found that even a "sniff of rf above 10MHz" affected the memory of his 10-memory telephone (PBT-200 series). He admits to effecting a complete cure by soldering three $0·0047\mu F$ (100V) ceramic capacitors across the pins of the socket where the line cord connects to the pcb (ie across pins 1-2, 2-3 and 3-4) although, here again, as the Editor warns, BT may not take kindly to do-it-yourself modifications to 'approved' telephone apparatus connected to their network.

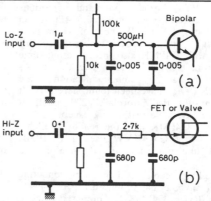

FIG 1. RF FILTERS POSITIONED CLOSE TO THE FIRST AMPLIFIER STAGE USING RF CHOKES OR RESISTORS ARE MORE SUITABLE FOR BLOCKING MF/HF ENERGY THAN FERRITE BEADS. (A) SUITABLE FOR LOW-IMPEDANCE CIRCUITS; (B) SUITABLE FOR HIGH-IMPEDANCE INPUTS.

THE LOW-COST SPECTRUM ANALYSER COMES GOOD

Following on the previous items (*TT*, July p521 and *TT*, April pp262-3) on the low-cost spectrum analyser as described by Al Helfrick, K2BLA of Doty RFL Industries in *RF Design* (January 1988), further reports and suggestions have come from Roger Blackwell, G4PMK and Stuart Jones, GW3XYW, both of whom have successfully built instruments based on this design, with G4PMK also incorporating some ideas from K2BLA's earlier *QST* design. As noted in the July *TT*, some modifications to the basic *RF Design* have been found necessary. It also seems that the Motorola MV209 varactor is no longer available in the UK except at very high cost; G4PMK uses the readily available BB209 while GW3XYW uses a BB105B, resulting in a somewhat reduced range of 10 to 100MHz.

There have been several enquiries wondering whether anybody has produced a pcb drawing for this device. G4PMK has prepared a set of circuit diagrams and notes on his prototype which differs considerably from the *RF Design*.

Since the information could not be fitted into *TT* (perhaps there is a need for a full-length article?), he offers to send his four sheets to members sending him an A4-sized stamped-addressed-envelope (Roger Blackwell, G4PMK, 57 Station Road, Scholes, Leeds LS15 4RY). He points out that despite its limitations, compared with a professional high-cost spectrum analyser, his unit has more than repaid the trouble taken to make it. Apart from such conventional uses as hf transmitter alignment he has found it useful (as a panoramic receiver) for looking for Sporadic E openings, connecting an antenna to the input socket and displaying the spectrum up to 90MHz or so. He writes in his notes:

"My prototype works well up to 90MHz or so, with a linear frequency sweep up to 80MHz. Maximum input to the analyser is −20dBm, and it will detect signals down to at least −90dBm. It has two selectable i.f bandwidths of 250 and 15kHz and a calibrated frequency sweep range of 10MHz/div to 50kHz/div. A frequency marker circuit gives one and/or 10MHz pips over the range of the instrument. Despite the comments in Helfick's *RF Design* article, the addition of the narrow i.f. bandwidth has proved very useful. Please note the *RF Design* article contained an error in the capacitor values in the

NE602 second mixer stage. The values shown in my circuit diagram are correct."

The capacitor values referred to in G4PMK's notes are the ones mentioned in the July *TT*.

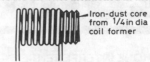

Iron-dust core from 1/4 in dia coil former

FIG 4. HOW GW3XYW CONSTRUCTED COIL L4 FOR HIS LOW-COST SPECTRUM ANALYSER BASED ON K2BLA's DESIGN. THE COIL WAS ORIGINALLY WOUND ALONG AN OLD IRON-DUST CORE. THE CORE IS THEN UNSCREWED AND CHOPPED IN HALF.

Stuart Jones, GW3XYW appears to have stuck more closely to the original design. He writes:

"Apart from a few small spurious responses which may be due to overloading the circuit works very well. I was unable to get a MV209 varactor diode and used a BB105B with slightly reduced range (10 – 100MHz). The NE602 and MC3356 devices were available from: Macro Marketing, Burnham Lane, Slough, SL1 6LN, telephone 06286-4422. The 145MHz helical resonator filters were available from Cirkit and Bonex: 2-section type 271MT1006A (145MHz, 3MHz bandwidth, 500-ohm impedance). Cirkit Stock No 17-10062, £4.20p. 3-section type ▶

Reducing rfi from computers

TT, April 1988, pp266-7, noted under the heading 'minimising rfi from digital equipment' that, unlike the USA and West Germany, the UK still has no legislation restricting electromagnetic emission from home or office computers or other digital information-technology equipment, despite the existence of British Standard BS6527 which specifies conducted noise limits on mains terminals between 150kHz and 30MHz, and radiated field strength limits from 30MHz to 1GHz. One result is that amateurs who find their weak signal reception, and sometimes even their broadcast reception, upset whenever their neighbour's children switch on their computers, tend to find themselves in a 'no-win' situation, even when the neighbours are sympathetic. Manufacturers of personal computers often express disbelief that 'their' models could be causing rfi and decline to do anything about it: yet many (if not most) of the models sold in the UK would fail both the American and German regulations. Legislation relating to BS6527 has been postponed pending the need to review the whole emc situation to comply with the European Community emc directive which, as I write, is still subject to discussion and negotiation.

The April *TT* included some American suggestions on reducing rfi by means of mains filters and the reduction of common-mode signals on the outer shield of screened cables. John Greenwell, G3AEZ draws attention to information reprinted from *Electronic Product Review* (February 1988) on the use of Citec BC-series, 1W dc/dc converter chips, together with opto-couplers, to provide isolation for RS232 and similar interfaces.

This notes that: "External cables can be particularly troublesome due to circulating common-mode currents (Fig. 2) which both radiate directly and can also raise mains-terminal noise voltages due to common impedance coupling (see April *TT*) . . .

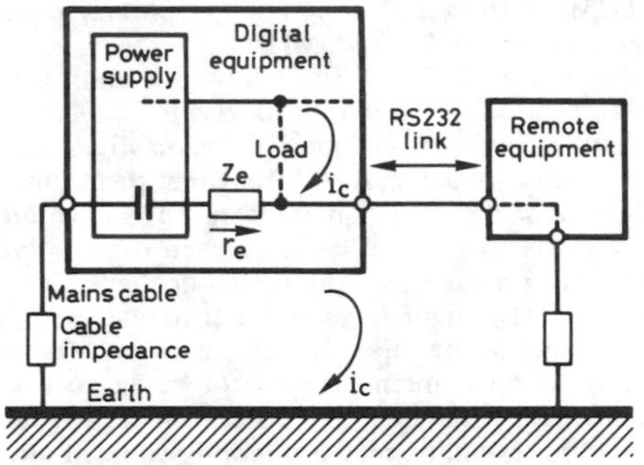

FIG 2. CIRCULATING COMMON-MODE CURRENTS IN MAINS CABLES AND INTERFACING LINKS BETWEEN DIGITAL INFORMATION-TECHNOLOGY EQUIPMENTS RESULTS IN INTERFERENCE SIGNALS BEING INJECTED INTO THE MAINS SUPPLY OR RADIATING DIRECTLY.

FIG 3. MEANS OF ISOLATING AN RS232 INTERFACE BY ▶ MEANS OF AN OPTO-ISOLATOR AND 1-WATT DC-DC CONVERTOR AVAILABLE IN CHIP FORM. NOTE BIASING RESISTORS, SPEED-UP COMPONENTS ETC HAVE BEEN OMITTED FOR CLARITY.

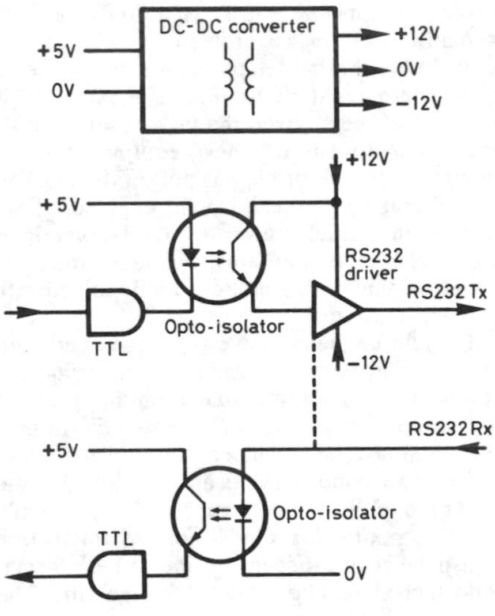

Common-mode circulating currents, and the problems they cause, can be substantially reduced by incorporating electrical isolation into equipment interfaces. Additional benefits (to the computer user) include much reduced susceptibility to externally induced noise, and the elimination of earth potential-difference hazards. RS232 and similar interfaces can be readily isolated through the use of opto-couplers for data isolation, together with isolated dc-dc conversion to power conventional line drivers and/or receivers (Fig. 3). Until recently the cost of dc-dc converters has prevented this approach being widely adopted. However, the impending legislation together with the availability of very low-cost dc-dc converters from BICC Citec now makes the isolated interface a practical reality. Designers can produce equipment which is both robust in terms of non-susceptibility to external

interference, and inherently superior with respect to electromagnetic emissions arising from cable-coupled mechanisms."

While this approach is clearly directed at professional rather than the smaller personal-computer installations, the principle of electrical isolation is of general interest. The Citec BC series of devices are miniature, high-efficiency isolated dc-dc converters in dil and sil ic packages. Designed for input voltages of 5V or 12V they deliver outputs, according to type, of ±5V, 100mA; ±12V, 40mA; ±15V, 30mA with an input-to-output isolation of 500V dc. No heat sinks are required for the rated performance; switching frequency is nominally 100kHz. As noted before in *TT* ic dc-dc converters also provide a convenient means of obtaining, for example, ±12V from a single battery. Efficiency at full load is about 75-80 per cent.

272MT1006A (145MHz, 2·8 MHz bandwidth, 500Ω, Cirkit Stock No 17-10063, £4.90p.

"I used the two-section filter as in April the three-section filter was out of stock. I only found out about Bonex later. Multiturn pots were used for 'sweep width' and 'centre frequency'. The spare amplifier section of IC3 (TL084) is used to amplify further the Y-output together with a Y position (zero) control. The blanking signal was fed to a Z input on a surplus vdu that was available. For L2 I used three turns of 20swg tinned copper wire with the same diameter of 3/16-in. For L4 I used six turns of 24swg tinned copper wire with a small iron dust core, see Fig. 4. I would be interested to know if there are any alternatives to the Motorola MV209 giving the same sweep range as I have found that very high prices are being asked for this device." GW3XYW does not mention any modification to the capacitor values of the NE602 mixer.

ELEVATED RADIALS VINDICATED

TT has referred on several occasions to the sterling work done in 1980-81 by Arch Doty, K8CFU, John Frey, W3ESU and Harry Mills, K4HU (retired professional engineers) in investigating the characteristics of electrically-short vertical antennas using elevated counterpoise and insulated radials, and comparing them with those of antennas using large numbers of buried radials, as customary for mf broadcast antennas ever since the classic paper "Ground systems as a factor in antenna efficiency" by the late Dr George Brown and his RCA colleagues R F Lewis and J Epstein (*Proc IRE*, June 1937, pp753-787). The K8CFU team made literally thousands of measurements which strongly suggested that, for equal efficiency, a counterpoise comprising insulated radials elevated a few feet above ground would require fewer radial wires than the 120-150 buried radials normally mandated for US medium-wave transmitters by the FCC. Their findings were, of course, applicable to amateur antennas, particularly for 1·8, 3·5 and 7MHz, and their report was published in detail in *QST*.

A recent *IEEE Trans on Broadcasting* paper by a team comprising American university and broadcast engineers, using a 'Method of Moments' computer program, seems to bear out the measurements made by K8CFU team although no reference is made to their pioneering work. The paper concludes: "Studies of vertical monopole antennas, using the NEC-GS computer code, indicate that a radiator elevated several metres above ground and having only four elevated horizontal radials can outperform a ground-mounted antenna with 120 buried radials, over any type of soil. Field measurements are planned for the purpose of verifying these computer predictions. If the NEC output is correct, then the construction, cost and complexity of vertical monopole antenna systems can be reduced significantly. At the same time, the elevated-radial antenna provides increased groundwave field intensity while attenuating skywave radiation."

In effect, they suggest that the elevated ground-plane antenna, as widely used on hf/vhf, represents a superior approach to using a grounded monopole with an extensive system of buried radials, at frequencies down to below 1MHz.

AIR-CORED BALUN

In *Radio ZS* (March 1988, p23), ZS2LR describes an effective home-constructed "dipole insulator and air-cored balun" based on information on a commercially made balun published in *QST* (October 1980) rated at up to 4kW peak with less than 0·5dB loss. The 3-30MHz unit comprises 12 turns, 16swg wire, trifilar wound on a one-inch phenolic former.

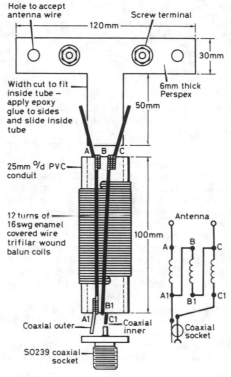

FIG 5. EXPLODED VIEW OF ZS2LR's DIPOLE-CENTRE INSULATOR AND 1:1 AIR-CORED BALUN.

For 1·8 to 7MHz, use 13 turns on a two-in former.

ZS2LR writes: "The *QST* information mentions that ferrite-cored baluns do a fine job but if overloaded or subjected to high standing wave ratios, harmonics are generated that can cause tvi. The air-cored balun cannot saturate, ring or generate harmonics. It is lightweight, causes little sag in the antenna and can be constructed from cheap and readily available materials. The losses are indeed very low. Owing to the cost, scarcity and possible problems with toroidal ferrite cores, the writer decided to construct an air-cored balun as an integral part of a dipole insulator (Fig. 5). The insulator was made of laminated perspex; tee-shaped with the vertical portion dimensioned to fit inside a piece of 25mm pvc conduit where the insulator was secured with epoxy glue. In the drawing the interconnections of the coils are shown outside the coil for reasons of clarity, but in practice are routed on the inside of the coil. Only two soldered connections are required on the balun coils, apart from the joints to the coax socket. Terminals were provided on the insulator for connection of the antenna and balun wires.

"A chassis mounting SO239 coax socket was connected at the bottom of the pvc coil former, pushed up against the former and secured. The coils were first wound, balun connections made, then the insulator secured to the former; the socket was connected and the balun connected to the insulator terminals. The balun was then wrapped with cotton gauze bandage to cover the windings and filling all gaps that might allow the ingress of rain water as well as securing the connector to the balun former. The cotton was impregnated with epoxy glue and allowed to cure. The antenna was then attached to the insulator and connected to the terminals. The feedline was plugged into the coaxial socket and terminals, and the socket sprayed with 'Tectyl' to prevent ingress of moisture and corrosion."

VOLTAGE GAIN FROM SOURCE FOLLOWER

Gordon Crayford, VE6LI in *QST* (April 1988, p45) shows how it is possible to obtain a moderate voltage-gain from a source-follower (cathode-follower) stage working into a high-impedance load, rather than the usual small voltage-loss. Such gain can be very useful when, for example, the output from a vfo source-follower buffer stage is required to drive a frequency multiplier. As shown in Fig. 6, this can be achieved by tapping the source terminal into one section of a multi-section rf choke (eg 2·5mH choke) which acts as a voltage step-up autotransformer. C1 is optional when the value of R1 represents only a small percentage of the impedance of the rfc, and its omission can sometimes improve circuit performance.

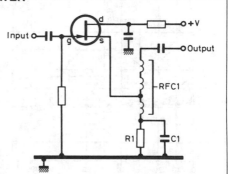

FIG 6. TAPPING INTO AN RF CHOKE TO OBTAIN VOLTAGE-GAIN FROM A SOURCE-FOLLOWER AS SUGGESTED IN QST BY VE6EI.

BATTERY LORE

Gordon Hudson, GM4SVM, draws attention to press reports that the Swedish firm of Ericsson recently had to recall some 30,000 of their 'Hotline Combi' mobile radiotelephones, following three explosions brought about by incorrect placement of a lithium battery giving rise to short-circuits. GM4SVM writes: "It might

be worth reinforcing previous *TT* warnings about the care that manufacturers and users need to take to ensure safety of these cells. Lithium cells are becoming commonplace in amateur equipment, particularly for memory back-up in synthesised equipment. It also seems an opportunity to remind readers that although lithium batteries have a very long lifetime in such applications, problems can arise in some, ▶

equipments if the batteries are permitted to fail or if no steps are taken to maintain voltage during their replacement (*TT*, December 1984, p1052). There are large numbers of FT290 transceivers using lithium cells for memory back-up which will soon need new batteries to be fitted. Many were purchased about five years ago and are thus reaching the end of the manufacturer's recommended life span for their factory-fitted cell."

The problem posed by the possible loss of information stored in a ram arises most seriously in equipments where the 'memory' forms a central brain, replacing manual switches and controls. The 1984 *TT* item noted that the IC751, 745, 271 and 451 transceivers fall specifically in this category, but there are many other models where the ram memory needs to be continuously powered since it forms a vital part of the basic unit. Loss of frequencies or channels stored in a memory is of little consequence since the rig can easily be reprogrammed. However, some manufacturers now suggest much longer than five years lifetime for their factory-fitted lithium batteries. GM4SVM continues:

"Also on the topic of FT290 batteries, I have encountered several cases of the nicad cells fitted to these sets overheating and melting because the incorrect size of dc plug was used to connect the set to a car or power supply. Although there are several plug sizes which will fit the socket and power the set, some are not large enough fully to engage the battery shut-off switch which is incorporated in the dc supply socket. The result is that the batteries are able to draw on the psu without any current limiting and they overheat. This is another safety area which should be considered when using rechargeable cells."

A long article 'Choosing the best battery for

TABLE 1 – PRIMARY AND SECONDARY CELL CHARACTERSITICS (condensed from a comprehensive table in IEEE Spectrum)						
System	Nominal cell voltage	Weight (Wh/kg)	Practical Energy Density* Type	Volume (Why/1)	Typical Operating Temperature	Shelf Life (to 80% capacity)
Zinc-air	1·4	310	– button –	1150	0 to 50	5-10 yrs unactivated
Lithium-sulphur dioxide	3·0	275	– cylindrical –	440	–40 to 71	5-10 yrs
Lithium-manganese dioxide	3·0	175	– coin –	505	–20 to 60	5-10 yrs
Alkaline-manganese dioxide	1·5	130	– cylindrical –	315	–20 to 54	3-4 yrs
Zinc-carbon	1·5	75	– cylindrical –	140	– 5 to 45	1-2 yrs
Mercuric-oxide	1·35 or 1·4	110	– button –	445	– 9 to 54	3-5 yrs
Silver-oxide	1·5	130	– button –	500	–20 to 54	2-3 yrs
Nickel-cadmium (rechargeable)	1·2	35	– cylindrical –	88	–40 to 45	3-6 mnths
Lead-acid (rechargeable)	2·0	30	– cylindrical –	90	–40 to 60	6-12 mnths
		35	– flatplate –	80	–40 to 60	6-12 mnths

*Button cells rated at the 500-1000h rate at 21°C. Cylindrical cells at 50-100h rate. Cut-off voltage 80 per cent of nominal voltage. In practice under typical conditions the capabilities can be higher.

portable equipment' by Trudy Bell, *IEEE Spectrum*, March 1988, pp30-35 provides a useful survey of disposable (primary) and rechargeable (secondary) cells for consumer electronics, hearing aids, communications devices etc. It includes a table listing in detail the salient characteristics of seven primary cells: zinc-air, lithium-sulphur, lithium-manganese dioxide, zinc-carbon, mercuric oxide and silver oxide; and also rechargeable nickel-cadmium and lead-acid cells. Table 1 is a much cut-down version of the *Spectrum* table.

While very large zinc-air industrial batteries have been mentioned several times in *TT*, zinc-air cells are now also manufactured as 'button' cells in diameters from 5·8 to 30·5mm, with capacities up to 1150mAh and also larger cells to

8·5Ah. Zinc-air batteries use oygen from the air as the active cathode material and have the distinction of having the highest energy density on continuous discharge of any of the primary cells including lithium. They have excellent shelf life while unactivated but once the air holes are unsealed, they need to be discharged within a few months. Zinc-air cells are thus best suited to devices used frequently with low to medium loads, such as hearing-aids, radiopagers, hand-helds in regular use, etc. Zinc-air button cells can cost around twice as much as mercury cells of the same size but their much superior energy density can make them competitive for some applications. Nominal cell voltage is 1·4V.

The *Spectrum* article, however, suggests that the most significant advance in recent years has been the development of high-power lithium cells for consumer products, including their use for powering all functions of fully-automatic cameras with integral flash. Self-discharge can be as low as one per cent per year at room temperature. The multiple safety features built into these consumer lithium batteries were described in *TT* (November 1987, p834). On the safety of lithium batteries, the *Spectrum* article comments: "More than a decade ago, lithium-sulphur dioxide cells had a bad reputation for safety, because the cells are pressurised and contain materials that are toxic or flammable. High internal temperatures resulting from continuous high current drain or a short-circuit could cause them to explode. The lithium battery industry since then has devoted much research to safety, and most lithium batteries have progressed well beyond their safety probationary period. Two lithium electrochemical systems – lithium-manganese dioxide and lithium-polycarbon monofluoride – were introduced (in the USA) in the late 1970s and have an unblemished safety record. Furthermore, (American) Underwriters Laboratories has recognised many manufacturers' lithium products, and more leading equipment manufacturers are now using lithium batteries in their consumer products". Nominal voltage of lithium cells is 3V.

For high-drain applications, including hand-held transceivers, nicad or sealed lead-acid batteries are usually the most economical long-

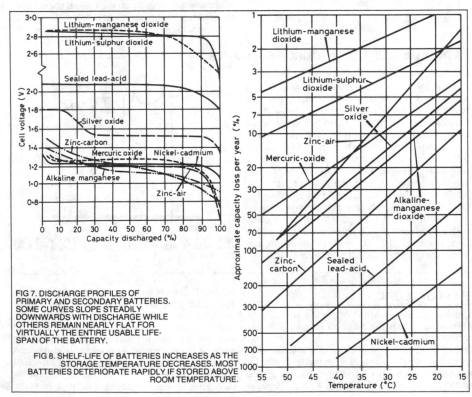

FIG 7. DISCHARGE PROFILES OF PRIMARY AND SECONDARY BATTERIES. SOME CURVES SLOPE STEADILY DOWNWARDS WITH DISCHARGE WHILE OTHERS REMAIN NEARLY FLAT FOR VIRTUALLY THE ENTIRE USABLE LIFE-SPAN OF THE BATTERY.

FIG 8. SHELF-LIFE OF BATTERIES INCREASES AS THE STORAGE TEMPERATURE DECREASES. MOST BATTERIES DETERIORATE RAPIDLY IF STORED ABOVE ROOM TEMPERATURE.

term solutions. Trudy Bell points out that there are now two types of sealed lead-acid cells which differ not only in construction but also in performance. The *gelled electrolyte* type, manufactured with capacities up to 50Ah, is basically similar to vehicle batteries other than the electrolyte being not a liquid but a polymeric gel. The *starved electrolyte* cell, with little or no free fluid electrolyte, is made in cylindrical form (smallest is a D cell, larger sizes designated X, J and BC) with capacities ranging from 2·5 to 30Ah. She adds:

"Soon to become a factor among portable rechargeable batteries are small secondary batteries using a lithium negative electrode. These are expected to have an energy density of the order of 100W-hrs per kilogram, good charge retention, and an acceptable cycle life. For example, the most advanced lithium secondary cell is the lithium-molybdenum disulphide system, which is manufactured in (small) AA cylinders. This cell uses a spiral-wound construction and a nonaqueous organic electrolyte. The expected advantages of the lithium rechargeable battery are its higher energy density and excellent charge retention when compared to nickel-cadmium". Whether the appearance of lithium rechargeable batteries for consumer applications will reduce their cost remains to be seen; at present rechargeable lithium cells are very costly.

A NOT SO TECHNICAL TOPIC

THE PHRASE IN THE ITU Radio Regulations *identifying radio amateurs as "duly authorised persons interested in radio technique" (see TT, June 1988, p421) deserves consideration, though I have no wish to appear to be moralising. It does not mean, surely, that in order to become an amateur one should be expected to have the knowledge and training of a professional radio engineer or technician – or even, initially, any real understanding of modern radio equipment. But to my mind it does imply a genuine interest in radio techniques and a willingness to learn as one goes along. It does not mean that only those who build their own equipment on the kitchen table can be considered true amateurs – useful and rewarding as a degree of home construction can be in the self-training process. It accepts that when authorised to venture on the airwaves, newcomers may have only the minimal technical knowledge required by their own national authorities. The Radio Regulations make no attempt to stipulate any requirement for a technical examination, although this is taken for granted, or to define the speeds to be achieved in the obligatory morse test for operation below 30MHz.*

But an "interest in radio technique" does indicate that licensed amateurs should not be content to be purely users of entertainment appliances. A television licence, a cb licence and even a driving licence impose no such obligations, and nobody would criticise a viewer for having no interest in, or knowledge of, the electronics he or she switches on and off.

There is no shame in starting amateur radio young or as a beginner with a bare minimum of technical understanding – but surely no excuse for remaining a complete technical ignoramus, year in, year out, time spent filling the spectrum with idle chatter. This does not require that we should all become experts in theory or mathematics. But one must hope that Jim Cookson, G4XWD is wrong when he suggests (June TT) that many of us are content to remain appliance operators, openly professing no real technical interest or knowledge. The radio amateur has always been well-served with technical publications, books and periodicals, and opportunities for self-training. But books are meant for a modicum of study, and not just for propping up a wonky transceiver or looking good on a shelf.

A NEAR-RECORD SOLAR CYCLE?

G8VR and G8KG have, in the "News & Views" columns, reported the growing body of evidence that solar cycle No 22 will peak much earlier and much higher than was being predicted only a few months ago. So far, cycle 22 has repeatedly thrown predictions (made several months in advance) out of kilter – by starting earlier than expected; by the way sunspot activity has advanced in odd fits and starts; and by confounding the strongly-held views that we were due this time for a very low maximum, several years into the 1990s. Some predictions put the maximum smoothed monthly mean sunspot number as low as 36.

In the scientific correspondence columns of *Nature* (12 May 1988), Dr Geoffrey Brown of the University College of Wales, Aberystwyth writes, under the heading "Solar cycle 22 to be one of the highest on record?": "It now seems virtually certain that the value of 12·3 for the smoothed monthly mean sunspot number for September 1986 defines the minimum of solar cycle number 21, and hence the conventional beginning of cycle 22. Since then, activity has increased unusually steeply. Because it has

generally been found that rapid initial rises in sunspot activity have been followed by large maxima, there is already wide interest in the development of cycle 22 . . . The consensus seems to be that cycle 22 will peak in 1990±1. Magnetic predictions are based on a variety of techniques . . . Recent predictions have all been at the top end of the range (international sunspot number as great as 190) . . . One prediction technique which generally gave near-correct forecasts for the previous cycle makes use of experimentally-observed precursors . . . One such precursor method is based on the occurrence of so-called geomagnetic abnormal quiet days (AQDs) determined at a temperate latitude station in the preceding sunspot mimimum . . . This relationship holds good back to 1885, the earliest year for which data are available."

Using such a prediction technique leads Dr Brown to forecast, for cycle 22, a maximum sunspot number of about 175±35 and to suggest that "it seems likely that cycle 22 could be second only to cycle 19 as the largest cycle on record."

ORIGINS OF THE 'KALLIROTRON OSCILLATOR'

In the February *TT*, Ray Howgego, G4DTC, raised the question of the correct spelling and origins of the push-pull oscillator he uses in his 'ultimate' hybrid front-end (*TT*, December 1987) and which he has found "exceptionally reliable, providing a very high output, independent of the LC ratio". In the May *TT*, I reported tracing earlier appearances of this form of oscillator in the *RSGB Bulletin* in 1953 (unnamed) and 1958 (spelt "kalitron") and also the receipt of a note from Don Nappin, G3LMS concerning a "kallirotron: an aperiodic negative resistance triode combination" developed by an L B Turner in 1920 as a means of reducing static crashes. But I had to admit failure in tracing the origins of this oscillator. Among the reference books I had checked without success was the first edition of Terman's *Radio Engineering* which did include a section on push-pull oscillators but no mention of any prefixed kali- or kalli-.

However, F R Wilson, G3ETX dipped into a later edition of Terman's classic textbook and found an added footnote referring to a paper "A low distortion audio-frequency oscillator" by Herbert J Reich (University of Illinois) in *Proc IRE*, Vol 24, November 1937. This has finally solved the mystery although, curiously enough, it shows that the oscillator is, in fact, based on the Turner 'kallirotron' circuit of 1920.

The summary of Reich's *ProcIRE* paper reads: "In the first portion of this paper, which deals with the theory of negative resistance oscillators, it is shown that for small harmonic content the form of the negative resistance characteristic in the vicinity of the operating point should be such that the average negative resistance increases with amplitude of oscillation. It is then shown that Turner's Kallirotron ▶

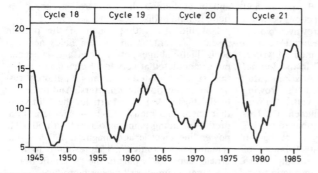

FIG 9. VARIATIONS OF THE ANNUAL NUMBER OF AQDs (GEOMAGNETIC ABNORMAL QUIET DAYS) IN SOLAR CYCLES 18 TO 21. SOME SCIENTISTS NOW SUGGEST THAT THE HEIGHT OF THE SUCCEEDING CYCLE IS INVERSELY PROPORTIONAL TO THE NUMBER OF AQDs IN THE DECLINING PERIOD OF THE PRECEDING CYCLE PUTTING CYCLE 22 UP TO NEAR-RECORD HEIGHTS.

circuit has negative resistance characteristics of the desired form. The final part of the paper describes an audio-frequency oscillator based on Turner's circuit. The second and third harmonic content of the output may be kept below 0·2 per cent by the use of low-resistance coils and diode automatic amplitude control. Higher harmonics are negligible. At 1000Hz the frequency drift relative to a tuning fork oscillator does not exceed 0·04Hz. The frequency drift caused by a 22·5V change in anode supply voltage is 0·04Hz".

In his introductory text, Reich wrote: "No study appears to have been made of the suitability of the 'Kallirotrun' negative resistance of Turner as the basis of a negative resistance oscillator. It is the purpose of this paper to show that the characteristics of this circuit are ideal for its use in an oscillator and to describe a low distortion oscillator based upon it."

It is thus now quite clear that we owe the "Kallirotron oscillator" to Reich, 1937 and Turner, 1920 (*Radio Review*, Vol 1, p317) and that it provides a useful configuration at frequencies from af to vhf (or beyond). Since writing the above notes further information has come from Isaac Lederer, ORS87664 in Israel and this will appear hopefully next month.

LOW-LEVEL RADIATION AND HEALTH

There are some questions that just will not go away no matter how much one would wish to have once-and-for-all definitive answers. For radio amateurs, one of the most important is whether or not non-ionized electromagnetic radiation, at levels below the current official standards, constitutes a potential health hazard. In the April *TT*, I drew attention to a trenchant article by the American university scientists Foster and Pickard (*Nature*, 10 December 1987) that highlighted the need to establish guidelines for *halting* some of the protracted and inconclusive research into possible biological effects of non-ionised radiation, at the sort of levels found at reasonable distances from amateur transmitting antennas, etc. This article, as might be expected, has been bitterly attacked by a considerable number of scientists involved in bio-research into possible radiation hazards.

In *Microwave News* (January/February 1988) no less than 19 prominent workers in this field, who obviously greatly resented the idea of their research projects being 'halted', went on record with highly critical remarks about the Foster and Pickard article. The critics included Dr Ross Adey of the Veterans Administration at a hospital in California who has been very prominent in investigating possible tissue interactions with weak electromagnetic fields. He has renewed his attack on Foster and Pickard's paper in *Nature* (2 June 1988) claiming that their commentary on the risks of microwaves is "wide of the mark and unreasonably denigrates the efforts of the many who have established structural and functional substrates for essential aspects of these interactions at cellular and subcellular levels" and ignores "a wealth of findings that relate to the role of cell membranes in transdictive coupling of electrical and chemical signals from the outside to the inside of the cell; in interactions at cell surfaces between weak elec-

Grant Dixon, G8CGK confesses to having originated the useful paper-clip component-puller praised by GW0IER (*TT*, May 1988, Fig. 11, p349). It was originally published a few years ago in one of the electronics magazine. G8CGK mentions that it can be further improved by filing the hook to resemble the tip of a screwdriver as in Fig. 10. This enables it to go under any wires which are very tight against a pcb.

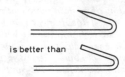

is better than

FIG 10. G8CGK POINTS OUT THAT HIS PAPER-CLIP COMPONENT-PULLER CAN BE IMPROVED BY FILING THE HOOK TO FORM A SCREWDRIVER SHAPE.

Peter Pitts, G3GYE/A4XGC finds the tune-up protection device featured several times recently in *TT* very worthwhile but comments: "Nobody has mentioned that the unwanted radiation (at balance position) is proportional to the power into the 50Ω dummy load so one can still radiate sufficient signal to interfere with local stations when used for extended measurements etc. For example at 100W output of the transmitter, rather over 1·25W is likely to be radiated." I seem to recall mentioning that this type of device comes into the 'quiet tune-up' rather than the 'silent tune-up' category required by the military. G3GYE has added another switch position to isolate the bridge when full power is required to load.

Paul Tregear, G8PQM draws the attention of constructors to the Wien Bridge Oscillator. He believes that they may have been put off by the apparent need to use a costly thermistor to stabilise the level of negative feedback. The arrangement of Fig. 11 dispenses with this item and, as a bonus, provides adjustment of the output level at source. D1 conducts at the positive peaks of the output waveform at a level set by adjustment of RV1.

Notes (1) The output frequency is equal to $1/(2\pi CR)$ where C is in farads and R in ohms. (2) The ratio R2/R1 must be only just greater than 2 to

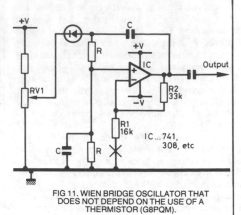

FIG 11. WIEN BRIDGE OSCILLATOR THAT DOES NOT DEPEND ON THE USE OF A THERMISTOR (G8PQM).

preserve good sinusoidal output form. (3) Values of C should be closely matched to ensure oscillation (positive feedback just predominates). (4) Circuit may be 'keyed' at point X.

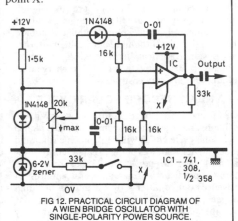

FIG 12. PRACTICAL CIRCUIT DIAGRAM OF A WIEN BRIDGE OSCILLATOR WITH SINGLE-POLARITY POWER SOURCE.

Fig. 12 shows a practical arrangement of a Wien Bridge oscillator for morse practice with a single 12V power supply. This will drive a high impedance headphone directly or a loudspeaker via an audio amplifier. Other uses suggested by G8PQM, are for a side-tone oscillator or for a two-tone signal source.

tromagnetic fields (elf fields and rf/microwave fields amplitude or pulse-modulated at elf) and the gamut of natural and artificial chemical molecules that stimulate cell surfaces at specific receptor sites . . . Beyond the evidence for these modulation-dependent effects further research is needed to evaluate the nature and extent of possible resonant interactions between biomolecules and millimetre microwave fields".

Jim Ballard, G0AOT, has drawn attention to a long article by Simon Best, a medical writer, on "The electropollution effect" in the *Journal of Alternative & Complementary Medicine* (May 1988). This surveys what is termed "the growing body of evidence linking high voltage power lines with cancer, especially leukaemia". This includes Dr Adey's recommendations to the US House Committee that: "There is a growing and even urgent need for early establishment of national safety standards that would govern exposure to non-ionising electromagnetic fields

in the workplace, in the home and in the general environment. These standards should be regarded as interim since current epidemiological knowledge and experimental evidence remain incomplete in precisely defining mechanisms of em field interaction with body tissues and in evaluating the exact role of these em fields in human disease."

I would stress that much of the present research is centred on the em fields near 50/60Hz high-voltage power lines and rf signals pulse-modulated at very low frequencies, rather than signals radiated by mf/hf/vhf/uhf broadcast or communications transmitters. And to be fair to the Foster & Pickard article, they did write that there are many effects – "perhaps hundreds" including many associated with 50/60Hz power line electric and magnetic fields – that remain to be studied". The response to their article seems to be part of the "scientific noise" that, they claimed, risk research produces. ∎

TECHNICAL TOPICS

PAT HAWKER · G3VA

MULLARD BECOMES PHILIPS COMPONENTS

As noted for an address in the item on phasing-type ssb, Mullard Ltd, for many years the UK's largest component firm, has become, since April 27, Philips Components Ltd, although (up to now) their London headquarters offices are still at Mullard House in Bloomsbury. Old-time amateurs may regret the vanishing of this link with the late Stanley R Mullard who died a few years ago at a ripe old age. Captain Mullard's connection with valve development stretched all the way back to the first world war and the first British high-vacuum receiving valve (type R5). Afterwards he set up the Mullard Radio Valve Company and proved a good friend of the early British experimental amateurs of the 1920s: for example he gave Gerry Marcuse, G2NM the very large valves which allowed him to pioneer 'Empire Broadcasting' in 1924 with a transmitter power on 10MHz of about 1·5kW. In 1924 he sold half of his company stock to N.V. Philips Gloeilampenfabrieken of Eindhoven. Three years later in 1927 the Mullard Radio Valve Co Ltd became a wholly-owned subsidiary of Philips – although for very many years (right up to the 1970s) the Philips ownership was never stressed publicly. It was, however, reflected in the early 'PM' (Philips-Mullard) series of valves such as the PM2DX used in many amateur regenerative receivers in the 1930s, and the development of the famous EF50 series. There were few *T&R Bulletins* (original name of *RadCom*) that did not carry a full-page Mullard advertisement, at first claiming "The Filament that cannot be broken except by the very roughest handling" for Mullard 'The Master Valve'. It was the support given by the few such advertisements that carried our journal through the depression of the 1930s. In those financially stringent days, few members could have been in a position to respond to the later advertisements featuring such transmitting valves as the DO/40 "a dull emitter transmitting valve capable of working on anode voltages up to 1000 volts and tested dissipating 40W at the anode . . . suitable for short-wave transmission (down to 40 metres) with total emission 300mA". Its 1931 price of £5.5s must have represented more than a week's wages for many members.

PHASING-TYPE SSB

Although phasing-type ssb exciters (and a few phasing-type ssb demodulators) were quite widely used in the early days of amateur ssb, it is a long time since any approach other than crystal or ceramic sideband filters has been used in factory-built amateur equipment. Yet it should not be forgotten that quadrature (90°) phasing of rf and af signals (combined with balanced modulators) remains a valid and low-cost approach in its basic form, or as the Weaver 'third method', or as the 'polyphase' system which has the

UK PIONEERS OF SSB

The July *TT* item on 'pioneers of ssb' included some notes on the Collins KWM–1 (10 × 100kHz between 14 and 30MHz) mobile rig, the first ssb/cw transceiver to reach the amateur market, although separate transmitters and receivers for ssb operation had been available in the USA in the early 1950s. But as a result of a printing error, the KWM–1 was dated 1965-69 instead of G4KSG's 1956-59 before being superseded by the KWM–2 covering 14 ×200kHz segments between 3·4 and 30MHz.

Douglas Kay, G3AAE had good reason to correct the printed dates. He writes: "The KWM–1 was available well before 1965. I used one on Alderney, as GC3AAE, between 16 to 30 May, 1958. GC3AAE was situated at Essex Castle, Alderney and was operated 24-hours-a-day for two weeks by G3AAE (John), G3BQR (Chas), G3IFB (Frank) and G3JUL (Geoff), making over 2000 contacts with 112 countries using a Collins KWM–1 transceiver running 150W on ssb and cw with a G8KW multiband trap dipole. It was the first KWM–1 to leave the USA and resulted from a direct appeal to Art Collins, W0CXX."

I should have spotted the error in proof since I obtained my photograph of the KWM–1 in 1958. Checking some back issues of *QST* etc I find the KWM–1 was being advertised as early as 1957, while the KWM–2 was introduced well before 1963 by which time there were over a dozen ssb transceivers on the American market (Davco, Drake, Eimac, Galaxy, Hallicrafters (2), Heath, National, SBE, Sonar and Swan) with several using hybrid transistor/valve designs. In the late 1950s, Collins were, however, still concentrating

advantage that it can be implemented entirely from preferred value resistor and capacitor networks.

Last year Chris Randall G4RBR drew my attention to an article 'A new approach to low-power ssb circuits' published in *Semiconductor Magazine* (28 August 1987). This article drew on a good deal of material from the Signetics Application Note AN1981, written by Bob Zavrek, W7SX, plus material from ARRL publications. As mentioned in *TT*, November 1986, p784, AN1981 'New low power single sideband circuits' is available in the UK from

on 'separate' receivers and transmitters, including the admirable 75A4 receiver and their new 'S-line' equipment.

SSB began to gain UK adherents in the early 1950s and a bimonthly *CQ Single Sideband* column, initially written by H. F. Knott, G3CU, was published in the *RSGB Bulletin* from October 1951. This set the ssb scene of the day as follows:

"It has often been heard said: 'What is ssb? Where are these stations to be found? What is it all about? . . . The single-sideband system was first introduced to amateurs in October 1947, and so immense are its advantages that a complete change in equipment and operating is certain. Today there are approximately 150 stations using ssb – seventeen in Europe. The first British amateur to adopt the system G2NX (Oswestry) August 1949 was quickly followed by G3CWC (Norwich), G3FHL and G3FDG (Ironbridge), G2CR (Lincoln) and G3CU (all mostly on the 3·5MHz band). After a pause of some months G3AIH (New Malden) and G8RC (Brentwood) made their appearance, and more recently G3BVA (Bromley). At least a dozen other UK amateurs are building equipment". In 1951 all the British ssb transmitters (phasing and filter types) had to be home constructed.

Curiously, although never a frequent user of ssb, I can claim to have written the first article to appear in the *RSGB Bulletin* on the new mode: an unsigned piece 'Amateur single-sideband telephone tests' commenting on the reports in the January 1948 *QST* and describing how to tune in an ssb signal. This must have been in either the February or March 1948 issue.

THE FIRST SSB/CW TRANSCEIVER, THE COLLINS KWM–1 MOBILE TRANSCEIVER, WAS INTRODUCED IN 1957 AND PAVED THE WAY FOR THE CHANGE FROM SEPARATE TRANSMITTERS AND RECEIVERS TO THE MODERN TRANSCEIVER SCENE. IT WAS NOT UNTIL JUST OVER TEN YEARS LATER THAT THE JAPANESE "BLACK BOXES" BEGAN TO APPEAR ON THE UK MARKET.

Technical Publications Department, Philips Components (then Mullard) Ltd, New Road, Mitcham, Surrey CR4 4XY.

In the early days of ssb, phasing methods were used to generate ssb signals directly at the output signal frequency rather than at a fixed 'intermediate' frequency. This called for balanced modulators and rf phasing networks that remained in good quadrature over a wide range of frequencies. This, together with a tendency of the circuits to suffer from significant heat drift and the requirement for unusual precision component values, all tended to turn amateurs ▶

towards crystal sideband filters (or mechanical filters below 500kHz), despite the high cost of good factory-built filters. This trend has been confirmed among home builders since the cost of a home-built crystal ladder filter can be kept low by the use of colour television or other low-cost crystals.

Today, a valid use of phasing-type networks is for their use in direct-conversion ssb receivers. For example this technique is used by Gary Breed, K9AY for "A new breed of receiver" (*QST* January 1988, pp16-23). His design (outlined in Fig 1) makes use of audio phase-shift networks made by cascading op-amp stages with each stage providing a phase shift centered on a particular frequency. Such filters, known as 'all-pass' filters provide a stable phase shift characteristic over a band of frequency, rather like using stagger-tuned rf or i.f filters. Each filter (Fig 2) can be formed from 1% tolerance value components, with K9AY noting that such parts are easy to obtain and inexpensive "quite a change from those early days of ssb!" He had rather greater difficulty in implementing his rf phase shift networks but comes up with several possibilities (eg Fig 3). His receiver achieves an unwanted sideband rejection ranging from about 34dB to 65dB at his 1kHz af balancing frequency on 7150kHz. For the European 7MHz band it might be possible to achieve better than say 40dB over the full band at audio frequencies between 350 and 2900Hz. An explanation of op-amp all-pass filters was given by G4YKT in the August *RadCom*, in this case without stagger tuning.

As the *Semiconductor Magazine* article points out: "The availability of new integrated circuits now makes it possible for the older techniques to be reappraised, with the prospect of low-cost circuits offering more than adequate suppression." Later on it notes that: "High-quality (professional and military) ssb specifications require greater than 70dB of sideband suppression, but the (phasing and third method) circuits so far described offer only 35-40dB. The addition of an inexpensive two-pole crystal or ceramic filter (in a super-dc-gainer configuration) will achieve this higher rejection, with the additional benefit of an improvement in the intermodulation performance of the receiver. Fig 4 shows a block diagram of a complete ssb receiver using the phasing-filter technique with the sensitive NE602 allowing a low gain and low-consumption rf amplifier and first mixer. The synthesised local oscillator could be built from either the TDD1742T or the dual-chip HEF4750/4751." Clearly, a tunable vfo could be used rather than a synthesized oscillator.

It is perhaps worth stressing that the op-amp all-pass quadrature phasing networks would appear to take most of the hassle out of a phasing-type ssb generator or demodulator. Whereas it used to be considered quite difficult to obtain an accurate phase shift over say an audio range of 300 to 2700kHz, one now finds all-pass filters being used to obtain 90° phase shifts for broadcast applications involving audio frequencies up to 15kHz.

It is also interesting to note that the 'super-dc-gainer' technique, with a superhet mixer in front of a phasing-type direct-conversion receiver (ie no i.f. stages), is currently being regarded favourably as particularly suitable for the application of digital signal processing (dsp).

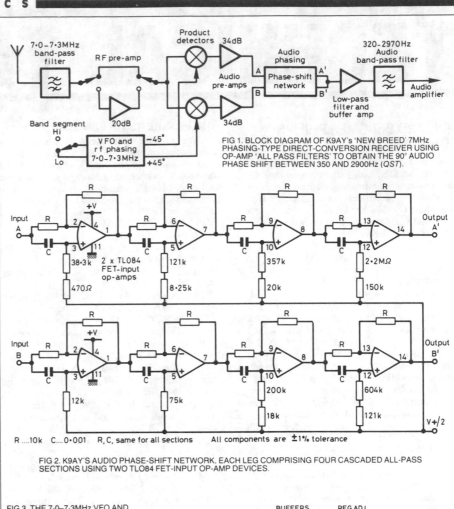

FIG 1. BLOCK DIAGRAM OF K9AY's 'NEW BREED' 7MHz PHASING-TYPE DIRECT-CONVERSION RECEIVER USING OP-AMP 'ALL PASS FILTERS' TO OBTAIN THE 90° AUDIO PHASE SHIFT BETWEEN 350 AND 2900Hz (*QST*).

FIG 2. K9AY'S AUDIO PHASE-SHIFT NETWORK, EACH LEG COMPRISING FOUR CASCADED ALL-PASS SECTIONS USING TWO TLO84 FET-INPUT OP-AMP DEVICES.

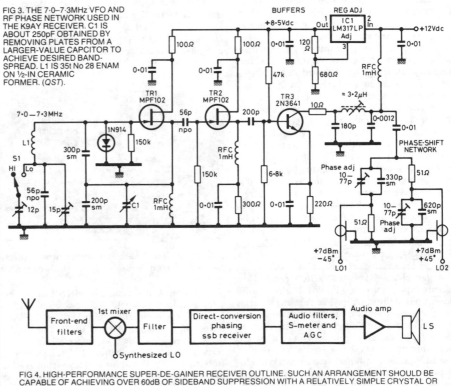

FIG 3. THE 7·0—7·3MHz VFO AND RF PHASE NETWORK USED IN THE K9AY RECEIVER. C1 IS ABOUT 250pF OBTAINED BY REMOVING PLATES FROM A LARGER-VALUE CAPCITOR TO ACHIEVE DESIRED BAND-SPREAD. L1 IS 35t No 28 ENAM ON ½-IN CERAMIC FORMER. (*QST*).

FIG 4. HIGH-PERFORMANCE SUPER-DE-GAINER RECEIVER OUTLINE. SUCH AN ARRANGEMENT SHOULD BE CAPABLE OF ACHIEVING OVER 60dB OF SIDEBAND SUPPRESSION WITH A RELATIVELY SIMPLE CRYSTAL OR CERAMIC FILTER.

PL519 GROUNDED-GRID LINEAR

George Moorfield, GW3DIX has been following with interest *TT* notes on the use of PL519/PL509 valves in high-power linear amplifiers. Ever since these valves were introduced about 1967 for use as line-output (sweep) valves in hybrid colour television sets, he has used them very successfully in a series of home-built linear amplifiers. To cope with a considerable number of on-air requests, GW3DIX last year consolidated and crystallised his experience in the form of a preferred design and has described this in eleven pages of hand-written notes and circuit diagrams. He notes that, with four PL519s (each

saturating on peak demand. A transformer rated as say 650V rms at about 800mA used with a conventional full-wave bridge (doubler) circuit, or alternatively one providing 1200-1250V at 400mA, would be suitable. A combination of suitable transformers may be used, with secondaries in series, etc. Note that if windings are connected in series, it is important to use good quality components with well-insulated windings, otherwise there is the risk of a seondary winding short-circuiting to the core or to the primary winding since it is required to withstand much higher voltages than for which it was originally intended. Suitable components are still readily and cheaply obtainable at rallies, junk sales, etc.

In the GW3DIX psu shown in Fig 7, T1 and T2 have their secondaries in parallel, a practice that has to be approached with caution since voltage differentials will result in circulating currents. However GW3DIX comments: "T1 and T2 are available from Marco of Wem, Salop as 175W units at £2.50 each. When tentatively tried with the secondaries in parallel to obtain the necessary current, I could not find any two (I built four amplifiers with this psu and cheap (40 for £1!) 60V dc relays) which produced a circulating current in the secondaries of more than 3mA.

GW3DIX admits that some components are not easy to acquire these days. PL519 (B9A) valveholders are available from Jack Birkett at ▶

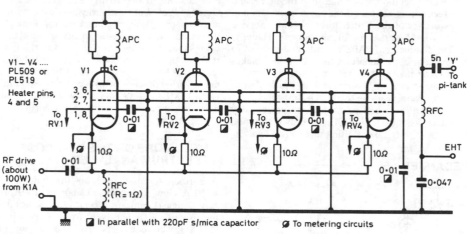

FIG 5. BASIC FOUR-PL519/PL509 GROUNDED-GRID LINEAR AMPLIFIER AS DESCRIBED BY GW3DIX

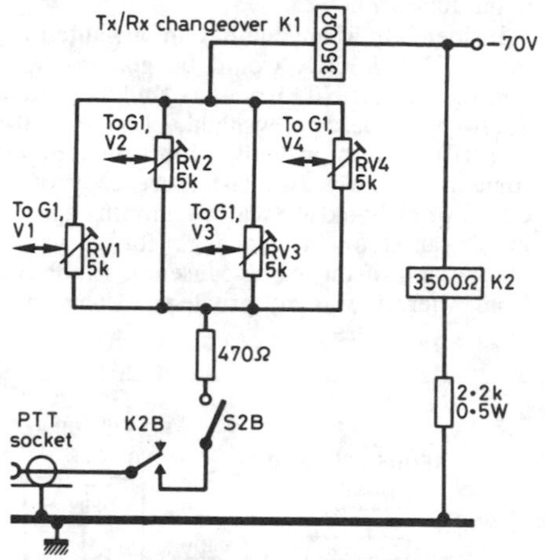

FIG 6. INDIVIDUAL BIASING POTS AS USED IN THE GW3DIX LINEAR.

30W anode dissipation) in parallel, it is possible to run up to 750W pep input, producing about 400W pep output with a 750V supply. However, he prefers to use a higher voltage (1·6 to 1·8kV) resulting in lower distortion with good efficiency. As sweep valves, the PL519 is designed to withstand up to 2·5kV anode voltage if operated correctly. In the ssb linear application, operating conditions (unless a large amount of speech compression is used) are "nowhere near as exacting as those of their regular television service. In class AB2 with 1·6kV and an input of 750W pep, an anode load of 2500 ohms is perfectly practicable. This overcomes the shortcomings of the older designs, and an operating Q of 12 is usable, with the resultant pi-tank components having normal values."

Of all the many enquiries received, GW3DIX reports that "no one who actually constructed the amplifier has failed to get it going satisfactorily." Figs 5, 6 and 7 have been extracted from GW3DIX's notes which include a total of six diagrams.

Although EL519 valves with 6·3V heaters are available in Europe, GW3DIX prefers the PL519 (40V, 0·3A heater) for the reasons already suggested by G4DTC (*TT*, May 1988) and also because, in the UK, the PL519 generally costs less than the EL519 and considerably less than American/Japanese sweep valves. Both the PL519 and EL519 have heavy duty cathodes capable of peak emission to 500mA.

GW3DIX believes that the rock on which such designs may survive or founder is the power supply. It is essential to use a mains transformer of sufficient power rating to prevent it from

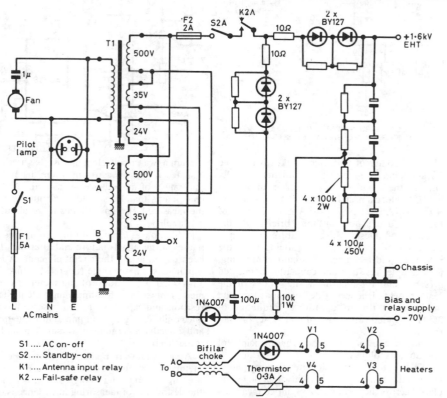

FIG 7. POWER SUPPLY UNIT FOR THE GW3DIX LINEAR. COMPONENTS MAY VARY TO SOME DEGREE TO SUIT AVAILABILITY PROVIDED THAT THE UNIT DOES NOT SATURATE ON PEAKS (SEE TEXT).

about 25p each; he also stocks twin-gang 500pF capacitors (for the pi-tank output loading) and 0·01µF 500V working disc ceramic capacitors. The bias pots are 5KΩ 1·6W wirewound television 'convergence' pots, available from Marco at about 32p each. Other components such as the various relays, 225 + 25µF (350V wkg) capacitors etc can usually be picked up at rallies or from Electronic Component Distribution, Horton, Telford. The "real stinker" tends to be the pi-tank high-voltage tuning capacitor. Available at a price at Telford but can sometimes be found at low-cost if you really hunt for them.

GW3DIX is not at all happy at the idea of anyone using the "darkened-room/glowing-anode" method of setting the standing current for this type of valve (as mentioned by G0DLN in the June *TT*).

Incidentally, if anyone has an unwanted copy of *ART7* GW3DIX would be glad to buy it (George Moorfield, Bryniau, Bull Bay Road, Amlwch, Anglesey, Gwynedd, LL68 9EA, 0407 830710). He "foolishly" lent his copy to someone . . . My own last spare copy of this out-of-print book went a few months ago to a Dutch amateur in exchange for a wartime photograph of the Abbe Museum, Eindhoven, from where it was my privilege to have many

contacts, on behalf of the Dutch Intelligence Bureau (BI), with Jack Verhagen and Jan Zandbergen, PA0ZY who were operating under extremely hazardous conditions from Alkmaar (G11) in the still occupied part of Holland. A detailed account of their remarkably successful clandestine operation, from September 1944 to May 1945, has been published in *Electron* (May 1988) by Dick Rollema, PA0SE (kindly translated into English for me by J. D. Lutterot, G5AQZ/PA0LUT). Jack Verhagen, who died in 1968, was a pre-war radio officer on the 'Zwarte Zee' ocean-going tugboat and I can testify that he was able to send perfect five-letter cipher traffic on a straight key at over 27 groups per minute even under the extreme stress of a covert operation which had seen the arrest and execution of almost all the radio operators and associates of the Dutch Internal Radio Service (OD/RvV Resistance organizations). Happily, Jan Zandbergen, PA0ZY is still, at the age of 75 years, an active amateur, though PA0SE makes it clear that he has not forgotten the terrible hunger-winter of 1944-45, and his wartime work over several years for the Dutch Resistance.

To return, albeit reluctantly, to present day radio, R. Hague, G4XOU has drawn attention to the 'Carrig Linear' using three PL519 valves,

described by EI8EI over several issues of the journal of the Irish Radio Transmitters Society and representing a high-power linear which can be built for under £50. However it uses a tranformerless voltage-tripling power supply with an output of about 900V dc. Personally, I feel reluctant to advise such an approach, not only because of the difficulty of achieving really good regulation without the use of really massive-value electrolytic capacitors (EI8EI uses six 350µF 350V wkg capacitors) but also because of the inherent danger of a mains-connected transmitter chassis and rf output socket. I recognise that in some circumtstances such an approach is entirely valid (eg the Danish lightweight 10W ac/dc 'Telephone Directory' clandestine transmitter-receiver, see *TT* October 1985) but this hardly applies to normal amateur operation. Remember, for example, that many UK domestic mains sockets have been shown to be incorrectly wired so there is a real risk of connecting the 'phase' (live) lead to 'chassis'. Furthermore, with traditional UK mains wiring practice or with protective multiple earth (PME) wiring, the mains neutral should never be connected directly to a real earth.

STILL MORE ON THE LOW-COST SPECTRUM ANALYSER

A further success story on the building of K2BLA's low-cost spectrum analyser (*TT* April, July, August) came in too late for inclusion in the August *TT*. This was from Steve Hunt, G3TXQ who considers that the use of the MC3356 fsk decoder ic for this application represents a "brain-wave". He writes:

"I made up the analyser as shown in the April *TT* and after one or two minor modifications it worked like a dream – it has completely changed the way I go about my circuit design! The changes I found necessary were: C7 from 5pF to 6·8pF, C13 from 6pF to 6·8pF, C14 from 2·2pF to 3·9pF. I used a ready-wound coil for L4 (Cirkit stock number 35–10864).

"At this stage I had a working analyser, but I have since made further improvements: (a) Add a 50-ohm resistor from ICL pin 20 to ground to terminate the low-pass filter. (b) The original design moves the trace off-screen on fly-back. I fed the vertical output through a 10k resistor and 'clamped' the output to ground on fly-back using an npn transistor (emitter to ground, collector to vertical output, base to blanking line through a 22k resistor). (c) I restricted the tuning range to 0 – 50MHz and added a 'single break-point' linearising network to IC3c. Replace R14 with two 27k resistors in series. Take the mid-point of these resistors through a 19k resistor and a diode to a potential divider (8·2k and 3·3k) between +12 and −12V lines. I now have acceptable linearity. (d) I get about 50dB 'on-screen' dynamic range. I added a switchable 20dB + 20dB + 10dB attenuator at the front end to give a total of 100dB dynamic range (−85dB to +15dBm).

"Like Roger Blackwell, G4PMK, I recommend a look at *QST* (November 1985) with K2BLA's earlier, rather more complex design. Readers may like to know that a company in the USA (A & A Engineering, 2521 W. La Palma, Unit K, Anaheim, CA92801 USA (714) 952-2114)) advertises a complete kit of parts for a

---

IMPEDANCES

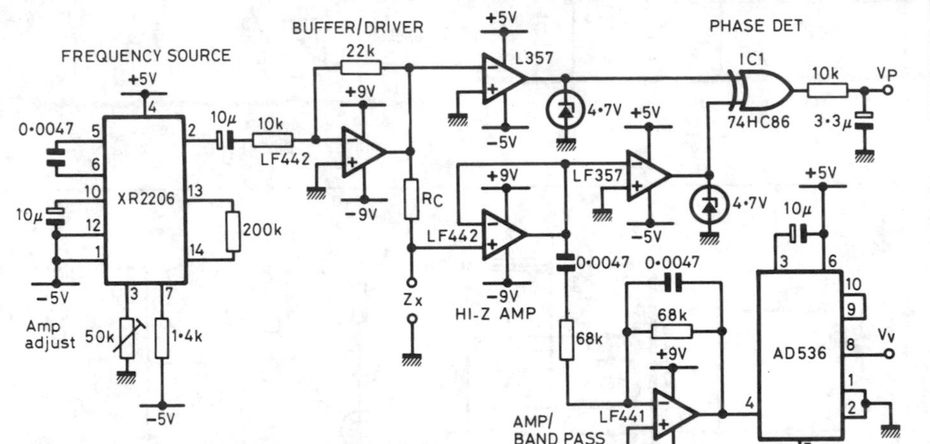

FIG 8. TEST INSTRUMENT FOR MEASURING COMPLEX IMPEDANCES. ETC (*ELECTRONICS AUSTRALIA*).

The availability of ic devices makes it possible for amateurs to build test instruments normally outside their budget range; for example the K2BLA spectrum analyser unit. In *Electronics Australia* (August 1987, p48) Andrew Stewart of Pialba, Queensland, outlines briefly, in the 'Circuit and Design Ideas' feature, an impedance meter capable of determining both the resistance and reactance of circuits comprising, for example, resistors and capacitors connected in series and for measuring the values of the reactance (and hence value) of capacitors and inductors. With an operating frequency of 25kHz the meter is for use primarily at af rather than hf.

Andrew Stewart describes the principle of operation as follows:

"This circuit (Fig 8) calculates the impedance magnitude and argument (phase) of a circuit placed across the terminals Zx. Impedance magnitude is calculated using a voltage divider network formed by the calibration resistor Rc and

the unknown circuit element. Rc has not been assigned a value because its value depends on the range of impedance measured. A basic guideline is that Rc should be about 10 (times the measured ?) ohms. Values up to about 1M work well.

"The phase circuit simply compares the phases of the signals before and after they have been passed across the circuit element. A basic rule here is: Phase Angle (degrees) equals 36 × Vp (volts). Calibration of the meter is performed simply using a few impedance elements (eg resistors and capacitors joined in series) to produce calibration graphs of impedance magnitude and impedance argument versus Vm and Vp respectively".

Andrew Stewart points out that impedance meters are extremely useful test instruments but are rarely seen owing to high prices. As a result the desirability of measuring impedance is often waived in favour of more familiar measurements.

spectrum analyser adaptor based on the *QST* design. It offers 0 – 400MHz, digital readout and two bandwidths for $399.

"I reckon the use of the MC3356 in this application is a 'brain-wave'. I now intend building another even simpler analyser by using just one conversion to 35·4MHz – a frequency for which you can get crystal roofing filters and at which the MC3356 works directly. The next step then has to be a matching tracking generator."

G3TXQ would be happy to help advise any readers who may be having difficulty in building their own unit (0604 858090 or stamped addressed envelope to Steve Hunt, 21 Green Street, Milton Malsor, Northampton NN7 3AT).

"ONE HOUR" TRANSMITTERS

In *TT* (April 1981, p333) I included some extracts from a letter that Al Rechner, VK5EK had written to the Australian *Amateur Radio* (February 1981, p38). In this he commented on designs for 5W cw solidstate QRP transmitters containing almost 100 components as "a stunning example of solid-state technology gone berserk . . . If we are trying to overcome the black box syndrome by inducing people to build their own equipment, then we will maximize our chances of success by presenting simple, cheap projects. Good applied engineering is concerned primarily with securing a good design objective in the simplest and cheapest manner."

With his letter, he presented an alternative design for a 5W crystal-controlled 3·5/7MHz transmitter based on a single triode-pentode valve (eg ECL82, ECL84, ECL85 or ECL86) as co-pa using only about 20 components and which he claimed could be built in about an hour or so yet would do substantially the same job as the 100-component solidstate transmitter.

Seven years later I was interested to note a basically similar valve design (Figs 9, 10), with some useful additions, described by Paul Harrison, G4VAM in *Sprat* (Journal of the QRP Club, Summer 1988, p11) as the "Car-boot-sale special". His title derived from the fact that the valve, the mains transformer and the smoothing capacitor had all been salvaged from an old tape recorder bought at a car-boot sale for 50p. With an ECL86 valve it provides some 6W output on 1·8MHz, about 5W on 3·5 or 7MHz, 4W on 10·1MHz and a modest 1·5W on 14MHz. He uses negative block keying to provide a crisp clean note. With 4 to 6W output, such a rig (even with a modest antenna) is capable of providing plenty of good 100-per-cent contacts at first-hop ranges.

TWO-TERMINAL KALLIROTRON OSCILLATOR

A rewarding result of delving back into early valve circuitry is that one stumbles across ideas that could be readily adapted to mosfet semiconductors – apart from the pleasure to be derived from hunting down the origins of an interesting circuit. *TT* (August) showed, with the help of a number of readers, that the push-pull 'kallitron' oscillator stems from "The Kallirotron, an aperiodic negative-resistance triode combination" by L. B. Turner, published in *The Radio Review* (Vol 1, No 7, April 1920. This journal was later renamed *The Wireless Engineer* and continued to be published by Iliffe's until the 1950s. The merits of the kallirotron circuit, later corrupted (by mistake?) to 'kallitron', as a variable push-pull oscillator, were later stressed, as noted in the July *TT*, by Herbert J. Reich in *Proc IRE*, November 1937.

I recently tracked down in the Science Museum Library, the original paper by Turner which, incidentally, explains that 'kallirotron' pronounced with the second syllable accented, vowel short, is derived from Καλλξροοτ, the Greek word meaning 'easy flowing'. In his introduction, L. B. Turner notes that: "In a recent triode invention known as the 'Dynatron' (A. W. Hull, *Proc IRE*, February 1918) by virtue of the phenomenon of copious emission of secondary corpuscles from a plate under sufficiently violent bombardment by primary corpuscles, the same negative resistance effect is obtained in quite another way (than by exalting the amplifying action of a triode by introducing magnetic or electric retroaction). The dynatron, being applicable to circuits containing resistance only, as well as to oscillatory circuits, is competent to reduce indefinitely the impedance of a circuit for currents of any frequency, including even steady current.

"The arrangement to be described here consists of a combination of circuits, which may be aperiodic, including two ordinary triodes in which secondary emission plays no part, whereby electrical resistance is annihilated – the result achieved in the dynatron by dependence on secondary emission."

It is also clear that Turner foresaw numerous applications, apart from its use as a limiter-amplifier. A short Section 8, headed 'Kallitorton as oscillator', was as follows:

"Any negative-resistance device can obviously be used to produce sustained oscillation. One simple arrangement is that shown in Fig 11 ►

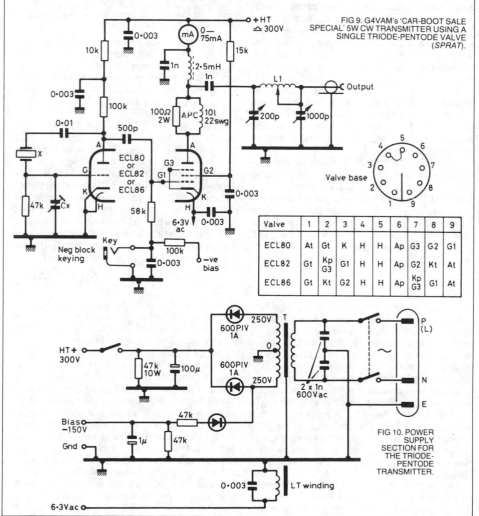

FIG 9. G4VAM's 'CAR-BOOT SALE SPECIAL' 5W CW TRANSMITTER USING A SINGLE TRIODE-PENTODE VALVE (*SPRAT*).

Valve	1	2	3	4	5	6	7	8	9
ECL80	At	Gt	K	H	H	Ap	G3	G2	G1
ECL82	Gt	Kp G3	G1	H	H	Ap	G2	Kt	At
ECL86	Gt	Kt	G2	H	H	Ap	Kp G3	G1	At

FIG 10. POWER SUPPLY SECTION FOR THE TRIODE-PENTODE TRANSMITTER.

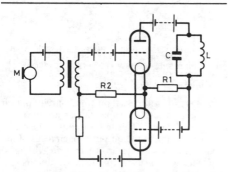

FIG 11. THE ORIGINAL 1920 'KALLIROTRON' (EASY FLOWING) OSCILLATOR/TRANSMITTER AS DESCRIBED BY L. B. TURNER.

where the circuit *LC* begins to oscillate with approximately its own independent frequency as soon as the retroaction (ie positive feedback – G3VA) has been increased sufficiently to reduce the resistance of its action below zero. Where such an oscillator is to be used for wireless telephony, speech control can be effected by a microphone M and transformer, the secondary of the latter being conveniently inserted between either grid and its resistance *r*." But note well that *TT* does not recommend the use today of a 1920 modulated power oscillator producing a mixture of a.m. and fm!

Isaac Lederer, ORS87664 has drawn attention not only to Reich's 1937 *Proc IRE* paper but also to a modified 'Two-terminal push-pull oscillator' described by E. J. Cuddy in *Electronics* (August 1955). This begins: "Of the many types of two-terminal oscillators in use at the present time, the Kallitron has the advantage of push-pull action. This circuit has one drawback, however; the fact that the tank is at dc plate potential and not easily adapted to use with the usual tuning capacitor.

"One possibility is an arrangement such as shown in Fig 12 (a). When the circuit is redrawn as in Fig 12 (b) it is seen to be a bridge-type circuit balanced with respect to the tank until oscillation starts. This conformation has another

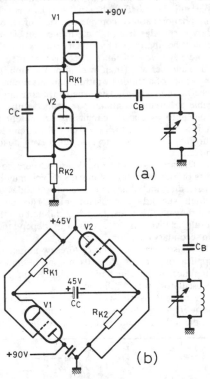

FIG. 12. (a) THE TWO-TERMINAL PUSH-PULL OSCILLATOR DERIVED FROM THE 'KALLITRON' OSCILLATOR BY E. J. CUDDY IN 1955. (b) REDRAWN TO SHOW THE BRIDGE CONFIGURATION. THE CIRCUIT COULD BE READILY ADAPTED FOR FET DEVICES.

advantage over the usual push-pull circuit in that the tube grid-to-plate capacitances are in parallel across the tank. This tends to lower the effect of any variation in the output capacitances of the tubes with a change in their grid voltages. Capacitor Cb is used to block dc and is not critical although it should have only a small impedance at the lowest frequency used. Cc should offer a low impedance at the frequency

HINTS

Geoff Bagley, G3FHL offers a useful tip on tuning capacitors for stable variable frequency oscillators. He writes: "Most single-ended variable capacitors have some form of wiping contact to short out any resistance, which may fluctuate, in the bearings. Both the contact resistance of the bearings and the wiping contact springs may exhibit unstable contact resistance, be it only a fraction of an ohm. This is often a source of flicker-noise since it carries the main circulating current of the vfo tank circuit. The problem is avoidable by using a small twin-gang variable as a split-stator capacitor. The path of the main circulating current now lies along the solid shaft of the variable capacitor and there is no fluctuating contact resistance in series with the oscillating current."

G3FHL has also been considering the potential use of copper-foil adhesive tape for winding stable inductors: "I obtained some tape from RS Components (512-266) and its width (10mm) should ensure a good Q factor. It can also be silver plated for reduced rf ohmic losses. A further advantage: the windings won't slip."

Electrolube, makers of contact lubricants, point out that even keeping contact surfaces clean and dry does not necessarily remove the problems of noise caused by high contact resistance in switches. Four main factors influence contact resistance: contact surface condition, contamination, frettage and contact bounce. A contact lubricant evens out the peaks and troughs of the contact surface, thus increasing the contact surface area. This in turn reduces contact resistance, minimises the formation of hot spots and reduces surface deformation due to friction wear. Lubrication also reduces the effects of arcing since the lubricant forms a bridge between the partially-open contacts to prevent current concentration of the contact-surface peaks and thus reduces current flow on switching more gradually.

John Greenwell, G3AEZ draws attention to 'Metashrink MSB' a lay-flat pvc with an aluminium outer skin forming a shrinkable tubing intended for such applications as rfi/emc shielding. According to the stockist (Bowman Electronics Plc, Europa Trading Estate, Fraser Road, Erith, Kent DA8 1QL, tel 03224-38182) this can be used as an inexpensive outer shield on cables and as an inner shield for wire termi-

nation within connectors; it can apparently also be used to reduce emission from small pcbs – and conversely improve their immunity to rfi. The shrinkable tubing is supplied in six 'lay-flat' widths from 10 to 100mm. Shrink temperature is 98°C with a shrink ratio of 2·5:1. It is not clear if such sheets are available in quantities and prices geared to amateur budgets.

To add to the earlier suggestions on how to feed 12V equipment from 24-28V vehicle batteries (*TT*, March 1988, p182), G B Wolfe in *Electronics Australia* notes that it is possible to obtain a voltage-regulated supply at up to 10A by using two 78H12A three-terminal TO-3 ic regulators (Fig 13) provided that low-value

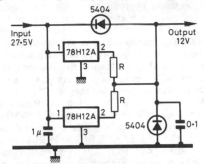

FIG 13. ARRANGEMENT PROVIDING 12V AT UP TO 10A FROM 27·5V VEHICLE BATTERY. NOTE THAT EFFICIENCY OF ALL SUCH ARRANGEMENTS WILL BE LESS THAN 50 PER CENT. (*ELECTONICS AUSTRALIA*).

resistors R are used to ensure equal sharing of the load. His resistors were each made from a piece of toaster-element 0·5-in in length. To the ends of these he crimped lengths of thick copper wire to form pigtails for connecting into circuit. For heavy current loads the regulators need to have good heatsinking.

On the same topic, Christopher Henn-Collins, GU5ZC has often used an arrangement similar to Fig 6 of the March *TT* but adds a further suggestion: "Put a car/truck bulb, with a current rating appreciably greater than that required by the load, in series with the collector of the power transistor (2N3055). In normal use its resistance is low and the bulb does not light. Under fault conditions, it lights and saves the power pack. I have also found the idea useful with car-battery chargers saving short-circuit problems and rectifier burn outs."

AND TIPS

of oscillation. However, it may be replaced by a series-resonant circuit. For fixed frequency operation this may be a crystal used at its series-resonant frequency. Rk1 and Rk2 should be approximately the recommended cathode bias resistors for class A operation . . . The most important factor contributing to good frequency stability and low harmonic content seems to be the class A mode of operation. The simplest method found for adjusting the circuit to these conditions was variation of the plate voltage. This makes it simple to adjust for each range when switching bands, by means of a series resistor simultaneously cut into the plate circuit.

"As in other types of oscillators, a high tank *Q* seems to increase frequency stability but some low-Q tank circuits were made to operate in a

satisfactory manner by adjustment of the plate voltage. Loading of the tuned circuit can be prevented by taking the output from the cathode of V2 when amplitude is not important.

"When tried in a superhet receiver this oscillator worked well from 500kHz to 15MHz and over the vhf/fm band using a 7F8 duotriode. It was also possible to use it as a locked oscillator by feeding a signal between the cathode of V2 and ground, as long as the method of coupling did not interfere with normal circuit action. With an antenna attached at the cathode of V2 and a load in the plate circuit between V1 and ht+, a stable regenerative receiver was formed. By inserting the correct RC combination between the grid of V2 and ground it is possible to obtain superregenerative action with this same arrangement . . ."

TECHNICAL TOPICS

PAT HAWKER · G3VA

LOW COST SYSTEMS
AID THE THIRD WORLD

Technical Topics (July 1988) recalled how a combination of professional engineers and amateurs was responsible for the development and widespread introduction of carrier-suppressed hf ssb, not only on the amateur bands but also profoundly influenced the course of mobile radio generally: "the amateurs, initially in the USA but soon world-wide, truly blazed the way for the general adoption of the suppressed carrier form of ssb." But that was 40 years ago. Can amateur radio still contribute usefully to the far more sophisticated radio scene today?

My answer would be yes, although perhaps not in quite the same way. Today, the need in many parts of the world is not for the latest 'new technology' systems but for low-cost, thin-line communications. There are vast areas of Africa, for example, where virtually the only way of getting a message to a village, a few miles away, is to take it in person or find a runner. No telephones, no regular postal services – and little of the hard-currency needed to buy, install and maintain the advanced telecommunication services that we take for granted. Even in the UK there are situations where better communications are needed but are ruled out by the cost of the equipment. The amateur is still in a position to try out and develop new ideas in advance of the necessarily more cautious large organisations.

In recent months, several innovative, ongoing projects have come to my notice involving radio amateurs aiming at reducing the cost of radio services or establishing new systems.

(1) At a recent IEE conference on rural telecommunications, Dr S A G Chandler, G3UDD of Warwick University, described a project now being implemented in Sierra Leone. This will eventually provide more than a thousand communal 'village' radiophones based on 27MHz cb-type transceivers under microprocessor control and powered by solar arrays: Fig 1. The control units provide selective calling and automatically close down the network overnight as well as providing remote monitoring, performance logging and supervision of the power system. Cost of a complete terminal station is just £304 plus transport costs, the most expensive item being the microprocessor control unit (£110). The villagers, themselves, are shown how to use the equipment and carry out simple repairs and have shown enthusiasm at being personally involved. The cb antenna is erected on a bamboo pole.

(2) In Cornwall, Lionel Sear, G3PTT has shown, with the help of a few other amateurs, that low-cost cb equipment plus a long-length of 75-ohm twin-feeder (terminated with a 75-ohm resistor) can form a poor man's 'leaky-cable' system for underground communications in support of small, cost-conscious mining operations (described in *Mining Magazine*, August 1988, pp110-111). While such a system would not be applicable to underground coal-mining (on

grounds of safety), G3PPT believes that the principle, which has been tested with cb equipment modified for use in the 28MHz band, should be of interest to the small mine, decline or tunnelling operations and would be cheap enough for the speleologist. He notes that the DTI is willing to consider varying the terms of the standard 27MHz cb licence to allow experiments with underground communications.

(3) At the rural telecommunications conference it was disclosed that the next University of Surrey UoSAT, due to be launched early next year, will use 'experimental' as well as amateur frequencies in order to permit demonstrations of third-world commercial applications of low-earth-orbit satellites operating in a store-and-forward mode using the AX-25 'packet' protocol, as already tested by amateurs on the present UoSAT etc. It would make possible a global electronic mail service permitting messages from remote areas to be delivered overnight virtually anywhere in the world at costs far below those normally associated with satellite communications systems. The earth terminals would cost from about £2000 to £10,000. The paper by Dr Martin Sweeting, G3YJO and Jeff Ward (former ARRL staff member and now part of the UoS team) points out that "it is well within the current state-of-the-art to build a portable, solar-powered terminal using a lap-top portable computer, a 10-watt vhf transceiver, a single-

channel uhf receiver, and collapsible vertical or helical antennas all capable of fitting into a suitcase, and invaluable to technical, agricultural or medical workers who need to communicate with their support bases from remote, rural areas."

Rag Otterstad, LA5HE/OZ8RO draws attention to a six-page article 'A worldwide packet radio network' by Cmdr R. E. Bruninga, USN, in the American military-communications journal *Signal* (June 1988). This traces the rapid growth since 1983 of AX.25 packet radio communications on hf/vhf/satellite networks now amounting to some 40,000 nodes worldwide, the number roughly doubling every six months for five years. These networks are, of course, the amateur-radio networks and their digirepeaters. Packet-switching techniques were originally developed by computer/telecommunications experts for line telecommunications networks. Amateurs were the first to adapt the X.25 protocol for hf/vhf radio circuits and it is only recently that the idea is being taken up by the American and British armed services. Amateurs were aided by the collective efforts of "a number of leading hardware and software engineers and communications professionals unbounded by fiscal, budgetary, political and bureaucratic limitations of government. Often overlooked are a number of unique characteristics that frequently make the amateur radio service a seed-bed in ▶

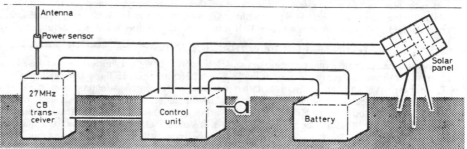

FIG 1. A VILLAGE TERMINAL IN THE SIERRA LEONE LOW-COST RURAL TELECOMMUNICATIONS PROJECT BEING IMPLEMENTED WITH THE ASSISTANCE OF DR S A G CHANDLER, G3UDD/9L1SC OF THE UNIVERSITY OF WARWICK.

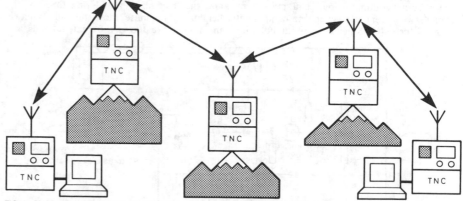

FIG 2. CMDR BRUNINGA, USN, IN SHOWING HOW RADIO AMATEURS HAVE RAPIDLY DEVELOPED A PIONEERING WORLD-WIDE PACKET-RADIO NETWORK SHOWS A TYPICAL ARRANGEMENT FOR A STATION-TO-STATION PACKET RADIO CIRCUIT THROUGH THREE REPEATER NODES SPANNING FROM 200 TO 600 MILES. THE CIRCUIT IS ROUTED AUTOMATICALLY THROUGH INTERMEDIATE NODES AS NECESSARY.

the development and demonstration of new technology".

Cmdr Bruninga, who is Project Manager for the Integrated Communications System/ Shipboard Communications Area Network (ICS/SCAN) shows how AX-25 techniques are now being adopted by the US Navy. He lists among the amateurs' unique characteristics: frequency agility; quality of service; ability to use many modes; flexibility ("the amateur radio user abhors fixed, centralised, vulnerable, high cost, critical hardware"); dependence on hf ("the amateur community probably holds the greatest expertise in the art of real time hf communications"); state-of-the-art "usually a communications technique is tried out first on the amateur bands. Many of the leading communications engineers and professionals in both academics and industry are radio amateurs anxious to try out their ideas before committing them to corporate investment. There is no greater motivation for excellence and productivity than working for one's self towards one's own imaginative goals".

THE TONSCHREIBER "B" TAPE RECORDER

Most of us accept the magnetic tape recorder in its various forms as a standard consumer-electronics product, both for entertainment and for its various applications to amateur radio, including the recording of meteor-scatter morse bursts for replay at slower speed. Home recording has never been easier, with DAT (digital audio tape) yet to come. It was not always so. I recall my first attempts, in collaboration with Charles Bryant, GW3SB, using blank aluminium discs which then had to be replayed with fibre needles with appalling signal-to-noise (or sometimes noise-to-signal) ratios.

Magnetic recording was first invented by the Dane, Valdemar Poulsen as long ago as 1901

and was revived in the 1930s in the form of the steel tape Blattnerphon/Marconi-Stille machines, still remembered by old-time broadcast engineers for their very dangerous cutting edge when anything went wrong. But the wartime reports, for example, of Wilfrid Vaughan-Thomas made over Berlin in a Lancaster bomber by Reg Pidsley, G6PI were on wind-up disc-cutting machines. The Americans developed the short-lived magnetic wire-recorders in the early 'forties (I first came across these being used for telephone surveillance in 1945); they were also used as part of the airborne Joan-Eleanor vhf clandestine 250MHz r/t links with OSS agents in Germany in the closing stages of the war in Europe. In those days high-speed morse was recorded on paper tape by the ink-pen of an 'undulator'.

The use of coated plastic tape and high-frequency biasing to achieve good linearity were both German developments. Telefunken demonstrated a domestic "magnetophon" recorder at a pre-war Berlin Radio Show but their first extensive use was by the German armed services for telephone monitoring during the second world war. A special model developed by AEG-Telefunken was to prove the "parent" of the domestic tape recorder (captured machines were taken to the UK and the USA for thorough examination and led directly to the early British and American tape decks of about 1948). My first encounter with the truly-remarkable "Tonschreiber b" was in 1945. One of these had been acquired along with other German military radio equipment, by colleagues in Special Communications including Roy

PHOTO: THE GERMAN MAGNETIC TAPE RECORDER USED FOR MONITORING IN THE SECOND WORLD WAR WAS NOT ONLY ANOTHER EXAMPLE OF THE EXCELLENCE OF THEIR MECHANICAL DESIGN BUT PROVIDED THE INSPIRATION FOR THE POST-WAR DOMESTIC MACHINES (PHOTO PAoSE).

Wilkins, G2ALM and the late John Bowers, ex-G4NY. It was used mostly for entertainment purposes but also to record some cw signals in which we were interested.

Dick Rollema, PA0SE (whose *Reflecties door PA0SE* column in *Electron* (VERON) has just celebrated its 200th appearance!) has contributed a detailed article on the Tonschreiber b in the July 1988 issue of *CQ* (English text) based on a machine in immaculate condition that forms part of the magnificent collection of German second world war communication equipment of Arthur Bauer, PA0AOB. The machine can still record and replay on standard ¼" tape, although it uses dc rather than rf biasing.

Tape drive is by a synchronous motor fed from a powerful valve-type audio generator providing about 20watts output on frequencies of 22, 32, 44, 63, 88, 125, 175 and 292Hz to give no less than nine tape speeds. A dc motor on the same shaft, controlled manually, brings up the speed until the synchronous motor locks and takes control. Fast morse is recorded with a high audio tone permitting replay at slower speeds. Perhaps the most interesting feature of this machine was the 'Dehner' (stretcher) drum carrying four heads which can be rotated in such a way that when a speech recording is replayed at lower tape speed, the relative velocity of the head in contact with it is similar to the recording speed; thus the speech is slowed down without affecting the pitch of the voice – a facility that has been possible by purely electronic means only within the past few years. On the Tonschreiber, speech played out at only quarter the recording speed is still intelligible, as PA0AOB demonstrated to PA0SE.

NO MORE MAGNETIC REF?

At the 1988 National Radio Science Colloquium of URSI, held at King's College, London (which

---

SIMPLE QUIET-TUNING FOR 100W TRANSCEIVERS

In discussing the Australian quiet tune-up device with an swr resistive bridge, reference was made (*TT*, February 1988) to the alternative, rather simpler, approach described earlier by Les May, G4HHS ('safe tune-up with the FT7', *Rad Com*, August 1981, p715). This had been based on a design in the ARRL's *Solid-state for the radio amateur*. Unlike the Australian design, this does not give a direct swr reading but is rather simpler to implement (especially for those who already have a suitable dummy load and built-in or external swr meter). However, the component ratings of the G4HHS device were intended for

low-power (10W) transmitters such as the FT7.

Alf Heinrich, DL1BT (*cq-DL*, 6/88, p357) in 'Einfache Stummabstimmung fuer die 100W Urlaubsstation' describes an adaption of this arrangement for higher-power transceivers: Fig 3. It similarly allows the antenna to be matched to the transmitting without radiating more than about 0·5W. In effect, a Wheatstone-bridge (which could be integrated within the atu) and dummy load is switched between the transceiver and the 'matchbox' atu during tune-up, thus helping to minimise those tune-up 'squawks' that remain a feature of the amateur bands.

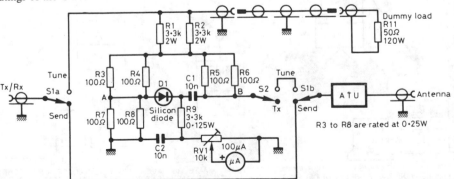

FIG 3. THE DL1BT QUIET-TUNING BRIDGE ENABLES 100W TRANSCEIVERS TO BE TUNED UP AND MATCHED TO ANTENNA WHILE RADIATING ONLY ABOUT 0·5-WATT.

---

has numbered amongst its professors Sir Charles Wheatstone, James Clerk Maxwell and Sir Edward Appleton), Dr W. F. Stuart of the British Geological Survey warned that the Government-funded scientists and technicians, who maintain the data bases on radio and geophysical phenomena on which the radio sciences, radio communications and navigation ultimately depend, are facing a financial crisis. Funding of 'routine' work of collecting and distributing geomagnetic and ionospheric data is in direct competition with what are seen as new and more 'exciting' scientific projects.

In a letter to *The Times* (15 June, 1988) Dr Stuart warned of the consequences that will follow within the next few years if, as seems possible, the magnetic reference may no longer be available for navigation in and around the British Isles: charts, Ordnance Survey maps, air traffic lanes, beacons, and runway approach plates will not be able to include an up-to-date, accurate magnetic reference.

Solar-terrestrial monitoring has been at the heart of the identification of the 'greenhouse effect', the 'ozone hole', the solar cycle, the solar winds, the Earth's fluid core, etc. The problem is not confined to the UK: cut-backs in monitoring projects have been reported from Canada and New Zealand.

CUTTING THE COST

For many years, Doug De Maw, W1FB has been encouraging the readers of *QST* to build simple equipment. Now in 'semi-retirement' he writes to *Ham Radio* (August 1988) about the high cost of entry to the hobby and to plead for simpler, lower-cost transceivers. Noting that hf transceivers are now priced at up to about $6000, with even the bottom of the scale about $1000, he comments:

"It is not difficult to visualise the shock coefficient associated with a teenager asking his parents to finance a new transceiver . . . I rebel against the cost of the new amateur equipment . . . What has been needed in the United States for a long time is a no-frills cw/ssb transceiver. Maximum output power 100 watts is adequate. It would not contain a speech processor, i.f shift or width circuit, nor would it need to have computer interface capability. A noise blanker is by no means a necessity since most blankers are ineffective for the more common types of QRN, and they degrade the receiver dynamic range when activated. I also question whether or not a basic rig needs memory channels and two internal vfo's . . . Someone needs to take the initiative towards encouraging the US and foreign manufacturers to develop a *practical* transceiver that can serve our basic operating needs – especially those of the Novice and other new amateurs . . . we need to get them started with the minimum of economic stress. Whatever happened to the concept of high volume and reduced per-unit-profit (shades of Henry Ford)? Small volume and high markups are not in the best interests of amateur radio."

In the early 1980s, the Japanese manufacturers, guided by sales and market research, decided there was little demand for basic transceivers; everyone seemed to want rigs with all possible bells and whistles. An American visitor told me: "The hobby is being changed out of all recognition by amateurs having too much money or too easy access to credit."

DESIGNING LINEARS FOR LOW POWER DRIVE

As a series of *TT* items over the past few months have indicated, low-cost, high-power linear amplifiers can be put together without undue difficulty using a few PL519/PL509 television 'sweep' valves, which are still available with their B9D bases for about £5 new. But some readers may scorn this approach which inevitably results in relatively high inter-electrode capacitances and hanker after an amplifier using a single modern transmitting valve, although these do not come cheaply unless they are secondhand ex-equipment valves of uncertain provenance – and the same goes for the special bases they need.

In the United States, under FCC regulations brought in many years ago to discourage kilowatt 'after-burners' being added to 27MHz cb rigs, linear amplifiers may not be supplied with the 28MHz band wired, and similarly, it is forbidden to market 1kW-class amplifiers designed to be driven by an exciter or transmitter delivering less than 50 watts. The result is that the vast majority of factory-built linear amplifiers are designed for use with 100-watt 'black box' transceivers. Were it not for the FCC regulations significantly lower levels of drive would be technically feasible.

In *QST* (August 1988) Dick Stevens, W1QWJ describes the home-construction of a six-band, grounded-grid, single-valve amplifier capable of delivering 750 watts output at 14MHz with less than 25 watts of drive; 440 watts with 10-watt drive; and 220 watts with about 5-watt drive. An attractive specification for anyone with a home-built or factory-built exciter in the low-power ranges.

There is a snag, the Eimac 3CX800A7 high-mu power triode and associated Eimac SK-1900 socket are clearly in an altogether different price category to the PL519, although it is claimed not so different from the prices being asked for much older transmitting valves and sockets at this power level.

Another interesting feature of W1QWJ's design is the use of a pi-L output network, capable of reducing harmonic output by about 15dB compared with the conventional pi-network, although it does mean that the 1000pF loading capacitor needs to cope with higher rf voltages, and in this design is rated at 1·5kV which adds to the cost. The result is a straightforward, clean-looking design, that has third order products about 42dB below the pep output, with fifth order about 51dB down.

RF CHOKE RESONANCES

For those who do not like the idea of having their pi-network output coil at high dc as well as high rf potential in the arrangements outlined in *TT* (April, July etc), there is little alternative to tackling the difficult problem of making your own custom-design rf choke that does not overheat, due to resonances on any of the bands you wish to use. In *QST* (June 1988, pp50-1),

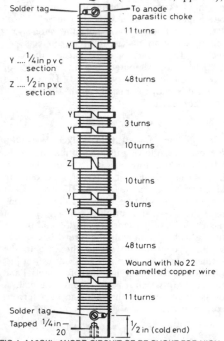

Solder tag
To anode parasitic choke
11 turns
Y .... ¼ in p v c section
48 turns
Z .... ½ in p v c section
3 turns
10 turns
10 turns
3 turns
48 turns
Wound with No 22 enamelled copper wire
11 turns
Solder tag
Tapped ¼ in – 20
½ in (cold end)

FIG 4. AA6GK's ANODE-CIRCUIT OF RF CHOKE FOR HIGH-POWER AMPLIFIERS AVOIDS RESONANCES ON MOST HF BANDS. BUT ALL SUCH CHOKES SHOULD PREFERABLY BE CHECKED *IN SITU* SINCE NEARBY METALWORK WILL SHIFT THE RESONANCE FREQUENCIES.

AA6GK outlines an rf choke design which he finds copes with the traditional five amateur hf bands plus 1·8MHz and 24MHz (although he still has some problems on 18MHz and does not mention 10·1MHz) at powers up to the full American legal limit: Fig 4. He emphasises the need to use a former having extremely good dielectric and thermal properties. He uses an 8" length of 1" diameter 'Delrin' rod (UK equivalent?) which has a 450°F melting point, an excellent dielectric constant and is easily machinable. Once the choke was completed he sprayed it with polyurethane varnish and baked it in an oven for 30 minutes at 150°F. Although Fig 4 shows his original arrangement using pvc sections between the windings, these tended to melt under the heat from his 4-1000 valve and he subsequently removed them and liberally applied some quick-curing ('five-minute') epoxy glue to the gaps.

On the same page of *QST* KH6CP warns that choke resonances should, wherever possible, be checked with the choke mounted where it is to be used, rather than away from the surrounding metal objects which shift the resonant frequencies.

One thing emerges clearly, it is far from easy to design a high-power rfc that will show no installed resonances within 20 per cent of any of the nine amateur bands from 1·8 to 30MHz – and that a design that suits one amplifier will not necessarily work without overheating in a different layout.

Peter Chadwick, G3RZP has pointed out that amateurs often overlook the fact that very high rf currents flow through the by-pass capacitor at the 'cold' end of the rf choke of a high-power pi-network – even with a low-voltage, solid-state amplifier.

MORE ON BATTERIES

The item in the August *TT* on exploding lithium batteries, has led to some confusion. There *is* a real problem in changing lithium memory-backup cells with some transceivers. But these two problems, fortunately, do not coincide. There is no risk of a cell designed as a memory back-up cell exploding as John Wilson, G3PCY/

5N2AAC of Lowe Electronics explains:

"I'm sure that the linkage between exploding batteries and memory backup in amateur equipment in *TT* was unintentional, but perhaps it is worth a further comment to reassure readers that there should be no danger of any damage whatsoever from memory backup cells.

"The type of cell used in most amateur radio

transceivers is the lithium-manganese dioxide cell designed to have a high internal resistance of about 200 ohms, which rises to several kilohms when the cell is shorted. The cells are designed to be wave-soldered into printed circuit boards which results in them being (temporarily) shorted out by the solder wave.

"The cells which may overheat when shorted

HINTS

When Evan Boden, N3DEO (QST, June 1988, p50) decided his alternative nicad battery pack for his handheld TR-2500 144MHz transceiver was *kaputt*, he separated the two halves of the plastic pack, removed the cells, pcb and miniature switch and then built into the container a dc adapter providing a regulated 9V source from the 12V cigarette-lighter socket of his vehicle electrics: Fig 5. The heat sink comprises a 1- x 2-in piece of ⅛-in-thick aluminium. Now he keeps his remaining good nicad pack for use when not in the car.

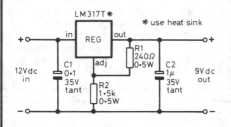

FIG 5. N3DEO BUILDS THIS ADAPTOR IN A DISCARDED NICAD BATTERY PACK TO PROVIDE A REGULATED 9V DC SOURCE FOR HIS TR-2500 HAND-HELD TRANSCEIVER WHEN IT IS OPERATED IN HIS CAR. HE USES A THIN MICROPHONE CABLE TO A FUSED CIGARETTE-LIGHTER SOCKET BUT LATER REALISED HE COULD HAVE LEFT THE BATTERY-PACK CHARGE CONNECTOR WITH A SUITABLE DC POWER PLUG ON THE ADAPTER END OF THE 12V CABLE. NOTE THAT THE LM317T'S MOUNTING TAG IS ELECTRICALLY CONNECTED TO ITS OUTPUT PIN AND MAY IN SOME CASES REQUIRE AN INSULATOR BETWEEN THE REGULATOR AND THE HEAT SINK.

● ● ● ● ● ● ●

At one time I used thermocouple rf meters to indicate the rf current flowing into the transmission line or long-wire antenna but soon found how easy it is to burn them out. Since then I have used a shunted torch bulb as a satisfactory substitute, suffering far less trauma when occasionally one is accidentally 'blown'. The lamp also scores over the meter in providing continuous visual reassurance from the operating position that all is working normally. Bill Orr, W6SAI (*Ham Radio*, July 1988, p60) quotes WoSVM for one version of this old dodge: "He shunts a No 47 pilot lamp (6-9V, 0·15A) with a 33ohm 1W resistor. This little assembly has

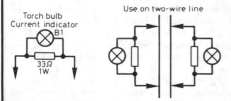

FIG 6. USING INEXPENSIVE PILO-LAMP BULBS AS RF CURRENT INDICATORS. CLIP ACROSS A FEW INCHES OF ANTENNA FEED-WIRE. VARY RESISTOR VALUE TO MATCH LINE CIRCUIT ETC.

copper alligator (crocodile) clips on it and he snaps it across a few inches of his feedline at his antenna tuner: Fig 6. He uses two of these gadgets for a two-wire line. Vary the tap spacing to accommodate your power level."

● ● ● ● ● ● ●

In addition to the papers in *IEE Conference Publication No 284* "HF radio systems & techniques", a further paper, providing more background information, on the SRI ctl and hla receiving loop antennas (*TT*, July 1988, pp520-1) appears in the 'special issue on short-wave broadcasting' of the *IEEE Transactions on Broadcasting* (June 1988, pp159-166) as 'Interference-reducing antennas for short-wave broadcast listeners' by Dr O G Villard, Jr. Incidentally, Mike Villard, W6QYT would be glad to correspond with amateurs who have built and used these antennas: his address is: Dr O G Villard, Jr, Senior Scientific Advisor, System Technology Division, SRI International, 333 Ravenswood Avenue, Menlo Park, CA94025, USA.

● ● ● ● ● ● ●

In connection with current work on the development of neural network computers (ie computers organised in much the same way as a brain) the US DARPA has estimated that the human brain contains 10^{11} neurons, each having roughly 1000 dendrites giving the brain a storage potential of 10^{14} interconnects. Nerves fire at 100Hz so a human brain (not mine surely) has the potential to make 10^{16} interconnects per second. This is far, far in advance of the Cray XMP1-2 supercomputer with its potential of 50×10^6 interconnects per second. Even a fly's brain, it is said, can manage some 10^9 interconnects per second.

● ● ● ● ● ● ●

A *QST* hint from Edwin Walker, WA4DFS suggests the following method of making small, adjustable coil formers: cut a short piece of heat-shrink tubing that is just large enough in diameter to pass a No4-40 or 6-32 screw. Coat the screw with silicone lubricant, slip the tubing over the screw and shrink the tubing. After it has cooled and hardened, wind the coil on the tubing without removing the screw. Use quick-setting epoxy glue to secure the wire to the former. Once the glue has set, you can adjust the inductance by varying the core material and the depth to which it is turned into the coil. A brass screw reduces the inductance; a ferrous core increases it.

● ● ● ● ● ● ●

Desmond Barry, G3ONU adding to the Collins saga notes that the KWM-2 was

announced from 15 October, 1959 to be succeeded by the KWM2-A a couple of years later. In September 1976, a Rockwell-Collins advertisement claimed that "in the last 15 years some 27,000 Collins KWM-2A units have been sold" – possibly a production record for a fully-valved hf transceiver. He still speaks highly of the Collins S-line with their good performance, good service manuals and requiring a minimum of test gear to maintain to specification. He adds: "It seems strange to me that so much new equipment suffers defect in design and/or production and how on earth does the average amateur know if his latest purchase meets its claimed specification? Having read "In Practice" in the July *Rad Com* why should the 20 manufacturers of the 20 commercially-built power amplifiers not be named so that they and RSGB members can take appropriate action? Does not the Society have a duty to those who have to suffer poorly designed and or manufactured equipment?" Perhaps the writer of "In Practice" feared the type of reaction I received after naming telephone apparatus in the August *TT*!

● ● ● ● ● ● ●

TT has recently shown several ways of powering 12V equipment from 24-28V vehicle batteries. W9OBG (*QST*, June 1988, p49) shows one way of powering 28V relays from a centre-tapped 12V power supply unit simply by adding two diodes: Fig 7. He adds: "Two addi-

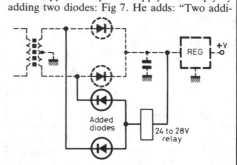

FIG 7. W9OBG'S METHOD OF POWERING 24-28V RELAYS FROM A CENTRE-TAPPED 9 OR 12V PSU SIMPLY BY ADDING TWO DIODES.

tional diodes furnish a negative voltage approximately equal in magnitude to the regulator's positive supply. The potential difference between the two supplies is about right for powering 24- to 28V relays. If the resulting voltage is too high, use a dropping resistor or try moving the positive end of the relay to the *output* of the positive regulator (if there is one in your circuit). Two warnings: (1) Both ends of the relay solenoid, and any associated switching lines, must be kept *above ground* to avoid short-circuiting the seondary of the power transformer. (2) This circuit cannot be used with a full-wave bridge supply."

AND TIPS

are probably the high-energy lithium thionyl chloride types, but these are not normally used for such light duty applications as memory backup, and would not be encountered in any amateur application. The cells certainly pack quite a punch, the 'D' size, 3·5-volt cell being 14Ah capacity with a continuous current rating of 10A. One can imagine the results of a short circuit."

I agree with G3PCY that memory-backup cells as found in amateur radio equipment incur no risk of explosion but I am a little unhappy at the suggestion that this applies to lithium-manganese cells in general, unless they have adequate built-in protection: see *TT*, November 1987, p834. Unprotected high-energy lithium-manganese cells can deliver many amperes of current and it was the risk of explosion when short-circuited that delayed their appearance on the consumer market for a number of years until cells with double or triple protection broke into the flash-camera market. These, of course do not have the high internal resistance of the memory cells.

While there is no danger in short-circuiting these memory cells for a short period, if done for a lengthy period it will of course exhaust the cell. In QST's *Hinks and Kinks* column (June 1988, p47) VE3HCD and WB3HAE describe how they accidentally plugged their memory back-up cell replacements into battery *dischargers*. Otto Cepella, VE3HCD writes:

"Recently, I purchased a pair of lithium cells for backing up cmos memory. Two ½-inch long radial leads protruded from each cell. To prevent the leads from shorting together against metallic objects in my junk box, I placed the cells, leads first, into the black conductive foam I use to protect static-sensitive integrated circuits. My haste to protect the cells resulted in their demise! . . . Antistatic foam isn't called 'conductive foam' for nothing. The resistance of the foam over a distance equivalent to the cell's lead spacing was about 500ohms. By the time it came to install one of the cells, its terminal voltage measured 0volts."

A similar experience was reported by WB3-HAE except that in his case the cell arrived in plastic foam and he left it in the packet for several weeks. The foam was conductive and his

'new' battery was dead before it was installed. David Newkirk, AK7M adds the note that it doesn't pay to put a powered-up pcb down on a piece of conductive foam; one of his friends had to replace a 40-pin microprocessor chip after doing this. It is not only conductive foam that one has to worry about; conductive plastic-bubble packing material can provide a leakage path.

In *QST* (June 1988, p50), Joe Mehaffey, K4IHP reports a problem on his 4½-year-old FT-980 transceiver (digital display garbage when the rig first switched on) which he traced to low voltage of the cpu memory battery (two AA cells). His recommendation: "Change your FT-980 memory backup battery about every three years, and you'll avoid experiencing this sort of problem."

Hazards arising from short-circuited batteries and low-voltage, high-current power supply units are not confined to lithium cells. *TT* has referred on several occasions to the dangers arising from wearing rings or metal watchstraps while working on 12V solid-state transceivers etc. Very serious burns can result if the metal gets across the supply and rapidly heats up. It has also been pointed out previously that a short-circuited nicad battery can cause a fire or even an explosion. This is underlined in a letter from Ian Barnes in *Practical Wireless* (September 1988, p15) who carried home in his car a spare battery pack for his FT-23R in his wife's shopping bag, where the unprotected contacts came into contact with some silver foil. By the time he had reached home the area around the contacts had melted with the heat, and the complete case and nicad cells were ruined. The battery pack burnt through the shopping bag, fortunately without causing a fire as could easily have happened. He believes the manufacturers of battery packs should add thermal cut-outs or a slide-on plastic cover, or at least provide a printed warning drawing attention to the danger. The Editor of *PW* adds a warning that considerable respect should be paid to all forms of storage batteries: "I even protect the terminals of dry cells if carrying them loose. Though there may not be enough power to start a fire, they're too expensive to risk flattening them by shorting across the terminals."

Incidentally when Duracell recently closed a watch-battery making plant with the loss of 350 jobs, the management claimed this was because their batteries were lasting too long. Reminds me of the story that in the 1940s, British battery manufacturers were most reluctant to change from cylindrical-cell ht batteries to layer batteries, and the more recent complaint by UNESCO that they have experienced problems in developing a low-cost solar-powered radio receiver for Third World countries because of lack of co-operation from specialised plastics firms associated with battery manufacturers. ∎

SULPHATION OF LEAD-ACID BATTERIES

The conventional lead-acid vehicle battery has acquired the reputation of staying in good shape for only a few years. As noted on previous occasions in *TT*, one of the main problems is sulphation although it is sometimes possible to revive – at least temporarily – an apparently dead battery by using Glauber's salt provided that the procedure given in *TT*, December 1984, p1057 is carefully followed.

An interesting letter in *Electronics Australia* (June 1988, pp6-7, 145) from Frank Walker suggests that the best form of protection against sulphation is to keep the battery fully charged at all times. He writes:

"A fully charged battery has a positive plate of lead dioxide and a negative plate of lead, both in finely-divided form. On discharge the negative plate reacts with the sulphate ions of the sulphuric acid electrolyte to give lead sulphate, whilst the lead dioxide is reduced to lead on the positive plate and water is generated at the same time. When fully discharged, the negative plate

is now finely-divided lead sulphate, the positive plate is fine lead and the electrolyte is weaker. When we re-charge the battery all this is reversed . . .

"If the battery is left in a discharged state for some time, a problem occurs. Lead sulphate is very slightly soluble in sulphuric acid. It will dissolve and slowly re-crystallise on the negative plate, but this time in large crystals which do not react easily with the hydrogen during the charging process. This re-crystallising is helped by the normal day-to-day temperature fluctuations, as lead sulphate is more soluble at higher temperatures. A further problem is the mechanical effect of the growing crystals which tend to loosen portions of the plate material.

"This change from finely-divided lead sulphate to big crystals in a partially or fully discharged battery is the process generally called 'sulphation'. What can be done about it? Once it has occurred it is almost irreversible. Certainly any mechanical damage cannot be repaired. A

very long, very slow trickle-charge may restore some capacity but this will only put off the evil day for a short time . . . I once tried the wartime dodge of using sodium solution (Glauber's salts) on a motor-cycle battery and restored some capacity but it eventually shorted out due to the mechanical damage to the plate.

"Prevention is the only way. Keep the battery fully charged at all times. Even a partly discharged battery will undergo some sulphation. If the battery is to be left unused for a time, regular top-ups of charge or a very small trickle charge is necessary, because internal leakage will gradually discharge the battery, even if it is disconnected. A figure as high as 1% of charge per day has been quoted for this."

In view of the number of amateurs who use vehicle batteries, not only for mobile operation but also for use in the shack, this advice should help prolong the life of their batteries. Then if they do fail, it it worth giving them a dose of Glauber's salts.

TECHNICAL TOPICS

PAT HAWKER · G3VA

SOLDERING – THE BASIC CRAFT

Being myself an abuser rather than a user of tools, I still recall with admiration an excellent series of articles 'In the workshop' by Donex (the late Ken Alford, G2DX) in the *RSGB Bulletin* back in 1950, introduced as follows: "It has long been considered a fundamental principle of Amateur Radio that every enthusiast should be capable of constructing the apparatus used in his or her station, even if, in practice, commercial equipment is employed . . . It is in the field of construction and practical design that the amateur still possesses one great advantage over his professional colleague: he is not constantly confronted with the necessity of cutting down the time spent on production in order to reduce labour costs . . . There still remains almost unlimited opportunities in the development of amateur equipment; for example, full advantage is not yet being taken of the wide range of miniaturised components now available, perhaps because of the additional skill in construction . . . So before the amateur can establish a tradition of craftsmanship – and that surely should be his aim – it is necessary to acquire a sound knowledge of the fundamental processes involved in the construction of radio equipment: the use and care of tools; the handling of metal; tapping; soldering; and the basic elements of sound workshop practice."

Donex devoted his second article (February 1950) entirely to "the technique of soldering"– still the most important workshop skill needed by everyone from practical experimenter and designer, through kit construction to the all-factory-built-equipment installer. But although the basics of soldering electronic components has remained unchanged since 1950, the introduction of printed component boards and heat-sensitive and current-leakage sensitive semiconductors, wave-soldering techniques in commercial production, etc has changed the emphasis and increased the degree of skill involved. Yet even today, intermittent faults arising from 'dry joints' remain a common problem.

In his 1985 book *Soldering and Brazing*, "Tubal Cain" (Tom Walshaw, ex-G2PI) notes that soldering electronic equipment differs from the fabrication of engineering models, etc: "First, the parts are small, often very small indeed. Second, the components are, in the main, very vulnerable to heat. Thirdly, the slightest trace of corrosion will almost certainly cause failure of the device after a while. Finally, stray electric currents can damage many of the devices used, and as no electric soldering iron operating at mains voltages is entirely free from leakage this may cause problems. . . .

"Corrosion is avoided by using nothing but resin flux and the special 'electronics grade' cored solder for all joints. Active flux should never be needed, as the component terminations are almost universally treated to make them easily 'wetted' by solder . . . Bear in mind that there are few joints which will *never* need 'unsol-

dering'. It is a golden rule that where possible all wires and terminations should 'stay put by themselves' before soldering, but to crimp over a wire end to a perforated tag (etc) is asking for trouble later . . . A small but hot soldering bit must be used, so that the joint can be made very quickly, prolonged application of heat may ruin the component . . . For pcbs a fine bit may be necessary with nothing larger than 22 gauge flux-cored solder. For components *very* sensitive to heat (transistors, diodes, ic devices etc) use a

heat shunt. This may require three hands, and proper clip-on heat sinks costing only a few pence (or made from spring brass) are a useful alternative.

"The most common fault is 'dry' joints, due to imperfect 'wetting' of the solder; such joints are the most common cause of 'noise' in electronic circuitry. 'Cold joints' in which the solder is rough and nobbly, caused as a rule by overworking the soldering iron, which should be hot enough (with the bit clean enough) to melt the

50MHz VCRI – A CASE HISTORY

Jerry Sanderson, G2DBT notes the recent *TT* references to the continuing problem of interference to the output of domestic video cassette recorders, and contributes a case-history of his experience of 50MHz breakthrough that affected two models: a Sanyo VTC-5000 (Betamax format); and Hitachi VT14E (VHS format). He writes:

"After reports from my neighbour of interference to his Hitachi vcr, I found that my own Sanyo model was also affected in the same way; this enabled me to get my own house in order first. My 50MHz transmissions caused breakthrough only on audio, and only on playback. I had no reported breakthrough on hf and only very low level interference on 144MHz which could be removed by removing the vcr antenna plug. There was no interference to vision on the associated tv set or to the record mode. The level of the audio breakthrough, although unintelligible, could be classed as *very* annoying, usually requiring abandoning the use of the vcr while transmitting on 50MHz.

"My transmitting set-up was as follows: (a) hf bands, 120watts to G5RV-antenna at a height of. 27ft; (b) 144MHz, FT290R plus 2N6084 home-made linear amplifier with bandpass clean-up filter and five-element Yagi antenna on rotator in roof-space; (c) 50MHz, TS10V hf transceiver with *Practical Wireless* transverter with 100MHz series pi-type trap filter in output feeding 20watt underrun 6146B valve linear amplifier with pi-tank network followed by a 100MHz coaxial-stub filter and a pi-type low-pass filter then three-element homebrew Yagi antenna with gamma matching at 30ft, designed from the NBS parameters (ARRL ·Handbook). Approximate distance from 50MHz antenna to Sanyo vcr 35ft, and to Hitachi vcr 60ft.

"My first efforts to cure the 50MHz audio breakthrough involved several types of filters: high-pass, braid-breaker (both capacitive and inductive), coax wound on RSGB toroid cores (10 turns to two cores) and toroid cores on the vcr mains lead while the other filters were tried. All to no avail. Transmitter output was carefully checked with a wavemeter but no spurious emissions were found between 1·5 and 250MHz; only the 50MHz carrier.

"These negative results suggested that the interfering signal was being picked up within the vcr (plastic case!). Not having a suitably large

metal box available, the vcr was completely encased in 450mm-wide aluminium kitchen foil. This completely cured the problem but only when the foil was earthed to the outer sleeve of the antenna socket at the rear of the vcr. If the foil were connected only to the base screen plate, the interference increased, suggesting that the foil then acted as antenna. A check with a multimeter showed that a very low resistance dc path existed between the two screens, but not at rf.

"A final cure was effected by strapping together the screened box behind the antenna input socket, the base plate and the screen over the tape-transport. This was done using the shortest possible lengths (3-4in) of braiding from an offcut of RG58U coaxial cable. Surprisingly, both recorders, although of different makers and formats, used very similar mechanical layouts and both suffered the same problems with their screens, with the result that the same cure worked for both. The Sanyo recorder was also modified by connecting a 470pF capacitor from the input of the audio-amplifier ic to earth. This was found necessary with the Hitachi recorder as the reduction of interference with the straps installed was already deemed sufficient, and there seemed no point in tempting fate!

"On both vcr's interference was reduced by about 90 per cent by the use of the straps; breakthrough could then be heard only faintly, during totally silent periods of a tape, whilst monitoring two feet from the loudspeaker. As a bonus, vision interference from the village overhead power distribution and the Eastleigh airport radar were also greatly reduced during replay."

An important lesson to be learned from this case history is the vital need, particularly at vhf and above, to ensure that all screens and shielding, including the shield of screened cables, really are at zero rf potential. This point was made in connection with cable booting in the April *TT* (p267) where Fig 8 shows clearly that any (drain) wire connecting a cable shield to the equipment 'chassis' will have an inductive reactance that results in rf voltages on the cable shielding, and hence radiating. It is worth keeping in mind that a straight 1in length of 23swg wire has an inductive reactance at 100MHz of about 16ohms.

solder wire almost instantaneously . . . Another fault is a 'burnt joint' due to applying the bit too long so that the copper foil parts from the pcb substrate. 'Solder bridges' where excess solder forms a conducting path between adjacent strips of foil can be removed (in the absence of a desoldering tool) by fluxing a piece of clean stranded wire (or better a piece of copper braiding from an offcut of coaxial cable) then heating the offending solder and applying the end of the stranded wire or braid."

Donex defined a 'dry joint' as one in which the solder is 'adhered' to the connection by a layer of undiffused resin, thereby introducing resistance into the circuit. "This can vary from a few to an infinite number of ohms. The main cause is an iron too cool or not applied long enough. The remedy is to locate the area of the fault and then reheat every joint in the neigbourhood with a hot, clean iron." In effect the solder must 'wet' to clean surfaces on both the wire and the termination in order to make an electrically good joint. The particular problem with 'dry' joints is that they may form a mechanically secure joint, with the electrical resistance showing up only intermittently.

Construction or servicing of pcbs calls for considerable skill and care in soldering. The use of a large (50-60watt) iron can cause blistering and damage to laminated boards and semiconductors. Use a low-wattage (under about 35W) iron with a small point or wedge bit and 60/40 resin-cored solder. Use the solder sparingly to avoid causing solder bridges which may prove difficult to clear. Other useful tools include a soft wire brush, a pair of diagonal wire cutters, a pair of long nose pliers, a small wire 'pick' (soldering aid), a needle point probe for circuit testing and a magnifying glass for detection of small cracks.

Be very careful, when removing faulty components from pcbs, not to cause breaks in the foil. Avoid applying excessive bending pressure to the boards as this may cause breaks in the foil. Make sure that any small particles of solder are not left sticking to the board. Remove such particles with a cloth dipped in solvent.

REDUCING SCREENED CABLE LEAKAGE

It has been noted several times in *TT* that the effective coverage of the outer copper braiding on typical television coaxial download cables has been progressively reduced in order to neutralise the rising cost of copper. This has relatively little effect on the performance of the cables as transmission lines but it does mean that many cables are 'leaky' in respect of their shielding properties, both ingoing and outgoing. The percentage coverage of the copper braid may now be only 60 per cent or less, although high-quality cables manufactured to meet milspec/defspec requirements may have a braid coverage of the order of 95 per cent or so. Coaxial cable may thus not be the optimum solution for use as a shielded cable when dealing with emc problems, for example radiation from or into digital equipment including home computers etc.

M.A. Sanders, G3CRH draws attention to an article 'Choosing a screen' by R.G. Sarney of Anixter UK Ltd (UK agents for Beldon cables) in an issue of the *Cable Buyers' Guide*. This notes that: "Digital computing devices are prone

SHORT LOADED HARMONIC DIPOLES

Gerald Stancey, G3MCK draws attention to an article 'Multi-band antennas using loading coils' by William J Lattin, W4JRW which appeared in *QST*, April 1961 (pp43, 148, 150). Although this was more than a quarter of a century ago, the information remains valid, fresh to many, and possibly of interest to those amateurs who have not the space available to put up resonant half-wave dipoles yet wish to use a co-ax feeder without requiring the use of an atu.

W4JRW recalled a Bureau of Standards Circular C74 *(Radio Instruments and Measurements)* first published in 1924 which showed that while the use of loading coils decreases the natural resonant frequency of antennas, it means that the harmonic frequencies are no longer integral multiples of the fundamental, as in the case of the conventional unloaded resonant antenna. An inductively loaded antenna also represents a higher Q system, decreasing the operational bandwidth over which an swr of, say, less than 2:1 can be achieved.

In his article, W4JRW showed that with careful placement of two 120µH loading coils (low-loss construction, close-wound with No 18 Nyclad wire on bakelite tubing 7/8in outside diameter, 14in long) it is possible to achieve a low swr on both the (American) 3·5 and 7MHz bands, with an overall span of around 80ft, without the use of 'tuned' traps.

For European operation, there is the problem that the optimum results achieved by W4JRW represented resonant frequencies more suited to the extended American (Region 2) bands (3·5-4·0MHz and 7·0-7·3MHz) than our restricted (Region 1) bands. However it would seem that with some experimentation, and parameters approximately as in Fig 1 (a), it should be possible to achieve a satisfactorily low swr over the Region 1 bands.

W4JRW stresses that: "There are no capacitors to break down as in traps and the 120µH coils have been used with a kilowatt transmitter input with no difficulty." He also adds: "We have not found any exact formulae to determine the relationship between the lengths of wire, loading coils and the two (resonant) frequencies. The antennas are very simple to adjust with a grid-dip meter coupled to a single-turn loop connected to the feed terminals, as quite small changes in the wire lengths result in appreciable

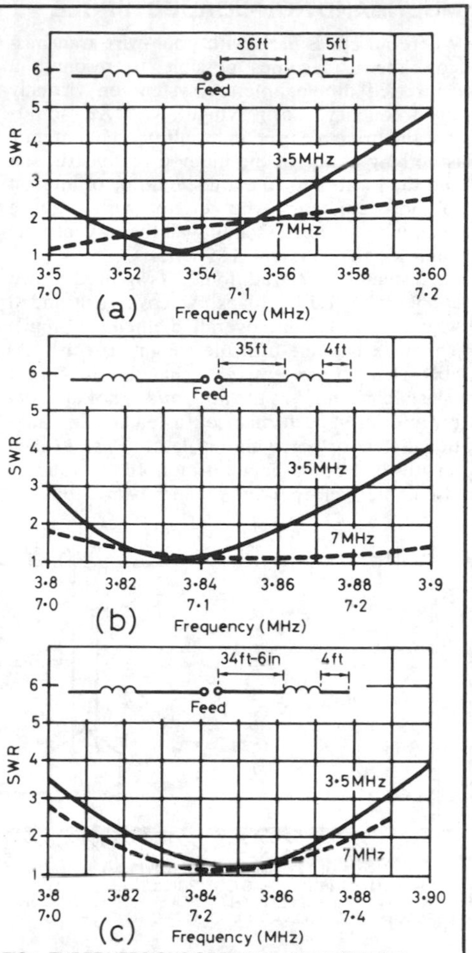

FIG 1. THREE VERSIONS OF THE W4JRW (1961) TWO-BAND LOADED DIPOLES USING TWO 120µH LOADING COILS (SEE TEXT), ILLUSTRATING THE EFFECT OF SMALL VARIATIONS IN THE DIMENSIONS.

in resonant frequencies.

"This principle can be extended: that is, by using two sets of coils, operation on three frequencies is possible, on four frequencies with three sets of coils, and so on. However these get very complicated to adjust, since the second set of loading coils changes operation of the first set somewhat, and the adjustment process gets rather tedious.

to a wide range of interference problems, both as receivers and emitters. In the USA, the FCC has addressed this problem with Docket 20780 which governs emission limits for both industrial

(class A) and consumer (class B) digital computing systems. . . . These regulations do not apply in the UK, but it can only be a matter of time before similar regulations are drafted."

TABLE 1
Comparison of various forms of shielding for rf cables

	Copper Braid	Copper Wrapped	Aluminium Polyester
Shield effectiveness at audio frequencies	good	good	excellent
Shield effectiveness at radio frequencies	good	poor	excellent
Normal % coverage	60-95	90-97	100
Fatigue life	good	fair	fair
Tensile strength	excellent	good	poor
Termination method	comb & pigtail	pigtail	drain wire
Limpness	good	good	fair
Cost*	most	more	less

*Relative assuming maximum coverage on braid and spiral wrapped shield

Source Anixter UK Ltd

MULTIBAND NON-LOADED DIPOLE

Where an atu is used with open-wire transmission line it becomes possible to resonate a centre-fed dipole antenna system on virtually any frequency. Lorin Knight, G2DXK admits that the principle used in his all-band hf antenna is nothing new, but the method of construction and the location of the atu should be of interest to those amateurs who do not wish to have open-wire feeders extending all the way into the domestic environment. He writes:

"Instead of the traditional 14swg hard-drawn copper wire, I use a black pvc-covered stranded wire (14 × 0·2mm, overall diameter 1·5mm). This wire has one-fifth the weight, is considerably cheaper, is easier to handle, is almost invisible when up in the air – and is not noticeably inferior in performance. Instead of the traditional glass or porcelain insulators I use 12-inch lengths of 1·5mm diameter monofil nylon line – also lighter, cheaper and practically invisible.

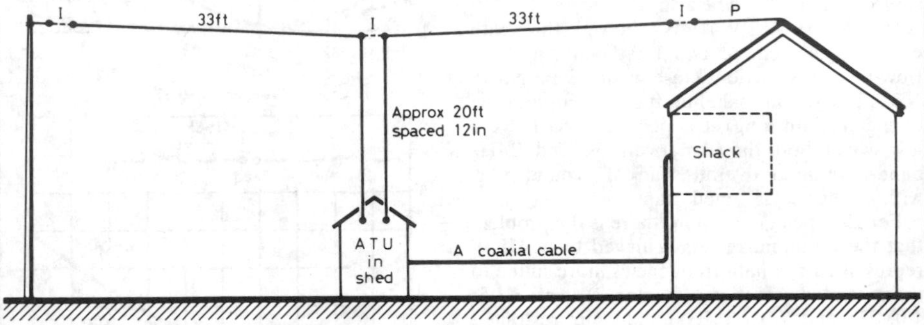

FIG 2. G2DXK'S MULTIBAND DIPOLE ANTENNA. I REPRESENTS INSULATORS COMPRISING 12IN LENGTHS OF NYLON LINE. P IS LENGTH OF POLYPROPYLENE CORD THROWN OVER ROOF AND ANCHORED TO EAVES.

"The feeder wires drop down to two standoff insulators mounted 12 inches apart on my garden shed which, very conveniently, stands right under the centre of the antenna: Fig 2. The wires are cut so that they are under slight tension and they maintain a nominal spacing of 12 inches without the use of any spreaders. In a very strong wind the actual spacing half-way up the feeder can fluctuate ± 2″ or so, but this appears to have negligible effect on the performance.

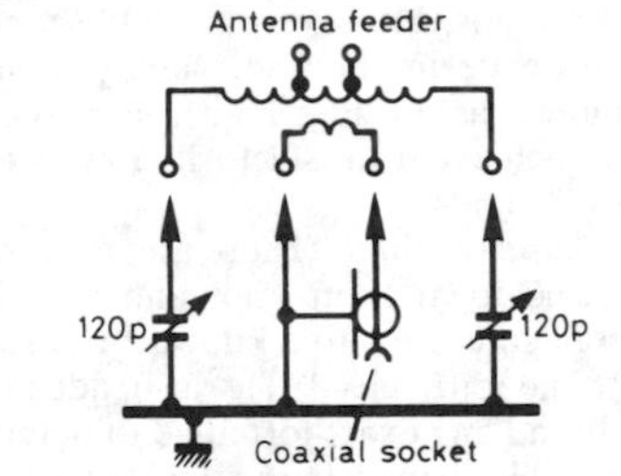

"I have an atu in the shed and a coaxial cable feed from there to the house. (This means that I have to go out to the shed every time I want to tune up the antenna for a different band but as I do not change bands all that often this is no great hardship.) The atu is homemade and has a separate plug-in coil assembly for each band from 3·5 to 28MHz (see Fig 3). Each coil assembly has written on it the relevant capacitor settings so that band-changing is a fairly simple operation.

"It will be noted that on 3·5MHz the active part of the antenna is only a quarter-wave long, but this does not prevent it from loading up and operating very satisfactorily. On 7MHz the antenna is a simple half-wave dipole; on 14MHz it acts as two half-waves in phase, giving some gain in the broadside direction. On the other bands it has multiple-lobe polar diagrams."

FIG 3. THE ATU USED WITH THE MULTIBAND DIPOLE IS SITED IMMEDIATELY UNDER THE CENTRE OF THE DIPOLE.

R.G. Sarney notes that there are several methods of screening cables to reduce rfi problems but not all are equally effective. He lists the most common cable screens as wire, braid, foil tape with an aluminium coating and drain wire, and spiral wire shields. Table 1, from his article, compares the properties and costs of various types of shielded cables based on samples from the Beldon range. Foil screens usually comprise a layer of aluminium deposited on a polyester tape, then wrapped helically around a cable with a longtitudinal copper drain wire used to terminate the screens. The Beldon cables of this type use a longitudinally applied screen which may have a shorting 'z' fold providing metal-to-metal contact so that the cable closely simulates the optimum 'metal-tube' form of screen, highly

FIG 4. TEST RESULTS OF MEASURING 'TRANSFER IMPEDANCE' OF SIX DIFFERENT SHIELDED CABLES AT DIFFERENT FREQUENCIES. A, 95% COPPER BRAID (BELDON 8221); B, 91% TINNED COPPER SPIRAL (BELDON 9456); C, FOIL WITH FOUR SPIRAL DRAIN WIRES (BELDON 9234); D, FOIL WITH 95% ALUMINIUM BRAID (BELDON 81008); E, FOIL/ALUMINIUM-BRAID/FOIL (BELDON DUOBAND PLUS, 9052); F, OPTIMISED BRAID. NOTE THE *LOWER* THE VALUE OF TRANSFER IMPEDANCE THE MORE EFFECTIVE THE SCREENING.

effective in preventing rf leakage into or out of the cable. Screening performance of such cables can be better than braid from audio to radio frequencies.

One way of comparing shielding effectiveness is by measuring the 'transfer impedance' of the

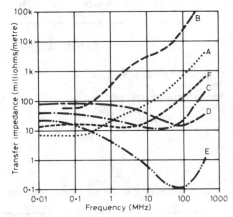

shield in terms of milliohms per metre. This represents the voltage per unit length generated on one surface of a shield by a longitudinal disturbing or interfering current on the other surface. The *lower* the transfer impedance the more effective the shielding. Fig 4, from R.G. Sarney's article illustrates the transfer impedance of six forms of shielded cable over a wide frequency range. The example A of copper braid cable represents a high-grade cable with 95 per cent copper coverage; consumer-type coaxial cables would have appreciably higher transfer impedances towards the higher-frequency end of the radio spectrum.

MORE SPECTRUM ANALYSER IDEAS

The low-cost spectrum analyser adapter described by Al Helfrick, K2BLA in *RF Design* (January 1988, see *TT* April, July, August and September) continues to attract attention and demands further coverage. But first, some information on how this design originated and the reason why the 'spread' of characteristics of the wired-in ic devices etc has given rise to problems to those building replicas of this design.

Who better to explain the background to this useful concept than the original designer? K2BLA writes: "I never realised that the design would achieve so much world-wide attention. A few notes of explanation are in order. First, I had no intention of the spectrum analyser becoming a constructional article. I designed the unit as an entry for the annual *RF Design* contest over the period of a weekend to see how few common parts could be used to generate a workable spectrum analyser. Therefore there is no printed circuit board and the only unit built to this specification was mine. I can, however, offer insight into solutions of some of the more common problems that have been reported to me by constructors.

"First, since the unit was built without a circuit board, *the distributed capacitance and inductance of a pcb layout is not present.* The breadboard is constructed with the chips 'on their backs with their feet in the air' a technique that, many years ago, I called 'dead-bug construction'. The leads to the components, especially those in the oscillators, are *very* short. This is necessary to obtain the required tuning range for the first local oscillator.

"There is one error on the schematic. The coil L4 does not return to the 5V supply but through a 1000pF capacitor to ground. There are no other errors and I recently checked the actual circuit to the schematic to be sure. Because many of the tuned circuits are well into the vhf region and will be affected by the internal capacitances of the chips and the distributed reactances of the wiring, each builder will have to tailor the coils for his own situation.

"The spectrum analyser described in *QST* ("An inexpensive spectrum analyser for the radio amateur" by Al Helfrick, K2BLA, *QST*, November 1985) is being made available in kit form by A&A Engineering (see *TT*, September 1988, p680). This unit has a zero to 400 or 450MHz range, depending on the converter used, and has a dynamic range of about 60dB, again depending on the converter. A&A had some early start-up problems but I understand they are now shipping units."

The 1985 design used an American catv tuner as the front-end converter. D.P.T. Evans,

GW31VK has combined some ideas from the 1985 *QST* and 1988 *RF Design* articles and also of his own to achieve a unit covering 0-400MHz with a sensitivity of about 30µV and a resolution of 150kHz. Improving the resolution beyond this introduced problems caused by a lower sweep rate needed giving rise to display flicker. He writes:

"Having obtained the specified parts, some with considerable difficulty, for the *RF Design* model, I assembled them on a pcb. Although it was possible to make IC1a oscillate to 245MHz, with suitable component values, it proved impossible to obtain a 100MHz sweep. About 30MHz was the maximum sweep obtained. Incidentally a Mullard BB809 variable capacitance diode performed slightly better than the specified MV209 in this circuit. The remainder of the circuit worked satisfactorily but because of the above problems it was decided to try a different approach.

"Fig 5 shows the overall block diagram and Fig 6 the circuit diagram of the basic unit. If the basic analyser of Fig 6 is constructed first (ie, tv tuner, MC3356 and TLO84 sweep generator) one has immediately a working display of the uhf television bands IV-V and this gives confidence that everything is going well. I made my first one in about two hours using a breadboard (I already had suitable power supplies). The final circuit was built on standard stripboard all the difficult parts already made in the tv tuner.

"*Points of note:* Power supplies required are +12V, −12V, +5V and +33V. The +33V supply should be well established and well smoothed in order to prevent horizontal drift and jitter on the display. Do not use tv varicap supply regulators such as the TAA550 as they are not good enough in this application. The zener diodes in the BFX85 collector improve sweep linearity. The agc potentiometer provides about 30dB of input level control. The frequency of the crystal used with the MC3356 is not critical, anywhere in the range 40·7 to 50·7MHz should prove suitable. The tuner i.f is

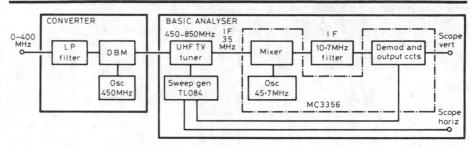

FIG 5. BLOCK DIAGRAM OF GW3IVK'S SPECTRUM ANALYSER UNIT.

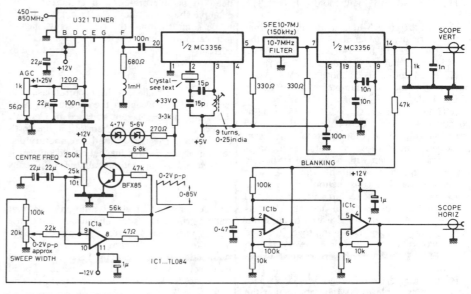

FIG 6. CIRCUIT DIAGRAM OF THE BASIC ANALYSER SECTION.

broad and may be peaked for maximum with its output trimmer. Use a ten-turn potentiometer for the centre-frequency control. If the unit is set to the test waveforms shown, then success should be immediate. My final version included a switched sweep-width control with six positions, maximum 50MHz/div, minimum 0·5MHz/div. The tv tuner used is a Philips U321 (available from P.M. Components).

The 0-400MHz converter (Fig 7) is quite simple. The diode bridge mixer (dbm) is readily available. Mount it on double-sided copper-clad board, with suitable holes and clearances on the appropriate pins. Note that in this application the input is taken to the i.f port and the output taken from the rf port as indicated in Fig 7. The local oscillator uses a BFW10 jfet device, mounted on the same board close to the dbm. The output level at 450MHz was rather less than 0dBm. The mixer requires +7dBm oscillator

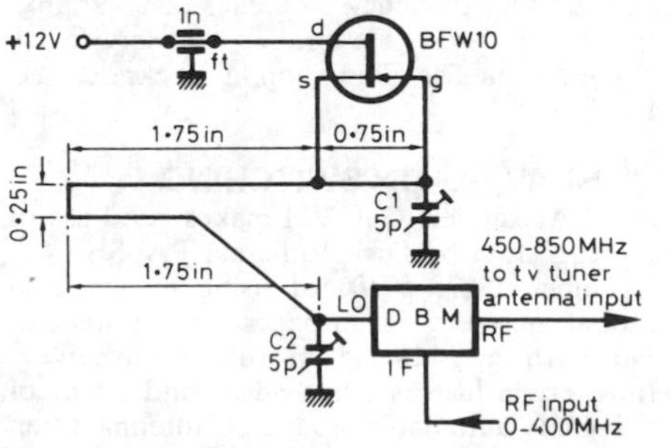

HIGH-POWER TETRODES LIVE ON

H. A. Sanders, G3CRH sends along the final part of a series of articles on broadcast transmitters that appeared in the trade journal *International Broadcasting* (Part 3, Transmitter tubes: the tetrode, January/February 1988 issue). This article by James Wood is concerned primarily with the very high-power tetrodes developed and still manufactured by Brown Boveri, English Electric, Philips, Thomson-CSF and Varian-Eimac; for example, the Thomson super-power TH526 with a rated dissipation of 1500kW! An important modern development has been the development, in an increasingly solidstate era, of the Thomson 'Pyrobolic' grid, using pyrolitic graphite (crystallised carbon). This material has very good mechanical stability with its mechanical strength *increasing* with increasing temperature.

But it is also pointed out that the post-war development by Varian-Eimac of the more familiar 4CX250B "revolutionised all previous design concepts . . . the interesting thing is the way in which all modern tetrodes at medium power levels have retained a close resemblance to the 4CX250B". Later, James Wood comments: "The uhf tetrode is championed by many

senior engineers . . . sadly though, the theory of vacuum tubes is no longer taught in most universities . . . we have a new generation of transmitter design engineers many of whom have an engineering education limited to the application of solidstate technology . . . Critics of the power grid tetrode are mainly those engineers who are not directly familiar with them, but have heard stories of short life."

Unlike solidstate, catastrophic failure is rare with tetrodes, although he notes that their life can be shortened by (a) inadequate cooling of the anode and electrode seals; (b) excessive (or inadequate – G3VA) filament supply voltage; (c) overdriving the control grid; (d) incorrect screen supply voltage or current; and (4) too lightly loaded output stage (a factor often overlooked by amateurs who may believe that this actually prolongs the life of the valve – G3VA).

James Wood adds: "These factors are effects rather than causes. The real cause of shortened tube life can boil down to either a badly designed transmitter stage, or a badly maintained transmitter. No amount of loving care and maintenance can ever remedy a substandard transmitter design."

FIG 7. FRONT-END CONVERTER SECTION OF THE GW3IVK ANALYSER.

power for optimum but the lower level did not appear to cause any problems. Use thick tinned copper wire for the tuning lines. Adjust C1 for frequency, again not critical but around 450MHz. The oscillator output is displayed on the basic analyser at the bottom end of the uhf tv Band IV. Adjust C2 for maximum output using this display.

"The input low-pass filter, 0-450MHz, was included as a precaution to prevent direct breakthrough from strong signals in the uhf tv bands. The completed spectrum analyser adapter is inexpensive, easy to make and surprisingly good." If required, further details can be obtained from: D.P.T. Evans, GW3IVK, 11 Hill View, Bryn-y-Baal, Mold, Clwyd, CH7 6SL.

The importance when using the original design of reducing to an absolute minimum the stray reactances in the connections to off-the-shelf MC3356 and NE602 devices is underlined by the experience of Ted Elliott, G3BYY. As he puts it: "Maybe some samples of the MC3356 are reliable up to beyond 260MHz but my NE602, no matter what L or C I tried would not go above 140MHz." G3BYY used 'ugly' construction with most components on the earth plane side and hard-wiring underneath, probably less strays than with a pcb, but probably rather more than would be the case with K2BLA's 'dead bug construction'. However he finds his unit – now boxed up – very useful and providing hours of delightful fiddling. He feels that KL2BLA has provided a well-thought-out roduct, and that to try to improve just one aspect would be a waste of time: "every portion is working at a level of performance where nothing is wasted."

He has settled for coverage 0–105MHz with linearity reasonable to 70MHz; above that the space between the 10MHz markers increases considerably. With a 3ft piece of wire on the input acting as a makeshift antenna, his six major Band 2 fm broadcast signals produce pips about 50mV in amplitude; between 0-20MHz there is a solid wedge of signals; around 27MHz cb signals coming and going, similarly two-way mobiles around 80-90MHz. His final modifications were: L2 2t, 3/16in id 20swg 3/16in long. C6 4pF (2·2pF and 1·8pF in parallel). He found it essential to increase voltage on the first half of the MC3356 to 13·8-14V. The original display circuitry suited his Trio CS-1560A scope perfectly. With only a single-range scan he sees no point in reducing the bandwidth of the i.f below 250kHz which represents a blip only 0·25mm wide, less than the spot size. With a much reduced sweep there would, he feels, be too much jitter in view of the rather crude method of sweeping the frequency by means of a variable capacitance diode. He praises the service be obtained from The Chip Shop in Stockport (see May *TT*).

12V HEAVY-DUTY SWITCHING

Derek Alexander, G4GVM makes good use of the suggestion by Dick Rollema, PAoSE (*TT*, December 1987, p910) of using a car radio antenna not only for broadcast reception but also with a 144MHz mobile transceiver. However, in his case, he had to find a way of raising his automatic broadcast antenna when required for 144MHz without first having to switch on the car radio.

Les Cobb, G3UI passes along a word of caution from Dr L. M. Dougherty, a keen astronomer of considerable repute and former Head of Physics at Huddersfield Polytechnic, on the 'kilner jar magnetometer' of G3UKV *TT*, based on the 1983 BAA 'Recording jamjar magnetometer' originally described by H. R. Hatfield. Dr Dougherty and a colleague constructed one of these instruments, as near as possible to the original 1983 specification. They carefully evaluated it over a considerable period and came to the conclusion that while it may well be an instrument worthy of experiment, the results need to be interpreted with great care. For example the temperature coefficient was found to be some 64 times the typical daily magnetometer range in the UK. Dr Dougherty is currently working on a device designed to minimise such variations.

The intense solar flare which occurred last June is believed to have been the reason why hundreds of homing pigeons released in CentraL France failed to return to their lofts in the north of England. The flare caused a temporary distortion of the Earth's magnetic field on which the remarkable navigational abilities of pigeons is thought to depend.

The September *TT* included a tip on using pilot bulbs as rf indicators for antennas in lieu of the once widely-available thermocouple rf ammeters. An alternative approach, recommended by Les Cobb G3UI is to use a toroid core wound with a few turns of wired, slipped over the feeder, with a diode rectifier and voltmeter. He considers that has the advantage of being indestructible and also provides a remote reading facility.

R S Andrews G3 BNG notes that many amateurs use the standard form of jack plug (known, for example, as the Air Ministry Phone/Mic Jack Plug AM No IOH986 with ¼in diameter shaft) used with a two-contact socket (AM IOH/1049). The panel mounting bush of the socket bears a black bakelite hexagon casting which, if undue force is used to tighten or loosen the bush, is liable to crack and break off, thus leaving the brass entry to the bush exposed, rendering the socket unsuitable for panel mounting. He writes: "This may easily be repaired by removing the brass locking nut from the mounting bush of a defunct potentiometer, soldering it over the exposed brass bush end, and then seating a brass ¼in washer over the two as in Fig 9. This renders the socket serviceable again."

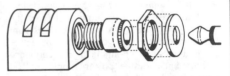

FIG 9. G3UI'S METHOD OF REPAIRING A BROKEN PANEL MOUNTING BUSH OF A STANDARD JACK SOCKET.

W3SHP (*QST* "Hints & Kinks") has found that when winding coils a useful tip is to wind double-stick transparent tape on the former before beginning the winding. Then if you relax your pull before anchoring the winding the turns will still stay put.

G4GVM found that the current required to raise the antenna was 75mA and feared that this

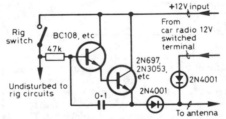

FIG 8. G4GVM'S METHOD OF RAISING HIS CAR RADIO ANTENNA WITHOUT SWITCHING ON THE CAR RADIO OR ADDING ANY SIGNIFICANT EXTRA SWITCHING CURRENT TO HIS 144MHZ TRANSCEIVER. THE SAME CIRCUIT CONFIGURATION COULD FIND OTHER APPLICATIONS WHERE A SUBSTANTIAL CURRENT NEEDS TO BE SWITCHED FROM A VERY SMALL ONE.

extra current might be sufficient to damage the 144MHz rig's on/off switch if a direct connection were made. Instead, he devised the arrangements shown in Fig 9. The current to activate this varies with the load current, but is only about 5µA to switch 75mA and only about 70µA to switch 450mA. In his case this means that the transceiver switch needs to cope only with a negligible extra 5µA. The diodes are required in order to stop the 144MHz rig supplying 12V to the car radio "through the back door" and vice versa.

While G4GVM's particular application may seem rather specialised, the circuit configuration and approach could be used for other applications where a substantial currenmt needs to be switched from a very small one.

MEMORY BATTERIES IN YAESU RIGS

Kjell Ström, PA/SM6CPI of Yaesu Europe BV adds to the comments on GM4SVM's worries about the memory back-up battery for the Yaesu FT-290R (and FT-290R II): see August *TT* with comments in September *TT*. He writes: "These worries are completely without foundation since all the vital software for all Yaesu radios is in rom (read-only-memory) devices and cannot be erased. The only slight inconvenience that will be caused by a discharged back-up battery in FT-290R is that the radio falls back to the default mode and frequency and that it cannot keep other data in its memory when it is being switched off. All other functions are available regardless of the state of the back-up battery. There is even a switch provided in the circuit so that battery life can be preserved when the radio is stored for a longer time.

"There are no tricks involved in replacing the back-up battery: if necessary, just make a note of what you have got stored in the memory, replace the battery and reprogram the radio. Knowing a little bit about human nature quite a few FT-290R owners will wait until one day they find that their radio does not keep memory data. Nothing bad will happen to their Yaesu radio.

"Regarding the dc supply plug: if you have lost the plug which comes with the radio, any Yaesu dealer can supply an exact replacement."

TECHNICAL TOPICS

PAT HAWKER · G3VA

DIRECT DIGITAL SYNTHESIS OSCILLATORS

TT has frequently referred to the problems created by oscillator phase noise on both receive and transmit modes, particularly in the case of the low-cost pll frequency synthesisers used in many transceivers. Admittedly, some manufacturers have succeeded during the past decade in significantly improving the performance of their synthesisers. But it remains true that a good free-running vfo can provide superior noise performance than a synthesiser. One recalls for example that Peter Hart, G3SJX in his equipment review of the Ten-Tec Corsair hf transceiver (*Rad Com* November 1984) – a model using a low-noise, permeability-tuned vfo covering 5·0 to 5·5MHz – admitted that after thoroughly testing this transceiver in the laboratory and on-the-air he decided to purchase one to replace an ageing FT101. Most of us are, however, not in a position to carry out exhaustive laboratory measurements before deciding which model to buy.

For those who value the convenience of digital control from microprocessors and memories etc, the synthesiser retains its attractions; otherwise, presumably, the transceiver manufacturers would have dropped them. However there is now new hope that digital synthesisers can be radically improved. In *TT* (March 1988) I mentioned an article in *Ham Radio* (November 1987) 'Tomorrow's receivers: what will the next 20 years bring?' by Robert J Zarvel, W7SX noting that: "W7SX considers that synthesisers offer distinct advantages in that they can be directly controlled by microprocessors and do not require special mechanical rigidity or moving parts, but admits that at present it is difficult, if not impossible, to duplicate the permeability-tuned oscillators of the 'sixties with pll synthesis, given the constraints of typical amateur budgets. He quotes, however, that another type of synthesiser – 'the direct digital synthesiser (dds)' – holds great promise for the future."

Ham Radio returns to this subject in its October 1988 issue with the article "A direct digital synthesis vfo" again by Robert Zarvel, W7SX (Digital RF Solutions of Santa Clara, California). This introduces DDS as follows: "The direct digital synthesizer has arrived in Amateur Radio (the new high cost Icom 781 uses DDS). In the past several months DDS state-of-the-art has progressed to the point where good radio performance is obtainable using DDS. The DDS offers some attractive features over the analogue or phase-locked loop (PLL) synthesizer. DDS is digitally controlled. Tuning is regulated by either memories or counters which, in turn, are controlled by rotary optical couplers. Unlike the PLL, DDS doesn't use a vco, loop filter, phase detector, or digital divider and prescaler. Waveform information is generated using digital information only. The last step uses a digital-to-analogue converter (DAC) to generate the rf signal."

W7SX shows that an important feature of the DDS system (Fig 2) is the NCMO vfo (NCMO stands for 'numerically controlled modulated oscillator'), which creates digitally defined rf waveforms and is now a trademark of Digital RF Solutions. It was conceived and designed by Earl McCune Jr, WA6SUH and it is described as follows:

"The NCMO is a highly integrated cmos phase accumulator with numerous interface and modulation features. It uses a 24-bit phase accumulator counter controlled by a 24-bit tuning word. The 24-bit tuning resolution implies over 16-million equally spaced discrete frequencies in an NCMO system; 16-million "channels" suggests about 1·2Hz steps with a 20MHz clock. Half of the frequencies appear between the Nyquist and clock frequencies. These are simply

NICAD PULSE CHARGER

An extensive list of 'facts and fallacies' about rechargeable nicad (NiCd) cells and batteries, based on an article by ZS5JF, appeared in *TT* May 1988, p349. But there is little doubt that many amateurs still do not appreciate that the useful life of these batteries can be significantly reduced by failure to recognize the way in which nicads can be damaged during charging.

In his 'The Weekender' column in *Ham Radio* (September 1988, pp18, 20 and 21), R L Measures, AG6K provides a useful description of why it is necesary to charge nicad cells at not less than 0·1C (Where C is the Ah capacity of the cell) but at the same time to avoid overheating the cell once it is fully charged. He writes: 'If the charging current of 0·1C (or more) is maintained after a wet cell NiCd battery is fully charged, the surplus charging energy that the battery can't store converts the water in the liquid electrolyte to hydrogen and oxygen gas. This causes no damage to the cell as long as distilled water is added periodically. . . . It's not convenient to add water in a sealed NiCd cell; an internal process of turning the hydrogen and oxygen gas back into water is designed into the cell. When hydrogen and oxygen unite as water they release energy in the form of heat. . . . If the cell is continuously cooled enough to maintain cell temperature below about 35°C during charging, the sealed cell won't be damaged by overcharging. If the temperature is allowed to rise above about 35° during charging the cell won't last long. . . . You can eliminate overcharging by using a constant-voltage charger (about 1·43V per cell) but then unfortunately, as the cells become charged, their voltage rises and the charge current decreases below the critical 0·1C level. This is both good and bad . . . the cells won't overheat when overcharged but bad because not enough current will be supplied near the end of the charging process to charge fully the deep parts of the plate.'

AG6K's answer to this dual problem is a pulsed constant-voltage charger: Fig 1. With the half-wave rectification, in the absence of a large-value 'reservoir capacitor' (C1), the output is in the form of 'rectified (raw) ac' or "dirty dc", a succession of current/voltage pulses with the voltage limited by the three-terminal ic regulator (eg LM3217T for currents up to 1A). Remember that the secondary winding of the mains transformer needs the current rated at about 1A where the 0·1C value is about 100mA. The charger is adjusted as follows:

With no battery connected, depress the push-button switch S1 thus bringing a reservoir capacitor into circuit and adjust R1 for a charger output of about 1·43V per cell to be charged. Release S1, connect the nicad battery with a multimeter across R3 to determine the average charging current. The initial average charging current for a fully discharged battery should be about 0·3C. When the battery is fully charged reset R1 to show an average charging current of 0·02C. If you have a suitable oscilloscope, the measured peak current should be about 0·1C. With the charger set up in this way it should then be safe to leave a battery on charge for up to several days without the cell temperature rising to 35°C.

FIG 1 AG6K's NICAD PULSE CHARGER PROVIDING VOLTAGE-LIMITED "DIRTY DC" PULSES WITH PUSH-SWITCH S1 OPEN. D1 IS A SMALL (9mm SIZE) METAL-OXIDE VARISTOR RATED AT LINE VOLTAGE (UK 240V). D2 3A 100PIV OR GREATER SILICON RECTIFIER. C1 220μF (35V), C2, C3 1♂F (35V) TANTALUM CAPACITOR MOUNTED NEAR REGULATOR IC. F1 0·2A FUSE FOR 240V SUPPLIES. R1 1K MULTITURN TRIMPOT. R2 100OHM ¼W, R3 CURRENT SAMPLING RESISTOR (1OHM 2W FOR AA BATTERIES, 0·1OHM 2W FOR C OR D BATTERIES). WITH 0·1OHM RESISTOR 1mV EQUALS 120mA. TRANSFORMER SECONDARY 1·1 TIMES NUMBER OF CELLS PLUS 3V RMS. NO-LOAD SECONDARY VOLTAGE MUST BE LESS THAN 24V RMS.

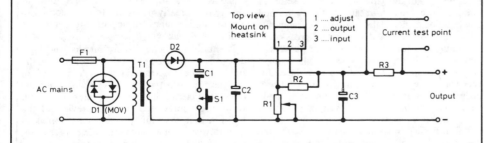

'folded back' below the Nyquist frequency, so there are actually only about 8-million possible discrete frequencies. Only the most significant 12 bits are used in this project. . . . The NCMO can be tuned in three ways: (1) a parallel mode connecting to 24 pins on the ic device; (2) a strobed mode for three eight-bit words, mainly for microprocessor interface; and (3) a serial mode which allows direct connection to a rotary optical coupler so that it can 'feel' like an analogue tuner."

Later in his long article, W7SX writes: "For on-the-air tests I have a Corsair II which uses a super low-noise permeability tuned oscillator (PTO). The output level of the TRW1012 dac is similar to the requirements of the Corsair (about +5dBm). Switching back and forth between the PTO and the NCMO vfo proved to be a good 'qualitative' test. Results were excellent; only a few weak spurs were noted." The specifications of the 18X 2070 NCMO VFO as described in the article gives: Phase noise at 1Hz offset −95dBc/Hz; 10Hz offset −115dBc/Hz; 100Hz offset −128dBc/Hz; and 1kHz −135dBc/Hz. Spurious signal generation −75dB (worst case), −90dB (typical). Frequency stability is equally as good as for a PLL, synthesizers in both cases being determined by the stability of the crystal reference oscillator.

Clearly this is a highly promising development, though more complex and costly than the PLL approach, for those who want digital control from microprocessors, memories or 'analogue-feel' rotary optical couplers. W7SX concludes, however with a word of warning: "You can purchase assembled DDS boards from Digital RF Solutions Inc. These boards are recommended for advanced experimenters. As a minimum, a low-frequency spectrum analyser is required before attempting experimentation. For more information contact Doug Hammed at 3080 Olcott St, Suite 200d, Santa Clara, CA95054, California." For those who are not deep into digital electronics, there remains much to be said for a good free-running vfo, such as the PTO used in the Corsair models.

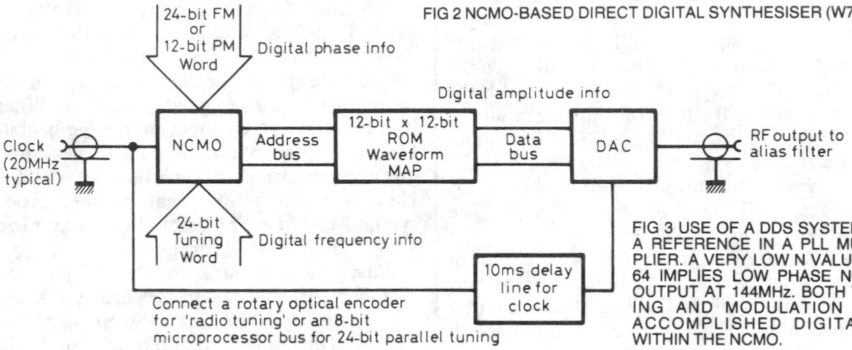

FIG 2 NCMO-BASED DIRECT DIGITAL SYNTHESISER (W7SX).

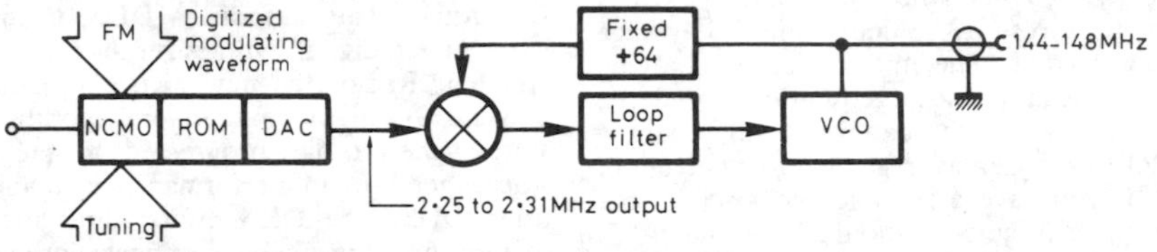

FIG 3 USE OF A DDS SYSTEM AS A REFERENCE IN A PLL MULTIPLIER. A VERY LOW N VALUE OF 64 IMPLIES LOW PHASE NOISE OUTPUT AT 144MHz. BOTH TUNING AND MODULATION ARE ACCOMPLISHED DIGITALLY WITHIN THE NCMO.

BROADBAND CAN BE VULNERABLE

On many occasions *TT* items have doubted the wisdom of adopting uncritically the trend towards 'broadband' configurations in both receiver front-ends and transmitter amplifiers. Unquestionably, though, such approaches can offer useful operational advantages and cost savings in eliminating multi-ganged variable-capacitor tuned circuits. It has been frequently stressed that good pre-mixer selectivity is a great help in overcoming the problems presented by limited dynamic range, particularly where very strong signals from local transmitters or broadcast stations are involved.

In the case of stand-alone receivers, it is often possible to add an external selectivity unit in the form of a low-gain pre-amplifier with two or more tuned circuits (see, for example, *TT* August 1981). Carried to the extreme such a selectivity unit may take the form of signal-frequency crystal filters as developed and proposed by Peter Haylett, G3IPV (*TT*, July 1985, pp 541-2 and *TT*, February 1986, p109).

Really sharp small-signal filters cannot readily be fitted to typical 100Watt transceivers, unless relay bypass switching is provided. The best that can be done without such switching is a sub-octave bandpass filter constructed to handle the transmitter output power as described in the accompanying item "Bandpass filters for co-sited transmitters". Such filters will provide limited attenuation of broadcast signals on adjacent bands (eg the 7·1MHz and 21·5MHz broadcast bands, or, on 14MHz, the not quite adjacent 15MHz band).

Gerald Stancey, G3MCK carries the debate forward to the broadband antennas which deliver to the receiver, at full strength, the many strong signals from those modern 250kW, 500kW and more broadcast transmitters working into their high-gain antennas to give effective radiated powers of many megawatts along the beam. Receiver emf input across 50ohms of these signals can be of the order of 0·1V, 100dB (μV), about a million times greater

---

'SQUEEZE' (IAMBIC-MODE) KEYING

As a result of my review of the Samson ETM8c keyer (*Rad Com*, October 1988, pp777-8) it has become clear that a number of readers are hazy as to the difference between 'iambic-mode' dual-paddle keyers and the traditional form of single-paddle elbugs. Although, as mentioned in the review, the dual-paddles of iambic-mode keyers can in practice be operated with the same hand-movements as the single-paddle elbug, this throws away the advantage of being able, with iambic-mode logic, to form many letters with just one single controlled squeeze of the paddles.

I noted in my 1972 review of the original ETM-3 keyer: "On a manual 'straight' key, all symbols are made manually and the 'shape' of every dit and dah depends entirely upon the operator; some 82 contact closures are needed to send the alphabet. The semi-auto ('bug') key replaces multiple dits with a single timed-closure, and the shape and spacing of the dits is taken care of automatically; an alphabet needs 66 contact closures. The (single-paddle) elbug replaces multiple dits and multiple dahs with single closures and can include self-completing

and character-spacing 'memory'; the alphabet now represents 53 closures.

"With 'iambic-mode' operation we enter a rather different world; those who remember the rules of metrical scansion of poetry will grasp that iambic means that when the paddles are squeezed together, the keyer produces a series of interspersed dits and dahs – short-long, short-long, short-long continuously, all accurately spaced, formed and completed. Because there are two paddles, it is possible to do more than this; if the paddles are closed in the reverse sequence (ie the other paddle makes its closure first) out comes dah-dits; one paddle closure gives a series of dits; the other alone a series of dahs. So we have four automatically formed combinations: dits, dahs, dit-dahs and dah-dits all with correctly timed spaces and cross-overs maintained as long as one or both paddles is activated. We are now down to 45 contact closures per alphabet, compared with the 82 for the straight key. Furthermore, such useful procedure signals as AR, VA, CT can all be made with what amounts to a single squeeze; CQ with two squeezes.

"So it is easy to come to the conclusion that, theoretically, iambic-mode squeeze keying does

represent a very real and useful advance on earlier types of keyers and keys. Having decided this, one must add a rider: it makes possible higher speeds and is less tiring at the cost of introducing the timing errors that result in jibberish, with the machine trying to take over from an increasingly flustered operator."

John Piggott, G2PT, in an excellent survey article (*RSGB Bulletin*, May 1956) pointed out that an operator's mind must be ahead of his hand movements since 'it is fairly certain that there is no individual nerve signal for each transmit movement of the key' – in other words, the times involved in morse are less than human reaction times. In acquiring a new form of keying it is clearly necessary to be prepared to put in many hours of practice, to program the brain so to speak.

It should also be pointed out that the logic design of a squeeze keyer differs from that of the single-paddle electronic keyer. A number of designs for both types of keyers, using mainly integrated circuit devices, have been published. It will be appreciated from the review of the ETM-8c that it is a fairly complex and sophisticated device, though amateurs have, of course, successfully built iambic-mode keyers.

than the weak amateur signal with which the receiver may be trying to cope. Remember that the effects of strong signals are cumulative.

G3MCK writes: "With regard to some recent *TT* items on broadband antennas, I wonder how much they degrade the performance of many modern receivers. With such a set-up you have a broadband antenna picking up some very strong signals, feeding through a wideband (sometimes 0 – 30MHz) front-end into a receiver with a fairly wide roofing filter. This does not seem to me to be good design practice even though the actual effects may not appear to be too bad.

"My own view is that for an optimum receiver system you should have a narrow-band antenna, as much front-end selectivity as possible and the narrowest first i.f filter you can use. This would seem to put out of court many current hf rigs which not only have no significant front-end selectivity but also have an fm (25kHz) filter as their first selectivity element. It would seem that the provision of 1001 memories etc is considered to more than compensate for such 'trivial' shortcomings as not being able to receive weak signals among the mass of spurious intermodulation products etc!"

G3MCK's remarks can also be considered in relation to the question of matching an antenna to a receiver. In the September, 1988 issue of *QST* (Technical Correspondence p46), Zachary Lau, KH6CP of ARRL staff, points out that properly matching receivers to a transmission line is much more complicated than matching transmitters to the line: "The latter is relatively simple – just obtain the largest power transfer. With receivers, the goal is a low system noise figure . . . Good receivers are optimized for 50-ohm source impedances . . . Note *source impedance* and *not* input impedance. Just because a receiver is designed to work well with 50-ohm sources doesn't mean it has a 50-ohm input impedance . . . the receiver input impedance may be far from 50 ohms, particularly if the noise figure is pretty good and obtained with a fet amplifier. As a result, feeding a receiver with an antenna matched to 50-ohm coaxial cable usually works pretty well, at least on hf. The mismatch is important if you have a big station with phased and matched beams."

KH6CP reminds us that laboratory-quality instruments for measuring power transfer cost hundreds of dollars, while noise figure measurement equipment costs run into thousands.

The difference between noise-figure matching and power-transfer matching, KH6CP suggests, explains why using a receiver to tune a Transmatch doesn't always work. When you tune a Transmatch for maximum (received) signal, you are tuning for maximum power transfer into a load which often isn't 50ohms. There is in fact a good reason why it is not desirable to have receiver matching adjusted for maximum power transfer: many modern receivers, with noise figures of the order of 6dB or so, have some 20-30dB more sensitivity than is required on the lower hf bands, leading to the type of overloading on strong signals that G3MCK has in mind. Even today, manufacturers design for good weak signal reception rather than for handling very strong signals, if necessary including rf attenuators between the antenna and the first stage. What you want out of a receiving antenna is a good signal-to-noise ratio, not necessarily maximum microvolts.

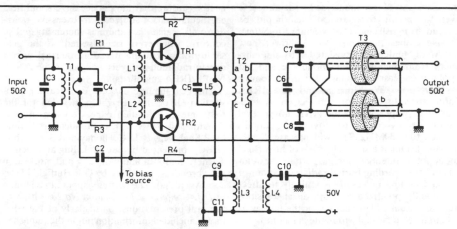

SOLIDSTATE RF POWER AMPLIFIERS

In the April and July *TT*s, I drew attention to the growing belief, at least as far as broadcast engineering is concerned, that the future of high-power solid-state power amplifiers will increasingly depend on mosfet rather than bipolar devices. The July *TT* provided details of a state-of-the-art Motorola design for a 300watts-carrier-output, broadband (10 to 175MHz) amplifier based on the "Gemini MRF151G" push-pull mosfet package. In general terms, rf power mosfets tend to work with higher voltage (50 to 70V) supplies than bipolars, reducing the heavy-current problems. They also provide rather higher power gain per stage and are free from secondary breakdown problems.

At present, however, the upper frequency limit of state-of-the-art rf power mosfets is about 150MHz although there are signs that some semiconductor firms are frantically working towards devices suitable for use up to about 1000MHz in order to meet the requirements of television broadcasting.

The broadband fet amplifier described in the July *TT* was designed by Helge O Granberg (*Microwaves & RF*, November 1987). An earlier design, based on push-pull bipolar devices, is described by him in Motorola Applications Note AN-758 "A two-stage 1kW solidstate linear amplifier" and remains a good guide to the design, construction and setting up of high-power bipolar transistor amplifiers. AN-758 describes two basic push-pull amplifiers, 1·6 to 30MHz, operating from 50V supplies. The design (Figs 4, 5) is based on combining the output from four 300Watt amplifiers each using two MRF428 (150Watt) bipolar transistors, with a 50Watt driver amplifier using a similar push-pull design with two MRF427A (25W) devices. The complete 1kW linear amplifier thus uses eight MRF428 and two MRF427A devices, and has a minimum total power gain of 30dB. For ssb has a third-order intermodulation distortion (IMD) of −30dB maximum (1kW p.e.p, 50V supply, or at 800W p.e.p with 40V supply) and can provide continuous cw output of 1kW with

FIG 4 BASIC 300W AND 50W SOLIDSTATE BIPOLAR PUSH-PULL AMPLIFIERS AS DESCRIBED IN MOTOROLA APPLICATIONS NOTE AN-758. COMPONENT VALUES DIFFER BETWEEN THE 300W POWER MODULE AND THE 50W DRIVER AMPLIFIER. COMPONENT LAYOUT AND FULL DETAILS OF COMPONENT VALUES AND CONSTRUCTION OF L1-4 AND T1-3 ARE GIVEN IN AN-758, TOGETHER WITH THE FOUR-PORT POWER DIVIDER AND OUTPUT COMBINER, MEASUREMENT TECHNIQUES ETC.

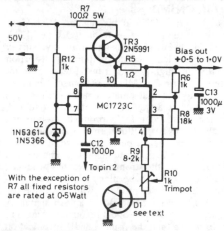

FIG 5 BIAS VOLTAGE SOURCE FOR THE MOTOROLA AMPLIFIERS. D1 IS BASE-EMITTER OF 2N5190 TEMPERATURE-TRACKED.

50% duty cycle over 30-minute periods with heatsink temperature less than 75°C. While the construction of this 1kW amplifier would represent for a radio amateur an ambitious and costly project in totality, it may be worth noting that the information in AN-758 covers, in effect, 50Watt and 300Watt linear amplifiers and associated regulated bias voltage source that would be suitable as stand-alone amplifiers. The 150Watt Motorola MRF428 device is currently listed in a *Ham Radio* advertisement at $50 (RF Parts, 1320 Grand Avenue, San Marcos, CA92069, USA) and in *Rad Com*, with VAT-added etc, at about £69. I would again stress that it would be unwise to attempt to build either amplifier without careful study of the 16-page AN-758 Application Note available from Motorola (see July *TT*).

RADIATION WORRIES

The continued public concern and controversy surrounding the safe level for extended periods of exposure to non-ionizing radiation has taken a new turn which could affect a few amateurs using high-power on hf with monopole vertical antennas. A few years ago both the British

National Radiological Protection Board (NRPB) and the American National Standards Institute (ANSI) proposed new guidelines that recognised for the first time that at frequencies between 30 to 300MHz, our bodies tend to act as dipole antennas and absorb more rf energy than, for example, from equivalent mf or lower-hf ▶

radiation. ANSI recommended that the safe level for public exposure at vhf should be reduced from 10W/m² (10mW/cm²) to 4W/m². *TT* (November 1986, pp780-781) showed how the ANSI guidelines translated into safe distances from medium-wave monopole and vhf dipole broadcast antennas at various power levels up to 1kW. More recently the IRPA (International Radiation Protection Association) has proposed that the ANSI lower level should be extended to cover frequencies between 10 to 30MHz. This will increase slightly the safe distances around the base of hf vertical (monopole) antennas and is perhaps another reason for discarding buried radials in favour of elevated ground planes. It is unlikely to affect horizontally polarized antenna distances since these are usually high-enough for the energy at ground level to be well within the guidelines.

Broadcasters, with co-sited transmitters increasingly run for 24 hours per day, have special problems in carrying out maintenance work on antennas without having to shut down all or some channels at the site for extended periods. They are increasingly recognising the need to ensure that the public, riggers and field engineers are not subjected to excessive radiation and realise that there is increasing public concern, whether or not justified, at the possibility of potentially harmful athermal effects due to radiation at levels well below the ANSI/NRPB/IRPA guidelines.

This year the International Broadcasting Convention (IBC88) at Brighton included for the first time two detailed papers on this subject: 'Health and safety with rf broadcast radiation' by P Shelswell, R D C Thoday and S Wakeling (BBC), presented by Sue Wakeling and Dennis Turner, and 'Radiation levels and protection near broadcast antennas' by G E Hatfield (Telecom Australia). The written papers can be found in *IEE Conference Publication No 283* although the oral presentations, particularly of the BBC paper, included information not in the published paper.

The BBC paper has resulted from surveying over 70 papers and 140 abstracts on this subject and is claimed to represent the current understanding of the problem of interaction of electromagnetic radiation with the body. The thermal effects include those caused by directly heating of tissue; those caused by a thermal loading of the body's thermo-regulatory system; and those that appear to be caused by an interaction with the field components themselves. The IRPA and ANSI guidelines are deemed to include a safety factor of about ten times in protection against thermal effects. (Though amateurs need to note that radiation from vhf/uhf 'rubber-duck' antennas held very near the eyes can represent a potential hazard at power levels of more than about 7Watts – G3VA).

Much of the current debate centres on whether there are harmful athermal effects caused by em fields interacting directly with the body. The BBC paper points out that: "These are very controversial because they do not have an obvious method of interaction of em fields on tissue and the theories put forward have not been confirmed by other experimenters . . . Two plausible methods of interaction have been proposed; the interaction of the field with calcium or other divalent ions, and the reception of magnetic fields by the pineal gland . . . Any link between em radiation and cancer has yet to be established and propositions are tenuous because of the way in which cancer occurs."

The conclusions to this paper include the following: "The levels of rf field which are safe are under close scrutiny. It is clear that the old limits which are based on the cooking effects of fields are well known and there is little difficulty in agreeing the physical basis of the safety standards, although the safety margins are often the causes of differences of opinion.

"More recently there has been concern that athermal effects are important. There is no firm evidence that athermal effects can cause any irreversible change in the body. Such changes that do occur are not seen to be dangerous. However there is pressure to recognise these effects and reflect them in the safety standards especially for public (as opposed to occupational) exposure. This may present some difficulty in the measurement techniques necessary, especially if there is a dose limit applied."

W1JR ON IMD

Joe Reisert, W1JR in his regular 'VHF/UHF World' column in *Ham Radio* (October 1988, pp71-74, 79-80) provides an informative survey of the problem of intermodulation distortion (IMD) in high-power transmitters: a more common term for IMD is, of course, 'splatter'. He points out that amateur-radio exciters and linear power amplifiers are often specified as having third-order IMD products at between about −26 to −30dB at a specific peak-envelope-power output. The third-order products are those generated closest to the desired signal and are the strongest unwanted products, but there will also be many higher-order products. Third-order products will be outside the 2·5kHz to 3kHz passband of an ssb signal. A figure of −26dB to −30dB is roughly some 6 to 10dB worse than the usual −36dB specification for professional, commercial or military transmitters. It should also be appreciated that the "specified" performance is likely to be that measured under optimum laboratory conditions. Much stronger IMD products will be produced if any attempt is made to squeeze more output from a rig by speaking loudly into the microphone and/or by turning up the audio gain.

W1JR agrees with the view often expressed in *TT* that a valve linear amplifier will usually have superior IMD performance than can be expected from solid-state amplifiers, particularly those with 12V supplies. He also agrees that the trend towards the use of rf power mosfets, with 'ht' rails up to about 60V represents a promising development. However he also stresses that "the fact that an amplifier uses a vacuum tube is no guarantee that it will be linear. Certain operating parameters must be met." As GW3DIX pointed out in the September *TT* (p679) one of the rocks on which designs may survive or founder is the power supply which must have sufficient rating to prevent it from saturating on peak demand.

With respect to vhf/uhf linear amplifiers, W1JR notes that tetrodes usually provide the highest power gain and are often operated in the grounded-cathode configuration: "However, the newer high-mu triodes driven in the grounded-grid configuration, while having less gain, will generally deliver the best IMD performance". Table 1 is derived from W1JR's article though omitting some of the highest-power valves rated well above UK legal power limits. W1JR stresses that the figures given in Table 1 have been extracted from manufacturers' data sheets and the IMD performance at the specified output is likely to prove an optimized target figure that will vary somewhat with different valves and will have been achieved under tight laboratory conditions with good instrumentation.

ELEVATED VERTICAL ANTENNAS

An item in the August *TT* "Elevated radials vindicated" (p599) made reference to a paper in *IEE Transactions on Broadcasting* (March 1988, pp75-77), "AM broadcast antennas with elevated radial ground systems" by Al Christman and Roger Radcliff of Ohio University. This reported computer modelling studies that have indicated that a lower-cost elevated vertical monopole antenna with four elevated horizontal radials can be expected to produce more ground-wave (low-angle) field strength than a conventional (broadcast) grounded monopole with 120 buried radials. I pointed out that this goes a long way to confirm, at least theoretically, the important practical work of Arch Doty, K8CFU and his colleagues, based on thousands of field measurements, first reported in *TT* (February, 1983, p131) and in more detail in *QST* (February 1983, pp20-25) and *CQ* (April 1984, pp24-42).

It transpires that Al Christman is KB8I and an expanded version of the *IEE Trans* paper, with emphasis on amateur-radio applications, appears under his name in *QST* (August 1988, ▶

TABLE 1
IMD specifications for a selection of transmitting valves used by amateurs on hf/vhf/uhf extracted by W1JR from valve manufacturers' data sheets

Type	Dissipation (Watts)	Peak Envelope Power output (Watts)	Specified IMD (dB down on p.e.p o/p)
Triodes			
3CX400A7/8874	400	590	35
3-400Z/8163	400	590	28
3CX800A7	800	750	36
3-1000Z/8164	1000	1080	29
Tetrodes			
4CX250R/7580W	250	470	23
8930 (formerly DX393	350	350	27
7650	600	680	27

Note that the specified IMD performance applies to the valve operated with correct parameters at the specified output. IMD will increase significantly at higher output powers.

BANDPASS FILTERS FOR CO-SITED TRANSMITTERS

The first time that I encountered the difficulty of operating simultaneously several transmitters and receivers from a single site was in a house in the XVI-th arrondissement of newly-liberated Paris in September 1944 when we were running several different links for Special Communications using HRO receivers and 40-watt (Mark III) and 150-watt (Mark X) transmitters. Every time one of us pressed a key it would disrupt every receiver in the room: a problem normally minimised in professional communications, other than Naval, by locating receivers well away from transmitters (with several HROs close together one could also experience the less serious problem of interference from local oscillators).

Today, 44 years later, the problem of co-sited and local transmitters still exists for amateurs, particularly during multi-operator, multiple-transmitter Field Days and contests. Indeed in some respects it has become worse due to design trends in modern transceivers (see "Broadband can be vulnerable").

In "Bandpass filters for hf transceivers" (*QST*, September 1988, pp17-19, 23), Lew Gordon, K4VX points out that when Field Day events are ruined by there being a number of transmitters on the same or nearby sites: "All that planning and anticipation down the drain! Frustrations and tempers immediately mount: someone yells 'Eighty metres is wiping me out!' or 'Every time you transmit, all I hear is noise!' . . . Although interference caused by receiver front-end overload from adjacent transmitters has existed since the earliest days of multiple-transmitter operations, the mutual interference problem has been exacerbated in the past few years by the widespread use of solidstate synthesized exciters. These rigs have not only greatly expanded operating ease and capabilities but

Table 2
Component values for K4VX's bandpass filters

Band	C1/C3 (pF)	C2 (pF)	L1/L3 (µH)	L2 (µH)	T-86-core L1/L3	T-86-core L2	T-80-6-core L1/L3	T-80-6-core L2	F$_r$ (MHz)
1·8	4000	400	2·2	22	22t	69t	23t	70t	1·75
3·5	2000	200	1·1	11	16t	48t	16t	50t	3·38
7	1000	100	0·55	5·5	11t	35t	11t	35t	6·78
14	500	50	0·28	2·8	8t	25t	8t	25	13·56
21	330	33	0·18	1·8	7t	20t	7t	20t	20·65
28	250	25	0·14	1·4	6t	17t	6t	18t	27·39

Table 3
Filter loss

Band (MHz)	Loss in decibels on different bands 3·5	7	14	21	28
3·5	<0·5	29	50	65	65
7	30	<0·5	32	41	49
14	56	32	<0·5	16	40
21	63	44	8	<0·5	15

also, as new devices and techniques are introduced, greater dynamic ranges than have previously been possible.

"There is a shortcoming in the new generation of transceivers, however. *Phase noise* . . . Not only is phase noise transmitted (and propagated) along with your signal on the band on which you are operating, but some noise energy is also transmitted on adjacent bands . . . fortunately not usually a major problem unless stations are

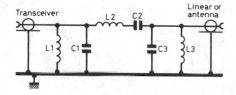

FIG 6 K4VX'S THREE-POLE BUTTERWORTH BANDPASS FILTERS FOR REDUCING TRANSCEIVER NOISE RADIATION ON ADJACENT BANDS AND FOR PROVIDING ADDITIONAL RF SELECTIVITY FILTERING IN RECEIVE MODE.

operating in close physical proximity.

"Filters constructed with components that can handle 100Watts of exciter output fitted between the exciter and the linear amplifier (if any) or the antenna would 'do the job nicely' providing filtering also in the receive mode, helping to reduce front-end overload problems. Even with new components the cost of filters should not exceed $10 each."

K4AVX provides layout and constructional details of these three-pole Butterworth bandpass filters in his *QST* but Fig 6 and Tables 2 and 3 will, it is hoped, provide a digest of this information in the space available in *TT*. It should also be noted that this form of band-pass filter will help to clean-up the harmonic output of any low- or medium-power transmitter and limit the number of strong broadcast signals entering the receiver in circumstances where the phase noise radiation on adjacent bands does not present a practical problem. Each filter was constructed on a 2- by 4-in single sided pcb.

pp35-42) as 'Elevated vertical antenna systems'. In this he writes:

"In agreement with the findings of Arch Doty,

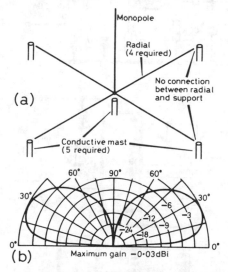

FIG 7(a) THE BASIC FOUR-RADIAL, ELEVATED VERTICAL-MONOPOLE (GROUND-PLANE) ANTENNA DESIGN AS SUBJECTED TO COMPUTER INVESTIGATION BY KB8I (QST). (b) ELEVATION-PLAN RADIATION PATTERN WITH ANTENNA ISOLATED FROM SUPPORT MAST WITH FEED-POINT HEIGHT OF 15 FEET (COMPUTER SIMULATION, GROUND CONDUCTIVITY NOT STATED).

K8CFU, I believe that the use of elevated, rather than buried, radials provides superior performance, because it allows the collection of electromagnetic energy in the form of *displacement currents*, rather than forcing *conduction currents* to flow through lossy earth.

"I will be doing field studies to verify the computer predictions. . . . If the information gathered from (the) NEC-GSD software is correct, the construction, cost and complexity of effective vertical-monopole antenna systems can be greatly reduced over that of comparable buried-radial systems now widely in use. At the same time, ease of installation and low-angle gain will be increased. The elevated-radial technique appears to be equally valid in the medium-frequency broadcast band and at the lower end of the hf range, so perhaps the ground-plane vertical is 'the antenna for all bands'!

"My studies on vertical monopole antennas (eg Fig 7) using the NEC-GSD computer code indicate that a radiator elevated 10 to 20 feet above ground and having only four elevated horizontal radials can outperform a ground-mounted monopole with 120 buried radials. At 3·8MHz an elevation of about 15 feet is adequate for average soil, while a lower height is satisfactory for shorter wavelengths. Higher elevation above ground is necessary over soil with poorer electrical characteristics and at lower operating frequencies."

REMOTE-TUNED 5·5M VERTICAL

A review of the type TCS80 antenna developed by DJ2UT in *Radio-REF* (09/1988, pp20-21) illustrates a novel use of a variometer-type arrangement to provide electrical loading of a 5·5m vertical antenna (quarter-wave resonance of the rod 13·6MHz) to enable it to work over the full range 3 to 30MHz, remotely tuned by means of the motorized variometer: Fig 8. In his review, Francois Rouais, F6CTK suggests that a six-month trial has shown that the TCS80 functions reasonably effectively throughout the hf spectrum when used with fewer radials than for more conventional verticals. The search for resonance is stated to be relatively quick and its efficiency is the same or better than a vertical antenna of the same height.

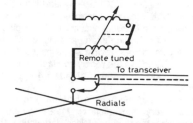

FIG 8 DJ2UT'S MULTIBAND (3-30MHZ) VERTICAL ANTENNA WITH VARIOMETER LOADING, MARKETED AS TYPE TCS80.

TECHNICAL TOPICS

PAT HAWKER · G3VA

COMPLEX ICs SIMPLIFY RECEIVERS

In so often advocating a 'kiss' (keep it simple, stupid) approach to amateur radio generally and home-constructed equipment in particular, I am acutely aware of the paradox presented by the increasing availability of medium, large and very-large-scale integrated circuits (MSI, LSI and VSLI). These often provide extremely complex circuitry yet represent to the constructor relatively simple devices with a minimum of external passive components. The 'one-chip' receiver is already with us, although it may still present some problems of lay-out etc, and is more applicable to broadcast than amateur reception. But there can be no doubt that LSI opens the way for the home-constructor to build 'complex systems' without breaching 'kiss' advice.

An informative article 'Simple receivers from complex ICs' by Bill Parrott, W6VEH (*Ham Radio*, annual receivers issue, November 1988, pp10-12, 14, 17, 18, 20, 22-23) describes the use of the recently introduced Signetics/Philips NE602N, in conjunction with the high-gain audio amplifier Plessey SL6310-DP etc, to form simple direct-conversion and super-DC-gainer receivers; in his case to form part of a portable noise-bridge detector. The NE602N comprises a double-balanced mixer, associated bipolar oscillator and integral buffering: Fig 1. The mixer portion resembles the MC1496G except that the eight external resistors usually required with the MC1496 have been moved on to the chip. The oscillator is internally biased and it should be noted that the external circuits need either to be isolated from earth and the 6V power line or blocking capacitors used. The mixer outputs however can be connected to the positive source voltage through the output circuit. W6VEH claims that "the chip is very easy to hook up and the oscillator seems to work with almost any breadboard lash-up". Like a multi-electrode frequency changer valve it can be used as a product detector, or frequency converter for HF or VHF, up to about 200MHz. The NE602N is optimised for 6V operation and in order to use a 9V battery without the power waste involved in zener diodes, W6VEM used a National LM2931 adjustable voltage regulator intended for vehicle applications which has a quiescent current of only 400µA and an input/output differential of only 0·6V. It is self-protecting against short-circuits, overloads, reversed input voltages and 60V transients. It sounds a very useful device for such purposes.

Figs 2 and 3 from the *HR* article show the basic front-end of a 28MHz DC receiver and the use of the NE602N as a crystal-controlled converter with extremely simple external circuitry and providing a simple means of adding extra bands to an existing direct-conversion receiver. In some cases it may prove possible to use the widely-available, low-cost 'clock-oscillator' crystals intended for digital systems.

The November 1988 issue of *Ham Radio* also contains a very long article by James M Larson, KF7M which is the reverse of 'kiss'. It describes the complete rebuilding of a Collins 75A-4 receiver in solid-state. More than 5,000 of these excellent

amateur-bands receivers were manufactured from 1955 to 1958 and they quickly gained the reputation of being one of the best communications

receivers ever built for the amateur-radio market. I must admit that if I had a 75A-4 in good condition, the last thing I would want to do would be to change

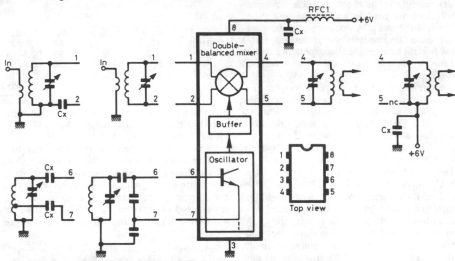

FIG 1. SOME POSSIBLE CONFIGURATIONS OF THE SILICONIX (PHILIPS) NE602N WHICH HAS BEEN CONFIRMED AS AVAILABLE IN THE UK. W6VEH POINTS OUT THAT BALANCED CIRCUITS ARE TO BE PREFERRED BUT MAY BE MORE DIFFICULT TO IMPLEMENT. CX BLOCKING/BYPASS CAPACITORS 0·001 to 0·1µF DEPENDING ON FREQUENCY. RFC1 FERRITE BEADS OR RFC RECOMMENDED AT HIGHER FREQUENCIES. UNMARKED COMPONENTS ARE TUNED CIRCUIT ELEMENTS. TYPICAL NE602N OPERATING PARAMETERS: SUPPLY VOLTAGE 6V DC, 2·5mA. MAXIMUM FREQUENCY 200MHZ. NOISE FIGURE 5dB. MIXER GAIN 20dB. THIRD-ORDER INTERCEPT −15dBm. INPUT AND OUTPUT IMPEDANCES BOTH 2×1·5KILOHMS.

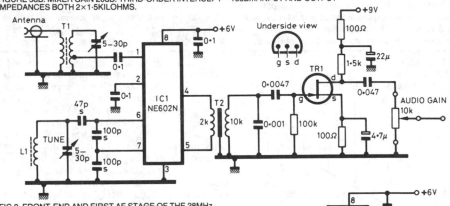

FIG 2. FRONT-END AND FIRST AF STAGE OF THE 28MHz VERSION OF W6VEH'S '3×8' DIRECT-CONVERSION RECEIVER. CAPACITORS MARKED 'S' ARE STABLE TYPES (IE POLYSTYRENE, SILVER MICA OR NPO CERAMIC). FOR 28MHz, L1 19 TURNS ON AMIDON T-50-12 CORE. TR1 MPF102, MPF106 OR SIMILAR FET. T2 MINIATURE 2K:10K AUDIO TRANSFORMER. THE FOLLOWING LOW-NOISE AF AMPLIFIER (NOT SHOWN ON THIS DIAGRAM) IS A SIGNETICS NE5230N DEVICE.

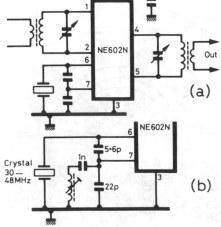

FIG 3. USE OF NE602N AS A CRYSTAL-CONTROLLED CONVERTER. THE 5dB NOISE FIGURE IS LOW ENOUGH FOR OPTIMUM SENSITIVITY UP TO ABOUT 50MHz WITHOUT AN RF AMPLIFIER.

it to solid-state, but there is no accounting for taste. KF7M set out "to get the tubes out yet retain or improve the original operating features and performance. I wanted a receiver that looked and felt like a 75A-4". His major project certainly resulted in considerably improved stability (to ±10Hz/hour) but his improved IMD performance depends on the use of an AGC-controlled input attenuator without any pre-mixer amplification, although retaining the pre-mixer tuned circuits as a double-tuned filter, rather than attempting to maintain the basic dynamic range of the original model which used the special 6DC6 valve with its good signal-handling performance. Nevertheless anyone contemplating rebuilding an old valve receiver as a long-term project would find KF7M's article instructive.

SIMPLE OVERCURRENT PROTECTION

M R Perry, G8AKX believes that many of us have overlooked an effective 'kiss' system of providing current overload protection that he has found invaluable over many years in electrical, radio and television engineering; it saved him many RF power transistors in his early days of building transistor transmitters and recently in tracing an intermittent and unpredictable fault in a high-voltage switch-mode power supply that resulted in

several blown transistors. It has also proved useful in a digital multimeter when a change to nicad batteries underlined the fact that during switching operations there was a temporary short-circuit of the battery, no problem with batteries having appreciable internal resistance but resulting in burning of the PCB track.

So what is this simple solution? A solution that also provides a visual indication of an overcurrent situation. It is, as you may have guessed, the common tungsten lamp which has a much lower resistance when the filament is cold, than when hot and which is designed to dissipate considerable power. The lamp is connected in series with the load requiring protection. As a very rough guide the cold resistance of most tungsten lamps is about one-tenth of the resistance as calculated from its rating as a lamp, but G8AKX warns that there are exceptions and considerable variation between different samples of nominally similarly-rated lamps.

He points out that the two basic requirements in using this method is that the lamp voltage should be roughly equal to the supply rail voltage and the normal lamp current should be above the normal load current by a factor of about five. For example, in the test-meter application with a 6V battery and presenting an 80mA load, a 0·3A pilot (dial) bulb

was used which gave less than 0·5V drop under normal operation. A 300V PSU was protected during testing and fault tracing using three 240V, 100W lamps in parallel. Apart from the possible problem of thermal inertia, applicable to the fastest acting devices where there is no overvoltage protection, the only snags could be for equipment where even a small voltage drop cannot be tolerated or for equipment taking many amperes; for example it could not be used to provide overcurrent protection for the 30A PSU described on page 38.

G8AKX gives some examples of the cold resistance of lamps, though these should be regarded only as a very rough guide:

Lamp Rating	Cold Resistance (ohms)	Rating	Cold Resistance (ohms)
6V 100mA	6	12V 21W	0·6
6V 0·5A	2	24V 50mA	50
12V 50mA	25	130V 15mA	800
12V 2·2W	7	240V 100W	40
12V 6W	1		

This is a simple yet effective technique provided that, in the case of RF power transistors etc, it is remembered that it does *not* provide protection against *overvoltages*. Semiconductors can be destroyed by a very short-duration transient overvoltage.

EMC – SLOW PROGRESS OF EUROPEAN DIRECTIVE

There is still only slow progress being made in connection with the European Commission's EMC Directive and the UK legislation that will be needed to make a number of BSI/CISPR standards legally enforceable. According to the DTI, on present timescales, the Directive should come into force on 1 January, 1992. However, it will allow a transitional period in the event of non-completion of standards at the date of its implementation, but with a deadline currently limited to 31 December 1992. Thereafter the Directive would apply to *all* apparatus and, if standards were still not drawn up, manufacturers would be asked to certify compliance with its general requirements by means of the proposed technical file route. But it would seem possible that even these deadlines may slip again.

BSI/CISPR standards that are still not legally enforceable include the spurious radiation limits of industrial, scientific and medical equipment (BS4809/CISPR11); radiation from information technology equipment including computers (BS6527/CISPR22); and the immunity of television and radio receivers to local RF fields (BS905, Part 2/CISPR20). All of these are of considerable importance to radio amateurs but it looks as though enforcement is still several years away.

Last year I visited the DTI's Kenley Radio Technology Laboratories on the former RAF aerodrome near Whyteleafe, Surrey, the main UK laboratory for approvals testing. It was frustrating to watch a demonstration of the measurement of the radiation, under the conditions specified in BS6527, from an Amstrad personal computer that showed it was radiating 40dB(μV) at 128MHz, 10dB more than the still unenforceable BS6527 limit of 30dB – and thus a potential hazard to aeronautical radio. Similarly Kenley showed their large TEM cell for testing the immunity of television receivers, etc, in a measurable, evenly-spread level of RF energy at frequencies up to 150MHz, but unfortunately there is still no way in which the DTI can insist on set makers complying with BS905 Part 2.

Even when these eventually become legally enforceable in the UK amateurs should not expect too much benefit from immunity regulations which are difficult to 'police' and enforce. The DTI last year made it known that although it expects to be given power under the European Directive to forbid the marketing of apparatus or insist on their withdrawal from the market if it does not meet the appropriate standards, it expects to act only on receipt of specific complaints rather than insisting on a pre-marketing 'approval test' for the bulk of consumer electronics.

Even where, as in the Federal Republic of Germany, there has been for a number of years an established system whereby anyone buying a radio or television set receives a letter from the German Post Office, EMC problems may still arise. This letter, according to Hans Ruckert, VK2AOU (*Amateur Radio*, July 1988) is as follows:

"Dear radio listener/television viewer: (1) This equipment has been permitted to be purchased and used for the reception of radio and television signals. (2) The equipment must be used only to receive broadcast sound and television signals within West Germany. It is illegal to listen to police, maritime and mobile land radio stations. (3) Marking with the FTZ Test Number offers you the guarantee that this equipment does not interfere with other telecommunication services including radio services. Marking with the letter 'S' or 'SK' beside the FTZ Test Number indicates that this equipment is largely immune against disturbance by other radio services (eg amateur radio and CB radio). Please contact the local Radio Disturbance Measuring Office if, in special circumstances, disturbance occurs.

"Notes: *Disturbance* is caused by lack of immunity of a piece of equipment from licensed transmissions affecting it. *Interference* is caused by illegal transmissions."

To a British amateur such a letter reads almost like manna from Heaven! But tests carried out in 1986 by the German consumer-goods testing

organisation on 12 prominent makes of television receivers showed that in seven cases the sets did not meet the standard implied by their certification.

Apparently, the FTZ tests only one prototype receiver and this is not necessarily representative of mass-production. As VK2AOU puts it: "Regulations which are not effectively policed are worse than no laws at all. They are misused by those who attempt to be 'smarter' than the authorities, to the detriment of the public."

Personally, I feel that it would be naïve to expect too much from future UK or EC regulations on television set and video cassette recorder immunity, I suspect that there will be occasional problems of TVI, VCRI and spurious radiation from digital equipment and switched mode power supplies for years to come; welcome though the 'immunity' regulations will be.

J M Osborne, G3HMO suggests that: "In investigating possible TVI with neighbours it is often difficult to obtain confirmation of whether this really happens, when it happens, and what are the actual effects on the screen or sound. Without assistance one cannot go around and see while the transmitter is being operated normally. It is not even always convincing if the XYL says she did or did not notice anything untoward. I recently acquired (for another purpose) a 5·5-in. mini monochrome television set, about the size of an Avo multimeter. It now sits on my ATU. If I have 100W SSB radiating without any observable TVI on any channel, I can feel reasonably certain that any interference problem is not at my end. It can also be a useful point to make when discussing TVI with a neighbour as he will understand such an explanation or demonstration and not feel you are attempting to blind him with science. Of course, it is not an infallible test but it does boost confidence."

Incidentally, I wonder whether we should follow the German lead and distinguish between the words 'disturbance' and 'interference'. Perhaps we should cease talking about TVI and use TVD instead.

Pat Hawker's observations on this complex subject are strictly personal and do not reflect the views of the RSGB.

20A POWER SUPPLY UNIT

Although there are now evident advantages in running medium and high-power amplifiers from 50V or 28V power supplies, the majority of current equipment continues to be based on the use of 12-14V supplies and, if operated directly from AC mains supplies, calls for power supply units capable of delivering very high currents without saturating on peaks. Since an SSB rig represents a variable load with intermittent peaks, there is much to be said in favour of using, in the shack, as well as during mobile operation, a trickle-charged vehicle-battery, preferably a modern sealed type. This type of arrangement has been discussed many times in *TT* and remains a cost-effective approach provided that due care is taken to maintain the battery in good condition. Vehicle batteries, designed to deliver the heavy load of a starting motor, are capable of delivering very high peak currents, always provided that the battery leads offer very low ohmic resistance. However, the lifetime of a neglected, poorly-maintained battery can be short.

Despite the attraction of heavy-duty lead-acid batteries, there are many situations where users prefer to obtain power directly from the mains supplies. This can call for units able to deliver up to about 20A continuously. Several 13V, 20A units have been described over the years in *TT*, the most recently being G3LBA/PA3ACQ's unit with a hex fet (IRF150) pass device, 723-based voltage regulator and over-voltage protection in the form of a thyristor crowbar (*TT*, October 1985, p785). This remains a most useful design although not all suppliers appear to stock the IRF150 device which comprises six power fets in a single package. See also the *Practical Wireless* 30A 'Marchwood' PSU in *TT*, May 1984 pp402-3.

Over the past 20 years, the Moorabbin and District Radio Club of Victoria, Australia has published a number of designs in *Amateur Radio* (VK)

for high-current power supply units in support of their kit projects. From time to time, the Moorabbin PSU has been redesigned, in part to take advantage of new components but also because of the perennial problem of some devices (eg 78HG primary regulator) vanishing from the marketplace.

The Moorabbin Mark IV PSU is described in *Amateur Radio* (VK) August 1988, pp4-6 rated at a continuous output of up to 20A and featuring overvoltage and overcurrent protection and a 275V metal-oxide-varistor (MOV) to clip transient high-voltage spikes from the mains supplies (General Electric V275LA20A). Another useful, though uncommon, feature on low-voltage supplies is the 200-ohm, 10W resistor (two 100-ohm, five-watt resistors in series) across the very high-capacitance 33,600µF reservoir capacitor (six 5,600µF, 40V high ripple-current capacitors in parallel) to ensure that the large and potentially dangerous amount of energy stored in these capacitors is quickly bled off when the PSU is switched off.

A 723 (14-pin DIL) device is used as the primary voltage regulator, fitted with 1nF ceramic bypass capacitors to prevent malfunctions in strong RF fields. The 723 drives the base of a single 2N3055 DC amplifier which in turn drives the eight, paralleled 2N3055 pass transistors. The use of eight of these devices, each of which has a maximum current rating of 10A, needs some explanation. This is given as follows: "It is true that a 2N3055 can pass 10A but, at this current level, the DC gain has dropped to an alarmingly low level and little or no regulating capability remains. Assuming that the 2N3055 is at the lowest end of its DC gain specification then each pass transistor should carry no more than 2·5A if the capabilities of the driver transistor and the 723 primary regulator are not to be overtaxed."

The rectifier and the pass transistors *must* be

mounted on adequate heat-sinks. A 75mm length of 'Minifin' should be suitable for the 35A bridge rectifier; four 150-mm lengths for the eight 2N3055 pass transistors, two mounted on each length. If a PCB is used, all high-wattage (5W) resistors should be mounted on standoff spacers to reduce the amount of heat applied to the circuit board. Eight 0·22ohm 5W current-sharing resistors are connected in the emitter connections to the pass transistors. The combined output current passes through three paralleled 0·1ohm 5W resistors to form a voltage drop for overload protection. When the total output reaches 20A the voltage drop across the 0·033ohm resistance will equal or exceed 0·67V and is applied across pins two and three of the 723. This has the effect of progressively reducing the voltage output of the 723 and consequently the voltage and current supplied to the external load.

The overvoltage protection is described as follows: "For outputs up to 15V the zener diode does not conduct. Above 15V it conducts and a voltage appears across the 470ohm resistor between the zener diode and earth. This voltage is filtered and applied to the BD136/BD140 combination causing them to draw current through the relay coil. This breaks the DC supply to the regulating section and energises the overvoltage indicator LED. The supply will remain in the cut-off condition until AC is removed from the transformer primary and the capacitors discharged through the 200-ohm bleed resistors. Optional voltage and current monitoring can be obtained by means of a 30A FSD meter in series with the output from the circuit board and the output terminal on the enclosure; similarly a 20V FSD meter can be connected across the output terminals for voltage monitoring.

It should be noted that the supply as shown in Fig 4 is 'floating' with the mains earth connected only to the electrostatic shield of the transformer. *Amateur Radio* recommends that this mains/shield/case

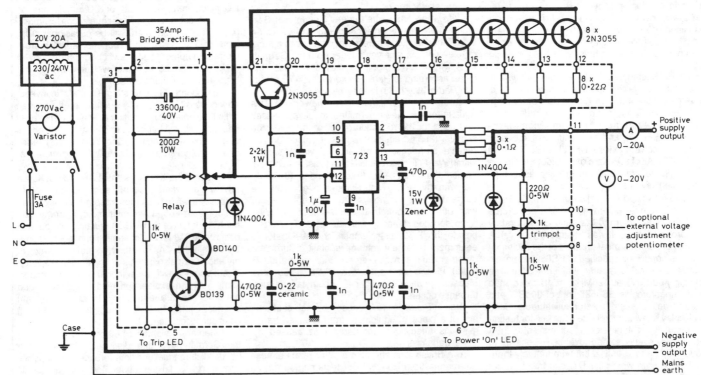

FIG 4. THE MOORABBIN MARK IV 20A POWER SUPPLY UNIT WITH OVERVOLTAGE AND OVERCURRENT PROTECTION. COMPONENTS WITHIN DOTTED LINES CAN BE MOUNTED ON A 150mm-SQUARE CIRCUIT BOARD (LAYOUT SHOWN IN *AMATEUR RADIO*, AUGUST 1988) BUT THIS IS NOT ESSENTIAL.

earth lead be brought to a separate front panel terminal for connection to the negative supply output terminal if required. Normally the voltage setting trimpot is mounted on the control board and is set to give one specified voltage output. Optionally this potentiometer can be omitted from the board and replaced with a 1K *linear* potentiometer mounted on the front panel. This will enable the output voltage to be varied as required between a low of eight volts and the upper limit of 15V determined by the overvoltage circuitry.

The transformer secondary must be rated to supply at least 20A continuously. The 'heavy' leads in Fig 4 shold be capable of carrying 30A or so.

DIRECT-READING CAPACITANCE METERS

Twelve years ago, *TT* (January 1977, p35, Figs 2 and 3) included information on two direct-reading capacitance meters based on the 555 timer IC that had originally appeared in the magazine *Television*. One had five switched ranges covering capacitor values from a few picofarads to about 10μF: Fig 5.

The other unit was intended for measuring electrolytic capacitors in the range 10μF to about 4000μF.

The basic principle of the unit shown in Fig 5 is to charge the unknown capacitor to a fixed voltage (4·5V) and then to discharge it into the meter circuit; the average current is directly proportional to the capacitance; the whole process being continuously repeated by the astable operation of the 555. The meter needle remains steady, although some vibration can be observed on the higher capacitance ranges. The unit which draws about 3mA battery current, delivers unidirectional voltage to the capacitor under test; this means that it can be used to measure polarised capacitors, such as electrolytics, and it will also cope with reverse-biased semiconductor junction capacitances which can be a useful guide to the f_T of an unknown transistor.

In 1977 it was noted that: "To avoid overloading the meter movement, large value capacitors should not be connected with the range switched to a low capacitance range: it is therefore useful to arrange the switch so that one starts at the highest value

range, rotating the switch clockwise until reasonable deflection is obtained, and the value read off. The five S1 switch positions give FSD ranges of 1μF, 0·1μF, 10nF, 1nF and 100pF. S3 provides a 'times ten' extension, for example providing measurement up to 10μF on the 1μF range. S2 is a 'divide by two' facility, providing FSD ranges of 0·5μF, 0·05μF etc. The 50pF 'divide by two' range is unlikely to be accurate, but it does allow estimation of values down to 1 or 2pF."

Recently, Ray Pascoe, G3IOI built this capacitance meter but noted that the 100pF range was reading approximately 10% low compared with the other ranges. A second 555 IC was substituted but showed the same effect. G3IOI's remedy was to connect a switched 100kΩ preset resistor in parallel with the existing 47kΩ range-setting potentiometer on all ranges *except* the 100pF range: Fig 5 (b). He writes:

"Ideally, the 100kΩ preset would be switched into circuit with another bank on the range switch but mine did not have any spare contacts so I use a small toggle switch with legends 1 and 2-5 corre- ▶

EUROPEAN VALVE NOMENCLATURE

It is difficult for some of us always to appreciate that many present-day radio amateurs and enthusiasts have never used valves, either in receivers or transmitters and have little idea of how they progressively evolved over more than 60 years into effective, flexible and rugged devices. It is often forgotten that the Post Office Research Station, while at Dollis Hill, developed a range of valves for use in submarine cable repeaters with a guaranteed operational lifetime of 20 years. Dr Tommy Flowers who led the wartime Post Office team that developed the pioneering 'Colossus' computers for Bletchley Park – generally recognised now as the world's first programmable, operational, digital-electronics computers although possibly challenged for this title by the work of Dr John Atanasoff and Clifford Berry whose 'ABC' machine developed between 1939 to 1942 was held in 1973 to upset the Sperry Rand Corporation's patents for the ENIAC machine which, until the disclosure of the 1943-44 work on Colossus by the PO team under the guidance of Bletchley Park cryptanalysts Max Newman, Alan Turing and Gordon Welchman, had been widely accepted as the first working digital electronic computer.

Last year, Dr Flowers described how it proved possible to develop equipment using as many as 2400 valves yet capable of providing reliable 24-hour operation. That thermionic valves and copper-oxide rectifiers could be used as switches at much higher speeds than electromagnetic relays was recognised in the 1930s, but put to little practical use because of cost and fear of valve failures. On Colossus, to achieve long and reliable valve life, heaters were *never* turned off, not even during maintenance. The use of relatively large pre-war valves such as the EF36, 6V6, 807 etc meant that they were not mounted very close together resulting in fewer 'hot spots' than in later valve equipment based on 'miniature' (B9A etc) valves. In practice, after the usual few initial failures, the valves in Colossus proved as reliable as the passive components.

Today, of course, vastly more computer power than that of Colossus is available on one or two chips and nobody would dream of using valves for such applications. However, it must be remembered that this is not the case where we need to handle or generate high RF power.

Even those who have long used valves, however, tend to be more familiar with American type numbers than with the considerably more informative European valve nomenclature. Did you know, for example, that the type number EF80 tells you immediately that the valve is an RF pentode, has a 6·3V heater and a B9A base? Two standard codes were originated in Continental Europe but were progressively introduced into the UK via the Philips/Mullard group of companies and were ultimately used by most UK valve manufacturers. The first applied to power valves for transmitters and industrial equipment; the second to valves used in receivers and general-purpose equipment.

Transmitting valves: The first letter of the type number denotes the general class of the valve: M audio (low-frequency) power amplifier or amplitude modulator triode; P RF power pentode; Q RF power tetrode (QQ double RF tetrode); R rectifier; T RF power triode. The second letter (or with QQ types the third letter) indicates the type of cathode/filament: G oxide-coated filament in mercury-vapour rectifier; V indirectly-heated oxide-coated cathode; X directly-heated pure tungsten filament; Y directly-heated thoriated tungsten filament; Z directly-heated oxide-coated filament (except in mercury-vapour rectifiers). A third letter S indicates a silica envelope. The first number (one or two digits) indicates the anode voltage (CCS rating) in kilovolts (eg 05 indicates 0·5kV, ie the valve is conservatively rated for an anode voltage of 500V; similarly 5 means 5kV etc). The second number (following a dash) shows for valves up to 5kW anode dissipation, the maximum permissible (continuous) anode dissipation in watts.

To show how this system works, the following are some types that have been used in amateur transmitters: QV04-7 indicates an RF power tetrode with an indirectly-heated oxide-coated cathode with its anode conservatively rated to work from a 400V HT line and to dissipate up to seven watts continuously. QQV06-40 tells you that this is a double-tetrode RF power valve with indirectly-heated oxide-coated cathode, the anodes rated for 600V and 40 watts dissipation. QV08-100 RF power tetrode with oxide-coated cathode rated for 800V (in amateur practice up to about 1250V) able to dissipate up to 100 watts continuously. QY3-125 is a directly-heated RF power tetrode with thoriated

tungsten filament suitable for use with up to 3kV on the anode and able to dissipate 125 watts continuously (ie near European equivalent to the well-known 813). One cannot, however, tell from the type number the type of valve socket required.

The European receiving valve code does provide this information. Unfortunately it was, for many years, not used by a number of British valve manufacturers who insisted on using their own type numbers and their own bases even when the valves were direct equivalents of types also available in the European code.

In this code, the first letter denotes the heater/filament rating in volts or amperes as follows: A 4V; B 180mA (DC); C 200mA (AC/DC); D 1·4V (DC filament); E 6·3V; F 13V; K 2V (DC filament); P 0·3A AC/DC; U 100mA (0·1A) AC/DC; V 50mA (0·05A) AC/DC.

The second, and where applicable, third and fourth letters in multi-electrode valves indicate the general type of valve: A diode; B double-diode; C triode; D output triode; E tetrode; F RF pentode; H hexode or heptode; K octode; L output pentode (including line-output pentode etc); M magic eye (tuning indicator); X full-wave rectifier, gas-filled; Y half-wave rectifier (vacuum); Z full-wave rectifier (vacuum).

The number following the letters shows the individual type but also the type of its base (socket): side-contact numbers 1 to 10; 'footless' 11 to 20; loctal 21 to 30; international octal 31 to 39 and 300 series; B8A 40 to 49 and 140 to 149; B9A 80 to 89, 180 series, 800 series; B7G 90 to 99; B10B 200 series; B9D 500 series.

Some examples will show how this code works: EF85 RF pentode with 6·3V heater, B9A base (in practice a useful variable-mu RF pentode for HF receiver front-ends); EABC80, 6·3V heater, diode plus double-diode, triode with B9A base (ie triple-diode-triode widely used as FM discriminator/AM detector/AF amplifier in old AM/FM broadcast receivers); EL84 output pentode with 6·3V heater and B9A base; PL500 0·3A heater, (line) output pentode with B9D base.

The code does not eliminate the need to know the electrodes to which the pins are connected and often the more detailed valve characteristics etc, but are, nevertheless, useful as a preliminary source of information.

sponding to the main switch range positions.

"Calibration is first done on the 100pF range with a 100pF, 1% tolerance capacitor connected across the test socket (Cx) and the 47k preset adjusted for full scale. Next, on the 1000pF range with the 100kΩ preset switched in and a 1000pF, 1% capacitor across Cx, the 100kΩ preset is adjusted for full scale deflection. Calibration on the higher capacitance ranges should then be correct. To calibrate the 'divide-by-two' position I used a 500pF 1% capacitor on the 1000pF range and adjusted the 10kΩ preset for full scale deflection with the switch closed. The 'times 10' facility adjustment can be carried out on the same range with a 1000pF, 1% capacitor across Cx and the 470-ohm preset adjusted for 10% of FSD with the switch closed.

"The accuracy is remarkable for such a simple instrument. Using several different value 1% tolerance capacitors on the 100pF, the readings obtained were almost 'spot on'. Similar results were obtained on the higher ranges. It's proving an excellent use for a large round 50µA meter that has been in my junk box for many years!"

For those without a good spare µA meter, a rather different form of adaptor unit to permit an existing digital or analogue multimeter, switched to read resistance, permits direct reading of capacitance values from a few picofarads up to about 2000µF in two ranges is described by Barry Kauler in Electronics Australia (August 1988, pp86-87). The unit is constructed in the form of a plug-in adaptor, uses only a few components and is claimed to be very easy to get going.

In this unit, the basic idea is an adaptor which plugs into the multimeter to convert it into a capacitance meter with two ranges, one reading in picofarads, the other in nanofarads and suitable for polarised capacitors such as electrolytics. The meter reading in ohms is divided by 10 to give the capacitance value in pF on the 'low' range or nF on the 'high' range.

The unit comprises a 74HC132 quad Schmitt trigger IC with 2-input NAND gates. The first (IC1a) forms a relaxation oscillator with a frequency depending on the value of the unknown capacitor connected across Cx. IC1b and IC1c acts as a monostable to convert the oscillator output into a stream of narrow pulses of constant width but with a duty cycle (mark/space ratio) proportional to the Cx. The pulses are squared off and inverted in polarity by IC1d and then used to switch TR1, a VN10KM enhancement-mode power mosfet. TR1 provides very fast switching with very low 'on' resistance and it is claimed that the adaptor is capable of providing accurate results (always pro-

vided that the resistance measurements on the multimeter are sufficiently accurate). Barry Kauler describes adjustment of the adaptor as follows:

"When the board is complete, plug it into your meter set to a suitable ohms range (initially with 1MΩ near full scale). Then switch S1 to the low (pF) range, and plug in a 0·1µF capacitor, preferably of known high accuracy (low tolerance). It should then be possible to adjust the 2kΩ trimpot to give a reading of 1MΩ, corresponding to 100,000pF. If you have any difficulty in achieving the correct reading, you may have to reduce the value of the fixed resistor in series with the 2kΩ trimpot from its value of 3kΩ. All four fixed resistors in this circuit should preferably be 1% tolerance.

"Next remove the 0·1µF capacitor and plug in a 10pF NPO or styroseal capacitor of known accuracy. Switch the meter down until it can read a value of 100Ω accurately, and adjust the trimmer capacitor to give this reading. Finally plug in the 0·1µF capacitor again, switch S1 to 'high' (nF) range, adjust the meter to read 1000Ω accurately and adjust the 200Ω trimpot for this reading." ∎

FIG 7. THE PCB PATTERN (ACTUAL SIZE) AND COMPONENT PLACEMENT.

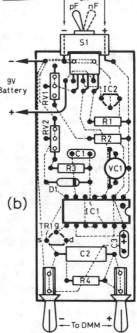

(a)

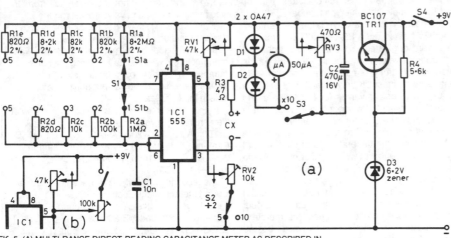

FIG 5. (A) MULTI-RANGE DIRECT-READING CAPACITANCE METER AS DESCRIBED IN 'TELEVISION' AND IN TT, JANUARY 1977. THE ARROWS AGAINST THE PRESET POTENTIOMETERS INDICATE THE DIRECTION OF MOVEMENT WITH CLOCKWISE ROTATION. THE UNIT IS CAPABLE OF MEASURING CAPACITORS WITH VALUES FROM A FEW PICOFARADS TO ABOUT 10µF. D1, D2 OA47 GOLD-BONDED GERMANIUM DIODES. D3 BZY88 C6V2 400mW 6·2V ZENER DIODE. RESISTORS ARE 5% TOLERANCE UNLESS OTHERWISE INDICATED. CLEAR READING 50µA FSD METER RECOMMENDED. (B) MODIFIED ARRANGEMENT BY G3IOI TO OVERCOME A 10% CALIBRATION ERROR ON 100pF RANGE, RESULTING IN "SPOT ON" CALIBRATION THROUGHOUT THE RANGES.

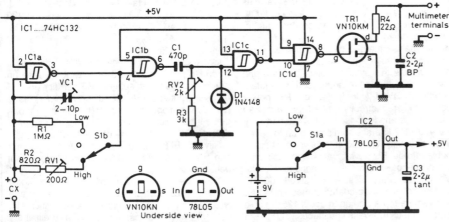

FIG 6. THE ELECTRONICS AUSTRALIA CAPACITOR METER ADAPTOR FOR USE WITH A DIGITAL OR ANALOGUE MULTIMETER.

TECHNICAL TOPICS

PAT HAWKER · G3VA

EMC – A GROWING TECHNICAL PROBLEM

Recent letters in *RadCom* reporting horrendously difficult social problems with neighbours, in which the amateur is cast in the role of a social outcast, have brought home to many the unhappy fact that electromagnetic compatibility (EMC) has once again become a major technical problem that poses a threat to the operation of amateur stations in residential areas.

The problem of causing 'disturbance' (to use the German term) to television receivers reached a peak in the early 1950s and led to a complete and agonising re-appraisal of transmitter shielding and the introduction of low-pass-filters in order to mini-

mise harmonic output. By the 1960s, the threat of harmonic radiation had been largely overcome, and the switch of British television to UHF Bands IV and V in the late 1960s and early 1970s brought further relief, at least to HF operators. It has been the progressive introduction of easily overloaded solid-state devices in TV sets and more recently 24-hour TV that have highlighted the poor 'immunity' of so many sets to strong out-of-band signals or direct audio breakthrough. Although undoubtedly the fault is primarily in the receiver rather than the transmitter, it is often virtually impossible for the amateur himself to convince neighbours of this. The position became much worse when the DTI, in a government cost-cutting exercise, abandoned

suddenly its long-established free radio interference service just about the time that many highly-vulnerable video cassette recorders were being installed in so many homes, along with an electronic telephones, microprocessor-operated domestic appliances and the like. Furthermore the public is becoming increasingly concerned with 'radiation hazards', seldom appreciating the important difference between ionizing (nuclear) radiation, the strong magnetic fields immediately under the power lines of the electricity grid and non-ionizing radiation from radio transmitters.

Once again, there is a real danger that the public will come to consider anyone with a transmitter as a social outcast, if not as a social leper. ►

IMPROVING LINEARITY OF SSB POWER AMPLIFIERS

Tony Preedy, G3LNP believes that there is a real need to improve "some of the grotty signals one hears these days" and points to the IMD specifications for tetrode valves steaming from W1JR (Table 1 in the December *TT*, p960). He considers these indicate a very poor performance for tetrode amplifiers if driven to the specified output powers. He writes:

"Many older valve types are capable of better performance than shown in Table 1. The QY4-400 for example will deliver 600watts PEP at −36dB IMD. (Note that the American method of specifying IMD tends to differ from the system often used in the UK – G3VA).

"I have found that a worthwhile improvement in IMD performance is easily obtainable by using simple negative feedback techniques. NFB makes the amplifier more tolerant of output tuning and

loading errors. As an alternative to reducing distortion, NFB can be used as a means of achieving greater output or allowing use of less critical power supply regulations, or lower quiescent current – all for a given level of distortion!

"Fig 1 shows how I obtain simultaneously both 3dB of RF of 3dB of envelope NFB with a pair of QY4-400 tetrodes. To offset the reduction with NFB of voltage gain, it is necessary to increase the value of the grid damping resistance if only a constant amount of drive power is available. The knock-on effect of this is that neutralisation may become necessary. I use the wideband grid input and neutralisation arrangement shown in Fig 2 to achieve a low input-VSWR from 3·5 to 30MHz. Drive power is about 50W for 400W output with 1·8kV on the anodes. An old NCX5 transceiver is used as the driver. Even when using a home-made RF-type speech-clipper I consistently receive complimentary reports on signal quality.

"Incidentally, I find that the best way to test SSB amplifiers is to use white noise at the microphone input. This allows the amplifier to be operated continuously at the full PEP output while the average power in the dummy load is similar to that obtained with speech (ie, about one-tenth of the PEP figure). A selective receiver can then be used to inspect the unwanted sideband while making linearity adjustments. A good source of white noise is a VHF

receiver with the antenna disconnected."

One point that emerges strongly from recent *TT* items on high-power (legal limit) SSB linear amplifiers is the requirement that these need to be designed, built, set up and operated to good professional standards and with a real understanding of the engineering and technology. It should also go without saying that it is essential to take safety precautions when working with high voltages. The following notes are taken from *QST*, October 1988, p89:

"Working with valve amplifiers involves voltages and currents that can kill you instantly should you come into contact with them. Take proper precautions whenever you work on such equipment.

"Before working on an amplifier: (1) Turn off the amplifier. (2) Unplug the amplifier from the AC line. (3) Wait until the high-voltage meter indicates less than 100V. (4) Use a shorting stick, *in series with a 100-ohm, 24W resistor*, to short-circuit the amplifier B+ (high-voltage bus) to earth to discharge the HV-supply filter capacitors. The resistor protects the amplifier's anode and grid current meters – and their shunt resistors if any – from damage as the capacitors are discharged by the shorting stick.

"*Pulling the plug* and following these steps is the only *safe* way to work on an amplifier. Most interlocks do not disconnect the line voltage from the amplifier when the amplifier lid is removed."

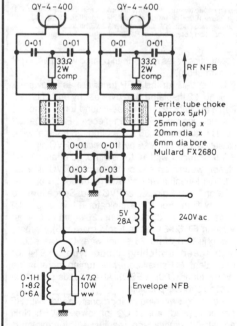

FIG 1. G3LNP's FILAMENT CIRCUIT OF HIS QY4-400 AMPLIFIER SHOWING HIS METHOD OF OBTAINING BOTH ENVELOPE AND RF NEGATIVE FEEDBACK THAT OFFERS A NUMBER OF ADVANTAGES INCLUDING LESS INTERMODULATION DISTORTION.

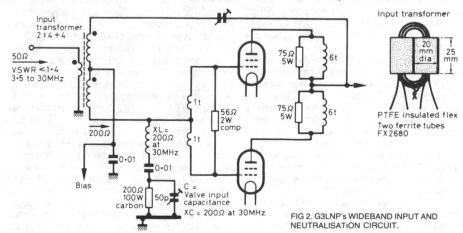

FIG 2. G3LNP's WIDEBAND INPUT AND NEUTRALISATION CIRCUIT.

It is important to ensure that newcomers to our hobby be aware of the problems they are likely to face and be encouraged to acquire the basic technical knowledge needed to understand the many aspects of EMC. This does not mean that an amateur should attempt to modify his neighbour's appliances other, perhaps, than by fitting an add-on filter unit. But he does need to be able to show that he or she knows what they are doing and understands what EMC is all about. Amateur radio has always been primarily a scientific and technical hobby. If we are content to become non-technical 'appliance fun-operators' its long-term future will indeed be at peril.

David Reynolds, G3ZPF is one of several recent *TT* correspondents who are concerned at the increasing number of consumer-electronics appliances with little built-in immunity to strong – and not so strong – local signals. He writes (in early December):

"It will soon be Christmas and I bet I will get the usual procession of neighbours complaining that their brand-new electronic gadget is wilting in the presence of my modest RF.

"I know the problems can be cured, if Joe Public acts rationally, but we have now gone from the

stage where each house had just one 'wireless' and maybe one 'TV' to the typical family home with a main colour TV set and VCR, one or two transportable TV sets, possibly with one having a video or used with a microcomputer, a 'tower hifi system', ghetto blasters for the youngsters, computers, radio alarms, radio-controlled toys, electronic and cordless telephones, microprocessors in this, that and the other and so on *ad infinitum*.

"Even with the best will in the world, it may take several weeks sorting that lot out . . . and just when you finally think it safe to go back on the air, it's somebody's birthday and another new gimmick in their home! And I firmly believe that trying to sort it all out by yourself without involving the DTI, is a positive *disservice* to the hobby."

The problem of EMC, spectrum pollution and spectrum management are now at the forefront of professional technology. Unless, as amateurs, we recognise that we too have a real part to play in their solution, then inevitably we shall see our privileges wither away. This is something that involves us all and will *not* be met by regarding amateur radio as purely a fun hobby. We should do well to remember that a general WARC, at which the entire International Frequency Allocation Table

will be reviewed, is now almost certain to be held within the next five years, possibly as early as 1992 or 1993. It will once again be necessary to justify the allocation of valuable parts of the radio spectrum to a 'hobby'.

SOLID-STATE RF POWER AMPLIFIERS

There have been several mentions in recent *TTs* of Motorola 'Application Note' publications which give detailed information on the design, construction and setting-up of power amplifiers based on the company's range of solidstate RF power devices. This has prompted Mike Grierson, G3TSO/KD3CL to pass along the information that several of these amplifiers are available in kit form from: Communication Concepts Inc, 121 Brown Street, Dayton, Ohio 45402, USA Tel: (513) 220-9677. US prices for complete kit of parts (less the heatsink) and presumably subject to six per cent import duty and 15 per cent VAT are: AN758 300W $160,70; AN762 140W $93·25 (this design is featured in the *ARRL Handbook* and is ideal for adding to the recently described G3TSO transceiver); AN779 20W $83·79; EB63 140W $88·65; EB27A 300W $139·20; and EB104 600W $448·15. G3TSO states that these kits can be purchased by means

RESONANT ATU WITH PARALLEL INDUCTORS

It is common practice to connect two or more capacitors in parallel in order to obtain a required value of capacitance. It is much less often that one sees the same technique applied to inductors in order to obtain a lower value of inductance, even though this can sometimes provide a useful simplification in band-switching etc.

This is well-illustrated in the article 'A simple resonant ATU' by Doug DeMaw, W1FB (*QST*, September 1988, pp26-28). His design eliminates both roller inductors and tapped inductors and reduces band changing to three simple on-off switches. While his design is for low-power (1 to 15 watts) operation, with the ATU feeding resistive (resonant) loads from 15 to 1000ohms impedance, the basic principle of parallel inductors in such ATUs is equally applicable to high power operation provided that high-voltage components are used.

W1FB justifies his approach as follows:

"Are you weary of looking for expensive roller coils? Do tapped coils in ATUs fail to provide the inductance resolution you need for matching a broad range of impedance? We are kindred souls if your answer to these questions are 'yes'. The roller-coil problem is even more acute for a QRPer: tiny roller inductors that fit the small format of QRP gear are not available. The remaining option is a tapped coil and switch.

"The circuit in this article is by no means new or original. The manner in which I am using it is, however, a bit uncommon. Fig 3 illustrates the circuit. Unlike other Transmatch circuits, this one is resonant at the operating frequency. Most tuners contain elements of L and C, which are used to cancel inductive or capacitive reactance in an antenna circuit. Circuit resonance is not a criterion. The popular T-mat that is used in most commercial Transmatches is an example of a non-resonant ATU. A resonant Transmatch offers the advantage of simplicity and harmonic reduction."

Fig 3 includes the circuit diagram of a simple SWR indicator plus the Transmatch proper, but the SWR-sensing circuit can be eliminated in those

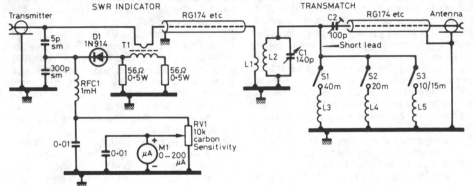

FIG 3. CIRCUIT DIAGRAM OF W1FB'S QRP SWR INDICATOR AND TRANSMATCH SHOWING HIS USE OF PARALLEL INDUCTORS TO ELIMINATE THE NEED FOR ROLLER-INDUCTOR.

Fixed capacitors are disc ceramic unless marked silver mica. C1 miniature 100pF or 140pF air variable capacitor. C2 10-100pF trimmer with shaft. RV1 linear-taper 10-kilohms carbon composition potentiometer. RFC1 miniature 750μH or 1mH RF choke.

cases where there is already available a separate SWR meter to use with the tuner. Since W1FB's concern was to obtain a matched condition between the transmitter and the antenna, the SWR indicator provides only reflected-power information with the ATU adjusted for minimum deflection. A sensitivity control, R1, is included to prevent the meter from reading off scale during adjustments. As shown, a transmitter output of 1W or more should provide full-scale deflection of the meter.

The problem of multiband operation is solved very simply by arranging for L1 and L2 and 3·5MHz (or the lowest band required) and then adding L3, L4 and L5 switched in parallel with L2 by means of either separate single-pole, single-throw switches S1, S2 and S3. The L1/L2 turns ratio remains the same as when only the main coil is being used (L1 could be eliminated by tapping L2 six turns above the earthy end). As described by W1FB L2 has an inductance of 28μH. The effective circuit inductance becomes 7·5μH. when L2 and L3 are in parallel; 2·4μH with L2 + L4; 0·82μH with L2 + L5 (L5 is misprinted as L3 in the original article); and 0·6μH if all four coils are in parallel. Although W1FB's tuner is made from pieces of single- and double-sided printed-circuit board, the unit has

connecting wires rather than printed wiring (ie 'ugly' construction).

Coil details for the QRP tuner are as follows: L1 6t of no. 22 insulated wire over earthy end of L2. L2 28μH inductor with 70 close-wound turns of no. 22 enamel wire on a 7⁄8 by 2in piece of PVC pipe. L3 10μH inductor with 30 turns of no. 26 enamel wire, closely wound, on a 5⁄8 by 1in piece of PVC pipe. L4 2·6μH inductor with 16 turns of no. 20 enamel wire, closely wound, on a 5⁄8 by 1in piece of PVC pipe. L5 0·85μH inductor with nine turns of no. 20 enamel wire on 5⁄8 by 1in piece of PVC pipe. Space turns to occupy 5⁄8in. For SWR indicator T1 is a toroidal transformer with 35 turns of no. 26 enam wire on an Amidon FT-50-61 ferrite toroid (μ = 125). Primary has one turn of no 26 enam wire. D1 is a silicon high-speed switching diode type 1N914 or equivalent. M1 small edgewise tuning meter in the W1FB tuner (200μA FSD). All RF leads should be kept as short as possible.

Adjust by switching to appropriate band. With RF power applied, adjust C2 for lowest SWR. Next adjust C2 slightly and readjust C1 for minimum SWR, repeating this process until minimum SWR is achieved, preferably using maximum possible value of C2 consistent with low SWR.

of Visa or Mastercharge (Access) cards. The 300W AN758 unit is the bipolar push-pull amplifier forming the basic module of the 1kW four-module power amplifier outlined in the December *TT*.

G3TSO also adds a rider to the December *TT* notes on the DDS (direct digital synthesiser) boards being offered by Digital RF Solutions. He has discovered that these are priced at $895 (ie £492 plus six per cent import duty plus 15 per cent VAT making the cost to a UK purchaser about £500). As G3TSO comments, this must put the DDS "somewhat outside the price bracket of the average homebrewing amateur even if they have a suitable spectrum analyser." While it is possible that the costs of DDS will come down in future, it all bears out my feeling that the problem of excessive phase-noise in amateur-budget synthesised transceivers is likely to be with us for some time to come.

Returning to the subject of solid-state power amplifiers, it is clear that Motorola have become one of the main American suppliers of state-of-the-art RF power devices, both bipolar junction transistors and field effect transistors. A review of some interesting, if still costly, devices was given by Barry Manz in "Tap real power with solid-state RF designs" (*Electronic Design*, 12 May, 1988). He highlights the introduction in 1985 of the Motorola MRF154 MOSFET (capable of 600W output up to 100MHz) as a 'milestone', being the first device that made it possible for just two solidstate modules to be paralleled to provide an amplifier capable of delivering 1kW continuous-wave output with up to 16dB gain. But he believes that bipolar devices will also continue to improve, using such techniques as gold-metallisation and the inclusion of input and output impedance matching *within* the package, so lowering the *Q* and enabling devices to deliver bandwidths of the order of 10%. A Motorola example of integral matching is the MRF898 which can provide 60W output at 850 to 960MHz with 8dB gain, 65% per cent efficiency and input and output impedances of 10ohms. A state-of-the-art UHF device is the SGS-Thomson gold-metalized SD1492 bipolar transistor capable of 150W CW output between 470 and 870MHz with 7dB gain and collector efficiency of 40%, as noted in *TT*, April 1988. p265.

Barry Manz, in looking to the future, calls attention to the little-known 'static induction transistor (SIT)'. This type of device was first discovered almost 40 years ago by J Nishizwza, Tohku University, Japan and has been the subject of long-term development by a number of companies including GTE Laboratories. Such devices, it is anticipated, will permit the use of DC supply voltages up to 150V and promise lower noise figures and higher gain than bipolar devices, plus better forward-bias current distribution, absence of secondary breakdown and greater tolerance to VSWR. The triode-type characteristics should also reduce design problems. Barry Manz suggests that a 350W SIT device might have a load impedance of 8ohms and 70V supply, whereas a comparable 28V bipolar device would have a load impedance of only 2-3ohms. While there are no SIT devices yet on the market, GTE have developed an experimental, water-cooled SIT delivering 280W CW at 400MHz with 8dB gain and 70% efficiency.

MORE ON PHASING-TYPE D-C RECEIVERS

Last September, *TT* in the item 'Phasing-type SSB' (pp877-879) described recent ideas on SSB demodulation based on all-pass-filters in direct-

EMC AND PACEMAKERS

From time to time, *TT* has referred to the uncertainty that has long surrounded the use of implanted cardiac pacemakers in close proximity to medium- and high-power transmitters and their associated antennas. There can be no doubt that early designs of these vital life-saving devices were often vulnerable to strong RF fields. It is only within the past decade or so that the problems of electromagnetic compatibility (EMC) have begun to be taken seriously in some segments of the electronics industry.

To improve what has now been recognised as an extremely unsatisfactory situation, attempts are being made to establish standards covering immunity and RF radiation. For implanted cardiac pacemakers, draft standards were issued in the Federal Republic of Germany in 1985 (DIN VDE 0750 Part 9) and in an European context by CENELAC (pr EN50 061 'Safety of implantable cardiac pacemakers').

However, at the 1988 'Sixth International Conference on Electromagnetic Compatibility', a paper "Hazards from electromagnetic fields; influence on cardiac pacemakers by powerful radio transmitters" by T Bossart and M Dahme of the German broadcast research institute (IRT) revealed that

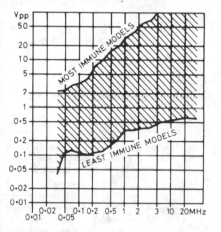

FIG 4. ENVELOPES OF THE IMMUNITY TO VOLTAGES PRODUCED BY PULSED AM SIGNALS OF 34 DIFFERENT PACEMAKER MODELS TESTED BY IRT IN GERMANY SHOWING THE WIDE DIFFERENCE OF UP TO 40dB BETWEEN THE MOST AND LEAST IMMUNE DESIGNS.

tests on 34 different cardiac pacemakers showed a difference of about 40dB RF voltage compatibility between the best and worst of these designs: Fig 4. They also showed that even the least susceptible of these models to RF fields could be improved by a further 32dB voltage compatibility by means of relatively simple, low-cost modifications. Were such techniques to be universally adopted it would ensure that patients fitted with pacemakers could be assured that these would not be affected in any way by exposure to electromagnetic fields at levels right up to the ANSI limits for normal healthy persons not having an implanted pacemaker. Such reassurance is clearly not possible with most, if not all, current models (or at least those tested in Germany).

The paper suggests that external RF signals (particularly those of pulsed, amplitude-modulated form) can have two effects on pacemakers: (1) they may cause an inhibited pacemaker to begin stimulation (this would normally present no severe danger); and (2) they may cause a stimulating pacemaker to return to its inhibited state; this could be most dangerous for the user and is likely to occur at lower RF levels than (1). It is thus the second effect that is the critical design factor.

The paper shows how susceptibility can be reduced by shunting the input/output leads with 1nF RF-type capacitors; inserting a passive low-pass filter between the input/output leads and the high-sensitivity amplifier; and by avoiding non-linearities by choosing adequate clipping levels of about 10 to 20V. Of course, I do not suggest that anybody other than the original pacemaker designer could do anything to modify such devices, but the techniques listed above are applicable to most consumer electronics etc. It is also hoped that by giving further publicity to this problem (which should be understood by all involved in the operation of broadcast, communications and radar transmitters), it may help to underline that EMC remains an important topic in many branches of electronics other than communications.

Meanwhile, it seems reasonable to suggest that persons depending on implanted cardiac pacemakers should avoid areas subject to strong electromagnetic fields, either as operators or as visitors, or as members of the family, unless they are certain that their particular device is guaranteed not be affected up to the range of levels involved.

conversion receivers designed to reject the unwanted sideband. This included some details of a *QST* design by Gary Breed, K9AY (who, incidentally, is editor of *RF Design* for professional engineers) and also referred to the earlier Signetics/Philips Application Note AN1981 written by Bob Zavrek, W7SX.

In *QST*'s *Technical Correspondence* column (September 1988, pp46-47), W7SX comments most usefully on K9AY's design which he regards as capable of achieving close to the optimum performance that can be expected from a D-C receiver. He writes:

"Gary obviously went through laborious considerations of op-amp performance, because the op-amps (NE5534s) largely determine the receiver noise figure . . . The NE5534 is an outstanding op-amp for its price. It is used in expensive professional audio-recording equipment because of its low noise and excellent linearity. Many people don't

know that it is available in a quad version, the NE5514, which is preferable to the TLO84s used in the all-pass networks. There is also a low-noise version of the NE5534, the NE5534A, available from Signetics. K9AY's receiver can be improved by replacing the NE5534s, with NE5534As the TLO81 with an NE5534 and the TLO84s with NE5514s . . . contributing to low-noise and wider dynamic range."

W7SX suggests that it is possible to eliminate the major problem of phasing-type D-C receivers: insufficient rejection of the unwanted sideband. He introduces an arrangement he calls a 'doubly-nulled D-C receiver, in which, by adding another quad op-amp to K9AY's receiver, it should be possible to achieve over 50dB of rejection of the unwanted sideband. He emphasises a point that has been made a number of times in *TT*, (stemming from the original article 'Synchronous Communications' by J P Costas, W2CRR in *ProcIRE*, Decem- ▶

ber 1956, pp1713-1718) that D-C phasing-type receivers offer freedom from spurious responses, simplify design and can be configured to detect USB and LSB simultaneously. He writes: "There is no reason why D-C receivers cannot be built to achieve performance levels approaching – or even exceeding – that of superhets."

He adds: "A block diagram/circuit diagram is shown in Fig 5 of the doubly-nulled technique. By adding another quad op-amp to K9AY's existing circuit, unwanted sideband rejection of over 50dB is possible. LSB and USB are detected simultaneously using the traditional phasing method. For additional sideband rejection, the undesired sideband signal is attenuated (about 30dB), phase inverted and used as a second cancellation signal in a second summing amplifier. (As shown in Fig 5 the second summing amplifiers are actually difference amplifiers.)

"K9AY tried this technique but got only an additional 6dB of sideband rejection. This limited improvement is caused by the bandpass ripple of the all-pass sections . . . attributable largely to gain variations resulting primarily from the feedback

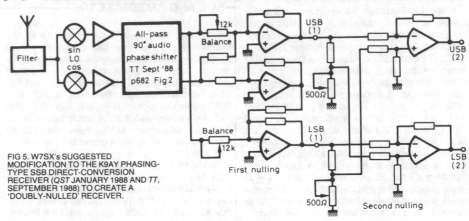

FIG 5. W7SX's SUGGESTED MODIFICATION TO THE K9AY PHASING-TYPE SSB DIRECT-CONVERSION RECEIVER (*QST* JANUARY 1988 AND *TT*, SEPTEMBER 1988) TO CREATE A 'DOUBLY-NULLED' RECEIVER.

resistors in the all-pass sections. Much better filter gain linearity is possible if 0·1% integrated resistors are used instead of the specified 1% 10ohm resistors. A single integrated multi-resistor would (also) reduce the component count of the filter

section. Alternatively, trimmer potentiometers could replace some, or all, of the feedback resistors. The additional nulling stages could be added to achieve outstanding unwanted-sideband rejection."

BINAURAL RECEPTION

The suggestion by W7SX in his comments on improved phasing-type direct-conversion receivers of using simultaneous demodulation of both upper and lower sidebands, while tuning, in order to spread out the band subjectively as a form of binaural pseudo-stereo is one that has arisen before, with particular reference to the reception of double-sideband AM signals (with or without carrier suppression) and also for CW reception. The basic idea (Fig 6) is to take advantage of the 'cocktail-party effect' (the ability we have with two ears to concentrate on just a single speaker in a crowded noisy environment) by moving unwanted interference 'away' from the wanted signal. This topic was discussed at some length in *TT*, August 1973, pp549-550 and October 1973, pp694-695, and especially by 'Dud' Charman, G6CJ and Richard Harris, G3OTK in 'Subjective selectivity and stereocode' *Rad Com*, September 1975, pp674-681 which described fully the construction of their stereocoder unit for CW reception. *TT* August 1973 also included details of an improved AM detector investigated by the CCIR for broadcast reception (Fig 7) and the 'Frequencieschaar' (ie 'frequency scissors') system developed in 1958 by Hans Evers, PA0CX. PA0CK used phasing techniques to cut the wanted double-sideband signal into two halves to give a pseudo-stereo presentation which helped overcome selective fading and interference: Fig 8. It won for him a prize from the Dutch 'Veder Scientific Radio Fund' normally awarded only to professional engineers. Dick Rollema, PA0SE who attended a demonstration wrote: "On reception under normal conditions one observes nothing unusual; both sidebands provide exactly similar interference. But if one sideband suffers interference from an adjacent channel then this is heard predominantly in one ear. . . . One has the feeling of sitting on a 'band' with the other signals to the right and left".

It is perhaps relevant to note that in the long-banned *Spycatcher*, Peter Wright describes how binaural techniques have been used for many years by MI-5 phone-tap transcribers to improve the intelligibility of noisy tapes. It is a technique that could prove capable of further development.

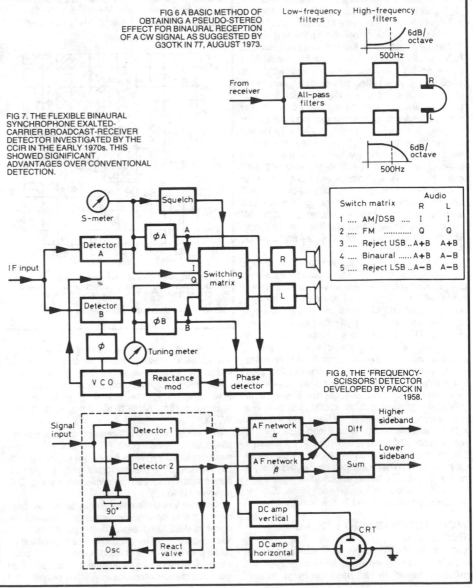

FIG 6 A BASIC METHOD OF OBTAINING A PSEUDO-STEREO EFFECT FOR BINAURAL RECEPTION OF A CW SIGNAL AS SUGGESTED BY G3OTK IN *TT*, AUGUST 1973.

FIG 7. THE FLEXIBLE BINAURAL SYNCHROPHONE EXALTED-CARRIER BROADCAST-RECEIVER DETECTOR INVESTIGATED BY THE CCIR IN THE EARLY 1970s. THIS SHOWED SIGNIFICANT ADVANTAGES OVER CONVENTIONAL DETECTION.

Switch matrix	Audio R	Audio L
1 .... AM/DSB	I	I
2 .... FM	Q	Q
3 .... Reject USB ..	A+B	A+B
4 .... Binaural	A+B	A−B
5 .... Reject LSB ..	A−B	A−B

FIG 8, THE 'FREQUENCY-SCISSORS' DETECTOR DEVELOPED BY PA0CK IN 1958.

W7SX notes that for CW reception it would be possible to optimise rejection across only the CW passband, so achieving greater rejection than for SSB bandwidths. He also notes that simultaneous LSB and USB detection can be used with dual-channel audio stages and headphones so as to listen to the LSB channel in one ear, USB in the other, while tuning across the band: (see the item 'Binaural Reception').

TELEPHONE INTERFERENCE FOLLOW-UP

Personally, I feel that British Telecom over-reacted to my comments (*TT*, August 1988) on the varying susceptibility of various 'approved' telephone instruments to RFI but the Society appears to take the view that anything published in *RadCom* is liable to be interpreted as representing official Society policy!

Many of the early, RFI-vulnerable electronic telephones are, unfortunately, still in use, and some apparently are still being installed. It is perhaps fortunate for radio amateurs that the main problem tends to be the breakthrough of broadcast programmes. It was this that appears to have led to BT setting up their special EMC field team. One reader telephoned me to say how useful a *BT engineer* had found the *TT* item when curing his telephone-interference problem. Another, who had also better remain unidentified, put it thus: "I was dismayed to note that BT were quicker to criticise *TT* than they are to sort out their telephones. I am still waiting, after 4½ years, for them to come back to sort mine out, which is why I did it myself. Incidentally, the Audioline 201 telephone, which retails from about £15, appears to be completely RF-proof and makes a good checking telephone. The 'works' are all mounted in the handset and, as a result, do not pick up RF on the cable from the base unit."

Occasionally, interference to telephones arises from coupling of RF through the AC power lines and can be eliminated without touching the telephone. Dave Zinder, W7PMD, in *QST*'s *Hints and Kinks* column (April 1988, p44) writes: "WA6BSJ in April 1984 *QST* p43, suggested the addition of line filters to eliminate telephone interference. Each of WA6BSJ's filters contained four RF chokes and three capacitors. After experiencing telephone RFI with my Yaesu FT-101EE transceiver, I found a simpler – and possibly more universal – cure. First I installed an AC-line filter in the transceiver power cord *within two inches* of the rig. Next, I connected the filter case to a cold water pipe earth by means of heavy wire. This simple solution entirely eliminated my interference problem". An editorial note pointed out that the use of plastic pipe fittings in modern plumbing makes the cold water pipe earth an increasingly unsure option: "Before depending on cold-water plumbing for electrical earthing of *any* kind, be sure that the system is conductive between your intended earth point and the main water inlet to the house." It also seems appropriate to remind readers of the potential hazards of separate earthing in premises where PME (protective mains earthing) is used (see *TT*, April 1987 and *RadCom* "Killing ground, earth your station safely' by Peter Chadwick, G3RZP, June 1987).

MAKING PCBS – THE SIMPLEST WAY?

R. G. EVANS, G4XAT has taught some 300 youngsters (12/13-year-olds) how to make printed circuit boards and believes that the method described below is the simplest, quickest and cheapest method to implement. He considers that while John

SOLAR FLARE DETECTOR

In his VHF/VHF column, Ken Willis, G8VR has referred to the technique of monitoring VLF transmissions in order to detect the sudden enhancement of signals that denotes a solar flare. This has prompted John Power, W2AXU to send him details of a simple monitoring receiver (Fig 9) suitable for operation between about 15 and 100kHz with three sets of coils. G8VR has kindly passed along the circuit information for inclusion in *TT* although he will be commenting himself on its use as a solar flare detector.

W2AXU considers that optimum results can be achieved when monitoring the most distant possible station along an East-West path at the lower frequency end of VLF, ie about 15 to 40kHz. The effect of a solar flare is to produce D-layer enhancement with the monitoring receiver showing a sudden enhancement of the signal.

He warns that, with an automatic strip recorder, paper costs tend to be about four times that of a magnetometer with the receiver using about one roll of paper per month, whereas a roll can last about four months with a magnetometer. However since solar flares occur *only* in daylight it is possible to reduce paper costs by switching off the strip recorder during darkness. W2AXU points out that while a strip recorder is a great convenience, the receiver could almost certainly be connected to a computer printer.

Components details: L1-C1 and L2-C2 are tuned to the required frequency. For 15 to 25kHz, L1 and L2 are 45 to 215mH, spaced 2in. centre to centre (Miller 6330). For 25 to 50kHz 8 to 60mH spaced 1¾in. centre to centre (Miller 6319). For 50 to 100kHz 0·5 to 5mH spaced ¾ to ⅝in. (Miller 6313). C1 and C2 will depend on frequency and the value of L1-L2 in the range 240 to 1000pF (capacitance of the coaxial feeder will appear across L1). T1 miniature audio transformer 2k to 20k or so. L1-C1, L2-C2 and TR1 to TR3 can be mounted at the antenna. Use two-wire shielded cable from TR3 to 2·2k potentiometer. Should greater signal voltage be required, another amplifying stage can be inserted before or after TR4.

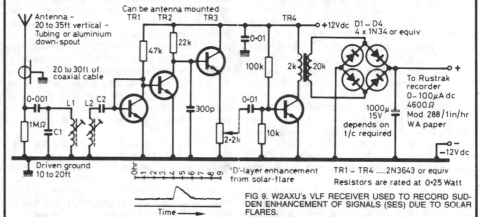

FIG 9. W2AXU's VLF RECEIVER USED TO RECORD SUDDEN ENHANCEMENT OF SIGNALS (SES) DUE TO SOLAR FLARES.

Case, GW4HWR in 'Making printed circuit boards – a different view' (*Rad Com* March 1988, pp176-179) has done a very good job of simplifying photographic reproduction of published board designs, for the beginner the investment required, even as a group, may put him or her off for good. He writes:

"The method I have been using for years and which I teach to youngsters at my school is as follows:

"Take a photocopy of the desired board layout or design and lightly glue it on the copper side to a piece of copper clad board using 'Pritt-Stick' or similar. Next drill all the holes as marked. By leaving the photocopy on the board you can (a) see what size to drill the holes; and (b) check that you have indeed drilled them all simply by holding the drilled board up to the light.

"After drilling the holes, carefully peel off the photocopy (try to do this immediately after drilling and before the glue really dries hard) and then clean the board thoroughly. Take care to remove burrs from around the drill holes as they can tear the nib; I have found that 400-grade wet or dry paper is the best, coarser materials cause the ink to run by capillary action. Next, using a 'Dalo Etch Resist Pen' copy the board layout using the holes already drilled as aiming points. In this fashion, board layouts from simple to very complicated have been made; some of my pupils have even successfully made double-sided boards. In the event of two tracks touching, it is best to leave the ink to dry and *then* to scratch the ink away with a scriber; the best

tool in my opinion for this. There seem to be several etchpens on the market; the genuine 'Dalo' seems best although the RS version is a close second, the main problem is that the nib dries up too quickly. I have found that the Staedler Lumocolour 218, although finer and less prone to drying up, cannot resist hot agitated ferric chloride long enough for a good board to be etched; since it was designed as an OHP pen this is not surprising!

"Although this may seem only a variation on the theme of 'mark the holes with a centre-punch' approach, I feel the above method offers many advantages. Since printed circuit boards provide such a reliable and repeatable method of circuit construction, I feel that this simple method of board manufacture would allow many more beginners to experience the joy of their first constructional project. Finally, two other tips: (1) Use SRBP board for maximum drill life – GRP will ruin even good drills after about 50 holes; and (2) Cheap drills can be bought from J & N Bull, 250 Portland Road, Hove, Sussex, BN3 5QT (Telephone 0273 734648 and 0273 203500)."

TIPS AND TOPICS

My apologies for giving (*TT*, October 1988) incorrectly the name of that great broadcaster and raconteur, the late Wynford Vaughan Thomas. No excuse is possible since I once had the great pleasure of hearing some of his anecdotes at an HTV dinner in Cardiff which he hosted in the style that made his broadcasts so memorable. ∎

ANOTHER FORECAST FOR CYCLE 22

'A near-record solar cycle?' in *TT*, August 1988, p601 included a forecast that sunspot cycle 22 may have a maximum number of 175±35, peaking in 1990±1. This was based on the prediction made in *Nature* (12 May 1988) by Dr Geoffrey Brown of the University College of Wales arising from a study of the occurrence of geomagnetic abnormal quiet days (AQDs) observed during the minimum period between cycles 21 and 22. Dr Brown suggested that "It seems likely that cycle 22 could be second only to cycle 19 as the largest cycle on record."

However, his prediction of 175±35 encompasses the relatively wide range of 140 to 210. More recently Robert M Wilson of the NASA Marshall Space Flight Center; Alabama, in a letter to *Nature* (27 October 1988, p773) ventilates an alternative approach which suggests that the peak may be close to the lower limit of Dr Brown's forecast. Dr Wilson believes that predictions based

on 'bivariate fits' combining the effects of the geomagnetic index and the level of sunspot number at the beginning of the cycle appear to be more accurate historically. He writes:

"Of several bivariate fits, the most reliable for predicting maximum amplitude, $R(max)$, is one that uses the minimum annual averages of sunspot number, $R(min)$ and the Ap index, $Ap(min)$, having a correlation coefficient of 0·997 and a standard error of only 3·9. For cycle 22, $R(min)$ occurred in

1986, having a value of 13·4, and $Ap(min)$ occurred in 1987, having a value of 11·0, implying that $R(max)$ should be about 144·6±7·8. Based on cycles 17 to 21 this particular fit has never erred by more than 4·1 units of sunspot number. Providing that cycle 22 is statistically no different from that of cycles 17 to 21, one infers that cycle 22 should be smaller than both cycles 21 (164·5) and 18 (151·8) and probably about the size of cycle 11 (140·5) making it the fourth or fifth largest sunspot cycle of the modern record . . . Cycle 22 probably will not be an exceptionally large, record-setting sunspot cycle, although it will be above average."

SETTING UP VHF/UHF SSB TRANSMITTERS

At one time it used to be suggested that nobody should use SSB who did not have access to a two-tone generator and an oscilloscope. Today, factory-built black boxes suffer relatively little drift

PRE-HISTORY OF AMATEUR SSB

In *TT* (July 1988) I noted how SSB became established in amateur radio following the 1947 experimental SSB project run by Dr O G 'Mike' Villard, W6QYT. He had been impressed by wartime use of SSB but felt that the filters required were too complex for amateurs and 're-invented' the phasing method of SSB generation that, unknown to him, had been invented and patented in the late 1920s. Following the publication of these early efforts in the January 1948 *QST*, SSB gradually caught on and, in the September 1988 *TT*, I recalled how SSB spread to Europe with G2NX of Oswestry the first British amateur to start the SSB mode rolling.

However, I had pointed out that the theory of SSB had been proved mathematically by Carson as early as 1922, had been used for the long-wave, VLF, transatlantic radio telephone service that opened in 1929 and, with pilot carrier, had been pioneered for commercial HF point-to-point working in the 1930s. What I did not make clear was that there had been various attempts by amateurs to introduce SSB working in both the USA and the UK even before the results of the Stanford project became evident.

A detailed article 'The development of amateur SSB: a brief history' by John J Nagle, K4KJ (*Ham Radio*, September 1984, pp12-16, 19-23) explains how two groups of amateurs tried to establish SSB on the amateur bands in the 1930s. Pride of place would seem to go to Robert M Moore, then W6DEI, who described a 3·5MHz SSB transmitter (Fig 1) in

that one-time excellent American magazine *R/9* (renamed *Radio* in 1933) using low-frequency filter techniques based on work published by Bell Telephone Laboratories. A second group was led by James J Lamb of crystal-filter fame while technical editor of *QST*. In September 1933 he produced a 12-page report describing the feasability of amateur SSB but the ARRL management decided not to pursue development on the assumption that SSB equipment would prove too complicated for the average amateur. His report was never published in full.

What I believe has never been revealed before is that one of those who were much impressed by the military use of SSB during the second world war for long-distance point-to-point circuits was a senior British signals officer, Christopher Henn-Collins, who was also a peacetime radio amateur G(U)5ZC. It is rather a sad story but worth telling as further evidence that amateur radio can interact with professional engineering to the benefit of both. GU5ZC writes:

"As Head of the Radio Division of the Signal Section of AFHQ in Algiers in 1942-43 I soon became acquainted with, and was much impressed by, the Western Electric independent sideband equipment and linear amplifier with which the US Signal Corps worked to the States running a plurality of RTTY and other circuits. The Royal Signals had only a single channel of high speed morse back to the UK. Yet, at four times the range, the Americans often operated their transmitter at less power than we found necessary.

"I quickly became hooked on the merits of SSB.

In 1944 I returned to the UK to head the Wireless Branch of the Directorate of Signals at the War Office. I managed to give things something of a technical wash-and-brush-up, including making a start with RTTY working in the British Army. I was, however, stopped in my tracks by the then Chief Superintendent of the Signals Research and Development Establishment (SRDE) who firmly minuted my boss, the late Brigadier Hickman, that due to the frequency stability requirements and complexity, SSB was quite unsuitable for military communications. However, I gained an ally in the GPO who promised to update some of their SSB equipment for use on main-line Army circuits, though I still wonder how many years the Army had to wait for a mobile SSB rig for use in the field (1960s I think, G3VA)..

"In 1945 I was posted away from the War Office to a job that had little to do with radio communications. The only place where I could build any equipment was here in Guernsey where my parents then lived. I became determined to build a mobile SSB rig to prove its feasibility for military use.

"I consulted the late Sir Archibald Gill, then Engineer-in-Chief of the GPO, whom I knew and much respected. He warned that it was a considerable project to build an SSB station from scratch but added that should I encounter any difficulties with his engineers in regard to the conditions of the Amateur Licence, I was at liberty to refer to him any GPO inspector or engineer raising difficulties.

"There were no text books to rely on. The Germans had left behind on Guernsey a Trager Frequenz Gerat equipment that provided the basic SSB signal at 36kHz. I bought a surplus Canadian C43 transmitter to house the equipment and provide the basics of a linear amplifier. A leave was then spent building test gear to check what I had done. On one leave in 1947 it all worked. However, contacts proved disappointing since nobody seemed to know then how to tune an SSB signal!

"The disappointment stayed with me for about ten years. Then, on a visit to my mother, I put the equipment on the air again. By then SSB had become established on the amateur bands and I must be a candidate for an award for creating one of the biggest pile-ups on 14MHz when I put the beam on to North America. Later I gave the whole equipment to the local radio club, I believe the receiver is still in use."

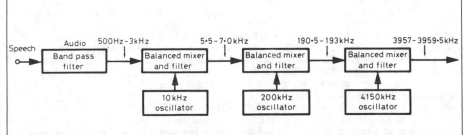

Fig 1. Block diagram of the 3·5MHz SSB transmitter developed and described by Robert Moore, W6DEI in the Amateur Radio Magazine R/9 about 1933 based on commercial practice in using LC filters at low frequencies about 1933 as reproduced by K4KJ in Ham Radio. It was not until many years later that suitable filters (crystal) were available at HF.

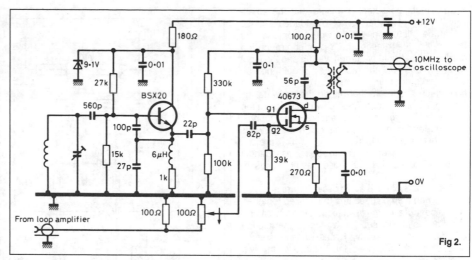

while solid-state devices do not show the gradual change in characteristics associated with gradual, but progressive, loss of valve emission. The result is that many amateurs operate SSB equipment with little or no test equipment suitable for checking linearity. Nevertheless, access to test equipment is still essential for anyone building their own equipment, and still extremely useful for occasionally checking the overall performance of equipment to guard against 'flat-topping' etc.

Ian Waters, G3KKD has sent along an item originally written for the *Cambridgeshire Repeater Group Newsletter* which shows succinctly a technique that makes it possible for VHF/UHF to display a two-tone waveform on an oscilloscope of limited bandwidth. G3KKD also provides an outline of two-tone testing applicable to all SSB transmitters. The following notes are based directly on G3KKD's newsletter article:

Those who listen on the SSB segments of our VHF and UHF bands will know that while there are many good clean signals to listen to, there are some that fall far short of this ideal. Badly over-driven rigs can make DX contacts a waste of time: over-driven local stations can spread over a hefty chunk of spectrum.

So, how do we set up our transmitters to prevent this happening?

Our text books will tell us how to set up HF transmitters: (**1**) Modulate with a two-tone audio test signal. (**2**) Run the transmitter into a good resistive load. (**3**) Observe the waveform across the load on an oscilloscope.

This is all very well – but how does a VHF/UHF operator do this?

Few of us have an oscilloscope that has a bandwidth up to 50MHz let alone the other VHF/UHF bands, up to say 1296MHz.

The solution adopted at G3KKD is to provide a small down-converter for each band used. The idea has so far been tested on 50 and 144MHz using two converters based on the circuit shown in Fig 2 with output on about 10MHz. It is intended to make others for 432 and 1296MHz, similar in principle but with circuit details adjusted to cope with these higher frequencies.

The converters are fed with a small sample of the transmitter output from a forward loop coupler in the transmission line after the harmonic filter. The output frequency is about 10MHz but this is not at all critical provided that the frequency is within the bandpass of the oscilloscope. The general arrangement is shown in Fig 3.

A correctly adjusted transmitter should result in a display similar to Fig 4. The two-tone PEP waveform should not exhibit any compression or clipping on the peaks and the cross-over at the base line should not be distorted. If one tone is switched off, the amplitude (a) should be half that of the two-tone signal (b). Since power varies as voltage squared, the two-tone PEP power will be four times the single-tone power, which is as it should be. If your dummy load can also act as a wattmeter, reading RMS power, the power measured with two tones should be twice that measured with only one tone present.

Adjust the level of the modulating signal or the drive to the linear (power) amplifier to limit the envelope peaks. If the amplifier operates biased in class AB, the stading current with no drive applied should be set to minimise the bottom bend distortion of the output device, transistor or valve, which shows up as cross-over distortion on the waveform.

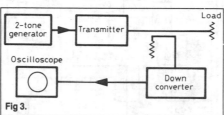

Fig 2. 50MHz to 10MHz down-converter used by G3KKD to check the linearity etc. of a 50MHz SSB transmitter without a requirement for a high-cost oscilloscope. Basically similar down-converters can be used for the other VHF/UHF bands.

Fig 3. Set-up for checking or adjusting VHF/UHF SSB transmitters using small-signal down converters.

Fig 4. Oscilloscope waveforms of a correctly adjusted ssb transmitter modulated by one and two sine-wave tones.

Fig 5. Circuit diagram of a two-tone generator (*Radio Handbook*).

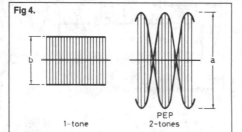

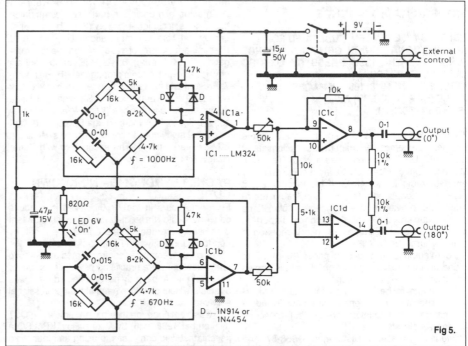

Care must be taken to ensure that the small-signal down-converter is not overloaded and so introduce distortion which would confuse the results. For this reason, the Y-gain control on the oscilloscope should be turned well up and the input potentiometer on the converter should not be advanced more than necessary. You can discover how much headroom there is on the converter by turning the oscilloscope gain down and turning the converter input up until the overload point is found.

A two-tone generator consists of two sine-wave audio oscillators with frequencies, which are not harmonically related, within the speech passband. I used 1·45 and 2·2kHz but these may not necessarily be ideal.

The outputs of each audio oscillator are adjusted to have equal amplitudes and then mixed together. A final control sets the level fed to the transmitter. I find it necessary to feed the two-tone signal into the SSB modulator directly, bypassing the speech processor, which distorts the balance of the two audio tones.

It seems appropriate to complete G3KKD's notes by adding an outline of an easy-to-build compact two-tone generator. Fig 5 shows the circuit diagram of a generator described in the *Radio Handbook* (22nd Edition, 1981, pp31.35/36) although many other suitable units have been published. This generator provides a pair of linearly added sine waves with second harmonic and intermodulation products reduced at least 35dB below one tone. It operates from an internal 9V battery with no inductors or transformers that might induce mains hum.

Two Wien-bridge AF oscillators and associated buffer/mixer stages are based on a single LM324 quad IC. One generator is adjusted for 1000Hz, the other for 670Hz although of course the oscillators could be modified for other combinations. The original model was enclosed within an aluminium utility box (3·5 by 2 by 1·5 inches) with all components mounted on a perforated circuit board. The 9V battery was mounted below the board in a small clip. The unit provides either balanced or unbalanced output.

MODERN RADIO SCIENCE

EDITED BY A L CULLEN. PUBLISHED FOR THE INTERNATIONAL UNION OF RADIO SCIENCE (URSI) AND THE ICSU PRESS BY OXFORD UNIVERSITY PRESS.
FIRST EDITION 1988. 166 + X PAGES.
PRICE (HARD COVERS) £25.
ISBN 0 19 856223 3.

This book comprises eleven 'tutorials' papers originally presented by eminent radio scientists at the 1987 URSI General Assembly at Tel Aviv. While it is not a book likely to find a place on many amateur radio bookshelves, it includes excellent papers on ionospheric propagation, radio astronomy, etc, providing understandable explanations of the current state of thinking on important subjects. It would well repay any efforts required to obtain a library copy.

For example, in two succinct pages (87-8) will be found an up-to-date explanation of what is known about Sporadic E propagation.

It is much to be welcomed that many professional specialist conferences are now including 'tutorial days' or tutorial papers that set the scene for non-specialists.
Contents: 1, Laser measurement 1968-87 and

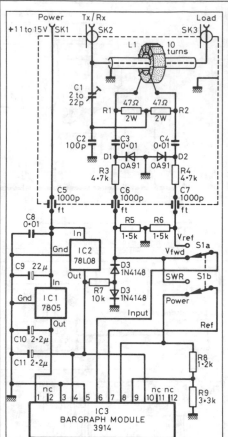

Fig 8. Direct-reading VSWR/power bargraph indicator developed by G3TXQ.

beyond (W Wolinski); 2, Waves and spectra; a modern perspective (Leopold B Felsen); 3, Queuing and coding in multi-user communications; ideas, techniques, theory (S. Csibi); 4, Coherent optical fibre communications (T. Okoshi); 5, Present and future of research on wave propagation (R K Crane); 6, Aspects of ionospheric physics relevant to radio propagation (H. Rishbeth); 7, Present and future trends in research in waves in plasmas (W S Kurth and S D Shawhan); 8 Radio astronomy – new horizons (Wm J Welsch); 9 New communication networks (Helga Seguin); 10, Digital optical techniques in computing and switching (J E Midwinter); and 11, The encounters with Comet Halley, March 1986. Index.

PACKET SYNDROME – NO KNOWN CURE

For some years in the 1950s I lived in a house converted into three flats in a most pleasant Bloomsbury garden-square until thrown out by London University who wanted to convert the building into a computer centre. Immediately above and below me were practising psychiatrists, but to my relief they apparently never detected that I was a radio amateur clearly in need of their professional services.

I was reminded of this by an article in *QST* (November 1988, p46) by Mike Bailey, KB6LSO a psychiatrist who confesses to using amateur radio

DIRECT-READING VSWR/POWER INDICATOR

Steve Hunt, G3TXQ has devised a useful-looking direct-reading VSWR/power indicator (Fig 8) which avoids the complexity and costs of some previously published designs for this type of unit. He writes:

"Components within the screened area (dotted line in Fig 8) comprise a conventional VSWR bridge producing voltages dependent on *forward* (FWD) and *reflected* (REF) power (energy). With the values shown, the bridge works well over the HF bands at power levels from 1W to 100W.

"With S1 in the 'power' position, the REF voltage is fed to the LED bargraph display module IC3. The reference input to IC3 (pin 7) is a fixed voltage derived from the on-board voltage regulator (IC2). In this mode the LED display gives a useful indication of power output over the range 1W to 100W and has the important advantage of indicating instantaneous peak power.

"With S1 in the 'SWR' position, the REF voltage is fed to the input of IC3 but the reference input for IC3 is now the FWD voltage. In this way, the bargraph indicates the *ratio* of VFWD and VREF and can be calibrated to display VSWR independent of the power level. No longer should the problem be experienced of adjusting an ATU for minimum reflected power, only to find that what has actually been done is to tune for a very *high* VSWR which has automatically caused the solidstate power amplifier to shut down!

"R7, D3 and D4 apply a small voltage to the bargraph module in order to extinguish all the LEDs when the transceiver is in the 'receive' mode."

G3TXQ adds that he has produced a PCB for this design, together with assembly instructions. He can also supply the required components. For details telephone him on 0604 858090 after 7pm (his postal address is 21 Green Street, Milton Malsor, Northampton NN7 3AT).

as an escape from a busy practice. He claims that over the past year he has become aware of a new psychiatric disorder which he names the 'Packeteer Addictive Syndrome (PAS)'. A first stage of this disorder is marked by an increase in energy and a heightened mood; the second stage frustration and discouragement when the amount of hardware and software needed becomes apparent; the third, chronic stage begins as the packeteer gets on the air and spends increasing periods of time at his computer and radio – compulsively connecting with others, searching for new packet modes and exploring bulletin boards until he becomes obsessed, ignoring social and family obligations: "He is heard less and less on local radio (speech) nets, ignores HF completely, forgets Morse code and speaks a vocabulary punctuated by terms such as digirepeater, CTEXT, PACLEN etc."

As the syndrome progresses, KB6LSO claims, the victim spends more and more time hunched over his video screen. If, at this stage, his equipment fails, he will frantically attempt to get back on the air. If unable to do so, he appears distant, depressed and listless, akin to someone with a severe organic or endogenous depression.

With no known cure to PAS, KB6LSO believes that self-help groups, 'Packeteers Anonymous', may prove useful in controlling the progression of this syndrome. With the benefit of hindsight I would suggest that similar syndromes have been observed before, marking the times when new modes or new activities have erupted on the amateur-radio scene. Even in the 1930s ARRL found it necessary to devise a six-point 'Amateur's Code' of which the fifth commandment was: 'The Amateur is Balanced ... Radio is his hobby. He never allows it to interfere with any of the duties he owes to his home, his job, his school, or his community.' Ah me, if only we had been able to observe that commandment, how different some of our lives might have been!

For packet-radio enthusiasts, a book worth seeking out in good technical libraries is 'Packet Radio Networks – Architectures, Protocols, Technologies and Applications' by Clifford A Lynch and Edwin B Brown (Pergammon Press, 1987, 292 + xviii pages, £43, ISBN 0-08-035913-2). Although a 'professional' book (at a professional price) it is virtually non-mathematical and readable by non-specialists. The authors are at the University of California, Berkeley.

1·8 – 10·1MHz MOSFET POWER AMPLIFIER

The other day I found myself working a Dutch amateur who was running 500mW on 7MHz CW quite successfully. But, personally, I would never recommend this order of QRP to anyone just starting up on HF. It needs a good, well-matched antenna and even then the outgoing signals are all too vulnerable to interference and fading. On the other hand, with an RF output of, say, five watts or more, a newcomer should have little difficulty in making satisfactory CW or SSB contacts on 1·8, 3·5, 7 or 10·1MHz, even with an indifferent antenna.

A broadband amplifier using a pair of D-MOS power FETs in push-pull and capable of providing about five Watts CW or six Watts PEP output with 100mW input, using 13V supplies, has been described in the *Novice Notes* of WIA's *Amateur Radio* October, 1988 by Drew Diamond, VK3XU. This uses two D-MOS, n-channel, enhancement mode FETs intended primarily for switching applications but useful as HF amplifiers up to about 10MHz. IRF510 devices are available in the UK at about £1·50p or less. VK3XU gives the amplifier gain as about 17dB and two-tone IMD characteristics as at least −30dBc (typically −35dBc). When used with the suggested band-filters all harmonics should be at least −50dBc. This amplifier should withstand short-circuited or open-circuited loads without damage and should remain stable regardless of load SWR. Such characteristics would seem to make such an amplifier a good project for anyone making a start in homebrewing a solidstate transmitter, as a beginner or for QRP operation.

The drain-to-drain impedance of the push-pull FETs is 2×24=48 ohms so that no elaborate impedance transformation is needed to match into 50ohms. T3 converts the balanced output to provide the usual unbalanced output. T2 forms a balanced choke feed for the devices. Negative RF feedback is provided by R3 and R4, stabilising the amplifier and helping to keep the frequency response level throughout the range. The heatsink of the bias zener, ZD1, is positioned against the heatsinks of TR1 and TR2 with a small blob of petroleum jelly so that it tracks the temperature of the FETs, causing the bias voltage to be influenced by their operating temperature. The polarity of the zener diode should be carefully observed and the

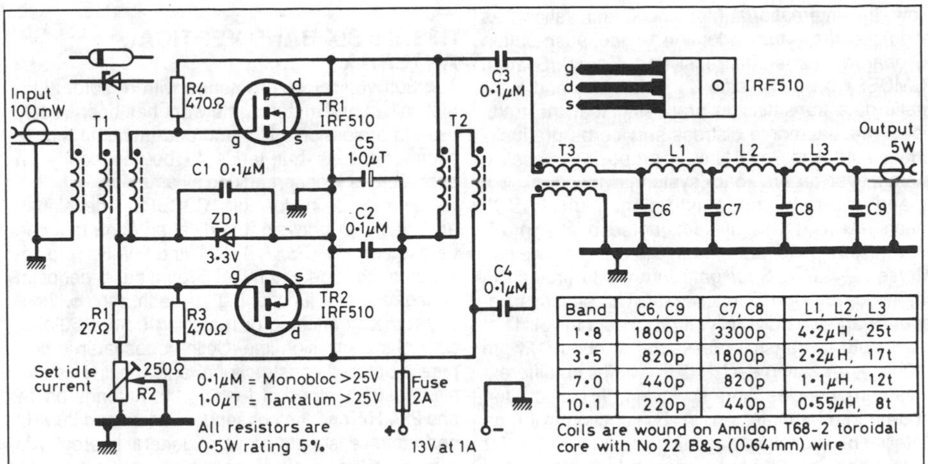

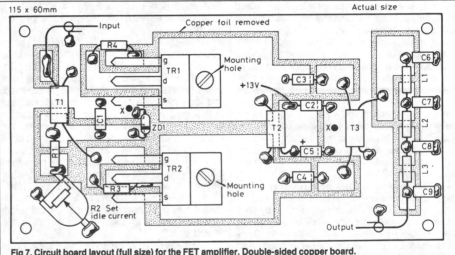

Fig 6. Circuit diagram of the 1·8MHz to 10·1MHz push-pull FET power amplifier capable of providing 5W (CW), 6W (pep) output as described in *Amateur Radio* by VK3XU.

TR1, TR2 and ZD1 attached to 6030 heatsinks in physical contact to enable ZD1 to temperature-track the fets. T1 comprises 11-turn loops of 24 B&S (0·5mm) enam. Wire on amidon FT50-43 core. T2, T3 11-turn loops of 22 B&S (0·64mm) enam. Wire on Amidon FT50-43.

*Indicates start of winding.

Band	C6, C9	C7, C8	L1, L2, L3	
1·8	1800p	3300p	4·2µH,	25t
3·5	820p	1800p	2·2µH,	17t
7·0	440p	820p	1·1µH,	12t
10·1	220p	440p	0·55µH,	8t

Coils are wound on Amidon T68-2 toroidal core with No 22 B&S (0·64mm) wire

Fig 7. Circuit board layout (full size) for the FET amplifier. Double-sided copper board.

enclosure for the amplifier should have adequate ventilation. The complete amplifier (with one band filter) can be built on a double-sided, 115mm by 60mm PCB. For stability, the unetched 'ground plans' should be connected to the etched-side common-earth (positive polarity) in at least two places near the input and output areas. The prototype has through links at the source of TR1 and at the point where C2 and C5 have their earth connections marked on the board layout diagram with a small circle, marked 'X'. Drill the holes with a one millimetre drill.

If multiband operation is required, the highest band-filter should be accommodated on the PCB and kept permanently in circuit; lower frequency band filters can then be built on an additional board. Polystyrene/Styroseal capacitors should be used for the band-filters, it may prove difficult to obtain the larger values such as 1800pF and 3300pF. Silver mica capacitors can be used if available. Provide a 2A fuse in the supply circuit.

When setting up, with R2 set for minimum resistance, the ideal no-signal current is about 200 to 300mA. Output must be terminated with a 50ohm dummy load resistor. Current drawn with 100mW drive should be about 1A. With suitable heatsinks, no discomfort should be experienced when the heatsinks are lightly touched after some minutes operation at the five watts level. While 100mW drive should suffice on the lower bands, up to 300mW may be needed at 10·1MHz which is about the limit for these devices. Do not overdrive or flat-topping will result. With larger heatsinks it would presumably be possible to obtain more RF power output by using a higher supply voltage, but before attempting this check the detailed characteristics of the IRF150 etc.

LONG LIVE MANUAL MORSE!

As Bruce Morris, GW4XXF has pointed out, many of the British and foreign 500kHz coast stations have been closed down during the past few years. ▷

Now, the International Maritime Organisation has endorsed the future adoption of the push-button 'Global Maritime Distress and Safety System (GMDSS)' based on satellite technology and automatic data transmission proposing that the traditional manual morse distress service be gradually phased out. The Royal Navy is proposing to abolish morse, even as a fall-back system, in favour of slow speed diversity modems using 7-unit ASCII machine code. This system, noted briefly in *TT*, May 1985, p356 and in an article 'Farewell to Morse . . .?' *DTE Spotlight*, June 1988 brought to my notice by Ron Cannon, G8OTG, employs frequency and time diversity. It requires a full 3kHz of bandwidth to transmit messages at about 12wpm (10bit/s), repeating each 'bit' five times on different audio frequencies and so using, in effect, ten 100-baud channels, all in conjunction with an 'intelligent' detecting decoding algorithm. It is far from a 'kiss' system but designed to achieve copy in conditions of poor propagation and/or severe interference. However even so, this is roughly of the same order as that of a human operator limited by fixed frequency operation.

With such developments, manual morse is being written off by some observers as an old-fashioned, obsolete form of communication. In fact, it is a highly efficient binary, non-return-to-zero, digital code. I admit to prejudice and make no apology for believing that, within amateur radio, there is and will continue to be an essential and fundamental role for manual morse.

Just one example. In a *TT* item (February 1986, p105), Nigel Neame, G2AUB, stressed the unique value of morse to those suffering from deafness or with extreme loss of hearing. He wrote, "CW enables a licensed deaf amateur to communicate *on equal terms* with any other person virtually throughout the world. The words 'on equal terms' are most significant, since there is no other means of direct *human* to *human* communication available between the deaf and non-deaf apart from 'signing' and lip-reading – and how many non-deaf people learn those skills?"

On other occasions it has been noted in *TT* that many people 'deaf' to normal speech can 'hear' the single tone of CW. Others can receive by their tactile sense, detecting the vibrations. A recent item in *Radio-ZS* noted that 79-year-old Denis Richardson, ZS1B was active again after ten years off the air. This was due to total deafness that had followed ten years of deteriorating hearing. Then a fellow amateur suggested he should try copying morse by vibration. ZS1B simply removed the cap from one of his earpieces and gently placed his forefinger on the diaphragm. He describes what happened: "A chill went down my spine. I could feel the dits and dahs of Morse coming though my finger . . . in no time at all I was able to read up to 20wpm." Soon he had fired up a small valve transmitter and his 40-year-old communications receiver. ZS1B was back on the air.

TRANSMITTING CLOTHES RACK

At the 1988 BBC Radio Show at Earl's Court, I noted that all of the modern equipments on the Royal Signals stand featured either a keyboard or microphone, only the 'museum pieces' such as the paramilitary Mk123 had a built-in key for CW operation.

What I did *not* see was the antenna, temporarily mounted on the roof of the hall, used by the Royal Signals in conjunction with the Army's national data

G3SBI's SIX-BAND VERTICAL ANTENNA

The 30ft vertical whip antenna with remote, automatically-tuned matching network has been widely used in professional HF land and maritime mobile communications but tends to be too costly an approach for widespread use by amateurs.

However, Colin Horrabin, G3SBI has developed an ingenious lightweight vertical antenna that can be used on 1·8, 3·5, 7, 14, 21 and 28MHz, providing on each band a nominal 50ohm base feedpoint impedance and functioning on each band without any remote switching or matching from a 50-ohm coaxial transmission line. Colin hopes later to prepare a detailed constructional article but feels that his unusual method of feeding the antenna on 14 and 28MHz, and the consequent enhanced 28MHz performance, should prove of general interest. His method of using stubs appears to be novel. His antenna was initially developed using a one-tenth scale model enabling current distributions and feedpoint impedance to be measured.

Fig 9 shows the complete antenna and Fig 10 the current distribution on 14 and 28MHz. G3SBI writes:

"On 14MHz the current distribution is similar to a 200° (electrical degrees) vertical; on 21MHz it resembles that of an 'elevated-feed' vertical one-wavelength high; over good earth this provides a main lobe at an elevation of only 10° above the horizon.

"To set-up the stubs initially, the 14MHz stub is adjusted for minimum SWR (Note that the length is such that a 90° bend is required as in Fig 9). The tapping point is moved up and down the element until an SWR better than about 1·3:1 is achieved. The same method is used with the 28MHz stub; but in this case a length of nylon rope is attached temporarily by means of PVC tape so that the length of the stub can be adjusted from ground level with minimum SWR centred on 28·5MHz.

"The 14MHz stub wire should not be more than 2-in from the vertical element since at any greater distance it will affect the resonance on 21MHz where the antenna functions as a ¾-wave monopole. It may prove necessary to readjust the length of the 14MHz stub slightly after adjusting the 28MHz stub."

G3SBI has recently expanded his original notes to give some further explanation of the feed mechanism for 14 and 28MHz: "The tapping point for the stubs on the 2-in OD aluminium mast-element determines the minimum SWR that can be achieved; the length of the stub determines at what frequency within the band this occurs. In my case the actual tapping points were within six inches of those predicted from my one-tenth scale model to obtain an SWR of less than 1·5:1.

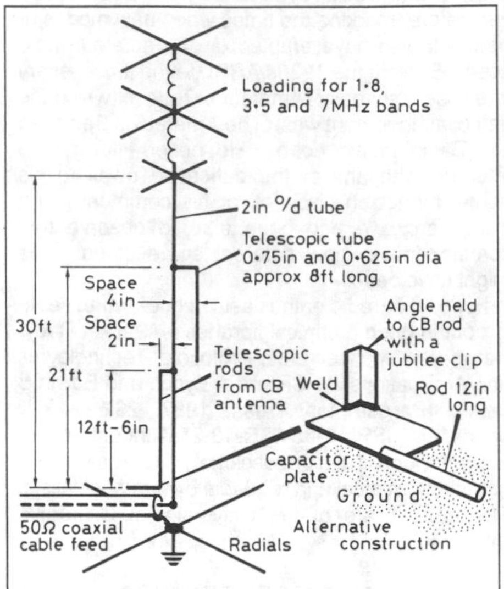

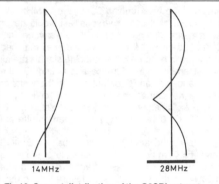

Fig 9. G3SBI's six-band vertical HF antenna.

Fig 10. Current distribution of the G3SBI antenna on 14 and 28MHz.

"What did surprise me was that, with base feed, the current distribution on 28MHz, where the vertical height is roughly 1λ, is similar to that of the 1λ elevated-feed vertical derived from a Marconi D/F system described many years ago in TT and included in most editions of *Amateur Radio Techniques* though now out of print.

"My back garden is 36ft by 24ft and the results seem particularly good on 28MHz although the antenna has been used to work South America (LU) and Australia (VK6) on 3·5MHz. I am convinced that this feed method would be of use to anyone with a conventional 33ft vertical at the bottom of their garden, since no remote L-network is required to match the element to coaxial cable."

network. According to a cutting from *British Aerospace News*, sent in by Bob Connell, G4JQY, this was a transportable HF loop antenna, originally designed as part of an airborne military system "shaped somewhat like a clothes rack from a dress shop . . . It is portable, easily tunable and quickly assembled in a confined space."

The report claims that the BAe loop antenna has been tested by all three British services in field trials under arduous conditions, including the snows of Northern Norway. The success of the trials led the Royal Signals to borrow the BAe

antenna for the Radio Show. They successfully relayed high-speed signals for the Army's computerised national data network, despite the high degree of 'electronic noise' in the city environment."

It would seem that the 'clothes-rack' rectangular tubular loop is rather bigger than most other compact HF transmitting loops, and does not require the use of a ground plane. It provides another example of the growing use of transmitting loops. Some further details appear in *Electronics Wireless World* (February 1989, p108). ☐

ELEVATED VERTICALS

In April 1958, in introducing the first *TT*, I wrote: "All we can hope to do (in this new feature) is to survey a few ideas from the technical press; a few hints and tips that have come to our notice; with perhaps an occasional comment thrown in for good measure". *TT* has always aimed at encouraging a spirit of experimentation and novelty rather than purely the continuation of established systems, providing a technical and ideas forum in which nothing is guaranteed, everything subject to trial and error; heresay given priority over technical dogma as seen in the light of the ways in which amateur radio is evolving, for better or for worse. A recognition that most of what we do is rooted in the past but also that physicists today are having to learn to cope with entirely new theories of 'chaos' – those inexplicable situations where even the most fundamental laws are broken or thrown into confusion.

There are two extremely difficult tasks an amateur can set him or herself: (1) To invent something entirely new; and (2) to persuade others that long-established practice, as described in the standard handbooks, may not always be the optimum or even the correct solution. This applies particularly in those areas of radio physics where it is virtually impossible for an amateur to plot or quantify exactly what is happening. Notable examples are radio propagation and antennas, where very large numbers of variables affect the performance. For instance, one cannot easily measure vertical radiation patterns.

An important area in which our ideas may need to change is in the design of elevated vertical antennas, even though the "ground-plane" has a history dating back over 50 years and is currently used successfully by many thousands of amateurs.

T E C H N I C A L
TOPICS

PAT HAWKER G3VA

It has been noted previously in *TT* that there is still confusion between the true vertical monopole, with its 'infinite' ground plane, the real Earth, often assisted by a large number of buried earth radials or an earth mat, and the elevated ground plane with quarter-wave horizontal or sloping wire radials or rods as a 'non-radiating' artificial earth plane.

In 1981 I revealed, possibly for the first time, that the late Dr George Brown of RCA, who developed the ground-plane antenna in the mid-1930s for 30-40MHz police communications, had told me that his original system had just two radials and that this

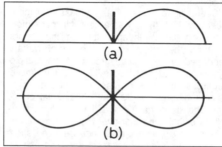

Fig 1. (a) Vertical radiation pattern of a quarter-wave monopole above an infinitely ground plane of perfect conductivity – this can be approached in maritime mobile operation. (b) VRP of half-wave dipole in free space.

was later altered to four radials for purely commercial reasons. Similarly, Les Moxon, G6XN has strongly advocated the use of a single short (inductively loaded) counterpoise (radial). If one thinks of the antenna as a *bent dipole*, it becomes evident that the antenna will radiate efficiently with just *one* elevated radial (counterpoise) but in this case there will be a tendency for the outgoing wave to have mixed horizontal/vertical polarisation with its maximum lobe at a relatively high angle to the horizon: nevertheless a perfectly satisfactory arrangement as a general purpose antenna. For DX operation with the desirable low angle of vertical radiation, the trick is to find some method of reducing the radiation from the wire forming the horizontal side of the 'dipole'.

Some years ago Canadian engineers W V Tilson and A H Secord in 'The radiation patterns of ground rod antennas' (*Electronics & Communications*, August 1967, pp27-30) showed that the VRP of ground rod antennas varies markedly with changes in element lengths and the degree to which RF currents can be kept off the outer braid of coaxial feed lines. Only in a limited number of cases does it provide its lobe directed towards the horizon to resemble the radiation pattern of a quarter-wave monopole above an infinitely perfectly conducting ground plane, or that of a vertical half-wave dipole in free space, Figs 1 and 2. Professional engineers tend to assume that the lobe of an elevated ground-plane antenna must always be tilted upwards. Tilson and Secord concluded: "It is clear that one cannot merely say that ground rod antenna patterns tilt up and leave it at that. The pattern depends on both the length of monopole and ground rods, and also on how well the currents can be kept off the feed cable. Secondly, when the ▷

HIGH CURRENT 50V PSU

It has been frequently suggested in *TT* that one way of improving the linearity of solidstate RF power amplifiers can be found in the availability of higher-voltage devices, particularly power MOSFET devices. Chris Gare, G3WOS, has been transversing this path but stresses that it does call for a new approach to high-current power supply units. He writes:

"In attempts to improve the linearity of various high-power VHF amplifiers built over the years I have migrated, as the technology has changed, from 12-volt to 28-volt transistors. 1988 brought the need for 50V devices. However, it always seemed to be more difficult to build the PSU than the amplifier itself and this was never more so than building a 50-volt PSU.

"The basic problem is that the ubiquitous 723 has a maximum voltage rating of 40volts and thus cannot be used by itself as in earlier, lower-voltage supplies. Having tried several published designs, including one based on a floating regulator (G3WZT, *Radio Communication*, June 1986, p409), I found none of them entirely satisfactory from the viewpoint of performance. For example, the G3WZT design needs at least 9.5volts across the regulator in order to maintain the regulation. If the supply is to be capable of supplying more than 10A this means 95watts dissipated in the pass transistors alone. I wanted to design a supply that would regulate with Vin(min) at 54 volts at a full load of 15A.

"The problem was solved by translating the regulated 26V output voltage of the 723 up to 50V

by means of a 24V zener diode as in Fig 3. The circuit works very well, has excellent regulation and is capable of meeting the above requirement with ease. The 723 supply is regulated to 36V by the use of a simple regulator. My earlier PSUs used *very* large and heavy conventional transformers which took up too much space in the shack and in the car when going portable. This present design uses a 45V-0-45V, 750VA toroid transformer (2.5-in high, 6in. diameter) allowing it to be built into a 5in. high cabinet (available from Airlink Transformers, Unit 6, The Maltings, Station Road, Sawbridgeworth Tel: 0279 724425).

'The design uses a conventional over-voltage detection arrangement (not described) and utilised fold-back over-current protection. The over-current detection circuit needs to use an external BD135 transistor as the internal 723 detection cannot be used."

G3WOS provides a worked example based on the formulae given in the *Motorola Linear Databook* for calculating the value of current foldback components. Unfortunately, recent printing problems with *TT* discourage the inclusion of this example, owing to the possibility of errors creeping in at a late stage, and pressure on space.

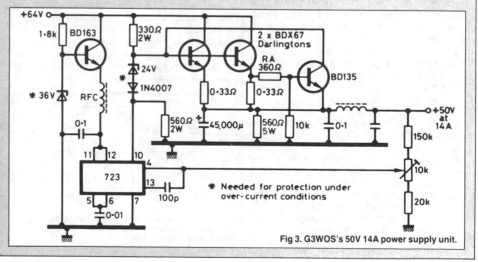

Fig 3. G3WOS's 50V 14A power supply unit.

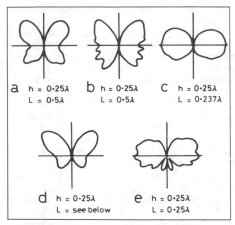

Fig 2. Some typical VRPs of ground rod antennas showing the effect of radial lengths (L) and of chokes on the feedline: (a) with chokes, (b) without chokes, (c) with chokes, (d) circular ground plane of radius 0.03 with chokes, (e) without chokes. (Tilson & Secord, 1967)

monopole radiator is a half-wavelength, the pattern resembles a typical dipole pattern even with no ground rods or chokes present on the feed cable. When a quarter-wave monopole is used with no chokes, suitable patterns may be obtained with ground rod lengths near three-eighths of a wavelength."

TT (March 1981) reported that Les Moxon, G6XN had developed an effective short (loaded) 'counterpoise' technique and this is explained in more detail in his *HF Antennas for all Locations* (RSGB 1982). G6XN was careful not to claim originality since military manuals often show pack sets working into a dipole in which one arm is run just above the ground while *TT* had earlier included notes on using trap verticals by converting them into vertical dipoles and had also shown how loaded 'counterpoises' can be used to remove unwanted RF-voltages from otherwise 'hot' metalwork or chassis in upstair shacks.

At about the same time, Arch Doty, K8CFU and colleagues carried out hundreds of measurements that showed that a few elevated 'radials' perform as well as or better than the 120 or more buried radials traditionally used for medium-wave broadcasting and often advocated for 1.8 and 3.5MHz DX operation despite the cost and effort required in such construction. As noted in *TT*, August 1988 and December 1988, K8CFU's laborious field measurements have been confirmed as the result of computer studies by a team of professional engineers including Al Christman, KB8I (*QST*, August 1988, pp33-42). Both studies have been based on the use of four or more elevated radials. There has also been some interest in the concept of a 'zero-extent' ground-plane antenna using lossy ferrite chokes to absorb energy fed back down the outer of the coaxial feeder (*TT*, March 1988 and November 1987).

But it would seem that the penny has yet to drop. Amateurs the world over continue to spend time, money and energy in improving earth systems for vertical monopoles, vertical arrays and erecting multi-radial systems for their ground-plane antennas. To quote from a recent letter from G6XN, parts of which it is hoped to cover later: "Despite proof of the efficiency and major practical advantages, my advocacy of short radials clearly stood no chance since, as you have related, even the inven-

tor of ground-plane was unable to get away with two radials but had to bow to commercial pressure. To suggest shorter radials and, beyond that, the possible use of only a single radial, provided it is *short* enough, is clearly heresy of the worst kind. It still seems to be universally accepted that a radial length of a quarter-wave is necessary; moreover from *TT* and elsewhere it appears that an enormous amount of effort continues to be misdirected at 'improving' earthed and radial systems which inflict a maximum of inconvenience and inhibit the use of vertical elements for beam arrays. Furthermore multiple quarter-wave radials offer no advantages but instead involve the major disadvantage that the rapid change of impedance close to resonance can cause problems of electrical equalisation of the radials. Short radials are superior also for multiband operation although grounded verticals have the edge in this respect, provided that the extra radiation loss due to ground losses is acceptable.

"Searching for ways to put my case over more effectively, I felt there was a need for more information on bandwidth and other limiting factors including the effect of the height of radials (shortened or not) above ground. A few simple experiments led to what, relative to my limited resources, became a massive research programme digging deeply into fundamental questions. The results have included a few surprises as well as establishing that *over a very wide range there is no significant difference between short and long radials in respect of any important aspect of performance.* This applies regardless of height although the so-called ground-plane, at extremely low height, turns into a completely different kind of antenna, ie, a *genuine* ground plane (monopole), whereas in the normal case, ie, height of radials more than a foot or two, it is a *dipole*. The fact that it is basically a dipole is implicit given that it works in

free space where monopoles cannot exist. As I see it the practical distinction between dipole and monopole depends on whether current flows from one pole to the other of the source as it would in free space, or whether it does so at least in part via the ground."

I hope to return to G6XN's letter on another occasion but for the present reproduce his summary of main conclusions relating to "unsymmetrical dipoles":

(1) Ground plane antennas with radials at normal heights are dipoles not monopoles.

(2) Over a wide range there is virtually no difference between short radials with a shared loading coil and quarter-wave radials in respect of any aspect of performance. Bandwidth is reduced by excessive shortening, typically 30% reduction for two 0.08-wave radials or four 0.06-wave radials.

(3) Ground losses for quarter-wave vertical antennas operating with a set of radials and fed at the base are virtually zero at 14MHz for heights more than 4ft and only just over 0.5dB for a height of 2ft. There are no losses in the case of parasitic beam elements of this type.

(4) Variation of such losses with frequency is likely to be negligible but this has not yet been determined.

(5) For a base-fed element the maximum loss resistance for radial heights less than 4inches is in the region of 35ohms for two radials and can probably be halved with four radials. Comparable losses were observed with buried radials (poor soil).

(6) Horizontal dipoles may also be loaded asymetrically, for example a quarter-wave radiator can be fed against the equivalent of a pair of short-loaded radials or even a single short resonant helix. Loading does not affect the current distribution or the height at which ground loss disappears, even if carried to extremes.

HI-C LO-L TANK CIRCUIT FOR TRANSISTOR AMPLIFIERS

QRP enthusiast John Cronk, GW3MEO recently built a very simple 1.8MHz transmitter using a BFY50 bipolar transistor amplifier. He writes:

"This transmitter is so simple that it provided an ideal opportunity to optimise every component and component value. The calculated values for the Class C output stage proved particularly interesting. Values were determined using the well-known recommendation that the tank circuit should have a loaded Q of 12. In this case the values turned out to be 10,000pF (0.01F) for the capacitor and 0.7H for the inductor: Fig 4.

"Since 0.01µF variable capacitors are not to be found in the real world, most transistor tank-circuit

designs avoid these extreme values by using a tapped coil (or series resonance) to match the very low impedance of a transistor power amplifier. Yet, in practice these values can be achieved quite easily by using a 0.01µF mica capacitor and a 0.7µH coil provided that the inductor becomes the variable component. Ten turns of 16SWG enamel wire on an Aladdin former with core seem satisfactory.

"It was only while testing this arrangement that I realised that tapping the amplifier down the tank coil does not fully use the flywheel effect of a tank circuit in restoring the pulse-like output of a Class C stage to near sinewave. I use the well-known analogy as the full electrical explanation of the flywheel effect is long-winded and in this case not a good analogy.

"I feel that it is of interest that in spite of this parallel-tuned tank being the conventional arrangement for valve amplifiers, none of the many small solidstate transmitter/transceiver designs that I have come across use such an arrangement. The result of using these unusual but technically correct values is a simple transmitter with such low harmonic output that the usual low-pass/bandpass filter is unnecessary. Remember that to obtain an 80ohm output the coupling link will need more turns than the tank coil to provide a step-up ratio (tank impedance 10ohms). The arrangement has the virtue of being physically small and in keeping with the other components in such a QRP rig."

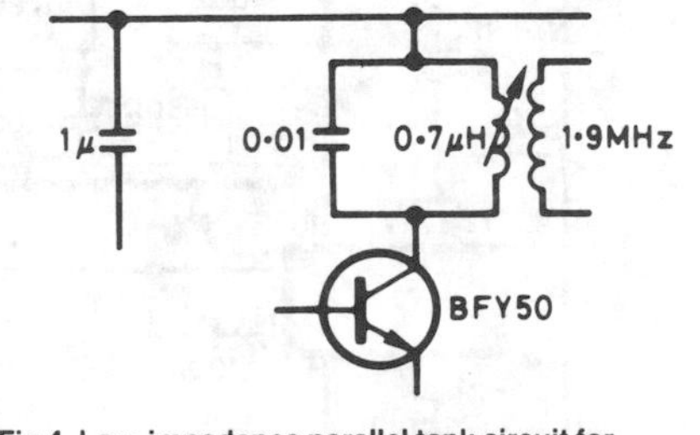

Fig 4. Low-impedance parallel tank circuit for transistor amplifier as used by GW3MEO for a 1.9MHz QRP transmitter.

(7) Horizontal antennas, whether loaded or not, have negligible ground losses above a height of about 0.16-wave.

(8) Comparisons of ground loss information from several sources suggest that it is much less variable than the DX signal performance of vertical antennas and not directly related to it. There is no connection between DC resistance and RF resistance of earths, nor would one expect any, although this point has seldom if ever been discussed in print.

13.8V 5A POWER SUPPLY UNIT

Despite the advantages of using 28V bipolar or 50V MOSFET devices for linear RF power amplifiers, most amateur transceivers are still being designed for use with vehicle supplies, nominally 12V but in practice usually 13.5-13.8V. Dropping the power supplied to the equipment to 12V will generally reduce the RF output power by 10-20% and may severely degrade the intermodulation distortion (IMD) on SSB.

It is thus important, both when operating mobile or when the rig is used as a base or fixed station, to ensure that the power leads between the equipment and the battery/PSU do not introduce a significant voltage drop; heavy gauge wire should always be used. A mains PSU should be well regulated for loads up to the peak current drawn by the equipment and the output voltage capable of adjustment to 13.5-13.8V preferably as measured at the transceiver unit.

In May 1978, *Electronics Australia* described a 'VK Powermate' 5A unit specifically intended for domestic operation of amateur radio and CB transceivers designed for mobile operation from a nominal 12V battery supply. Apparently this unit has enjoyed continued popularity, exceeding that of PSUs of higher and lower power ratings. The result is that the magazine has recently published (EA, October 1988, pp66-71) constructional details of a 'Powermate II' design utilising updated or more economical components. It is claimed that the revamped unit (Fig 7) provides a clean, well-regulated 13.8V DC output at up to 5A continuous. Voltage output, for loads from 0-6A, drops only about 10mV with less than 6mV peak-to-peak ripple with mains voltages from 220 to 260V AC.

The unit has a conventional circuit arrangement with an 18V/6A mains transformer, bridge rectifier, using four low-cost 3A diodes such as the IN5404 or a suitable encapsulated 6A bridge rectifier which

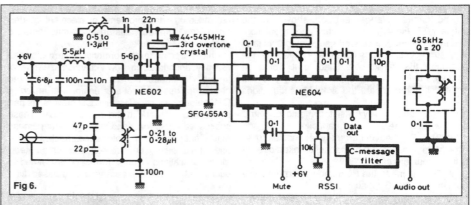

Fig 6.

Fig 5.

THE NE604-NE602 RECEIVER

A very simple pocket VHF/FM receiver is possible using an NE602 in conjunction with the associated NE604 device. The Signetics/Philips NE604 is a monolithic low-power FM/IF system incorporating two limiting IF amplifiers, quadrature FM detector, muting, logarithmic signal strength indication and voltage regulator integrated into a single 16-lead dual-in-line package: Fig 5. Product specification and application notes, originally prepared by Signetics were republished by Mullard (Philips Components) in 1985-86 as: Product specification 'SA/NE604 Low Power FM IF System' (12pp) and Application Note 'AN199: Designing with the SA/NE604' (10pp). Fig 6 shows how the NE602-NE604 combination can form the basis of a VHF receiver.

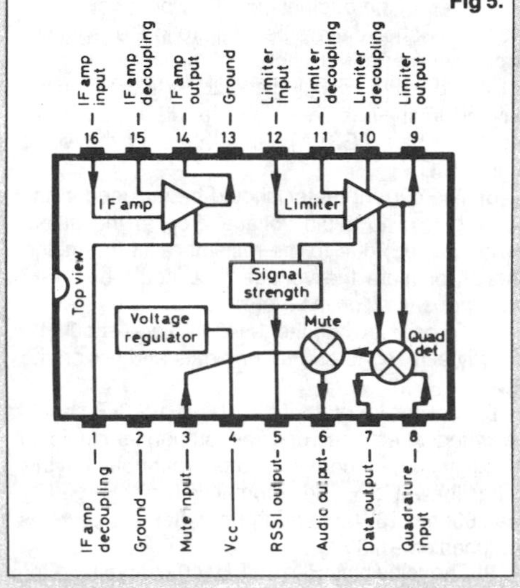

Fig 5. The Signetics NE604 FM/IF system showing functions and pin layout.

Fig 6. Simple VHF 'cellular radio' receiver based on NE602 and NE604 devices.

tends to cost more than separate diodes. The unit, although running quite warm, is capable of continuously powering a 5A load or supplying 6A for short periods as found with a transmit/receive duty cycle. The author, Jim Rowe, suggests that "to make it capable of delivering 6A continuously, the 3A diodes D1-D4 should be replaced by a suitably rated bridge rectifier preferably mounted on the inside of the rear panel for improved heat dissipation, with the value of C1 and C2 increased to 5.6 or 6.8 millifarads (ie. 680µf) and with a second

2N3055 power transistor with current-sharing resistors preferably each with its own heat sink. The 5A unit uses a finned heat sink section (single-sided) 110 by 33 by 74mm.

A possible additional safeguard would be to incorporate mains-transient suppression using a metal oxide varistor (eg, V275LA20A) as shown for the 'Moorabbin Mark IV' 13V, 20A unit outlined in the January *TT*. The Mark IV has relay-operated over-voltage protection and this has led J R Hooper, G3PCA, to suggest a number of ▷

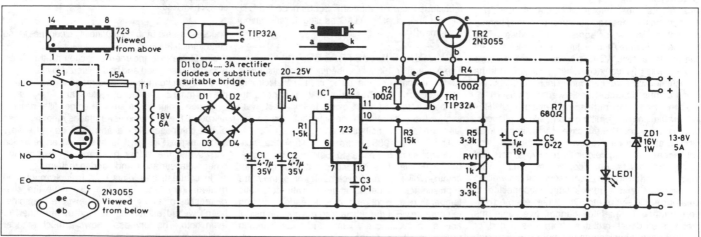

Fig 7. 'Powermate II' 13.8V 5A PSU (*Electronics Australia*).

improvements to this heavy current unit. He writes:

'The circuit arrangement, as shown in the January *TT*, Fig 4, provides very poor regulation, and in the event of a sudden rise in output voltage (eg, short-circuited pass transistor) there is the possibility that a rig connected to it would be damaged before the trip operated. In my view the trip circuit and relay are too slow. My suggestions are:

(1) The 200ohm 10W resistor should be wired directly across the 33,600 µF capacitor.

(2) The OV heavy current line should come directly from the 33,600 µF capacitor taken directly to the output terminal.

(3) The 0V line to the PCB should come directly from the 33,600 µF capacitor.

(4) The 'power on' LED with its 1k feed resistor should be wired across the 33,600µF capacitor. As connected in the original circuit it would now show 'power on' should there be a failure in the regulator circuit.

(5) The voltage sensing should be taken from the output terminals (or remotely from the transceiver input terminals – G3VA) rather than from the wiring or the PCB.

(6) The current meter should be included in the sensing loop to avoid voltage drop at the output (when loaded) due to the resistance of the meter. At 20A or more the voltage drop could be 1V or more depending on the meter.

(7) To be effective, the 1N4004 diode should be directly across the output terminals and not on the PCB.

(8) A capacitor of about to 500 to 1000µF should be wired directly across the output terminals to maintain a low impedance output (but note that this capacitor would not be automatically discharged by the 200ohm 10W bleed resistor when the power is switched off – G3VA).

(9) The relay plus BD139/BD140 overvoltage trip would be too slow acting to save the connected rig should the output rise suddenly (eg, short-circuited 2N3055 etc). G3PCA feels this circuit should be replaced with a 'crowbar and fuse' type of arrangement on the output side of the regulator.

(10) The current sensing line (pins 2-3 on the 723) should go directly to the 3 × 0.1ohm resistors.

With the above changes, the PSU should hold its output voltage to within 0.01V at the full load of 20A and be safe to use with any equipment.

NEW RANGE OF MAINS FILTER CHOKES

One of the most useful weapons in the EMC armoury has always been the use of mains filters to prevent the ingress or egress of RF 'noise' along the mains leads. At one time, such filters often comprised a few AC-rated capacitors and two chokes, each typically comprising 50 to 200 turns of insulated wire wound on a 1inch diameter former, (lengths of broom-handle were often used).

With the ever-increasing amount of RF-vulnerable and RF-emitting domestic appliances, there is a real need for effective mains filtering to be incorporated in a wide range of domestic and office appliances including colour TV receivers, personal computers, VDUs, photocopiers etc, many with 'noisy' switched mode power supplies, as well as for cleaning up the mains supply connected to amateur transceivers etc. Of course, even a high-performance mains-filter cannot overcome the problem of direct radiation from unshielded or poorly-shielded enclosures but there is a very high

proportion of cases where an effective mains-filter can overcome the problems of electrical interference and amateur 'disturbance' of domestic appliances.

Philips Components (formerly Mullard Ltd) has recently announced a newly-developed range of high-performance current-compensated ferrite chokes for use in consumer equipment, including CTV sets, monitors, VTRs and CD players, as part of the filter network in the power supply. These chokes can also be used as a general-purpose mains filter choke in professional applications – and would clearly be suitable also for amateur-radio applications. The performance is claimed to equal that of more expensive toroid-based filter chokes.

The new CU15/d3 and CU20/d3 families are small, high-permeability ferrite chokes suitable for PCB mounting. There appear to be about five members of the CU15/d3 family and four of the CU20/d3 family based on U15 and U20 Ferroxcube cores with current-ratings up to 2.5A. To reduce the winding capacitance each winding is split into two sections. Insertion loss over the range 0.5 to 30MHz is given as up to 65dB for the CU15 chokes, 55dB for the CU20 series. The chokes offer high inductance; CU20/de family offering self-inductance ratings up to 47mH with a self-capacitance of around 10 to 25pF. DC resistance usually less than 1ohm.

Philips Components are only available through their own distributors.

The firm emphasises that such chokes minimise both the effects of mains pollution on the equipment as well as mains pollution by the equipment itself. It is much to be hoped that equipment makers will increasingly incorporate effective mains filtering in their products.

The other side of the coin is illustrated by the introduction of an 'ATAC' system made by the Swedish company Cominvest, brought to my notice by Dave Ansten, G1EHF. This device is claimed to prevent 'eavesdropping' of information from computer radiation. It is well known that computer data can be secured by unauthorised interceptors within a few hundred feet of the installation. Military equipment is protected under the 'Tempest' regulations which specify very effective shielding. The ATAC system, on the other hand, seeks to protect the security of information by adding a large number of signals to those emitted from information technology equipment. As G1EHF comments: "So it seems the solution to computer-generated RF rubbish is more RF rubbish!" Let us hope the DTI will in future classify ATAC as illegal transmitting equipment!

DRY JOINTS ILLUSTRATED

The November 1988 *TT* underlined the truism that soldering remains "the basic craft" of electronic construction, emphasising that a continuing bugbear is the 'dry joint' owing to imperfect 'wetting' of the solder which remains 'adhered' to the joint by a layer of undiffused resin.

The October 1988 *Electronics Australia* was able to devote some 5½ pages to 'Soldering: the basics' by Jim Rowe. This described many of the finer points involved in the choice of an iron or the more sophisticated 'soldering stations' with automatic temperature control and digital readout of iron temperature. But the article also gave some useful advice on avoiding dry joints and other common problems. It gave the three golden rules for

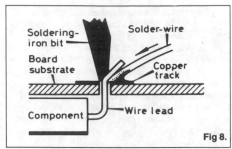

Fig 8. Soldering a component lead to a PCB pad. The iron tip heats the lead and pad directly (*Electronics Australia*).

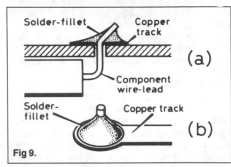

Fig 9. (a) With a good solder joint, the solder meets the metal surfaces at a low angle. (b) The solder forms a smooth fillet all round.

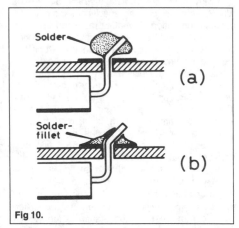

Fig 10. (a) A dry joint where the solder has not wetted the PCB pad. (b) Where the solder has not wetted the component lead.

successful soldering: cleanliness, cleanliness and cleanliness! Fig 8.

Jim Rowe also included a section on the difference between good and bad soldered joints:

"How can you tell if you've made a good joint or not? In most cases, just by looking at it.

"A good joint has a smooth solder fillet running all round it, with the solder surfaces meeting those of the component lease and PCB pad at a very small angle (Fig 9). It is this small angle which shows that the solder has properly 'wetted' the other metal surfaces, and bonded to them.

"In contrast, bad joints tend to look rough and matted. Very likely they will also have the characteristics of a 'dry' joint – one where the solder hasn't wetted either one surface or the other, or even both. The 'dryness' shows a much steeper angle between the solder and metal surfaces.

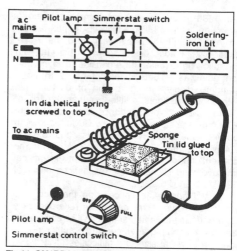

Fig 11. GM1RPJ uses a 'Simmerstat' control to stop overheating his soldering iron during 'stand-by' periods.

"If the solder hasn't properly wetted the PCB pad, but only the component lead, you'll get a small spherical blob shape rather like that shown in Fig 10(a). Conversely if it hasn't wetted the component lead, but only the PCB pad, you'll get a tiny 'groove' around the top of the lead as shown in Fig 10(b). This can be quite subtle and hard to see, so if you're in any doubt it's desirable to reheat and try again – perhaps scraping the metal first to clean it.

"Why is a 'dry' joint bad? Because where there isn't any wetting, there isn't any true bonding either. Even though the joint may seem firm and secure, and perhaps measure as a very low resistance with your multimeter, it won't stay that way.

"Sooner or later, perhaps years later, oxidation will take place and the resistance will rise – possibly going to a full 'open circuit'. Even more likely is that it will start changing resistance with temperature and vibration, causing all manner of weird and wonderful symptoms. Sometimes a dry joint can be hard to spot because the top of the solder can be covered by a thin layer of glassy resin after everything cools. This can make the joint look good even though it's not... Good soldering takes care, as well as practice. Even experts can make dry joints, if they don't watch what they're doing."

David Norrie, GM1RPJ, found that his 25watt soldering iron had a tendency to overheat the bit and burn off the tinned surface when 'standing by'. As he had recently replaced a 'simmerstat' control switch on his electric cooker, and found that one of the two spiral resistive ring was still good, he connected this in series with his soldering iron and found it all worked 'a treat': Fig 11. In use it is turned 'full on' until the solder melts and then turned to the stand-by position except for heavy joints when it has to be turned full on again. The thermostat clicks on and off in the stand-by position. GM1RPJ fitted it in a box about 120 by 80 by 60mm with a spring and tray for the sponge on top.

MORE ON THE NE602 FREQUENCY CHANGER IC

'Complex ICs simplify receivers' (*TT*, January 1989 pp36-7) drew attention to the value of the Siliconix/Philips NE602 integrated double-balanced mixer plus oscillator device as a product detector in simple direct-conversion receivers and also as a very simple VFO or crystal-controlled frequency-converter for either up or down conversion. It may also be recalled that the NE602 was one of the

three ICs used in K2BLA's low-cost spectrum analyser (*TT*, April 1988, p262) where it functions as a 0-100MHz mixer and swept oscillator over the range 150-250MHz. In *TT*, November 1988, p871, K2BLA explained that to achieve a reasonably linear oscillator sweep range of 145 to 245MHz he used 'dead bug construction' ie, chips with their 'legs' in the air glued to the board and resulting in extremely short leads. In the data sheets, the NE602 oscillator is specified as suitable for use up to 200MHz and the Gilbert Cell mixer to beyond 500MHz.

Multiple use of this device in low-power RF systems turns up in 'An NE602-based QRP transceiver for 20-meter CW' by Rick Littlefield, K1BQT (*Ham Radio*, January 1989, pp9-12, 14, 17-18). Built as a three-module unit this little rig fits into a 1.75 by 4.0 by 4.0-inch Ten-Tec-type enclosure (external battery or PSU) to provide 5watt RF output between 14.0 and 14.1MHz, semi-QSK T/R switching, provision for adjustable CW off-set and sidetone monitoring. The superhet receiver with a double-tuned bandpass LC filter input has a 10MHz four-crystal ladder filter with the third-module providing an additional four-crystal 10MHz ladder filter and an active audio-filter intended for 'serious CW work'. In effect, the new rig is a further development of K1BQT's 'Travelradio' (*Ham Radio*, June 1987 and see *TT*).

A complete kit of parts, including PCBs and enclosure is available from Radiokit, Box 973, Pelham, New Hampshire 03076, USA, priced in the US at $124.95. A set of PCBs only is priced at $8.95. The new rig uses three NE602 devices: front-end frequency-changer (Fig 4(a)) and 'vxo' product detector (Fig 4(b)), and one in the transmitter section as a crystal-controlled frequency-changer (9.9985MHz crystal). Although no detailed performance characteristics of this compact rig are given in the article, there seems no reason to suppose that it is not capable of forming a reasonably effective miniature 14MHz CW transceiver.

K1BQT warns that "although billed as a double-balanced mixer, be aware that the NE602 is not "state-of-the-art" for HF (receiver) applications. It's a high-Z device with lots of gain and a third-order intercept of only -15dBm, so it's prone to stray pick-up and occasional (over-load) symptoms of intermodulation distortion. On the other hand, the NE602 has many attributes. It has (for HF) a very low noise figure (lower than 5dB at 45MHz), needs no external local-oscillator circuitry and a minimum of external parts, comes in a small package with low power consumption, and is inexpensive. For the QRP microphile, these are very attractive pluses!".

Three useful information sheets on the NE602 were produced by Signetics in 1985 and republished by Mullard (now Philips Components) in 1986: (1) 'Designing with the SA/NE602' Application Note AN198 (4pp); (2) 'SA/NE602 double-balanced mixer and oscillator' Product Specification (6pp); and (3) 'AN1982: Applying the oscillator of the NE602 in low-power mixer applications' by Donald Anderson (3pp). As noted above the device provides mixer operation to beyond 500MHz, a versatile oscillator to 200MHz, typical 18dB conversion gain at 45MHz and total current consumption of about 2.4mA. Absolute voltage rating is 9V but optimum performance is achieved with about 6V. The device is available in various packages; the NE602N is 8-pin dual-in-line plastic with a temperature range 0 to +70°C. The SA602- ▷

SIMPLE VHF MODULATED GENERATOR

Construction and modification or alignment of VHF receivers is much facilitated when there is a suitable signal source. In the absence of a good VHF signal generator, even the simplest adjustable and optionally modulated oscillator can be an invaluable aid. Charles Guilbert, F3LG, in 'Un tres simple generateur VHF module' (*Radio-REF*, January 1989, p39) describes just such a device: Fig 12. TR1 (BF184 or equivalent) forms a VHF oscillator with an RF output of a few milliwatts; the frequency is set by L-Cv where Cv is a 6-25pf trimmer and L is a 'hairpin' inductor, about 25mm high. This provides an adjustable range of about

105 to 200MHz. Other ranges can be achieved by replacing L with a small coil; for example, a coil of 4.5 turns, 1mm wire, diameter 18mm with turns spaced 2mm would give a range of about 37 to 60MHz etc. TR2 (B775, eg, BC547 or similar) is a bridged-T audio oscillator with an output tone adjustable over a range of about 220 to 500Hz. Adjustment of the regenerative (positive feedback) capacitor Ca (3 – 13pF trimmer) is not critical and can be adjusted for maximum output.

Clearly one should not expect such a device to be very stable and the signal will tend to be a mixture of AM and FM but it can be a life saver if nothing better is available and it can still form a useful gadget.

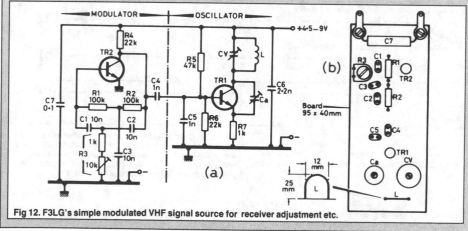

Fig 12. F3LG's simple modulated VHF signal source for receiver adjustment etc.

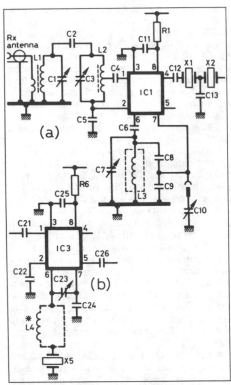

Fig 4. (a) Front-end NE602 mixer/oscillator and (b) NE602 product detector as used in N1BQT's compact 14MHz 5W transceiver.

series is suitable over the (military) temperature range −40 to +85°C. Small outline and cerdip packages are available. Basic pin outlines and oscillator configurations were given in the January *TT*.

As noted by K1BQT, this device is not intended for use in the front-ends of HF receivers having a very wide dynamic range. For such applications the Plessey IC double-balanced mixer type SL6440 would clearly be more suitable but does not include the in-built oscillator that makes the NE602 an attractive device for small-signal HF/VHF applications, where 'state-of-the-art' performance is not a requirement.

MININEC LOOK AT CAPACITIVE LOADING

TT has referred on several occasions to the increasing use of sophisticated computer software to analyse the characteristics of antennas without any requirement actually to construct either a full-scale or a model antenna. One of the best-known techniques is the so-called 'Method of Moments' using various NEC (Numerical Electromagnetic Code) programs. The original NEC programs tend to be rather costly for purely amateur use but, as with the various programs for propagation prediction, simplified versions are being developed. For example, the US Naval Postgraduate School in California has written MININEC for use with readily available personal computers and able to analyse basic wire antennas. While there is no doubt that such computer techniques are providing a valuable new tool for the antenna engineer, there is always the danger of writing off antennas that in the real world may have practical advantages not catered for by the software. One *must* treat computer simulations with caution.

Almost 28 years ago, 'Dud' Charman, G6CJ, introduced to radio amateurs the principles and potential applications of dipoles, monopoles and ground planes, and long-wire antennas with their elements 'stretched' by the insertion of capacitance loading at intervals along their length ("Loaded wire aerials" F J H Charman, *RSGB Bulletin*, July 1961 and see also most editions of *Amateur Radio Techniques*). He showed that the capacitors could conveniently be formed using 80ohm flat-twin feeder line for the element cut to form overlapping sections. Later designs in American and Australian publications have tended to use conventional capacitors.

Because most of us have locations of restricted length, there has always been more interest, at least on HF, in antennas of compressed rather than stretched size. Capacitive loading has never attracted a great deal of attention, and when it has, some of the claims made for it have been rather extravagant (compare with those made for the T2FD antenna). In one small respect, the *G6CJ/ART* information is misleading in suggesting that a terminated stretched long-wire has only a single main lobe; in practice the radiation pattern has the usual split lobes of its non-stretched equivalent.

G6CJ showed that a dipole stretched by a factor of two, ie, a half-wave dipole 'stretched' to the span of a full-wave element, has only a modest gain of about 1dB, a similar broadside radiation pattern with slightly reduced beamwidth (56° instead of 78°) and a central resistive feedpoint of about 200ohms rather than the nominal 70ohms of a conventional dipole. It needs a lot of stretching to obtain substantial gain: see Table 1. But as noted in 1961 there are other advantages. A unique feature of stretched antennas is that they can be placed quite close to an unstretched wire without the radiation pattern being distorted by mutual coupling. For example, a 14MHz 'stretched' dipole could be hung directly beneath a conventional 7MHz dipole with both elements providing the radiation pattern of a half-wave dipole. The higher feedpoint can also be beneficial for monopole, Marconi or ground-plane vertical antennas, though stretching does unfortunately call for a very high mast if advantage is to be taken of the much lower ground losses for earthed monopoles, resulting from their higher impedance feed point.

A recent article 'The capacitively loaded dipole antenna – some new findings' by Dick Turrin, W2IMU in the Australian *Amateur Radio* (Novem-

ber 1988) presents the results of analysing a stretched antenna using a MININEC-3 program on an AT&T 6300 PC. He investigated the 7MHz capacitively loaded dipole shown in Fig 4(a) with the following results: The broadside radiation pattern gain was +3.0dBi instead of the +2.1dBi of a standard dipole, giving a gain of 0.84dB with reference to a dipole, a little less than the 1dB of Table 1. Feed-point impedance came out at about 200ohms, the same as given by G6CJ. Bandwidth between the 2:1 VSWR points is about 6.65 to 7.45MHz compared with 6.8 to 7.2MHz for the conventional dipole; a useful but not exceptional improvement. Higher order resonances occur at 12.6, 19.5 and 26.5MHz.

W2IMU comments critically on the factor-two stretched dipole: "This cannot be regarded as a high-performance antenna nor can it be considered an ultra-broadband antenna. In the author's opinion, the physical size and difficulties of including capacitors along a wire antenna do not justify the predicted increase in performance". He notes that in contrast the gain from a 'double Zepp' (two half-waves in phase) is +3.69dBi, about 0.7dB more than the stretched wire of similar overall span and about 1.5dB more than a conventional dipole of half the length.

Clearly if 'gain' is the only consideration, there would be little justification in still regarding capacitive loading as a useful weapon in the antenna armoury. At least in some circumstances. It could prove unwise to write-off entirely capacitive loading, where the capacitors are formed by overlapping, purely on the basis of a MININEC run which largely confirms the earlier performance figures of G6CJ. It seems to me that what W2IMU has done is to underline the credibility of the MININEC program. As he points out: "The MININEC program permits a fairly straightforward and rapid analysis of complex wire antennas using readily available personal computers, a facility which, ten years ago, was virtually impossible'.

His computer has also shown that because of the resulting improved current distribution, an antenna using mixed inductance/capacitance loading with four inductors and six capacitors as in Fig 4(b) would achieve a broadside gain of 3.51dBi, virtually the same as the double Zepp, and a feedpoint impedance very close to 300ohms resistive, making such an arrangement convenient to feed with the low-cost 300-ohm ribbon feeder widely used for TV reception in the USA. □

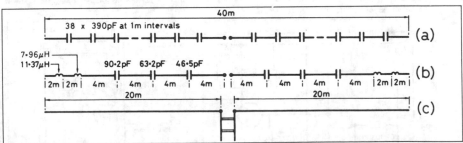

Fig 14. (a) Capacitively loaded 7MHz half-wave dipole as computer-analysed by W2IMU. (b) Combination of inductive and capacitive loading to give rather more broadside gain. (c) Double Zepp (two half-waves in phase, voltage fed with open-wire feeders).

n-factor	No of C(pF)	No of Sections	½ dipole length (ft)	Input Z Ω	Beam-width	Gain (dBd)
1	—	2×1	33	70	78°	0
2	68	2×6	66	200	56°	1
3	50	2×9	99	400	42°	2·1
4	43	2×12	132	550	32°	3·1

For other bands change C and section length proportional to wavelength eg for 21MHz reduce values by two-thirds, *G6CJ, 1961.*

Table 1. Basic information on 14MHz dipoles Capacitive loading at 5ft 6in intervals.

PHANTOM TRANSMISSIONS

It has sometimes been observed that as soon as your neighbours realise that you operate a transmitter every subsequent disturbance to their television or radio reception, whether or not you were at home, is laid at your door. An unusual example of such 'phantom' transmissions was in evidence on BBC and ITN News Bulletins following the recent sentencing of 'Erwin van Haarlem' to 10 years imprisonment for 'Acts preparatory to the commission of an offence under Section 1 of the Official Secrets Act.' Evidence was given that he had been working for over 13 years as an agent of SFGF, the Czech Secret Service and had been arrested while *receiving* morse transmissions from Prague.

Statements made in open court indicated that over the years more than 200 such messages had been sent to him, enciphered on one-time pads. But it was clear that these messages had been sent 'broadcast' and when arrested he was using a standard all-band broadcast-type receiver. Although part of the trial was held in camera, there seems to have been no evidence that he had used a *transmitter*.

TECHNICAL TOPICS

PAT HAWKER G3VA

It is evident that two-way clandestine radio contacts are not a common feature of peace-time espionage in European countries: outgoing reports are normally conveyed by less-detectable methods.

Yet the television bulletins featured an interview with neighbours who were convinced that 'Van Haarlem' had been regularly using a transmitter that had been interfering with their television reception, and cameras were focused almost accusingly on broadcast-receiving antennas. The neighbours even claimed to have recognised the interference as morse code. Perhaps the answer to such TVI is to fit 'phantom' filters!

For those experiencing 'real' EMC problems, often in the form of interference *from* digital appliances, a massive amount of technical information is becoming available now that this topic figures high on the list of professional investigations and research projects.

In 'Modelling the electromagnetic radiation from electrically small table top products' by Todd H Hubing and J Frank Kaufman (*IEEE Trans on EMC*, February 1989) it is concluded that: "Electrical small circuits are very inefficient sources of radiation. When these circuits are operating in the vicinity of relatively long power or signal cables, the currents induced on the cables are generally the primary sources of electromagnetic radiation. This is true even when the circuit has been isolated from the cables with ferrites, filters, transformers or metal plates." In effect mains-borne interference is not necessarily overcome solely by installing effective filtering at the input to the appliance. The leads beyond the filter act as a receiving antenna and can re-inject RFI into the mains or act as radiating elements.

The IEEE paper illustrates the importance of the environment of the source in determining the overall radiation. This implies that one needs to know how small radiation sources interact with relatively large metallic objects or wires in their neighbourhood. Surprisingly, it is shown that in some circumstances radiation can be significantly higher from a shielded circuit than from an unshielded one. Perhaps not so surprising when one recalls how a transmitter cabinet can become 'hot' to RF, particularly when used in an upstairs shack.

Another paper in the same issue of the *IEEE Trans* 'Shielding effectiveness of "pigtail" connections' by Hassan A N Hejase *et al* (Syracuse University) provides another look at a problem that was highlighted in the item 'Minimising RFI from digital equipment' (*TT*, April 1988, pp266-7) where it was shown that the inductance of a 'drain-wire' (pigtail) connection in a poor 'cable-boot as in **Fig 2** can cause appreciable RF noise to appear on the outside of a screened cable. The IEEE paper provides a detailed analysis, based on the method of moments, of the effectiveness of various forms of pigtail connections at various frequencies. The type and length of pigtail connection is shown to be crucial, although the pigtail itself does not radiate significantly. It is shown that not all pigtails are equal, even when electrically short in terms of wavelength: "A short pigtail is significantly better than a longer one … multiple pigtails yield significant improvement over the single pigtails; the difference in shielding effectiveness may be 10dB or more … Different load impedances lead to different input parameters and may cause appreciable changes in shielding effectiveness, especially at frequencies close to resonance." A practical example of the importance of earthing connections of minimum RF resistance was described in the November 1988 *TT* item '50MHz VCRI — a case history' stemming from Jerry Sanderson, G2DBT, **Tables 1-3** provide useful information when tackling EMC problems.

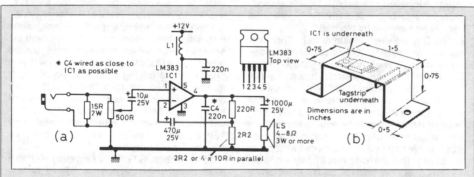

Fig 1. K8KWD's external one-Watt audio amplifier for use with handheld transceivers etc in noisy environments.

BEEFING UP HANDHELD AUDIO

The use of 'handheld' transceivers in vehicles or in noisy environments where an additional power source is available is by no means uncommon, although it should be recognised that if actually held in the hand by the driver of a moving vehicle this practice goes against the recommendations of the current Highway Code. An article 'A speaker amplifier for handheld transceivers' by Leonard Van Prooyen, K8KWD (*QST*, January 1989, pp20-22) is introduced as follows: "Does background noise make it difficult for you to hear your handheld talking to you? By spending a couple of enjoyable hours at the workbench, you can build this external amplifier unit (**Fig 1**) to boost your transceiver's audio output."

L1 is a choke used when the amplifier is powered from a 12V vehicle supply to eliminate alternator whine. While K8KWD suggests that suitable chokes can be salvaged from some broadcast car radios, he notes that one can also be made from two '8d' 1½-in nails wound with about 100 turns of 18g enamelled wire secured at the ends by a layer of electrical tape. The LM383 requires a heat sink which in K8KWD's design takes the form of U-shaped

aluminium strip (Fig 1(b)) which is also used to hold a tag strip. If power is drawn from the vehicle electrics make sure that the lead is suitably fused close to the source.

While the LM383 is readily available, it seems appropriate to note that Philips Components have recently claimed to be first on the market with two audio ICs that require no external components, apart from decoupling components, to form a 1W mono (TDA7052) or 2 x 1W stereo class B high quality audio power amplifiers. Featuring 'bridge-tied load (BTL)' configurations', the new ICs can be used over an unusually wide operating voltage range (3-15V). The mono TDA7052 has a typical quiescent current of only 4mA, a closed-loop voltage gain of about 40dB, low total harmonic distortion (typically 0·2%) and an output protected against short circuits. The announcement adds: "Both ICs have a high supply ripple rejection of 40dB (typical) between 100Hz and 10kHz and produce no switch-on or switch-off clicks". This new device would thus seem useful both for an add-on amplifier for handhelds etc and also for a receiver output stage. The stereo chip (two mono units on the same chip) could also be of interest to anyone experimenting with pseudo-stereo or binaural reception (see *TT*, February 1989).

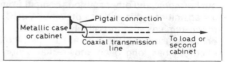

Fig 2. A poorly 'booted' shielded cable with a long 'pigtail' connection results in RF radiation from the outer braid of the co-axial cable or conversely reduces the immunity of the shielded equipment: for more detailed explanation see *TT*, April 1988.

Table 1. Noise-immunity level (NIL) and noise margins for some popular logic families

Logic family[1]	NIL, mV	Nominal voltage swing, V	Noise margin,[2] dB
CMOS	1000	5	14
CMOS-HS	1000	5	14
LS-TTL	300	3	20
S-TTL	300	3	20
LP-TTL	400	3	18
TTL	400	3	18
ECL-10k	100	0·8	18
ECL-100k	100	0·8	18

Source: Vendors' data sheets and catalogues
1. Legend: CMOS — complementary metal-oxide silicon; CMOS-HS — high-speed CMOS; LS-TTL — low-power Schottky transistor-transistor logic; S-TTL — Schottky transistor-transistor logic; LP-TTL — low-power TTL; ECL — emitter-coupled logic; 10k — medium-speed version; 100k — high-speed version
2. Ratio of voltage swing to noise immunity level, expressed in decibels

Table 2. Relative radiation levels for some popular logic families

Logic family	Typical gate current, mA	Typical bandwidth, MHz	Relative radiation level,[1] dB
CMOS	0·1	3	-10
CMOS-HS	0·1	30	10
LS-TTL	8	40	50
S-TTL	30	120	71
LP-TTL	8	21	45
TTL	16	32	54
ECL-10k	1	160	44
ECL-100k	1	420	52

Source: Vendors' data sheets and catalogues
1. Relative radiation in terms of the product of gate current and bandwidth, expressed in decibels with respect to 1 milliampere megahertz

Table 3. Effectiveness of shielding materials

Shielding material	Surface resistance,[1] ohms/square	Shielding effectiveness, dB At 10MHz	At 100MHz	At 1GHz
Silver acrylic paint	0·004	67	93	97
Silver epoxy paint	0·1	59	81	87
Silver deposition	0·05	57	82	89
Nickel composite	3.0	35	47	57
Carbon composite	10·0	27	35	41
Arc-sprayed zinc	0·002	106	92	98
Wire screen (0·64-mm grid)	NA	86	68	48

Source: Vendors' data sheets and catalogues
1. For 25-micrometre thickness and for frequencies for which the largest dimension of the shielding plate is less than a quarter of a wavelength

(Source of Tables 1-3 'Taming EMI in Microprocessor Systems' by White, Atkinson, Osburn in *IEEE Spectrum*, December 1985)

RUSTY-BOLT TVI

Although it is almost always possible to filter out harmonic and other spurious content from a transmitter sufficiently to prevent TVI/BCI, there remains the possibility of problems being caused by the so-called 'rusty-bolt effect'. It has long been known that a non-linear junction can be created by rusty metal contacts and that these can generate harmonics from induced RF currents, by acting as diode mixers and rectifiers. This problem is particularly important at professional mobile base stations, where a single mast may support the antennas of half-a-dozen transmitters. In such circumstances rusty-bolt rectification can result in the generation of hundreds of intermodulation products which seriously affect local reception.

A research project a few years ago at City University, London supported by the Science & Engineering Research Council and the Home Office, then the Radio Regulatory authority, sought to provide a practical engineering solution to the suppression of such structural intermodulation interferences ('Intermodulation interference in radio systems' by P S W Ho et al, AGARD-CPP-420, NATO).

As background, this report noted that intermodulation interference (IMI) can be divided into two types: "First, those due to active devices in the communication systems, such as the non-linearity of the power amplifiers where common antennas are employed, and overloading the receiver front-end. The second type is due to the passive components and these include cables, feeders, aerials and supporting structures. Effective methods have been found to solve the problems of the active type by careful shielding of equipments, using filters in the transmitter outputs and receiver inputs. However, the passive type is a much more intractable problem, and once generated cannot be removed by filtering."

The City University team noted: "There are two major causes for the generation of passive IM products, namely non-linear junction effect and B/H non-linearity which is inherent in any ferromagnetic material. Earlier investigations into ferromagnetic materials have shown that nickel-plated RF connectors can cause a high level of IMI and should be avoided for coaxial cables carrying large RF currents in systems susceptible to IMI. Steel masts can also cause problems. But the B/H non-linearity of bulk ferromagnetic materials is much less important than the non-linear junction effect, ie the rusty-bolt effect."

The most effective way of overcoming rusty-bolt IMI problems appears to be to offer an alternative high-conductivity path to RF, by-passing the non-linear junction once this has been located, but this is not always an easy task as noted later. The amateur situation, where it is unusual for several transmitters to be operating simultaneously at the same site, is less commonly affected than with shared mobile base antenna towers. Nevertheless, a 'rusty-bolt' generates harmonics from a single transmission and it is not uncommon for this to give rise to TVI etc.

In describing experimental results using a test cell in which deliberately corrroded metal junctions were fed with two 50-watt signals working into a dummy load (f_1 155·2125MHz, f_2 152·0875MHz, f_{im} 148·9625MHz, ie 2 x 152·0875 = 304·1750 − 155·2125 = 148·9625) the City University report states:

"Joint samples, in a test cell, were made and were corroded for IM measurements. By doing this we were able to convince ourselves that the rusty joint is a first order effect in IM generation, although the ferromagnetic effects of steel are still important . . . For a new antenna tower, the structural elements are galvanised. However, the joints between structure elements could lose their initial protection during construction of the tower, and suffer more rapid deterioration giving rise to corrosion due to fretting at the joint. Moreover, a joint will tend to be a moisture trap. Corrosion at these joints can probably be assumed to be the major source of intermodulation. Our approach to solve the IM problem is to offer an alternative high conductivity path to RF current. An initial experiment involved the covering of a corroded cylindrical steel sample with zinc coating (by electroplating) . . . the IM level was (then) very close to the system floor level . . . The problem now is to develop a practical way to carry out the metallic coating of the joints. Methods being considered are metal spraying and electroless plating . . . It was found that metal-based paints would not work because the bulk conductivity of the paint is much less than of the metal."

WHERE THERE IS NO TELEPHONE

"Low-cost systems aid the third world", a *TT* item last October (p779), discussed some ways in which radio amateurs are attempting to help those vast areas of Africa where at present virtually the only way of sending a message is to take it in person or find a runner: "no telephones, no regular postal services — and little of the hard currency needed to buy, install and maintain the advanced telecommunications services that we take for granted."

This problem affects not only the indigenous population but also the many missions and aid agencies even where these do have limited funds. The outstations often need a relatively cheap way of talking to their regional headquarters in the capital cities or with other outposts over distances of some hundreds of kilometres. The obvious solution is HF radio, using amateur-grade transceivers and such systems are increasingly filling the gap left by the absence of telephones.

John Corbett, G3TWS has recently written a most useful 100-page booklet 'Where there is no telephone' specifically intended to assist those with or without formal electronics education to whom the successful operation of an HF radio system appears shrouded in mystery: 'something more akin to art than science'. Although written from the perceptive of experience of HF radio communications in Zaire, much of the information is applicable to HF radio in any underdeveloped, Third World country. Indeed much of the contents would prove interesting also to newcomers to amateur radio anywhere though not aimed at the setting up of a 'hobby' station. The main sections include: 1, How radio waves travel; 2, aerials; 3, transceivers; 4, how to plan your radio network; 5, costs and choices; 6, how to install a radio system; 7, how to operate a radio network; 8, how to maintain a radio network; and 9, additional facilities.

The booklet has been printed and published in Kinshasa, Zaire but is available in the UK from the Baptist Missionary Society, 93 Gloucester Place, London W1H 4AA (price £2·50, A4 format, paper covers).

It is believed to be the only radio publication specifically written for the conditions experienced in some Third World countries. Written in a thoroughly practical, yet technically sound, manner it should assist both technical and non-technical readers as a reliable guide to planning, selecting, installing, operating and maintaining an SSB radio-telephone network in difficult circumstances.

LIVING WITH ELECTROMAGNETIC RADIATION

On many occasions, *TT* has referred to the long-lasting and seemingly insoluble controversies surrounding the biological effects of electro-magnetic, non-ionized, radiation at frequencies all the way from near-DC to visible light. These controversies, in the years since the publication of a book *The Zapping of America*, have changed from being a matter of specialist concern to the stage where they are regarded by a growing minority of the public as part of the environmental pollution debate.

For radio amateurs, the important consideration is the question of exposure to strong RF fields in the immediate vicinity of transmitting antennas. It has long been accepted that when RF energy is absorbed by biological material, particularly moist material such as tissue and the eye, there will be a rise in temperature, just as must occur in a dummy-load resistor. In most cases a modest rise in body temperature has no permanent adverse effect but it is clearly necessary to limit this rise.

There have long been official safeguards designed to limit continuous exposure to a safe figure that includes a 'factor-of-ten' safety margin. The present safety guidelines are designed to limit exposure to a maximum of 0·4W/kg of body weight. This translates into a power flux level of 10mW/cm² for continuous exposure (Note: G6HD has pointed out that there was an error in the equivalent figures I gave in the December 1988 *TT* in attempting to equate mW/cm² with W/m²). More recently it has been recommended that the figure of 10mW/cm² should be reduced to 4mW/cm² at VHF, with a progressive reduction from 10mW/cm² between 10MHz and 30MHz and a progressive rise between 300MHz and microwaves. This reduction is to take account of the greater absorption of the human body at VHF due to the dipole and monopole resonances of the body in all its shapes and sizes from infancy to adulthood.

TT, November 1986, pp780-781 summarised how the American ANSI levels translated into distances from MF and VHF broadcast antennas at power levels below 1kW, indicating that amateur HF and VHF antennas sited out-of-doors at normal heights are unlikely to infringe these guidelines, although this may not always be the case within a couple of metres of ground-mounted HF verticals. It is also becoming important to recognise that due to the sensitivity of our eyes, a problem could arise when using VHF handheld transceivers with short (rubber-duck etc) antennas held within a few inches of our eyes: in these circumstances it is now usually recommended on the basis of American work that the RF output should not exceed seven watts — a figure approached in some recent models. Care may also need to be exercised close to a mobile VHF/UHF antenna.

In *TT* (December 1983) I included a note from Bill Hall, G6ZRB reporting how he had suffered severe head pains the night after watching a demonstration of a 25W mobile transceiver while standing alongside the vehicle quite close to the antenna. Roberto Craighero,

I1ARZ. sensibly included a warning in his article on an 'Electrically tunable HF loop' (*Rad Com,* February 1989, pp38-42) on the potential hazard that could arise from the strong near-field magnetic component of an HF loop at other than QRP, particularly a loop used indoors without remote tuning.

Peter Simpson, G3GGK adds a further warning. He writes: "Having more time to experiment since taking early retirement, I decided to try my hand at building a one-metre diameter loop antenna for use with a 100W HF rig. Having no method of remote tuning, I was obliged to stand quite close to the loop whilst making adjustments ... After a few minutes, I became aware that I had developed a slight headache, not a condition I am usually troubled with. It was mealtime, so I switched off the rig and left the shack thinking no more about it. A few days later I resumed work on the loop and, after about five minutes or so, back came the headache. I decided there might possibly be a hazard so I have abandoned work on the project until I can motorise the tuning capacitor. *One hears now and again warnings about RF damage to human tissue at UHF and microwave but can there really be risk at 14 to 30MHz?*" (Italics added).

The answer, as noted earlier, is a definite *yes!* although an HF antenna element does not represent a 'point source' in the near field so it is not possible to calculate the power flux close to the element(s); obviously, a compact loop produces an unusually strong magnetic component in the immediate vicinity. Amateurs should not be misled into believing that the thermal effects of EM radiation are confined only to UHF and microwaves.

One suspects, although it is not possible to be sure, that the headaches experienced by G6ZRB and G3GGK were manifestations of thermal effects, possibly absorption in the high water content of the eyes, the most vulnerable organ of the human body. There is some evidence that high levels of radiation can result in eye cataracts, a very much more serious matter than a passing headache. It is thus important that amateurs should be fully aware of — and avoid — the hazards of exposure to RF fields appreciably above the safe limits recommended by the National Radiological Protection Board. As G3GGK puts it: "The publicity attached to any injury to a radio amateur from RF exposure would do untold damage to the hobby and heaven knows what the tabloid press would make out of any incident which involved a hobby already under social pressures due to RFI/EMC problems."

Indeed hanging as a Sword of Damocles over all users of the radio spectrum is the growing

concern, found among sections of the public and a number of scientists, about both long-term and short-term biological effects of low-level radiation as a form of 'environmental pollution'. The power of suggestion and fear is very strong, particularly when fuelled by those individuals who are always ready to suspect that there may be a 'conspiracy of silence' on the part of the authorities.

Widespread publicity was given recently in the Surrey/Hampshire area linking 'cot deaths' with nearby radar stations. Ned Row, G8GZZ sent me the front-page of the *Surrey Mail* (February 18, 1989) headlined: 'Why are we killing our children? Sinister secret could hide truth of cot deaths mystery.' G8GZZ assumed this was the fervent imagination of a local journalist but enquiries show that the story was based on statements by qualified medical researchers, although other experts point out that a far more tenable theory is that these particular infant deaths coincided with a sudden drop in temperature.

I recently attended a IEE discussion meeting 'Biological effects of electromagnetic radiation' at which a number of workers in this field described attempts to reproduce the many 'positive' results achieved, for example, by the use of pulsed EM radiation to stimulate bone growth, as now used widely throughout the world. Yet 14 years work at Sheffield, including the use of 'double blind' experiments, have failed to confirm that the radiation plays any significant part in effecting the many successful cures. But it is clearly extremely difficult to prove or disprove whether there are any long-term effects of low-level radiation. It was apparent during an unusually heated 'discussion period' — not often a feature of IEE meetings — that the idea of 'electromagnetic pollution' is taking firm root in what at present appears to be 'fringe circles' unwilling to be swayed by engineers or to appreciate that a biological effect may not in fact be hazardous. My personal view is that if eventually it is shown that there are still unproven long-term athermal effects then, compared with other natural hazards, they will prove to be statistically very small indeed. But it is becoming more difficult to state positively that there are *no* athermal effects of low-level RF radiation, possibly at microbiological levels.

AUDIO DECIBEL LEVEL METER

The April *TT* referred to the Signetics application notes reissued by Philips Components (Mullard) on the NE602 and NE604 devices. This series also includes: 'AN1991 Audio decibel level detector with meter driver' by Robert J Zavrel, W7SX originally published by Signetics January 1986 and republished by Mullard June 1986. There are several uses for such an audio meter of interest to amateurs. Among those listed by W7SX are: S-meter for direct-conversion radio receiver; VU meter; microphone tester; audio analysers; portable acoustic analysers; audio dynamic-range testers; and audio spectrum analysers.

The NE604 can provide a logarithmic response proportional to the input signal level over an 80dB range, at frequencies from audio up to about 15MHz. **Fig 3** shows a sensitive (10·5µV) audio level indi-

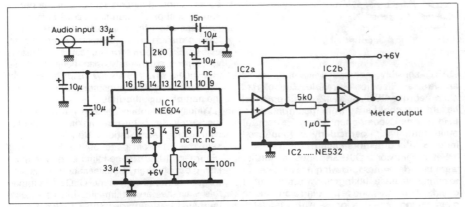

Fig 3. Audio decibel level meter based on the Signetics NE604 IC.

cator circuit based on two IC devices (NE604 and NE532) that draws less than 5mA from a 6V supply. A standard 5V FSD voltmeter can be linearly calibrated in decibels (within ±1·5dB) over a single 80dB range for audio frequencies from 100Hz to 10kHz: **Fig 4.** If higher level measurements are required an attenuator should be incorporated ahead of the input capacitor. Input impedance is high, about 50k, so lower impedance terminations, 50 or 600ohms, will not be affected. The application note provides a description of the circuit functions of the two amplifier sections in the NE604 used to provide a current proportional to the $\log_{10}$ of the input audio signal. The 532 op-amp is used as a buffer and meter driver although a digital voltmeter could replace both the op-amp and the meter shown reducing the device to a single 604 and the few external components.

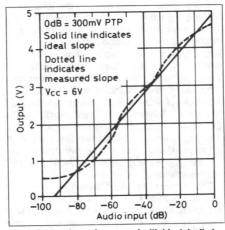

0dB = 300mV PTP
Solid line indicates ideal slope
Dotted line indicates measured slope
V_{cc} = 6V

Fig 4. Comparison of measured with ideal decibel calibration of the audio level meter.

MORE ON ELEVATED VERTICALS

The April *TT* introduced the important concept, put forward by Les Moxon, G6XN, that the popular elevated ground-plane antenna should be regarded as basically a *dipole* rather than a quarter-wave monopole antenna. Some readers may have been tempted to say: "So what. As long as it works with my rig, I couldn't care less that the boffins say it's a dipole!"

But it *does* matter. For years the reputable sources of technical information, such as the *ARRL Antenna Handbook,* have described the radials of a ground-plane antenna (GPA) as 'simulating' a solid (circular) plate, and thus resembling a grounded monopole, adding that four radials are sufficient to achieve this effect but implying that the more radials the better. It was not until 1981 that I was able to reveal, following a pleasant lunch with the late Dr George Brown and his wife Elizabeth, that the GPA, as originally conceived in the 1930s, used only two radials, later increased to four in order to make it more marketable for American police radio communications. Some years before this, I had successfully tried out and described in *TT* an 'inverted ground-plane' in the form of a T-antenna or single-element 'Bobtail antenna' with two quarter-wave horizontal radials: **Fig 6.** I still believe this is a useful antenna for those wishing to use vertical polarisation, have two supports and are prepared to use an outdoor antenna matching network to provide a high-impedance, voltage feed. It has the advantage of raising the high-current section of the radiating element well above surrounding fences, shrubs etc which can

TRACING RUSTY-BOLT AND DIODE INTERFERENCE

A method of sniffing out non-linear junctions has been described recently by Jack Holmes, W6BUY (Technical Correspondence, *QST*, December 1988, p46). He wrote:

"About 30 years ago, I had a TVI problem that nearly drove me mad! It didn't take long to analyse the problem — RF rectification — but it took nearly three years to locate the *source* ... TVI can be caused by RF rectification in unexpected places: a rain gutter, a fence, a household appliance or any number of other sources.

"The method I devised for locating a rectification source is a relatively simple one that hit the bull's-eye. My RF sniffer produces a small radiation field. When this field encounters an object that rectifies the RF, the harmonic energy is picked up by an antenna and sent back to a portable TV set: **Fig 5.**

"The sniffer probe consists of a broom handle on which is mounted a dummy load with a wire loop, the receiving antenna, around it. Energy from a low-power transmitter is fed to the dummy load (50ohms, non-inductive resistor of appropriate wattage) ... The sniffer must be within approximately 10ft of the rectification source (to produce observable TVI) and this immediately narrows the search area. Prior to use, place the test set-up in a clear area and check that there is no TVI with

power applied to the dummy load ... save time and energy by initially trying to locate the general area of rectifictaion ... In my case I found the house walls were the culprits. They were plaster on PegBoard and had overlapping 10ft lengths of six inch wide heavy wire mesh between the plaster and the boards. The pieces of wire mesh were at the top of walls. Rectification was at some of the overlapped joints ... That's when I called my builder."

I believe that a basically similar techique (but using a radio receiver rather than a portable TV set) is sometimes used for 'sweeping' rooms to ensure that no electronic 'bugs' have been installed. The transistors in the 'bug' act as diodes and generate harmonics or IMI, although I cannot recall seeing any published designs for such 'sweepers'.

Further examples of IMI/harmonics generated

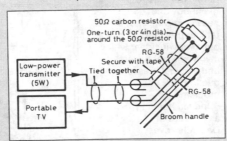

Fig 5. The RF sniffer used by W6BUY to trace 'rusty-bolt' (diode junction) radiation causing TVI.

by 'diodes' in unpowered equipment have been described by David Barker and AK7M in *QST* (November 1988, p38) in an item 'Un-powered computer generates RFI.'

David Barker contributes: "Reception from 1·8 to 30MHz was marred by severe splatter from a broadcast station one and a half miles away. The interference came and went for no apparent reason. After several weeks I tracked the apparent source to a 30ft shielded RS-232-C data cable connected to my unpowered computer. Disconnecting the cable made the interference go away but attaching a new cable brought it back. Further investigation revealed a poorly soldered joint on the computer's RS-23-C DB25 connector. Evidently this solder joint was acting as an effective frequency multiplier."

AK7M added the following editorial note: "Turned-off electronic equipment can generate interference even *without* faulty wiring. Investigating pops, sizzles and crackles on all medium and high frequencies, I discovered that my unpowered, general-coverage receiver was generating the junk in step with the modulation peaks of a medium-wave broadcast transmitter one and a quarter miles away ... My hunch is that the interference is caused by the unpowered receiver's unbiased input network switching diodes and/or the RF amplifier (MOSFET). Turning the receiver 'on' makes the problem disappear. Solution: Disconnect the antenna from the receiver when not in use."

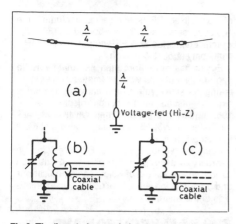

Fig 6. The 'inverted ground plane' antenna using two horizontal radials. (b) and (c) show two possible matching networks for voltage feeding at the base of the quarter-wave radiating element.

absorb an appreciable amount of the RF energy from ground-mounted verticals.

As explained last month, G6XN takes the further step of advocating the use of a single *short* loaded radial, otherwise counterpoise, an arrangement that must seem illogical if you still regard the GPA as a monopole with a simulated earth plane.

In *Ham Radio* (October 1988), Bill Orr W6SAI retold my account of how the RCA ground-plane antenna came to have four radials and my 1981 conclusion that "a two-radial ground plane certainly serves the purpose the inventor had in mind!". In the March 1989 issue, W6SAI returns to this subject on the basis of letters received from readers. He writes:

"A letter from Don Norman, AF8B says that experiments he ran in 1982 on an elevated 147MHz ground-plane showed two radials were a considerable improvement over one, three radials were a considerable improvement over two. He said his tests also showed conclusively that the radials served to decouple the feedline from the antenna. Don's opinion is that HF multiband verticals planted in backyards around the world would probably perform much better if they were placed on rooftops and equipped with two radials for each band."

Certainly, as mentioned last month, the degree to which RF currents can be kept off the feedline is an important factor in determining the vertical radiation pattern of a GPA no matter how many radials are used. Nevertheless it should be possible to minimise such current by the use of chokes, including a coiled length of the coaxial feeder, stub filters etc or ferrite absorbing toroids as in the zero-extent GPA described in *TT*, November 1987, rather than depending on multiple radials.

Another *Ham Radio* reader, Bill Bringler, K5CSJ ran the ground-plane programme on his computer using MININEC (see April *TT*) and compared the field patterns of two and four radial configurations for a GPA with base 25ft above 'average' earth and with the radials sloping down to 15ft elevation at their ends: "At a vertical radiation angle of 10°, the horizontal pattern of the two-radial design was omni-directional within a fraction of a decibel. In the vertical plane, the angle of the main lobe above the horizon was less than 20°." This corresponded to the pattern of the equivalent four-radial design. K5CSJ concluded that there was no significant difference in operation between the two antennas. He also did a computer-run to compare a ground-mounted monopole vertical against the elevated two-radial design and found it about 1·5dB worse at an elevation angle of 10°. His conclusion was that "A two-radial ground plane, when elevated, works just fine!"

L-MATCH ATU WITH FINE ADJUSTMENT

Doug DeMaw, W1FB in introducing 'A VFO with bandspread and bandset' made me feel my age when he wrote: "Are you old enough to recall those days when we amateurs had receivers that had two readout dials? One was a bandset dial for coarse tuning and the other was for bandspread or fine tuning. When I compare that method to modern digital-readout techniques I wonder how we managed to get on frequency...". Old enough to *recall* ... gosh, I still *use* a 40 year old general coverage Hammarlund HQ129-X receiver with its two readout dials! The trick now, as then, is to use a crystal band-edge marker when setting the coarse tuning and then who really needs to know the *precise* in-band frequencies?

However, the point I wish to make this month is that the coarse/fine adjustment principle has other valid applications. Hector Cole, G3OHK uses a 100ft end-fed Marconi antenna, using 20g enamelled wire, with his TS530SP HF transceiver. Over the years he has made and used many different ATUs for end-fed random-length antennas including some with roller-coaster variable inductances. The most satisfactory has proved to be his present ATU which achieves variable inductance without the use of either a roller coaster or a variometer.

He writes: "It's an L-match using an old idea that seems to have fallen out of use for many years **(Fig 7)** that enables me to select an inductance of any number of turns. There are three adjustments, the variable capacitor and two multi-position rotary switches but it is not at all complicated to tune. One switch provides fine 'unit' adjustment with the first 10 turns of the coil tapped at every turn; the remainder of the coil is then tapped only at intervals of 10 turns with the taps taken to the 'tens' switch.

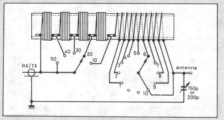

Fig 7. G3OHK's L-match ATU permits switch selection of from one to 50 turns of a 50-turn coil with just 14 taps. This two-switch technique can prove more economical and more convenient than using a roller-coaster inductance. As shown it provides a step-up impedance transformation suitable for use with end-fed antennas.

The single turn taps go to the 'units' switch and the 'tens' taps go to the 'tens' switch. With the 'tens' switch at position '1' you can select a coil of 1 to 10 turns, likely to prove suitable for use on at least the 28, 24, 21 and 18MHz bands. On the lower frequency bands, with the 'tens' switch at '2' this allows the 'unit' switch to cover from 10 to 20 turns; with the 'tens' switch at '3' you can select from 20 to 30 turns and so on.

Unlike a roller-coaster, you do not need to have a turns counter and the coil can be quickly re-set to any number of turns previously found to be suitable. The ATU can be set more quickly to a different band than one with a roller coaster.

"The switches I use are similar to those sold by Cirkit and Maplins; all plastic body and shaft. These have given no trouble at the power levels of my transceiver although higher-grade components may be required at legal-limit powers."

G3OHK is puzzled why the simple, two-component L-match circuit is not more popular. It is as efficient as the 'Ultimate' T-match and can provide better harmonic suppression. It is very convenient for voltage-fed antennas and, by reversing connections, can also provide an impedance step-down. At G3VA much use has been made of both L-match and Pi-network antenna matching units, both configurations providing satisfactory results — G3VA.

G3OHK recalls that the first radio he ever built was a crystal set using two stud switches to vary the inductance and no tuning capacitor. But it's a long time since he twiddled with a cat's whisker!

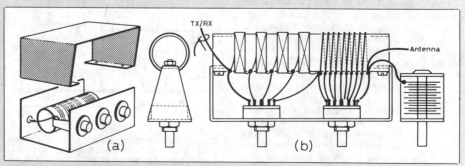

Fig 8. Constructional details of the L-match ATU.

PROFESSIONAL-AMATEUR PIONEERS

Six years ago, in describing something of the role of radio amateurs in the second world war ('The Secrets of Wartime Radio' *Amateur Radio* (London), March 1983) I pointed out that the large amateur-radio market in North America led, by the mid-thirties, to some excellent high-performance communications equipment whereas, by comparison, British military communications planning had progressed relatively slowly in the inter-war years, with crude, heavy and far from reliable designs still in use. An exception was the adoption by the RAF of VHF R/T equipment for fighter aircraft following experimental 56MHz demonstrations by George Jessop, G6JP, and Douglas Walters, G5CV, then the radio correspondent of the old *Daily Herald*.

In the 'thirties, many of the leading American firms, such as RCA and General Electric, employed large numbers of engineers who had become interested in amateur radio as youngsters. But in addition, a number of firms were established by enthusiastic amateurs, initially to cater for the amateur market. These included Collins Radio (Arthur Collins, W0CXX), Hallicrafters (Bill Halligan, W9WZE) and the specialist RF power valve firm of Eitel-McCullough Inc 'Eimac' set up in 1934 by Bill

Eitel, W6UF and Jack McCullough, W6CHE. They launched the company on a $5000 stake and the belief (or dream) that they could build more powerful and reliable valves, which would operate at higher frequencies than any then available. Although Eimac valves were originally designed for amateur radio transmitters, they were soon taken up by commercial and military designers. Old-timers still remember the 35T triode which with 2kV HT could provide 225 watts (CW) or 120 watts (AM) output and which sold in the USA for about $6, and the powerful 75T (375 watts CW output) for $9. The big boys fitted the 100TH triode (300 watts CW output) or the 152-TL (two 75T triodes in a single envelope) handling 500mA at 3000V for $20.

In 1965 Eimac, with a staff of 1800 at its San Carlos factory, could claim to be 'The World's Largest Manufacturer of Transmitter Valves', and then merged with Varian Associates. As the Varian Eimac Division, the firm remains a major supplier

of specialised RF power valves, including the 4CX250B series and the air-cooled 30X800A7 – which can provide 2kW PEP output up to 30MHz, yet is only about 2.5-in high.

Eimac has never forgotten its amateur radio beginnings with many active amateurs on its staff, taking an active role in the early moonbounce experiments, helping to set up Project OSCAR in 1965 and with both Bill Eitel, W6UF and Jack McCullough, W6CHE remaining active amateurs in their retirement.

Sadly I have to report that Bill Eitel died on February 26 at the age of 81 years. His contribution to both amateur and professional communications and broadcasting should not go unnoticed on this side of the Atlantic.

THE KALLI(RO)TRON AND OTHER OSCILLATORS

When at last I was able to present (*TT*, September 1988, pp681-2) a round-up of information on the 'kalli(ro)tron' oscillator, based in part on the original 1920 paper by L B Turner and the variation proposed by E J Cuddy in 1955, I felt that it was time to put this topic to rest for the time being. But it is clear that Ray Howgego, G4DTC, in first raising this topic in *TT*, December 1987, page 916, has succeeded in stirring up a lot of interest in

---

LINEARITY OF AMPLIFIERS

Several recent items in *TT* have discussed the problem of the unwanted intermodulation products produced by the non-linearity of heavily driven or incorrectly biased valve and solid state power amplifiers. One point that emerged from Table 1 of the December 1988 *TT* (page 960) ("IMD specifications for a selection of transmitting valves used by amateurs on HF/VHF/UHF extracted by W1JR from valve manufacturers' data sheets") is that even such highly-regarded valves as the 4X250/4CX250 series perform poorly if an attempt is made to maximise RF output rather than optimum linearity at reduced output. It should always be recognised that better IMD performance than was indicated in Table 1 can be achieved with reduced drive, with the proviso that the bias and screen voltages are correctly set and regulated for the conditions under which the amplifier is to be operated. There is much to be said for using power valves or semiconductors for the more demanding small-signal applications.

My first encounter with this approach was in 1942 when Dud Charman, G6CJ designed a large number of distribution amplifiers for feeding each of the outputs from rhombics and vee antennas to 8 or 16 of the seventy or so HRO receivers at the 'Country Farmyard' special intercept station, using 807 medium-power transmitting valves as linear small-signal amplifiers. In the crowded, non-channelised HF bands, splatter may not always be readily traced to a specific transmission and/or wrongly attributed to the linearity in the front-end of the receiver. This is not so often the case on VHF where there continue to be complaints of 'dirty', unduly broad signals, particularly during contests.

For many years it has been usual to specify intermodulation distortion (IMD) of SSB transmitters by measuring the third-order product (2f1-f2) of a two-tone signal, either with respect to the level of one of the test tones or relative to peak envelope power. Since the level of each tone is –6dB relative to PEP it is important to appreciate that these two

different ways of specifying IMD performance differ by 6dB. For example, –28dB relative to one test tone is equivalent to –34dB relative to PEP. Amateur practice is not consistent, although dB relative to a single tone is the more common.

At one time, a specification of –28dB relative to one tone was regarded as acceptable for commercial SSB transmitters, but for many years the more stringent figure of –42dB relative to PEP (–36dB relative to one tone) has been specified for professional/military SSB transmitters etc. since these are often required in independent sideband (ISB) transmitters. Few commercially-made amateur transmitters come within 10dB of the professional specification. This is why such feedback techniques as those described by Tony Preedy, G3LNP (*TT*, February 1989) could do much to clean up the bands, though it has to be recognised that often the worst splatter is not basically the fault of the amplifier but of the operator shouting into the microphone with the audio gain turned up too far!

Checking with that one time bible of SSB *'Fundamentals of Single Sideband'* (3rd edition,

1960, published by Collins Radio) one finds the following notes on the use of the 4X250B tetrode as a grid-driven or cathode-driven linear power amplifier:

"**Fig 1** is a simplified schematic of a grid-driven tetrode power amplifier. This amplifier, operating Class AB2 produces 250 watts per tube using the 4X250B tetrode. In general, the same design considerations exist for tetrode amplifiers as for triode amplifiers. That is, grid circuit swamping is required to hold the input impedance constant if the tetrode is driven into the grid current region, and neutralization is generally required if the tube is to operate over the entire high-frequency range. However, since the plate-to-grid capacitance is small in the tetrode, neutralization is much simpler. The tetrode amplifier, being a high gain tube requires relatively little driving power and a relatively small grid-swing for operation. This permits the paralleling of tubes with a common input network and a common output network which reduces the number of stages and simplifies tuning. In the tetrode power amplifier, the screen voltage has a very pronounced effect on the dynamic characteristic of the tubes. By lowering the screen voltage, the static current required for optimum linearity is lowered. This permits greater plate RF voltage swing which improves efficiency. The use of lower screen voltage has the adverse effect of increasing the grid drive for class AB2 operation and lowering the power output for class AB1 operation. The tetrode tube can be used in the cathode-driven circuit and can be so used without neutralization in the HF range."

This is, of course, all well-established practice, but one has the feeling that for many present-day amateurs, the fundamentals of good *valve* practice have often been largely forgotten, if ever known. Similarly, there is a tendency to forget that without careful design problems may arise, particularly if simple audio speech processors are used on SSB transmitters not designed to handle the higher duty-cycle and flattened waveforms of heavily processed speech.

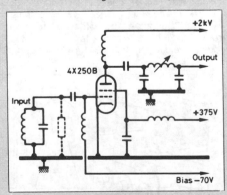

Fig 1. Simplified schematic of basic grid-driven tetrode power amplifier with grid circuit swamping resistor to hold the input impedance constant if the tetrode is driven into the grid current region.
(Fundamentals of SSB)

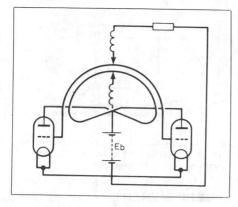

Fig 2. Mesby VHF oscillator of the 1920s.

Fig 3. 70MHz kallitron oscillator by G8SEQ. The two source resistors could be replaced by a single resistor selected for optimum results.

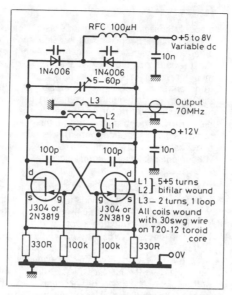

push-pull, two-device, oscillators and their origins.

Brian Bower, G3COJ, recalls attending lectures on RF engineering at Cambridge University in 1949-50 given by the self-same L B Turner who, it turns out, was also largely responsible in the mid-1920s for the design of the VLF antenna system for Rugby Radio (GBR, 16kHz) which at the time was the world's most powerful radio transmitter.

K H Green, G1NAK recalls using this form of tuned multivibrator in an attempt to encourage a reluctant 10kHz bar crystal to oscillate; this it did so violently that it self-destructed after about 10 seconds!

J W Noble, G8FEQ consulted the original paper which L B Turner delivered to the Wireless Section of the IEE in November 1919 describing his two-valve circuit which gave very high amplification of audio frequencies and embodied a limiting action for the reduction of static, but remains unconvinced that the modern push-pull 'kallitron' is directly

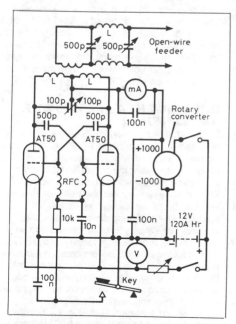

Fig 4. A kallitron power oscillator/transmitter that made history as AC4YN, providing the first amateur contacts with Tibet in the 1930s.

derived from Turner's oscillator as then presented (reproduced in *TT*, September 1988). He draws attention to a form of two-valve oscillator developed by Mesny in the early 1920s from which an output of several watts at 150MHz could be obtained: no mean achievement at that time. G8FEQ writes: "In the early 1920s there was a great deal of interest in the VHF bands despite the poor performance at high frequencies of the components of the day. One of the workers in this field was Mesny. His circuit (**Fig 2**) shows that this is a push-pull oscillator resembling the 'pseudo-kallitron' but with the unusual feature that feed-back is by inductive coupling (as used in the traditional regenerative detector)"

Neither G8FEQ nor I can trace anything further on the work of Mesny, but it is worth pointing out that both the Franklin and Ross-Gunn oscillators of the 1920s (both included in *Theory and Design of Valve Oscillators* by Dr H A Thomas, 1939) use cross-coupled two-device configurations basically akin to the G4DTC form of kallitron oscillator, although in the case of the Franklin the tank circuit is connected to earth rather than between the anodes.

A solid-state kallitron also turns up in *Sprat* (Issue Nr 38) built by John Beech, G8SEQ to provide a test signal source on 70MHz: **Fig 3**. G8SEQ notes that in the form shown it can be continuously tuned, frequency modulated, or scanned by applying a sawtooth waveform to the varicap diodes. It was built using copper PCB pads stuck to a groundplane of plain PCB material, 30mm square, the layout resembling the schematic.

The April 1989 issue of *OT News* (quarterly journal of the Radio Amateur Old-Timer's Association) also recalls that the famous mid-1930s British Political Mission to Tibet, during which Sir Evan Nepean, G5YN operated the first amateur station from Tibet (AC4YN), used a kallitron power oscillator/transmitter built by Lt Sidney Dagg, Royal Corps of Signals. This was intended for use by the Mission on about 10MHz but capable of being tuned to 14MHz: **Fig 4**. *Note:* I would not recommend anyone today to venture on to 14MHz, even from Tibet, with a keyed self-excited power oscilator running at up to about 100 watts input!

However, the final word on this subject surely must go back to G4DTC who launched us into this

world of 'smooth running' oscillators. He writes: "I have followed with interest those ever-deepening excavations into the archaeology of the kallirotron oscillator and would thank all concerned with the dig. I also use an identical oscillator to that shown in December 1987 in a band-switched VHF tuner covering 30MHz to 480MHz in ten bands, the balanced outputs feeding an SBL-1 diode mixer for conversion to a 30MHz IF. The 2N5458 FETs were replaced by J310 low-noise UHF FET devices, the 56pF feedback capacitors by 3.3pF, and the variable capacitor reduced to 15 + 15pF. Selected signal-frequency pre-amplifiers can then be placed in front of the mixer to give immediate access to any part of the VHF spectrum. Long term stability of 5kHz per hour at 450MHz is easily achieved and is quite adequate for a general-purpose receiver. If the oscillator is placed in a thermally-insulated diecast box, sudden changes in external temperature are largely ignored.

"While on the subject of oscillator stability, it is worth mentioning the exceptional stability of many of the older mechanically-tuned UHF TV tuners. These were commonly used in British television receivers until the advent of the far less stable varicap diode tuners; they commonly used BF180/BF181 transistors. *Practical Wireless* (March/April 1987) published my 'Blandford' design for a receive converter tuning near DC to 400MHz in a single band. This made use of a mechanically-tuned TV tuner to provide a tunable IF from 464 to 860MHz. Incoming signals were fed to an SBL-1 doubly-balanced mixer with a 464MHz (4 x 116MHz) crystal-controlled local oscillator. Three switched tunable signal pre-amplifiers were placed ahead of the mixer to give a total system noise figure across the spectrum of 3 to 4dB. During the development of this converter (which failed to attract the interest it surely deserved if you will excuse my lack of modesty!) extensive measurements were made on UHF TV tuners. Long term stability was about 2kHz per hour after an initial warm-up drift of about 100kHz in the first few minutes. This is exceptional for a free-running L/C oscillator at 800MHz. External temperature changes accounted for most of the drift: approximately -10kHz/°C, corresponding closely to the calculated drift on a quarter wave copper line due to thermal expansion. To achieve automatic colour locking, varicap tuners soon replaced the inherently-superior mechanically-tuned units. While these are in themselves equally stable, the problem is the supply voltage variations; to achieve a stability equal to that of the mechanical units would require tuning-voltage stabilisation of the order of 1 part in 10^7 or better!

The problem of spurious responses in the various low-cost spectrum analysers using UHF tuners etc, as described recently in *TT*, has in fact been raised by other correspondents and it is hoped to treat this subject separately in *TT* shortly.

NICAD MEMORY — FACT OR FICTION?

Several earlier *TT* items have noted that the common advice to discharge fully nicad batteries before recharging, in order to overcome the so-called condition of nicad 'memory', is not good advice but can shorten the life of these batteries. Deliberately discharging nicad battery packs can, in fact, lead to polarity reversal of one or more cells since it is unlikely that all the cells making up a battery will be in exactly the same state of charge.

What then is the reality of the memory effect so often advanced as the reason to avoid partial recharging? It should be noted that a useful list of facts and fallacies, stemming from an article by J Fielding, ZS5JF (*TT*, May 1988, page 349), strongly rejected the idea that "You should not charge only partially discharged cells as this causes a loss in capacity," giving the reply: "*Not true*: It is not necessary to fully discharge nicad batteries before recharging. In fact, *the opposite* is true. Repeated partial charging gives an increase in the number of charge/discharge cycles compared with fully-discharged cells." But the ZS5JF notes did not refer specifically to nicad memory.

However, an article by Anton Wilson ('Rechargeable Power Supplies, Part 3: The Mystery of Memory' *International Broadcast Engineer*, March 1989, pages 48 & 51) explores this topic in some depth, introduced as follows:

"Battery memory is undoubtedly the most often mentioned and least understood of all nicad battery anomalies. To further this confusion, there are actually two separate and distinct conditions that might be called 'memory'. Most people believe that the so-called memory phenomenon is manifest by a loss of capacity, that a battery so inflicted will run the equipment for only a fraction of the time normally expected. This turns out to be the first point of confusion. In almost all cases memory does *not* involve any significant loss of capacity but rather a voltage depression. Battery engineers use the term 'voltage depression phenomena' to refer to these conditions, avoiding the ambiguous term memory."

Later in the article it is noted: "There are two basic causes of so-called memory. The name memory ironically originates with a very rare phenomenon that is almost never encountered in professional video *(and probably equally seldom in amateur radio — G3VA)*. A fully-charged nicad battery that is only partially discharged before being recharged, and then repetitively cycled to precisely the same point of partial discharge... may exhibit a voltage depression at the memory point if an attempt is made to discharge the battery past the previous point of partial discharge... The most prevalent cause of memory phenomena turns out to be long-term trickle charging... In this case the continuous current can cause a metamorphosis to occur within a fully charged nicad cell... Over a period of time the charged nicad compounds are transformed into a secondary alloy called NI_5CD_{21} which exhibits a lower voltage potential than a normal nicad cell."

IN PRACTICE

In practice, the article explains, the unaffected nicad discharges first, providing the usual initial voltage output. But then the cell begins to use the secondary alloy exhibiting a voltage depression (**Fig 5**). In the case of a battery with a fully charged potential of say 12, 13.2 or 14.4 volts as commonly used for professional portable TV cameras and video recorders, the cumulative voltage depresssion at the point of change to the secondary alloy can amount to a rapid drop of more than one volt, and this may be sufficient to take it below the minimum end-point operating voltage of the equipment, although the battery may still be holding a large part of its total charge. In these circumstances the effective operating period of the battery may be reduced by up to 70% or so of the time per charge that it should power the equipment, even though the total capacity per charging cycle may not have been seriously diminished.

Anton Wilson points out that long-term trickle charging can also result in the appreciably more serious problem of 'accelerated ageing' which can reduce the useful life of a battery, in terms of charge/discharge cycles, to only one-eighth of normal. As noted by AG6K in the December 1988 *TT*, the prime cause of this form of accelerated ageing of sealed nicad cells is the conversion of the water in the liquid electrolyte to hydrogen and oxygen gas when the temperature of the cell rises above about 35°C by overcharging. AG6K suggested that a valid answer to this problem is to use a pulsed constant-voltage charger of the type shown in *TT*, December 1988, Fig 1, page 957, claiming that such a charger when set up correctly is unlikely to result in overheating even if the battery is left on charge for several days. Because of the significant rate of self-discharge of nicad batteries, it is difficult to ensure that a battery is always kept in a fully charged condition over an extended period of time without the use of various fairly complex chargers.

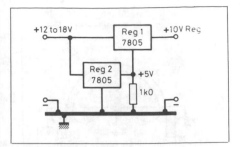

Fig 6. Use of cascaded three-terminal IC voltage regulators (Electronics Australia).

HERE & THERE

Peter O'Connell in the "Circuit & Design Ideas" feature of *Electronics Australia* (December 1988, page 93) shows how cascading two five-volt three-terminal IC regulators (7805) can provide a regulated 10V supply, one of several possible ways of obtaining regulated outputs at voltages different from that of the regulator. For applications requiring heatsinking it is necessary to insulate the top regulator from the heat sink as the common lead no longer connects to earth: **Fig 6.**

The world of hi-fi magazines produces some remarkable prose poems. One wonders how *Rad Com* readers would react to equipment appraisals couched as follows: (This £825 valved audio pre-amplifier) "worked beautifully after as little as 30-minutes warm-up time. And it is a cracker, offering as it does a delightful blend of classic valve virtues with some modern refinements. The sound is warm and rich, without being too romantic or bloated, and it handles wide dynamic swings with absolute grace..." (*Hi-Fi News & Record Review*, April 1989).

The G4DTC hybrid 'ultimate' receiver stimulated enormous interest and Ray Howgego received about 80 requests for PCB layout plans but he has so far not received any comments from anyone who may have completed the receiver. The major problem appears to have been the acquisition of the 623 chip which is made only to "mil-spec" standards and retails at around £13. However, G4DTC points out, it is possible to substitute any of the classic detector circuits, although in this case AM AGC might be a problem. He was impressed to find so many old-timers showing interest in constructional work "after many years of black-box-boredom".

EXPERIMENTAL FET POWER AMPLIFIER

I hope that Peter Haylett, G3IPV will not be offended if I suggest that he is one of those amateurs who like to tread idiosyncratic paths rather than following the crowd. His latest offering is 'an experimental non self destruct power FET RF amplifier' which includes some off-beat features. He introduces his design as follows: "Recent observation of RF amplifiers indicates that RF voltages generated across RF chokes and wire-wound resistors cause unnecessary feedback, not only degrading amplifier performance by producing noise and IMD but also, owing to lack of control of the feedback, capable of resulting in random violent parasitic self-oscillation which can immediately destroy solid-state RF power devices.

"In my experimental unit (**Fig 7**), providing some 30watts CW output on 3.5MHz, feedback is reduced and controlled by the very light coupling of the input circuit to the first stage, using about a

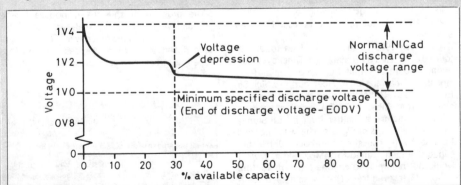

Fig 5. Discharge curve of a nicad cell suffering from a pronounced 'voltage depression' at about one-third discharge.. Most probable cause is overlong trickle charging although the effect is often attributed to the so-called 'memory' of nicad cells.

1pF capacitor and resistance-capacitive inter-stage coupling. **Fig 8** shows the difference in feedback arrangements between the conventional RF amplifier circuit and the experimental unit."

G3IPV suggests that his technique overcomes the problems of parasitic and self-oscillation. In front of this unit, he uses a special driver amplifier which remains stable with very light loading. This all seems logical enough though I am not sure that I follow entirely his notes on operation as follows:

"During operation, it was found that an SWR meter did not function correctly. It was thought that this was because an SWR meter may read the correct neutralization point of an amplifier rather than the SWR on the output coaxial cable; the neutralization occurring when the output parameters of an amplifier are varied by an ATU. With my experimental amplifier owing to very low feedback capacitance this would no longer occur. Difficulty was observed in obtaining power to an antenna when using an ATU and field strength meter near the antenna. However, good power output was achieved by connecting the feeder directly to the drain of the Power FET and monitoring the output with an oscilloscope in parallel with the antenna socket. High power output was achieved in this manner even with the antenna off resonance and unmatched."

G3IPV concludes that power FETs are superior in such applications both to valves and to bipolar transistors once the problem of safely soldering them into the circuit has been achieved. I would, however, stress that the unit developed by G3IPV should be considered experimental rather than established practice, as I suspect that not everyone would agree with his explanations.

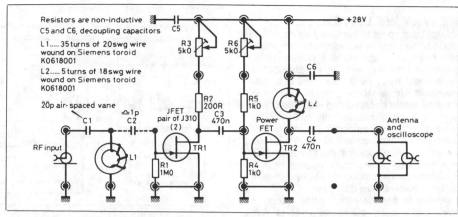
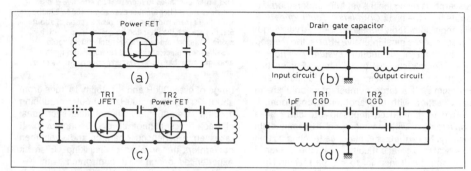

Fig 7. Experimental 3.5MHz FET power amplifier developed by G3IPV and intended to minimise the risk of destructive self- or parasitic-oscillation.

Fig 8. (a) Conventional RF amplifier with uncontrolled feedback; (b) feedback circuit of (a); (c) G3IPV amplifier with 'controlled' feedback; (d) feedback circuit of (c) as suggested by G3IPV.

THE FRINEAR LINEAR

During 1988, the attractions of the relatively low-cost and still readily available European colour-television line-output valves, types PL519/PL509, as RF linear amplifiers were discussed in a number of *TT* items. This has prompted Frits Geerligs, PA0FRI to contribute his design for a single-valve linear suitable for use with QRP transceivers (**Fig 9** and **10**). With about 5 watts input, the amplifier provides an RF output of about 80 watts on 28MHz rising to about 110 watts on 3.5MHz, using a single PL519 that had already

seen ten years service in a colour television receiver.

PA0FRI points out: "A new (100%) PL519 is capable of providing more than 200 watts output when used with forced air cooling. As G4DTC stated (*TT*, May 1988) the PL519 seems to be virtually indestructible with its performance limited only by envelope temperature. After ten years television service, cathode emission remains near perfect and the valve is capable of sustaining over 1.1kV on its anode. In my opinion, anode dissipation, with adequate cooling, is of the order of 65 watts.

The anode is in fact about the same size as that of the old 814 RF power valve, although, in the case of the PL519, closer to its glass envelope. This is why forced air cooling is needed to get maximum power from this valve.

Using two 400V mains transformers in the PSU, the amplifier can be constructed in a compact enclosure of about 27 x 22 x 9cm, smaller than most solid-state amplifiers of equivalent power."

PA0FRI does not indicate the degree of linearity achievable with the PL519 when output is increased beyond about 100 watts.

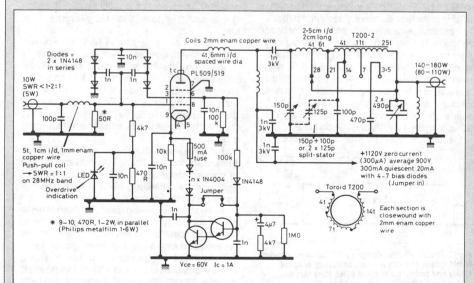

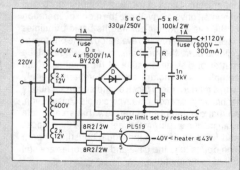

Fig 9. The PA0FRI 'Frinear' power amplifier for use with low-power transceiver or exciter. The maximum output power of 140 to 180 watts requires the use of ducted air cooling and 80-110 watts output is possible without forced-air cooling.

Fig 10. Power supply for the 'Frinear' using two 400V mains transformers.

THE WAY WE LISTEN

Although hand-speed Morse is, and seems certain to remain, the simplest and most effective weak-signal communications mode, it should not be assumed that the way we listen to either CW or speech under noisy conditions is by now fully understood. Samuel Morse, it may be recalled, in the period before he teamed up with Alfred Vail, thought in terms of mechanically recording the incoming signals, not appreciating that the human brain could be 'programmed' to perform instant decoding at realistic speeds. As *TT* has pointed out in the past, it is necessary to consider both receiver and operator as a complete 'system' with a complex man-machine interface.

Listening to and 'decoding' either morse or speech under noisy conditions involves very complex processes in the human brain and auditory system which, in spite of years of research, is by no means yet fully understood. To quote from the book *Correlation Techniques* by F H Lange, admittedly published some 20 years ago: "In spite of the most intensive efforts, the method of operation (of the auditory system) has not yet been completely clarified...Meyer-Eppler has described the problem as the 'Cocktail Party Problem'...If a large number of people are in conversation with one another in one room, it should in general be impossible to carry on a conversation with someone in the immediate vicinity. Nevertheless experience teaches us that this raises no great difficulty, in fact the reverse, if a person has 'tuned in' to the partner and the subject of conversation. This implies, therefore, the existence of a tuning (modulation) mechanism in the human ear, certainly one of another kind than is used in the radio receiver; for, in the radio receiver, the only transmitters which are distinguished from one another clearly are those the frequency ranges of which do not overlap. On the other hand all the conversations which the ear would be capable of separating lie in the same frequency range, roughly between 80 and 6000Hz. The human ear therefore achieves more than all the methods of analysis hitherto known...Classical filter theory with its band-pass and rejection bands break down here."

Professor Lange quoted the physiologist Kraus who in 1953 wrote: "Because of its smallness, the ear presents some of the most disputed problems of human physiology. While the mode of operation of the eye is quite clear and its basic principles have been imitated and evaluated in the photographic camera, the mechanism of hearing is still a matter of dispute. In spite of the small size and complicated structure, the ear compares roughly with a modern radio receiver and, regarded purely technically, is of comparatively simple construction, so that one might hold the view that an accurate examination would immediately expose the purpose and function of each individual constituent part. The opposite is the case and all theories are still full of contradictions."

Correlation techniques and research into directional hearing have led to the recognition of the value of various pseudo-stereo and binaural techniques (see *TT* February 1989, p36) for the reception through interference of speech and (more effectively) narrowband CW signals, though contributing little to intelligence at reasonable signal-to-noise ratios.

It has often been pointed out that the human ear can provide an effective narrow-band filter with a minimum bandwidth of only about 50Hz, a dynamic

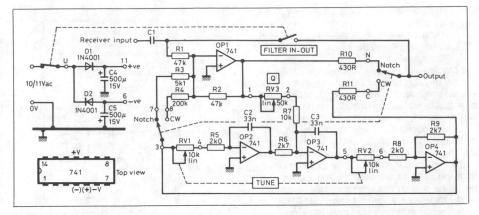

Fig 11. Versatile active analogue AF filter for speech or CW reception as described originally by DJ6HP in 1974 and which continues to represent an effective design. It provides a CW filter tunable over about 450 to 2700Hz with the Q (bandwidth) variable over a range of about 5:1. For speech the filter can be switched to a notch mode. Although modern digital audio filters could provide more precisely shaped tunable filtering, this analogue filter has received many endorsements over the years.

range of over 100dB and the ability to 'tune' from about 200 to over 100Hz without introducing 'ringing'. Unfortunately, in practice, such ideal characteristics cannot always be achieved. It takes an experienced operator and even then encounters the problem of 'masking'. Even an experienced operator, if confronted with two nearly similar tones, will normally find it impossible to distinguish between them unless they are separated by about 100 to 500Hz or so depending on their position in the audio spectrum.

Recent professional interest in reducing the transmission bandwidth of high-quality digital stereo sound has revived interest in this phenomenon of 'masking'.

In 1967, E Zwicker and R Feldtkeller published a study 'Das Ohr als Nachrichten empfaenger' (The ear as a receiver of information) showing that there exist between 30Hz and 20kHz, 24 audio sub-bands within which the most powerful component conceals (masks) adjacent, less powerful components, including noise, making them imperceptible to the ear. The widths of these sub-bands varies from 100Hz in the low-frequency domain up to 2kHz in the high-frequency domain. Applied to hi-fi music this means that while the dominant components have to be transmitted accurately, other components within each of the critical sub-bands may be transmitted digitally with a much lower (less accurate) number of bits, permitting the total bit-rate to be reduced by from three to seven times, thus permitting digital stereo of CD-quality to be transmitted digitally at 256kB/s rather than the 1.4MB/s of CD recordings.

It seems to me that the Zwicker masking

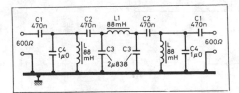

Fig 12. Passive AF filter design by DJ1ZB using standard 88mH toroids and with a centre frequency of about 420Hz and bandwidth of about 80Hz. Note that this design is for 600ohm input/output impedance. (*Sprat* No 58)

phenomenon explains why our ears alone cannot filter out a weak wanted CW signal if there is a more powerful interfering signal *within the same* sub-band, even though in other circumstances our ears have a selectivity of only 50Hz or so. Appreciation of Zwicker masking also encourages the reception of CW signals at relatively low audio frequencies (say 300-500Hz) rather than the usually recommended 700-1000Hz. Interestingly, the same recommendation is made in respect of CW audio filters in the current issue of *Sprat* (Issue No 58 — dated 'Autumn 1989' but presumably the 'Spring' issue). In "The best audio frequency for CW reception" by DJ4SB and DJ1ZB, on the basis of a 1979 German publication, it is suggested that the selectivity (discrimination) of the human ear peaks around 300 to 400Hz being some ten times better at these frequencies than at 1000Hz. The former belief in using the higher frequencies presumably stems from the fact (Fletcher-Munson curves) that the *sensitivity* of the ear is greater at around 1000 to 2000Hz: **Fig 11** and **12** illustrate two filters mentioned in the *Sprat* article.

Meanwhile, the age-old arguments about easing the entry into HF amateur radio by removing the obligatory (ITU Radio Regulations) Morse Test continue on both sides of the Atlantic.

John Rabson, G3PA draws attention to a remarkable example of an unexpected use of CW reported in the Belgian journal *CQ-QSO*, December 1988. His translation is as follows: "It's the end of March 1985. A Belgian family is involved in a road accident. The parents are badly injured, their son is in a coma. The doctors say there is no hope for him.

"The parents refuse to give up hope. For two years they visit their son every day. One day, in desperation, the father, a radio amateur who before the accident was preparing his son for the Morse test, has the idea of sending CW by pressing on his son's arm. To his astonishment, the lad responds. The doctors say 'you're imagining things' they insist death will come within three weeks.

"But three weeks later their son is transferred to a university hospital. There, in front of an audience of doctors and lecturers, he is able to send CQ quite clearly whenever asked...gradually the coma becomes less deep.

"Several months have passed. The boy is able to communicate by signs. He indicates that he is thirsty but doesn't want any of the offered drinks. He seizes his morse key and sends 'grapejuice'.

"This is not a fairy story. The father is Jan, ON1FV of Malines. His son Willem has now left hospital; he can say several words and can even take a few steps." □

FREEMATCH LINE MATCHING UNIT

Frits Geerligs, PA0FRI, whose PL509 linear design appeared in the June *TT*, also contributes details of his 'Freematch' line matching unit (LMU) for reducing the SWR seen by a transmitter on the coaxial cable feeder to resonant antennas (see **Fig 1**). It is a modified version of the well-known Z-match and is designed as the result of experiments in flattening the SWR on the five HF bands between 3.5 and 28MHz (plus the WARC bands) without the necessity for switching coils and with a minimum of knobs. It is essentially a 'kiss'

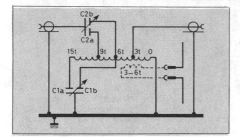

Fig 1. The PA0FRI 3.5/28MHz line matching unit for minimising the SWR presented to the transmitter output. Such a unit is suitable for use with reasonant antennas nominally matched to the transmitter and should not be expected to cope with a very wide range of reactive impedances.

approach, cheaper and faster than an automatic ATU provided that the calibrated settings on each band for minimum SWR are known so that the capacitors can be quickly reset.

PA0FRI writes: "The 'Freematch' (PA0FRI-match) has been devised as an unbalanced tuner for improving the SWR at the transmitter end of coaxial feeders to *resonant* antennas (eg verticals, dipoles, trapped dipoles, G5RVs, Yagis, loopquads, European FD4 etc). In practice it has proved more flexible than expected and in some cases permits matching to non-resonant antennas. With an extra 3-6 turn bifilar winding over the earthy end of the coil (as indicated) a 'balanced' output for 75ohm twin wire or 300ohm ribbon feeder is feasible. However, it should be noted that this design cannot satisfy all possible matching conditions (eg random length wires), though it is possible that this can sometimes be overcome by increasing or decreasing the length of the coaxial feeder and/or reversing the input/output terminals of the Freematch. To meet all possible matching conditions a more complex arrangement would be necessary."

Component information: Coil 15 turns of 2.5mm

diameter enamelled copper wire on 5cm (2-in) inner diameter. For powers lower than 200 watts, a T200-2 toroid can be used with 15 turns on ¾ of the body covered with plumbers PTFE tape. Taps 3, 6 and 9 turns from earthy end. Variable capacitors can be receiver-type twin-gang (10-490pF per section) for powers up to about 100 watts or for higher powers if power is reduced during tuning. For QRP operation a T200 toroid and two air-dielectric variable capacitors discarded from transistor radios can be used. If random sized coils are used the taps should be ratio n, 2n, 3n for a coil having 5n turns.

SMALL ENOUGH?

I must admit that for fixed-station HF operation, I have never been attracted by the decreasing size and weight of modern amateur radio equipment, although I can understand its appeal for mobile or portable operation or where the station has to be squeezed into a small space. Surface-mounted components, VLSI devices with their many leads etc just do not suit my increasingly clumsy fingers and call for watch repairer's skills. Such miniature components seem to me to be one of the factors that have moved the hobby so far away from home construction. I feel lucky in that my junk boxes still include a number of components and valves from the vintage years of home construction when there was no nonsense about squeezing a quart

OVER-VOLTAGE, OVER-CURRENT PROTECTION

For those determined to power 13.5V equipment from the mains supply without an intermediate car battery, the protection of equipment against over-voltage and over-current transients remains an evergreen topic. Ken Atack, G4WAS offers the following advice:

"The circuit of **Fig 2** provides a number of safety features which operate entirely independently of the voltage regulating circuit, which for this reason is not shown in detail.

"The use of a 'soft start' circuit allows the rating of the mains supply fuse, F1, to be equal to the value of the (240V) full load current. Without this feature the high magnetic in-rush current which can occur will necessitate a much higher fuse rating or a more expensive anti-surge fuse. It should be noted that the PSU must be 'off-load' at the time of switch-on, otherwise excessive voltage drop across the 100ohm resistor will prevent the operation of relay RL2. This is not a bad thing, since the output voltage should always be checked before use.

"There are two stages of over-voltage protection. Stage 1 is provided by thyristor THY2 the gate voltage of which is set by RV2 to trip at 14.3V thus shorting out the coil of RL2, which drops out, opening the mains-transformer primary circuit. At this time, the neon lamp N1 will light and N2 go out.

"In the event of a major fault in the regulating circuit causing an 'instantaneous' rise in output volts, the 'crowbar' circuit (THY4) is triggered via the more sensitive thyristor THY1, which is set to fire at 14.8V. As the 'crowbar' effectively reduces the output voltage to zero, RL2 will drop off and again disconnect the mains supply. Meanwhile, one or both fuses will have blown. If N1 is lit, fuse F1 is good, indicating that F2 must have blown.

"Apart from the normal over-current protection offered by the two fuses, additional and more

sensitive overload protection is provided by means of the relay RL1, the operation of which triggers the gate of THY3. This in turn short-circuits the coil of RL2 and thus disconnects the mains.

"Relay RL1 was made up from an old open-type relay having an adjustable tension-spring-controlled armature. The original coil was removed, the winding stripped and replaced with six turns of 18swg enamelled copper wire and the spring tension carefully adjusted so that the relay pulled in at 27.5A (the normal full load being 25A).

"Finally and perhaps most importantly is the use of the large value electrolytic capacitor C2 (39,000µF) across the *output* of the PSU. This effectively increases the rise time of the output voltage in the event of an 'instantaneous' breakdown of the regulating circuit and allows the 'crowbar' time to operate well before the voltage rises to a dangerous level.

"It is a very worthwhile exercise to check the performance of any over-voltage-protected PSU by observing the output voltage on a good quality (20MHz) oscilloscope as the regulating circuit is deliberately bypassed. In the arrangement shown here, before C2 was fitted, the output voltage was seen to rise from 13.5V to around 25V, albeit as a very short duration 'spike'. With C2 at 39,000µF, this 'spike' was reduced to about 16V."

The above notes from G4WAS illustrate well the need for quite complex, fast-acting protection arrangements for any high-current PSU feeding voltage-sensitive solid-state equipment which could be severely damaged by even a short-duration transient. Series voltage regulating power transistors (not shown in **Fig 2**) can and do break down in short-circuited form resulting in a hefty increase in the voltage output from the PSU unless fast-acting protection is provided.

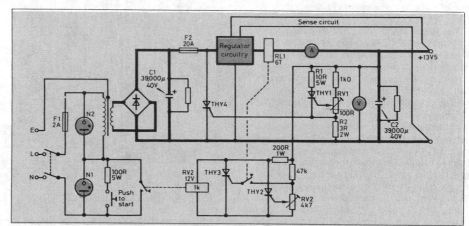

Fig 2. Circuit diagram of G4WAS's over-voltage and over-current protected PSU. THY1, 2, 3 are any small thyristors (SCRs) with Igt about 0.2mA and Vgt about 1.2V. THY4 is a heavy current device with Igt up to 100mA and Vgt up to 3V. The values of R1 and R2 should be chosen so that the voltage across R2 when THY1 fires is about 10% higher than the trigger voltage (Vgt) of THY4.

into a pint pot. There was a time when the larger and heavier the station equipment, the more adorned with meters and weighed down with door-stop mains transformers and smoothing chokes, the more it was prized.

I still use for an ATU, a hefty (3-in inner diameter) ten-turn coil made from self-supporting copper tubing bought from Webb's Radio (of cherished memory) about 1937 for 4d per turn. This was for my first 10-watt (6L6-T20) transmitter though it would not have been out-of-place in a 5 or 10kW amplifier! Because of its large size and air-spaced turns, taps can be made simply with a large crocodile clip avoiding the use of high-voltage RF switches and multiple taps. I still find uses for the plug-in coils once made by Eddystone, Raymart (and the long-forgotten 'Formo' range). Components were made to last though there were some notable exceptions. Old capacitors tend to leak. Even today electrolytic capacitors that have not been in use for some time, require 're-forming' in the manner described in *TT*, June 1987. Quite old electrolytics will usually respond to this treatment but be warned that some don't and will overheat and are liable to explode if put back into service. Anybody who has ever had to clean up the mess that can be caused by an exploding electrolytic capacitor will afterwards always make certain that a capacitor has successfully reformed before using it in a high-voltage power supply!

Nowadays, with dimensions in microns, times in nanoseconds and chips with hundreds of thousands of active devices, it seems we have reached the ultimate practical stage of microminiaturisation. Drop a modern component and you'll be lucky if you can find it again. But now two factors are combining to place limitations on the size of even portable and pocket equipment: controls still have to be related to fingers, and its operation is governed by the size and weight of the batteries.

It has been pointed out in the *New Scientist* (May 6, 1989) that "Portable electronic equipment is now about as small as it will ever be. The designers of portable video cameras and video recorders, personal computers and pocket (radio-transceiver) telephones all face the same problem. if the equipment is made too small it becomes impractical to use, and the rechargeable battery needed to provide its power will weigh almost as much as the equipment itself ... developments in the miniaturisation of electronic circuitry have now outstripped developments in battery technology."

The article points out that this problem is typified by some of the new pocket cellular radio telephones such as the Motorola 9800X (162mm long by 61mm wide) with the body including its keypad, display panel and antenna weighing less than 200g. The transmitter can radiate 0.6 Watt but the chip continuously monitors the strength of the (incoming) signals and reduces the transmitter's power to match these signals in order to save battery current. Incidentally adaptive power control designed to minimise radiated power to that required to maintain a low error rate is a feature of some modern naval HF systems and could usefully be applied to amateur communications on both HF and VHF to minimise intererence in crowded bands.

The *New Scientist* points out that "There are virtually no further savings in power that can be made. So manufacturers face a trade-off between length of time the unit can operate and the size of the battery."

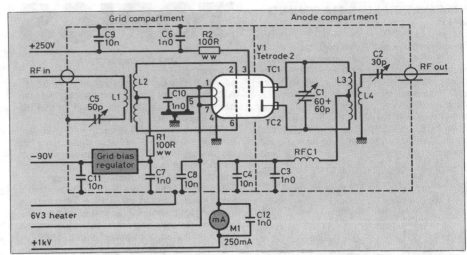

Fig 3. Circuit diagram of G4IDE's updated 50MHz 80W power amplifier using a QQVO6-40A double-tetrode valve with modern solidstate regulation and control circuits. L2 is 8 + 8 turns of 24swg enamelled copper wire on Amidon T50-10 toroid core, tuned by stretching/compressing the winding. L1 is a 3-turn coupling link winding. L3 is 4.5 + 4.5 turns of 16swg copper wire, 1-in diameter, air-spaced. L4 is a 2-turn link with adjustable coupling. Note that the rotor of C1 is *not* grounded.

UP-DATED 50MHz VALVE AMPLIFIER

A new twist to the perennial valve vs solid state debate has appeared over the horizon with the disclosure of current research work on 'vacuum microelectronics' as described, for example, by Dr Rosemary Lee (GEC Hirst Research Centre) in 'Return of the vacuum valve' (*Electronics & Wireless World*, May 1989, pp443-447). She also described on a BBC Radio 4 science programme the rationale behind the intensive work now in progress at various research centres throughout the world aimed at developing a range of micron-sized vacuum electronic devices based on field emission of electrons rather than the thermionic technology of hot cathodes.

Dr Lee writes: "Semiconductor devices are poorly equipped to survive certain environments

and there is a need for devices which can work at high temperatures, withstand high voltage pulses and have the potential to provide high-frequency operation. Vacuum valves offer such properties. Ironically, it is the semiconductor fabrication technology which has been developed over the past few years which now offers the opportunity of producing vacuum valves as small as transistors." There is a military spur to such work to overcome the fear of massive disruption of telecommunications and computers etc by the electromagnetic pulse that would result from exploding a nuclear bomb in the upper atmosphere (NEMP).

At present GEC seems to have reached the stage of producing tiny vacuum microelectronic diodes (shades of Ambrose Fleming) but it is already being claimed that such work is leading the way to the creation of whole families of new

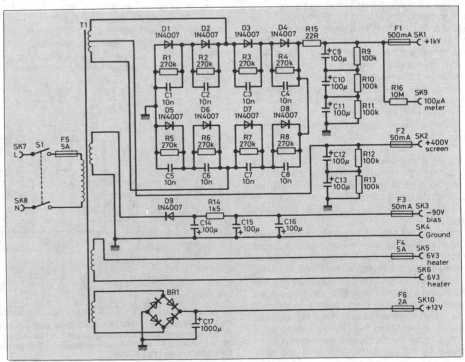

Fig 4. Basic PSU for the 50MHz amplifier.

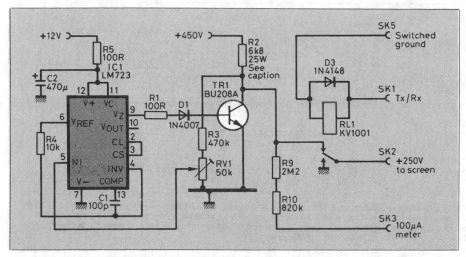

Fig 5. Screen-voltage regulator. Set RV1 to give 250V for the screen at the collector of TR1. R2 should be chosen to give 25-30mA through the BU208A when the screen is not being supplied.

microelectronic devices based on the valve approach that so many branches of the electronics industry have already virtually forgotten.

I suspect that it will be some years, if ever, before vacuum microelectronics comes to play a significant role in amateur radio. But meanwhile there are very good reasons for continuing to use conventional valve technology if only for RF power amplification (or indeed for many other applications if the fancy and junk boxes move you in that direction). Even so there is no reason to ignore the value of current solid state devices in implementing equipment based on valves, with particular reference to the regulation, protection and implementation of power supplies.

Roger Barker, G4IDE, believes that the availability of the 50MHz band has given a renewed impetus for amateurs to start building at least some of their own equipment again, despite the headaches induced by the problem of acquiring the necessary bits and pieces — particularly difficult in the case of high-voltage components suitable for use in valve amplifiers, etc. The QQV06-40A double-tetrode valve, once a popular choice for 144MHz, remains an excellent performer at either 50, 70 or 144MHz.

G4IDE writes: "I have recently built a new QQV06-40A power amplifier for 50MHz; **Figs 3-7.** When I started the project my theme was 'ancient and modern' — the ancient bit being the 6-40A! I wanted the rest of the design, essentially the power supplies, to reflect current practice. Probably the most interesting feature is the screen supply. My then-existing amplifier used a standard OA2/OB2 voltage regulator arrangement. This performs quite adequately but to have duplicated it for the new amplifier would have meant two more valves and extra metal bashing! I did not fancy the idea of a string of zener diodes and

finally developed the shunt stabilisation design shown in Fig 5.

"If nothing else, this must be one of the most unusual applications yet devised for an LM723 regulator! Since the output voltage from the LM723 needs to rise as the feed-back voltage rises (to drive the BU208A harder and so lower the circuit output voltage), the reference voltage pin on the LM723 is connected to the inverting input and the feed-back voltage to the non-inverting input — the reverse of the usual configuration. It should also be noted that the feed-back voltage represents only a small percentage of the circuit output voltage. This, together with the fact that the drive needed to the base of the BU208A is only about 1V, means that the loop gain around the LM723 is very high. Despite this, the performance of the circuit is excellent. It appears to be extremely stable and I have tested it with a scope on the output while driving the PA to 80W PEP with two-tone input. The ripple on the screen

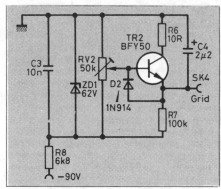

Fig 6. Grid bias regulator. Set grid bias to around -30V by adjusting RV2.

supply is no more than 0.1V. The same test with the conventional OA2/OB2 arrangement showed a ripple of several volts. No doubt a string of zener diodes would be even worse.

"A number of other points concerning the power supply should be noted:

1) The series-zener output on the LM723 is used to allow the true output of the device (V_{OUT}) to fall into its normal operating range. Driving the BU208A from V_{OUT} gave very poor regulation.

2) R2 needs to be of adequate wattage and should be chosen to give 25 to 30mA through the BU208A when the screen is not being supplied.

3) The BU208A needs a heat sink since, with the PA idling, it will be dissipating around 7W.

4) Any attempt to decouple the inputs to the LM723 is guaranteed to turn it into a very potent saw-tooth oscillator!

"Another feature of the design that may be of interest is the relay-switching arrangement: Fig 7. The IRF510 MOSFET is kept turned on by the presence of the 1,000V HT. If the HT should fail then it is impossible to energise the relays. This seems a very simple way to implement HT-failure protection compared with some of the circuits I have seen. Note that the 500k resistor must be a high-voltage item.

"Some other points that may be of interest include:

1) The toroid for the grid-tuned circuit is an idea passed to me by G3ENY. It is a bit fiddly to tune up, but once done seems to offer excellent long-term stability and saves the cost of a grid tuning capacitor.

2) The emitter-follower in the grid-bias circuit was more or less copied from my original PA which was built by G4PBP (at the time when he was G8BHH of 144MHz contest fame). I do not know whether it has any advantage compared with the orthodox arrangement of taking the grid-bias direct from a lower value potentiometer across the bias supply, but it seemed to work well, so I copied it.

3) For the 50pF variable capacitor on the input coupling loop I used nothing more than a compression trimmer accessed through a hole in the chassis. Most designs specify an airspaced capacitor in this application but the Jackson C804 is not exactly cheap; since the PA can be driven to 80W output with only a couple of hundred milliwatts of drive, the compression trimmer is more than adequate."

HF COST OF ENTRY

For many years, a major objective in amateur radio was to puzzle out ingenious ways of avoiding the need to invest large sums of money in what is basically a spare-time hobby that hopefully should appeal to all sections of society including the impecunious. In earlier times, few newcomers, particularly the younger ones, expected to start straight away with high-power, multiband equipment even during the years when good value-for-money, factory-built units were available. Later these may have been purchased after a spell with relatively crude equipment used as an excellent form of hands-on training and for finding out which of the many aspects of amateur radio were likely to prove of lasting appeal. There is still no better way of understanding the elements of radio communication than by actually tackling the problem of making something you have built work or coaxing an old secondhand piece of equipment back to its original specification, or modifying it for improved performance, though this is not

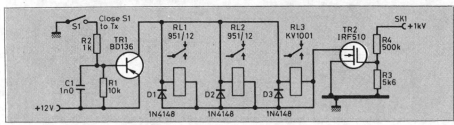

Fig 7. Transmit/receive control unit for the QQVO6-40A 50MHz power amplifier.

always practicable with modern forms of construction.

Few of us seek to acquire the mathematical skills and expertise of a professional design engineer but struggle along lifting circuits and design ideas from the periodicals, using parts of published designs to create our own individual equipment. In real money terms, current equipment prices are probably not unreasonable, but that surely does not mean that the entry to HF operation should involve a £1,000-plus transceiver, possibly as much again for a high-power linear, and a costly rotary beam antenna array. It sometimes seems to be a lost cause to continue to argue the case for starting off on HF with a simple home-built two or three-band, 15/25-watt CW transmitter, possibly even crystal-controlled, simple ATU and an end-fed all-wire antenna supported from roofs/trees etc. Such rigs can still bring plenty of enjoyable contacts on the HF bands, if not consistently the most exotic DX, and form an effective means of becoming a proficient CW operator (a skill that will last a lifetime even if subsequently you opt for speech or data). One has only to listen on 21 and 28MHz to the many excellent signals from Russian operators using home-built 10-watt transmitters and delta-loop or ground-plane antennas to realise that there is a happy medium for the newcomer between the skills of extreme QRP and the factory-built 100-watt transceiver.

Recently I enjoyed putting together a classic beginner's transmitter (6AG7/CO-807/PA) using purely junk-box components. Even if one had to buy new components such a rig — or its solid state equivalent — would put one on the air for a lot less than a £1,000 economy rig!

ECONOMICAL POWER SUPPLIES

An aspect of station building in which significant savings can still be made without undue constructional skills is in the area of power supplies, both medium and high-voltage PSUs for valve equipment and high-current supplies for solid state. For a simple CW rig, either entirely valved or with a valve power amplifier (PA), there is no need for elaborate regulation or even protection (a simple fuse will suffice). A single mains transformer with a 250-0-250V or 350-0-350V, preferably rated for about 100mA current, salvaged from an old radio receiver or preferably (because of the higher current rating) from an old Hi-Fi audio amplifier, plus a few silicon diodes or bridge rectifier of adequate peak-inverse-rating can provide a useful two-voltage supply. **Fig 8** shows such a unit as described by Charles Aud, F8CV in *Radio-REF* October 1988.

The availability of low-cost silicon diodes in lieu of the now obsolete double-diode valve rectifiers makes possible a variety of configurations that would have been impractical in the days when one needed separate, well-insulated heater/filament supplies for bridges or voltage-doubling circuits. **Fig 9** shows the basic characteristics of a number of standard arrangements.

For low-voltage, high-current equipment, it has been stressed many times in *TT* that a car battery and simple trickle charger provides one of the safest and most economical ways of running 12V equipment from the mains supply, provided always that care is taken to ensure that there is no possibility of the output from the unregulated trickle charger by-passing the battery (which needs to be maintained in good condition).

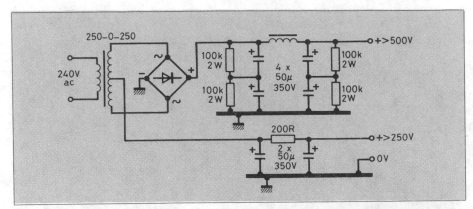

Fig 8. Dual-voltage (anode/screen) PSU for typical medium-power valve amplifier using for example a salvaged 250-0-250V mains transformer from thrown-out domestic radio, television or hi-fi equipment. Unfortunately heavy-current isolating transformers, found in some foreign TV sets, were not used in British TV valve receivers, but suitable transformers can be found in many old audio amplifiers. (F8CV)

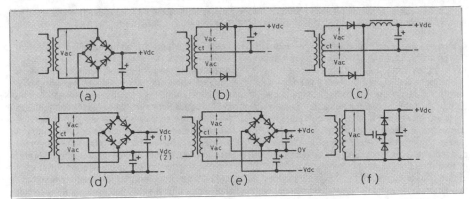

Fig 9. Basic diode rectifying circuits. (a) Full-wave (bi-phase) bridge with capacitive input ripple filter (ie reservoir capacitor) in which Vdc approximately equals 1.4Vac. PIV of each diode section 1.4Vac. (b) Full-wave with capacitive-input filter. Vdc approximately 1.4Vac. PIV of each diode 2.8Vac. (c) Full-wave with choke-input filter. Vdc approximately Vac. PIV 1.4Vac. (d) Dual-voltage bridge with centre-tapped transformer and capacitive input filter. Vdc (1) about 2.8Vac, Vdc (2) approximately 1.4Vac. (e) Bridge with balanced output voltage. Vdc about ±1.4Vac. (f) Voltage doubler (unsuitable for heavy current supplies) (unsuitable for heavy current supplies). Relatively poor voltage regulation. Note that the inclusion of a large-value reservoir capacitor raises the maximum DC output voltage significantly above that obtained with an inductive or resistive load. An inductive filter (smoothing choke) reduces the voltage variation between no-load and full-load conditions.

In this connection, John Osborne, G3HMO draws attention to an article he wrote for *Short Wave Magazine* in March 1987 shortly before it emerged primarily as a magazine for listeners. His title 'The biggest electrolytic in the world' emphasised that a battery can be considered as an enormous capacitor in that it similarly stores electricity; and like a capacitor it forms a very effective ripple filter. A battery in good condition provides very stiff voltage regulation, although the actual voltage depends on the stage of charge. G3HMO points out that, as with mobile operation, the exact voltage depends on the state of charge of the battery and to some extent the charging current if the charger is left on during operation,

varying from about 12.5V to about 13.8V, but changing by not more than about 0.2V for a typical full load.

G3HMO recommends that a voltmeter should be kept in circuit to enable the operator to keep an eye on things. Note that it is a false economy to use old clamps and it is advisable to use two sets of clamps for charger/battery and battery/transceiver in order to ensure that corrosion or disconnection of a single pair of battery clamps does not leave the equipment connected directly to the charger: **Fig 10**.

In his 1987 article, G3HMO reported using this system for over two years to power an FT77, FT290 and a 28MHz FM 'talk box' (converted CB

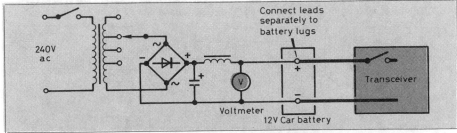

Fig 10. Use of a car battery and simple charger to provide a safe and effective 13V power supply for domestic operation of solidstate transceivers at relatively low cost compared with factory PSUs.

equipment), adding: "I have twice topped up with distilled water in that time. Very little was needed. I have resisted the temptation to overcharge as this would cause loss of water through gassing. This could also be undesirable in that corrosive fumes would be released into the shack. Watching the voltmeter is the key; never charge (typically about 2-4A) unless the volts are down. Bearing in mind the (tough) life a car battery normally leads, in this application it is running very light.

Perhaps one should add the warning given in *TT* (April 1989, page 35) that transceivers nominally rated as 12V, are designed for operation between 13.5-13.8V and that dropping the voltage supplied to such equipment to about 12V will generally reduce the RF output power by 10-20% (not ᴐally significant) but may also severely degrade the linearity and hence increase intermodulation distortion on SSB. In his covering letter, G3HMO comments that the car battery approach is a form of 'kiss' that has served him well and avoided the necessity of paying around £150 for the factory-built PSU intended for his equipment: "With the advent of 24V equipment, two batteries in series along these lines should prove equally effective."

HERE AND THERE

The use of low-cost aluminium kitchen foil to form indoor antennas has been mentioned several times in *TT*, dating back to the 1970 broadband aluminium foil dipole of DJ7VYA and to W8AP's 1971 'quickie quad for two', a 144MHz window-pane single-element square loop using household aluminium foil mounted on cardboard and then taped to the inside of a high-rise window. Both of these antennas were subsequently included in *ART* and it is worth remembering that window glass imposes virtually no attenuation at HF or VHF so that the quickie quad can provide a very effective antenna at least in the direction outwards from the building. Aluminium foil turns up again as the basis of N5NBU's 'Nice but Ugly $1.29 Antenna' (*Ham Radio*, May 1989, pp39-40) this time as a 66ft length of foil to provide an end-fed HF antenna with the foil unrolled in a roof space. Aluminium foil, of course, is not suitable for use outdoors because of the wind loading but can work well in roof spaces or along the sides of walls. Incidentally I would expect 66ft of strip to resonate as a half-wave antenna at a frequency below 7MHz because of the large width/length ratio that produces the broadbanding effect. The DJ7VYA broadband dipole had foil elements of 2 x 6.2m for 7MHz using 45cm wide foil.

USING FAST-SWITCHING POWER FETs AS RF AMPLIFIERS

TT (July 1988) presented circuit details of two broadband HF amplifiers using modern RF power MOSFETs: a 300W amplifier based on the Motorola 'Gemini' push-pull package (MRF151G); and a more modest 40W PEP unit by VK3AFQ using a single MRF138. The March 1989 *TT* included a broadband push-pull FET power amplifier capable of providing 5W output (from a 13V supply) using two IRF510 switching-type power FETs which cost considerably less than the devices specifically intended for use in HF or VHF amplifiers.

Power FETs are increasingly seen as offering useful advantages over bipolar devices, including higher voltage operation (28V or 50V), absence of thermal runaway (with a FET the main *decreases* with increasing temperature) and greater immunity

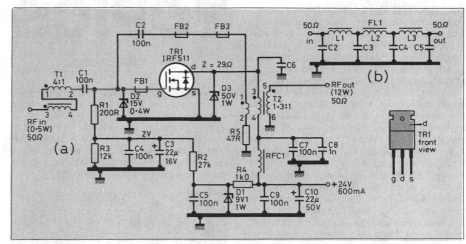

Fig 6 (a) Circuit diagram of W1FB's 12W power-FET class C amplifier with negative feedback. (b) The 7-element pi-type filter (FL1) which proved satisfactory for both 12W and 25W amplifiers after earlier problems with an alternative filter resulting in destruction of a number of power-FETs. For details see Table 1.

from destruction when unloaded or working into a significantly high SWR.

Unfortunately, RF power FETs tend to be more expensive than bipolar transistors providing equivalent output power. They are also very liable to instant self-destruction if they go into parasitic oscillation that can easily result in an excessively high voltage appearing on the gate, puncturing the thin layer of silicon-oxide insulation. This can of course also occur with such devices out of circuit due to electrostatic charges.

"Power-FET switches as RF amplifiers" by Doug DeMaw, W1FB (*QST*, April 1989, pp30-33) provides a useful review of the pros and cons of FET devices and presents details of two amplifiers using low-cost IRF511 devices. These devices are intended for use as high-speed switches but are capable of providing Class C or linear amplification throughout the HF spectrum. A single IRF511 in Class C for CW operation can provide 12W RF output from 0.5W drive with a 28V supply. Although push-pull rather than parallel operation of power-FETs is to be recommended, W1FB also presents the design of a 25W linear amplifier (1W drive) using two IRF511 devices in parallel. The single-device amplifier is shown in **Fig 11(a)**.

All polarized capacitors are electrolytic or tantalum. Others are disc ceramic, 100V or more. R1, R4 ½-watt, others ¼-watt. C6 is used to bypass VHF harmonic currents at TR1 drain, its capacitive reactance should be at least four times the drain impedance to avoid power loss. For 20-ohm drain

impedance Xc is 116ohms (ie 200pF is largest value for 7MHz). RFC 10t, No 26 enam on Amidon FT-37-43 toroid. T1 has 12 bifilar turns, No 28 enam on Amidon BN-43-302 balun core. T3 1.3:1 impedance ratio, use 1t No 24 hook-up wire for winding 1-2, 4t No 26 enam for 5-6, wound on Amidon BN-43-3312 balun core observing winding polarity indicated on diagram by the dots. FB1-3 mini ferrite beads (Amidon FB-43-101). Power FETs are enhancement-mode devices and require positive gate voltage to turn them on. Typical +2V for CW. Set by R2 for 25-50mA Idq for linear operation. Negative feedback is set by R5. Use no more than necessary to avoid excessive reduction of power gain (feedback may not be required but as shown improves stability). FB1 helps suppress VHF parasitics and should not be omitted. For detailed information on this and the 25W version refer to W1FB's *QST* article.

His experiments were prompted by discovering the low prices at which these useful devices can sometimes be purchased in the USA for around $1 each (a possible source is listed as: All Electronics Corporation, PO Box 567, Van Nuys, California CA91408, USA). However he does admit to destroying six of these devices by attempting to use a 7-element T-network harmonic filter (resulting in parasitic oscillation) before changing to the conventional 7-element pi-filter arrangement of **Fig 11(b)** and **Table 1**. The T-network filter caused both his 12W and 25W amplifiers to self-oscillate so there is obviously need to take care.

TABLE 1 — COMPONENT VALUES FOR THE FL1 BAND-PASS HARMONIC FILTER USED BY W1FB BUT SUITABLE ALSO FOR MOST LOW-POWER 50 OHM TYPE SOLID STATE AMPLIFIERS

Band (MHz)	C2, C5 (pF)	C3, C4 (pF)	L1, L3	L2	Wire	Cores
3.5	560	1200	2.46µH, 21t	2.89µH, 23t	No 26	enam T-50-2
7	470	820	1.4µH, 17t	1.56µH, 18t	No 24	enam T-50-2
10.1	220	470	0.96µH, 15t	1.13µH, 17t	No 24	enam T-50-6
14	110	300	0.6µH, 11t	0.65µH, 14t	No 24	enam T-50-6
18	100	250	0.52µH, 11t	0.65µH, 13t	No 22	enam T-50-6
21	110	240	0.48µH, 11t	0.56µH, 13t	No 22	enam T-50-6
24	120	270	0.54µH, 12t	0.63µH, 13t	No 22	enam T-50-6
28	56	150	0.3 µH, 8t	0.38µH, 10t	No 22	enam T-50-6

Note: Various cut-off frequencies and ripple factors used to achieve preferred value capacitors. Coil turns may be spread or compressed with an insulated tool to peak output. Capacitors are silver mica or polystyrene, 100V or greater.

HANDLING CHEMICALS

Many of the substances involved in electronics fabrication and servicing are potentially hazardous or damaging to the environment and need to be handled with care. For example, cleaning solvents including acetone, benzene carbon tetrachloride, ethyl alcohol, isopropyl alcohol, methylene chloride etc are all to some degree potentially harmful — some very harmful; most are highly flammable and the vapours can form dangerously explosive mixtures with air and may attack internal organs and the nervous system. When heated, some solvents are especially dangerous; chlorinated and fluorinated hydrocarbon fumes decompose into hydrochloric acid and phosgene, both highly toxic and corrosive to eyes, throat and lungs. Even the fumes given off by the fluxes used in some cored solders, long regarded as completely harmless, have been found to cause asthma symptoms, among those employed in electronic assembly factories and good ventilation is advisable when carrying out a lot of soldering.

It is well known that when using ferric chloride for the fabrication of printed circuit boards, it is necessary to use plastic dishes, teaspoons, stirrers etc and to keep the etchant away from children, your fingers and clothes (it stains badly) as well as metal objects. But what about disposing of it once the boards have been completed?

Fred Longman, G3HOH has recently become interested in making his own PCBs for a range of QRP equipment but has been feeling a little uneasy about how to dispose of the ferric chloride afterwards. Although he searched through *TT* and *RadCom* articles on PCBs since 1983, he had found nothing on this particular aspect. In these days of growing environmental concern, it seemed advisable to seek expert opinion and I mentioned this to a very helpful member of DTI's Radio Investigation Service. In turn he got in touch with several authorities including *Thames Water*. The advice is that it is considered quite safe to flush a couple of pints of ferric chloride down a toilet — the authorities might become worried if they felt that several thousand people were likely to be doing this at the same time. Ferric chloride could be rendered harmless by adding washing soda but it is felt this is unnecessary for small quantities. One precaution: do *not* empty the ferric chloride into a stainless steel sink!

Unfortunately there are some materials used in electronics that require extremely high temperature furnaces. A number of warnings have been given in *TT* and elsewhere on such deadly substances as berrilyium oxide and the deadly polychlorinated biphenyl (PCB) that still turns up in old dummy loads, high-voltage transformers and capacitors as a coolant (*TT*, September, 1984, p 861).

AMPLIFIER-DRIVER COMPATIBILITY

Without wishing in *TT* to harp too much on the question of SSB non-linearity problems, there can be little doubt that the increasing use of relatively high-power linear amplifiers on both HF and VHF bands does impose the need for high technical standards if transmissions are to be confined to a single channel. Intermodulation distortion in either the basic transceiver-exciter or the final amplifier or in both will spread out the signal in the form of 'splatter' causing interference to other transmissions on nearby frequencies. Several readers have commented that some recent 'equipment reviews' of HF transceivers show that even the products of

TECHNICAL TOPICS

PAT HAWKER G3VA

well-respected manufacturers have a third-order IMD performance on some bands significantly worse than on other bands, falling well short of what they consider to be desirable for neighbour-friendly amateur operation. I have never been certain whether such variations between bands are due primarily to the basic design or to the factory alignment and setting-up.

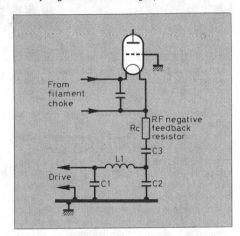

Fig 1. Addition of a negative feedback resistor (Rc) makes a grounded-grid amplifier more resistant to overdrive (AG6K, *QST*).

SWITCHED-VOLTAGE RECTIFICATION

The July *TT* included a brief review of a number of the standard rectifier arrangements used in both high-voltage and high-current power supply units, including basic dual-polarity and dual-voltage PSUs. By coincidence, shortly before this item was published, Alan Hobden, G3YNN sent along a novel arrangement that he is using for a switched-voltage supply. He writes:

"Whilst recently building a low-voltage power pack which turned out to have too low an output voltage, I was surprised to find how little it needed altering to make the bridge rectifier into a full-wave voltage doubler. The circuit (**Fig 2**) is extremely simple yet I cannot recall having ever seen it in print.

"My unit was a low-voltage power pack with a five-amp bridge rectifier and 1000μF 50Vwkg capacitors but I see no reason why this arrangement could not be used at other voltage levels with appropriate components."

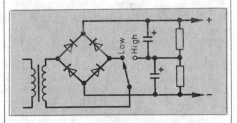

Fig 2. Bridge cum voltage-doubler rectifier circuit for switchable dual-voltage power pack (G3YNN).

Problems can also arise due to incompatibility between a transceiver and an add-on linear amplifier. This topic is discussed in some detail by Richard L Measures, AG6K in *QST* (April 1989, pp 17, 18, 20). This emphasises that some modern factory-built amplifiers require much less drive than the 100watts many transceivers provide, and that this may cause splatter even where automatic level control circuits are supposed to take care of this problem. His opening paragraphs are:

"About ten years ago, when amplifier tubes were much less costly, the two-tube amplifier was in vogue. During the last few years, a number of new amplifier designs, many of which use only one high-mu triode operating grounded-grid in class AB2, have appeared on the market. A single-tube amplifier has some advantages over a two-tube design: reduced parts count and cost, and the elimination of the possibility of a push-pull parasitic oscillation between two tubes. But the high-gain triodes now commonly used in single-tube amplifiers have a major drawback; they require *much* less drive (less than 20-75watts per tube for full (US legal limit) output) than that produced by contemporary transceivers (100watts or more). Overdrive is *guaranteed* when one of these tubes is driven with 100W; depending on the tube type (the 3CX800A7, for instance) 100W can overdrive *two* (or even three!) high-gain tubes.

"Overdrive pushes an amplifier tube out of linearity, and into gain compression. Increasing drive beyond the point at which compression begins causes a slight increase in power output but a great increase in IMD products. In theory amplifier-to-transceiver ALC is supposed to take care of the overdrive problem ....ALC has a serious flaw: *It doesn't act until the amplifier has already been overdriven* ... ALC is like trying to close the barn door when the horse is halfway out of the barn ... **Fig 1** shows a simple and inexpensive way of correcting the overdrive. Addition of a cathode resistor, Rc, adds negative feedback to an amplifier and makes it more resistant to overdrive. Because Rc increases the amplifier input impedance, the values of the (existing) input-network reactances (C1, C2 and L1) may require adjustment when Rc is added. C3 is a DC blocking capacitor."

AG6K describes in the *QST* article how to determine value and rating of Rc and gives some examples:
Single 3-500Z: Rc 20ohms (four 20ohm, 2W flame-proof resistors connected in series-parallel).
Single 8777: Rc 10ohms (four 10ohm, 2W metal-film flameproof resistors in series-parallel).
Two 3CX800A7: 40ohm resistor in series with cathode of each valve (each resistor made from five 200ohm, 2W (3W for RTTY) metal-film resistors in parallel.

MAKING BATTERIES LAST

Although all *TT* ideas should be regarded as "experimental", I am always relieved when from time to time I get the opportunity or need to try one myself, if I find they work for me! This certainly proved to be the case with the German idea, brought to notice by Tim Harrowell, G3IMI (*TT*, February 1988, p106) for rejuvenating "Dryfit" sealed lead-acid batteries. The 6V (three cell) battery of this type fitted in my ageing Uher 4000 Report IC portable tape recorder recently 'died' refusing to hold any charge whatsoever although still exhibiting a no-load voltage.

Although convinced it had reached the end of its useful life, on the off-chance I tried the

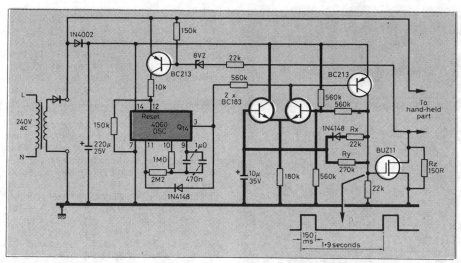

Fig 3. Nicad battery charger incorporating a timer to reduce greatly the charging rate after about seven hours to provide safe trickle charging.

suggested rejuvenation technique of drilling into each cell as shown in *TT* and adding a little distilled water (produced by boiling a kettle and directing the steam into a succession of upturned saucepans as cooling devices arranged so that the condensed water ran into a dish). All very primitive and I did not even attempt to measure the amount dripped into each cell which was then later resealed. Yet it all worked a treat. The Dryfit battery now once again powers the Uher recorder for several hours per charge. If only all cures were as easy and as effective!

Mike Brown, G4RAA, after reading the notes on Nicad 'memory' in the June *TT*, tells me that he is still not convinced that in practice repeated partial discharges of nicad cells do not bring about serious 'memory effects', 'voltage depressions' call them what you will. He finds with nicad batteries used in many domestic appliances, that it is necessary, at least occasionally, to discharge the batteries deeply before recharging. Otherwise the batteries power the equipment only for much reduced times. What he feels may contribute to this effect is that the factory-made chargers supplied for nicad charging are virtually never true constant-current units but instead are normally similar to those intended for charging lead-acid batteries.

There can be little doubt that over-charging, often in the form of continuous trickle charging, can much reduce the life and efficiency of both lead-acid and nicad batteries. Doug Eaton believes that even the commonly accepted nicad charging rate of 0.1C (where C is the nominal capacity of the battery in ampere-hours (Ah)) is too high a rate for long-term charging of nicads (some sophisticated fast-charge units for broadcast applications charge at much higher rates than 0.1C but take precautions against over-charging). He found that the charger for his first Texas Instruments LED-display calculator would heat the battery up after only four hours on charge. As AG6K pointed out (*TT*, December 1988, p957) unless the cell temperature is maintained during charging below 35°C, (a very modest rise on a warm summer day) the battery won't last long.

Doug Eaton finds that some appliance manufacturers consider it safe to leave batteries continuously under trickle charge at up to 0.1C and then to completely discharge the batteries once or

twice a year. His own solution is to change automatically the continuous charge current to about 0.01-0.02C by means of a timer after charging the unit for the first seven hours after it is returned to the charger after use. **Fig 3** shows an updated circuit now used to provide such a charger. The 4060 is connected as a 7-8 hour monostable, the oscillator being inhibited when the last output (Q14) goes to a logic '1'. This causes the BC213 transistor and the BUZ11 FET to turn off, leaving Rz to set the long term charging current. The 4060 is triggered whenever the hand-held part is removed from the charging cradle. Thus removing the handheld part allows the output voltage to rise to 11-12 volts. This turns on the 8.2V zener diode during the 50Hz-rate voltage peaks, and, via the other BC213 transistor, resets the 4060 counter and thus restarts the monostable action.

The two BC183 transistors and associated circuitry form a simple oscillator that flashes the LED in the hand-held unit once every two seconds to show that everything is working correctly after the monostable times out. It does this by restoring the charging current to its 0.1C value for 7-8% of the time. The flash rate and duration are controlled by Ry and Rx respectively. The total long term charging current is thus the sum of two currents, a continuous component (controlled by Rz) and an intermittent component (timing controlled by Rx and Ry).

Doug Eaton (28 Combermere Road, St Leonards on Sea, E. Sussex, TN38 0RS) would be interested to have comments on the optimum values for the various parameters (times, charging currents etc) with such a circuit. The values shown in **Fig 3** reflect his own thoughts. He points out that the 'flash' oscillator is a very useful design, very well suited to a number of low-current applications, including medical electronic aids, since it offers significantly lower quiescent battery consumption than most other arrangements.

Dr Roy Hill, GM0IJF comments on some recent *TT* items in regard to the use of vehicle batteries to supply transceivers, etc. He points out that it is not the very high peak currents, lasting milliseconds, that result in under-powering equipment but the average current of say ten amps or so lasting seconds which causes polarization and a fall in battery voltage. He writes: "In my experience even

a large truck battery will not hold up to 12V if you try to run 100W SSB from it, the voltage soon dropping to about 11.5V resulting in the rig not operating correctly." He also notes that while an ammeter is handy for checking transmitter current, it can introduce an undesirable voltage drop. To overcome this problem he uses one of the supply leads as a shunt for a sensitive meter which then needs to be calibrated.

GM0IJF, on other topics, points to a slip of my pen in referring (*TT*, May) to 'non-ionized' rather than 'non-ionizing' electromagnetic radiation. *Mea culpa*. Unlike X-rays and nuclear radiation etc, RF radiation is not powerful enough to eject electrons from biological or other matter!

TUNING THE I1ARZ LOOP

Dick Kelsall, G4FM recently moved from a farm-house where he had had plenty of unrestricted space for antennas into an old cottage in the village with limited room for antennas and what there is tending to be screened by other cottages. This has encouraged him to build a 1.2m diameter I1ARZ-type loop antenna (*RadCom* February) using 22mm copper pipe and covering the 7, 10 and 14MHz bands. This has proved very satisfactory when mounted at a height of only 2m above ground. The experience has, however, indicated some ways of facilitating remote tuning which could be of interest to anyone building one of these transmitting loops. He writes:

"Covering three bands makes it necessary to have some visual indication of the angular position of the tuning capacitor when changing bands. I used a simple 15k wire-wound Colvern potentiometer coupled to the shaft of the tuning capacitor, having first removed the end-stop pin from the shaft. This is fed from the 24V DC supply used for the tuning motor. The output from the wiper arm feeds a DC voltmeter through a trimming resistance to set the scale. I found it better to off-set the meter below zero to keep the wiper arm of the potentiometer away from the end of the track for zero indication on the meter.

"A stabilised supply would result in improved accuracy of indication but as the tuning is so very sharp, I found it better to introduce a phase detector into the co-ax feed to show which way to drive the tuning capacitor when within the bands, since the potentiometer indicator cannot discriminate this with sufficient accuracy. The circuit arrangement I used (**Fig 4**) is a simple one made from an old SWR meter.

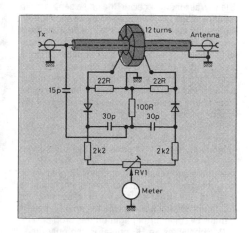

Fig 4. Phase detector for use with I1ARZ loop aerial.

"Good matching has been achieved on all three bands, better than 1.2:1 at resonance. Bandwidths for an SWR of 1.5:1 are: 7MHz ±3kHz; 10.1MHz ±7kHz; and 14MHz ±12kHz. I'm sure cleverer people may have better ideas but with these two additions to the system described by I1ARZ, I have found the loop easy to use. Neighbours are unconcerned and believe I'm on satellite TV!

"Over 36 contacts with Europe, Australia and the USA I have compared performance on reception with a Butternut HF6V elevated at 35ft with the loop axis on SW/NE. Noting the plus or minus 'S' points relative to the Butternut, the average indicated that the loop performed equally as well. Many stations were a few points better than the omnidirectional Butternut antenna.

"The tuning motor is an ex-Luftwaffe 24V PM DC motor with 25mm diameter by 50mm long together with two stages of worm reduction from the same 50-year-old source — beautiful workmanship. Having a 12-0-12V secondary on the transformer feeding the bridge rectifier for the motor supply, I was able to introduce a change-over switch to give 12V for fine tuning. I hope my experience may help others trying this interesting small antenna."

BROADBAND TRANSMITTER NOISE

The problem of spurious emissions from transmitters, including harmonics, mixer products, intermodulation distortion, is universally recognised and methods of minimising them well-publicised, if not always heeded. Similarly it is usually appreciated that oscillator phase noise, particularly from low-cost frequency synthesisers, adversely affects transmission as well as reception.

Now Edmund Ramm, DK3UZ draws attention to a form of unwanted broadband noise that can adversely affect local amateurs yet is seldom discussed, virtually never in practice considered, despite the fact that on VHF/UHF bands it can significantly degrade weak signal reception at distances up to several kilometres from the transmitter.

DK3UZ writes. "With the advent of solid state VHF transmitters, it has become fashionable to align all stages of a transmitter so that the output power remains stable across the entire band without retuning. This means that a transistorised amateur VHF transmitter represents a broadband high-gain amplifier from the first to the final stage. Clearly, as for any receiver, the noise generated in an early stage will be amplified by all subsequent stages so that the noise from the first stage is crucial. Amplified noise, across the full bandwidth of the amplifier, will be radiated from the antenna along with the desired signal, spread thinly but evenly across the band. Whenever the transmitter is operating, the radiated noise will raise the noise floor of any sensitive receiver within range of the radiated noise.

"While this sad fact has occasionally been noted before, for example by Ari Dogteram, PA0EZ (Dubus-magazin, 4/87 pp352-4) there is still no sign that it is being taken into account by designers, professional or amateur. Should we be designing our VHF/UHF transmitter amplifiers, as well as the front-ends of our receivers, for minimum noise? I wonder whether any TT readers can throw some further light on this problem?"

Personally, as an HF operator, the only time I recall encountering the problem of transmitter

GRAY-LINE GLOBES

Almost twenty years ago, I included in TT (later ART) a table giving approximate local times of sunrise and sunset for different parts of the globe (taken from R. Keen's classic book on Wireless Direction Finding) together with some small maps indicating seasonal variations in 'twilight' paths. The information was intended to help readers to ascertain the most likely times at which HF signals would be subject to long-distance chordal hop propagation. Later, others gave to these twilight paths, highly favourable for DX contacts on the lower-frequency MF/HF bands (1.8, 3.5 and 7MHz), the term 'gray-line propagation'. Chordal-hop propagation had by then been put forward as the explanation of the strength and regularity of the reception of European signals in Australia by Hans Albrecht, VK3AHH/DL3EC and enthusiastically endorsed by Les Moxon, G6XN.

It was the publication in the late 1970s of the book 80-meter DXing by John Devoldere, ON4UN that provided a stimulus to the use of gray-line propagation as well as much useful advice on 3.5MHz antennas etc. K6UA and W6NLZ, in an article in CQ (September 1975) seem to have originated the term 'gray-line' rather than 'twilight' paths.

Colin Horrabin, G3SBI writes: "Ever since I read ON4UN's excellent book I have been looking out for one of these 'Gray Line' globes. They are, in fact, Columbus Verlag 'Planet Earth' globes. They are internally illuminated to show darkness, sunlight and three twilight zones. There is a date control, and the globe can be used to predict the possibility of long-distance paths on the lower frequency bands. I have used my globe to check contacts made on 1.8MHz with VK6 and 9M2. In each case signals peaked when the first twilight ring before dawn in VK and 9M2 fell across the position of the stations. I have also checked other DX contacts on 7 and 3.5MHz and find a good degree of correlation, including where the distant station is experiencing dusk.

"After a number of enquiries I found that the 'Planet Earth' globes can be obtained from Edward Stanford Ltd, 12 Long Acre, London WC2. They are not cheap but I am convinced that anyone really serious about low-HF DXing should think about investing in one. They are made to high standards of accuracy and look quite attractive. Size 1. 10.5-in diameter. This model does not have a ring round the equator so the time has to be read from the disc at the top of the globe. Price (inc VAT) £69.95, postage £3.50. Size 2. 13.5-in diameter as used by ON4UN and with a ring around the equator for reading the time of day. Price (inc VAT) £129.95, postage £3.50.

noise was many years ago when, for a time, I worked full break-in without the use of relays, with oscillator keying and the final Class C power amplifier biased partly from grid current so that there was appreciable standing current in the key-up position. Under these circumstances the noise radiated from the transmitter with the key-up, centred on the frequency in use, was sufficient to spoil reception of all but the strongest signals. In my case, the problem was solved simply by increasing the standing bias on the PA to beyond cut-off. This, however, is not a solution for the type of situation that DK3UZ has in mind since it is noise radiation while the PA is functioning that causes the problem.

In Dubus, PA0EZ presents calculations based on a good 100watt 430MHz transmitter showing that its wideband noise could raise the noise floor of a sensitive receiver 5km distant from -137dBm to -117dBm, representing an increase of 18dB (three S points) in the noise floor. His main conclusion is that "stations going portable, expose themselves to very high requirements if they are not to destroy the pleasure of nearby stations (and vice versa). The main effort should be to create an output level at the last narrowband filter in the transmitter which is as high as possible. One solution could be extra amplification between the modulator (mixer) and the filter, lowering the gain after the filter by the same amount. (One would need to take care that a crystal filter is not driven into non-linearity — G3VA). A filter output level of 0dBm can be aimed at. The first transistor after the filter should be a very low-noise device. An FET would be a good choice taking into account the impedance levels concerned in such a change. For stations using a transceiver with a common transmit-receive filter, there are clearly some disadvantages in this proposed solution since the noise levels around the filter would not be well suited to the conflicting requirements of reception and transmission."

PA0EZ also suggested that transmitter noise should be at least 90dB below signal output and outlined how this could be checked. He added: "To check whether the noise created in your receiver is due to a local transmitter or your own transmitter, ask the other amateur to transmit without speech or carrier and to switch his transmitter on and off. If you do not see his switching influencing your receiver noise level when tuned about 500kHz away from his frequency, then his wideband noise is not the source of your problem."

Edmund Ramm, DK3UZ (Postfach 1338, D-2358 Kaltenkirchen, FRG) comments that changing to FET rather than bipolar devices could come close to involving a major rebuild and believes there must be simpler solutions using low-noise bipolar devices. He would welcome comment and suggestions from those with more fundamental design knowledge.

AIRCRAFT-ENHANCED PROPAGATION DEBATE

In 1985 two Australian amateurs, Doug McArthur, VK3UM and Gordon McDonald, VK2ZAB were engaged in investigating the use of forward-scatter as mode of propagation of VHF/UHF signals between Melbourne and Sydney. They were surprised at times to hear strong, but short-lived signals from Ian Cowan, VK1BG near Canberra, a distance of about 450km. The signals lasted from just a few minutes to tens of minutes and were clearly not due to meteor scatter. Careful observations and enquiries soon showed that these 'openings' coincided with the flight of large aircraft between Melbourne and Sydney.

The connection between the signals and aircraft was quickly confirmed by a number of other Australian enthusiasts and there is no dispute that this is a form of aircraft-enhanced propagation. But ever since 1985, there has been a continuing and lively debate about the cause: one faction led by Gordon McDonald believes that it can be explained fully as a form of bilateral radar brought about by direct reflections (scattering) from the metal surfaces of large aircraft. Others, including VK1BG and Roger Harrison, VK2ZTB believe that an important factor is the large amount of hot gases ejected from the engines.

Ian Cowan, VK1BG in the latest of a number of articles on AE propagation *(Amateur Radio* (VK), March 1989, pp18-20) argues strongly that it is not only a matter of reflection of signals from the metal surfaces but "there is also a mode of hot gas supported propagation that gives very good results indeed when the conditions are right." He is convinced that an aircraft can produce what in effect is a temporary temperature-inversion. He lists the following circumstances in which such AE can occur:

(a) A baseline distance of about 450km.

(b) Air reasonably still and stable (ie, where pilots do not report turbulence or strong winds).

(c) VHF/UHF terrestrial propagation is normal (ie natural big temperature inversions are unhelpful to AE, although of course desirable for conventional forms of tropospheric propagation).

(d) The aircraft track is nearly parallel to the radio-wave path and the intersection of the two is roughly the mid-point of the radio path.

(e) Both stations have line-of-sight paths to the aircraft.

(f) Both stations have SSB (or CW) equipment, with 20watts or more transmitter output power, reasonable antenna gain and low-noise receiver pre-amplifiers (or first signal amplifiers). The mode can work on FM, but the average FM-operator generally lacks the necessary ERP and receiver sensitivity.

VK1BG considers that it can be shown that a large aircraft delivers a large amount of heat to the atmosphere with the geometric shape of its wake very much like a two-dimensional copy of the temperature inversions produced in nature and which provide so many openings for serious VHF/UHF operators.

His article is thus a fairly convincing rebuttal of the view advanced by VK2ZAB *(Amateur Radio,* February 1986) that reflection from the metallic skin of an aircraft fully accounts for the AE mode of propagation. Those with reasonably long memories may recall a fascinating three-part article by Rev Paul Sollom, OSB, G3BGL *(RadCom* December 1970, January & February 1971) under the deliberately intriguing title "Flare-spot — a radio-detective story in three parts." G3BGL in conjunction with the Radio & Space Research Station (now part of the Rutherford-Appleton Laboratory) carried out an intensive investigation into the phenomenon of "steam-train (chuff-chuff) fading" on VHF/FM broadcast signals and showed conclusively that the cause was reflections from aircraft. At Douai Abbey near Reading, he recorded the TV-sound transmissions from Lille (174.1MHz, 5kW) over a path length of about 280km, relating them to the records of the London Air Traffic Control Centre. The incoming signals were spectrum analysed and the fading frequencies automatically measured. The *RadCom* articles showed very clearly the temporary signal enhancements from aircraft.

Although G3BGL was primarily interested in the effect of aircraft as a fade and interference producing mechanism, he did conclude that as a communications mechanism "the air traffic density in south-east England (in 1970) is probably sufficient to provide a reliable service by passive reflection, given adequate information on the whereabouts of the aircraft and suitable antenna equipment at the terminals." The Doppler shifts he recorded indicated that the signals were reflected from a moving aircraft. He does not appear to have observed or considered the possibility of aircraft giving rise to temporary temperature-inversions. If VK1BG is correct in his belief that this can occur in some circumstances, the Australian work would seem to be breaking interesting new ground.

MORSE VERSUS AMTOR

Garry Orford, G4FRO takes issue with a comment I made in "The way we listen" *(TT,* June 1989, p36). He writes: "Your contentious statement that 'hand-speed Morse is... the simplest and most effective weak signal communications mode cannot be allowed to remain unchallenged. Simple maybe but most effective? Many think otherwise. Let me quote from G3PLX in *RadCom* June/July 1980: 'Experience of the use of Amtor system by the author and others, both on HF and VHF bands, indicates that under typically bad conditions of fading and interference, Amtor (Mode A) performs better than any other mode of transmission currently used by amateurs, including morse code'. Or from G3OSS in *Buyer's Guide to Amateur Radio:* 'Amtor... I had one remarkable contact for over an hour with an Australian amateur with very few errors in conditions that would have been impossible for SSB, and exceptionally difficult with CW.' I believe G3PLX is correct and have duplicated the G3OSS VK feat with ease with a typical suburban amateur set-up. Morse has its uses but this does not give it unique mystical powers. Amtor must be considered for the title of most effective amateur mode."

CONVERTERS AND COMPONENTS

TT (January 1989) showed how a single Signetics/Philips NE602 IC could be used to form a very simple crystal-controlled HF or VHF converter. Since then some readers have mentioned that they have had difficulty in obtaining these devices, although others have found that they are available (as mentioned in connection with the low-cost spectrum analyser last year) through some of the specialised chip shops. The problem of publishing circuits using other than the most commonly available components is touched upon in a letter from Stephen Gilbert, G3OAG below. However an alternative one-device band-converter using just one common-type mosfet is outlined by AK7M in a recent *QST:* **Fig 5**. This was based on design in the Japanese *CQ Ham Radio* and features the use of a drain trap tuned to the crystal frequency (L1/82pF). It could prove a little more tricky to get to work than the NE602 and would not represent a 'state-of-the-art' front-end but could be useful in some circumstances.

On components, G3OAG writes: "The comments on the G4DTC receiver in June *TT* prompt me to point out that the SL623 chip is readily available from Quarndon Electronics in Derby whose address was published in a *RadCom* article about component suppliers a few years ago. This is a very helpful company who can offer the data sheets and specifications on the devices they supply. I have built the back-end of G4DTC's design with some modifications. Although I have used double-sided PCB, with good by-passing and screening, with the top as a ground-plane, I find the 623 can still be extremely unstable. Good supply bypassing is essential with plenty of capacity right at the chip pins in order to stop low-frequency instability. I feel that replacing the 10k trimpot by a 1.5k fixed resistor (as suggested in the data sheet) would probably reduce the time spent trying to tame the 623... I have also modified the S-meter circuitry and added a series choke (330 μH) in the SL1612 IF amplifier AGC rail, right against the pins to prevent some desensitising of the IF chain when the BFO is switched on.

"Usually I loathe using specialised chips such

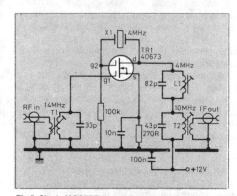

Fig 5: Single MOSFET 14-to-10MHz band converter based by AK7M on a *CQ Ham Radio* design. L1 is slug-tuned coil set to approximately 19.3μH. T1 slug-tuned coil about 3.9μH (primary three turns of No 26 enam wire over "earthy" end of secondary). T2 slug-tuned coil about 5.9μH (secondary four turns of enam wire over "earthy" end of primary).

as the 623 which is available from only a few suppliers and I am puzzled that G4DTC picked on this device... Have you noticed the increase in the cost of basic RF components such as coil formers? Apart from the usual difficulty in obtaining a choice of RF components locally, prices have shot up. A simple plastic coil former obtainable for about 10p not long ago is now around 25p. Add to that the cost of the slug and screening can and you are up to the cost of a ready wound component (if you can get it) from say Cirkit at around 65p. For my present project I need 33 coils for the seven input bandpass filters plus a lot of capacitors...

"I note that nearly all technical and constructional articles appearing in *RadCom* and elsewhere are from amateurs holding the older licences. Could it be that the newer licensees never build anything at all (as some suspect) and are not really all that interested in electronics, as opposed to communication? Articles specifying obscure chips and components do not help. While here in Manchester we are blessed with both a Maplin and an Electrovalue, and there are good mail order services such as STC and Electromail, and of course Cirkit, there is still a problem in obtaining specialised RF components for those of us who have no connection with the electronics industry. I am a retail pharmacist and all my electronic interest stems from the 1960s when everything I had was home brew. I have to trek around the Rallies and search for bits and pieces!" G3OAG also included some notes on building the crystal ladder filter for the G4DTC receiver which I will try and squeeze in another month.

Considered perhaps, but surely rejected. I have no wish to cross swords with either G3PLX or G3OSS, though I believe that G4FRO is wrong on solid technical grounds without the need to ascribe mystical powers to Morse code! Certainly Amtor has proved a far more effective communications mode than basic radioteleprinting with simple frequency-shift-keying without any form of 'automatic request for repetition' (ARQ).

Historically the 5-unit Murray RTTY code was developed for line communication and the difficulties experienced with it on HF radio circuits soon led to the introduction of the seven-unit RCA ARQ code and then to various forms of forward error correction (FEC) for use where a return link was not available. Both these systems were well-established before the development of computer codes such as ASCII, and throughout the period 1945-1965 much effort was put into developing systems more resistant to the effects of fading, multipath and interference. For fixed point-to-point services diversity reception was considered virtually essential for RTTY. For less ambitious installations, a number of multi-tone systems were developed including various 'marks' of Piccolo used by the British Foreign Office to overcome the growing shortage of experienced manual operators. Piccolo and similar systems *are* capable of extremely good weak signal communications though at the cost of using more bandwidth, as well as requiring extremely good frequency stability and complexity. For passing traffic rather than conventional amateur contacts, it would be possible to argue that Piccolo outperforms manual Morse, but amateurs have never shown any interest in the more complex multitone transmission systems.

Then again, since about 1982, the Admiralty Research Establishment has been developing the complex slow-speed frequency and time-division diversity modem using 7-unit ASCII machine code reported in *TT,* May 1985, p356 and March 1989 p38 using ten 100-baud channels on SSB to provide a single 10-baud throughput. It was claimed at an IEE Conference in 1985 that trials had shown that this modem was capable of providing the Royal Navy with a fall-back system performance equivalent to or better than that of an experienced manual operator. In the subsequent discussion period I pointed out without being challenged that the trials methodology gave no scope to the flexibility possible with manual operating. Perhaps G4FRO might consider why if AMTOR (or its professional equivalent protocol SITOR) were really better in difficult conditions than manual CW, the Royal Navy should have gone to the trouble of developing this unique slow-speed modem in its wish not to have to train morse radio operators? FSK, even in Amtor form, remains extremely vulnerable to multipath conditions. I wonder if he finds his AMTOR set-up as reliable as manual CW on, say, the trans-Arctic path to Alaska as he apparently does on the UK-Australia path where the chordal-hop paths are usually relatively free of multipath and fast fading?

The manual operator can readily adjust his speed to suit path conditions, repeat key words, shift frequency to minimise interference, adjust the bandwidth of his receiver to optimise signal-to-noise ratio, use language-redundancy and intelligent guesswork to fill in gaps and correct errors (the fact that Morse is not a fixed time-unit-per-letter code can assist this process). The normal amateur contact is not concerned with achieving a high throughput of traffic but with the

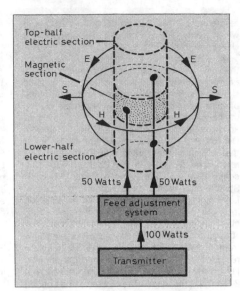

Fig 6. Basic configuration of the GM3HAT/GM3DTI controversial 'crossed-field antenna'. Does it really work by direct synthesis of the Poynting Vector cross product?

exchange of what, in difficult conditions, is reduced to: signal report, QTH, name, etc. Machine and electronic telegraphy can be made to cope with poor signals by means of complex signal processing and by reducing the speed of transmission; just as CW can be further improved by adopting coherent techniques, although this is seldom attempted in practice. Not just for nostalgic reasons I stick by my claim that manual Morse is not only the simplest but also the most effective weak signal communications mode for amateur radio: Amtor represents a major advance on conventional HF RTTY but lacks the flexibility achievable with human decoding and the electronic sophistication of some of the more recent adaptive systems of data transmission.

The 'boom' technology of packet radio is spectrum-efficient but unfortunately is all too vulnerable to interference. There is a considerable body of opinion that doubts whether its use should be encouraged or is really feasible on crowed HF bands. While it is important that amateurs should advocate an experimental approach to new technology, one has to recognise that some systems are likely to upset existing operators, giving rise to such protests as that delivered by John Shelley, WA1IAQ in *Ham Radio*, June 1989: "An electronic plague has descended upon Amateur Radio. Long-standing nets and discussion groups have been pushed out of existence by the agonizing, screeching tide of packet radio... Who can stand that piercing sound that has been likened to that of fingernails on a blackboard?... The basic pleasures of hearing a voice from afar, sensing its emotions, its unique sounds, are being bittered. It is bad enough to lose frequencies to commercial interests, but it is much worse to have them rendered unlistenable by your own group. This could be the final assault in which Amateur Radio, like all the great empires, falls from within."

'NEW' ANTENNA?
With a century of antenna development behind us, it takes some courage to claim to have developed an antenna system that depends on

doing something "for the very first time in the history of radio-communications". Indeed, anyone making such a claim has to expect that it will be received with a degree of scepticism, particularly when the system is claimed to overcome most of the disadvantages traditionally associated with electrically-short antennas.

Maurice Hately, GM3HAT and F M Kabbary, GM3TDI have certainly stirred things up by describing their new "crossed-field antenna (CFA)" as exploiting "for the very first time, radio waves that have been efficiently generated by direct synthesis of the Poynting Vector cross product, by using separately stimulated electric and magnetic fields cutting at right angles." In effect they claim that reversing the form of Maxwell's original equations has led to the realisation and development of a revolutionairy new antenna system **(Fig 6)** for which they have applied for patents in a number of countries and are marketing through Hately Antenna Technology, the firm associated with GM3HAT's dipole of delight!

An article (with B G Stewart) "Maxwell's equations and the crossed-field antenna" appeared in the March issue of *Electronics & Wireless World* that I for one found virtually impossible to understand and which has since been savaged by a number of antenna specialists including Dr A G P Boswell, G3NOQ, who points out: 'The value or otherwise of the CFA could be very quickly established by an experiment conducted by any generally-accepted method. The radiated field produced at some large distance from the antenna should be measured and related to the RF power being fed to the antenna terminals. The *IEEE Standard Test Procedure for Antennas* (IEEE Std 149-179) offers one such procedure by which the authors could (maybe) silence their critics immediately. Can they explain why this has not been done? Until it is, the verdict on the CFA must remain 'not proven'." Others have suggested the article was an April Fool article published a month too soon! My own ill-informed opinion is that it rather proves that if you can feed RF to any lump of metal in the sky it will radiate effectively on HF in good conditions. It may well be advisable to wait for the results of a carefully controlled test before accepting that GM3HAT and GM3TDI are really generating radiowaves in a unique and revolutionary manner, despite their claim that many prototypes smaller than 1m in height and 0.4m in diameter have been tested and have radiated any frequency from 1.8 to 30MHz at powers up to 400W with the only adjustment necessary to change the wavelength generated is a change of proportional feed voltage and phase to the two field-stimulating electrodes. Wonderful, if it really works as claimed and in the manner claimed! Meanwhile they have certainly blinded me with science and Maxwell's equations.

Gary Milton, G0CUQ provides a cautionary tale for owners of FT-747GX HF transceivers and possibly also relating to some other equipments. On the rear of the FT747 is a socket which provides 13.8V for powering keyers etc. The manual points out that it is intended only for supplying loads of a few hundred mA. G0CUG was unlucky enough to fit a homebrew connector to this socket which proved to have a short-circuit between the power rail and 0V. This resulted in excessive current which burnt the 13.8V supply track off the PCB. Too late he realised that this supply is not separately fused. He warns readers to check carefully any connectors, accessories etc for short-circuits before plugging into the rear panel socket. It could save them a nasty repair bill.

WHATEVER HAPPENED TO AMATEUR RADIO?

Few readers born before 1940 will need reminding that September 1939 — 50 years ago this month — marked the beginning of the second world war. An event, for those radio amateurs who survived intact, that inevitably changed attitudes to radio communication as well as proving a forcing house for changes in the technology. It underlined that a radio link can be a vital, life-saving facility; yet, as was so often the case in those hectic years, a link that often failed when most needed. This was for a variety of reasons: unreliability of equipment in difficult environments; failure of batteries or generators; use of unsuitable frequencies; propagation conditions; lack of operating skills; hostile action and so on. If truth is told, radio failures were common and cost many lives. The near complete failure of communications during the 'Market Garden' operations at Arnhem has passed into history, but there were many similar episodes that have been lost in the mists of time. Most of the Resistance operators survived only a few weeks, RAF aircrew W/T operators often only a few flights. It left many of us with a strong feeling that there is more to amateur radio, as a self-teaching medium, than just a 'fun hobby'. By comparison the early months of 1939, as reflected below, were an age of innocence. How fortunate it is that amateur radio could potentially be as useful for a world at peace as for a world at war!

The special April 1989 issue of *Electronics Australia* marked the 50th anniversary of a magazine that began life as *Radio & Hobbies*. The enlarged 260-page issue was supplemented by a reprint of its complete first 72-page issue which vividly brought back memories of pre-war radio. It included such nostalgic articles as 'Your first transmitter — 50 watts on three bands' (6L6G tritet crystal oscillator and 809 neutralised triode power amplifier, rack constructed), **Fig 1**. 'The 2JU Special Six amateur receiver', a 'high-frequency buzzer for code practice' and 'an antennna relay, how to make and use it'. There was also a page advertisement for a new Brimar (STC) range of 1.4-volt battery valves 'specially designed to operate economically from a single dry cell' — forerunners of the miniature 1.4V series Introduced by RCA about a year later that made possible such wartime receivers as the MCR-1 miniature communication receiver, built for SOE by Philco (GB) Ltd.

In the anniversary issue itself, an article that caught my eye was 'Whatever happened to amateur radio?' by *EA's* editor Jim Rowe, a long-time licensed amateur. He writes: "This month I'm really going to stick my neck out, and tackle a subject that to some is almost sacred: amateur radio. The question is, does it still exist? Is there any real difference nowadays between hams and those dreaded CB operators — apart from the number of fancy knobs, pushbuttons and dials on their transceivers?".

He points out that, like many other hobby-electronics magazines, *EA* for several years has published few specifically amateur-radio projects. He finds that even in those magazines devoted entirely to amateur radio the amount of actual amateur radio gear described for construction is "quite modest. Most of the technical material (and there really isn't much of it anyway) deals with reviews of the latest commercially-made gear, while the rest of the magazines seems to be devoted to endless reports of operating contests. The other thing that became pretty clear was that

TECHNICAL TOPICS

PAT HAWKER G3VA

most of the advertisements were offering fully built-up, all-singing, all-dancing, whizzbang transceivers. Multi-band, multi-mode marvels offering almost every conceivable technical feature in either a desktop or handheld package. Very neat, very elegant, very impressive — but also very complete in almost every detail. Nothing much left to do except hook them up to an aerial, plug them in and twiddle the knobs ... there really isn't much difference between this equipment and that sold for CB — essentially pre-packaged *appliances*. The 'amateur-radio' gear tends to have more knobs and buttons, and carries a bigger price tag ... The main activities of today's radio amateurs seem to be very little different from that of the CB operators they've traditionally viewed with such scorn. They both seem to use the equipment almost exclusively as 'black boxes' for communication with each other. The only obvious difference is that CB-ers seem to be interested in 'socialising' over the air, while amateurs seem mainly interested in notching up the largest possible number of token and ever briefer contacts in the shortest possible time — or to/from the weirdest-possible locations. Whatever happened to the original idea of amateurs as people interested in experimenting with radio and communications technology?"

I should make it clear that Jim Rowe is not attacking the hobby. He recognises that not *all* radio amateurs "have become appliance operators and/or contest freaks ... there are still a small

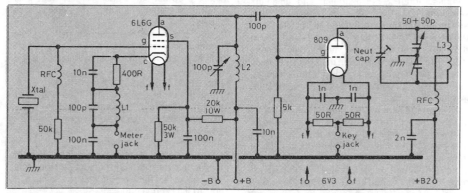

Fig 1. 50-watt three-band CW transmitter from the age of innocence. Without having to worry about TVI construction was easy and the component count, including PSU, less than one per watt! From the first Issue of *Radio & Hobbies* reissued to mark the 50th anniversary of *Electronics Australia*.

SIMPLE TWO-TONE GENERATOR

Jack Hollingworth, ZF1HJ in Grand Cayman, British West Indies, noted the inclusion in G3KKD's item on setting up VHF/UHF SSB transmitters

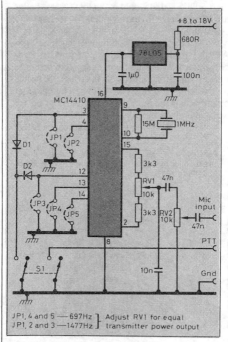

Fig 2. Simple two-tone generator (ZF1HJ).

(*TT*, March 1989, pp34-36) of a *Radio Handbook* design of a two-tone generator using an LM324 device as two Wienbridge oscillators. He writes:

"I feel that information on an alternative 'quick and dirty' two-tone generator suitable for checking SSB transmitters may be of interest. The design **(Fig 2.)** utilises a readily available 'touch-tone' generator IC (MC14410). Whilst the output waveforms may not be quite as clean as those from the *Radio Handbook* design, they are quite adequate for most purposes and the component count is much lower.

"By temporarily jumpering the points indicated, single tones of 697 or 1477Hz are generated, enabling the balance of the tone levels to be set using RV1. This is best done by observing the transceiver output power rather than by looking at the output level from the generator. Closing S1 produces simultaneous 697 and 1477Hz and also keys the transmitter. The output is adequate to drive most HF transceivers from the microphone input but a simple op-amp buffer amplifier could be added if desired.

"In some transceivers it is possible to replace the built-in tone generator by this two-tone unit, thus producing a two-tone drive whenever 'tune' is selected.

"The jumpers may be replaced by two sets of three diodes (anodes to MC14410 pins 3, 4, 12 and 3, 13, 14 respectively), with the cathodes of both sets commoned and grounded via single pole (normally-open) switches or push-buttons. This is more convenient if frequent adjustment of the balance control is required when using the unit with different transceivers."

number of hardy experimenters, carrying on the old tradition of amateur radio with work in areas like 'QRP', microwaves, moon-bounce and so on. I just have the feeling that these people represent no more than about 5% of all amateurs — quite a small minority... It's a great shame that the old spirit of amateur radio seems to have almost gone." He recalls the many major contributions made in the past by amateurs to radio communications, but accepts that *EA* is now publishing few amateur radio projects. This stems from what he feels has happened to the hobby: "Because radio amateurs have largely lost interest in experimenting and building their own gear, and turned to buying and using 'appliance' equipment, they have neither asked us to publish such projects nor submitted any ,or publication. It's as simple as that."

It could be argued that Jim Rowe has got it wrong; that he underestimates the continuing technical interest of Australian and amateurs worldwide. One thinks of many interesting ideas and projects that have appeared in *TT* culled from the pages of WIA's *Amateur Radio* — and also of the interest still shown everywhere in new antenna ideas, in unusual propagation modes, in the whole area of developing technology, both analogue and digital. But, undoubtedly there is some truth in Jim Rowe's comments and we should applaud his wish to discover that "the original kind of amateur radio isn't really dead, after all." Make no mistake. If amateur radio loses the support and interest of those in positions of media or political influence, then the future outlook would be very uncertain. CB, introduced in the UK with so much hype in late 1981, soon had over 350,000 licensees — yet by April 1988 (the latest date for which I have seen figures) the number of licences in force had fallen to only just over 100,000 and were still falling, the UHF 902MHz allocation had been withdrawn, and the hobby now seems almost in limbo.

If editors, professional engineers, spectrum administrators and/or the politicians were to become convinced, rightly or wrongly, that experimental amateur radio is dead or dying, inevitably this will come to happen. It is perhaps fortunate that the ITU World Administrative Radio Conference now scheduled for 1992 will not, after all, involve a complete revision of the 1979 International Table of Frequency Allocations.

RECEIVING EXTREMELY WEAK SIGNALS

In the August *TT,* I claimed that for normal amateur operation, manual CW remains not only the simplest but also the technically most effective transmission mode, capable of outperforming in poor conditions such automatic data transmission systems as RTTY, AMTOR-RTTY and HF Packet as well as SSB. In this connection, the Editor of *QST,* Paul L Rinaldo, W4RI, in 'The Great 1989 HF Packet Design Quest' (*QST,* May 1989, pp54-55) underlines the difficulties involved with the present AX-25 ASCII protocol on HF now being used not only by amateurs but by an increasing number of commercial and official services. He stresses that while packet radio can be effective on VHF, the current protocol is too demanding for ionospheric transmission in rejecting all packets that contain even a single error: "The problem is efficiency, ie. too many retries to get past the dragons: multipath, intersymbol distortion, group delay, QRM,. QRN. bursty errors etc." He believes that the time has

FITTING CONSUMER COAXIAL PLUGS

TT has noted several times that there are various categories of coaxial plugs and sockets, some designed not to introduce any impedance mismatch even at high microwave frequencies. But many of us use, for less demanding purposes, the standard type marketed primarily for plugging into television sets. A 12pp leaflet 'Handy Tips' published by Antiference Ltd, the largest UK manufacturer of domestic TV and FM radio antennas, provides a clear illustration and text in a section 'fitting a coaxial plug' that may be useful to some readers. I would however emphasise that for most amateur radio applications, soldering the centre core connection should be considered mandatory rather than 'ideally'. In practice, many TV set installers do *not* solder these plugs, leading to signal losses later. The Antiference advice is as follows:

1) Slide cap over cable, ensuring that it is the correct way round.
2) Remove 25mm (1") of outer cover from the cable, being careful not to cut into the copper braid. Tease out the braid and twist it to form a tail.
3) Slip the cable grip over the braid and inner insulant with the claws towards the cap and place it so that it rests on the end of the outer cover.
4) Remove 20mm of the inner insulant taking care not to damage the centre conductor.
5) Wrap the braid around the remaining 5mm of inner insulant so that it is in contact with the cable grip. Ensure that there are *no* whiskers of braid to short to the centre conductor.
6) Slide the pin moulding over the centre conductor and push it down so that it compresses the copper braid between it and the cable grip.
7) Fit the body of the plug and screw the cap firmly onto it. This tightens the cable grip securing the

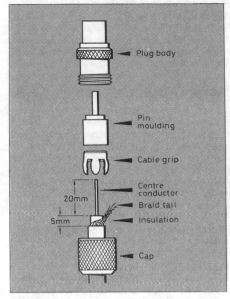

Fig 3. Exploded view of the Antiference coaxial plug type TVP2.

plug. Ideally the centre core connection should be soldered as signal losses may occur as the copper wire oxidises.

Antiference market through local retailers the standard plug type TVP2 but also a coaxial socket (TVS4) for joining cables; a coaxial coupler TVS5 for coupling a coaxial plug with another: and an interference filter TVI/U designed primarily to attenuate at UHF any 27MHz CB signals but useful against HF interference generally. They also produce a range of attenuators TVA/* with 3, 6, 10, 12, 18 and 24dB values available to prevent receiver overload.

come for serious designers to make a valuable contribution to HF packet radio by introducing modifications that would make this system better able to cope with the dragons of ionospheric propagation.

W4RI dimisses the solution of sticking with AMTOR (with five-unit code and forward error correction). With only three characters sent at a time at 100 bauds rather than the usual 300 bauds for the longer packets, AMTOR has a much better chance than "packet" of getting through on HF without endless repeats.

A point I was trying to make last month is that

when it comes to very weak signals it is important to be able to reduce drastically the speed of signalling and hence permit the use of very narrow receiver bandwidths to improve the signal-to-noise ratio. Carried to the extreme, signalling at rates of minutes per word rather than words per minute, it *is* possible to receive data automatically without the use of the human ear/brain combination even on signals that would be buried deep in the noise of a normal bandwidth receiver. The problem is that if you reduce the bandwidth of the receiver to the region of 1Hz, this imposes extremely stringent requirements on the frequency stability

For radio amateurs, 1939-45 saw the passing of that 1930s age of innocence. A still from the 1970 Mullard film 'The Electron's Tale.'

of both the transmitter and the receiver.

Many years ago, RCA showed that a 100mW HF pocket transmitter could be reliably received automatically over ranges of 2,000 miles or more with a receiver bandwidth of about 1Hz (low-frequency crystal filter). Recently, Ray Scrivens, GW3LNM of Minisig Systems Ltd of Aberystwyth has developed and is marketing a VHF telemetry system capable of collecting slow-changing measurements over distances of the order of 20 miles or so (not necessarily line-of-sight) from VHF transmitters having an output of only 1mW to a simple dipole antenna (this power level means that it can be operated, as DTI approved equipment, in the de-regulated 173MHz band without requiring a licence). The receiver bandwidth is about 1Hz and the signalling rate is only one bit every seven seconds!

For amateurs, an interesting point about GW3LNM's work on the development of special techniques pemitting the use of such narrow bandwidths for remote sensing is that the idea originated in amateur radio from his desire to exploit tropospheric scatter propagation using low power transmitters. He writes: "This was successful in that we were able to operate between mid-Wales and Sussex on 144MHz in 'flat' conditions using a 5-watt transmitter and simple antennas. Admittedly, communication was slow; it took about three minutes to send a three-digit number! As you would expect with tropo-scatter, the signal exhibited considerable fading and for most of the time the system was operating on a signal which was completely inaudible even through a narrow-bandwidth CW filter. Error correction coding was also used to ensure that odd missed 'bits' would not corrupt the whole message. We have done some calculations which indicate that it ought to be possible to operate moon-bounce with the system with quite reasonable transmitter powers and antennas. All we need is the time to do it!"

For commercial reasons, GW3LNM is not at present disclosing full technical details of how he has overcome the problem of the receiver automatically identifying and locking on to very weak signals in a reasonably short time. He writes: "In a normal receiver bandwidth the telemetry signal is well below the noise level and, due to oscillator inaccuracies at both transmitter and receiver, its precise frequency is indeterminate. It is here that digital signal processing has provided the answer at quite low cost. The bandwidth of the transmitted signal is extremely narrow (less than 10Hz) and channel spacing is determined almost solely by the frequency stability of the transmitter oscillator. This means that very good spectrum occupancy can be achieved. At present we are able to operate on five sub-channels, spaces at 2.5kHz intervals within each standard 12.5kHz channel."

With such slow signalling rates, one would expect such systems to be attractive for normal amateur contacts except for special modes such as tropo-scatter, moon-bounce etc, but the system provides a striking example of the advantages that slow sending can bestow. Alongside the existing HSC Club perhaps we should start a slow-senders club!

Another approach to weak signal reception at more conventional speed lies in the use of coherent (synchronous) CW systems in which the start and finish of each symbol is accurately anticipated by the receiver. Such a system was developed for amateur QRP operation by Raymond Petit, WA7GHM, in the mid-seventies. It was

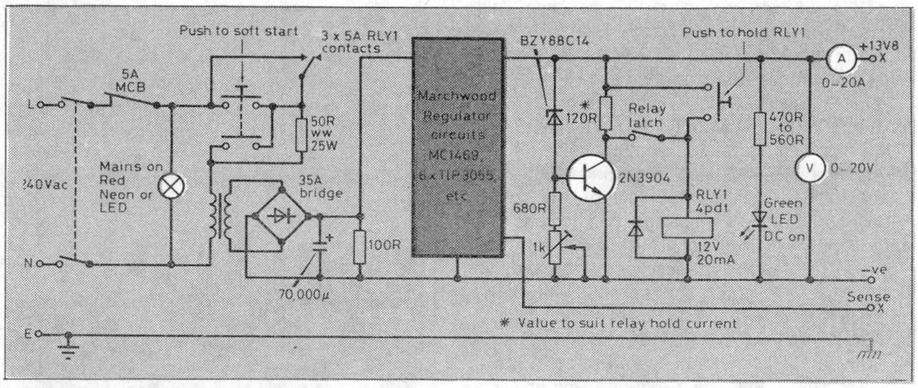

Fig 6. ZS6BVO's soft-start system for a heavy-current 13.8V power supply unit.

SOFT START FOR 13.8V PSU

In the past, *TT* has included a number of ideas and circuits designed to overcome the very real problem of the large in-flow of current at the instant of switching on a hefty power supply. Most of these were intended primarily for high-voltage supplies although due to the extremely high-value of the reservoir capacitors used in high-current, low-voltage PSUs, these units can offer serious switch-on problems.

John Woodcock, ZS6BVO writes: "The peak current demanded by large value filter capacitors can be enormous at switch-on and puts avoidable strain on the components involved. The arrangement shown in **Fig 4.** has been in use for about four years without problems and provides a 'soft' start that limits the peak current transient at switch-on. It really does remove that worrying switch-on 'thump'.

"The arrangement also provides an overvoltage-protection system utilising the same latching relay used for 'soft' starting. It should be noted that switching the low-current primary circuit is less demanding on the relay contacts than the high-current DC circuit, albeit an inductive load. A suitable RC combination across the contacts will suppress arcing on opening. The 'soft start' and 'hold' switches are biased double-pole 'make and break' panel-mounted, push-button types.

"The 'switch-on' sequence is as follows: **1)** AC mains 'on', 'red' indicator 'on'. **2)** Push 'soft start'. This switches the AC mains to primary via series 50-ohm wirewound 25-watt resistor, thus providing suitable surge limiting as the filter capacitor(s) charge. DC appears on output line and 'green' indicator comes 'on'. **3)** Push to 'hold' energises relay from DC output line and the latching contact holds relay energised. Release both push button

switches and the 'soft' start switch puts a short-circuit across the primary surge-limiting resistor. The system is now ready. **4)** AC mains 'off'. Red indicator 'off' and DC output line drops to zero volts. 'Green' indicator goes out and the latching relay de-energises ready for a new switch-on cycle.

"This system has certain advantages over a manually-switched system, one of which is that an AC mains interruption will cause the power supply to shut down and so avoid mains on/off surges.

"The over-voltage protection operates as follows: **1)** DC output voltage exceeds 14.5V and BZY88c14 zener diode conducts. This causes the switching transistor(2N3904) to conduct dropping the collector and relay supply voltage to near zero and the relay is latched out. Sensitivity is adjusted by the preset 1k resistor in the base circuit. **2)** The three pairs of 5A relay contacts in parallel, open-circuit the mains input and the DC output circuit decays to zero. The system is ready for another switch-on cycle.

"For example, a short-circuit condition in one of the regulating 2N3055 transistors can be investigated without the trauma of the conventional crowbar system. Although no overvoltage fault has occurred on my power supply, which runs an Icom IC730 transceiver at 13.8V, this condition has been simulated with an external voltage supply and works well."

The 'Marchwood' design for a high-current 30A power supply unit was originally described by G4JET in *Practical Wireless* June-July, 1983 and the circuit diagram reproduced in *TT*, May 1984, p402.

described initially in *The Milliwatt* and subsequently in *QST* etc (brief mention in *TT* June 1975 and July 1976). coherent CW is claimed to provide an effective advantage in SNR of the order of 20dB but has never gained wide acceptance by amateurs, primarily because it requires that both ends of the circuit are equipped for this mode and have accurate time-synchronisation (much easier to achieve now than in 1975).

Peter Lumb, G3IRM, (2 Briarwood Avenue, Bury St Edmunds, Suffolk, IP33 3QF) together with G3RHI is currently trying to get going on Coherent CW and to revive interest in this mode of communication. He writes: "It will be some time before we are able to operate but we would be interested to find out if there is anyone else who

may like to join us. We have a fairly complete set of articles on this subject. These are sufficient to get started using the mode and we are now building equipment."

FEEDBACK AND COMMENTS

Unfortunately, three errors crept into the circuit diagram of PA0FRI's 'Frinear Linear' (*TT*, June 1989, p35, Fig 9). The polarity of two of the four diodes between chassis and the screen grid of the PL519 was shown incorrectly and a 10nF coupling capacitor in the grid circuit was omitted. The relevant part of the amended diagram is shown in **Fig 5**.

QST (May 1989, p51) has published an important correction to the circuit diagram of W1FB's 12-

watt RF amplifier using power-FET switches. This diagram was included in *TT* (July 1989, p39). The RF input transformer T1 should be earthed at point 3 and the RF input applied at 1.

Peter Chadwick, G3RZP comments on G4IDE's 50MHz QQVO6-40A amplifier (*TT,* July, pp36-37): "This has getting on for enough volts on the anode. The valve was rated for around 2400V peak (600V, 100% modulated) but I feel that the screen supply could prove a bit dodgy. As shown with a 450V supply rail, the BU208A transistor is sitting right on the manufacturer's second-breakdown line, so that its reliability and reproducibility could be open to question. In practice of course it could last G4IDE for years but someone less lucky might experience device failures. Dare I say that EL84, 5763 or even a 6L6 valve regulator might serve better? It was this problem that, John Nelson, GW4FRX to use MOSFETs which are immune to secondary breakdown as their gain *reduces* with rising temperature. Just a thought!"

Just too late for inclusion this month, a considerable amount of information on power supply units, including comments on some aspects of the G4WAS and G4IDE designs in the July *TT,* has arrived from John Brown, G3EUR. *TT* will return to this subject hopefully in the October issue.

The idea of kite-supported antennas stretches right back to Marconi's work at the turn of the century. But this practice could be given a new boost by the findings of Dr Clive Eastman, a clinical psychologist at Birmingham University who believes that kite flying is therapeutic and excellent for reducing stress in executives: "As opposed to watching a bowl of goldfish, which is a passive pastime, kite flying gets you out into the fresh air and in tune with the elements. Kites are very colourful which is positive. People feel they are in control of them, which is very important... Adults are now getting over the embarrassment of admitting that they are kite flyers, though some still bring their kids and pretend the kites are for them." Good show, but what about the stress caused when the wind drops just as the band opens? And somehow I doubt if those German WW2 kite-borne observers at sea felt stress free while towed behind a U-boat, though that was a rather different kind of kite-flying to what Dr Eastman has in mind.

Joe Moell, K0OV (PO Box 2508, Fullerton, CA92633, USA) writes in support of the recognition by Mr Wilson that many of the popular beliefs about nicad 'memory' (*TT,* June, page 34) are nothing more than myths. He recalls making many of the same points in an article 'Forget Memory' (*Ham Radio,* January 1983, pp62-64) based on some mid-1970s publications by General Electric research engineers *Nickel-Cadmium Battery Appli-*

On 12 December, 1901, Guglielmo Marconi and his assistants used a kite-supported antenna on Signal Hill, Newfoundland for the first-ever DX feat in hearing signals transmitted from Poldhu, Cornwall, 2,200 miles away. Leading scientists of the day had declared that reception over such distances was impossible because of the curvature of the Earth. Marconi was later to declare: "You know I have always considered myself an amateur." *(Marconi Company)*

cation Engineering Handbook 2nd Ed 1975. He writes: "This shows that the truth about 'memory' has been well known in the battery industry for many years. The research described in these primary sources has never been challenged. Yet myths and incorrect statements about 'memory' and the desirability of fully discharging nicads continue to pop up regularly in electronics magazines and manufacturer's instruction books. Apparently the writers of these pieces read only each other's articles instead of the primary sources. I have had great success achieving rapid charging and long battery life on a variety of nicad sizes by using simple chargers which produce constant voltage (1.43V per cell) with current limit at about 3C rate. I disagree with AG6K when he states that insufficient current is supplied near the end of the charging process using this scheme. When the current falls below 0.1C charging is complete. The deep parts of the plate are charged by then. I get full capacity charges with no heating this way."

K0OV takes the opportunity of mentioning his recent 323-page book *Transmitter Hunting — Radio direction-finding simplified* (published by TAB books) written in collaboration with Thomas N. Curlee, WB6UZZ. Although amateur DF contests are organised on rather different lines in the USA to those in the UK, he feels that this book would be of general interest. It is available (price $17.95) from the retail outlets for TAB books and also by mail order from ARRL, *Ham Radio* and *73* Magazine. I have not seen a copy but it sounds a useful book. To my mind, HF DF remains a uniquely fascinating topic owing to the great difficulty in obtaining reliable bearings on sky-waves which do not always arrive on a direct bearing from the transmitter Some interesting work on an improved algorithm for use with the large Wullenweber arrays has *recently* been reported by a team at the University of Leicester in conjunction with practical experience with a Canadian array. With a large Wullenweber array it is possible to get bearings accurate to better than 1° on transmitters hundreds of miles away. But we have yet to meet an amateur who could contemplate

building a full-size HF Wullenweber array!

Rod Craddock, GW4SLK draws attention to a publication which he believes represents money well spent for anyone interested in solidstate RF design and construction. He writes: "Readers may be interested in my experience with the Motorola UK Literature Distribution Centre whose address you gave in *TT:* 88 Tanners Drive, Blakelands, Milton Keynes MK14 5BP. I recently sent them a very long request list. Next day they telephoned me 'yes, I could have most of what I had asked for but would I sent them a cheque for the one chargeable item.' This was for *RF Device Data,* 5th edition, 1988, £38.73). By return of post I received an enormous parcel including some useful items that I had not asked for. The *RF Device Data* book is in two thick volumes and I can honestly recommend it to RF constructors as it is not just a data book for Motorola devices but a text book in its own right. Vol 2 includes over 60 application notes, article reprints and engineering bulletins, including all the H O Granberg designs referred to in *TT* as well as comprehensive notes on impedance matching networks for RF transistors, RF design procedures using two-port parameters etc. Also included is a good cross reference to other makes of RF devices. Compulsive reading for anyone building a solid state linear."

THE PYE RADAR IF STRIP

G6HD's recollections reminded me of a paper by M Cosgrove outlining the contribution over many years of the Pye Group of companies to television history (prepared in connection with the 1986 IEE 50th anniversary conference but not included in *IEE Conference Publication No 271*). This paper includes a timely story that will bring back memories to the many pre and post-war amateurs who were concerned with wartime radar:

"A new (receiver) model had started in production, but had not been released for sale, when the war started (and the TV service, like all British amateur activity, closed down — *G3VA*) in September 1939. All assemblies, including 10,000 EF50 valves, were placed in store. All production and develop-

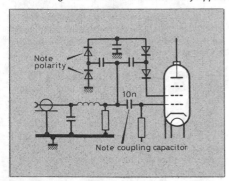

Fig 4. Amended part of the circuit diagram of PA0FRI's PL519 linear amplifier described in the June TT.

ment activities were concentrated on radiolocation (RDF, later 'radar') and radio-based proximity fuses. The RF amplifier (TV receivers then used single-channel 'straight' configuration) of the stillborn receiver became the basis of a standard radar IF strip, operating at the AP vision frequency of 45MHz, and using EF50 valves.

"This valve, which was conceived at Pye and produced by Philips (Eindhoven), had a red metallic screening can surrounding the glass envelope to improve stability. However the valves used in early airborne radar units were resprayed grey to disguise their origin (Holland was a neutral country until May 1940). The production jigs and tools for the EF50 were moved to Mullard (a Philips company) in the UK in 1940, just before the invasion of Holland.

"Instead of Mullard building a new 'shadow' factory, as requested by the British government, decentralisation of production was achieved by the then novel use of nearly 14,000 out-workers in local villages and individual homes to minimise possible disruption in the event of air raids..." So, in effect, many of the many EF50 valves used in the post war period were 'home-brew'. Today, two German enthusiasts have been overcoming many problems in successfully producing replicas of vintage bright-emitter radio valves in a garage, though handicapped in their work on more modern dull-emitter types by lack of tungsten filament wire containing about 1.5% of Thorium (*Vintage Wireless*, Vol 14, No 2, 6/89 pages 16-17).

DO's AND DON'TS WITH ATUs

John J Schultz, W4FA/SV0DX, in *CQ* (April 1989, p34) provides a succinct outline of 'Some general do's and don'ts regarding antenna tuners' that squeezes into seven items a lot of practical experience, based on a talk he gave to a local club. He recalls that "practically since the beginning of amateur radio, various forms of antenna tuners have come and gone along with various opinions as to their value in a station installation." The following notes are a brief digest of his main findings:

1) Don't use an ATU to disguise a poorly dimensioned or improperly constructed antenna. (In other words if a conventional dipole or other antenna which should provide a good match to the transmitter results in an excessive SWR find out why rather than using an ATU to overcome the problem — *G3VA*).

2) Don't waste power in an ATU by using a short random length of wire as an antenna if this can be avoided. The shorter the length of the antenna wire, the greater the proportion of output power that will be dissipated in the ATU. It is better to get out more wire even if it has all sorts of twists and turns than to use a very short (in terms of wavelength) length of antenna wire.

3) Do be kind to your ATU when using a (voltage-fed) random length of wire about a half-wave or multiple thereof in length antenna. Avoid arc-overs by increasing capacitor/component ratings or increase the length of the antenna to provide current feed.

4) Do use a good ground (earth) with an ATU even if the antenna itself does not 'work against ground'.

5) Don't rely on an ATU alone to provide harmonic attenuation. The amount of attenuation provided by an ATU can vary enormously from band to band, with the ATU providing insignificant attenuation with some antenna loads.

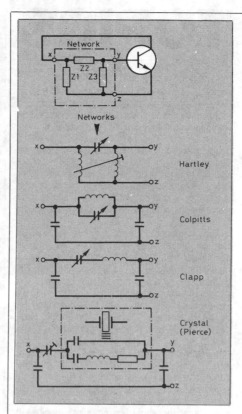

Fig 6. Basic single-transistor oscillator networks (G3LHZ).

OSCILLATORS — FUNDAMENTAL LIMITATIONS

Recently on 7MHz, I found myself eavesdropping on a net discussion between a group of retired BBC/IBA transmitter engineers. They were talking about the use during the second world war of a high-stability VFO as a broadcast transmitter drive, recalling that it was fitted with an HRO-type tuning mechanism. But nobody in the group seemed to know the bitter-sweet story behind this VFO which should have carried the name of its British inventor into posterity; Geoffrey Gouriet who in the early 1940s developed the series-tuned configuration later rediscovered and described in *Proc IRE* by the American engineer J K Clapp. If it had not been for wartime secrecy preventing publication, it would have been known as the Gouriet oscillator; only a few pedants still call it a Gouriet-Clapp oscillator.

Despite the development of frequency-synthesisers, there is still an important role for the tunable VFO with its significantly lower phase noise. But all oscillators, unfortunately, have limitations. At the IEE Conference 'Frequency Control & Synthesis' held at Leicester University last April, Professor M J Underhill, G3LHZ (MEL-Philips) gave a tutorial paper 'Fundamental limitations of oscillator performance' (*IEE Conference*

Publication No 303, pp18-31) from which the following brief extract is taken:

"There is a continuing need for better purity and stability of oscillators particularly as the frequencies of operation of communications and radar systems continue to extend ever higher. In principle, oscillators can be made more and more stable by better control of the physical elements that determine the frequency of oscillation. However the presence of phase noise on an oscillator **Fig 6** is fundamentally inescapable. The price to be paid for better phase noise is higher power or at least higher stored energy (PQ^2) in the oscillator system. Both these eventually are limited by physical breakdown of components... Temperature, as for example the expression for Johnson noise kT, is probably the only parameter which remains to be fully explored for the reduction of phase noise in oscillation. A reduction in temperature not only reduces the amount of noise that a given resistor produces but also in general reduces the value of the resistor... Although cryogenic temperatures remain an interesting area to be explored in the search for better oscillators it is highly probable that further physical barriers and limitations will prevent the perfect oscillator from ever being achieved."

At the same conference (of which Peter Chadwick, G3RZP was chairman of the organising committee) D Salt (Hy-Q International (UK) Ltd) provided a tutorial review of the use of quartz crystals as frequency controlling elements. He emphasised that compared to other resonators, such as LC circuits, mechanical or ceramic resonators, the quartz crystal still provides a unique combination of properties. Its material properties are extremely stable and highly repeatable. The internal friction (acoustic loss) is particularly low, leading directly to its extremely high Q. The intrinsic Q of quartz is 10^7 (ten-million) at 1MHz, with mounted crystals having Q factors ranging from tens of thousands to several millions. The Q of even the best wound inductors does not exceed a thousand (10^3) and that of ceramic resonators is at most ten-thousand (10^4).

The paper stated that the long term stability of crystal resonators depends on the manufacturing techniques used rather than the intrinsic properties of quartz. Ageing rates of about 5 parts per million per year or less are typical for commercially manufactured crystals; 2 to 3ppm can be achieved relatively easily. Precision quartz resonators can have ageing rates as low as parts per billion (10^9) though such crystals are costly: "The short term stability of quartz crystals is less well understood. From the experimental data there again appear to be a number of factors involved but identifying these with specific physical mechanisms is a matter of uncertainty."

6) Do be aware that some ATU networks can show false resonances. Obtaining a near unity SWR does not necessarily mean that all the power is going to the antenna. Occasionally it may indicate that much of the power is being 'dumped' into the ATU coil. In general, tuner settings should be such that the minimum amount of inductance is used that permits the system to tune-up properly. 'Dumping' can often be detected by the coil running warm — a sure sign that power is

being wasted.

7) Don't expect too much from 'automatic antenna tuners' which are meant to cope with only moderate SWRs (1:3 or, at most, 1:5) as may be encountered at band edges with a beam array or sometimes with a dipole: "if such tuners are grossly mistreated, their components can readily arc over or burn up. Just by the nature of their compact size, the components used in such tuners cannot be 'jumbo' size."   □

TECHNICAL TOPICS

PAT HAWKER G3VA

POWER SUPPLY COMPROMISES

Power supply units remain an area where home design and construction continues to interest many amateurs even in this era of black boxes. But it is an area where care is needed, particularly if the PSU is to be used to drive an expensive transceiver or linear amplifier without inducing a gnawing fear that one day it may inflict costly damage on itself or its load. Protection against excessive voltage output (transient or sustained), over-current and short-circuit protection, switch-on transients and current surges, including safeguards against all likely fault conditions are important, while always paramount should be the safety of users, their family, pets etc. The degree of voltage regulation and ripple filtering may vary widely according to the intended load (transceivers intended for mobile operation will include in-built voltage regulation). Then again, for some applications questions of size and weight and the desire to counter the rising cost of what we used to call the 'ironmongery' — mains transformers, smoothing chokes, metal cabinets etc — will need to be taken into account. In many areas of electronics, the 50Hz PSU is being superseded by switched-mode units and inverters with the tendency for these to function at ever higher switching frequencies and involving the need to counter radio-frequency-interference (RFI) problems by the use of good EMC practices. For 50Hz and higher frequency units the toroidal transformer has become established (see *TT* March 1986, pp 186-7 for a summary of the advantages of toroids based on information stemming from John Brown, G3EUR) as an alternative to conventional laminated-core transformers.

To meet *all* the requirements outlined above with a high-voltage or high-current transmitter/transceiver PSU is neither easy nor cheap, and in practice many of the designs published in *TT* and elsewhere tend to include compromises that reflect the designer's belief that, despite Murphy's Law, particular fault conditions are unlikely to befall him. A PSU designed to function perfectly under all fault conditions may in fact be over-designed and not truly cost-effective. Most of us only partly believe in the validity of Murphy's Law and comfort ourselves with the thought that sustains all those who live dangerously: 'It won't happen to me.' Thus most of the PSUs published in the amateur press tend to be based on units that have worked satisfactorily over a reasonable period of time rather than designs that would fully satisfy a top professional designer (though the same could be said for some factory-built PSUs). However, if compromises are to be made, it is highly desirable for those concerned to know and recognise what they are. For that reason it is my practice to publish constructive comments on *TT* designs, without this implying that the original design would not prove satisfactory in practice. Perhaps the main problem for the amateur designer is analysing what may happen in the event of a sequence of component failures and deciding what are the chances of particular components failing.

The components count of high-current PSUs can be significantly reduced by the use of specialised and over-rated components; unfortunately these may not be readily available in the UK to those not working in the electronics field. An interesting example of such a design is the 13.8V (adjustable), 20A maximum PSU described by Jean-Luc Barraud, FC1JEK (*Radio-REF,* No7/1989) using SGS and Thomson devices: **Fig 1.** The BUX21 series regulator is rated at 40A, 250W (alternatives BUX20, BUX22) is mounted on a heat sink at least 150-200mm (0.5°/W) and forced air ventilation of the unit by means of a fan is strongly recommended. The diode bridge can be mounted on the side of the metal cabinet or on another heat sink. Capacitors should be mounted very close to the SGS L200 regulator (alternative Thomson TDB200) which also requires heat sinking, for example by mounting on the side of the cabinet. The use of a 6A miniature circuit breaker as switch and 'fuse' is another feature. The design is included here primarily for interest rather than duplication.

John Brown, G3EUR, with much professional experience, offers some useful comments on several recent PSUs that have been shown in *TT,* including the two in the July issue: Fig 2 (p35) G4WAS's 13.5V high-current supply with crowbar over-voltage protection; and Fig 4 (p36) G4IDE's 600V/400V unit for the 50MHz valve amplifier. Both raise questions of the protection arrangements.

G3EUR writes: "In the event of a catastrophic failure of the series regulator in G4WAS's unit, due to collector/base-emitter short, the voltage across C2 (39,000 μF) will rise until THY1 fires, turning on THY4 to blow the fuse F2. But the coil of RL1 in series with C2 will present high impedance to the current surge. Feeding the network R1, RV1 etc from the junction of the regulator and RL1 would give much faster turn-off and could permit a smaller value for C2. This is advisable since a large-value C2 could deliver a lot of destructive energy to a short-circuit in the transceiver etc, although not as much energy as from a hefty 12-volt battery. I consider that *several* fuses are desirable at strategic points in the rig. For example, I found the scale lamps on the VSWR meter and the 12V outlet for 'accessories' on my rig were fed from the same 20A fuse that 'protected' the PA. For my peace of mind, I have added 20mm by 5mm holders and 500mA fuses.

"I have never experienced a breakdown in a series pass transistor, perhaps because I always use conservative ratings and like to keep devices cool. Many years ago, in a professional capacity, I found that different makes of 2N3055 transistors when opened up revealed a more than 2:1 variation in chip area, often with poor thermal coupling between chip and header. I decided that cheap chips are poor insurance. The firm I was with encapsulates many type of regulators using 2N3055 devices and has had almost zero fault records for a decade.

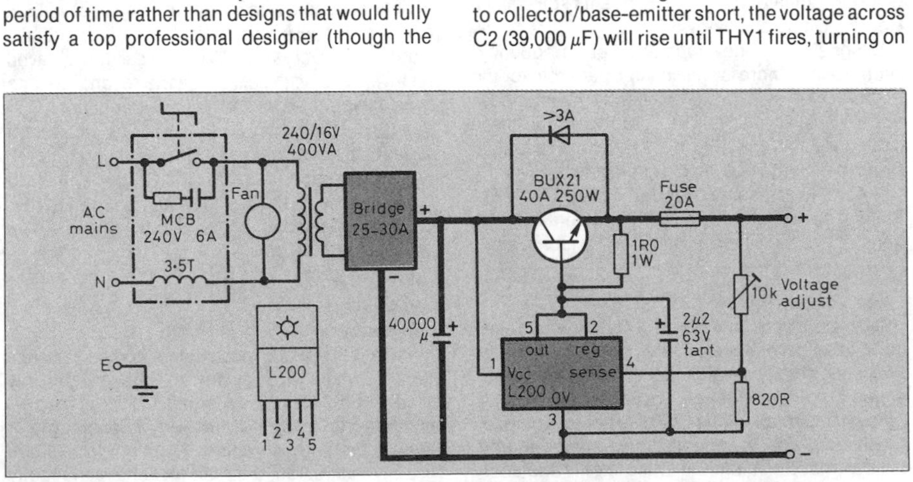

Fig 1. FC1JEK's 20A PSU based on relatively high-power components. Shown for interest rather than duplication as some components may not be readily available in the UK. MCB is a miniature contact breaker combined switch and 'fuse'. *(Radio-REF)*

COOKING THE VISION

Gina Moda, I7SWX draws attention to an article 'A microwave oven to amateur TV transmitter conversion' by David Pacholok (Creative Electronics Consultants) in *RF Design,* March 1989. This describes how he used a domestic 400-500 watt microwave oven as the basis for a 2.3GHz amateur television transmitter with an FM vision output of more than 200 watts, at a cost of under $200, and capable of being received on the low-cost 2.3GHz down-converters sold widely in the USA for the 'pirating' of MDS (microwave subsciption-television distribution systems). One must have doubts about the advisability of attempting to squirt out amateur TV signals from a 2M189A or 2M226A magnetron used as a self-contained, crossed-field power oscillator, with an HT supply of about 3.5kV even by those with a good knowledge of microwave engineering (the frequency can shift by up to about 6MHz if the load is varied). It opens up a new way of cooking the books. David Pacholok points out that the basic transmitter scheme should be adaptable to other emission modes, such as narrow-band FM, with additional phase-lock circuitry. The *RF Design* article describes the characteristics of microwave oven magnetrons and shows how the built-in cavities can be modified to couple RF to a transmission line instead of the oven compartment; it is also emphasised that safety must be considered paramount: "4kV DC and high power microwave energy are present in the transmitter. An inexpensive microwave leakage detector should be used to check the integrity of the modified unit, and door interlocks should be retained (the modulator was installed in the now-unused cooking cavity). Antennas can easily have high gain at this frequency, so avoid pointing them at people, buildings, etc." The author concludes: "Although this is not a 'high performance' television transmitter, it represents a low-cost effort to achieve significant power output at microwave frequencies." Some of the shortcomings are discussed, along with possible improvements.

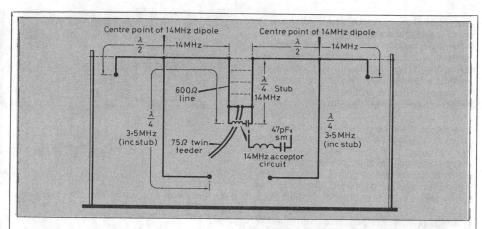

"But it has been my experience, more than once, that if RF gets into the control circuits of a regulated PSU, it can raise the output voltage sufficiently to turn on crowbar protection. This happened recently at a Duxford (part of the Imperial War Museum) demonstration when another transmitter was being tuned up.

"In connection with the above notes, an average linear regulator has a source impedance of the order of 10 milliohms from DC to about 1kHz and this is usually less than the impedance of the cable connecting the PSU to the load. The impedance rises with frequency to tens of ohms at say 10kHz, hence the need for a bypass capacitor, but *not* 39,000µF. More important is low equivalent series resistance (ESR). A 1000µF capacitor has a reactance of 0.16 ohms at 1kHz, adequate for bypassing audio, but the series-resistance may be higher, especially in old 'surplus' types. A new radial type, for SMPS use, will have an ESR of around 0.1 ohm at 1kHz and stay low up to tens of kHz. A mica or ceramic bypass for RF should then keep the PSU source impedance lower than the cable impedance, so that large values of C in this position represent only excess energy storage.

"PSU design should be related to need: the load variations in an SSB transmitter are relatively slow, modulation envelope sized; in CW there are fast square waves with a change in mean current related to keying speed (wpm). If the circuits prior to the final amplifier are voltage sensitive, it is better that they should be stabilised or decoupled at their own low-current level, which also gives some protection and time for the main-PSU protection circuits to work. This also applies to a receiver. Over-kill is not good design; costs money and space, and adds problems.

"Questions of protection also arise in the G4IDE PSU (July Fig 4). C9, C10, C11 together store about 16 joules of energy and in the event of a short-circuit in the power amplifier (and there are at least five points in the PA circuit which could break down to chassis) the destructive energy would probably explode the 500mA fuse (F1) unless this was of the specially-designed, high-voltage, sand-filled type. 16 watt-seconds in 1mS is 16kW! Hence the bang on arc-over.

"Then a common failing in such designs: most resistors of 1W or less are rated at 350V DC maximum regardless of their value and I would not recommend a single 10 megohm resistor (R16) for the 100µA voltmeter unless it was of the 50mm spiral track type rated at 1kV continuous working.

"Then one must question the use of half-wave rectification for the bias supply. Admittedly, the resulting small amount of DC in a big mains transformer will not saturate the core but a bridge-type rectifier is cheap (38p) and could save one of the 100µF capacitors (36p) yet providing less ripple. I frequently see designs using toroids with half-wave rectification; clearly it is not always recognised that the gapless core of a toroid means that it can be easily biassed by DC, and then blamed for core noise and excessive switch-on spikes."

SSB LINEARITY: THE MOVING GOAL-POSTS

The recent series of references in *TT* to the question of the linearity of amateur transceivers and linear amplifiers continues to attract comment. It was noted in the June *TT* that for many years the specification for most professional SSB/ISB transmitters has called for a third-order IMD performance

ANTENNA TOPICS

From a number of antenna ideas recently received from readers, this month's selection includes an ingenious 3.5/1.4MHz wire antenna from C W Farrell, G8GS and a method of ensuring resonance of narrow bandwith HF mobile antennas from Charles Wilkie, G0CBM.

G8GS writes: "After improving signals to VK/ZL on the long path by using a four-element wire beam comprising two colinear horizontal dipoles, each with a director, it was desired to incorporate a 3.5MHz facility into the system. This has been done and the arrangement works successfully on both bands. The method is shown in simple outline in **Fig 2,** utilising the voltage node points, switching being achieved with a 14MHz acceptor circuit fitted into the bottom of the quarter-wave stub. The array is compact, measuring approximately 52ft in length, the mast height being 30ft. No deterioration of the out-going 14MHz signals has been detected." The illustration does not show the 14MHz director wires.

G0CBM required an efficient mobile antenna for 3.5MHz and recognised that the key to efficiency with electrically-short (high Q) antennas is achieving accurate resonance when changing frequency. He writes: "The usual way of achieving resonance of mobile antennas is by means of a tapped loading coil, thus resonance occurs as a series of steps through the band with maximum efficiency only when the operating frequency coincides with the resonance of a tapping point. On the lower HF bands, bandwidth is often only about 10kHz or less, and would entail the use of some 30 taps on the loading coil. I found that by placing a variable capacitor at the base of the antenna, resonance could be achieved at any point in the band. Matching the antenna to a 50-ohm output of a transmitter is achieved by inserting a 4.5µH inductor between the variable capacitor and ground. In practice, I have found that the twin requirements of resonance and unity VSWR can be achieved with only three taps and a 365pF variable capacitor. In operation I simply peak the variable capacitor for maximum signal

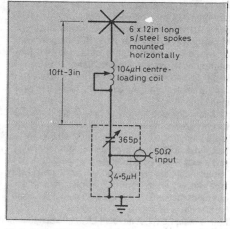

Fig 2. (top) G8GS's dual-band (3.5 and 14MHz) antenna.

Fig 3; G0CBM reduces the need for multiple loading-coil taps by adding a variable capacitor to peak for resonance while maintaining near-unity VSWR. Dimensions of his 3.5MHz mobile antenna for guidance only.

on a field strength meter. Dimensions shown in **Fig 3** are for guidance only."

John Heys, G3BDQ reports some very successful DX operation using a three-band (14, 21 and 28MHz) and a two-band (3.5 and 7MHz) inverted ground-plane antennas (see *TT*, May 1989 and many earlier references) based on the standard multi-band dipole principle of parallel wires of suitable resonant lengths. His triband unit (fed at the top of the three vertical radiators by means of tuned 300 ohm BOFA ribbon feeder) has the 14MHz wire inductively loaded 3.5MHz radiator with the bottom ends of both 3.5 and 7MHz radiators folded back so that the total support height is only 34ft (lower part 2ft above ground). This is end-fed to a single wire radiation feeder to an ATU which then also allows the antenna to be tuned up as form of long-wire antenna for any band. G3BDQ hopes to publish an article on them before long.

of at least -42dB relative to PEP output (equivalent to -36dB relative to one tone), whereas few factory-built amateur rigs come within 10dB of this figure, and some are appreciably worse than this.

It is worth recalling that many years ago, Les Moxon, G6XN pointed out in *TT* that the design and operation of high-power linear amplifiers requires a high level of good engineering practice,

particularly where any degree of speech-compression is used. Apart from the actual amplifier stages, including the exciter, the PSU must be able to handle the current peaks without drooping, including the increased duty-cycle found with compressed speech and with frequency shift keying (FSK) as used for RTTY, AMTOR and digital data.

Paul Essery, GW3KFE writes: "May I pick up on

your point recently about non-linear linears? Whilst I agree that many people overdrive linears, some points need to be stressed; firstly that by-and-large valve linears perform satisfactorily given reasonable design and subject to not being overdriven. However, in my humble opinion by far the biggest cause of problems is the fact that designers have moved the goalposts. In the early days of SSB — vide ARRL's *SSB for the Radio Amateur* for instance — it was accepted that a *minimum* of -30dB represented the figure for spurious output products. Nowadays, if you look at manufacturers' literature covering equipment with solidstate output stages — let alone solid-state 'big boot' amplifiers — you find specification figures for their IMDs of around -25dB at rated output.

"So where in 1989 is the problem with linears? Overdriving is a running problem of course, although ALC can at least reduce this tolerably. But with the present design specifications, a linear to perform adequately at 400W PEP output needs to be rated at much higher output so that they cannot be overdriven accidentally. It is surely better to be momentarily 'over the limit' cleanly than to be plastering the band with splatter at legal limit!

"Secondly, and so few people seem to realise this, whatever the type of linear, as soon as the input impedance changes the driver stage senses this and distorts. Thus to obtain adequate linearity one needs a low-pass filter (to provide a constant impedance) between a blackbox transceiver and a factory-built linear more, possibly, than at the output of the linear if this is feeding an ATU. I had handsome proof of this at my former QTH. Woe betide me if I did not have an LPF between linear and rig; the second LPF merely cleaned up the slight increase in spurious output due to the linear itself. For more than two decades, I have had a TV set built into the shack and switched on whenever the rig is in use. The problem was noted with Class AB2 and Class B linears, but nobody realised, it seems, that AB1 linears with ALC had the same problem. The point is that if the transceiver output stage is forced into distortion the linear faithfully reproduces that distortion!

"With solidstate, designers seem to have com-pounded the problem by selling what in effect is a PA tank circuit as an optional extra called 'automatic ATU'. In my opinion, the right way to go, in the long term, is to use FETs as transmitter amplifiers. But I still believe that many problems arise because the market demands 'modern solid-state technology' regardless of its suitability for a particular application. Leaving things to the mar-ketplace means in practice that 'fashion' rather than 'technical merit' is everything. It is fashion that puts all those confusing buttons and knobs on current transceivers. So many, that even after several months of use, it can be a problem to 'drive' the rig. A few old-style controls would be infinitely easier to operate. Similarly the handhelds are virtually impossible to use with gloved hands, as might be necessary in an emergency."

ECONOMICAL DUAL-VOLTAGE AND VOLTAGE-MULTIPLIER PSUs

John Brown, G3EUR, was stirred to take a long look back to the 1942 era, when he designed the Type 3 Mk II (otherwise known as the B-2) transmitter-receiver for SOE, when he saw F8CV's

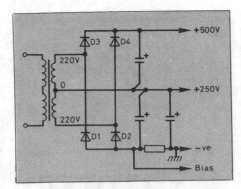

Fig 4. Dual voltage (plus negative bias) power supply as used by G3EUR in the 1942 B-2 transmitter-receiver still represents an economical arrangement.

dual-voltage (anode/screen) PSU for use with a typical medium-power valve transmitter or power amplifier (*TT*, July, Fig 8, p38). His Scottish instincts lead him to point out a cost saving can be made. He writes:

"The B-2 used a similar arrangement but with the negative of the bridge arrangement forming the negative HT connection as in **Fig 4.** I used selenium rectifier-stacks, big and heavy compared with modern silicon diodes, although nevertheless semiconductors. With this arrangement there is no need for the resistors across the capacitors since the centre-tap to the 250V line keeps the voltage across the capacitors to a maximum of 1.4 times 250V, though it may be advisable to retain two resistors to bleed the charge when the unit is switched off. In either case, the current in the 250V line is supplied by diodes D1, D2 in the bridge and the transformer rating is unchanged at the total wattage of the 250V and 500V loads. Note that 220-0-220V rms gives an off-load voltage of 600V DC."

The basic diode rectifying circuits of the July *TT*, Fig 9 were all familiar to G3EUR but he considers it worth adding a voltage-quadrupler arrangement which can provide a useful means of powering a QRP value transmitter from a low-voltage toroidal transformer: **Fig 5.** He included this arrangement in his article 'Using toroidal transformers' (*Mercury*, November 1985) to which reference was made in *TT*, March 1986. The

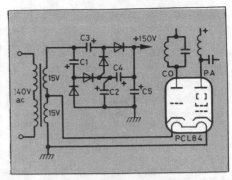

Fig 5. How a 15V + 15V toroid or laminated core transformer can be used to power a valve QRP (2-3W) transmitter. 15-20VA toroid transformer. D1-D4 1N4003. C1-C4 50µF (100V). C5 25µF (200V).

usefulness of this approach is underlined by the fact that the current 'economy' ranges of power transformers, both toroidal and stacked-lamination types, have twin identical-winding secondaries: eg 12V + 12V which can be used separately, in parallel or in series, for full-wave or bridge rectification, thus providing very flexible compo-nents. A 15V + 15V transformer in a quadrupler arrangement can provide 150V HT for a 2-3 watt transmitter from a 15/20V toroid. Basic voltage-multiplier circuits are shown in **Fig 6** and a triple output PSU is shown in **Fig 7.**

G3EUR adds: "Less obvious is the use of PSU circuits which give HT and LT from low-voltage. For example, using a TV-type valve, still cheap and plentiful, such as a PCL84 (triode-pentode with 15V heater) one winding of a 15V + 15V transformer can be used for the heater and the whole with a quadrupler to give 150V HT for the valve as a CO-PA as in Fig 5. Add a PCF80 (triode-pentode with 9V heater) as a simple receiver to the 15V heater of the PCL84, then use a 25V + 25V transformer and a tripler arrangement and you have power for a modest transceiver, using the triode of the PCL84 as an audio output valve on receive and as a crystal oscillator on transmit (a device used in the A MkIII of 1943). Even better, use DC for the heaters with an IC regulator such as the LM317 to provide stable DC for the receiver LT and so reduce the drift associated with valves. The possibilities are almost endless."

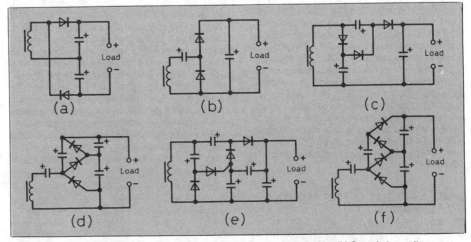

Fig 6. Basic voltage-multiplier PSU configurations. (a) Conventional voltage-doubler. (b) Cascade-type voltage doubler. (c) Voltage tripler. (d) Cascade-type voltage tripler. (e) Voltage quadrupler. (f) Cascade-type voltage-quadrupler (extendable to an n-times voltage multiplier). Note that voltage regulation between load and non-load conditions is very dependent on the value of the capacitors and that such circuits are more suitable for relatively low-current loads.

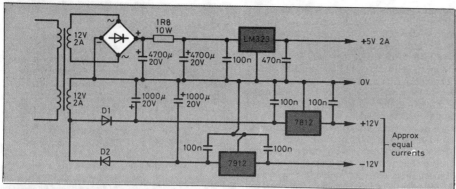

Fig 7. A triple-voltage, regulated supply using the twin-windings usually found in modern toroidal and laminated core transformers. With the back-to-back half-wave rectification of the two 12V outputs it is advisable to ensure that the loads are balanced to avoid a DC component in the gapless core of a toroid, if necessary by adding loading resistor(s). The top section uses a bridge and provides about 15V DC across the 4700µF capacitor. This is rather high for a 5V IC regulator and the heat dissipation can be reduced and smoothing improved by adding a low-value resistor as shown (1.8 ohms in this example) which drops about 3.6V at the full load of 2A with the second 4700µ capacitor giving extra smoothing. (G3EUR, *Mercury*, November 1985).

HF PACKET RE-THINK?

Without, this month, pursuing the CW/AMTOR debate, which arouses strong feelings on both sides, it seems worth drawing attention to an article by Paul Rinaldo, W4RI, the Editor of *QST*, 'The Great 1989 HF Packet Design Quest' (*QST*, May 1989) in which the 'dragons' of HF packet operation — multipath, intersymbol distortion, group delay, QRM, QRN, busty errors, contention and retries — are given an airing. W4RI believes that the time has come for amateurs as well as the increasing number of professional users to rethink the AX.25 protocol for HF operation, for which it is clearly far less satisfactory than AMTOR. He introduces his appeal for a quest to find a less vulnerable protocol as follows:

"Medieval mariners *knew* that the earth was flat. As they sailed near the edge of the earth, it was commonly accepted that 'beyond this place there be dragons.' Hams now *know* that amateur packet radio works well on VHF/UHF, but not too well on HF. Sure many of the HF bands are buzzing with packet activity... The problem is efficiency; ie, too many retries to get past the monsters. Because the AX.25 protocol includes an error-checking feature, packets with even itty-bitty errors are shunned by the receiving station. Then, the automatic repeat request (ARQ) feature of AX.25 takes over and keeps on retrying until a packet runs the ionospheric gauntlet of monsters completely unscratched... Why not just use AMTOR? Of course, it is a partial solution that's here today. There are even packet-to-AMTOR gateways. However AMTOR has its problems. AMTOR is based on the older Baudot charater set rather than the newer ASCII character set which is replete with upper and lower case, more symbols and computer control characters. At best, even when band conditions are perfect, AMTOR has a *maximum* efficiency of 50 per cent, as only three characters are sent at a time, then the sending station must get an acknowledgement (ACK) before proceeding with new characters. While the symbol rate is 100 bauds, the throughput is between 0 and 50 bauds depending on band conditions. When the concept on which AMTOR is based was first conceived some years ago, designers didn't have the luxury of today's microprocessors and other digital integrated circuits. Whether or not AMTOR is used as a point of departure for a new HF packet protocol, it nevertheless sets a standard for comparison."

If I were an AMTOR operator, which I am not, I would not be entirely convinced by W4RI's strictures on its efficiency. There is little doubt that in reasonable (and not so reasonable) conditions the throughput of anything between say 30 and 50 baud can shift a lot of words, at least in upper case letters! Even on VHF, AX.25 packet can involve a large number of retries which can bring its throughput tumbling down. Meanwhile I intend to keep plodding along with hand Morse!

BATTERY CHARGER CONTROLLERS

Recent items in *TT* have stressed that lead-acid and nicad rechargeable batteries can have their active lives shortened by subjecting them to frequent overcharging, sometimes when attempting to keep them fully charged by continuous trickle charging. The August *TT* included some suggestions on the use of timers designed to reduce greatly the charging rate after a fixed period of time. This approach is well suited to nicad batteries which have a fairly 'flat' voltage charge/discharge curve that makes it difficult to use a voltage-sensitive controller. However, for lead-acid batteries, where the voltage increases significantly as the battery approaches the fully-charged state, it is easier to use a voltage-sensitive controller which can be either an add-on unit or built into the charger.

Ron Wilson, G3DSV draws attention to a charger-controller of this type that was described by J P Bell, G4LSA and E J Barker in *Practical Wireless* (June 1985, pp20-21, 53). He writes: "I use a 12-volt vehicle battery for running my HF rig and have been following the notes in *TT* with some interest. You mention chargers taking batteries up to 13.8V. In practice, most of the chargers I have come across will take a battery up to 14.4V and indeed this is the voltage found on many cars, my Volvo for one. This voltage is a bit too close to the 15V maximum of some older rigs (although most newer rigs are now rated at 16V maximum). The policy of watching a voltmeter is sound but it is so easy to forget to adhere to, as I well know. I would like to draw readers' attention to the controller described by G4LSA. This cuts the charger almost out, in practice down to about 100mA, when the voltage reaches 13.5 to 13.8V (this can be adjusted and mine is set to 13.6V). The controller is simple and inexpensive to build, and can often be built within the charger enclosure."

The G4LSA controller was intended for use with lead-acid vehicle batteries (charging rate about 4-5A) used to power SSB transmitters with an output of up to about 100W requiring 13V DC at up to about 25A peak. When set to 13.5V it cuts out, reducing the charging current to a very low value, when the battery is roughly 85% fully charged and greatly reduces any tendency for the battery to 'gas'.

In the *PW* article, G4LSA pointed out that modern vehicle batteries of the 'low maintenance' type can be topped up with distilled water in the traditional manner. Plates now contain less antimony than before; this reduces the amount of gassing and the batteries require less topping up. With modern 'sealed for life' batteries, the plates have very little antimony or may replace this altogether, by the use of calcium. The sealed batteries cannot be topped up (without drilling into them) but since a small vent is provided to prevent the pressure

AIRCRAFT-ENHANCED PROPAGATION: A CONTRAIL HYPOTHESIS

Arising out of the item 'Aircraft-enhanced propagation debate' (*TT*, August 1989, pp36-37), Brian Measures, G0HKR puts forward an interesting hypothesis; he believes that an explanation of the mode discovered in the south of Australia may be found in the visible aircraft exhaust trails called condensation trails or 'contrails'. He writes:

"Water, a by-product of combustion, is ejected through the aircraft exhaust gases and tends to raise the relative humidity of the air whilst heat generated by the engines tends to lower the relative humidity by raising the temperature in the aircraft wake. The net result sometimes is a contrail.

"A contrail occurs when the air temperature is in the range -24°C at sea level to -45°C at 50,000 feet. It can also occur exceptionally when operating at full throttle. If the surrounding air is at, or near, saturation the contrail is long and persistent, whereas if the relative humidity is low the contrail is only a short plume behind the aircraft.

"In the tropical stratosphere, where the lowest temperatures are to be found, persistent contrails are formed by the aircraft exhaust gases. These gases contain sublimation nuclei so causing supersaturation with respect to ice with radio signals possibly bouncing off the resultant ice particles formed in the contrail.

"Therefore, it appears that the forward scatter propagation researches of VK2ZAB and VK3UM which found that the signals from VK1BG at Canberra (roughly mid-way between Sydney and Melbourne) 'lasted from just a few minutes to tens of minutes,' clearly point to the creation of contrails in low-level or high-level saturation conditions where contrails were either a short plume or of a long, persistant nature. It appears to me that the disciplines of meterology, flight and Amateur Radio need to come together in this debate and research."

Sydney/Canberra/Melbourne are roughly at latitudes that correspond in the northern hemisphere to the Mediterranean area (eg Spain/Morocco)

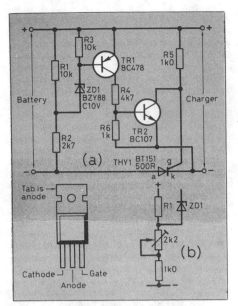

Fig 6. (a) G4LSA battery-charger controller (b) Modification for adjustable voltage replacing R2. (*Practical Wireless*)

building up if the battery is overcharged, frequent venting will make the battery unusable. Since most cars are now fitted with alternators rather than dynamos, the primary task of a car battery is to provide the initial heavy surge of current (hundreds of amps) and are not designed to be deeply discharged.

The G4LSA controller (**Fig 6**) is designed to charge the battery when this discharges to about 12V. Initially a partly charged battery should be connected since a fully discharged battery will not enable the controller to function. With a battery voltage of about 12V but less than 13.5V, ZD1 conducts and TR1 and TR2 are 'off'. The thyristor THY1, with its gate voltage derived through R5, will be 'on', effectively passing the charging current. When the voltage increases to about 13.5V (or as set), ZD1 conducts, turning both TR1 and TR2 'on', thus clamping the gate of THY1 to its cathode, switching the thyristor 'off'. Where a substantial load is being drawn from the battery, the effect will be to switch the charging current quite rapidly on and off.

THY1 requires heat sinking and this could be the metal lid of a small diecast aluminium box (114 x 54 x 30mm) with the thyristor mounted on the underside of the lid. With the specified device an insulating washer is not needed and the anode is bonded via the mounting tab to the box. Note

however that the DC output terminals of the charger must be independent of the mains earth, otherwise the controller may be bypassed.

A full-size overlay and PCB track pattern is given in the *PW* article together with notes on setting up and testing, but construction should not be critical and operation is quite straightforward. Perhaps the most important point to note is that if the battery is fully discharged ZD1 may not conduct and the battery will not be charging unless a switch or shorting jumper is added across THY1 (anode to cathode).

The July *TT* included a warning on the importance of using battery clamps that cannot result in the full voltage from a charger reaching the equipment. G3DSV points out that "available from caravan shops are snap on/snap off clamps suitable for batteries with round posts. Inside each clamp are two fixing screws, one for the charger and one for the rig. The clamps are rated at around 100A and make a very positive connection." Personally, I feel one would need to be fully convinced that the clamp could not under any circumstances become detached from the battery lug, since this would create just the situation that must be avoided. G3DSV also reminds us that a breakers yard can be a useful source of low-cost car batteries: "My son and I have purchased batteries for £8-£10. The main point is to look at the date on the battery. We have managed to purchase batteries less than a year old, from crashed cars."

Vincent Evans, G4AVT is another *TT* reader who uses a lead-acid car battery and charger for his 144MHz and HF transceivers. To avoid continual checking of voltages, he, like G3DSV, uses a voltage-sensitive controller but intead of a thyristor he uses an electro-magnetic relay: **Fig 7**. Full details of his 'Automatic Battery Charger' appeared in *Ham Radio Today* (September 1988, pp42-44). The action of his system is basically similar to that of the G4LSA unit in that the charger is left on continuously but is switched through to the battery only when the battery voltage is between about 11.5 and 13.5V after setting the cut-out adjustment RV1 with the aid of an accurate voltmeter. The relay must have heavy-current contacts, the specified unit being a 12V SPDT 320R, 10A at 240V contacts, PCB mounting, Maplin type YX97F. Full constructional details are given in the *Ham Radio Today* article. G4AVT adds: "The device is self-contained so that no alteration has to be made to the charger, and it is a reasonable DIY project. The charger is always on but current consumption is negligible. The more experienced amateur could very well build the device into a simple charger, and perhaps experiment by putting the relay contacts in the mains lead, although caution would be necessary since

HERE AND THERE

The August *TT* included a list of solvents used in the electronics industry that can cause health and environmental problems. As became clear several years ago (see, for example, *Electronics Week*, March 18, 1985 'Toxic chemicals jar industry') the semiconductor industry and the fabrication of printed circuit boards involve a large number of potentially harmful substances. Some experts have claimed: "no other industry on earth uses nastier chemicals than the semiconductor industry." The *Electronics Week* article noted that "the chemicals in question are those acids, gases and solvents used in every phase of semiconductor manufacture, from the silicon ingot to the finished chip. They are: (1) sulphuric and hydrochloric acids used in cleaning chips and hydrofluoric acids in etching them. They are all irritating to skin, eyes and the respiratory tract. Hydrofluoric acid also attacks bones. (2) Silane, arsine and phophine gases are used for doping and fluorinated hydrocarbons for plasma etching. Silane is pyrophoric, that, it can ignite spontaneously. And (3) organic solvents, which are used in vapour degreasing, pose one of the toughest problems because they can't be neutralised. They are blamed for cancer and birth defects as well as for systemic illnesses."

Clearly the risks are to those involved in manufacture or living in areas where effective waste disposal has not been employed, and not to users of semiconductor equipment. But it could be argued that it is the responsibility of us all to be aware of the potential hazards and to do what we can to see that the necessary steps are taken to prevent environmental pollution or the creation of fire or explosive hazards.

switching the transformer in the mains lead would cause a current surge, giving a momentary high output voltage and misleading the voltage-dependent switch. A resistor in the line to SW1 might provide an anti-surge device but this has not been tried.

Peter O'Keele, VK3YF, in *Amateur Radio (VK)*, April 1989, discusses the various types of lead-acid batteries now on the market, including various forms of 'Deep Cycle' batteries intended for non-vehicle use but imposing various charging constraints and often carrying only a six-months guarantee. He also notes that the sealed gel-type batteries sold for automobile use are intended strictly for engine-starting purposes and have a very limited stationary capacity. For conventional wet lead-acid batteries, he advises: (1) Keep the electrolyte up to the required level. (2) Check the specific gravity of the cells periodically using a hydrometer — cells should have a gravity of at least 1230 when the battery has been left overnight. (3) Charge at about 14.4V, 4A for nine plate batteries, 5A for eleven plate batteries, for about 12 hours. Four hours after gassing begins you can assume the battery is fully charged. The specific gravity will then depend on the condition of the battery.

Those who recall such books as the classic *Admiralty Handbook of Wireless Telegraphy* of the 1930s, with its stress on the care of batteries, may feel wryly that it all goes to show that technology often moves in circles. But then, it has long been evident that it is often easier to generate RF power than the necessary DC! □

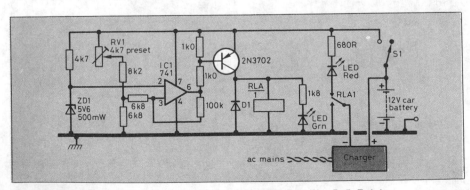

Fig 7. G4AVT's battery-charger controller using a relay rather than a thyristor. (*Ham Radio Today*)

TECHNICAL TOPICS

PAT HAWKER G3VA

ELEMENTS FATIGUED BY FLUTTERING

An article by Dick Weber, K5IU 'Vibration induced Yagi fatigue failures' *Ham Radio*, August 1989) reminded me of one of the most traumatic events of the years I spent with the IBA. About 5pm on the evening of March 19, 1969, the news broke that one of the two IBA 1265 ft masts (the tallest masts in the UK) had suddenly collapsed. This was the TV mast at Emley Moor, Yorkshire and its collapse, fortunately without causing injuries or deaths, threatened the entire project aimed at introducing 625-line UHF colour on the ITV network by November of that year. Fortunately the engineers were able to erect a temporary mast, brought from Sweden, and this enabled the colour service to begin on time; meanwhile the present Emley Moor concrete tower was built in quick time.

Naturally, there followed a lengthy inquest on why the cylindrical steel guyed mast, erected in 1966, should have collapsed on a cold but not particularly windy evening (wind speed at the time only about 19 mph). Some pundits claimed it was due to the effect of unequal ice loading on the guys, but the inquiry discounted this hypothesis and came to the conclusion that the mast had been excited into a resonant mode of violent oscillation by 'vortex shedding' induced by the moderate wind speed. It fell to my lot later to try to put together a layman's guide to vortex shedding when the IBA fought (and won) an action against the prime contractors, arguing that the effects of such vortex-shedding induced oscillation should have been foreseen by the designers. To prevent a repetition of this collapse in the remaining two masts of this type (1265 ft at Belmont, Lincolnshire and 1015 ft at Winter Hill, near Bolton) the IBA installed suspended counterweights inside the masts — over twenty years later both are still standing.

In his *Ham Radio* article, K5IU writes: "Yagi element failures can be attributed to two basic causes. The first type of failure occurs whan an element isn't strong enough to hold up when forces are applied. These forces may be caused by a thick layer of ice, high winds, or a combintion of the two. Under the stress of these forces the element either bends or breaks off, with signs of bending in the area of the break.

"The second type of failure takes place after an element has been fluttering, or vibrating, in a relatively low wind stream. The break caused by this kind of failure is quite different. There's no sign of bending in the area of the break; it's a jagged line through the element. Boom fluttering (although not as common as element fluttering) can also lead to this type of failure.

"Because there's no sign of bending you'll know that the stress levels in the material are relatively low, yet failure occurs. What causes the element to flutter in the wind? What causes the break although the stress levels are well below those required to bend the tube? And what methods will minimise this type of failure?"

In answering these questions at some length, K5IU stresses that an antenna element will have high-Q mechanical (as well as electrical) resonances that can be excited into large displacement oscillations by quite small exciting forces. Medium speed winds, at well under 35 mph, when they strike an elongated cylindrical object create vortices or swirls of air; if these are shed from the object in a regular, orderly manner related to a natural resonance of the object, they constitute an exciting force. A commonly cited example is the pronounced low-frequency hum that comes from overhead telephone wires when the wind blows at a specific speed.

Unfortunately, when aluminium is flexed at levels below its yield-stress, while no permanent bend results, the damage accumulates and if the flexing is repeated sufficiently often there will be a fatigue failure. In effect metal fatigue is the weakened condition induced in metal parts of machines, vehicles or structures by repeated stresses or loadings, ultimately resulting in fracture under a stress much weaker than that necessary to cause fracture in a single application (*Britannica Encyclopedia* definition). Metal fatigue was noted in the 19th century but only came to public (and engineering) attention in 1954 with the failure of the pressure cabins and consequent crashes of the early Comet airliners (the first jet airliner), although this problem in aircraft had been previously forecast with surprising accuracy by Neville Shute, engineer turned novelist, in his book *No Highway*.

What then can be done to minimise fatigue failures in antenna elements? The basic approach is to try and limit the amplitude of the stresses during fluttering by damping the Q of the mechanical resonances. K5IU notes that the following ideas have been suggested:

(1) Filling the inside of tubular elements with the type of foam intended for sealing and insulating cracks and holes in buildings.

(2) Modifying the shape of the element so that orderly vortices cannot be shed. A practical technique is to wrap a wire in a helix around the element; wire diameter about 0.09 times that of the element with the turns of he helix spaced about five times the diameter (K5IU recommends this method).

(3) By attempting to move the mechanical, resonances of the element out of the range of vortex shedding. Some amateurs have fitted damping ropes inside the elements (K5IU doubts the value of this). A small weight (eg 3oz) fastened to the tip of an element can alter its resonant frequency appreciably.

Many years ago, I reported in *TT* (and subsequently in many editions of *ART*) a technique used to overcome metal fatigue fluttering of Yagi and log-periodic HF arrays at Washington State Unversity originally published in *Electronic Design* (2 August, 1966) for use in locations where there are persistent winds and the risk of elements being flexed continuously over long periods.

As shown in **Fig 2,** flat rubber sheets, or sheets fashioned by splitting a length of rubber garden hose, can be used as energy absorbers (dampers). The mechanical (as well as the electrical) impedance of any rod-like element is high at its free end(s), regardless of the number of modes along the elements. This means that placing an energy-absorbent device at the ends can reduce the amplitude of the oscillations and minimise the chance of metal-fatigue breakage (although possibly slightly increasing the bending stresses in gale-force winds).

For the 1966 approach a short section of lightweight garden hose, split lengthwise every 90° is held in place on the end of the element by a hose clamp: **Fig 2.** A more efficient and durable protection can be made from a sheet of flat rubber

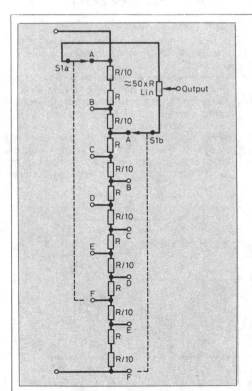

Fig 1. Lower-cost substitute arrrangement for a multi-turn potentiometer for varactor-diode tuning etc.

SUBSTITUTE FOR A MULTI-TURN POT

Some projects call for the use of multi-turn linear potentiometers; for example to 'bandspread' electronic tuning diodes. Such pots are neither cheap nor readily available; the cost is further increased where a counter-type dial has to be fitted.

In the 'Circuit & Design Ideas' feature of *Electronics Australia* (June 1989, p79), Jim Rowe points out that a low-cost but effective substitute can be devised using a double-pole rotary switch, a conventional linear pot and a handful of fixed resistors: **Fig 1.**

He writes: "The fixed resistor divider chain and the switch poles effectively 'step' the pot along, in increments roughly equivalent to a single turn of a multi-turn pot.

"Why the small additional resistors (R/10), as well as those marked with value R?. Without these, there would be small gaps in between the end of one adjustment segment and the beginning of the next. The R/10 resistors and staggered tapping points for SW1a and SW1b ensure that the segment ranges overlap slightly, to give contiguous adjustment over the full range.

"I developed this arrangement for an application where it was used to adjust the tuning voltage applied to varicaps. Here the divider values were 180 and 18 ohms, and the pot value was 10k. Although a six-stage divider is shown in Fig 1 to suit a readily available 2-pole six-position switch, further stages may be added if desired and a suitable switch is available."

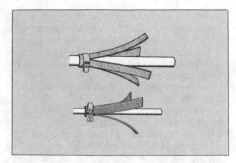

Fig 2. Energy absorbers fitted at the ends of antenna elements to reduce flutter-type oscillation due to vortex shedding.

or pliable plastic material ⅛in to ¼in thick by 5-6in long. If this is made just wide enough to wrap once round the element, the damping will be matched to the size of the element. This material is cut lengthwise to make four tabs. Ideally, such devices would be more effective if clamped at the very end of the elements, but in practice they are positioned so that the free end of the tabs are about 2in from the ends to prevent changes in the electrical length of impedance of the elements.

This system was used at a site exposed to the Pacific coastal breezes. Fitted to elements with diameters ranging from ⅜in to 1in, no breakages occurred over three years. Previously, breakages had been frequent. It occurs to me that if the energy-absorbers are made of plastics, it would be advisable to ensure that they are as UV-resistant as possible, or replaced occasionally.

For coping with the different problem of gale-force wind stresses, reference should be made to the two-part article 'Wind Loading' by David Reynolds, G3ZPF (*RadCom*, April/May 1988).

PUSH-PULL OSCILLATORS

There have been several matters arising from the notes in the June *TT* on the Kalli(ro)tron and other push-pull oscillators. Then it was mentioned that a 100W power-oscillator of this type was used in 1936 by Sir Evan Nepean, G5YN for the first amateur radio operation, as AC4YN, from Lhasa, Tibet. It was built by Lt Sidney Dagg a fellow officer in the then Royal Corps of Signals. By coincidence, I came across an obituary notice on Lt Col Sidney Dagg, who died in October 1988, in a recent *Journal of the Royal Signals Institution* and quoting from the Royal Signals book 'Through to 1970'. This notes that Sidney Dagg and G5YN provided communication and other scientific assistance to the Gould Political Mission from India to Lhasa. The object of this mission, in the days of the Raj, and with Lhasa then regarded as a Holy City, was to restore the balance of influence by outdoing the Russians in 'wireless, photography, public address equipment and fireworks'. Lt Dagg had charge of the fireworks and became a casualty when hit by one of his own maroons. However, 'valuable experience in the performance of static engines and accumulators at high altitudes and in extremes of temperature was gained. Lt Dagg designed and constructed the transmitter while Lt (later Lt Col Sir) Evan Nepean provided the receiver.' Sidney Dagg, MBE, later commanded a Brigade Signal Section with Wingate's Chindits in Burma. He became a Vice President of Lancashire Cricket Club in 1986.

Lyell Herdman, G6HD notes that a bibliography of early push-pull oscillators appeared in the book 'Phenomena in HF Systems' by August Hund (McGraw Hill, 1936). This book refers to push-pull oscillators as "a means of obtaining still higher frequencies" and credits their origination to W H Eccles and F W Jordan (*London Electrician*, Vol

Photo: Long before he became BBC National Governor for Scotland, a youthful Watson Peat (then BRS3740, later GM3AVA) as a Special Communications radio operator in Eindhoven in 1944 shortly before gaining his Royal Signals commission and departing for India where he operated as VU2WP. Equipment includes a Whaddon Mark III (6V6 - 807) transmitter, HRO receiver and a bug-key made by G6NM. (See 'Amateurs of Influence' page 39)

83, page 299, 1919). The Eccles-Jordan R-C oscillator is the modern multivibrator. I wonder if it was ever implemented by them as a resonant-circuit sine-wave oscillator. Dr W H Eccles, it should not be forgotten, was the 1923-24 President of the RSGB, having been a member of the original Wireless Society of London since 1913. He was for many years a professor at Imperial College and was always prominent in stressing

IC TUNING CONTROLLER FOR THE I1ARZ LOOP

The tuning system used by Roberto Craighero, I1ARZ for his 'Electrically tunable HF loop' (*RadCom*, February 1989, pp38-42) included a Bulgin receiver-type slow-motion tuning drive to provide the reduction gearing needed to achieve accurate remote-tuning of the high-Q transmitting loop. Recently, for a new portable loop, I1ARZ has devised an alternative IC electronic motor-controller with excellent results. He feels that such a controller is an improvement over mechanical gearing for such applications. He writes:

"The new method of powering the DC tuning motor is based on a high-power monolithic bridge-driver IC, type L293B made by SGS and allows the antenna to be accurately tuned without difficulty. The 16-pin DIL chip is not difficult to use and permits careful regulation of the motor speed and its direction of rotation.

"The L293B is a quad push-pull driver capable of delivering an output of 1A per channel; each channel is controlled by TTL-compatible logic input and each pair of drivers (a full bridge) has an inhibit input which turns off all four transistors of the IC.

"My circuit arrangement is shown in **Fig 3**. Only a half-bridge is used for controlling the tuning motor and the chip could control two DC motors simultaneously. Fig 3 includes the oscillator and modulator and allows independent regulation of the DC motor, the channel inputs being used to

control the sense of rotation. The inputs are simply commanded by two button-switches; however it would appear possible to construct an automatic tuning system by connecting the inputs to a suitable form of standing wave bridge, akin to autumatic ATUs although I have not tested such a possibility.

"An interesting feature of this simple circuit is that it takes advantage of the threshold of the enable/inhibit input to economise on a comparator. The TBA820M audio amplifier IC generates triangular waves, the DC level of which is varied from 0 to 5V by means of RV1. Since the switching

threshold of the enable/inhibit inputs of the L293B is roughly 2V, the duty cycle of the output current (and hence the motor speed) is controlled by RV1. The switching frequency is set by R1/C1 and the amplitude of the oscillator signal is set by the divider R2/R3. I recommend the use of a DC motor having a built-in reduction gear providing a shaft revolution speed not faster than 5—6 turns per minute and capable of operating at a minimum voltage of 0.75V. Then the controller as described makes it possible to obtain a shaft rotation of about 0.5rpm as set by RV1. Maximum current 1A."

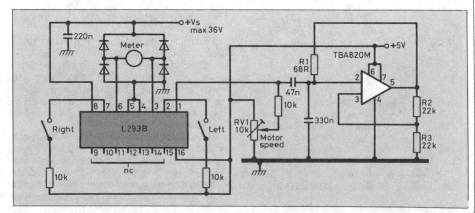

Fig 3. I1ARZ's electronic tuning controller used as an improved alternative to mechanical reduction gearing on his transmitting loop antenna.

the importance of the experimental amateur, taking an active part in urging the resumption of amateur licensing in 1919 and giving evidence on behalf of the RSGB when a Bill was introduced into Parliament in 1925 which threatened to restrict amateur radio activities severely.

The book by August Hund provides two references in French publications to the Mesny VHF push-pull oscillator mentioned, with circuit diagram, in the June *TT: Compt rend.* 177, 1106, 1923 and *L'Onde elec* 3, 25-37, 99-110, 1924.

G6HD, although he cannot recall where he first heard of the Mesny oscillator, actually used one when he built a low-power VHF television transmitter to provide a laboratory signal source for the Pye Television Laboratory at Cambridge shortly before the opening in November 1936 of the BBC 405-line television service. This was to assist in the development of TV receivers at Cambridge, then believed to be beyond the range of the forthcoming Alexandra Palace transmitter on 45MHz. The transmitter comprised a Mesny oscillator (using two Mazda AC/P valves) driving a push-pull pair of audio pentodes (Mazda AC/P or Mullard Pen 4VA) in Class B, with grid modulation from a flying-spot scanner developed by his colleagues. 'Spenny' (G6NA) was one of the engineers who developed the vision channel. A similar 'transmitter' was built for the 41.5MHz sound channel.

The Mesny oscillator's anode resonant circuit was formed from a piece of copper tube with the grid 'coil' (wire) fed through it, coaxial fashion, insulated by ceramic beads. When Ally Pally fired up, it was found that in practice weak signals could be received in Cambridge, aided by a receiving TW array designed by G6HD.

DON'T KNOCK THE SYNTHESIZER

I must confess that on a number of occasions *TT* has pointed out that low-cost frequency synthesizers tend to suffer from significantly more phase noise than good free-running VFOs, resulting in reciprocal mixing and poor close-in dynamic range on receive and local noise radiation on transmit, broadening the channel. It seems only fair to give the case for the defence as put by David Reynolds, G3ZPF. He writes:

"Synthesized rigs have been getting a lot of stick over the past couple of years. Whilst I agree entirely that there are a number of shortcomings when compared with a *well-designed* valve rig, the usual comments tend to give the impression that *all* valve rigs of yesteryear *were* well-designed. In practice that was far from being the case.

"Despite the suggestion that amateur radio is losing its appeal with numbers/activity falling, here in the West Midlands at least, it is unusual not to have one in your locality. I now have G0IRN directly across the road.

"Quite by accident, I discovered that even when he is beaming his signals right at me in order to work Japan on 21MHz, I can genuinely get within 50kHz of him, using a vertical, before I even know he is there. On a quiet band, even allowing about 20dB cross-polarization loss, this says as much for the output cleanliness of his TX140 as it does for the performance of the receiver in my TS930.

"With reasonably strong incoming signals I reckon I could operate within 15kHz of his frequency without too much trouble. There is no way I could have operated my old non-synthesized valve gear on the same band as such a near-neighbour. At my former QTH, I could always tell when my (then) nearest local, about a mile or so

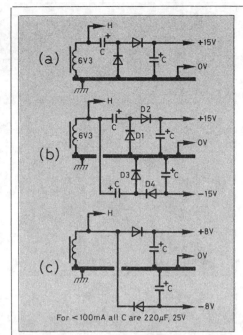

Fig 4. Using 6.3V heater lines to provide low-voltage DC to solidstate circuitry. (a) and (b) are common-terminal (cascade--type) voltage doublers.

MORE ABOUT VOLTAGE DOUBLING

John Brown, G3EUR, adds to his notes on the use of voltage doubling circuits to provide economical PSU arrangements (*TT* October) by drawing attention to some ways in which experimenters adding solid-state sections to existing valve rigs can make use of the 6.3V heater line. As shown in **Fig 4** it is quite simple to obtain an output of 12V DC (which could then be used with a three-terminal IC regulator to provide say 5V), plus or minus according to diode polarity, or even both simultaneously, ie +12V/0/-12V. These arrangements thus save having to add another mains transformer and most equipment heater windings can readily spare an extra 100mA or so. In the arrangements shown in Fig 4, (a) and (b) use cascade-type (common-terminal) voltage doublers; (c) is not a voltage doubler but note that all three of these circuits have 50Hz ripple on the DC output and may need further filtering, which would be provided by an IC regulator.

It is perhaps worth adding some further basic information to that provided in the October *TT* underlining the difference between the conventional (symmetrical) and the common-terminal (cascade) voltage doubler: **Fig 5** (a) and (b) respectively.

In (a) the diodes must be able to withstand twice the peak applied voltage in the reverse direction (ie 2 × 1.4Eac). The capacitors need a working voltage at least the peak applied voltage (1.4Eac). The ripple frequency is twice that of the applied AC (ie 100Hz on 50Hz supplies).

In (b) the ripple frequency is that of the applied AC (ie 50Hz). The rating of C1 must be equal to the peak applied voltage (1.4Eac) and rated to carry

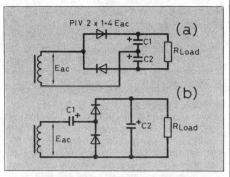

Fig 5. (a) Conventional (symmetrical) voltage doubler. (b) Common-terminal (cascade-type) voltage doubler. See text for main differences in component ratings.

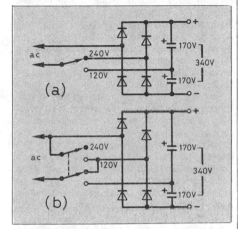

Fig 6. Use of switched bridge/voltage-doubler rectifiers to give 240/120V inputs with similar voltage output as described in Motorola AN837 of 1974. (b) improved version which parallels diodes not used on 240V in (a).

the RMS load current. The rating of C2 should be twice the peak applied voltage (2 × 1.4Eac).

Output regulation of both (a) and (b) is poor, but that of (a) is better than that of (b).

G3EUR was interested to see the dual-voltage (bridge/voltage doubler) circuit devised by G3YNN to up the voltage output of his PSU. (*TT*, August, p34). He comments: "Like many of these circuits, their origins date back a long way but are then rediscovered. **Fig 6** from a Motorola Application Note AN-737 of 1974 shows what was then a novel variation of the circuit. The same principles used by G3YNN work equally well for getting the *same* DC output from either 120 or 240V AC (or 12/24V AC) with Fig 6 (b) showing the improvement of switching the diodes (unused in G3YNN's arrangement) so that they are paralleled on the lower input voltage to share the higher currents. It should be noted that a voltage doubler has poorer regulation than a bridge, and the use of large capacitors means high peak forward currents in the diodes. But full marks to G3YNN for his use of logic in arriving at a solution to his problem; this is what Amateur Radio is all about, and part of the fun."

away, was on the same band...the AGC of my valve gear used to 'pump' if I got within 500kHz of his frequency.

"When I first had my TS930, for the first few nights I found myself constantly checking 7MHz

and discovered there really are gaps between the broadcast signals. Even with the subtle use of RF attenuators none of my valve rigs were ever this good. Now my complaint is that the noise of the twin fans in the TS930 sometimes drives me crackers. It's not that they are particularly loud, but then neither is a mosquito and they can be thoroughly annoying!

"So don't be too hard on solidstate synthesizers. Carefully designed they can be very good although this is perhaps true of all rigs. PS, I have no connection with Trio/Kenwood in spite of using only their equipment."

DX ANTENNAS FOR 3.5MHz

Earlier this year, Martin MacGregor, G4EZG gave a talk to a local club on the options and considerations surrounding the design of DX antennas for the lower HF bands (eg 3.5MHz) for sites of different sizes and terrains (sloping, low-lying, high-plateau etc). In this he was at pains to emphasise the concept of antenna directivity and radiation versus height and ground effects.

He has sent along some of his notes and relevant diagrams; unfortunately it is not possible to include in *TT* more than a very brief digest of some of his material but even so this should help clear the minds of those who wonder why their antennas work well on the higher HF bands and for medium-distance contacts on all bands, but leave much to be desired when striving to work DX on 3.5MHz or 1.8HMz.

He notes that it is well understood that, at least theoretically, horizontal dipoles at heights of 0.25λ or less have little or no horizontal directivity (ie are virtually omni-directional) and very little radiation at the lower vertical angles (say 10-30°) desirable for DX working under normal propagation conditions: **Fig 7**. At 3.5MHz, 0.25λ is roughly 66ft so that the basic horizontal dipole is of limited value to the majority of amateurs who cannot aspire to antenna supports higher than about 60ft. As previously noted in *TT* the effective height of an antenna is usually several feet more than its actual height above ground; this is particularly true at the lower frequencies where the ground behaves rather as a lossy conductor, changing to a dielectric at higher frequencies. Additionally, a 'real' (imperfect) earth has the effect of filling in the nulls between the theoretical vertical and horizontal radiation lobes.

As confirmed by experiments by DJ2NN some years ago an optimum cost-effective height for 14-28MHz arrays is about 18.5m and 60ft has become a median height for amateur HF towers. This height can be shown to be suitable for DX operation on all bands down to and including 7MHz although theoretically unsuitable for 3.5MHz DX *(unless used to support an inverted-vee dipole with its vertically-polarized component — G3VA).* Empirically this is not the case: dipoles and their variants at 60ft do show DX capabilities under those propagation conditions that favour high-angle openings. Even so, comparatively small height increases above 60ft can dramatically improve their DX performance.

Directivity (effective gain) of an antenna has an important if secondary effect on the vertical radiation pattern of an antenna, and this has a particularly important, if secondary, effect at low antenna heights in reducing the strength of unwanted incoming high-angle signals. In general, a Yagi or other array concentrates the vertical radiation lobe to much the same extent as its horizontal (HRP) directivity.

While a 3.5MHz array at 60ft, or possibly a little less, can give acceptable results it cannot challenge the superiority of an efficiently installed and well-sited vertically-polarized array in an area of reasonably good ground conductivity. *(Hence the*

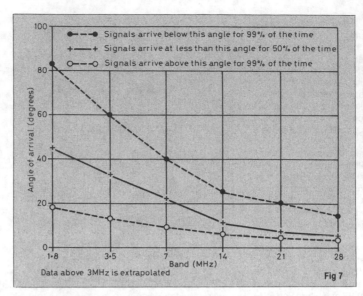

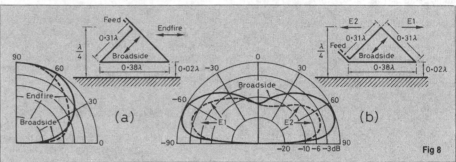

popularity of inverted-vees, slopers and top-loaded tower antennas — G3VA).

G4EZG adds: "Large 3.5MHz arrays apart, in my experience the best DX antenna of moderate dimensions for use with a 60ft tower, is the apex-up, bottom-corner-fed Delta loop: **Fig 8** (b). The best *local* antenna is the same but apex-up, apex-fed: **Fig 8** (a). My antenna was constructed from 2.5mm², PVC, stranded wire, fed with an 0.5λ (electrical length) of RG62A/U (93-ohm) coaxial cable. this gave a good match to the loop feed-impedance of roughly 100 ohms, and most rigs will happily load this arrangement. It obviates the need for a 0.25λ (72-ohm) matching section and the use of a 52-ohm cable. The absence of a matching section and the use of large-diameter wire resulted in a very broad-band system.

"By placing pulleys at each of the three corners I could physically move the feed point around one side of the loop to change the vertical radiation angle to suit conditions for DX and local operation. The difference such adjustments made had to be heard to be believed! It would have been interesting to motorize this operation to see what could be achieved with remote fine-tuning of the feed-point position."

For those who cannot aspire to a 60ft antenna-support, the system could be scaled down for 7 or 10MHz and 30ft height.

AMATEURS OF INFLUENCE

In the September *TT,* in commenting on Jim Rowe's 'neck sticking out' and rather depressing review of current trends in our hobby — 'Whatever happened to Amateur Radio?' I stressed that if those in positions of media or political influence were ever to become convinced that experimental

amateur radio is dead or dying, then the future outlook would be bleak indeed. The ideal situation is where the persons of influence are themselves in their spare time (if any) enthusiastic radio amateurs.

One who has for the past five years ideally fulfilled this situation has been Scottish farmer, Watson Peat, CBE, GM3AVA who has just retired as National Governor for Scotland of the BBC. It must have been unique for a member of the BBC Board of Governors to be an active radio amateur, Chairman of the Ariel Radio Group (the BBC's amateur radio club), making his interest in the hobby clear to the Board and to the staff, and including it in his *Who's Who* entry.

His knowledge of, interest in and concern with the engineering side of broadcasting — something not often found within the inner councils — has won him much respect and at the dinner held to mark his retirement I found genuine regret among senior BBC engineers that Watson (known to his wartime colleagues in Special Communications as 'Bill') has completed his five year term as National Governor. For us, as compensation, he is likely to be active for part of each year from a good site in Barbados.

250V DC/AC INVERTER

Several references have been made in *TT* to the series of general-purpose DC/AC inverters designed to provide 240V pseudo AC sine-wave output as published in recent years in *Electronics Australia.* Circuit details and waveforms of a low-power 15-watt 12-to-240V unit originally intended for powering portable CD players appeared in *TT,* December 1987, p915. For amateur applications, including their use instead of petrol-electric

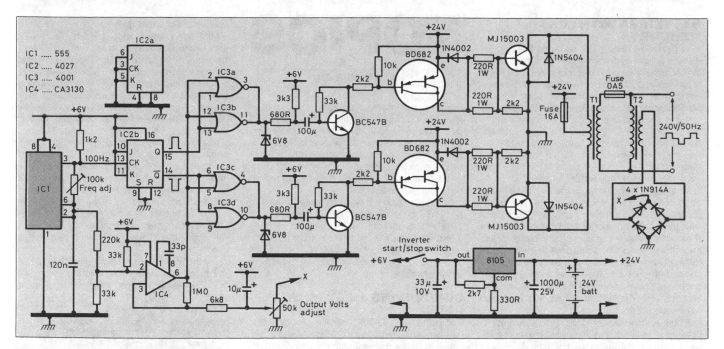

Fig 9. 250VA 24/240 DC/AC inverter (*Electronics Australia*).

generators for powering 240V mains-type equipment in the field or at locations where there is no mains supply, or as a stand-by power source in areas where the mains supplies are subject to frequent interruption, higher power inverters are needed.

The circuit diagram of an inverter providing a stepped waveform output with a power rating of 250VA appeared in *EA* (October 1988, p91) In a note from B Mortensen of Lae, Papua New Guinea where apparently there are frequent electricity blackouts.

His circuit, **Fig 9,** uses ideas from earlier *EA* inverters and functions as follows:

"The oscillator (555) and 4027 flipflop provide the 50Hz complementary square-wave which is fed via the 4001 to the BC547B devices through 100µF electrolytic capacitors. These serve to keep the 6V DC and 24V DC parts of the unit separate.

"The BC547B devices drive the BD682 Darlingtons which in turn drive the MJ15003 output transistors. Voltage regulation is achieved by the CA3130 comparing a proportion of the output voltage with the 6V regulated supply and inhibiting part of the drive circuit's waveform by turning low the output from the 4001 when required (ie a form of pulse width modulation).

"Transformer T1 is an 18-0-18/240V toroid transformer (300VA). T2 is a PCB-mount 240/2V transformer.

"I have had the inverter along with its mains-failure start-up (relay) circuit and voltage-sensing battery-charger in service for several months without any problems occurring. The transfomer and the MJ15003 devices were the only costly items, but the unit still proved to be a cheap and reliable 250-watt inverter."

FEEDBACK, FOLLOW-UPS & POT-POURRI

Geoff Perkins, G3VIJ, and John Brown, G3EUR, have drawn attention to a small but potentially misleading error that crept into the circuit diagram of ZS6BVO's soft-start system (Fig 6, *TT*, September, p41). As shown the 'push to soft start' switch appears to be a two-pole push-to-make switch As explained correctly in the text, this switch must be a 'biased double-pole make-and-break' switch, ie on push the mains supply is connected via the 50-ohm resistor while the contact across the resistor is moved to the 'open' position, and since the switch is 'biased' this means that it stays pushed until manually pulled out. When this happens the contact across the resistor closes while the other contact (now short-circuited by the three RLY1 relay contacts) *opens*. G3EUR has some other reservations. My apologlies to readers and to ZS6BVO whose original diagram made this clearer than Fig 6.

Gordon McDonald, VK2ZAB has re-entered the debate on Aircraft-Enhanced propagation with a trenchant article 'Signals reflected via aircraft' (*Amateur Radio*, May 1989 pp 10-11). This makes a strong attack on the artificial temperature inversion theory concluding: "VK1BG's theory has some parts which sound good but as every radioman worthy of the name knows you can't have two signal paths without interference and as there is no evidence of this the theory breaks down, ie it's wrong". VK2ZAB still puts his money on bistatic-radar-type scattering from the surface of the aircraft although he admits "there is still a lot to learn about contacts via aircraft reflections. For example, how can we estimate an aircraft's effective (bistatic) reflecting area which seems to be greater than we first thought." Then he puts an Australian four-X boot-in: "Amateur radio lore already has its fair share of myths, furphys, half-truths and plain nonsense without adding more." But surely scattering from a moving surface would show interference patterns (deep fading) as much as from both surface and inversion scattering? I still feel the debate could be settled by checking the Doppler shifts.

Mark Meyer, WA0NSY (*QST*, August 1989, p38) points out that ferrite cores from TV flyback transformers can serve well as core material for filament chokes (1.8 to 30MHz). He found that a rectangular core (inside dimensions about 1¾ by 1½ in) could handle 10V at 10A (for two 813 valves) without saturating. He made his choke as follows: "After removing the transfomer windings, I wound several layers of electrical tape on the core to protect the choke winding from the core's sharp edges. Next, I wound 34 bifilar turns of No 12 enamelled wire — as many as would fit — on the core (I obtained the wire from an electric-motor repair shop)." The choke's AC (60Hz) voltage drop measured as 0.2V at 10A and WA0NSY rewound his power transformer to deliver 10.2V under load.

By chance I came across in Vol 8 of the massive report of the CCIR Plenary Assembly of 1986 in Report 906 ('Frequency usage in the amateur service') a succinct review of why morse telegraphy (A1A) remains popular: "1.1.1. Morse telegraphy owes its popularity to the relative simplicity of equipment; its effectiveness under conditions of low power, weak signals or high noise; its inherent capability to bridge the language barrier between operators who do not speak the same language; and its narrow-bandwidth characteristics, which permit a very high density of stations in a heavily occupied band."

CLAPP OSCILLATOR

John Roscoe, G4QK, apropos my September note on the sad story of the Gouriet (Clapp) oscillator, writes: "I seem to recall seeing a circuit for a Gouriet oscillator in Sanderman's *Radio Engineering*. It used an AC/SP3 oscillator valve (very high slope for those days) followed by another as buffer, with a diode providing AOC feedback to the first valve. Point is, I thought this was used in the BBC HF transmitters immediately *before* the war, which would date its development about 1936. Its stability was certainly comparable with the crystal oscillators of the period." The article in Proc IRE by J K Clapp was in 1950 and it seems a pity that it had to be rediscoverd more than a dozen years after its first use and years after its publication in *Radio Engineering*.

In a fine tribute to the late Jim Kirk, G6ZO (also XAZO/CE3ZO/ON5Z0/F0AJB/G6ZO/HB) in *Amateur Radio*, Norm Hull concludes: "If Heaven were to appear on the DXCC list, Jim would have one of the first calls to be issued there." The DX bands seem to lack something without his polished and always courteous operating. □

BATTERIES WITH LESS MERCURY

In *TT*, March 1985, p192 an item 'Mercury is dangerous' drew attention to the fears in Japan of the possibility of mercuric poisoning resulting from the disposal of the many millions of alkaline-manganese batteries each year containing a significant amount of mercury: "Japan now manufactures some 3000-million dry batteries a year, the majority finishing up on municipal rubbish dumps and later used as landfill...some part of this mercury becomes converted into organic mercury by the action of bacteria and leached away (for example into water supplies)."

As a result I received a reassuring letter from Peter Poole, G3ENV, electrical adviser in the DTI's consumer safety unit (see *TT*, June 1985, p450). This included a number of safety hints including the need to keep the small mercury 'button cells' away from infants who could swallow them in the belief they were sweets, but took issue with the suggestion that alkaline-managanese batteries contained a potentially harmful amount of mercury. He considered the amount of mercury so small as to be insignificant.

Who was I to argue with the DTI's safety unit? It seemed possible that in Japan (where there had been serious outbreaks of the fatal Minimata disease in 1956 and 1964 caused by factory effluent getting into the food chain) they had become over-sensitive on this issue.

But — surprise, surprise — an item in *New Scientist* (7 October, 1989) states: "Duracell is reducing the amount of mercury in its new alkaline batteries to 0.02% by weight. Two years ago the amount was 5% *(that's what it says, though I suspect a decimal point or two may have gone missing — G3VA)*. Duracell says it plans to remove all mercury from its batteries... Manufacturers of zinc-carbon Leclanché cells have succeeded in removing mercury from their cells. Until the world became conscious of the risk of mercury pollution, battery manufacturers used a large dose of mercury to prevent 'gassing' — the formation of bubbles of hydrogen gas on the metal electrode."

The report makes it clear that it was a warning by the Swiss government that burning discarded cells with household rubbish releases mercury into the air that has led to the current efforts to reduce the amount of mercury. Why we should take note of Swiss fears but dismiss those from Japan seems puzzling.

CONCERNING 13.8V POWER UNITS

Bert Humphreys, GI3EVU wades in to add a few pertinent comments to the recent debate about power supplies for solid-state transceivers. In particular he draws attention to the article by E J Hatch, G3ISD '13.8V power units — an amateur's approach' (*RadCom*, July 1983, pp590-595) which he feels ought to be required reading for anyone contemplating the construction of a mains-operated PSU. G3ISD stressed that while it might seem he was making rather a song and dance about a fairly straightforward piece of equipment, his article should show that there is more to a PSU than meets the eye, and should assist readers in making use of whatever is available.

GI3EVU however adds a rider: "From bitter experience, however, I disagree with G3ISD about the amount of gain which is desirable in the voltage-control loop. Having had several 723 regulators die on me, although ostensibly working well within the outline ratings available to me at the time I constructed the PSU, I later obtained detailed data-sheets which disclosed that the devices were being asked to provide too much output power! This stemmed from a misconception about the Hfe of the single 2N3055 transistor which drives the paralleled output pass translators. When working near the maximum current of 20A or thereabouts from the PSU, the current gain of these devices falls far below the optimistic figure which the outline data might lead one to expect (*this point has been noted before in* TT-*G3VA*); so the poor old 723 was literally working itself to death.

"At the time these problems were arising, I had the opportunity of dissecting several commercially-built PSUs which had been designed for continuous

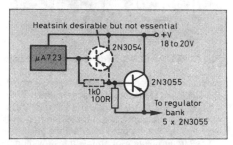

Fig 1. Adding a 2N3054 transistor in the darlington configuration to reduce the need for a 723 regulator to provide a high-current output that can shorten its life.

AN EARLY TRANSMITTING LOOP

Gerald Stancey, G3MCK was not taken by the idea of Richard Silberstein, W0YBF of putting a secret antenna under the floorboards (*RadCom*, September 1989) and my own concern at the idea was that no mention was made of the possible radiation hazard to anyone in the room immediately above (or below) the antenna. On the other hand the compact transmitting loop of high-conductivity copper tubing, out-of-doors if QRO, is establishing itself as an effective antenna for those with restricted sites.

G3MCK continues to find much of interest in the back copies of amateur journals, often unearthing items which attracted little attention when originally published. In this process he has come across an article 'Ham-band transmitting loops' by Richard Hay, W4LW (*QST*, September 1952, pp14, 118) that pre-dates by 15 years the US Army Loop of 1967 to which most recent loop ideas can be traced back. G3MCK writes: "This loop antenna appears to have the dimensions of a modern 'magnetic loop' but is not fed like one nor used in the vertical plane. However it seems certain to radiate better than something under the floorboards! At the worst it supports the theory that anything fed with RF will radiate!"

W4LW's horizontal square loop suitable for balcony mounting had 3ft sides and was connected directly in series with a conventional tank circuit (**Fig 3**). He reported that it gave him 7MHz CW contacts up to 2500 miles when fed with 40Watts

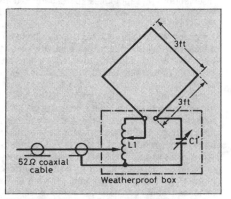

Fig 3. The 1952 horizontal-plane 'transmitting loop' of W4LW was simply connected in series with a conventionally tuned circuit. For a loop with 3ft sides at 7MHz, L1 had an inductance of 2.5μH and C1 a maximum capacitance of about 150pF (high-voltage spacing).

of RF, with 'reliable' contacts up to 1000 miles. He wrote: "The possibilities of this system have not been explored fully. However, two facts have been established: it works, and it is a wonderful subject for conversation during QSOs!"

W4LW's loop used No 12 wire for both the loop and for L1 but he pointed out "an improvement could probably be effected by the use of heavier wire or even copper tubing." In 1952, SWR meters were still uncommon and he described an adjustment technique that did not depend on their use. He wrote: Adjustment is as follows: (a) Substitute a 52-ohm dummy load for the antenna system and adjust transmitter for proper loading. (b) Remove dummy load and replace the loop antenna assembly. (c) Set the tap for the coax connection at about 3 turns and tune C1 to resonance at the transmitter frequency. (If necessary, reduce inductance of L1 by shorting turns with the second tap.). (d) Vary the position of the coax tap (retuning C1 each time) until proper loading is indicated. The position of the coax tap is a fairly critical adjustment and must be set to the nearest ¼-turn for best results. An SWR indicator would be very helpful, although it *can* be done by 'cut and try'... It would be desirable to make the loop as large as possible, with corresponding reduction in L1. The ultimate would be to reduce L1 to just enough inductance to match the coax line impedance; the larger the loop, the greater the (desirable) radiation resistance and the wider the band of frequencies that can be covered without re-adjusting." The square loop with 2-ft sides had a bandwidth on 7MHz of about 20kHz. W4LW reported "An unexpected by-product of this system is freedom from TVI and, on reception, marked reduction in local QRN with interference from the line output oscillator of a neighbour's TV set disappearing entirely."

The inclusion of the loop within the lumped inductance tuned circuit must inevitably increase the resistive losses compared with the present use of a small inductively coupled matching loop. However, there are circumstances in which W4LW's horizontal loop might be a useful, if makeshift, arrangement.

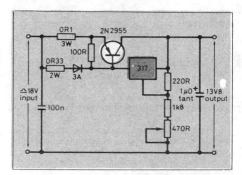

Fig 2. GI3EVU's 'beefier' constant-voltage charger arrangement for car batteries. Provided the charger is set to 13.8V it can be left permanently charging the battery.

high-current service, and found that none of them required more than a whiff of current from the 723. So I connected a 2N3054 in darlington configuration between the 723 and the 2N3055 (see **Fig 1**) whereupon my problems disappeared.

"Subject to the reservation mentioned about loop gain, it must be hard to better the control circuits of the 'Marchwood' 30A PSU originally described by G4JET in *Practical Wireless* June-July 1983, with the circuit diagram reproduced in *TT*, May 1984, p402. However, when built on the PCB obtainable from *PW* I have found it susceptible to RF pick-up. Although this was curable by the addition of bypass capacitors attached to strategic points on the board, they made a mess of the otherwise-attractive layout. A redesign, bearing in mind the amount of RF likely to be present in the average shack, would be welcome (*PW* to note?).

With further reference to the excellent advice given by G3ISD in 1983, I should like to suggest that prospective constructors give more thought to the ratings of the transformer they propose to use. If the component is adequately rated in terms of current (as it should be) an on-load secondary RMS voltage of 16 is quite adequate; anything appreciably higher merely aggravates the problem of heat dissipation. In practice, if the heatsinks become uncomfortably warm to the touch in normal CW operation, it's an odds-on bet that the secondary voltage is excessive!

"Finally, I share the reservation of GM0IJF (*TT*, August 1989, p35) about the use of car batteries. If used with a constant-voltage charger giving a charge of about 1A or thereabouts, the key-down voltage drops unacceptably after a few short overs. A beefier constant-voltage charger, capable

of delivering 5 or 6A at 13.8V is quite simple to construct (see **Fig 2**) and will keep the voltage to the transmitter at a reasonable value. Since the current from the charger drops virtually to zero when the battery reaches full charge, it can remain permanently in circuit without detriment to itself, the battery, or the transmitter."

50 WATTS RF FROM LOW-COST FET AT 7MHz

To judge from the trend in broadcast transmitters, the use of FET rather than bipolar devices is becoming firmly established, at least up to 250MHz. MOSFET devices are available delivering up to 200 watts RF at VHF, free from such problems as secondary breakdown. But such state-of-the-art devices are far too costly for their use in experimental amateur rigs where there is always the danger of destroying several devices during development. An alternative, for low power, noted in *TT* July 1989, p39, is to use low-cost switching-type FETs which can deliver say. 12.5 watts per device up to 30MHz.

David Bowman, G8PDW has sought out a different low-cost approach that has enabled him to obtain more than 50Watts output at 7MHz from a n-channel FET device costing under £5. He describes his bench work (his Class B licence means that his HF load is a power meter rather than an antenna) as follows:

"I was first made aware of the potential of using audio-frequency MOSFETs for RF power amplification when a friend attempted to build an audio amplifier. His neighbours discovered that while the amplifier provided the appropriate number of watts at AF, it was also generating a significant output across the higher end of the medium-wave broadcast band. Investigation revealed RF signals up to 4MHz.

"So started a search for a high-power FET device with fast turn-on/off times. I began with the devices used in my friend's oscillating AF amplifier: these were Hitachi 2SK135 enhancement-mode n-channel power FETs. These TO-3 transistors have 100-watts dissipation; although designed for audio, they gave good results as RF amplifiers — but only to 10MHz.

"Finally, I choose to investigate the 2SK413, also from Hitachi. This device appeared to be designed for, among other things, ultrasonic power amplifiers. This sounded promising. In addition they were not fitted with gate-protection diodes which had caused problems with the

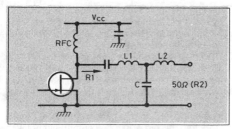

Fig 4. Narrow-band LCL 'T' output network adopted by G8PDW using values calculated from the design procedure set out in ARRL's *Solid-state Design for the Radio Amateur*.

2SK135."

G8PDW set himself the task of designing an RF power amplifier capable of reasonable power out (say 50 watts per device, roughly comparable to the old 807 valve), initially on 7MHz then at higher frequencies. Characteristics and maximum limits for the 2SK413 are: drain — source voltage Vds 140V; Gate — source voltage Vgs ±20V; channel dissipation Pch 100W; rise time 15 nanoseconds; fall time 50nsec.

G8PDW felt that the switching times were fast enough for his purpose but noted that the T03P package would require insulating if a grounded-source circuit was chosen. An input capacitance at 1MHz of 800pF showed that care would be needed in the network design.

G8PDW decided to use a narrow-band output circuit with an LCL 'T' network having a working Q of 12. Using the procedure given in the ARRL's *Solid-state Design for the Radio Amateur*, he obtained the values for the network of **Fig 4**, for 7.1MHz, 50Watt power and 36V supply line, as: L1 33.6μH, L2 6.63μH and C 222 pF (G8PDW provided in his letter a fully worked example but this has to be omitted in the limited space available for *TT*). The inductors were wound on iron-dust toroids type T-130-6 since the number of turns required can be found from the formula $L(nH) = n^2K$ where n is the number of turns required and K is a constant for the core. A variable capacitor is used to tune to resonance.

G8PDW continues: "Finding a suitable input network proved a real headache. Several types of narrow-band networks were tried without success. Disappointedly, I turned to W1FB's article in *QST* (April 1989, pp30-33). He used broadband transformers loading into part of the bias circuit. The explanation for this approach was that the input impedance of the IRF511 was extremely high and

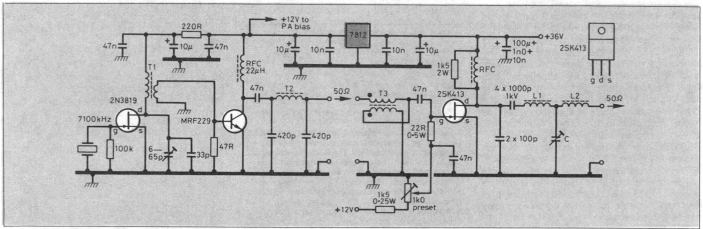

Fig 5. The 7MHz power amplifier and drive unit as designed by G8PDW for the 2SK413 audio-type power FET. For 14MHz the output network values need to be recalculated. Component details are shown under Table 1. Note that the 22-ohm resistor is mounted close to the case on the FET gate lead.

the effective input impedance could be controlled by using a resistor across the gate; both as a load for the incoming RF and as a source of bias. I was doubtful, but desperate!

"W1FB had used a 4:1 step-up transformer with a 200-ohm load as part of the bias circuit. This was reproduced and with 1.5W drive the unit was switched on... The result — nothing: 10:1 SWR and no output. A brief attempt was made at resonating the input capacitance with a parallel inductor. This did work (25W output) but not with unconditional stability and the required inductance values differed with different production batches of FETs. It seemed that was that; if subtle design and pages of calculations failed, perhaps brute force would.

"But W1FB's approach had rung a bell in a long-unused part of my memory: it rang out 'passive grid techniques'. Reverse the 4:1 transformer former to give a 12.5-ohm source and provide a partial load; 22 ohms should do it I thought... and it did, within ten minutes the circuit was up and running and the dummy load warming up nicely.

"As a Class B licensee, I did not have a readily available source of HF drive. So a simple crystal oscillator/amplifier was used. As shown in Fig 5 and Table 1 this approach yielded up to 73 watts output from just three devices. The RFC was constructed from a ferrite ring; normally this should have an XL of about ten times that of the output impedance of the transistors; in this case 12.5 x 10 = 125 ohms but not unduly critical. What is really important is that the Q-factor of the RFC is low. To ensure this a 1K5 resistor was wired in parallel; otherwise RF chokes can cause 'ringing' and other unwanted resonances which if ignored may cause the Vds rating of the device to be exceeded.

"I have also adopted W1FB's technique of including a capacitor from drain to ground. After extensive tests with a high frequency oscilloscope, I determined that a capacitor with a reactance of about nine times the output impedance of the amplifier is sufficient to remove any HF energy from the drain circuit without affecting the efficiency of the amplifier.

"The bias has two functions: (a) providing a bias voltage for the FET between 0 and 5V; and (b) providing a load for the incoming RF drive. The 2SK413 has the following bias characteristics: Conduction begins at Vgs +3.15V; Id = 50mA at Vgs +3.77V; and Id = 100mA at Vgs +4.04V. At 100mA, the amplification characteristics began to appear to be linear, the output power varying in direct proportion to power input. The IMD characteristics have not been measured but I would suggest that 100-250mA would be a suitable quiescent current for linear operation.

"At 14MHz results are incomplete but encouraging. Again using the T-network design formulae, the output network values were changed accordingly. The input circuit is inherently broadband and was left unchanged, as was the RFC. The drain by-pass capacitor was halved in value to 100pF according to the criteria given above. Unfortunately my source of RF drive, using a 14,330kHz crystal, was limited to 1W and this proved insufficient to drive the amplifier fully. However, by increasing the bias it proved possible to get 38W output. This represents a gain in excess of 15dB. I feel convinced that if more drive had been available, the results would have been similar to those obtained on 7MHz.

"I feel that the experiments with this low-cost device have been a success. The networks are

CO-AXIAL PLUG LORE

Ian Hamilton, GM3CSM comments on the September TT item on the method recommended by Aerialite for connecting co-axial cable to their consumer-type plugs. He prefers a slightly different method shown in some 1970s publications: "With this method, the braid is inserted with the centre conductor and insulation through the cable grip, teased out over the 'leading' rounded end of the cable grip, and cut off just short of the 'trailing' edge: (Fig 6). When the plug is assembled the braid is firmly clamped by the plug cap between the cable grip, the plug body and the bevelled end of the plug insulation. Most viewers/users seem to pull these plugs out of their sockets by the cable, but I have never been asked to remake any of those I have made up in this way. As you say in TT, soldering the centre conductor to the plug pin should be considered mandatory — but try telling that to the TV trade!"

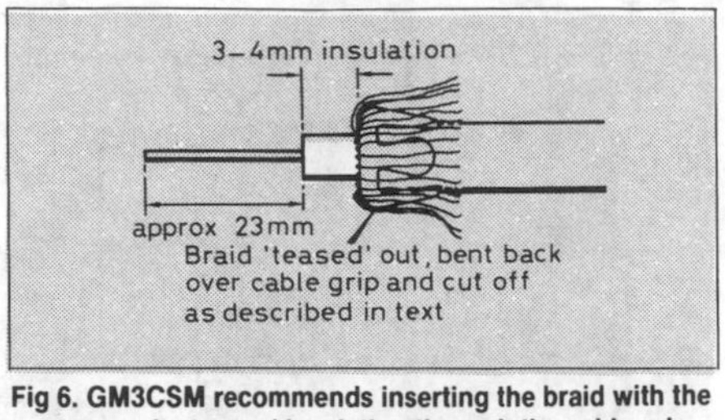

GM3CSM recalls several occasions when he has been able to improve viewers' reception simply by cleaning and soldering their oxidised plug connections — particularly in seaside or industrial environments. A well-soldered connection is the only long-term protection against a salt-laden or polluted atmosphere.

I once sat on one of the two BSI committees that, over many months, drew up BS6330: 1983 'Reception of sound and television broadcasting'. The committee spent time discussing the problem that trade installation technicians could seldom be persuaded of the need to solder plug connections. In the outcome 5.3.2.2 of BS6330, Installation, item (j) recommends, a shade ambiguously: "Coaxial plugs should be assembled in accordance with the manufacturer's instructions and the inner conductors soldered where applicable. A type

Fig 6. GM3CSM recommends inserting the braid with the centre conductor and insulation through the cable grip when fitting TV-type co-axial plugs. For details see text.

employing a crimped connection should only be used in conjunction with a proper crimping tool."

A 1984 TT item on BS6330 stressed that for any installation, wind forces, corrosion, oxidization and so on tend always to be more severe than one imagines. BS6330 reminds installers that any outdoor system that is erected in a situation where it is exposed to the rigours of the climate will experience wide ranges of temperature (from well below freezing to over 55°C), rain, snow, ice formation and high-velocity winds; it will be subject to metal fatigue, as are all stressed metal structures. The degree of exposure of the site needs to be considered very carefully: coastal sites, sites on hills or on or near very tall buildings need special care. It is worth remembering that most weather data are based on *statistical* information and are not absolute values. I pointed out then that an assurance that wind gusts are likely to exceed 100mph only, say, once in 20 years means, by Murphy's Law, that gusts will certainly exceed 100mph the following winter. For those in the south of England, Murphy was a couple of years out: the 'hurricane' did not arrive until October 1987!

totally stable and the use of the T-network may possibly allow the amplifier to be used on-air without additional filtering. There are many possible routes for the development of practical HF amplifiers from these humble beginnings. I am currently constructing a pushpull amplifier using a pair of devices which I believe should provide an output comfortably in excess of 120W between 3.5 and 21MHz. There are possibilities of building multiple-device designs along the lines of the Motorola EB104 design with the output power approaching the 400W UK limit. The 2SK413 is currently available from RS Components Ltd at £3.75 + VAT. The toroid cores were available from Bonex Ltd of Langley, Berks.

Frequency	Supply Voltage	CW Output Power	Efficiency
7100kHz	36V DC	52W	73-75%
7100kHz	43V DC	73W	73-75%
14,330kHz	43V DC	38W	—

Drive power input at 7MHz approximately 1.5W
Drive power input at 14MHz approximately 1W

Table 1 —— Performance of G8PDW's FET Amplifier.

Notes: Output power measured on Marconi absorption power meter, checked with peak-to-peak voltage measurement at dummy load. The efficiency was not measured at 14MHz due to increase in quiescent drain current used to compensate for lack of drive power. Component details (7MHz only) T1 34t of 0.4mm enam with 4t link of 0.56mm enam copper on T-50-2. T2 13 turns of 0.56mm on T-50-2. T3 4:1 broadband transformer. 8 bifilar turns of 0.5mm enam copper twisted 5 turns per inch on ferrite core od 12.4mm μ 125 (Bonex No 530090). L1 18 turns 1.2mm on T-130-6 toroid. L2 23 turns 1.2mm on T-130-6 toroid. C 150pF +

6-100pF variable in parallel. Capacitors rated at 350V. RFC 14 turns 1mm enam copper on 1-in od ferrite toroid.

UP-DATE ON WORKING EARS

In the TT item 'The Way We Listen' (June 1989), I quoted a 1953 comment by the physiologist Dr Kraus that "Because of its smallness, the ear presents some of the most disputed problems of human physiology... the mechanism of hearing is still a matter of dispute. In spite of its small size and complicated structure, the ear compares roughly with a modern radio receiver... one might hold the view that an accurate examination would immediately expose the purpose and function of each individual constituent part. The opposite is the case and all theories are still full of contradictions."

I doubt if Dr Kraus would express exactly the same puzzlement today. Since 1953 much effort has been put into solving the many mysteries of hearing — and also how our ears provide us with the sense of balance needed to walk on two legs. For most of us, our ears are the final link in amateur radio operation; yet many of us, along with 'the walkman generation,' tend to put our hearing at considerable risk by subjecting them to 'acoustic trauma'.

A long review article 'How the ear's works work' by A. J. Hudspeth (University of Texas South Western Medical Centre, Dallas) in the prestigious scientific journal *Nature* (5 October 1989, pp397-404) shows not only the enormous amount that has been learned about the working of our ears in recent years, but also the exceptional vulnerability of what is normally a reliable system. It appears that the key to greater understanding came with the recognition of the role of sensory receptors called 'hair cells' which can detect "motions of atomic dimensions and respond more than 100,000 times a second."

Dr Hudspeth introduces his article as follows: "The internal ear is an evolutionary triumph of miniaturization, a three-dimensional inertial-guidance system and an acoustical amplifier and frequency analyser compacted into the volume of a child's marble. That we are ordinarily oblivious to what goes on within the labyrinth reflects the ear's reliable performance: our bipedal stance, our capacity for locomotion on foot and in vehicles and our ability to communicate vocally, all stem from the ear's incessant activity. The internal ear, in turn, owes its success to its complement of hair cells, the epithelial receptors responsible in the cochlea for our sensitivity to sound, in the utriculus and sacculus for our perception of linear accelerations, and in the three semicircular canals for our appreciation of rotary accelerations...

"The volume of the human nervous system devoted to the auditory and vestibular systems also testifies to the ear's importance. The 32,000 hair cells of the two cochleae and the total of 134,000 cells found bilaterally in the organs of equilibrium forward their signals to the large cochlear and vestibular nuclear complexes of the brainstem's medulla and pons...

"The paucity of hair cells also accounts for the exceptional vulnerability of the auditory system...destruction of 166,000 hair cells would entail disequilibrium and profound deafness, both major impairments. Society is awakening only slowly to the cost of acoustic trauma in both industrial and recreational settings; within the next decade or two, the 'walkman generation' will find itself unexpectedly and ardently interested in auditory pathophysiology."

Much of the language of the *Nature* article is likely to be incomprehensible to those who are not physiologists, but the import is clear: stick an earpiece or pair of earphones running at high output on your ears for many hours a day and you will be exposing them to an unacceptable acoustic trauma: it could make your hair cells curl up and destruct! On the other hand, if the audio peaks are kept low all should be well.

The cocktail party effect is a good example of the astonishing ability of the way our ears can discriminate between phase differences that are measured in microseconds. Dr Hudspeth writes: "The localisation of sound sources, one of the most important roles of hearing, sets even more stringent limits on the speed of transduction. If a sound source lies directly to one side, an emitted sound will reach the nearer ear somewhat sooner than the farther; for a human-being the maximal delay is about 700μsec. Humans and owls can locate sound sources of much smaller temporal delays, less than 20μsec. For this to occur, hair cells must be capable of detecting accoustical waveforms with microsecond-level resolution; even more remarkably, this temporal information must be transmitted along axons whose individually signalling rate is less than 1kHz."

He also notes that the accoustic radar system of bats, with targets such as a 3mm-long insect, requires an auditory response extending to at least 150kHz! Pity the designer of hi-fi equipment for bats. Then, again, he writes: "Although the auditory system is capable of improving its signal-

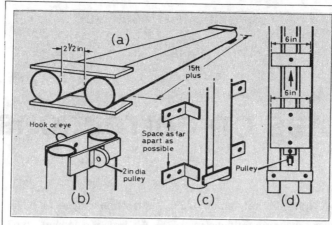

Fig 7. Details of G1JKX's method of constructing an extendable 30-ft mast using scaffold poles and 2-in alloy tube.

Fig 8. The completed mast.

D-I-Y EXTENDABLE MAST (LOW-COST)

John West, G1JKX writes: "After a few years trial-and-error in making low-cost masts, I think I have cracked the problem. Two metal scaffold poles, 15ft or more long, are placed side by side, about 2.5-in apart. Two mild steel spacers, about 6-in long, 2-in wide, 1/4-in thick, are welded or bolted at each end of the scaffold poles (**Fig 7** a). A 2-in pulley is welded on the top at the back (**Fig 7** b). Two wall-brackets are welded on about 2-ft below the highest point of the wall on the poles (**Fig 7** c).

Then an alloy-pole (20-ft-plus long) is placed between the two scaffold poles with a 2-in pulley placed on the bottom and bolted in place (**Fig 7** d). About 3-ft from the bottom of the alloy pole a stop bar is bolted on, with a slide bar bolted on the bottom. Wire rope is tied to the top of the scaffold pole, down to the bottom of the alloy pole, through the pulley and back up to the pulley at the top on the front, then down to the bottom again. Bolt the mast to the house wall, etc, add rotator and VHF antenna to the top of the alloy section. Pull the alloy tube up to its maximum height by means of the wire rope; tie rope securely to a wall bracket or similar fixing point. Result: a 'cheapie' 30-ft-plus extendable mast." (**Fig 8**).

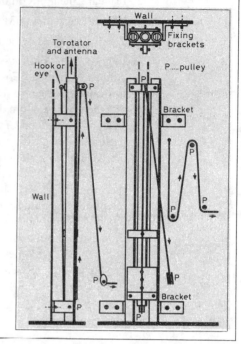

to-noise ratio to some extent by averaging responses over several cycles, the sensitivity of our hearing is ultimately limited because fainter sounds are drowned out by the thermal clatter of the components of the ear."

The June *TT* item drew attention to the discussion in *Sprat* of the advantages of listening to CW at an AF beat note of about 400Hz rather than about 1000Hz. I suggested that it has been firmly established that the selectivity/discrimination of the ear is higher at low frequencies and that this is borne out by the phenomenon of Zwicker 'masking' as now being used to reduce the bit-rate of digital-audio for transmission purposes.

Angus Taylor, G8PG (Communications Manager of the G-QRP Club) has now brought to my attention the Club's new 8-page 'A report on Project Frequency Band' compiled by G3XJS, GW0DYT and G8PG. This evaluates the use of outboard passive LC filters with centre frequencies of 750Hz and 450Hz for use with direct-conversion receivers. It has been produced at the request of Ed Wetherhold, W3NQN, technical adviser to ARRL on filter design. The three participants compared the usefulness in practice of both filters. In summary, it was found that 450Hz was more useful than 750Hz, although having both

available (switchable) gives additional flexibility. The investigation has thrown up some interesting unanswered questions: the 450Hz filter seemed better from a noise point of view, but is this due to the filter or the better aural discrimination at this frequency or both?

The report does seem to bear out the view that in receiver design we need to take fully into account the characteristics of the human operator, including the way our ears work. G8PG adds: "The use of an AF amplifier at the filter output will allow the attenuation in the filter to be restored easily, common telephony practice ever since the advent of the valve, but usually ignored in amateur radio designs. Provision of such a low gain amplifier allows the filter designer to concentrate on bandwidth and skirt sensitivity without the additional worry of pass-band loss.

"The use of AF oscillators in the 800-1000Hz range for morse practice and testing mitigates against maximum efficiency in aural CW reception; students become conditioned to these higher frequencies and have to be 'deconditioned' if they are to use lower-frequency filters. But once deconditioned, they soon appreciate the effectiveness of low-frequency beat notes and use them a great deal."

□

Notes on corrections

1. ZS6JC transmitter diagram, p227. A correction appears on p235.
2. Frinear Linear circuit diagram, p309. A correction appears on p323.
3. W1FB diagram on p315. A correction appears on p323.
4. The following statement was printed in the December 1988 issue of *Radio Communication*:

In good faith, Pat Hawker revealed the secrets of some British Telecom documentation in his August 'Technical Topics' feature. The subject was RF breakthrough to telephones. Some information came from a 'customer service information' leaflet identifying the various models and their behaviour in the presence of strong RF fields between 100kHz and 200MHz. British Telecom were concerned that the confidentiality of these documents was breached – in particular any publication of non-approved modifications to telephones which could result in a breach of their statutory approval.

G3VA did state that no attempt should be made to modify any telephone instruments that are the property of British Telecom, and warned against making modifications to 'approved' telephone apparatus connected to their network. This we must reiterate, and point out that BT respond to and thoroughly investigate all complaints regarding RFI to their systems. Indeed, they had a special unit which deals with such problems, as mentioned in 'TT'.

Sorry, BT. We believed that we were acting in everyone's best interests and were appreciative of your efforts to overcome RFI problems. We certainly had no wish to precipitate any upset – Ed.

Index